✳ **HAESE MATHEMATICS**

Specialists in mathematics publishing

Mathematics
for the international student
Mathematical Studies SL
third edition

Mal Coad

Glen Whiffen

Sandra Haese

Michael Haese

Mark Humphries

for use with
IB Diploma
Programme

MATHEMATICS FOR THE INTERNATIONAL STUDENT
Mathematical Studies SL third edition

Mal Coad   B.Ec., Dip.T.
Glen Whiffen   B.Sc., B.Ed.
Sandra Haese   B.Sc.
Michael Haese   B.Sc.(Hons.), Ph.D.
Mark Humphries   B.Sc.(Hons.)

Published by Haese Mathematics
152 Richmond Road, Marleston, SA 5033, AUSTRALIA
Telephone: +61 8 8210 4666, Fax: +61 8 8354 1238
Email: info@haesemathematics.com.au
Web: www.haesemathematics.com.au

National Library of Australia Card Number & ISBN 978-1-921972-05-8

© Haese & Harris Publications 2012

First Edition	2004
Reprinted	2005 three times *(with minor corrections)*, 2006, 2007, 2008 twice, 2009
Second Edition	2010
Reprinted	2011
Third Edition	2012
Reprinted	2013 *(with minor corrections)*, 2014, 2015

Typeset in Times Roman 10.

Printed in China by Prolong Press Limited.

The textbook has been developed independently of the International Baccalaureate Organization (IBO). The textbook is in no way connected with, or endorsed by, the IBO.

FOREWORD

Mathematics for the International Student: Mathematical Studies SL has been written to embrace the syllabus for the two-year Mathematical Studies SL Course, first examined in 2014. It is not our intention to define the course. Teachers are encouraged to use other resources. We have developed this book independently of the International Baccalaureate Organization (IBO) in consultation with many experienced teachers of IB Mathematics. The text is not endorsed by the IBO.

Syllabus references are given at the beginning of each chapter. The new edition reflects the new Mathematical Studies SL syllabus. Explanations have been reworded, making them easier for students who have English as a second language. Discussion topics for the Theory of Knowledge have been included in this edition. See page 12 for a summary.

To help students prepare for examinations, the final chapter contains 200 examination-style questions.

Comprehensive graphics calculator instructions for Casio fx-9860G Plus, Casio fx-CG20, TI-84 Plus and TI-*n*spire are accessible as printable pages online (see page 18) and, occasionally, where additional help may be needed, more detailed instructions are available from icons located throughout the book. The extensive use of graphics calculators and computer packages throughout the book enables students to realise the importance, application, and appropriate use of technology. No single aspect of technology has been favoured. It is as important that students work with a pen and paper as it is that they use their graphics calculator, or use a spreadsheet or graphing package on computer.

This package is language rich and technology rich. The combination of textbook and online interactive features will foster the mathematical development of students in a stimulating way. Frequent use of the online interactive features is certain to nurture a much deeper understanding and appreciation of mathematical concepts. This textbook also offers ◀) **Self Tutor** for every worked example. ◀) **Self Tutor** is accessed online – click anywhere on any worked example to hear a teacher's voice explain each step in that worked example. This is ideal for catch-up and revision, or for motivated students who want to do some independent study outside school hours.

The online interactive features allow immediate access to our own specially designed geometry software, graphing software and more. Teachers are provided with a quick and easy way to demonstrate concepts, and students can discover for themselves and re-visit when necessary.

continued next page

It is not our intention that each chapter be worked through in full. Time constraints may not allow for this. Teachers must select exercises carefully, according to the abilities and prior knowledge of their students, to make the most efficient use of time and give as thorough coverage of work as possible. Investigations throughout the book will add to the discovery aspect of the course and enhance student understanding and learning.

In this changing world of mathematics education, we believe that the contextual approach shown in this book, with the associated use of technology, will enhance the students' understanding, knowledge and appreciation of mathematics, and its universal application.

We welcome your feedback.

Email: *info@haesemathematics.com.au*
Web: *www.haesemathematics.com.au*

MC GAW SHH
PMH MAH

ACKNOWLEDGEMENTS

Cartoon artwork by John Martin. Artwork by Piotr Poturaj and Benjamin Fitzgerald.

Cover design by Piotr Poturaj.

Computer software by Thomas Jansson, Troy Cruickshank, Ashvin Narayanan, Adrian Blackburn, Edward Ross and Tim Lee.

Typeset in Australia by Charlotte Frost.

Editorial review by Catherine Quinn and David Martin.

Support material: Marjut Mäenpää

The authors and publishers would like to thank all those teachers who offered advice and encouragement on this book. Many of them read the page proofs and offered constructive comments and suggestions. These teachers include: Sara Brouwer, Duncan Smith, Chris Carter, and Julie Connah. To anyone we may have missed, we offer our apologies.

The publishers wish to make it clear that acknowledging these individuals does not imply any endorsement of this book by any of them, and all responsibility for the content rests with the authors and publishers.

ONLINE FEATURES

With the purchase of a new hard copy textbook, you will gain 27 months subscription to our online product. This subscription can be renewed for a small fee.

Students can revisit concepts taught in class and undertake their own revision and practice online.

By clicking on the relevant icon, a range of interactive features can be accessed:

INTERACTIVE LINK

- ◆ 🔊 Self Tutor
- ◆ Graphics calculator instructions
- ◆ Interactive links to spreadsheets, graphing and geometry software, computer demonstrations and simulations

Graphics calculator instructions: Detailed instructions are available online, as printable pages (see page 18). Click on the icon for Casio fx-9860G Plus, Casio fx-CG20, TI-84 Plus, or TI-$n$spire instructions.

GRAPHICS CALCULATOR INSTRUCTIONS

COMPATIBILITY

For iPads, tablets, and other mobile devices, the interactive features may not work. However, the digital version of the textbook and additional pages can be viewed online using any of these devices.

REGISTERING

You will need to register to access the online features of this textbook.

Visit www.haesemathematics.com.au/register and follow the instructions. Once you have registered, you can:

- • activate your digital textbook
- • use your account to purchase additional digital products.

To activate your digital textbook, contact Haese Mathematics. On providing proof of purchase, your digital textbook will be activated. **It is important that you keep your receipt as proof of purchase.**

For general queries about registering and licence keys:

- • Visit our Snowflake help page: http://snowflake.haesemathematics.com.au/help
- • Contact Haese Mathematics: info@haesemathematics.com.au

ONLINE VERSION OF THE TEXTBOOK

The entire text of the book can be viewed online, allowing you to leave your textbook at school.

SELF TUTOR

Self tutor is an exciting feature of this book.

The 🔊 Self Tutor icon on each worked example denotes an active online link.

> Simply 'click' on the 🔊 Self Tutor (or anywhere in the example box) to access the worked example, with a teacher's voice explaining each step necessary to reach the answer.
>
> Play any line as often as you like. See how the basic processes come alive using movement and colour on the screen.

TABLE OF CONTENTS

SYMBOLS AND NOTATION USED IN THIS BOOK

$\mathbb{N}$	the set of positive integers and zero, $\{0, 1, 2, 3, ...\}$
$\mathbb{Z}$	the set of integers, $\{0, \pm 1, \pm 2, \pm 3, ...\}$
$\mathbb{Z}^+$	the set of positive integers, $\{1, 2, 3, ...\}$
$\mathbb{Q}$	the set of rational numbers
$\mathbb{Q}^+$	the set of positive rational numbers, $\{x \mid x > 0, \ x \in \mathbb{Q}\}$
$\mathbb{R}$	the set of real numbers
$\mathbb{R}^+$	the set of positive real numbers, $\{x \mid x > 0, \ x \in \mathbb{R}\}$
$\{x_1, x_2, ...\}$	the set with elements $x_1, x_2, ...$
$n(A)$	the number of elements in set A
$\{x \mid ....\}$	the set of all x such that
$\in$	is an element of
$\notin$	is not an element of
$\varnothing$	the empty (null) set
U	the universal set
$\cup$	union
$\cap$	intersection
$\subset$	is a proper subset of
$\subseteq$	is a subset of
A'	the complement of the set A
$p \Rightarrow q$	implication 'if p then q'
$p \Leftrightarrow q$	equivalence 'p is equivalent to q'
$p \wedge q$	conjunction 'p and q'
$p \vee q$	disjunction 'p or q'
$p \veebar q$	exclusive disjunction 'p or q but not both'
$\neg p$	negation 'not p'
$a^{\frac{1}{n}}, \ \sqrt[n]{a}$	a to the power of $\frac{1}{n}$, nth root of a (if $a \geqslant 0$ then $\sqrt[n]{a} \geqslant 0$)
$a^{-n} = \dfrac{1}{a^n}$	a to the power $-n$, reciprocal of a^n
$a^{\frac{1}{2}}, \ \sqrt{a}$	a to the power $\frac{1}{2}$, square root of a (if $a \geqslant 0$ then $\sqrt{a} \geqslant 0$)

$\lvert x \rvert$	the modulus or absolute value of x $\lvert x \rvert = \begin{cases} x \text{ for } x \geqslant 0, & x \in \mathbb{R} \\ -x \text{ for } x < 0, & x \in \mathbb{R} \end{cases}$
$\equiv$	identity or is equivalent to
$\approx$	is approximately equal to
$>$	is greater than
$\geq$ or $\geqslant$	is greater than or equal to
$<$	is less than
$\leq$ or $\leqslant$	is less than or equal to
u_n	the nth term of a sequence or series
d	the common difference of an arithmetic sequence
r	the common ratio of a geometric sequence
S_n	the sum of the first n terms of a sequence, $u_1 + u_2 + ... + u_n$
$\displaystyle\sum_{i=1}^{n} u_i$	$u_1 + u_2 + ... + u_n$
$f(x)$	the image of x under the function f
$\dfrac{dy}{dx}$	the derivative of y with respect to x
$f'(x)$	the derivative of $f(x)$ with respect to x
sin, cos, tan	the circular functions
$A(x, y)$	the point A in the plane with Cartesian coordinates x and y
AB	the line through A and B, the line segment with end points A and B, or the length from A to B.
$\widehat{A}$	the angle at A
$\widehat{CAB}$	the angle between CA and AB
$\triangle ABC$	the triangle whose vertices are A, B, and C
$\parallel$	is parallel to
$\perp$	is perpendicular to
$P(A)$	probability of event A
$P(A')$	probability of the event 'not A'
$P(A \mid B)$	probability of the event A given B

$x_1, x_2, ...$	observations of a variable
$f_1, f_2, ...$	frequencies with which the observations $x_1, x_2, ...$ occur
μ	population mean
σ	population standard deviation
$\overline{x}$	mean of a data set
s_n	standard deviation of a data set
$N(\mu, \sigma^2)$	normal distribution with mean μ and variance σ^2
$X \sim N(\mu, \sigma^2)$	the random variable X has a normal distribution with mean μ and variance σ^2
r	Pearson's product-moment correlation coefficient
χ^2	chi-squared
χ^2_{crit}	critical value of the chi-squared distribution
χ^2_{calc}	calculated chi-squared value
f_o	observed frequency of a variable
f_e	expected frequency of a variable

THEORY OF KNOWLEDGE

Theory of Knowledge is a Core requirement in the International Baccalaureate Diploma Programme.

Students are encouraged to think critically and challenge the assumptions of knowledge. Students should be able to analyse different ways of knowing and areas of knowledge, while considering different cultural and emotional perceptions, fostering an international understanding.

The activities and discussion topics in the below table aim to help students discover and express their views on knowledge issues.

Chapter 2: Measurement p. 40	**MEASURES OF ANGLE - MATHEMATICS IN NATURE**
Chapter 5: Sequences and series p. 145	**HOW MANY TERMS DO WE NEED TO CONSIDER BEFORE A RESULT IS PROVEN?**
Chapter 6: Descriptive statistics p. 162	**MISLEADING STATISTICS**
Chapter 9: Probability p. 295	**APPLICATIONS OF PROBABILITY**
Chapter 11: Two variable statistics p. 345	**MODELLING THE REAL WORLD**
Chapter 12: Pythagoras' theorem p. 366	**MATHEMATICAL PROOF**
Chapter 13: Coordinate geometry p. 376	**ARE ALGEBRA AND GEOMETRY SEPARATE AREAS OF LEARNING?**
Chapter 15: Trigonometry p. 469	**MATHEMATICS IN SOCIETY**
Chapter 16: Functions p. 497	**MATHEMATICAL LANGUAGE AND SYMBOLS**
Chapter 18: Exponential functions p. 532	**THE NATURE OF INFINITY**
Chapter 20: Differential calculus p. 582	**ZENO'S PARADOX**
Chapter 21: Applications of differential calculus p. 606	**THE SCIENTIFIC METHOD**

THEORY OF KNOWLEDGE

There are several theories for why one complete turn was divided into 360 degrees:

- 360 is approximately the number of days in a year.
- The Babylonians used a counting system in base 60. If they drew 6 equilateral triangles within a circle as shown, and divided each angle into 60 subdivisions, then there were 360 subdivisions in one turn. The division of an hour into 60 minutes, and a minute into 60 seconds, is from this base 60 counting system.
- 360 has 24 divisors, including every integer from 1 to 10 except 7.

1 What other measures of angle are there?

2 Which is the most *natural* unit of angle measure?

See **Chapter 2, Measurement**, p. 40

WRITING A MATHEMATICAL PROJECT

In addition to sitting examination papers, Mathematical Studies SL students are also required to complete a **mathematical project**. This is a short report written by the student, based on a topic of his or her choice, and should focus on the mathematics of that topic. The mathematical project comprises 20% of the final mark.

The project should involve the collection of information or the generation of measurements, as well as the analysis and evaluation of the information or measurements. The project should be no more than 2000 words long, and should be written at a level which is accessible to an audience of your peers.

Group work should not be used for projects. Each student's project is an individual piece of work.

When deciding on how to structure your project, you may wish to include the following sections:

Introduction: This section can be used to explain why the topic has been chosen, and to give a clear statement of the task and plan. This should be a short paragraph which outlines the problem or scenario under investigation. Any relevant background information should also be included.

Method and Results: This section can be used to describe the process which was followed to investigate the problem, as well as recording the unprocessed results of your investigations, in the form of a table, for example.

Analysis of Results: In this section, you should use graphs, diagrams, and calculations to analyse and interpret your results. Any graphs and diagrams should be included in the appropriate place in the report, and not attached as appendices at the end. You should also form some conjectures based on your analysis.

Conclusion: You should summarise your investigation, giving a clear response to your aim. The validity of your project should be discussed, outlining any limitations or sources of error.

The project will be assessed against seven assessment criteria. Refer to the Mathematical Studies SL Subject Guide for more details.

The following two pages contain a short extract of a student's report, used with the permission of Wan Lin Oh. Please note that there is no single structure which must be followed to write a mathematical project. The extract displayed is only intended to illustrate some of the key features which should be included.

The electronic version of this extract contains further information, and can be accessed by clicking the icon alongside.

ELECTRONIC EXTRACT

This is an **extract** of a mathematics report used to demonstrate the components of a written report.

1. Title (and author)
A clear and concise description of the report

Population Trends in China
Written by Wan Lin Oh

2. Introduction
Outline the purpose of the task. Include background information and definitions of key terms or variables used.

Aim

To determine the model that best fits the population of China from 1950 to 2008 by investigating different functions that best model the population of China from 1950 to 1995 (refer to *Table 1*) initially, and then re-evaluating and modifying this model to include additional data from 1983 to 2008.

Rationale

The history class had been discussing the impetus for, and the political, cultural and social implications of China's "One Child Policy", introduced in 1978 for implementation in 1979[1]. This aroused the author's curiosity about the measurable impact that the policy may have had on China's population.

Table 1: Population of China from 1950 to 1995

Year (t)	1950	1955	1960	1965	1970	1975	1980	1985	1990	1995
Population in millions (P)	554.8	609.0	657.5	729.2	830.7	927.8	998.9	1070.0	1155.3	1220.5

Choosing a model

Values from *Table 1* were used to create *Graph 1*:

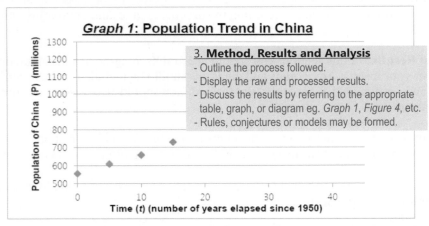

Graph 1: Population Trend in China

3. Method, Results and Analysis
- Outline the process followed.
- Display the raw and processed results.
- Discuss the results by referring to the appropriate table, graph, or diagram eg. *Graph 1*, *Figure 4*, etc.
- Rules, conjectures or models may be formed.

Graph 1 illustrates a positive correlation between the population of China and the number of years since 1950. This means that as time increases, the population of China also increases. *Graph 1* clearly shows that the model is not a linear function, because the graph has turning points and there is no fixed increase in corresponding to a fixed increase in P. Simple observation reveals that it is not a straight line. In addition, *Graph 1* illustrates that the function is not a power function ($P = at^b$) because it does not meet the requirements of a power function; for all positive b values, a power model must go through the origin, however *Graph 1* shows that the model's function does not pass through the origin of $(0, 0)$.

There is a high possibility that the model could be a polynomial function because *Graph 1* indicates that there are turning point(s). A cubic and a quadratic function were then determined and compared.

Analytical Determination of Polynomial Model

As there is a high possibility that the model could be a cubic function (3rd degree polynomial function), an algebraic method can be used in order to determine the equation of the function. In order to determine this cubic equation, four points from the model will be used as there are four... The middle section of this report has been omitted.

Conclusion

The aim of this investigation was to investigate a model that best fits the given data from 1950 to 2008. It was initially found that a 3rd degree polynomial function and an exponential function have a good possibility of fitting the given data from *Table 1* which is from year 1950 to 1995 by observing the data plots on the graph.

A cubic function (3rd degree polynomial function) was chosen eventually and consequently an algebraic method using simultaneous equations was developed to produce the equation of the function. Through this method, the equation of the cubic was deduced to be $P(t) = -0.007081t^3 + 0.5304t^2 + 5.263t + 554.8$. In addition, the use of technology was also included in this investigation to further enhance the development of the task by graphing the cubic function to determine how well the cubic function fitted the original data. The cubic graph was then compared with a quadratic function graph of $P(t) = 0.13t^2 + 8.95t + 554.8$. Ultimately, the cubic function was seen as the better fit compared to the quadratic model.

A researcher suggests that the population, P at time t can be modelled by $P(t) = \frac{K}{1+Le^{-Mt}}$. With the use of GeoGebra the parameters, K, L and M were found by trial and error to be 1590, 1.97 and 0.04 respectively. This consequently led to the equation of the logistic function of $P(t) = \frac{1590}{1+1.97e^{-0.04t}}$.

From the comparison of both the cubic and the logistic model, the cubic function was established to be a more accurate model for the given 1950 – 1995 data because the data points matched the model better, however the logistic model produced more likely values under extrapolation.

Additional data on population trends in China fro[...]d by the International Monetary Fund (IMF) was given in Tabl[...] graphed with the additional data points and compared. It w[...]er model compared to the cubic model because it was able [...]lation of China much more precisely.

Subsequently a piecewise function was used becau[...] have two distinctly different parts, each with a correspondin[...] domain $0 < t \le 30$. The researcher's model was modified to fit the data for $30 < t \le 58$.

The piecewise function was then defined as

$$P(t) \begin{cases} -0.007081t^3 + 0.5304t^2 + 5.263t + 554.8 & 0 < t \le 30 \\ \dfrac{1590}{1+1.97e^{-0.04t}} & 30 < t \le 58 \end{cases}$$

This modified model matched the data points of the population of China from 1950 to 2008 closely; the model also passed through both the minimum and the maximum of the given data. In addition, the modified model exhibited good long-term behaviour and was able to predict a sensible result beyond the known values.

Limitations

In this investigation, there were several limitations that should be taken into account. Firstly, the best fit model which is the piecewise function model does not take into account the possibility of natural disasters or diseases that may occur in China in the future which will lead to a mass decrease in population. Furthermore, the model also does not consider the population pressures in China such as the one child policy. The one child policy introduced in 1978 but applied in 1979 would cause a decrease in the population in the long term. It is shown in *Graph 14* that after 1979 (P_7), the rate at which the Chinese population is increasing is slower compared to the previous years. This is because this policy leads to an increase in the abortion rate due to many families' preference for males, as males are able to take over the family name. This will consequently lead to a gender imbalance, causing a decrease in population because of the increasing difficulty for Chinese males to find partners. In addition, the model of best fit does not consider the [...] countries, allowing more Chinese people to live longer, which wil[...] term.

---

[1]http://geography.about.com/od/populationgeography/a/onechild.htm

---

4. Conclusion and Limitations
- Summarise findings in response to the stated aim including restating any rules, conjectures, or models.
- Comment on any limitations to the approach used or of the findings.
- Considerations of extensions and connections to personal/previous knowledge may also contextualise the significance of the project.

5. References and acknowledgements
A list of sources of information either footnoted on the appropriate page or given in a bibliography at the end of the report.

USEFUL FORMULAE

STATISTICS

Mean
$$\bar{x} = \frac{\sum fx}{n} \quad \text{where} \quad n = \sum f$$

Interquartile range
$$\text{IQR} = Q_3 - Q_1$$

Standard deviation
$$s_n = \sqrt{\frac{\sum f(x - \bar{x})^2}{n}} \quad \text{where} \quad n = \sum f$$

The χ^2 test statistic
$$\chi^2_{calc} = \sum \frac{(f_o - f_e)^2}{f_e} \quad \text{where } f_o \text{ are the observed frequencies, } f_e \text{ are the expected frequencies.}$$

GEOMETRY

Equation of a straight line
$$y = mx + c \quad \text{or} \quad ax + by + d = 0$$

Gradient formula
$$m = \frac{y_2 - y_1}{x_2 - x_1}$$

Equation of axis of symmetry
$$x = \frac{-b}{2a}$$

Distance between two points (x_1, y_2) and (x_2, y_2)
$$d = \sqrt{(x_1 - x_2)^2 + (y_1 - y_2)^2}$$

Coordinates of the midpoint of a line segment with endpoints (x_1, y_2) and (x_2, y_2)
$$\left(\frac{x_1 + x_2}{2}, \frac{y_1 + y_2}{2} \right)$$

TRIGONOMETRY

Sine rule
$$\frac{a}{\sin A} = \frac{b}{\sin B} = \frac{c}{\sin C}$$

Cosine rule
$$a^2 = b^2 + c^2 - 2bc \cos A$$
$$\cos A = \frac{b^2 + c^2 - a^2}{2bc}$$

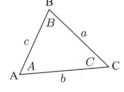

Area of a triangle
$$A = \tfrac{1}{2}ab \sin C \quad \text{where } a \text{ and } b \text{ are adjacent sides, } C \text{ is the included angle.}$$

PLANE AND SOLID FIGURES

Area of a parallelogram
$$A = (b \times h), \quad \text{where } b \text{ is the base, } h \text{ is the height}$$

Area of a triangle
$$A = \tfrac{1}{2}(b \times h), \quad \text{where } b \text{ is the base, } h \text{ is the height}$$

Area of a trapezium
$$A = \tfrac{1}{2}(a + b)h, \quad \text{where } a \text{ and } b \text{ are the parallel sides, } h \text{ is the height}$$

Area of a circle
$$A = \pi r^2, \quad \text{where } r \text{ is the radius}$$

Circumference of a circle
$$C = 2\pi r, \quad \text{where } r \text{ is the radius}$$

Volume of a pyramid	$V = \frac{1}{3}(\text{area of base} \times \text{vertical height})$
Volume of a cuboid	$V = l \times w \times h,$ where l is the length, w is the width, h is the height
Volume of a cylinder	$V = \pi r^2 h,$ where r is the radius, h is the height
Area of the curved surface of a cylinder	$A = 2\pi r h,$ where r is the radius, h is the height
Volume of a sphere	$V = \frac{4}{3}\pi r^3,$ where r is the radius
Surface area of a sphere	$A = 4\pi r^2,$ where r is the radius
Volume of a cone	$V = \frac{1}{3}\pi r^2 h,$ where r is the radius, h is the height
Area of the curved surface of a cone	$\pi r l,$ where r is the radius, l is the slant height

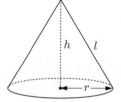

FINITE SEQUENCES

The nth term of an arithmetic sequence	$u_n = u_1 + (n-1)d$
The sum of n terms of an arithmetic sequence	$S_n = \dfrac{n}{2}(2u_1 + (n-1)d) = \dfrac{n}{2}(u_1 + u_n)$
The nth term of a geometric sequence	$u_n = u_1 r^{n-1}$
The sum of n terms of a geometric sequence	$S_n = \dfrac{u_1(r^n - 1)}{r - 1} = \dfrac{u_1(1 - r^n)}{1 - r},\quad r \neq 1$

FINANCIAL MATHEMATICS

Compound Interest	$FV = PV \times \left(1 + \frac{r}{100k}\right)^{kn},$

where FV is the future value,
PV is the present value,
$r\%$ is the interest rate per annum,
k is the number of compounds per year,
n is the number of years

PROBABILITY

Probability of an event A	$P(A) = \dfrac{n(A)}{n(U)}$
Complementary events	$P(A') = 1 - P(A)$
Combined events	$P(A \cup B) = P(A) + P(B) - P(A \cap B)$

Mutually exclusive events	$P(A \cup B) = P(A) + P(B)$
Independent events	$P(A \cap B) = P(A) \times P(B)$
Conditional probability	$P(A \mid B) = \dfrac{P(A \cap B)}{P(B)}$
Expectation	Expected value $= np$, where n is the number of trials, and p is the probability of the event

DIFFERENTIAL CALCULUS

Derivative of ax^n	If $f(x) = ax^n$ then $f'(x) = nax^{n-1}$
Derivative of a polynomial	If $f(x) = ax^n + bx^{n-1} + ...$ then $f'(x) = nax^{n-1} + (n-1)bx^{n-2} + ...$

GRAPHICS CALCULATOR INSTRUCTIONS

Printable graphics calculator instruction booklets are available for the **Casio fx-9860G Plus**, **Casio fx-CG20**, **TI-84 Plus**, and the **TI-*n*spire**. Click on the relevant icon below.

CASIO
fx-9860G Plus

CASIO
fx-CG20

TI-84 Plus

TI-*n*spire

When additional calculator help may be needed, specific instructions can be printed from icons within the text.

GRAPHICS
CALCULATOR
INSTRUCTIONS

Chapter 1

Number properties

OPENING PROBLEM   THE LEGEND OF SISSA IBN DAHIR

Around 1260 AD, the Kurdish historian Ibn Khallikān recorded the following story about Sissa ibn Dahir and a chess game against the Indian King Shihram. (The story is also told in the Legend of the Ambalappuzha Paal Payasam, where the Lord Krishna takes the place of Sissa ibn Dahir, and they play a game of chess with the prize of rice grains rather than wheat.)

King Shihram was a tyrant king, and his subject Sissa ibn Dahir wanted to teach him how important all of his people were. He invented the game of chess for the king, and the king was greatly impressed. He insisted on Sissa ibn Dahir naming his reward, and the wise man asked for one grain of wheat for the first square, two grains of wheat for the second square, four grains of wheat for the third square, and so on, doubling the wheat on each successive square on the board.

The king laughed at first and agreed, for there was so little grain on the first few squares. By halfway he was surprised at the amount of grain being paid, and soon he realised his great error: that he owed more grain than there was in the world.

Things to think about:

a How can we describe the number of grains of wheat for each square?

b How many grains of wheat would there be on the 40th square?

c Find the total number of grains of wheat that the king owed.

In this chapter we revise some of the properties of numbers. We consider operations with numbers and the order in which operations should be performed.

A   WORDS USED IN MATHEMATICS

Many words used in mathematics have special meanings. It is important to learn what each word means so we can use it correctly.

For example, when we write a number, we use some combination of the ten symbols: 1, 2, 3, 4, 5, 6, 7, 8, 9, and 0. These symbols are called **digits**.

There are four basic **operations** that are carried out with numbers:

> **Addition** $+$ to find the **sum**
>
> **Subtraction** $-$ to find the **difference**
>
> **Multiplication** $\times$ to find the **product**
>
> **Division** $\div$ to find the **quotient**

SUMS AND DIFFERENCES

- To find the **sum** of two or more numbers, we *add* them.
  The sum of 3 and 16 is $3 + 16 = 19$.
- To find the **difference** between two numbers, we *subtract* the smaller from the larger.
  The difference between 3 and 16 is $16 - 3 = 13$.

- When adding or subtracting **zero (0)**, the number remains unchanged.
  So, $23 + 0 = 23$ and $23 - 0 = 23$.
- When adding several numbers, we do not have to carry out the addition in the given order.
  Sometimes it is easier to change the order.

Example 1	◀ Self Tutor

Find: **a** the sum of 187, 369, and 13   **b** the difference between 37 and 82.

a $187 + 369 + 13$
$= \underbrace{187 + 13} + 369$
$=\quad 200 \quad + 369$
$= 569$

b   The difference between 37 and 82
$= 82 - 37$
$= 45$

PRODUCTS AND QUOTIENTS

- The word **product** is used to describe the result of a multiplication.
  The product of 3 and 5 is $3 \times 5 = 15$.
  We say that 3 and 5 are **factors** of 15.
- The word **quotient** is used to describe the result of a division.
  The quotient of 15 and 3 is $15 \div 3 = 5$.
  We say that 15 is the **dividend** and that 3 is the **divisor**.
- Multiplying by **one (1)** does not change the value of a number.
  So, $17 \times 1 = 17$ and $1 \times 17 = 17$.
- Multiplying by **zero (0)** produces zero.
  So, $17 \times 0 = 0$ and $0 \times 17 = 0$.
- Division by zero **(0)** is meaningless. We say the result is **undefined**.
  So, $0 \div 4 = 0$ but $4 \div 0$ is undefined.
- The order in which numbers are multiplied does **not** change the resultant number.
  So, $3 \times 7 \times 2 = 2 \times 3 \times 7 = 42$.

EXERCISE 1A

1 Find:

  a the sum of 4, 8, and 11

  b the difference between 23 and 41

  c the sum of the first 12 positive whole numbers

  d by how much 407 exceeds 239.

2 **a** What number must be increased by 249 to get 752?

  b What number must be decreased by 385 to get 2691?

3 Jose received €285 in wages whereas Juan received €312. How much more did Juan receive than Jose?

4 Emma's horse float has mass 406 kg. Her two horses weigh 517 kg and 561 kg. If Emma's car is allowed to tow 1500 kg, is she allowed to transport both horses at the same time?

5   To help buy an apartment, Agneta borrowed $26 200 from her parents. She has already paid them back amounts of $515, $872, and $664. How much does Agneta still owe her parents?

6   Find: **a**   the product of 19 and 23
           b   the quotient of 1008 and 36
           c   the product of the first 6 positive whole numbers.

7   How many £3 buckets of chips must I sell to earn £246?

8   My orchard contains 8 rows of 12 apple trees. If each tree produces 400 fruit, how many apples can I harvest?

9   How many laps of a 400 m track does an athlete need to complete in a 10 000 m race?

10   An apartment complex has 6 buildings, each 28 storeys high, and on each storey there are 5 apartments.

   a   How many apartments are there in total?

   b   Each apartment owner has to pay $3400 per year to maintain the buildings. What is the total annual budget for maintenance?

11   A cargo plane can carry 115 tonnes. How many plane loads are needed to transport 7245 tonnes of supplies?

B   EXPONENT NOTATION

A convenient way to write a product of *identical factors* is to use **exponential** or **index notation**.

For example,   32 can be written as $2 \times 2 \times 2 \times 2 \times 2$.

There are five identical factors, each a 2, so we can write $2 \times 2 \times 2 \times 2 \times 2$ as 2^5.

The small 5 is called the **exponent** or **index**, and the 2 is called the **base**.

Another example is: 7^4 ← exponent or index
                            ← base number

which tells us there are 4 factors of 7 multiplied together, or $7 \times 7 \times 7 \times 7$.

The following table shows the first five powers of 2.

Natural number	Factorised form	Exponent form	Spoken form
2	2	2^1	two
4	2×2	2^2	two squared
8	$2 \times 2 \times 2$	2^3	two cubed
16	$2 \times 2 \times 2 \times 2$	2^4	two to the fourth
32	$2 \times 2 \times 2 \times 2 \times 2$	2^5	two to the fifth

Any non-zero number raised to the power zero is equal to 1.

$$a^0 = 1, \ a \neq 0$$

0^0 is undefined.

Example 2   ◀)) **Self Tutor**

Write in exponent form: $2 \times 2 \times 2 \times 2 \times 3 \times 3 \times 3$

$2 \times 2 \times 2 \times 2 \times 3 \times 3 \times 3 = 2^4 \times 3^3$ {4 factors of 2, and 3 factors of 3}

Example 3   ◀)) **Self Tutor**

Write as a natural number: $2^3 \times 3^2 \times 5$

$2^3 \times 3^2 \times 5$
$= 2 \times 2 \times 2 \times 3 \times 3 \times 5$
$= 8 \times 9 \times 5$
$= 40 \times 9$
$= 360$

CALCULATOR USE

The **power key** of your calculator may look like $\boxed{\wedge}$, $\boxed{x^y}$, or $\boxed{y^x}$.
It can be used to enter numbers in exponent form into the calculator. Consult
the **graphics calculator instructions** if you need assistance.

GRAPHICS
CALCULATOR
INSTRUCTIONS

EXERCISE 1B.1

1   Copy and complete the values of these common powers:

   a $3^1 = ...$, $3^2 = ...$, $3^3 = ...$, $3^4 = ...$ **b** $5^1 = ...$, $5^2 = ...$, $5^3 = ...$, $5^4 = ...$

   c $6^1 = ...$, $6^2 = ...$, $6^3 = ...$, $6^4 = ...$ **d** $7^1 = ...$, $7^2 = ...$, $7^3 = ...$, $7^4 = ...$

2   Write in exponent form:

   a $2 \times 3 \times 3$ **b** $3 \times 3 \times 7 \times 7$ **c** $2 \times 2 \times 5 \times 5 \times 7$

   d $3 \times 5 \times 5 \times 5 \times 11$ **e** $2 \times 2 \times 3 \times 3 \times 3$ **f** $3 \times 3 \times 5 \times 7 \times 7 \times 7$

3   Convert each product into natural number form:

   a $2 \times 5 \times 7$ **b** 2×3^2 **c** $3^3 \times 5$

   d $2^2 \times 3^3$ **e** $2^3 \times 3 \times 5^2$ **f** $2^4 \times 5^2 \times 11^2$

4   Use your calculator to convert each product into natural number form:

   a $2^4 \times 3^5$ **b** $3^3 \times 5^5 \times 7$ **c** $2^5 \times 3^3 \times 11^2$

   d $7^4 \times 11^3 \times 13$ **e** $2 \times 3^6 \times 5^2$ **f** $2^2 \times 5^4 \times 7^3$

5   Consider $2^1, 2^2, 2^3, 2^4, 2^5, ...$ Look for a pattern and hence find the last digit of 2^{111}.

6   **a** Copy and complete:

        $2^1 = ...$ $2^2 - 2 = ...$

        $2^1 + 2^2 = ...$ $2^3 - 2 = ...$

        $2^1 + 2^2 + 2^3 = ...$ $2^4 - 2 = ...$

        $2^1 + 2^2 + 2^3 + 2^4 = ...$ $2^5 - 2 = ...$

   b Hence predict an expression for $2^1 + 2^2 + 2^3 + ... + 2^7$.
      Check your prediction using your calculator.

7 Answer the **Opening Problem** on page **20**. Use question **6** to help you with part **c**.

8 Teng is designing a house. In each room he can choose between tiles, floorboards, or carpet for the floor.

    a How many combinations of flooring materials are possible in the design of a 2-room "studio"?

    b How many flooring combinations are possible for a 3-room apartment?

    c How many flooring combinations are possible for a 4-room flat?

    d Find a pattern and write down a formula for the number of combinations of flooring materials for an n-room house.

    e Eventually Teng designs an 8-room house. How many flooring combinations does he have to choose from?

NEGATIVE BASES

Consider the statements below:

$$(-1)^1 = -1$$
$$(-1)^2 = -1 \times -1 = 1$$
$$(-1)^3 = -1 \times -1 \times -1 = -1$$
$$(-1)^4 = -1 \times -1 \times -1 \times -1 = 1$$

$$(-2)^1 = -2$$
$$(-2)^2 = -2 \times -2 = 4$$
$$(-2)^3 = -2 \times -2 \times -2 = -8$$
$$(-2)^4 = -2 \times -2 \times -2 \times -2 = 16$$

From these patterns we can see that:

> A **negative** base raised to an **odd** power is **negative**.
> A **negative** base raised to an **even** power is **positive**.

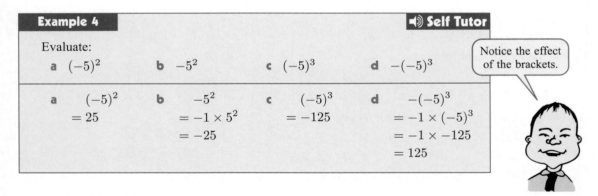

Example 4   ◀ㅇ **Self Tutor**

Evaluate:

  a $(-5)^2$ **b** -5^2 **c** $(-5)^3$ **d** $-(-5)^3$

Notice the effect of the brackets.

  a $(-5)^2$
      $= 25$

  b -5^2
      $= -1 \times 5^2$
      $= -25$

  c $(-5)^3$
      $= -125$

  d $-(-5)^3$
      $= -1 \times (-5)^3$
      $= -1 \times -125$
      $= 125$

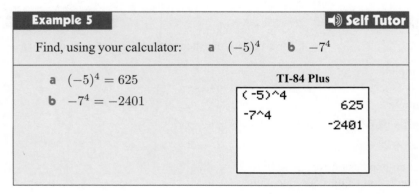

Example 5   ◀ㅇ **Self Tutor**

Find, using your calculator: **a** $(-5)^4$ **b** -7^4

  a $(-5)^4 = 625$

  b $-7^4 = -2401$

TI-84 Plus

```
(-5)^4
              625
-7^4
             -2401
```

EXERCISE 1B.2

1 Simplify:

a $(-1)^2$
b $(-1)^5$
c $(-1)^8$
d $(-1)^{23}$

e $(-1)^{10}$
f -1^{10}
g $-(-1)^{10}$
h $(-3)^2$

i $(-4)^3$
j -4^3
k $-(-7)^2$
l $-(-3)^3$

2 Use your calculator to evaluate the following, recording the entire display:

a 2^9
b $(-3)^5$
c -5^5
d 9^3

e 6^4
f $(-9)^4$
g -9^4
h 1.16^{11}

i -0.981^{14}
j $(-1.14)^{23}$

C — FACTORS OF POSITIVE INTEGERS

The **factors** of a positive integer are the positive integers which divide exactly into it.

For example, the factors of 8 are   1, 2, 4, and 8   since

$$8 \div 1 = 8$$
$$8 \div 2 = 4$$
$$8 \div 4 = 2$$
and $$8 \div 8 = 1.$$

3 is not a factor of 8 since $8 \div 3 = 2$ with remainder 2. We say that 8 is not *divisible* by 3.

All positive integers can be split into **factor pairs**.

For example: $8 = 1 \times 8$ or 2×4
$$132 = 11 \times 12$$

When we write a number as a product of factors, we say it is **factorised**.

10 may be factorised as a product of two factors in two ways: 1×10 or 2×5.

12 has factors   1, 2, 3, 4, 6, and 12.   It can be factorised as a product of two factors in three ways: 1×12, 2×6, and 3×4.

EVEN AND ODD NUMBERS

A whole number is **even** if it has 2 as a factor and thus is divisible by 2.

A whole number is **odd** if it is not divisible by 2.

EXERCISE 1C.1

1 a List all the factors of 15.
  b List all the factors of 16.
  c Copy and complete: $21 = 3 \times ....$
  d Write another pair of factors which multiply to give 21.

2 List *all* the factors of each of the following numbers:

a 9
b 17
c 22
d 24

e 28
f 42
g 60
h 108

3 Complete the factorisations below:

  a $36 = 6 \times$ ....
  b $38 = 2 \times$ ....
  c $48 = 12 \times$ ....
  d $90 = 5 \times$ ....

  e $88 = 8 \times$ ....
  f $54 = 3 \times$ ....
  g $72 = 12 \times$ ....
  h $60 = 12 \times$ ....

4 Write the largest factor other than itself, for each of the following numbers:

  a 18
  b 30
  c 35
  d 49

  e 88
  f 143
  g 126
  h 219

5 **a** Beginning with 6, write three consecutive even numbers.

  b Beginning with 11, write five consecutive odd numbers.

6 **a** Find two consecutive even numbers which add to 34.

  b Find two non-consecutive odd numbers which add to 8.

  c Find all the pairs of two non-consecutive positive odd numbers which add to 16.

7 Use the words "even" and "odd" to complete these sentences correctly:

  a The sum of two even numbers is always ......

  b The sum of two odd numbers is always ......

  c The sum of three even numbers is always ......

  d The sum of three odd numbers is always ......

  e The sum of an odd number and an even number is always ......

  f When an even number is subtracted from an odd number the result is ......

  g When an odd number is subtracted from an odd number the result is ......

  h The product of two odd numbers is always ......

  i The product of an even and an odd number is always ......

PRIMES AND COMPOSITES

Prime numbers can be written as the product of only one pair of factors, one and the number itself.

For example, the only two factors of 3 are 3 and 1, and of 11 are 11 and 1.

A **prime** number is a natural number which has exactly two different factors.

A **composite** number is a natural number which has more than two factors.

From the definition of prime and composite numbers we can see that:

The number 1 is neither prime nor composite.

Primes numbers are used in coding and cryptography.

PRIME FACTORS

8 is a **composite number** since it has 4 factors: 1, 8, 2, 4.

We can write 8 as the product 2×4, or as the product of prime factors $2 \times 2 \times 2$.

The **fundamental theorem of arithmetic** is:

Every composite number can be written as the product of prime factors in exactly one way (ignoring order).

So, although $252 = 2^2 \times 3^2 \times 7$ or $3^2 \times 7 \times 2^2$, the factors of 252 cannot involve different prime base numbers.

If 1 was a prime number then there would not be only one factorisation for each composite number. For example, we could write the prime factorisation of 252 as $1^3 \times 2^2 \times 3^2 \times 7$ or $1^7 \times 2^2 \times 3^2 \times 7$. For this reason 1 is neither prime nor composite.

To express a composite number as the **product of prime numbers**, we systematically divide the number by the prime numbers which are its factors, starting with the smallest.

Example 6   ◀) **Self Tutor**

Express 252 as the product of prime factors.

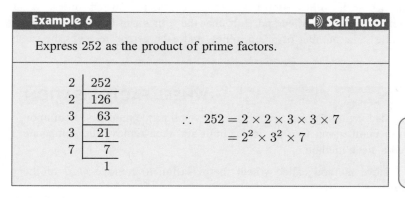

$$\therefore \quad 252 = 2 \times 2 \times 3 \times 3 \times 7$$
$$= 2^2 \times 3^2 \times 7$$

We divide by primes until we are left with 1. We usually write the result in exponent form.

EXERCISE 1C.2

1   **a**   List all the prime numbers less than 60.

  b   How many prime numbers are even? List them.

2   Show that the following are composites by finding a factor other than 1 or itself:

  a 985   **b** 7263   **c** 5840   **d** 1001

3   Express each of the following numbers as a product of prime factors:

  a 14   **b** 20   **c** 28   **d** 32   **e** 40

4   Use your list of prime numbers to help you find:

  a   the smallest odd prime   **b**   all odd two-digit composite numbers less than 30

  c   a prime number whose two digits differ by 7.

HIGHEST COMMON FACTOR

A number which is a factor of two or more other numbers is called a **common factor** of those numbers.

For example, 5 is a common factor of 25 and 35.

We can find the **highest common factor (HCF)** of two or more natural numbers by first expressing them as the product of prime factors.

Example 7   ◀) **Self Tutor**

Find the highest common factor (HCF) of 18 and 24.

2	18		2	24
3	9		2	12
3	3		2	6
	1		3	3
				1

$18 = 2 \times 3 \times 3$

$24 = 2 \times 2 \times 2 \times 3$

2×3 is common to the factorisations of both 18 and 24.

So, the highest common factor of 18 and 24 is $2 \times 3 = 6$.

EXERCISE 1C.3

1 Find the highest common factor of:

 a 8 and 12 **b** 9 and 15 **c** 14 and 21 **d** 27 and 36

 e 26 and 39 **f** 18 and 30 **g** 18, 24, and 45 **h** 32, 60, and 108

2 Alice has a packet containing 48 green lollies. Bob has a packet containing 56 red lollies. What is the highest number of friends, including Alice and Bob, that the lollies can be shared amongst so that each person receives the same number of green lollies, and each person receives the same number of red lollies?

INVESTIGATION	WHEEL FACTORISATION

There are several different methods for finding prime numbers. For small prime numbers, a common way to search is to start with all numbers up to a particular limit and then remove the composite numbers and one. This is called a **sieve** method.

In this investigation we use a sieve method called **wheel factorisation** to remove *most* of the composite numbers up to 100.

What to do:

1 The smallest prime numbers are 2 and 3.
$2 \times 3 = 6$, so we write the numbers from 1 to 6 in a circle.

2 We continue to write the numbers all the way to 100 by adding more circles as shown. Notice how the lines of numbers extend out like the spokes of a wheel.

Click on the icon to load a completed printable wheel.

PRINTABLE WORKSHEET

3 Cross out the number 1, since this is not prime.

4 For spokes 2 and 3, which were the prime numbers used in step **1**, cross out all numbers except these primes.

5 For spokes 4 and 6, which are composite numbers, cross out all numbers.

6 The remaining numbers in the wheel are *mostly* primes. Sort through them and identify those which are not. What do you notice about the prime factors of these numbers?

D | MULTIPLES OF POSITIVE INTEGERS

The **multiples** of any whole number have that number as a factor. They are obtained by multiplying the number by 1, then 2, then 3, then 4, and so on.

The multiples of 10 are 1×10, 2×10, 3×10, 4×10, 5×10, ...

  or   10, 20, 30, 40, 50, ...

Likewise, the multiples of 15 are 15, 30, 45, 60, 75, ...

The number 30 is a multiple of both 10 and 15, so we say 30 is a **common multiple** of 10 and 15.

Example 8   ◀⬥ **Self Tutor**

Find common multiples of 4 and 6 between 20 and 40.

The multiples of 4 are 4, 8, 12, 16, 20, 24, 28, 32, 36, 40, ...

The multiples of 6 are 6, 12, 18, 24, 30, 36, 42, ...

∴ the common multiples between 20 and 40 are 24 and 36.

LOWEST COMMON MULTIPLE

The **lowest common multiple (LCM)** of two or more numbers is the smallest number which is a multiple of *each* of those numbers.

Example 9   ◀⬥ **Self Tutor**

Find the lowest common multiple of 9 and 12.

The multiples of 9 are: 9, 18, 27, 36, 45, 54, 63, 72, 81, ...

The multiples of 12 are: 12, 24, 36, 48, 60, 72, 84, ...

∴   the common multiples are 36, 72, ... and 36 is the smallest of these

∴   the LCM is 36.

EXERCISE 1D

1 List the first six multiples of:

  a 4   **b** 5   **c** 7   **d** 11

2 Find the:

  a fourth multiple of 6   **b** sixth multiple of 9.

3 List the numbers from 1 to 40.

  a Put a circle around each multiple of 3.

  b Put a square around each multiple of 5.

  c List the common multiples of 3 and 5 which are less than 40.

4   Consider the following list of multiples of 12:   12 24 36 48 60 72 84 96 108 120
State the numbers from the list which are common multiples of:

   a   9 and 12   **b**   12 and 15   **c**   9, 12, and 15

5   Find the lowest common multiple of the following sets:

   a   2 and 5   **b**   3 and 7   **c**   4 and 5   **d**   6 and 8

   e   6 and 9   **f**   10 and 12   **g**   4, 5, and 7   **h**   6, 9, and 12

6   Find:

   a   the smallest multiple of 7 that is greater than 100

   b   the greatest multiple of 9 that is less than 200.

7   Three clocks start chiming at exactly the same instant. One chimes every 3 hours, one every 4 hours, and the other every six hours. When will they next chime together?

8   The football fields at three different schools were measured, and it was found that their perimeters were 320 m, 360 m, and 400 m. If the students at each school are to run the same distance, and this must be a whole number of laps, what is the shortest distance they need to run?

E   ORDER OF OPERATIONS

When two or more operations are carried out, different answers can result depending on the **order** in which the operations are performed.

For example, consider the expression $11 - 4 \times 2$.

Bruce decided to subtract first,
then multiply:

$$11 - 4 \times 2$$
$$= 7 \times 2$$
$$= 14$$

Poj decided to multiply first,
then subtract:

$$11 - 4 \times 2$$
$$= 11 - 8$$
$$= 3$$

Which answer is correct, 14 or 3?

To avoid this problem, a set of rules for the **order of performing operations** has been agreed upon by all mathematicians.

RULES FOR ORDER OF OPERATIONS

> - Perform operations within **B**rackets first.
> - Calculate any part involving **E**xponents.
> - Starting from the left, perform all **D**ivisions and **M**ultiplications as you come to them.
> - Finally, working from the left, perform all **A**dditions and **S**ubtractions.
>
> The word **BEDMAS** may help you remember this order.

Note: - If an expression contains more than one set of brackets, evaluate the innermost brackets first.
      - The division line of fractions behaves like a set of brackets. This means that the numerator and denominator must each be found before doing the division.

Using these rules, Poj's method is correct in the above example, and $11 - 4 \times 2 = 3$.

Example 10 ◀) **Self Tutor**

Evaluate: $35 - 10 \div 2 \times 5 + 3$

$$
\begin{aligned}
&35 - 10 \div 2 \times 5 + 3 \\
&= 35 - 5 \times 5 + 3 \qquad \text{\{division and multiplication working from left\}} \\
&= 35 - 25 + 3 \\
&= 10 + 3 \qquad \text{\{subtraction and addition working from left\}} \\
&= 13
\end{aligned}
$$

EXERCISE 1E.1

1 Evaluate the following:

   a $6 - 3 + 4$ **b** $7 \times 4 \div 2$ **c** $3 + 2 \times 5$

   d $3 \times 2 - 1$ **e** $16 \div 4 \times 2$ **f** $15 \div 5 + 2$

   g $9 - 6 \div 3$ **h** $4 + 7 - 3 \times 2$ **i** $3 \times 4 - 2 \times 5$

   j $3 + 9 \div 3 - 2$ **k** $7 - 9 \div 3 \times 2$ **l** $13 - 2 \times 6 + 7$

Example 11 ◀) **Self Tutor**

Evaluate: $2 \times (3 \times 6 - 4) + 7$

$$
\begin{aligned}
&2 \times (3 \times 6 - 4) + 7 \\
&= 2 \times (18 - 4) + 7 \qquad \text{\{inside brackets, multiply\}} \\
&= 2 \times 14 + 7 \qquad \text{\{evaluate expression in brackets\}} \\
&= 28 + 7 \qquad \text{\{multiplication next\}} \\
&= 35 \qquad \text{\{addition last\}}
\end{aligned}
$$

If you do not follow the order rules, you are likely to get the wrong answer.

2 Evaluate the following:

   a $(11 - 6) \times 3$ **b** $9 \div (7 - 4)$ **c** $(2 + 7) \div 3$

   d $4 \times (6 - 2)$ **e** $7 + (2 + 3) \times 5$ **f** $18 \div (1 + 5) - 1$

   g $2 + 3 \times (7 - 2)$ **h** $3 + (17 - 8) \div 9$ **i** $4 \times 3 - (6 - 2)$

   j $4 \div (3 - 1) + 6$ **k** $(7 + 11) \div (7 - 4)$ **l** $(4 - 1) \times (7 + 5)$

   m $2 \times (3 - 4) + (7 - 1)$ **n** $(14 - 3 \times 2) \div (7 - 3)$ **o** $(22 - 3 \times 5) \times (8 - 3 \times 2)$

Example 12 ◀) **Self Tutor**

Evaluate: $5 + [13 - (8 \div 4)]$

$$
\begin{aligned}
&5 + [13 - (8 \div 4)] \\
&= 5 + [13 - 2] \qquad \text{\{innermost brackets first\}} \\
&= 5 + 11 \qquad \text{\{remaining brackets next\}} \\
&= 16 \qquad \text{\{addition last\}}
\end{aligned}
$$

Evaluate the innermost brackets first.

3 Simplify:

 a $3 \times [2 + (7 - 5)]$ **b** $3 + [2 \times (7 - 5)]$ **c** $[(13 - 7) \div 2] + 11$

 d $[14 \div (2 + 5)] \times 3$ **e** $3 + [32 \div (2 + 6)] \div 2$ **f** $3 \times [(32 \div 2) + 6] - 2$

Example 13   ◀) **Self Tutor**

Evaluate: $\dfrac{16 - (4 - 2)}{14 \div (3 + 4)}$

For a fraction we evaluate the numerator and denominator separately, then perform the division.

$\dfrac{16 - (4 - 2)}{14 \div (3 + 4)}$

$= \dfrac{16 - 2}{14 \div 7}$ {brackets first}

$= \dfrac{14}{2}$ {evaluate numerator, denominator}

$= 7$ {do the division}

---

4 Simplify:

 a $\dfrac{19 - 3}{2}$ **b** $\dfrac{11 - 6}{4 \times 5}$ **c** $\dfrac{6 \times (7 - 2)}{10}$ **d** $\dfrac{18 - 2 \times 7}{6 \div 3}$

5 Simplify:

 a $3 + 5^2$ **b** $7^2 - 18$ **c** $5^2 - 6 \times 2$

 d $(13 - 4) \div 3^2$ **e** $48 \div (5 - 3)^2$ **f** $2 \times 3^3 - (11 - 7)^2$

6 Simplify:

 a $3 \times -2 + 18$ **b** $-3 \times -2 - 18$ **c** $23 - 5 \times -3$

 d $[3 - (-2 + 7)] + 4$ **e** $(18 \div 3) \times -2$ **f** $2(7 - 13) - (6 - 12)$

 g $-6 \times (2 - 7)$ **h** $-(14 - 8) \div -2$ **i** $-18 - (8 - 15)$

 j $-52 \div (6 - 19)$ **k** $\dfrac{38 - -4}{6 \times -7}$ **l** $\dfrac{28 - (-3 \times 4)}{10 \times -2}$

USING A CALCULATOR

Modern calculators are designed to use BEDMAS automatically. However, unless your calculator has a *natural mathematics* mode, you need to be careful that with fractions you place the numerator in brackets and also the denominator in brackets.

GRAPHICS CALCULATOR INSTRUCTIONS

Example 14   ◀) **Self Tutor**

Use your calculator to simplify $\dfrac{27 + 13}{5 \times 4}$.

We first write the fraction as $\dfrac{(27 + 13)}{(5 \times 4)}$.

So, $\dfrac{27 + 13}{5 \times 4} = 2$.

Casio fx-CG20

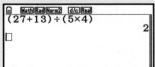

Notice the use of brackets.

EXERCISE 1E.2

1 Use your calculator to simplify:

a $6 \times 8 - 18 \div (2 + 4)$

b $10 \div 5 + 20 \div (4 + 1)$

c $5 + (2 \times 10 - 5) - 6$

d $18 - (15 \div 3 + 4) + 1$

e $(2 \times 3 - 4) + (33 \div 11 + 5)$

f $(18 \div 3 + 3) \div (4 \times 4 - 7)$

g $(50 \div 5 + 6) - (8 \times 2 - 4)$

h $(10 \times 3 - 20) + 3 \times (9 \div 3 + 2)$

i $(7 - 3 \times 2) \div (8 \div 4 - 1)$

j $(5 + 3) \times 2 + 10 \div (8 - 3)$

k $\dfrac{27 - (18 \div 3) + 3}{3 \times 4}$

l $\dfrac{620 - 224}{9 \times 4 \times 11}$

F · SPECIAL NUMBER SETS

You should be familiar with the following important number sets:

- $\mathbb{N}$ is the set of **natural** or **counting** numbers 0, 1, 2, 3, 4, 5, 6, 7, ...
- $\mathbb{Z}$ is the set of all **integers** 0, ± 1, ± 2, ± 3, ± 4, ...
- $\mathbb{Q}$ is the set of all **rational numbers**, or numbers which can be written in the form $\dfrac{p}{q}$ where p and q are integers and $q \neq 0$.
- $\mathbb{R}$ is the set of all **real numbers**, which are all numbers which can be placed on the number line.

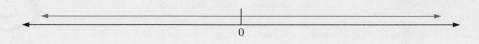

If we are considering positive numbers only, we indicate this with a + symbol:

- $\mathbb{Z}^+$ is the set of all **positive integers** 1, 2, 3, 4, 5, ...
- $\mathbb{Q}^+$ is the set of all **positive rational numbers**.
- $\mathbb{R}^+$ is the set of all **positive real numbers**.

Example 15	◀) **Self Tutor**

Explain why:

a any positive integer is also a rational number

b -7 is a rational number

a We can write any positive integer as a fraction where the number itself is the numerator, and the denominator is 1.

For example, $5 = \frac{5}{1}$.

So, all positive integers are rational numbers.

b $-7 = \dfrac{-7}{1}$, so -7 is rational.

All **terminating** and **recurring decimal numbers** can be shown to be rational.

Example 16   ◀) **Self Tutor**

Show that the following are rational numbers:

   a   0.47   **b**   0.135

   a $0.47 = \frac{47}{100}$,   so 0.47 is rational.

   b $0.135 = \frac{135}{1000} = \frac{27}{200}$,   so 0.135 is rational.

All **terminating** decimal numbers are rational.

Example 17   ◀) **Self Tutor**

Show that the following recurring decimal numbers are rational:

   a   0.777 777 7....   **b**   0.363 636 ....

   a   Let $x = 0.777\,777\,7....$

      $\therefore \;\; 10x = 7.777\,777\,7....$

      $\therefore \;\; 10x = 7 + 0.777\,777....$

      $\therefore \;\; 10x = 7 + x$

      $\therefore \;\; 9x = 7$

      $\therefore \;\; x = \frac{7}{9}$

    So, $0.777\,777.... = \frac{7}{9}$,

    which is rational.

   b   Let $x = 0.363\,636....$

      $\therefore \;\; 100x = 36.363\,636....$

      $\therefore \;\; 100x = 36 + 0.363\,636....$

      $\therefore \;\; 100x = 36 + x$

      $\therefore \;\; 99x = 36$

      $\therefore \;\; x = \frac{36}{99}$

      $\therefore \;\; x = \frac{4}{11}$

    So, $0.363\,636.... = \frac{4}{11}$,

    which is rational.

All **recurring** decimal numbers are rational.

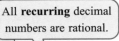

EXERCISE 1F.1

1   Show that 8 and -11 are rational numbers.

2   Why is $\frac{4}{0}$ not a rational number?

3   Show that the following are rational numbers:

   a   0.8   **b**   0.71   **c**   0.45   **d**   0.219   **e**   0.864

4   True or false?

   a -136 is a natural number.   **b** $\frac{15}{2}$ is a rational number.   **c** $\frac{14}{2}$ is not an integer.

5   Show that the following are rational numbers:

   a   0.444 444 ....   **b**   0.212 121 ....   **c**   0.325 325 325 ....

6   On the table, indicate with a tick or cross whether the numbers in the left hand column belong to $\mathbb{Q}$, $\mathbb{Q}^{+}$, $\mathbb{Z}$, $\mathbb{Z}^{+}$, or $\mathbb{N}$.

	$\mathbb{Q}$	$\mathbb{Q}^{+}$	$\mathbb{Z}$	$\mathbb{Z}^{+}$	$\mathbb{N}$
3					
-2					
1.5					
0					
$-\frac{1}{2}$					

IRRATIONAL NUMBERS

All real numbers are either rational or irrational.

> **Irrational numbers** cannot be written in the form $\dfrac{p}{q}$ where p and q are integers, $q \neq 0$.
>
> The set of irrational numbers is denoted by $\mathbb{Q}'$.

Numbers such as $\sqrt{2}$, $\sqrt{3}$, $\sqrt{5}$, and $\sqrt{7}$ are all irrational. Their decimal expansions neither terminate nor recur.

Other irrationals include $\pi \approx 3.141\,593\,....$ which is the ratio of a circle's circumference to its diameter, and exponential $e \approx 2.718\,281\,828\,235\,....$ which has applications in finance and modelling.

EXERCISE 1F.2

1 Which of the following are irrational numbers?

    a 3.127   **b** $\sqrt{8}$ **c** $\sqrt{4}$ **d** $\sqrt{1}$

2 Show that $\sqrt{\frac{9}{25}}$ is a rational number.

3 On the table, indicate with a tick or cross whether the numbers in the left hand column belong to $\mathbb{Q}$, $\mathbb{R}$, $\mathbb{Z}$, $\mathbb{Q}'$, or $\mathbb{N}$.

	$\mathbb{Q}$	$\mathbb{R}$	$\mathbb{Z}$	$\mathbb{Q}'$	$\mathbb{N}$
$\sqrt{2}$					
5					
$-\frac{1}{3}$					
2.17					
-9					

REVIEW SET 1A

1 Find: **a** the sum of 28 and 18   **b** the quotient of 425 and 17

          c the difference between 246 and 81   **d** the product of 29 and 12.

2 Arnold does 37 situps on Wednesday, 45 on Thursday, and 29 on Friday. How many situps has Arnold done over the three day period?

3 Write $2 \times 2 \times 5 \times 5 \times 5 \times 7$:   **a** in exponent form   **b** as a natural number.

4 Evaluate: **a** 3^2 **b** $(-5)^2$ **c** -7^2 **d** -2^3

5 The ancient Greeks compared the brightness of stars by giving them a "magnitude number". They said a magnitude 1 star (the brightest) was twice as bright as a magnitude 2 star, which was twice as bright as a magnitude 3 star, and so on.

    a How many times brighter was a magnitude 1 star than a magnitude 3 star?

    b The lowest magnitude was 6. How many times brighter was the brightest star than the faintest star?

6 List all the:

    a multiples of 7 between 80 and 100   **b** prime numbers between 30 and 40

    c pairs of positive even numbers that add to 22.

7 List all the factors of:

    a 34   **b** 31   **c** 36   **d** 45

8 Find the highest common factor of:

    a 16 and 20   **b** 54 and 72   **c** 56 and 70

9 Find the lowest common multiple of:

    a 6 and 10   **b** 7 and 8   **c** 3, 4, and 5

10 Evaluate: **a** $12 + 27 \div 3$ **b** $3 \times (5 - 2)$ **c** $(11 - 5) \times (3 + 4)$

11 Simplify: **a** $\dfrac{7 + 17}{3 - 1}$ **b** $7^2 - 4 \times 5$ **c** $-6 - 5 - 4$

12 For each of the following numbers, state if they are rational or irrational. If the number is rational, prove your claim.

    a $\frac{4}{7}$ **b** 0.165 **c** $\frac{8}{0}$ **d** 56 **e** $\sqrt{5}$ **f** $0.181\,818\,....$

REVIEW SET 1B

1 Zhang starts the day with \$487 in his wallet. During the day he buys lunch for \$12, pays \$175 in rent, and buys \$29 worth of phone credit. How much money is left in Zhang's wallet?

2 Every hour, a factory produces 23 boxes of soap. Each box contains 25 bars of soap. How many bars of soap are produced in an 8 hour working day?

3 Simplify: **a** $(-1)^4$ **b** $(-1)^{13}$ **c** $-(-2)^5$ **d** -7.1^2

4 Find the sum of all the odd numbers between 70 and 80.

5 Show that 2241 is a composite number.

6 Express each number as the product of prime factors in exponent form:

    a 33   **b** 60   **c** 56

7   **a** List all the pairs of factors of 42.   **b** Write down all the factors of 18.

8 Find the: **a** HCF of 48 and 45   **b** LCM of 12 and 20.

9 A shop runs a promotion in which every 500th customer receives a free gift, every 800th customer receives a voucher, and every 1200th customer gets a discount on their purchases. Which customer is the first to receive a free gift, a voucher, *and* a discount?

10 Evaluate: **a** $[8 - (1 + 2)] \times 3$ **b** $15 \div (2 + 3)$ **c** $6^2 \div 2 + 4$

11 Simplify: **a** $-3 \times (5 + 7)$ **b** $\dfrac{-4 \times 8}{24 \div 3}$ **c** $6 - (2 - 8)$

12 On the table, indicate with a tick or cross whether the numbers in the left hand column belong to $\mathbb{Q}$, $\mathbb{R}$, $\mathbb{Z}$, $\mathbb{Q}'$, or $\mathbb{N}$.

	$\mathbb{Q}$	$\mathbb{R}$	$\mathbb{Z}$	$\mathbb{Q}'$	$\mathbb{N}$
3.91					
$\sqrt{4}$					
-18					
π					
0					

Chapter **2**

Measurement

Syllabus reference: 1.2, 1.3, 1.4, 1.5

DISCUSSION

Write down five quantities which we commonly *measure*.

What devices do we use to measure these quantities?

What units are these quantities measured in?

What errors are associated with our measurements?

OPENING PROBLEM

On September 28, 2008, Ethiopian runner Haile Gebrselassie won the 42.195 km Berlin Marathon in the world record time of 2 hours 3 minutes and 59 seconds.

Things to think about:

a What is the length of the marathon in metres?

b Can you write the time taken by Haile in:

   i seconds   **ii** hours?

c What was Haile's average speed for the marathon?

A   TIME

For thousands of years people measured time by observing the passage of day and night, the stars, and the changes of season. This was necessary to help them with farming and other aspects of daily life.

The earliest inventions for measuring time included the sundial, the hourglass, and the waterclock or *clepsydra*.

Over the centuries many different devices were made to measure time more accurately, eventually leading to the watches and clocks we use today. The most accurate clock in the world, the cesium fountain atomic clock, is inaccurate by only one second every 20 million years.

© iStockphoto

UNITS OF TIME

The units of time we use are based on the sun, the moon, and the Earth's rotation.

The most common units are related as follows:

© iStockphoto

Musée de l'Agora antique d'Athènes, photo from Wikimedia Commons

> 1 minute = 60 seconds
> 1 hour = 60 minutes = 3600 seconds
> 1 day = 24 hours
> 1 week = 7 days
> 1 year = 12 months = $365\frac{1}{4}$ days

For times which are longer or shorter we either multiply or divide by powers of 10:

$$1 \text{ millisecond} = \frac{1}{1000} \text{ second}$$

$$1 \text{ microsecond} = \frac{1}{1\,000\,000} \text{ second}$$

1 decade = 10 years
1 century = 100 years
1 millennium = 1000 years

Example 1 ◀)) Self Tutor

Convert 3 hours 26 minutes 18 seconds into seconds.

3 h 26 min 18 s
$= (3 \times 3600) \text{ s} + (26 \times 60) \text{ s} + 18 \text{ s}$
$= 12\,378 \text{ s}$

We use h for hours,
min for minutes,
s for seconds.

Example 2 ◀)) Self Tutor

What is the time difference between 11:43 am and 3:18 pm?

11:43 am to 12 noon =   17 min
12 noon to 3 pm = 3 h
3 pm to 3:18 pm =   18 min
∴   the time difference is   3 h 35 min

Example 3 ◀)) Self Tutor

What is the time $3\frac{1}{2}$ hours before 1:15 pm?

$1\text{:}15 \text{ pm} - 3\frac{1}{2} \text{ hours}$
$= 1\text{:}15 \text{ pm} - 3 \text{ h} - 30 \text{ min}$
$= 10\text{:}15 \text{ am} - 30 \text{ min}$
$= 9\text{:}45 \text{ am}$

EXERCISE 2A

1 Convert into seconds:
   a   45 minutes
   b   1 hour 10 minutes
   c   2 hours 5 minutes 28 seconds

2 Convert into minutes:
   a $3\frac{1}{2}$ hours
   b   1440 seconds
   c   5 hours 13 minutes
   d   3 days 1 hour 48 minutes

3 Find the time difference between:
   a   2:30 am and 7:20 am
   b   10:14 am and 1:51 pm
   c   5:18 pm and 11:32 pm
   d   3:42 pm and 6:08 am the next day.

4 Joseph caught the 7:54 am train into town, arriving in the main station at 8:47 am. It took him 16 minutes to walk from the station to work.

    a How long was Joseph's train journey?   **b** At what time did Joseph arrive at work?

5 Find the time that is:

    a 3 hours after 7:15 am   **b** $5\frac{1}{2}$ hours before 10:26 am

    c $4\frac{1}{2}$ hours after 11:50 am   **d** $6\frac{1}{2}$ hours before 2:35 am.

6 I left for work $1\frac{1}{4}$ hours after I woke up. If I left at 8:05 am, at what time did I wake up?

7 My brother overseas telephoned me at 3:47 am. I was very angry and told him I would ring him back when I woke up in the morning. If I woke up at 7:04 am, how long did my brother have to wait for the return call?

THEORY OF KNOWLEDGE

There are several theories for why one complete turn was divided into 360 degrees:

- 360 is approximately the number of days in a year.
- The Babylonians used a counting system in base 60. If they drew 6 equilateral triangles within a circle as shown, and divided each angle into 60 subdivisions, then there were 360 subdivisions in one turn. The division of an hour into 60 minutes, and a minute into 60 seconds, is from this base 60 counting system.
- 360 has 24 divisors, including every integer from 1 to 10 except 7.

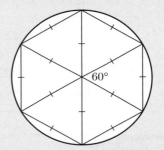

1 What other measures of angle are there?

2 Which is the most *natural* unit of angle measure?

B   TEMPERATURE

There are two units which are commonly used to measure temperature: degrees Celsius (°C) and degrees Fahrenheit (°F).

We can compare the two units by looking at the temperatures at which water freezes and boils.

	Celsius (°C)	Fahrenheit (°F)
water freezes	0	32
water boils	100	212

Using this information we can construct a **conversion graph** to help us change between units.

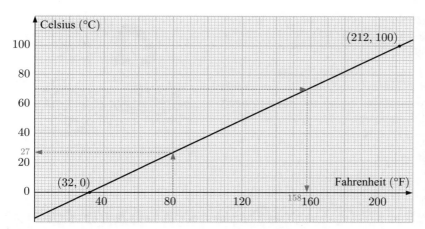

For example, we see that:
- 70°C is about 158°F
- 80°F is about 27°C.

CONVERSION FORMULAE

To convert between the temperature units exactly we can use the following conversion formulae:

If C is in degrees Celsius and F is in degrees Fahrenheit then:
- to convert °C to °F, use $F = \frac{9}{5}C + 32$
- to convert °F to °C, use $C = \frac{5}{9}(F - 32)$

Example 4 ◀) Self Tutor

Convert: **a** 392°F to °C   **b** 30°C to °F

a
$$C = \frac{5}{9}(F - 32)$$
$$\therefore \ C = \frac{5}{9}(392 - 32)$$
$$\therefore \ C = 200$$
So, 392°F = 200°C

b
$$F = \frac{9}{5}C + 32$$
$$\therefore \ F = \frac{9}{5} \times 30 + 32$$
$$\therefore \ F = 86$$
So, 30°C = 86°F

EXERCISE 2B

1 Use the conversion graph to estimate the temperature in degrees Celsius for:
  a 60°F   **b** 180°F   **c** 10°F

2 Use the conversion graph to estimate the temperature in degrees Fahrenheit for:
  a 60°C   **b** 40°C   **c** 15°C

3 Convert into °C:
  a 0°F   **b** 100°F   **c** 20°F

4 Convert into °F:
  a 70°C   **b** −10°C   **c** 400°C

5 Rearrange $F = \frac{9}{5}C + 32$ to show that $C = \frac{5}{9}(F - 32)$.

DEMO

6   **a**   Jonte, in Johannesburg, notices on the Weather Channel that the temperature in New York is $-16°F$. Convert this temperature into degrees Celsius.

   b   Mary-Lou lives in Los Angeles. She is going to Sydney for a holiday and is told to expect temperatures around $25°C$ during the day. Convert $25°C$ to degrees Fahrenheit.

7   Find the temperature which is the same in degrees Celsius as it is in degrees Fahrenheit.

C   SCIENTIFIC NOTATION (STANDARD FORM)

Many people doing scientific work deal with very large or very small numbers. To avoid having to write and count lots of zeros, they use **scientific notation** to write numbers.

Observe the pattern:

$$\div 10 \left(\begin{array}{l} 10\,000 = 10^4 \\ 1000 = 10^3 \\ 100 = 10^2 \\ 10 = 10^1 \\ 1 = 10^0 \\ \frac{1}{10} = 10^{-1} \\ \frac{1}{100} = 10^{-2} \\ \frac{1}{1000} = 10^{-3} \end{array} \right.$$

As we divide by 10, the **index** or **exponent** of 10 decreases by one.

We can use this pattern to write very large and very small numbers easily.

For example:
$$\begin{aligned} & 5\,000\,000 \\ =\ & 5 \times 1\,000\,000 \\ =\ & 5 \times 10^6 \end{aligned}$$
and
$$\begin{aligned} & 0.000\,003 \\ =\ & \frac{3}{1\,000\,000} \\ =\ & 3 \times \frac{1}{1\,000\,000} \\ =\ & 3 \times 10^{-6} \end{aligned}$$

Scientific notation or **standard form** involves writing a given number as a number between 1 and 10, multiplied by a power of 10.

The number is written in the form $a \times 10^k$ where $1 \leqslant a < 10$ and k is an integer.

A number such as 4.62 is already between 1 and 10. We write it in scientific notation as 4.62×10^0 since $10^0 = 1$.

Your calculator is also able to display numbers using scientific notation.

GRAPHICS CALCULATOR INSTRUCTIONS

Example 5   ◀)) **Self Tutor**

Write in scientific notation:

  a $9\,448\,800\,000$

  b $0.000\,000\,053\,04$

a $9\,448\,800\,000$ $= 9.4488 \times 1\,000\,000\,000$ So, $a = 9.4488$ and $k = 9$ The number is 9.4488×10^9.	**b** $0.000\,000\,053\,04$ $= 5.304 \div 100\,000\,000$ So, $a = 5.304$ and $k = -8$ The number is 5.304×10^{-8}.

Example 6   ◀)) **Self Tutor**

Use your calculator to evaluate:

  a $870\,000 \times 95\,000\,000$

  b $\dfrac{6.2 \times 10^3}{8 \times 10^{12}}$

TI-nspire

Casio fx-CG20	TI-84 Plus	

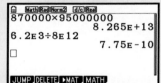
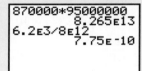

  a $870\,000 \times 95\,000\,000 = 8.265 \times 10^{13}$

  b $\dfrac{6.2 \times 10^3}{8 \times 10^{12}} = 7.75 \times 10^{-10}$

EXERCISE 2C

1 Which of the following numbers are *not* written in scientific notation?

  a 3.7×10^4 **b** 4.2×10^{-7} **c** 0.3×10^5 **d** 21×10^{11}

2 Copy and complete:

$$1000 = 10^3$$
$$100 = 10^2$$
$$10 =$$
$$1 =$$
$$0.1 =$$
$$0.01 = 10^{-2}$$
$$0.001 =$$
$$0.0001 =$$

3 Write as decimal numbers:

  a 8.2×10^4 **b** 3.6×10^1 **c** 8.7×10^0 **d** 4.9×10^2

  e 7.8×10^{-3} **f** 5.5×10^{-2} **g** 3.76×10^{-1} **h** 2.02×10^{-3}

4   Write in scientific notation:

    a   3900   **b**   17 000   **c**   0.04   **d**   0.000 071

    e   85   **f**   6.3   **g**   2 480 000   **h**   0.000 000 108

5   Write these calculator displays in scientific notation:

    a $\boxed{\text{4.5E07}}$ **b** $\boxed{\text{3.8E-04}}$ **c** $\boxed{\text{2.1E05}}$ **d** $\boxed{\text{4.0E-03}}$

    e $\boxed{\text{6.1E03}}$ **f** $\boxed{\text{1.6E-06}}$ **g** $\boxed{\text{3.9E04}}$ **h** $\boxed{\text{6.7E-02}}$

6   Write the numbers displayed in question **5** as decimal numbers.

    For example, $\boxed{\text{3.9E06}}$ is 3.9×10^6

$$= 3.900\,000 \times 1\,000\,000$$
$$= 3\,900\,000$$

> In an exam it is **not** acceptable to write your answer as a calculator display.

7   Use your calculator to evaluate the following, giving your answer in scientific notation:

    a $680\,000 \times 73\,000\,000$ **b** 900^4 **c** $0.0006 \div 15\,000$

    d $(0.0007)^3$ **e** $5.3 \times 10^8 \times 6.4 \times 10^5$ **f** $2.6 \times 10^4 \times 3.7 \times 10^{-9}$

    g $\dfrac{3.6 \times 10^4}{7.5 \times 10^{11}}$ **h** $\dfrac{4.9 \times 10^{-5}}{1.12 \times 10^6}$

8   Write as a decimal number:

    a   The estimated population of the world in the year 2020 is 7.4×10^9 people.

    b   The pressure at the edge of the Earth's thermosphere is about 1.0×10^{-7} Pa.

    c   The diameter of the Milky Way is 1.4×10^5 light years.

    d   The mass of a proton is about 1.67×10^{-27} kg.

9   Express the following in scientific notation:

    a   The Jurassic period lasted about 54 400 000 years.

    b   The ball bearing in a pen nib has diameter 0.003 m.

    c   There are about 311 900 000 different 5-card poker hands which can be dealt.

    d   The wavelength of blue light is about 0.000 000 47 m.

10   Last year a peanut farmer produced 6×10^4 kg of peanuts. If the peanuts weighed an average of 8×10^{-4} kg, how many peanuts did the farm produce? Give your answer in scientific notation.

INTERNATIONAL SYSTEM (SI) UNITS

HISTORICAL NOTE

The decimal **Metric** system was created at the time of the French Revolution.

Having decided that a new unit of length, the metre, should be one ten millionth of the distance from the North Pole to the Equator, **Pierre Méchain** and **Jean-Baptiste Delambre** set about surveying the 1000 km section of the meridian arc from Dunkirk to Barcelona. At the end of their survey, two platinum bars were deposited in the Archives de la République in Paris in 1799, defining the standard metre and standard kilogram.

Pierre Méchain

Despite the error in the calculations of Méchain and Jean-Baptiste, when it was decided in 1867 to create a new international standard metre, the length was taken to be that of the platinum bar still in Paris.

Jean-Baptiste Delambre

The **International system of Units**, abbreviated SI from the French *le Système international d'unités*, is the world's most widely used system of measurement.

It is founded on seven base units:

Quantity	Name	Symbol
Distance	metre	m
Mass	kilogram	kg
Time	second	s
Electric current	ampere	A
Temperature	kelvin	K
Intensity of light	candela	cd
Amount of substance	mole	mol

Other SI units, called **derived units**, are defined in terms of the base units.

Some of the common SI derived units are:

Quantity	Name	Symbol
Area	square metre	m^2
Volume	cubic metre	m^3
Mass	gram	g
Velocity	metres per second	$m\,s^{-1}$
Angle	radian	rad

Quantity	Name	Symbol
Force	newton	N
Pressure	pascal	Pa
Energy	joule	J
Power	watt	W
Frequency	hertz	Hz

When we multiply one unit by another, we leave a short space between the unit symbols.

When we divide one unit by another, we use an oblique line between the unit symbols, or a negative index. For example, we write metres per second as m/s or $m\,s^{-1}$.

Example 7   ◄)) **Self Tutor**

a   Density is defined as mass per unit volume. Write the SI unit for density.
b   A newton is defined as the force which accelerates a mass of 1 kilogram at the rate of 1 metre per second per second. Write down the combination of SI units which defines a newton.

a   The unit for mass is kg, and the unit for volume is m^3.
∴   the unit for density is kg/m^3 or $kg\,m^{-3}$.
b   1 newton = 1 kilogram × 1 metre per second per second = $1\ kg\,m\,s^{-2}$

In addition to the base and derived units, the SI allows the use of other units, such as:

Quantity	Name	Symbol	SI equivalent
Time	minute	min	60 s
	hour	h	3600 s
Mass	tonne	t	1000 kg
Capacity	litre	L	$0.001\ m^3$
Area	hectare	ha	$10\,000\ m^2$
Angle	degree	°	$\frac{\pi}{180}$ rad
Temperature	degree Celsius	°C	$K - 273.15$
Pressure	millibar	mb	100 Pa
Distance at sea	Nautical mile	Nm	1.852 km
Speed at sea	Knot	kn	$1.852\ km\,h^{-1}$
Energy	Kilowatt hour	kWh	3.6 MJ

The symbol for litre can be l or L depending on which country you are in. We use L here to avoid confusion with the number 1.

Smaller or larger multiples of these units are obtained by combining the base unit with a prefix chosen from a progression of powers of 10. The most commonly used are:

nano	n	$10^{-9} = \frac{1}{1\,000\,000\,000}$
micro	μ	$10^{-6} = \frac{1}{1\,000\,000}$
milli	m	$10^{-3} = \frac{1}{1000}$

kilo	k	$10^3 = 1000$
mega	M	$10^6 = 1\,000\,000$
giga	G	$10^9 = 1\,000\,000\,000$

The SI also accepts the prefix "centi" (10^{-2}) which can be used in conjunction with metre, litre, or gram.

When stating the value of a measurement, the prefix chosen should give the value as a number between 0.1 and 1000. Thus, one nautical mile is written as 1.852 km, not 1852 m.

The SI does not allow the use of other units. Imperial units of measurement, as used in the United States for example, are not acceptable in the international system.

For more information on SI units, visit   www.bipm.org/en/publications/si_brochure/

DISCUSSION

Does the use of SI notation help us to think of mathematics as a "universal language"?

Example 8   ◀)) **Self Tutor**

Convert:

a   3540 millimetres into metres   b   7.14 kilograms into grams

c   4 hours and 12 minutes into seconds   d   15 knots into kilometres per hour

a $1 \text{ mm} = 10^{-3} \text{ m}$

∴ $3540 \text{ mm} = 3540 \times 10^{-3}$

$= 3.54 \text{ m}$

b $1 \text{ kg} = 1000 \text{ g}$

∴ $7.14 \text{ kg} = 7.14 \times 1000$

$= 7140 \text{ g}$

c $1 \text{ h} = 3600 \text{ s}$

$1 \text{ min} = 60 \text{ s}$

∴ $4 \text{ h } 12 \text{ min} = (4 \times 3600) + (12 \times 60)$

$= 15\,120 \text{ s}$

d $1 \text{ kn} = 1.852 \text{ km h}^{-1}$

∴ $15 \text{ kn} = 15 \times 1.852$

$= 27.78 \text{ km h}^{-1}$

EXERCISE 2D

1   How many millilitres are there in 1 kilolitre?

2   How many micrometres are there in a:

   a   millimetre   b   kilometre?

3   How many μPa are there in 1 MPa?

4   Convert the following:

   a   0.025 L into mL   b   26 580 ns into μs   c   45 km into mm

   d   5840 kg into t   e   54 kWh into MJ   f   60 km h^{-1} into m s^{-1}

   g   0.14 m^2 into mm^2 h   16 m s^{-1} into km h^{-1} i   36 kn into km h^{-1}

5   Perform the following conversions, giving your answers in scientific notation:

   a   7 L into mL   b   3.8 km into mm   c   9.86 g into kg

   d   56 ha into m^2 e   10.8 s into μs   f   258 L into GL

6   Calculate the area of a rectangular field with side lengths 440 m and 75 m. Give your answer in hectares.

7   A kilowatt hour is the accepted commercial unit for selling energy. How many joules of energy are there in 60 kWh?

8   A ship has travelled 48 km in the past 3 hours. Calculate the average speed of the ship in knots.

9   A joule is defined as the energy required to exert a force of 1 newton for a distance of 1 metre. Write down the combination of SI units which describe a joule.

E | ROUNDING NUMBERS

There are many occasions when it is sensible to give an **approximate** answer.

For example, it is unreasonable to give the exact population of a country since the number is continually changing. We would not say that the population of Turkey is 71 158 647 people. It is more sensible to say that the population of Turkey is about 71 million people.

We use the symbol $\approx$ or sometimes $\doteqdot$ to show that an answer has been approximated.

RULES FOR ROUNDING OFF

- If the digit after the one being rounded off is **less than 5** (0, 1, 2, 3, or 4) we round **down**.
- If the digit after the one being rounded off is **5 or more** (5, 6, 7, 8, 9) we round **up**.

Example 9   ◀) **Self Tutor**

Round off to the nearest 10:

a 48   b 583   c 5705

a $48 \approx 50$ {Round up, as 8 is greater than 5}
b $583 \approx 580$ {Round down, as 3 is less than 5}
c $5705 \approx 5710$ {5 is rounded up}

EXERCISE 2E.1

1 Round off to the nearest 10:

a 75	b 78	c 298	d 637
e 3994	f 1651	g 9797	h 1015
i 783	j 835	k 2119	l 1995

Example 10   ◀) **Self Tutor**

Round off to the nearest 100:   a 452   b 37 239

a $452 \approx 500$ {5 is rounded up}
b $37\,239 \approx 37\,200$ {Round down, as 3 is less than 5}

---

2 Round off to the nearest 100:

a 78	b 468	c 923	d 954
e 5449	f 4765	g 13 066	h 43 951

3 Round off to the nearest 1000:

a 748	b 5500	c 9990	d 3743
e 65 438	f 123 456	g 434 576	h 570 846

4 Round off to the accuracy given:

   a The cost of an overseas holiday is $15 387. {to the nearest $1000}

   b The mass of a horse is 468 kg. {to the nearest ten kg}

   c A weekly wage of €610. {to the nearest €100}

   d The flight has length 5735 km. {to the nearest 100 km}

   e The annual amount of water used in a household was 117 489 litres. {to the nearest kilolitre}

   f The monthly income for a business was £28 817. {to the nearest £1000}

   g The box-office takings for a new movie were $6 543 722. {to the nearest hundred thousand dollars}

   h The area of a country is 32 457 hectares. {to the nearest thousand hectares}

   i In one year the average heart will beat 35 765 280 times. {to the nearest million}

   j The year's profit by a large mining company was $1 322 469 175. {to the nearest billion dollars}

ROUNDING DECIMAL NUMBERS

If a traffic survey showed that 1852 cars carried 4376 people, it would not be sensible to give the average number of people per car as 2.362 850 972. An approximate answer of 2.4 is more appropriate.

There is clearly a need to **round off** decimal numbers which have more figures in them than are required.

We can round off to a certain number of **decimal places** or **significant figures**.

Example 11	◀ Self Tutor

Round: **a** 3.27 to one decimal place   **b** 6.3829 to two decimal places.

a 3.27 has 2 in the *first* decimal place
and 7 in the *second* decimal place.
Since 7 is in the second decimal place and is greater than 5, we increase the digit in the first decimal place by 1 and delete what follows. So, $3.27 \approx 3.3$

b 6.3829 has 8 in the *second* decimal place
and 2 in the *third* decimal place.
Since 2 is less than 5, we retain the 8 and delete all digits after it.
So, $6.3829 \approx 6.38$

EXERCISE 2E.2

1 Round the following to the number of decimal places stated in brackets.

a	3.47	[1]	**b**	5.362	[2]	**c**	7.164	[1]
d	15.234	[2]	**e**	9.0246	[3]	**f**	12.6234	[1]
g	0.4372	[2]	**h**	9.276 43	[2]	**i**	0.0099	[2]

Example 12

🔊 **Self Tutor**

Calculate, to 2 decimal places:

a $(2.8 + 3.7)(0.82 - 0.57)$

b $18.6 - \dfrac{12.2 - 4.3}{5.2}$

TI-84 Plus

```
(2.8+3.7)*(0.82-
0.57)
               1.625
18.6-(12.2-4.3)/
5.2
         17.08076923
```

a $(2.8 + 3.7)(0.82 - 0.57) = 1.625$
≈ 1.63

b $18.6 - \dfrac{(12.2 - 4.3)}{5.2} \approx 17.080\,769\,23\,....$
≈ 17.08

---

2 Find, giving your answers correct to 2 decimal places where necessary:

a $(16.8 + 12.4) \times 17.1$

b $16.8 + 12.4 \times 17.1$

c $127 \div 9 - 5$

d $127 \div (9 - 5)$

e $37.4 - 16.1 \div (4.2 - 2.7)$

f $\dfrac{16.84}{7.9 + 11.2}$

g $\dfrac{27.4}{3.2} - \dfrac{18.6}{16.1}$

h $\dfrac{27.9 - 17.3}{8.6} + 4.7$

i $\dfrac{0.0768 + 7.1}{18.69 - 3.824}$

3 Over a 23 game water polo season, Kerry scored 40 goals for her team. Find Kerry's average number of goals, correct to 2 decimal places.

ROUNDING OFF TO SIGNIFICANT FIGURES

To round off to n significant figures, we look at the $(n + 1)$th digit.

- If it is 0, 1, 2, 3 or 4 we do not change the nth digit.
- If it is 5, 6, 7, 8 or 9 we increase the nth digit by 1.

We delete all digits after the nth digit, replacing by 0s if necessary.

DEMO

Example 13

🔊 **Self Tutor**

Round: **a** 7.182 to 2 significant figures

b 0.001 32 to 2 significant figures

c 423 to 1 significant figure

d 4.057 to 3 significant figures.

---

a $7.182 \approx 7.2$ (2 s.f.)

This is the 2nd significant figure, so we look at the next digit which is 8.
The 8 tells us to round the 1 up to a 2 and leave off the remaining digits.

b $0.001\,32 \approx 0.0013$ (2 s.f.)

These zeros at the front are place holders and so must stay. The first significant figure is the 1. The third significant figure, 2, tells us to leave the 3 as it is and leave off the remaining digits.

c $423 \approx 400$ (1 s.f.)

4 is the first significant figure so it has to be rounded. The second figure, 2, tells us to keep the original 4 in the hundreds place. We convert the 23 into 00. These two zeros are place holders. They are not 'significant figures' but they need to be there to make sure the 4 has value 400.

d $4.057 \approx 4.06$ (3 s.f.)

This 0 is significant as it lies between two non-zero digits. The fourth significant figure, 7, tell us to round the 5 up to a 6 and leave off the remaining digits.

In IB examinations you are expected to give answers to 3 significant figures unless otherwise specified in the question.

EXERCISE 2E.3

1 Write correct to 2 significant figures:

a   567   b   16 342   c   70.7   d   3.001   e   0.716
f   49.6   g   3.046   h   1760   i   0.0409   j   45 600

2 Write correct to 3 significant figures:

a   43 620   b   10 076   c $0.\overline{6}$ d   0.036 821   e   0.318 6
f   0.719 6   g $0.\overline{63}$ h   0.063 71   i   18.997   j   256 800

3 Write correct to 4 significant figures:

a   28.039 2   b   0.005 362   c   23 683.9   d   42 366 709
e   0.038 792   f   0.006 377 9   g   0.000 899 9   h   43.076 321

4 The crowd at an ice hockey match was officially 5838 people.

a   Round the crowd size to:

   i   1 significant figure
   ii 2 significant figures.

b   Which of these figures would be used by the media to indicate crowd size?

5 Calculate the following, giving answers correct to three significant figures:

a $56 \div 81$ b 503×904 c $\sqrt{17}$
d $\dfrac{36.2 + 19.1}{7.6}$ e $\sqrt{0.023}$ f $(0.132)^4$

6 A rocket travels at 2.8×10^4 km h^{-1} in space. Find how far it would travel in:

a   5 hours   b   a day   c   a year.

Give your answers correct to 2 significant figures.
Assume that 1 year ≈ 365.25 days.

7   Use your calculator to evaluate the following, correct to 3 significant figures:

   a $(4.7 \times 10^5) \times (8.5 \times 10^7)$ **b** $(2.7 \times 10^{-3}) \times (9.6 \times 10^9)$

   c $(3.4 \times 10^7) \div (4.8 \times 10^{15})$ **d** $(7.3 \times 10^{-7}) \div (1.5 \times 10^4)$

   e $(2.83 \times 10^3)^2$ **f** $(5.96 \times 10^{-5})^2$

8   Use your calculator to answer the following:

   a A rocket travels in space at 4×10^5 km h^{-1}. How far does
        it travel in:

        i 30 days   **ii** 20 years?

   b An electron travels 5×10^3 km in 2×10^{-5} hours.
        Find its average speed in kilometres per hour.

   c A bullet travelling at an average speed of 2000 km h^{-1} hits
        a target 500 m away.
        Find the time of flight of the bullet in seconds.

   d The planet Mars is 2.28×10^8 km from the sun, while
        Mercury is 5.79×10^7 km from the sun. How many times
        further from the sun is Mars than Mercury?

   e Microbe C has mass 2.63×10^{-5} g, whereas microbe D
        has mass 8×10^{-7} g.

        i Which microbe is heavier?

        ii How many times heavier is it than the other one?

There are 365.25 days in a year.

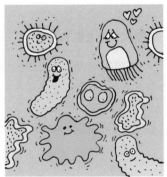

F   RATES

A **rate** is an ordered comparison of quantities of **different** kinds.

Some examples of rates are shown in the following table:

Rate	Example of units
rates of pay	dollars per hour, euros per hour
petrol consumption	litres per 100 km
annual rainfall	mm per year
unit cost	dollars per kilogram, pounds per kilogram
population density	people per square km

RESEARCH   RATE DATA

1   Obtain data from the internet for the average rainfall of your city, and the breakdown into
      average monthly rates. Compare these with rates for other cities.

2   Compare the rates of petrol consumption for different cars. Also compare the rates for 4 cylinder
      and 6 cylinder cars.

SPEED

One of the most common rates we use is **speed**, which is a comparison between the *distance travelled* and the *time taken*.

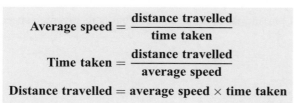

$$\text{Average speed} = \frac{\text{distance travelled}}{\text{time taken}}$$

$$\text{Time taken} = \frac{\text{distance travelled}}{\text{average speed}}$$

$$\text{Distance travelled} = \text{average speed} \times \text{time taken}$$

Cover the variable you are trying to find. You should then see it expressed in terms of the other two variables.

Because we are comparing quantities of different kinds, the units must be included. In most cases we express speed in either kilometres per hour (km h^{-1}) or in metres per second (m s^{-1}).

$$1 \ \text{km h}^{-1} = \frac{1000 \ \text{m}}{3600 \ \text{s}} = \tfrac{1}{3.6} \ \text{m s}^{-1}$$

To convert km h^{-1} into m s^{-1}, we divide by 3.6.

To convert m s^{-1} into km h^{-1}, we multiply by 3.6.

For example, suppose a car travels 144 km in 2 hours.

$$\begin{aligned}
\text{Its average speed is} \quad \frac{144 \ \text{km}}{2 \ \text{h}} &= 72 \ \text{km h}^{-1} \\
&= \frac{72}{3.6} \ \text{m s}^{-1} \\
&= 20 \ \text{m s}^{-1}
\end{aligned}$$

Example 14   ◀)) **Self Tutor**

A car is travelling a distance of 325 km.

a Find its average speed if the trip takes 4 h 17 min.

b Find the time taken if the average speed is 93 km h^{-1}.

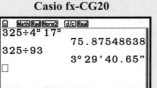

TI-*n*spire

Casio fx-CG20	TI-84 Plus

Casio fx-CG20:
```
325÷4°17'
            75.87548638
325÷93
            3°29'40.65"
```

TI-84 Plus:
```
325/4°17'
          75.87548638
325/93
          3.494623656
Ans▶DMS
        3°29'40.645"
```

TI-nspire:
```
  325
 ─────              75.8755
  4°17'

  325
 ──── ▶DMS      3°29'40.6452"
   93
```

a average speed

$$= \frac{\text{distance travelled}}{\text{time taken}}$$

$$= \frac{325 \ \text{km}}{4 \ \text{h} \ 17 \ \text{min}}$$

$$\approx 75.9 \ \text{km h}^{-1}$$

b time taken

$$= \frac{\text{distance travelled}}{\text{average speed}}$$

$$= \frac{325 \ \text{km}}{93 \ \text{km h}^{-1}}$$

$$\approx 3 \ \text{h} \ 29 \ \text{min} \ 41 \ \text{s}$$

GRAPHICS CALCULATOR INSTRUCTIONS

EXERCISE 2F.1

1 Find the average speed of a car travelling:

    a 71.2 km in 51 minutes   **b** 468 km in 5 hours 37 minutes.

2 The flight from London to Frankfurt is 634 km and takes 86 minutes. What is the average speed of the plane in $km\,h^{-1}$?

3 What is faster, $100\ km\,h^{-1}$ or $30\ m\,s^{-1}$?

4 Find the distance you would travel if you:

    a drove at an average speed of 95 $km\,h^{-1}$ for 3 h 23 min

    b rode at an average speed of 25.3 km h^{-1} for 1 h 17.5 min.

5 How long would it take to travel 42.3 km at an average walking speed of 5.7 $km\,h^{-1}$?

INVESTIGATION 1   STOPPING DISTANCES

A car does *not* stop the instant you want it to. It travels on for quite some distance before coming to rest.

Two factors control how far a car travels between when you see a problem and when the car comes to a halt.

The first is the **reaction time** it takes for the driver to react and hit the brake pedal. The distance travelled during this time is called the **reaction distance**.

The second is the **braking distance**, or distance the car travels after the brakes are applied.

Stopping distance = **distance travelled while reacting** + **distance travelled while braking**

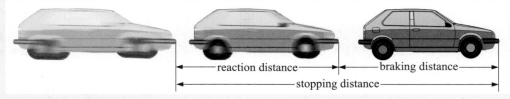

MEASURING REACTION TIME

You will need: • Electronic timer (measuring to hundredths of a second) with remote switching capability

            • Pedal simulator

            • Light for timer mechanism

What to do:

1 Position the pedal simulator in front of your seat, and place your right foot on the accelerator pedal. When the light flashes, rapidly move your foot to the brake pedal and press it.

2 Do this test five times, and find your average reaction time.

CALCULATING REACTION DISTANCE

Now that you have a good estimate of your personal reaction time, you can calculate your reaction distance for any given vehicle speed. To do this, multiply your reaction time by the vehicle speed in metres per second.

For example, if you are travelling at 30 km h^{-1} and your reaction time is 0.5 s, then

$Step\ 1:$ $30 \text{ km h}^{-1} = (30 \div 3.6) \text{ m s}^{-1} \approx 8.333 \text{ m s}^{-1}$

$Step\ 2:$ Distance travelled $\approx 0.5 \times 8.333 \approx 4.166$ m $before$ you hit the brake pedal.

What to do:

1   **a**   Convert 60 km h^{-1} to m s^{-1}.

   b   Calculate the reaction distance for a reaction time of 0.5 s and a vehicle speed of 60 km h^{-1}.

2   Use your personal reaction time to calculate reaction distances for each of the following speeds. Remember, this is the distance covered $before\ the\ car\ even\ begins\ to\ slow\ down!$

Speed in $km\,h^{-1}$	30	40	50	60	70	80	90	100	110	120
Speed in $m\,s^{-1}$	8.33									
Reaction distance										

3   In this experiment you were a fully prepared person waiting for a signal and then reacting to that signal. We therefore call the measurement your **simple reaction time**. In the real world of driving, many things can distract or impair a driver, resulting in much longer reaction times. As a class, discuss factors that could increase your reaction time. List them on the board.

CALCULATING BRAKING DISTANCES

The **braking distance** is the distance you travel $after$ you have applied the brakes as the car slows to a stop.

On a good dry bitumen surface, with a car in perfect condition, it takes about 18 m to stop from a speed of 60 km h^{-1}. The distance is longer on wet roads or gravel surfaces.

We can calculate the effects of different road surfaces on braking distances using the following formula:

$$\text{distance travelled (in m)} = \frac{\text{speed}^2 \ \left(\text{in } \text{m s}^{-1}\right)}{\text{surface factor}}$$

What to do:

Calculate the braking distances for each of the speeds and surface conditions listed in the table alongside.

Copy and complete the table which follows or set up a spreadsheet:

Surface factor	
Dry bitumen	15.7
Wet bitumen	11.8
Gravel	9.6
Ice	1.8

Speed (km h^{-1})	Speed (m s^{-1})	Dry bitumen	Wet bitumen	Gravel	Ice
30					
40					
50					
60					
⋮					
120					

CALCULATING STOPPING DISTANCE

> **Stopping distance = reaction distance + braking distance**

What to do:

Using your personal reaction distances, find your total stopping distances for each of the speeds and conditions listed previously. Copy and complete a table like this one or set up a spreadsheet:

Condition	Personal reaction distance	Braking distance	Stopping distance
30 km h^{-1}, dry bitumen			
40 km h^{-1}, dry bitumen			
50 km h^{-1}, dry bitumen			
60 km h^{-1}, dry bitumen			
⋮			

OTHER RATES PROBLEMS

There are many rates other than speed which we use each day. They include rates of pay which may be an amount per hour or an amount per year, and the price of food which is often written as an amount per kilogram.

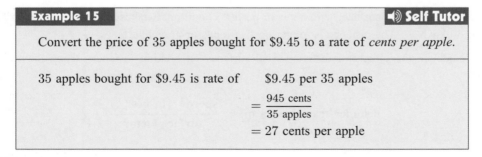

Example 15   ◀) **Self Tutor**

Convert the price of 35 apples bought for $9.45 to a rate of *cents per apple*.

35 apples bought for $9.45 is rate of $9.45 per 35 apples

$$= \frac{945 \text{ cents}}{35 \text{ apples}}$$

$$= 27 \text{ cents per apple}$$

EXERCISE 2F.2

1   Copy and complete:

   a   If 24 kg of peas are sold for $66.24, they earn me $...... per kg.

   b   My car uses 18 L of petrol every 261 km. The rate of petrol consumption is ...... km per litre.

   c   675 litres of water are pumped into a tank in 25 minutes. This is a rate of ...... L min^{-1}.

   d   Jasmin is paid $87 for working 6 hours. This is a rate of $...... per hour.

e A temperature rise of 14 degrees in $3\frac{1}{2}$ hours is a rate of ...... degrees per hour.

f 38.5 kg of seed spread over 7 m² is a rate of ...... $kg\,m^{-2}$.

g \$173.47 for 1660 kWh of power is a rate of ...... cents per kWh.

h Dominic types 220 words in 4 minutes. This is a rate of ...... words per minute.

2 A worker in a local factory earns €14.67 per hour.

    a How much does he earn in a 40 hour week?

    b If he receives the same weekly wage but only works a 35 hour week, what is his hourly rate for that week?

Example 16   ◀) **Self Tutor**

Suburb A covers 6.3 km² and has a population of 28 700 people.
Suburb B covers 3.9 km² and has a population of 16 100 people.
Which suburb is more heavily populated?

Suburb A has $\dfrac{28\,700 \text{ people}}{6.3 \text{ km}^2} \approx 4556$ people per km².

Suburb B has $\dfrac{16\,100 \text{ people}}{3.9 \text{ km}^2} \approx 4128$ people per km².

$\therefore$ suburb A is more heavily populated.

---

3 A farmer harvested 866 bags of wheat from an 83 hectare paddock (A) and 792 bags from a 68 hectare paddock (B). Which paddock yielded the better crop?

4 When the local netball club decided the winner of the trophy for the highest number of goals thrown per match, there were two contenders: Pat threw 446 goals in 18 matches, while Jo threw 394 goals in 15 matches. Who won the trophy?

5 A family uses 46 kilolitres of water in 90 days.

    a Find the rate of water use in litres per day.

    b If the water costs 65 cents per kilolitre, how much do they need to pay for the water used:

        i over the 90 day period   **ii** per day?

6 Phillipa types at a rate of 50 words per minute.

    a How long would it take her to type a 500 word essay at this rate?

    b How much longer would it take Kurt to type this essay if he types at 35 words per minute?

7 The cost of electricity is 13.49 cents/kWh for the first 300 kWh, then 10.25 cents/kWh for the remainder.

    a How much does 2050 kWh of power cost?

    b What is the overall rate in cents/kWh?

8 The temperature at 2:30 pm was 11°C and fell steadily until it reached −2°C at 1:45 am.

    a Find the decrease in temperature.

    b Find the average rate of decrease per hour correct to 2 decimal places.

9 Convert:

    a $12 per hour into cents per minute

    b 240 000 litres per minute into kilolitres per second

    c 30 mL per second into litres per hour

    d $2.73 per gram into dollars per kilogram

    e 1 death every 10 minutes into deaths per year.

G   ACCURACY OF MEASUREMENTS

INVESTIGATION 2   MEASURING DEVICES

Examine a variety of measuring instruments at school and at home. Make a list of the names of these instruments, what they measure, what their units are, and the degree of accuracy to which they can measure.

For example:

A ruler measures length. In the Metric System it measures in centimetres and millimetres, and can measure to the nearest millimetre.

When we take measurements, we are usually reading some sort of scale.

The scale of a ruler may have millimetres marked on it, but when we measure the length of an object, it is likely to fall between two divisions. We **approximate** the length of the object by recording the value at the nearest millimetre mark. In doing so our answer may be inaccurate by up to a half a millimetre.

> A measurement is accurate to $\pm \frac{1}{2}$ of the smallest division on the scale.

Example 17   ◀ Self Tutor

Ling uses a ruler to measure the length of her pencil case. She records the length as 18.7 cm.

Find the range of values in which the length may lie.

18.7 cm is 187 mm, so the measuring device must be accurate to the nearest half mm.

∴ the range of values is $187 \pm \frac{1}{2}$ mm

The actual length is in the range $186\frac{1}{2}$ mm to $187\frac{1}{2}$ mm, which is 18.65 cm to 18.75 cm.

EXERCISE 2G

1 State the accuracy of the following measuring devices:

    a a tape measure marked in cm   **b** a measuring cylinder with 1 mL graduations

    c a beaker with 100 mL graduations   **d** a set of scales with marks every 500 g.

2 Roni checks his weight every week using scales with 1 kg graduations. This morning he recorded a weight of 68 kg. In what range of values does Roni's actual weight lie?

3   Find the range of possible values corresponding to the following measurements:

    a   27 mm   **b**   38.3 cm   **c**   4.8 m

    d   1.5 kg   **e**   25 g   **f**   3.75 kg

4   Tom's digital thermometer said his temperature was 36.4°C. In what range of values did Tom's actual temperature lie?

5   Four students measured the width of their classroom using the same tape measure. The measurements were 6.1 m, 6.4 m, 6.0 m, 6.1 m.

    a   Which measurement is likely to be incorrect?

    b   What answer would you give for the width of the classroom?

    c   What graduations do you think were on the tape measure?

Example 18   ◀) **Self Tutor**

A rectangular block of wood was measured as 78 cm by 24 cm. What are the boundary values for its perimeter?

The length of the block could be from $77\frac{1}{2}$ cm to $78\frac{1}{2}$ cm.

The width of the block could be from $23\frac{1}{2}$ cm to $24\frac{1}{2}$ cm.

$\therefore$ the lower boundary of the perimeter is $2 \times 77\frac{1}{2} + 2 \times 23\frac{1}{2} = 202$ cm

and the upper boundary of the perimeter is $2 \times 78\frac{1}{2} + 2 \times 24\frac{1}{2} = 206$ cm

The perimeter is between 202 cm and 206 cm, which is 204 ± 2 cm.

---

6   A rectangular bath mat was measured as 86 cm by 38 cm.
What are the boundary values of its perimeter?

7   A rectangular garden bed is measured as 252 cm by 143 cm. Between what two values could the total length of edging required to border the garden bed be?

Example 19   ◀) **Self Tutor**

A paver is measured as   18 cm × 10 cm. What are the boundary values for its actual area?

The length of the paver could be from $17\frac{1}{2}$ cm to $18\frac{1}{2}$ cm.

The width of the paver could be from $9\frac{1}{2}$ cm to $10\frac{1}{2}$ cm.

$\therefore$ the lower boundary of the area is $17\frac{1}{2} \times 9\frac{1}{2} = 166.25$ cm^2

and the upper boundary of the area is $18\frac{1}{2} \times 10\frac{1}{2} = 194.25$ cm^2.

The area is between 166.25 cm^2 and 194.25 cm^2.

This could also be represented as $\dfrac{166.25 + 194.25}{2} \pm \dfrac{194.25 - 166.25}{2}$ cm^2

which is 180.25 ± 14 cm^2.

8 A rectangle is measured to be 6 cm by 8 cm. Find:

    a the largest area it could have   **b** the smallest area it could have.

9 Find the boundary values for the actual area of a glass window measured as 42 cm by 26 cm.

10 The base of a triangle is measured as 9 cm and its height is measured as 8 cm. What are the boundary values for its actual area?

11 Find the boundary values for the actual volume of a box measuring 4 cm by 8 cm by 6 cm.

12 Find the boundary values, correct to 2 decimal places, for the actual volume of a house brick measuring 21.3 cm by 9.8 cm by 7.3 cm.

13 A cylinder is measured to have radius 5 cm and height 15 cm. Use the formula $V = \pi r^2 h$ to find the boundary values for the cylinder's volume, correct to 2 decimal places.

14 A cone is measured to have radius 8.4 cm and height 4.6 cm. Use the formula $V = \frac{1}{3}\pi r^2 h$ to find the boundary values for the cone's volume, correct to 2 decimal places.

H   ERROR AND PERCENTAGE ERROR

An **approximation** is a value given to a number which is close to, but not equal to, its true value.

Approximations often occur when we round off results obtained by measurement.
For example, 36.428 97 is approximately 36.4.

An **estimation** is a value which has been found by judgement or prediction instead of carrying out a more accurate measurement.

For example, we can estimate 38.7×5.1 to be $40 \times 5 = 200$ whereas its true value is 197.37. A good approximation of this true value would be 197.

In order to make reasonable estimations we often appeal to our previous experience.

INVESTIGATION 3   A GRAM IN THE HAND IS WORTH ....

What to do:

  1 Measure in mm the length and width of a sheet of 80 gsm A4 photocopying paper.

  2 What is its area in m^2 and how many sheets make up 1 m^2?

  3 80 gsm means 80 grams per square metre. What is the mass of one sheet of A4 paper?

  4 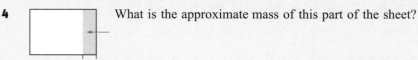 What is the approximate mass of this part of the sheet?

  5 Crumple the 6 cm strip into your hand and feel how heavy it is.

ERROR

Whenever we measure a quantity there is almost always a difference between our measurement and the actual value. We call this difference the **error**.

If the actual or exact value is V_E and the approximate value is V_A then the

$$\text{error} = V_A - V_E$$

Error is often expressed as a percentage of the exact value, and in this case we use the *size* of the error, ignoring its sign. We therefore use the **modulus** of the error.

$$\textbf{Percentage error} \;\; E = \frac{|V_A - V_E|}{V_E} \times 100\%$$

Example 20
◀)) Self Tutor

You estimate a fence's length to be 70 m whereas its true length is 78.3 m. Find, correct to one decimal place:

  a   the error   **b**   the percentage error.

a $\text{error} = V_A - V_E$
        $= 70 - 78.3$
        $= -8.3 \text{ m}$

b   percentage error

     $= \dfrac{|V_A - V_E|}{V_E} \times 100\%$

     $= \dfrac{|-8.3|}{78.3} \times 100\%$

     $\approx 10.6\%$

Example 21
◀)) Self Tutor

Alan wants to lay carpet on his 4.2 m by 5.1 m lounge room floor. He estimates the area of the lounge room by rounding each measurement to the nearest metre.

  a   Find Alan's estimate of the lounge room area.

  b   The carpet costs \$39 per square metre. Find the cost of the carpet using Alan's estimate of the area.

  c   Find the actual area of Alan's lounge room.

  d   Find the percentage error in Alan's estimation.

  e   Will Alan have enough carpet to cover his lounge room? How should he have rounded the measurements?

a   Area $\approx 4 \text{ m} \times 5 \text{ m}$
          $\approx 20 \text{ m}^2$

b   Cost $= 20 \times \$39$
          $= \$780$

c   Actual area $= 4.2 \times 5.1$
           $= 21.42 \text{ m}^2$

d   Percentage error $= \dfrac{|V_A - V_E|}{V_E} \times 100\%$

                   $= \dfrac{|20 - 21.42|}{21.42} \times 100\%$

              $\approx 6.63\%$

e   Alan only has 20 m^2 of carpet, so he will not have enough to cover his lounge room. He should have rounded the measurements *up* to make sure he had enough carpet.

EXERCISE 2H

1   Find   **i** the error   **ii** the percentage error   in rounding:

a   the yearly profit of €1 367 540 made by a company to €1.37 million

b   a population of 31 467 people to 31 000 people

c   a retail sales figure of $458 110 to $460 000

d   the number of new cars sold by a company in a year from 2811 to 3000.

2   Find   **i** the error   **ii** the percentage error   if you estimate:

a   the mass of a brick to be 5 kg when its actual mass is 6.238 kg

b   the perimeter of a property to be 100 m when its actual length is 97.6 m

c   the capacity of a container to be 20 L when its actual capacity is 23.8 L

d   the time to write a computer program to be 50 hours when it actually takes 72 hours.

3   Jon's lounge room is a 10.3 m by 9.7 m rectangle.

a   Estimate the floor area by rounding each length to the nearest metre.

b   Find the actual area of the floor.

c   What is the error in your calculation in **a**?

d   What percentage error was made?

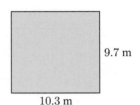

9.7 m

10.3 m

4   The cost of freight for a parcel is dependent on its volume. Justine lists the dimensions of a parcel as 24 cm by 15 cm by 9 cm on the consignment note.
The actual dimensions are 23.9 cm × 14.8 cm × 9.2 cm.

a   Calculate the actual volume of the parcel.

b   Calculate the volume given on the consignment note.

c   Find the rounding error in the calculation.

d   What percentage error was made?

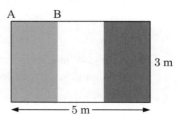

5   A hotel wants to cover an 8.2 m by 9.4 m rectangular courtyard with synthetic grass. The manager estimates the area by rounding each measurement to the nearest metre.

a   Find the manager's estimate of the area.

b   The synthetic grass costs $85 per square metre. Find the cost of the grass.

c   Find the actual area of the rectangle.

d   Calculate the percentage error in the manager's estimate.

e   Will the hotel have enough grass to cover the courtyard?

f   Find the cost of the grass if the manager had rounded each measurement *up* to the next metre.

6   The Italian flag is split into three equal sections.

a   Find, rounded to 1 decimal place, the length AB.

b   Use your rounded value in **a** to estimate the area of the green section.

c   Find the actual area of the green section.

d   Find the percentage error in the estimate in **b**.

A   B

3 m

5 m

7   Luigi estimates that he can drive at an average speed of 70 km h^{-1} between his house and the beach, 87 km away. One particular journey took him 1 hour and 20 minutes.

   a   Calculate Luigi's average speed for this journey.

   b   Find the error in his estimate.

   c   Find the percentage error in his estimate.

INVESTIGATION 4   ESTIMATING AND ACCURACY

When we measure quantities such as angle size, length, or area, it is possible that errors in measurement might occur. It is therefore a good idea to *estimate* the quantity first, so that we can recognise whether the results of our measurement are *reasonable*.

In this investigation you will make estimates of angle size, length, area, temperature, and time. You can then check your estimates by taking actual measurements.

What to do:

1   Angle size   *Equipment needed*:   Protractor

   a   Estimate the size of angle θ alongside.

   b   Stuart measured the angle, and obtained a value of 140°. Does this seem reasonable?

   c   Ellen measured the angle, and obtained a value of 40°. Does this seem reasonable?

   d   Use a protractor to measure the size of the angle.

2   Length   *Equipment needed*:   Ruler

   a   Estimate the length of the line segment alongside.

   b   Mei-Li measured the length, and wrote down 37 cm. Does this seem reasonable?

   c   Paul measured the length, and wrote down 3.7 cm. Does this seem reasonable?

   d   Use a ruler to measure the length of the line segment.

3   Area   *Equipment needed*:   Ruler

   a   Estimate the area of the rectangle alongside.

   b   One of the values below is the correct area of the rectangle. Use your estimate to identify the correct area.

      A 2 cm^2 **B** 5.25 cm^2

      C 11.25 cm^2 **D** 24 cm^2

   c   Use a ruler to check your answer.

4   Temperature   *Equipment needed*:   Thermometer in °C

   a   Estimate the temperature of:

      i   air in the classroom   **ii**   air outside the classroom

     iii   water from the cold tap   **iv**   water from the hot tap.

   b   Use a thermometer to measure the temperature of the air and water in **a**.

   c   Comment on the accuracy of your estimates.

5 Time   *Equipment needed*:   Stopwatch or watch with seconds

  a In pairs test each other at estimating a time interval of one minute.

  b Find the percentage error for your estimates.

  c Can you find a way to improve your method of estimating?

◾ I   CURRENCY CONVERSIONS

If you visit another country or buy products from overseas, you usually have to use the money or **currency** of that country. We use an **exchange rate** to find out how much your money is worth in the foreign currency, and vice versa.

Exchange rates are constantly changing, and so are published daily in newspapers, displayed in bank windows and airports, and updated on the internet. The rate is usually given as the amount of foreign currency equal to one unit of local currency.

SIMPLE CURRENCY CONVERSION

In this section we consider currency conversions for which there is **no commission**. This means that there are no fees to pay for making the currency exchange.

To perform these conversions we can simply multiply or divide by the appropriate currency **exchange rate**.

Example 22   ◀)) **Self Tutor**

A bank exchanges 1 British pound (GBP) for 1.65 Australian dollars (AUD). Convert:

  a 40 GBP to AUD   **b** 500 AUD to GBP.

a $1 \text{ GBP} = 1.65 \text{ AUD}$

  $\therefore$ $40 \text{ GBP} = 40 \times 1.65 \text{ AUD}$ {multiplying by 40}

  $\therefore$ $40 \text{ GBP} = 66 \text{ AUD}$

b $1.65 \text{ AUD} = 1 \text{ GBP}$

  $\therefore$ $1 \text{ AUD} = \dfrac{1}{1.65} \text{ GBP}$ {dividing by 1.65}

  $\therefore$ $500 \text{ AUD} = 500 \times \dfrac{1}{1.65} \text{ GBP}$ {multiplying by 500}

  $\therefore$ $500 \text{ AUD} \approx 303 \text{ GBP}$

Sometimes the exchange rates between currencies are presented in a table. In this case we select the row according to the currency we are converting *from*, and the column by the currency we are converting *to*.

currency converting to

	Hong Kong (HKD)	China (CNY)	Japan (JPY)
Hong Kong (HKD)	1	0.817	9.885
China (CNY)	1.225	1	12.106
Japan (JPY)	0.101	0.083	1

currency converting → from

For example, to convert 2000 Chinese yuan to Japanese yen, we choose the row for CNY and the column for JPY.

$$2000 \text{ CNY} = 12.106 \times 2000 \text{ JPY}$$
$$= 24\,212 \text{ JPY}$$

Example 23 🔊 **Self Tutor**

The table alongside shows the transfer rates between US dollars (USD), Swiss francs (CHF), and British pounds (GBP).

	USD	GBP	CHF
USD	1	0.640	0.91
GBP	1.56	1	1.43
CHF	1.10	0.70	1

a Write down the exchange rate from:

   i CHF to USD   **ii** USD to CHF.

b Convert:

   i 3000 USD to GBP   **ii** 10 000 francs to pounds.

a **i** 1 CHF = 1.10 USD   **ii** 1 USD = 0.91 CHF

b **i**   1 USD = 0.640 GBP   **ii**   1 CHF = 0.7 GBP

       $\therefore$ 3000 USD = 3000 × 0.640 GBP $\therefore$ 10 000 CHF = 10 000 × 0.7 GBP

       $\therefore$ 3000 USD = 1920 GBP $\therefore$ 10 000 CHF = 7000 GBP

EXERCISE 21.1

1 A currency exchange will convert 1 Singapore dollar (SGD) to 6.5 South African rand (ZAR).

  a Convert the following into South African rand: **i** 3000 SGD   **ii** 450 SGD.

  b Convert the following into Singapore dollars: **i** 21 000 ZAR   **ii** 1.35 ZAR.

2 Exchange rates for the US dollar are shown in the table alongside.

Currency	1 USD
Taiwan New Dollar (TWD)	30.3765
Norwegian Kroner (NOK)	5.8075
Chinese Yuan (CNY)	6.3627

  a Convert 200 USD into:

     i TWD   **ii** NOK   **iii** CNY

  b Convert 5000 NOK into:

     i USD   **ii** CNY

  c Convert 100 TWD into:

     i USD   **ii** CNY

3 A bank offers the following currency exchanges:

        1 Indian rupee (INR) = 0.1222 Chinese yuan (CNY)

        1 Indian rupee (INR) = 0.6003 Russian rubles (RUB)

  a Convert 15 750 INR to: **i** CNY   **ii** RUB.

  b Calculate the exchange rate from:

     i Chinese yuan to Indian rupee   **ii** Russian rubles to Chinese yuan.

  c How much are 30 000 Russian rubles worth in Chinese yuan?

4 The table alongside shows the conversion rates between Mexican pesos (MXN), Russian rubles (RUB), and South African rand (ZAR).

	MXN	RUB	ZAR
MXN	1	2.230	0.6018
RUB	0.4484	1	0.2699
ZAR	p	q	r

   a Convert 5000 rubles into: **i** rand **ii** pesos.

   b How many Russian rubles can be bought for 20 000 Mexican pesos?

   c Calculate the values of: **i** p **ii** q **iii** r

   d Which is worth more in rand, 1 peso or 1 ruble?

Example 24　　　　　　　　　　　　　　　　　　　　　◀ⅈ) **Self Tutor**

The graph alongside shows the relationship between Australian dollars and Great Britain pounds on a particular day. Find:

   a the number of AUD in 250 GBP

   b the number of GBP in 480 AUD

   c whether a person with 360 AUD could afford to buy an item valued at 240 GBP.

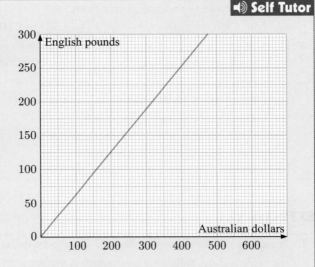

   a 250 GBP is equivalent to 400 AUD.

   b 480 AUD is equivalent to 300 GBP.

   c 360 AUD is equivalent to 225 GBP.

     ∴ the person cannot afford to buy the item.

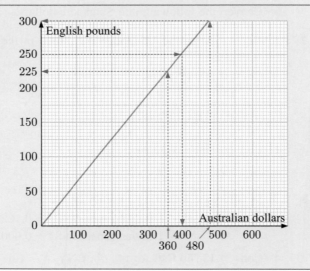

---

5 Use the currency conversion graph of **Example 24** to estimate:

   a the number of AUD in **i** 130 GBP **ii** 240 GBP

   b the number of GBP in **i** 400 AUD **ii** 120 AUD.

ACTIVITY	CURRENCY TRENDS

Over a period of a month, collect from the daily newspaper or internet the currency conversions which compare your currency to the currency of another country. Graph your results, updating the graph each day. You could use www.x-rates.com/calculator.html or www.xe.com/ucc .

FIXED COMMISSION ON CURRENCY EXCHANGE

When a currency trader (such as a bank) exchanges currency for a customer, a commission is often paid by the customer for this service. The commission could vary from $\frac{1}{2}\%$ to 3%, or could be a constant amount or 'flat fee'.

Example 25	◀) Self Tutor

A banker changes South African rand to other currencies at a fixed commission of 1.5%. Wendy wishes to convert 800 ZAR to Russian rubles where 1 ZAR buys 3.75 RUB.

a   What commission is charged?   b   How much does Wendy receive?

a   Commission $= 800$ ZAR $\times 1.5\%$ b   Wendy receives 788×3.75 rubles
$= 800 \times 0.015$ ZAR $= 2955$ rubles
$= 12$ ZAR

EXERCISE 21.2

1   A bank exchanges GBP for a commission of 1.5%. For the following transactions, calculate:

    i   the commission charged   ii   how much the customer receives.

  a   500 GBP is converted to US dollars where 1 GBP buys 1.5616 USD.

  b   350 GBP is converted to euros where 1 GBP buys €1.1605.

  c   1200 GBP is converted to New Zealand dollars where 1 GBP buys $2.0954 NZ.

2   A bank exchanges Singapore dollars for a commission of 1.8%. For the following transactions, calculate:

    i   the commission charged   ii   how much the customer receives.

  a   250 SGD is converted to UK pounds where 1 SGD buys 0.4907 GBP.

  b   700 SGD is converted to AUD where 1 SGD buys 0.7848 AUD.

  c   1500 SGD is converted to euros where 1 SGD buys €0.5695.

DIFFERENT BUY AND SELL RATES

Another way currency traders can obtain a commission is to offer different exchange rates which include their commission. They will buy currency from you at a rate lower than the market value, and sell it at a rate higher than the market value. The difference is their commission.

Suppose you live in the United States of America. The following table shows how much one American dollar (USD) is worth in some other currencies.

Country	Currency name	Code	Buys	Sells
Europe	Euro	EUR	0.7502	0.7354
United Kingdom	Pounds	GBP	0.6468	0.6340
Australia	Dollars	AUD	1.0341	1.0136
Canada	Dollars	CAD	1.0516	1.0308
China	Yuan	CNY	6.4263	6.2991
Denmark	Kroner	DKK	5.5828	5.4722
Hong Kong	Dollars	HKD	7.8705	7.7146
Japan	Yen	JPY	77.797	76.256
Mexico	Peso	MXN	14.150	13.870
New Zealand	Dollars	NZD	1.3566	1.3298
Norway	Kroner	NOK	5.8656	5.7494
Saudi Arabia	Riyals	SAR	3.7877	3.7127
Singapore	Dollars	SGD	1.3179	1.2918
South Africa	Rand	ZAR	8.5101	8.3416
Sweden	Kronor	SEK	6.9323	6.7951
Switzerland	Francs	CHF	0.9238	0.9055
Thailand	Baht	THB	31.598	30.972

The 'buy' and 'sell' rates are listed relative to the currency broker (bank or exchange) and are in terms of the foreign currency.

The foreign currency EUR will be bought by the broker at the rate $1 \text{ USD} = 0.7502 \text{ EUR}$, and sold by the broker at the rate $1 \text{ USD} = 0.7354 \text{ EUR}$.

Example 26   ◄)) Self Tutor

Use the currency conversion table above to perform the following conversions:

a Convert 400 USD into euros.

b How much does it cost in US dollars to buy 5000 yen?

c How many US dollars can you buy for 2000 Swedish kronor?

a Euros are sold at the rate
$$1 \text{ USD} = 0.7354 \text{ EUR}$$
$$\therefore \ 400 \text{ USD} = 400 \times 0.7354 \text{ EUR}$$
$$= 294.16 \text{ EUR}$$

b The currency broker sells yen at the rate
$$1 \text{ USD} = 76.256 \text{ JPY}$$
$$\therefore \ \frac{1}{76.256} \text{ USD} = 1 \text{ JPY}$$
$$\therefore \ 5000 \times \frac{1}{76.256} \text{ USD} = 5000 \text{ JPY}$$
$$\therefore \ 5000 \text{ JPY} = 65.57 \text{ USD}$$

c The currency broker buys kronor at the rate
$$1 \text{ USD} = 6.9323 \text{ SEK}$$
$$\therefore \ \frac{1}{6.9323} \text{ USD} = 1 \text{ SEK}$$
$$\therefore \ 2000 \times \frac{1}{6.9323} \text{ USD} = 2000 \text{ SEK}$$
$$\therefore \ 2000 \text{ SEK} = 288.50 \text{ USD}$$

EXERCISE 21.3

For questions **1** to **4**, suppose you are a citizen of the USA and use the currency table on page **68**.

1 On holiday you set aside 300 USD to spend in each country you visit. How much local currency can you buy in:

    a Europe (euros)   **b** the United Kingdom

    c Singapore   **d** Australia?

2 Find the cost in USD of:

    a 400 Canadian dollars   **b** 730 Swiss francs

    c ¥12 430   **d** 4710 DKK.

3 If you are shopping on-line for these items, find the price in USD of:

    a a computer worth 7000 Hong Kong dollars   **b** a rugby ball worth 35 NZD

    c a watch worth 949 SAR.

4 Find how many US dollars you could buy for:

    a €2500   **b** 57 000 rand   **c** £165   **d** 86 370 baht.

Example 27	◀) **Self Tutor**

A currency exchange service exchanges 1 euro for Japanese yen with the buy rate 105.3, and sell rate 101.4. Cedric wishes to exchange 800 euros for yen.

  a How many yen will he receive?

  b If the yen in **a** were exchanged immediately back to euros, how many euros would they be worth?

  c What is the resultant commission on the double transaction?

  a Cedric receives $800 \times 101.4 \approx 81\,120$ yen

                               {using the selling rate as the bank is selling currency}

  b Cedric receives $\dfrac{81\,120}{105.3} = €770.37$ {using the buying rate as the bank is buying currency}

  c The resultant commission is $€800 - €770.37 = €29.63$.

---

5 A currency exchange service exchanges 1 Mexican peso into Thai baht using the buy rate 2.26 and sell rate 2.20. Sergio wishes to exchange 400 peso for Thai baht.

    a How many baht will he receive?

    b If he immediately exchanges the baht back to pesos, how many will he get?

    c What is the resultant commission for the double transaction?

6 A currency exchange service exchanges 1 Chinese yuan into Indian rupees with buy rate 8.3101 and sell rate 8.1387. Lily wishes to exchange 425 yuan for rupees.

    a How much will she receive?

    b If she immediately exchanges the rupees back to yuan, how many will she get?

    c What is the resultant commission for the double transaction?

7 A bank exchanges 1 Botswana pula to Angolan kwanza with buy rate 12.595 and sell rate 12.306. Kefilwe wishes to exchange 3200 pula to kwanza.

    a How much will he receive?

    b If he immediately exchanges the kwanza back to pula, how many will he get?

    c What is the resultant commission for the double transaction?

REVIEW SET 2A

1 Find the time difference between 10:35 am and 4:52 pm.

2 What is the time:

    a $4\frac{1}{4}$ hours after 11:20 pm   **b** $3\frac{1}{2}$ hours before 1:20 pm?

3 A racehorse weighs 440 kg. Calculate its mass in grams.

4 It is 35°C in a town in Mexico. Use the formula $F = \frac{9}{5}C + 32$ to calculate this temperature in degrees Fahrenheit.

5 Express the following quantities as ordinary decimal numbers:

    a Jupiter has a radius of 1.43×10^5 km

    b a baker's yeast cell is approximately 4.5×10^{-6} m in diameter.

6 Sound travels along a telephone cable at 1.91×10^8 m s^{-1}. Use your calculator to find how long it takes Tetsuo's voice to travel from his office phone in Tokyo to his:

    a wife's phone, 3740 m away   **b** brother in Beijing, 2.1×10^6 m away.

7   **a** Round 6.376 to: **i** 1 decimal place   **ii** 3 significant figures.

    b Round 0.0473 to: **i** 2 decimal places   **ii** 2 significant figures.

8   **a** How accurate is a tape measure marked in cm?

    b Find the range of possible values for a measurement of 36 cm.

    c A square has sides measured to be 36 cm. What are the boundary values for its actual area?

9 A cyclist is travelling a distance of 134 km.

    a What is her average speed, if the trip takes 5 hours and 18 minutes?

    b If her average speed is 24 km h^{-1}, how long does the trip take?

10 Find the   **i** error   **ii** percentage error   if you:

    a estimate your credit card balance to be $2000 when it is $2590

    b round 26.109 cm to 26 cm.

11 A photograph was measured as 15 cm by 10 cm. What are the boundary values for its perimeter?

12 Currency exchange rates for the Canadian dollar (CAD), European euro (EUR), and Tajikistani somoni (TJS) are given in the table alongside.

	CAD	EUR	TJS
CAD	1	0.715	4.547
EUR	1.398	1	6.358
TJS	0.220	0.157	1

    a Convert 300 EUR into:

       i CAD   **ii** TJS.

    b How many somoni can be bought for 1780 Canadian dollars?

    c 1 euro is worth 3.088 Sudanese pounds (SDG). What are 2500 Sudanese pounds worth in somoni?

REVIEW SET 2B

1 Convert $2\frac{3}{4}$ hours to minutes.

2 Aniko left for work at 7:39 am and returned home at 6:43 pm. How long was she away from home?

3 Use the formula $C = \frac{5}{9}(F - 32)$ to convert 84°F to degrees Celsius.

4 Bianca is 1.68 m tall. Calculate her height in cm.

5 Write as decimal numbers:

    a 4.6×10^{11} **b** 1.9×10^{0} **c** 3.2×10^{-3}

6 Write in scientific notation:

    a The diameter of the earth is approximately 12.76 million metres.

    b A bacterium has a diameter of 0.000 000 42 cm.

7 Sheets of paper are 3.2×10^{-4} m in thickness. Use your calculator to find how many sheets are required to make a pile of paper 10 cm high.

8   **a** Round 59.397 to: **i** 1 decimal place   **ii** 4 significant figures.

    b Round 0.008 35 to: **i** 2 decimal places   **ii** 2 significant figures.

9 The cost of water is $0.97 per kL for the first 120 kL, then $1.88 per kL for the remainder. How much does 361 kL of water cost?

10 Jenny estimated the length of her front fence to be 32 m. Its exact length is 34.3 m. Find, correct to one decimal place:

    a the error   **b** the percentage error.

11   **a** Jorg works at a supermarket for 38 hours each week. He earns £332.50 per week. What is his hourly rate of pay?

    b After a promotion, Jorg earns £10.25 per hour, and only works 35 hours each week. What is this change in weekly income?

12 Roger has 640 Swiss francs. A currency exchange service exchanges 1 Swiss franc for Danish krone at a buying rate of 6.141 krone and a selling rate of 5.992 krone.

    a How many krone can Roger buy?

    b If Roger immediately sells the krone back for Swiss francs, how many will he now have?

    c Find the commission on this double transaction.

REVIEW SET 2C

1 Find the time difference between 11:17 am and 5:09 pm.

2 Calculate the time:

    a $5\frac{1}{2}$ hours after 9:17 am
    b $4\frac{1}{4}$ hours before 1:48 pm.

3 Use the formula $C = \frac{5}{9}(F - 32)$ to convert 50°F to degrees Celsius.

4 A yacht travels 26 nautical miles in 2 hours. Find the average speed of the yacht in kilometres per hour.

5 Write the following as decimal numbers:

    a 5.73×10^{-3}
    b 3.02×10^{3}
    c 9.875×10^{2}

6 Evaluate, giving your answers correct to 3 significant figures:

    a $(17.5 - 4.3) \div 3.2$
    b $\dfrac{16.52 - 0.041}{4.2 + 1.35}$

7 **a** How long would it take to travel 45.8 km at an average speed of 21.3 $km\,h^{-1}$?

    b A car travels 20 km in 24 minutes. Find the average speed of the car in kilometres per hour.

8 Store A sells 200 g packets of sugar for $1.79, while store B sells 500 g packets of sugar for $4.40. Which store offers better value for money?

9 The two shorter sides of a right angled triangle are measured as 6 cm and 8 cm. What are the boundary values for the area of the triangle?

10 A circular gazebo has a diameter of 2.8 m. In calculating the area of the gazebo, the diameter is rounded to the nearest metre.

    a Find the actual area and the calculated area of the gazebo.

    b Find the error in the calculation.

    c Find the percentage error in the calculation.

11 An architect designs a support beam to be $\sqrt{5}$ metres long. The builder working from the architect's plans converts this length to a decimal number.

    a Write down the length of the support beam correct to the nearest:

        i metre
        ii centimetre
        iii millimetre.

    b For each answer in **a**, write down how many significant figures were specified.

    c The architect insists that there be no more than 1% error. Which of the approximations in **a**, if any, will satisfy this?

12 A bank exchanges 5500 Chinese yuan to Japanese yen for a commission of 1.8%.

    a What commission is charged?

    b What does the customer receive for the transaction if 1 Chinese yuan $=$ 12.1385 Japanese yen?

Chapter **3**

Laws of algebra

Contents:

OPENING PROBLEM

a Fill out the table:

b	$(5+b)^2$	$(5-b)^2$	$(5+b)^2 - (5-b)^2$
0			
1			
2			
3			
4			
5			

b Can you explain why $(5+b)^2 - (5-b)^2$ is always equal to $20b$?

In this chapter we review some important laws that deal with algebraic expressions. These include the **laws of exponents** which describe what happens when different operations are performed on expressions containing exponents, and the **expansion laws** which describe how brackets can be removed from expressions.

A   LAWS OF EXPONENTS

INVESTIGATION 1

In this investigation we discover the laws of exponents by observing number patterns.

What to do:

1 Write out the first ten powers of: **a** 2   **b** 3   **c** 5

2 **a** Use your calculator to fill in the first column of numbers. Then use your answers to **1** to complete the second column.

$$2^3 \times 2^2 = \quad 32 \quad = \quad 2^5$$
$$2^2 \times 2^7 = \qquad =$$
$$2^5 \times 2^3 = \qquad =$$
$$3^4 \times 3^1 = \qquad =$$
$$3^3 \times 3^5 = \qquad =$$
$$3^2 \times 3^2 = \qquad =$$
$$5^3 \times 5^4 = \qquad =$$

  b Use your observations from **a** to complete these statements:

   i $2^m \times 2^n = \ldots.$ **ii** $3^m \times 3^n = \ldots.$ **iii** $a^m \times a^n = \ldots.$

3 **a** Use your calculator and answers from **1** to complete:

$$\frac{2^5}{2^2} = \quad 8 \quad = \quad 2^3 \qquad \frac{3^8}{3^3} = \qquad = \qquad \frac{5^6}{5^5} = \qquad =$$

$$\frac{2^6}{2^3} = \qquad = \qquad \frac{3^4}{3^3} = \qquad = \qquad \frac{5^9}{5^2} = \qquad =$$

  b Complete these statements:

   i $\dfrac{2^m}{2^n} = \ldots.$ **ii** $\dfrac{5^m}{5^n} = \ldots.$ **iii** $\dfrac{a^m}{a^n} = \ldots.$

4 a Use your calculator and answers from **1** to complete:

$(2^3)^2 =$ 64 $=$ 2^6
$(2^4)^2 =$ $=$
$(3^1)^3 =$ $=$
$(3^2)^5 =$ $=$
$(5^3)^3 =$ $=$
$(5^2)^4 =$ $=$

   b Complete these statements:

     i $(3^m)^n = ...$ **ii** $(5^m)^n = ...$ **iii** $(a^m)^n = ...$

5 a Use your calculator to find:

     i 2^0 **ii** 5^0 **iii** 79^0 **iv** 148^0

   b Write a rule showing what you have found.

6 a Evaluate using a calculator:

     i $\dfrac{1}{5^3}$ **ii** $\dfrac{1}{3^1}$ **iii** $\dfrac{1}{3^4}$ **iv** $\dfrac{1}{5^2}$ **v** $\dfrac{1}{2^1}$

     vi 5^{-3} **vii** 3^{-1} **viii** 3^{-4} **ix** 5^{-2} **x** 2^{-1}

   b Complete:

     i $\dfrac{1}{3^n} = ...$ **ii** $\dfrac{1}{5^n} = ...$ **iii** $\dfrac{1}{a^n} = ...$

The following are **laws of exponents** for $m, n \in \mathbb{Z}$:

$a^m \times a^n = a^{m+n}$	To **multiply** numbers with the **same base**, keep the base and **add** the exponents.
$\dfrac{a^m}{a^n} = a^{m-n}, \quad a \neq 0$	To **divide** numbers with the **same base**, keep the base and **subtract** the exponents.
$(a^m)^n = a^{m \times n}$	When **raising** a **power** to a **power**, keep the base and **multiply** the exponents.
$(ab)^n = a^n b^n$	The power of a product is the product of the powers.
$\left(\dfrac{a}{b}\right)^n = \dfrac{a^n}{b^n}, \quad b \neq 0$	The power of a quotient is the quotient of the powers.
$a^0 = 1, \quad a \neq 0$	Any non-zero number raised to the exponent zero is 1.
$a^{-n} = \dfrac{1}{a^n}$ and $\dfrac{1}{a^{-n}} = a^n$ and in particular $a^{-1} = \dfrac{1}{a}, \quad a \neq 0.$	

Example 1   ◀ᴺ) **Self Tutor**

Simplify: **a** $7^4 \times 7^5$ **b** $p^6 \times p^2$

     a $\quad 7^4 \times 7^5$ **b** $\quad p^6 \times p^2$
        $= 7^{4+5}$ $= p^{6+2}$
        $= 7^9$ $= p^8$

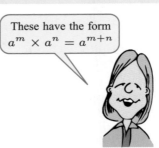

These have the form
$a^m \times a^n = a^{m+n}$

EXERCISE 3A.1

1 Simplify using $a^m \times a^n = a^{m+n}$:

   a $k^4 \times k^2$ **b** $5^2 \times 5^6$ **c** $d^3 \times d^7$ **d** $11^4 \times 11^a$

   e $p^6 \times p$ **f** $c^8 \times c^m$ **g** $x^k \times x^2$ **h** $r^2 \times r^5 \times r^4$

Example 2   ◀) **Self Tutor**

Simplify:

   a $\dfrac{5^6}{5^3}$ **b** $\dfrac{x^{11}}{x^6}$

   a $\dfrac{5^6}{5^3}$ **b** $\dfrac{x^{11}}{x^6}$

   $= 5^{6-3}$ $= x^{11-6}$

   $= 5^3$ $= x^5$

These have the form
$$\frac{a^m}{a^n} = a^{m-n}$$

2 Simplify using $\dfrac{a^m}{a^n} = a^{m-n}$:

   a $\dfrac{7^8}{7^3}$ **b** $\dfrac{b^7}{b^5}$ **c** $5^9 \div 5^6$ **d** $\dfrac{m^{10}}{m^4}$

   e $\dfrac{k^{12}}{k^a}$ **f** $\dfrac{y^6}{y}$ **g** $\dfrac{t^m}{t^4}$ **h** $\dfrac{x^{3a}}{x^2}$

Example 3   ◀) **Self Tutor**

Simplify:

   a $(3^5)^2$ **b** $(x^3)^k$

   a $(3^5)^2$ **b** $(x^3)^k$

   $= 3^{5 \times 2}$ $= x^{3 \times k}$

   $= 3^{10}$ $= x^{3k}$

These have the form
$$(a^m)^n = a^{m \times n}$$

3 Simplify using $(a^m)^n = a^{m \times n}$:

   a $(5^3)^2$ **b** $(c^4)^3$ **c** $(3^8)^4$ **d** $(v^5)^5$

   e $(7^6)^d$ **f** $(g^k)^8$ **g** $(m^3)^t$ **h** $(11^x)^{2y}$

4 Simplify:

   a $b^5 \times b^7$ **b** $\dfrac{t^9}{t^2}$ **c** $(p^6)^3$ **d** $\dfrac{7^6}{7^n}$

   e $(x^{2s})^3$ **f** $d^k \div d^3$ **g** $3^2 \times 3^7 \times 3^4$ **h** $(j^4)^{3x}$

   i $11^6 \times 11$ **j** $\dfrac{z^7}{z^{4t}}$ **k** $(13^c)^{5d}$ **l** $w^{7p} \div w$

Example 4

🔊 **Self Tutor**

Write as powers of 2:

a 16   b $\frac{1}{16}$ c 1   d 4×2^n e $\frac{2^m}{8}$

a 16
$= 2 \times 2 \times 2 \times 2$
$= 2^4$

b $\frac{1}{16}$
$= \frac{1}{2^4}$
$= 2^{-4}$

c 1
$= 2^0$

d 4×2^n
$= 2^2 \times 2^n$
$= 2^{2+n}$

e $\frac{2^m}{8}$
$= \frac{2^m}{2^3}$
$= 2^{m-3}$

5 Write as a power of 2:

a 4   b $\frac{1}{4}$ c 8   d $\frac{1}{8}$ e 32   f $\frac{1}{32}$

g 2   h $\frac{1}{2}$ i 64   j $\frac{1}{64}$ k 128   l $\frac{1}{128}$

6 Write as a power of 3:

a 9   b $\frac{1}{9}$ c 27   d $\frac{1}{27}$ e 3   f $\frac{1}{3}$

g 81   h $\frac{1}{81}$ i 1   j 243   k $\frac{1}{243}$

7 Write as a single power of 2:

a 2×2^a b 4×2^b c 8×2^t d $(2^x)^2$ e $(2^{-n})^{-1}$

f $\frac{2^c}{4}$ g $\frac{2^m}{2^{-m}}$ h $\frac{4}{2^{1-n}}$ i $\frac{2^{x+1}}{2^x}$ j $\frac{4^x}{2^{1-x}}$

8 Write as a single power of 3:

a 9×3^p b 27^a c 3×9^n d 27×3^d e 9×27^t

f $\frac{3^y}{3}$ g $\frac{3}{3^y}$ h $\frac{9}{27^t}$ i $\frac{9^a}{3^{1-a}}$ j $\frac{9^{n+1}}{3^{2n-1}}$

Example 5

🔊 **Self Tutor**

Express in simplest form with a prime number base:

a 9^4 b $\frac{3^x}{9^y}$ c 25^x

Decide first what the prime number base should be.

a 9^4
$= (3^2)^4$
$= 3^{2 \times 4}$
$= 3^8$

b $\frac{3^x}{9^y}$
$= \frac{3^x}{(3^2)^y}$
$= \frac{3^x}{3^{2y}}$
$= 3^{x-2y}$

c 25^x
$= (5^2)^x$
$= 5^{2x}$

9 Express in simplest form with a prime number base:

a 32   b 49   c 25^3 d 4^5

e 16^p f 27^t g $5^a \times 25$ h $4^n \times 8^n$

10 Express in simplest form with a prime number base:

a $\dfrac{8^m}{16^n}$

b $\dfrac{25^p}{5^4}$

c $\dfrac{2^{x+2}}{2^{x-1}}$

d 9^{t+2}

e 32^{2-r}

f $\dfrac{81}{3^{y+1}}$

g $\dfrac{16^k}{4^k}$

h $\dfrac{5^{a+1} \times 125}{25^{2a}}$

Example 6   ◀) **Self Tutor**

Write without brackets:

a $(3x)^3$

b $\left(\dfrac{x}{y}\right)^4$

a $(3x)^3$
   $= 3^3 \times x^3$
   $= 27x^3$

b $\left(\dfrac{x}{y}\right)^4$
   $= \dfrac{x^4}{y^4}$

These have the form $(ab)^n = a^n b^n$ or $\left(\dfrac{a}{b}\right)^n = \dfrac{a^n}{b^n}$

---

11 Write without brackets:

a $(2a)^2$

b $(3n)^2$

c $(5m)^3$

d $(mn)^3$

e $\left(\dfrac{a}{2}\right)^3$

f $\left(\dfrac{3}{m}\right)^2$

g $\left(\dfrac{p}{q}\right)^4$

h $\left(\dfrac{t}{5}\right)^2$

Example 7   ◀) **Self Tutor**

Simplify, giving answers in simplest rational form:

a 7^0

b 3^{-2}

c $3^0 - 3^{-1}$

d $\left(\dfrac{5}{3}\right)^{-2}$

a 7^0
   $= 1$

b 3^{-2}
   $= \dfrac{1}{3^2}$
   $= \dfrac{1}{9}$

c $3^0 - 3^{-1}$
   $= 1 - \dfrac{1}{3}$
   $= \dfrac{2}{3}$

d $\left(\dfrac{5}{3}\right)^{-2}$
   $= \left(\dfrac{3}{5}\right)^2$
   $= \dfrac{9}{25}$

Notice that $\left(\dfrac{a}{b}\right)^{-2} = \left(\dfrac{b}{a}\right)^2$

---

12 Simplify, giving answers in simplest rational form:

a 4^0

b 3^{-1}

c 7^{-2}

d x^{-3}

e $5^0 + 5^{-1}$

f $\left(\dfrac{5}{3}\right)^0$

g $\left(\dfrac{7}{4}\right)^{-1}$

h $\left(\dfrac{1}{6}\right)^{-1}$

i $\left(\dfrac{4}{3}\right)^{-2}$

j $2^1 + 2^{-1}$

k $\left(1\tfrac{2}{3}\right)^{-3}$

l $5^2 + 5^1 + 5^{-1}$

Example 8 ◀) **Self Tutor**

Write without negative exponents:

a $3x^{-1}$ b $(3x)^{-1}$ c $\left(\dfrac{3}{x}\right)^{-2}$

$a^{-n} = \dfrac{1}{a^n}$

a $\quad 3x^{-1}$

$\quad = \dfrac{3}{x}$

b $\quad (3x)^{-1}$

$\quad = \dfrac{1}{3x}$

c $\quad \left(\dfrac{3}{x}\right)^{-2}$

$\quad = \left(\dfrac{x}{3}\right)^{2}$

$\quad = \dfrac{x^2}{3^2}$

$\quad = \dfrac{x^2}{9}$

13 Write without negative exponents:

a $5n^{-1}$ b $(5n)^{-1}$ c $\left(\dfrac{5}{n}\right)^{-1}$ d $\left(\dfrac{n}{5}\right)^{-2}$

e $(mn)^{-1}$ f $m^{-1}n$ g mn^{-1} h $\left(\dfrac{m}{n}\right)^{-1}$

SIMPLIFYING ALGEBRAIC EXPRESSIONS

When given an algebraic expression we can use the laws of exponents to write it in **simplest form**. The resulting expression should not contain brackets or negative exponents.

Example 9 ◀) **Self Tutor**

Express the following in simplest form, without brackets:

a $(2c^3d)^4$ b $\left(\dfrac{3f}{g^4}\right)^{2}$

a $\quad (2c^3d)^4$

$\quad = 2^4 \times (c^3)^4 \times d^4$

$\quad = 16 \times c^{12} \times d^4$

$\quad = 16c^{12}d^4$

b $\quad \left(\dfrac{3f}{g^4}\right)^{2}$

$\quad = \dfrac{3^2 \times f^2}{(g^4)^2}$

$\quad = \dfrac{9f^2}{g^8}$

EXERCISE 3A.2

1 Express in simplest form, without brackets:

a $(5p)^2$ b $(6b^2)^2$ c $\left(\dfrac{5k}{m}\right)^{2}$ d $\left(\dfrac{t}{2s}\right)^{3}$

e $(2a)^3$ f $(3m^2n^2)^3$ g $\left(\dfrac{y^2}{3z}\right)^{3}$ h $\left(\dfrac{c}{3d^2}\right)^{0}$

i $(2ab^4)^4$ j $\left(\dfrac{2a^2}{b^2}\right)^{3}$ k $\left(\dfrac{4a^3}{b}\right)^{2}$ l $\left(\dfrac{3p^2}{q^3}\right)^{2}$

Example 10   ◄ᴺ) **Self Tutor**

Simplify using the laws of exponents:

a $4x^3 \times 2x^6$ b $\dfrac{15t^7}{3t^5}$ c $\dfrac{k^2 \times k^6}{(k^3)^2}$

---

a $4x^3 \times 2x^6$ b $\dfrac{15t^7}{3t^5}$ c $\dfrac{k^2 \times k^6}{(k^3)^2}$

$= 4 \times 2 \times x^3 \times x^6$ $= \dfrac{15}{3} \times t^{7-5}$ $= \dfrac{k^{2+6}}{k^{3\times2}}$

$= 8 \times x^{3+6}$ $= 5t^2$ $= \dfrac{k^8}{k^6}$

$= 8x^9$ $= k^2$

---

2 Simplify using the laws of exponents:

a $\dfrac{4b^5}{b^2}$ b $2w^4 \times 3w$ c $\dfrac{12p^4}{3p^2}$ d $5c^7 \times 6c^4$

e $\dfrac{d^2 \times d^7}{d^5}$ f $\dfrac{18a^2b^3}{6ab}$ g $\dfrac{24m^2n^4}{6m^2n}$ h $\dfrac{t^5 \times t^8}{(t^2)^3}$

i $5s^2t \times 4t^3$ j $\dfrac{(k^4)^5}{k^3 \times k^6}$ k $\dfrac{12x^2y^5}{8xy^2}$ l $\dfrac{(b^3)^4 \times b^5}{b^2 \times b^6}$

Example 11   ◄ᴺ) **Self Tutor**

Write without negative exponents:

a $(2c^3)^{-4}$ b $\dfrac{a^{-3}b^2}{c^{-1}}$

---

a $(2c^3)^{-4} = \dfrac{1}{(2c^3)^4}$ b $a^{-3} = \dfrac{1}{a^3}$ and $\dfrac{1}{c^{-1}} = c^1$

$= \dfrac{1}{2^4 c^{3\times4}}$ $\therefore \quad \dfrac{a^{-3}b^2}{c^{-1}} = \dfrac{b^2 c}{a^3}$

$= \dfrac{1}{16c^{12}}$

---

3 Write without negative exponents:

a ab^{-2} b $(ab)^{-2}$ c $(2ab^{-1})^2$ d $(5m^2)^{-2}$

e $(3a^{-2}b)^2$ f $(3xy^4)^{-3}$ g $\dfrac{a^2b^{-1}}{c^2}$ h $\dfrac{a^2b^{-1}}{c^{-2}}$

i $\dfrac{1}{a^{-3}}$ j $\dfrac{a^{-2}}{b^{-3}}$ k $\dfrac{2a^{-1}}{d^2}$ l $\dfrac{12a}{m^{-3}}$

Example 12   ◄ᴺ) **Self Tutor**

Write $\dfrac{1}{2^{1-n}}$ in non-fractional form. $\dfrac{1}{2^{1-n}} = 2^{-(1-n)}$

$= 2^{-1+n}$

$= 2^{n-1}$

4 Write in non-fractional form:

   a $\dfrac{1}{a^n}$ **b** $\dfrac{1}{b^{-n}}$ **c** $\dfrac{1}{3^{2-n}}$ **d** $\dfrac{a^n}{b^{-m}}$ **e** $\dfrac{a^{-n}}{a^{2+n}}$

Example 13   ◀ϑ **Self Tutor**

Write in non-fractional form:

   a $\dfrac{x^2 + 3x + 2}{x}$ **b** $\dfrac{x^3 + 5x - 3}{x^2}$ **c** $\dfrac{2x^5 + x^2 + 3x}{x^{-2}}$

a $\dfrac{x^2 + 3x + 2}{x}$

    $= \dfrac{x^2}{x} + \dfrac{3x}{x} + \dfrac{2}{x}$

    $= x + 3 + 2x^{-1}$

b $\dfrac{x^3 + 5x - 3}{x^2}$

    $= \dfrac{x^3}{x^2} + \dfrac{5x}{x^2} - \dfrac{3}{x^2}$

    $= x + 5x^{-1} - 3x^{-2}$

c $\dfrac{2x^5 + x^2 + 3x}{x^{-2}}$

    $= \dfrac{2x^5}{x^{-2}} + \dfrac{x^2}{x^{-2}} + \dfrac{3x}{x^{-2}}$

    $= 2x^{5-(-2)} + x^{2-(-2)}$

        $+ 3x^{1-(-2)}$

    $= 2x^7 + x^4 + 3x^3$

---

5 Write in non-fractional form:

   a $\dfrac{x+3}{x}$ **b** $\dfrac{3-2x}{x}$ **c** $\dfrac{5-x}{x^2}$ **d** $\dfrac{x+2}{x^3}$

   e $\dfrac{x^2+5}{x}$ **f** $\dfrac{x^2+x-2}{x}$ **g** $\dfrac{2x^2-3x+4}{x}$ **h** $\dfrac{x^3-3x+5}{x^2}$

   i $\dfrac{5-x-x^2}{x}$ **j** $\dfrac{8+5x-2x^3}{x}$ **k** $\dfrac{16-3x+x^3}{x^2}$ **l** $\dfrac{5x^4-3x^2+x+6}{x^2}$

6 Write in non-fractional form:

   a $\dfrac{4+2x}{x^{-1}}$ **b** $\dfrac{5-4x}{x^{-2}}$ **c** $\dfrac{6+3x}{x^{-3}}$ **d** $\dfrac{x^2+3}{x^{-1}}$

   e $\dfrac{x^2+x-4}{x^{-2}}$ **f** $\dfrac{x^3-3x+6}{x^{-3}}$ **g** $\dfrac{x^3-6x+10}{x^{-2}}$

B   THE DISTRIBUTIVE LAW

To find the product of 4 and 103, it is helpful to write 103 as $100 + 3$.

$$4 \times 103 = 4(100 + 3)$$
$$= 4 \times 100 + 4 \times 3 \qquad \{\text{4 lots of } 103 = \text{4 lots of } 100 + \text{4 lots of } 3\}$$
$$= 400 + 12$$
$$= 412$$

This method uses the fact that $4(100 + 3) = 4 \times 100 + 4 \times 3$, which is an example of the **distributive law**:

$$a\overparen{(b + c)} = ab + ac$$

Each term inside the brackets is multiplied by the value outside the brackets.

Example 14   ◄》 **Self Tutor**

Expand and simplify:

  a $3(x+5)$ **b** $4x(x-2)$ **c** $-2x(x-5)$

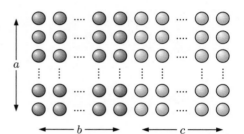

a $3(x+5)$
$$= 3 \times x + 3 \times 5$$
$$= 3x + 15$$

b $4x(x-2)$
$$= 4x \times x + 4x \times -2$$
$$= 4x^2 - 8x$$

c $-2x(x-5)$
$$= -2x \times x + -2x \times -5$$
$$= -2x^2 + 10x$$

EXERCISE 3B

1   A collection of balls has been arranged into a rectangle with a rows, as illustrated. There are b columns of green balls, and c columns of red balls.

     a   Explain why there are $a(b+c)$ balls in total.

     b   Find an expression for the number of:

         i   green balls   **ii**   red balls.

     c   Hence, show that $a(b+c) = ab + ac$.

2   Expand and simplify:

     a $4(x+3)$ **b** $5(x-2)$ **c** $8(3-x)$

     d $-(2x+5)$ **e** $-3(x-7)$ **f** $2x(x+6)$

     g $-6x(x+5)$ **h** $4x(3x-5)$ **i** $-5x(x-2)$

     j $-3x(6-5x)$ **k** $7x^2(x-4)$ **l** $-9x(4x^2-9)$

Example 15   ◄》 **Self Tutor**

Expand and simplify:

  a $3(4x+1) + 2(3x-4)$ **b** $x(3x+2) - 4x(1-x)$

> We simplify by **collecting like terms**.

a $3(4x+1) + 2(3x-4)$
$$= 12x + 3 + 6x - 8$$
$$= 18x - 5$$

b $x(3x+2) - 4x(1-x)$
$$= 3x^2 + 2x - 4x + 4x^2$$
$$= 7x^2 - 2x$$

3   Expand and simplify:

     a $2(2x+3) + 5(3x+1)$ **b** $4x + 3(6x-5)$

     c $3(3x-4) - 2(x-7)$ **d** $-2(4x+3) - 3(8-5x)$

     e $x(2x-1) + 3x(x+4)$ **f** $3x(x-9) + 5(5x+2)$

     g $4x(2x-5) - (3x+7)$ **h** $3x(7x-2) - x(6-x)$

     i $-8x(4-3x) - 5x(3x-2)$ **j** $-6x(2x-3) - 4(5-3x)$

C   THE PRODUCT $(a+b)(c+d)$

We can find the product $(a+b)(c+d)$ by using the distributive law several times.

$(a+b)(c+d) = a(c+d) + b(c+d)$ $\{(a+b)X = aX + bX\}$
$\qquad\qquad\quad = ac + ad + bc + bd$

$$(a+b)(c+d) = ac + ad + bc + bd$$

Notice that this final result contains four terms.

This expansion is sometimes called the **FOIL** rule.

$\quad ac$ is the product of the **First** terms of each bracket.
$\quad ad$ is the product of the **Outer** terms of each bracket.
$\quad bc$ is the product of the **Inner** terms of each bracket.
$\quad bd$ is the product of the **Last** terms of each bracket.

To demonstrate this rule, we find expressions for the shaded area alongside in two ways:

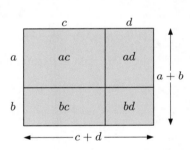

- Shaded area $= (a+b)(c+d)$
    $\qquad$ {area of large rectangle}

- Shaded area $= ac + ad + bc + bd$
    $\qquad$ {sum of areas of the 4 smaller rectangles}

So, $(a+b)(c+d) = ac + ad + bc + bd$.

Example 16	◀) Self Tutor

Expand and simplify: **a** $(x+4)(x+5)$ **b** $(3x+1)(4x-3)$

a $(x+4)(x+5)$

$= x \times x + x \times 5 + 4 \times x + 4 \times 5$
$= x^2 + 5x + 4x + 20$
$= x^2 + 9x + 20$

b $(3x+1)(4x-3)$

$= 3x \times 4x + 3x \times -3 + 1 \times 4x + 1 \times -3$
$= 12x^2 - 9x + 4x - 3$
$= 12x^2 - 5x - 3$

EXERCISE 3C

1 Expand and simplify:

$\quad$ **a** $(x+2)(x+7)$ $\qquad$ **b** $(x+8)(x-3)$ $\qquad$ **c** $(x-5)(x+4)$

$\quad$ **d** $(x-3)(x-6)$ $\qquad$ **e** $(2x+3)(x-4)$ $\qquad$ **f** $(3x-5)(2x+7)$

$\quad$ **g** $(5x-2)(4x-5)$ $\qquad$ **h** $(3+x)(4x-1)$ $\qquad$ **i** $(5-3x)(x+4)$

$\quad$ **j** $(6x-1)(8-3x)$ $\qquad$ **k** $(9-x)(3x+4)$ $\qquad$ **l** $(7x-3)(4-5x)$

Example 17   ◀) **Self Tutor**

Expand and simplify: **a** $(2x+5)(2x-5)$ **b** $(3x+4)^2$

a $(2x+5)(2x-5)$
$= 4x^2 - 10x + 10x - 25$
$= 4x^2 - 25$

b $(3x+4)^2$
$= (3x+4)(3x+4)$
$= 9x^2 + 12x + 12x + 16$
$= 9x^2 + 24x + 16$

> What do you notice about the middle two terms in **a**?

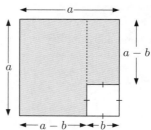

2   Expand and simplify:

a $(x+4)(x-4)$

b $(a+6)(a-6)$

c $(7+x)(7-x)$

d $(3x+1)(3x-1)$

e $(4k+3)(4k-3)$

f $(5+6a)(5-6a)$

3   Expand and simplify:

a $(x+7)^2$

b $(x-5)^2$

c $(2x-3)^2$

d $(5+3x)^2$

e $(7-2x)^2$

f $(4x+y)^2$

D   DIFFERENCE OF TWO SQUARES

Consider the product $(a+b)(a-b)$.

Using the FOIL rule to expand this product, $(a+b)(a-b) = a^2 - ab + ab - b^2$
$= a^2 - b^2$

$$(a+b)(a-b) = a^2 - b^2$$

This expansion rule is called the **difference of two squares** since the expression on the right hand side is the difference between the two perfect squares a^2 and b^2.

This result can be demonstrated geometrically.

In the figure alongside, the
shaded area = area of large square
                 − area of small square
$= a^2 - b^2$

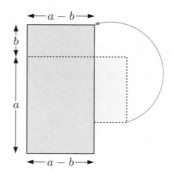

If the rectangle on the right hand side is rotated and placed on top of the remaining shaded area, we form a new rectangle.

Now, the shaded area $= (a+b)(a-b)$

So, $(a+b)(a-b) = a^2 - b^2$.

DEMO

Example 18   ◀)) **Self Tutor**

Expand and simplify:

    a $(x + 8)(x - 8)$ **b** $(4 - y)(4 + y)$

    a $(x + 8)(x - 8)$ **b** $(4 - y)(4 + y)$

          $= x^2 - 8^2$ $= 4^2 - y^2$

          $= x^2 - 64$ $= 16 - y^2$

EXERCISE 3D

1   Expand and simplify:

   a $(x + 3)(x - 3)$ **b** $(x - 1)(x + 1)$ **c** $(6 + x)(6 - x)$

   d $(10 - x)(10 + x)$ **e** $(x - 10)(x + 10)$ **f** $(a - 7)(a + 7)$

   g $(9 + y)(9 - y)$ **h** $(k + 5)(k - 5)$ **i** $(x + y)(x - y)$

Example 19   ◀)) **Self Tutor**

Expand and simplify:

    a $(3x + 2)(3x - 2)$ **b** $(4x - 3y)(4x + 3y)$

    a $(3x + 2)(3x - 2)$ **b** $(4x - 3y)(4x + 3y)$

          $= (3x)^2 - 2^2$ $= (4x)^2 - (3y)^2$

          $= 9x^2 - 4$ $= 16x^2 - 9y^2$

2   Expand and simplify:

   a $(2x + 1)(2x - 1)$ **b** $(5x - 3)(5x + 3)$ **c** $(4x + 7)(4x - 7)$

   d $(6x - 5)(6x + 5)$ **e** $(8t + 1)(8t - 1)$ **f** $(5 - 9x)(5 + 9x)$

   g $(7 - 4k)(7 + 4k)$ **h** $(10 + 3m)(10 - 3m)$ **i** $(1 - 12z)(1 + 12z)$

3   Expand and simplify:

   a $(3x + y)(3x - y)$ **b** $(m - 4n)(m + 4n)$ **c** $(3p + 7q)(3p - 7q)$

   d $(8c - 5d)(8c + 5d)$ **e** $(9x - 2y)(9x + 2y)$ **f** $(5x + 6y)(6y - 5x)$

E   PERFECT SQUARES EXPANSIONS

The expressions $(a + b)^2$ and $(a - b)^2$ are known as **perfect squares**. Expanding the expressions using the FOIL rule, we get:

$$(a + b)^2 = (a + b)(a + b) \qquad \text{and} \qquad (a - b)^2 = (a - b)(a - b)$$

$$= a^2 \underbrace{+ ab + ab}_{\substack{\text{the middle two terms} \\ \text{are identical}}} + b^2 \qquad\qquad\qquad = a^2 \underbrace{- ab - ab}_{\substack{\text{the middle two terms} \\ \text{are identical}}} + b^2$$

$$= a^2 + 2ab + b^2 \qquad\qquad\qquad\qquad\qquad = a^2 - 2ab + b^2$$

So, the perfect square expansion rules are:

$$(a + b)^2 = a^2 + 2ab + b^2$$
$$(a - b)^2 = a^2 - 2ab + b^2$$

A useful way to remember the perfect square expansion rules is:

Step 1:   Square the *first term*.

Step 2:   Double the product of the *first* and *last terms*, adding or subtracting according to the sign between the terms.

Step 3:   Add on the square of the *last term*.

Example 20   ◀) Self Tutor

Expand and simplify:

a $(x + 5)^2$ b $(x - 4)^2$

a $(x + 5)^2$ b $(x - 4)^2$
$= x^2 + 2 \times x \times 5 + 5^2$ $= x^2 - 2 \times x \times 4 + 4^2$
$= x^2 + 10x + 25$ $= x^2 - 8x + 16$

EXERCISE 3E

1   Use the rule $(a + b)^2 = a^2 + 2ab + b^2$ to expand and simplify:

a $(x + 3)^2$ b $(x + 6)^2$ c $(x + 2)^2$

d $(a + 9)^2$ e $(5 + k)^2$ f $(7 + t)^2$

2   Use the rule $(a - b)^2 = a^2 - 2ab + b^2$ to expand and simplify:

a $(x - 3)^2$ b $(x - 1)^2$ c $(x - 8)^2$

d $(b - 2)^2$ e $(4 - x)^2$ f $(7 - y)^2$

Example 21   ◀) Self Tutor

Expand and simplify using the perfect square expansion rules:

a $(3x + 2)^2$ b $(1 - 5x)^2$

a $(3x + 2)^2$ b $(1 - 5x)^2$
$= (3x)^2 + 2 \times 3x \times 2 + 2^2$ $= 1^2 - 2 \times 1 \times 5x + (5x)^2$
$= 9x^2 + 12x + 4$ $= 1 - 10x + 25x^2$

3   Expand and simplify using the perfect square expansion rules:

a $(3x + 5)^2$ b $(4a - 2)^2$ c $(2b + 7)^2$

d $(3k + 1)^2$ e $(5y - 4)^2$ f $(3 - 2x)^2$

g $(4 + 3y)^2$ h $(1 + 5z)^2$ i $(2 - 3n)^2$

Example 22

Self Tutor

Expand and simplify: **a** $(3x^2 - 1)^2$ **b** $4 - (x + 3)^2$

a $(3x^2 - 1)^2$
$= (3x^2)^2 - 2 \times 3x^2 \times 1 + 1^2$
$= 9x^4 - 6x^2 + 1$

b $4 - (x + 3)^2$
$= 4 - (x^2 + 6x + 9)$
$= 4 - x^2 - 6x - 9$
$= -x^2 - 6x - 5$

4 Expand and simplify:

   a $(x^2 + 3)^2$
   b $(y^2 - 7)^2$
   c $(5z^2 + 1)^2$

   d $(3 - 2a^2)^2$
   e $(m^2 + n^2)^2$
   f $(x^2 - y^2)^2$

5 Expand and simplify:

   a $2x + 5 - (x + 2)^2$
   b $4 - 3x + (x - 1)^2$

   c $(x + 3)(x - 3) + (x + 2)^2$
   d $(x + 7)(x - 7) - (x + 4)^2$

   e $(5 - x)^2 - (x + 3)(x - 2)$
   f $(2 - 3x)^2 + (x - 4)(x + 1)$

   g $(3x + 1)(3x - 1) + (x - 7)^2$
   h $(2x - 5)(x + 3) - (1 - x)^2$

   i $(x - 2)^2 + (3x - 4)^2$
   j $(4 - x)^2 - (x - 3)^2$

6 Answer the **Opening Problem** on page **74**.

F   FURTHER EXPANSION

When expressions containing more than two terms are multiplied together, we can still use the distributive law. Each term in the first set of brackets is multiplied by each term in the second set of brackets.

If there are 2 terms in the first brackets and 3 terms in the second brackets, there will be $2 \times 3 = 6$ terms in the expansion. However, when we simplify by collecting like terms, the final answer may contain fewer terms.

Example 23

Self Tutor

Expand and simplify: $(3x + 2)(x^2 - 4x + 1)$

> Each term in the first brackets is multiplied by each term in the second brackets.

$(3x + 2)(x^2 - 4x + 1)$

$= 3x^3 - 12x^2 + 3x$ {$3x$ multiplied by each term in the 2nd brackets}
$\quad + 2x^2 - 8x + 2$ {2 multiplied by each term in the 2nd brackets}
$= 3x^3 - 10x^2 - 5x + 2$ {collecting like terms}

EXERCISE 3F

1 Expand and simplify:

   a $(x + 2)(x^2 + 3x + 5)$
   b $(x + 3)(x^2 - 4x + 2)$
   c $(x + 5)(x^2 + x + 2)$

   d $(x - 2)(x^2 + 3x - 4)$
   e $(2x + 3)(x^2 - 2x + 1)$
   f $(4x - 1)(x^2 - x - 1)$

   g $(2 - x)(x^2 + 7x - 3)$
   h $(3x + 2)(2x^2 - 5x + 3)$

Example 24

🔊 Self Tutor

Expand and simplify: $(x+3)^3$

$(x+3)^3$
$= (x+3) \times (x+3)^2$
$= (x+3)(x^2 + 6x + 9)$

$= x^3 + 6x^2 + 9x$ {$x \times$ each term in the 2nd brackets}
     $+ 3x^2 + 18x + 27$ {$3 \times$ each term in the 2nd brackets}
$= x^3 + 9x^2 + 27x + 27$ {collecting like terms}

2 Expand and simplify:

     a $(x+2)^3$ **b** $(x+1)^3$ **c** $(x-1)^3$

     d $(x-2)^3$ **e** $(3x+1)^3$ **f** $(2x-3)^3$

Example 25

🔊 Self Tutor

Expand and simplify: **a** $x(x+3)(x+2)$ **b** $(x+2)(x-3)(x+1)$

a $x(x+3)(x+2)$
   $= (x^2 + 3x)(x+2)$ {$x \times$ each term in the first brackets}
   $= x^3 + 2x^2 + 3x^2 + 6x$ {expanding remaining factors}
   $= x^3 + 5x^2 + 6x$ {collecting like terms}

b $(x+2)(x-3)(x+1)$
   $= (x^2 - 3x + 2x - 6)(x+1)$ {expanding first two factors}
   $= (x^2 - x - 6)(x+1)$ {collecting like terms}
   $= x^3 + x^2 - x^2 - x - 6x - 6$ {expanding remaining factors}
   $= x^3 - 7x - 6$ {collecting like terms}

3 Expand and simplify:

     a $x(x+1)(x+2)$ **b** $x(x-2)(x+3)$ **c** $x(x-4)(x-1)$

     d $2x(x+2)(x+1)$ **e** $2x(x-3)(x-4)$ **f** $-x(2+x)(x-3)$

     g $-3x(x+4)(x-5)$ **h** $3x(2-x)(x-1)$ **i** $-x(x+6)(1-x)$

4 Expand and simplify:

     a $(x+1)(x+3)(x+2)$ **b** $(x-3)(x+2)(x-1)$ **c** $(x-2)(x-4)(x-6)$

     d $(x+1)(x-2)(x-1)$ **e** $(2x-3)(x+2)(x-1)$ **f** $(2x+3)(2x-3)(x-2)$

     g $(2-x)(4x-1)(x+5)$ **h** $(2+x)(5-x)(3x+1)$

5 State how many terms would be in the expansion of the following:

     a $(a+b)(c+d)$ **b** $(a+b+c)(d+e)$ **c** $(a+b)(c+d+e)$

     d $(a+b+c)(d+e+f)$ **e** $(a+b+c+d)(e+f)$ **f** $(a+b+c+d)(e+f+g)$

     g $(a+b)(c+d)(e+f)$ **h** $(a+b+c)(d+e)(f+g)$

INVESTIGATION 2   THE EXPANSION OF $(a+b)^3$

The purpose of this investigation is to discover the expansion of $(a+b)^3$.

What to do:

1   Find a large potato and cut it to obtain a 4 cm by 4 cm by 4 cm cube.

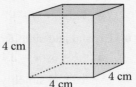

2   By making 3 cuts parallel to the cube's surfaces, divide the cube into 8 rectangular prisms as shown.

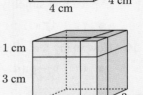

    How many prisms are:

    a   3 by 3 by 3   **b**   3 by 3 by 1

    c   3 by 1 by 1   **d**   1 by 1 by 1?

3   Now instead of 3 cm and 1 cm dimensions, suppose the potato was cut to give dimensions a cm and b cm. How many prisms are:

    a a by a by a **b** a by a by b

    c a by b by b **d** b by b by b?

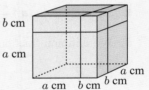

4   Explain why the volume of the cube in **3** is given by $(a+b)^3$.

5   By adding the volumes of the 8 rectangular prisms, find an expression for the total volume. Hence write down the expansion of $(a+b)^3$.

REVIEW SET 3A

1   Simplify: **a** $x^4 \times x^2$ **b** $\left(2^{-1}\right)^7$ **c** $\left(ab^3\right)^6$

2   Write without negative exponents:

    a 3^{-3} **b** $x^{-1}y$ **c** $\left(\dfrac{a}{b}\right)^{-1}$

3   Express in simplest form with a prime number base:

    a   27   **b** 9^t **c** $\dfrac{4}{2^{m-1}}$

4   Simplify using one or more of the laws of exponents:

    a $\dfrac{15xy^2}{3y^4}$ **b** $\dfrac{j^6}{j^5 \times j^8}$ **c** $\dfrac{36g^3h^5}{12h^2}$

5   Express the following in simplest form, without brackets:

    a $\left(\dfrac{t}{4s}\right)^3$ **b** $\left(\dfrac{m^2}{5n}\right)^0$ **c** $\left(5p^3q\right)^2$

6 Write in non-fractional form:

    a $\dfrac{x^2 + 8}{x}$
    b $\dfrac{4 + x + x^3}{x^{-2}}$
    c $\dfrac{k^{-x}}{k^{x+6}}$

7 Expand and simplify:

    a $7x(x - 7)$
    b $x(3 - x) - 7x(x + 5)$

8 Expand and simplify:

    a $(x - 3)(x + 3)$
    b $(2x - 5)(x + 6)$
    c $(7x - y)^2$

9 Expand and simplify:

    a $(x + 4)(x + 9) + (x + 6)(x - 6)$
    b $(x - 5)(x^2 + 7x - 2)$

10 How many terms are in the expansion of:

    a $(a + b + c)(d + e)$
    b $(a + b)(c + d + e + f)$?

REVIEW SET 3B

1 Simplify:
    a $\dfrac{m^9}{m^5}$
    b y^0
    c $\left(\dfrac{7z}{w}\right)^{-2}$

2 Simplify:
    a $\dfrac{k^x}{k^2}$
    b $11^r \times 11^{-4}$
    c 9×3^b

3 Write in non-fractional form:

    a $\dfrac{1}{11}$
    b $\dfrac{a}{b^2}$
    c $\dfrac{jk^4}{l^a}$

4 Express in simplest form with a prime number base:

    a $\dfrac{1}{16}$
    b $3^k \times 81$
    c $\dfrac{125^a}{5^b}$

5 Write in simplest rational form:

    a 2^{-3}
    b 7^0
    c $3^{-1} + 3^1$

6 Simplify, writing your answer without brackets:

    a $\left(\dfrac{2a^6}{8b^2}\right)^3$
    b $\left(5d \times d^{-5}\right)^2$
    c $\dfrac{16z^2 \times z^5}{(2z)^3}$

7 Expand and simplify:

    a $4x(5 - x)$
    b $(3x + 2)(2x + 3)$

8 Expand and simplify:

    a $(x - 9)(x + 4)$
    b $(x + 7)^2$
    c $(2 - x)(x + 3)$

9 Expand and simplify:

    a $7 - (x + 4)^2$
    b $(6x + 1)(x + 5) + (x - 2)^2$

10 Expand and simplify:

    a $(x + 7)(x - 2)(2x + 3)$
    b $(x - 4)^3$

Chapter 4

Equations and formulae

Syllabus reference: 1.6

OPENING PROBLEM

Holly is studying overseas and makes a lot of calls back home. She is comparing two different mobile phone plans, both of which give free local calls, but which charge international calls at different rates. Plan A costs €25 for the monthly access fee and international calls are billed at 17 cents per minute. Plan B costs only €10 for the monthly access fee but international calls are billed at 23 cents per minute.

Things to think about:

a Can you write a *formula* for each plan that connects the total cost €C with the number of minutes m used on international calls per month?

b Use the formula to find the total *cost* for each plan if Holly's international calls total:

   i 150 minutes per month   **ii** 300 minutes per month.

c Find the values of m such that the cost of each plan is the same.

d What advice would you give to Holly regarding her choice of plans?

Algebra is a tool which we use to write mathematical ideas in a convenient way. In algebra we use letters or symbols to represent unknown quantities, or values which can vary depending on the situation.

There are several important words associated with algebra that you should be familiar with:

- $2x + 3$ is an **expression** for the quantity which is three more than twice x.

- $2x + 3 = 5$ is an **equation** which says that the quantity $2x + 3$ has the value 5. We can **solve** the equation to find the value of x.

- $2x + 3 > 5$ is an **inequality** or **inequation** which says that the value of $2x + 3$ is more than 5.

- $y = 2x + 3$ is a **formula** which connects the two **variables** x and y. If we know the value of one of the variables then we can **substitute** this value to determine the other variable. We can also **rearrange** formulae to write them in more convenient forms.

A   ALGEBRAIC SUBSTITUTION

We can think of an expression as a number crunching machine. We feed an input number into the machine, and the machine produces a related output number.

For example, the machine for the expression $4x - 1$ starts with the input number x, multiplies it by 4, and then subtracts 1.

If we feed the number 3 into the machine, the machine **substitutes** the number 3 in place of x, then **evaluates** the result:

$$4x - 1 = 4 \times 3 - 1$$
$$= 12 - 1$$
$$= 11$$

So, the machine produces the output number 11.

When we substitute a negative number, we place it in brackets to make sure the negative sign does not become confusing.

For example, if we feed the number -5 into the machine, the machine calculates

$$4x - 1 = 4 \times (-5) - 1$$
$$= -20 - 1$$
$$= -21$$

Example 1   ◀» **Self Tutor**

If $p = -2$, $q = 3$, and $r = 4$, find the value of:

    a $p + 5q$ **b** $pr - 7q$ **c** $\dfrac{2r - 4q}{qr + p - 1}$

a $p + 5q$
     $= (-2) + 5 \times 3$
     $= -2 + 15$
     $= 13$

b $pr - 7q$
     $= (-2) \times 4 - 7 \times 3$
     $= -8 - 21$
     $= -29$

c $\dfrac{2r - 4q}{qr + p - 1}$

     $= \dfrac{2 \times 4 - 4 \times 3}{3 \times 4 + (-2) - 1}$

     $= \dfrac{8 - 12}{12 - 2 - 1}$

     $= \dfrac{-4}{9}$

EXERCISE 4A

1   If $l = 2$, $m = -3$, and $n = -1$, find the value of:

    a $4l$ **b** $-n$ **c** $2mn$ **d** lmn

    e $2l + m$ **f** $4m - 3l$ **g** $ml - 2n$ **h** $nl - 2mn$

2   If $e = 4$, $f = 2$, and $g = -3$, evaluate:

    a $\dfrac{g}{e}$ **b** $\dfrac{e + f}{g}$ **c** $\dfrac{2g + e}{f}$ **d** $\dfrac{3f - e}{2f - g}$

    e $g - \dfrac{e}{f}$ **f** $\dfrac{fg}{e}$ **g** $\dfrac{2g + f}{e}$ **h** $\dfrac{g - f}{e + g}$

Example 2   ◀» **Self Tutor**

If $x = 2$, $y = -4$, and $z = -5$, evaluate:

    a y^2 **b** $yz^3 - 3x$

a y^2
     $= (-4)^2$
     $= 16$

b $yz^3 - 3x$
     $= (-4) \times (-5)^3 - 3 \times 2$
     $= 494$

Notice the use of brackets.

3 If $a = 4$, $b = -1$, and $c = -3$, evaluate:

   a b^2 **b** c^3 **c** $a^2 + c^2$ **d** $(a + c)^2$

   e $a^3 + b^3$ **f** $(a + b)^3$ **g** $(2c)^2$ **h** $2c^2$

Example 3   🔊 Self Tutor

If $k = 5$, $l = -1$, and $m = 2$, evaluate:

   a $\sqrt{k + l}$ **b** $\sqrt{m^2 + 3k}$

   a $\sqrt{k + l}$ **b** $\sqrt{m^2 + 3k}$

        $= \sqrt{5 + (-1)}$ $= \sqrt{2^2 + 3(5)}$

        $= \sqrt{4}$ $= \sqrt{19}$

        $= 2$ ≈ 4.36 {3 significant figures}

---

4 If $k = -2$, $l = 3$, and $m = 7$, evaluate:

   a $\sqrt{l + k}$ **b** $\sqrt{m + 3l}$ **c** $\sqrt{m - k}$ **d** $\sqrt{lm - 2k}$

   e $\sqrt{k^2 + m^2}$ **f** $\sqrt{l^2 - m}$ **g** $\sqrt{2m + 6l - 5k}$ **h** $\sqrt{m^2 - l^2 + 2k}$

B   LINEAR EQUATIONS

Many problems can be written as **equations** using algebraic notation. So, it is essential we are able to **solve** equations.

> **Linear equations** are equations which can be written in the form $ax + b = 0$ where x is the **variable** or **unknown** and a, b are constants.

To solve linear equations we need to rearrange the equation to **isolate** the unknown. We first look at how the expression involving the unknown was built up, then undo it using **inverse operations**. The inverse operations are performed on both sides of the equation to **maintain the balance**.

Once you have found a solution, you should check it is correct by **substitution** back into the original equation.

Example 4   🔊 Self Tutor

Solve for x:

   a $2x - 3 = 5$ **b** $8 - 4x = -2$

> The inverse of -3 is $+3$.
> The inverse of $\times 2$ is $\div 2$.

   a $2x - 3 = 5$

       $2x - 3 + 3 = 5 + 3$ {adding 3 to both sides}

       $\therefore \quad 2x = 8$

       $\therefore \quad \dfrac{2x}{2} = \dfrac{8}{2}$ {dividing both sides by 2}

       $\therefore \quad x = 4$ *Check:* $2 \times 4 - 3 = 8 - 3 = 5$ ✓

b $8 - 4x = -2$

∴ $8 - 4x - 8 = -2 - 8$ {subtracting 8 from both sides}

∴ $-4x = -10$

∴ $\dfrac{-4x}{-4} = \dfrac{-10}{-4}$ {dividing both sides by -4}

∴ $x = \frac{5}{2}$ *Check*: $8 - 4 \times \left(\frac{5}{2}\right) = 8 - 10 = -2$ ✓

Example 5   ◀)) Self Tutor

Solve for x: **a** $\dfrac{x}{4} + 7 = 5$ **b** $\frac{1}{3}(x + 2) = 6$

> The inverse of $+7$ is -7.
> The inverse of $\div 4$ is $\times 4$.

a $\dfrac{x}{4} + 7 = 5$

∴ $\dfrac{x}{4} + 7 - 7 = 5 - 7$ {subtracting 7 from both sides}

∴ $\dfrac{x}{4} = -2$

∴ $\dfrac{x}{4} \times 4 = -2 \times 4$ {multiplying both sides by 4}

∴ $x = -8$ *Check*: $\dfrac{-8}{4} + 7 = -2 + 7 = 5$ ✓

b $\frac{1}{3}(x + 2) = 6$

∴ $\frac{1}{3}(x + 2) \times 3 = 6 \times 3$ {multiplying both sides by 3}

∴ $x + 2 = 18$

∴ $x + 2 - 2 = 18 - 2$ {subtracting 2 from both sides}

∴ $x = 16$ *Check*: $\frac{1}{3}(16 + 2) = \frac{1}{3} \times 18 = 6$ ✓

EXERCISE 4B.1

1 Solve for x:

   a $x + 5 = 3$ **b** $4x = 28$ **c** $-18 = -3x$ **d** $7 - x = 11$

   e $2x + 3 = 14$ **f** $3x - 4 = -13$ **g** $5 - 2x = -9$ **h** $7 = 11 - 3x$

2 Solve for x:

   a $\dfrac{x}{3} = 15$ **b** $\frac{1}{4}x = 16$ **c** $1 = \dfrac{x}{-3}$ **d** $\dfrac{x}{2} - 4 = 7$

   e $\dfrac{x - 4}{3} = -1$ **f** $\frac{1}{2}(x + 5) = 6$ **g** $\dfrac{2x - 3}{5} = 4$ **h** $\frac{1}{3}(2 - x) = -5$

EQUATIONS WITH A REPEATED UNKNOWN

If the unknown appears in the equation more than once, we follow these steps:

- Expand any brackets and collect like terms.
- If the unknown appears on both sides of the equation, remove it from one side using an inverse operation. Remember to balance the other side.
- Isolate the unknown and solve the equation.

Example 6   ◀》 **Self Tutor**

Solve for x: $4(2x + 5) - 3(x - 2) = 16$

Use the **distributive law**
$a(b + c) = ab + ac.$

$4(2x + 5) - 3(x - 2) = 16$
$\therefore \ 8x + 20 - 3x + 6 = 16$ {expanding brackets}
$\therefore \quad 5x + 26 = 16$ {collecting like terms}
$\therefore \ 5x + 26 - 26 = 16 - 26$ {subtracting 26 from both sides}
$\therefore \quad 5x = -10$
$\therefore \quad x = -2$ {dividing both sides by 5}

Check: $4(2 \times (-2) + 5) - 3((-2) - 2)$
$= 4 \times 1 - 3 \times (-4) = 4 + 12 = 16$ ✓

Example 7   ◀》 **Self Tutor**

Solve for x: **a** $4x - 3 = 3x + 7$ **b** $5 - 3(-1 + x) = x$

a $4x - 3 = 3x + 7$
$\therefore \ 4x - 3 - 3x = 3x + 7 - 3x$ {subtracting $3x$ from both sides}
$\therefore \quad x - 3 = 7$
$\therefore \quad x - 3 + 3 = 7 + 3$ {adding 3 to both sides}
$\therefore \quad x = 10$

Check: LHS $= 4 \times 10 - 3 = 37,$ RHS $= 3 \times 10 + 7 = 37$ ✓

b $5 - 3(-1 + x) = x$
$\therefore \ 5 + 3 - 3x = x$ {expanding the brackets}
$\therefore \quad 8 - 3x = x$
$\therefore \ 8 - 3x + 3x = x + 3x$ {adding $3x$ to both sides}
$\therefore \quad 8 = 4x$
$\therefore \quad \dfrac{8}{4} = \dfrac{4x}{4}$ {dividing both sides by 4}
$\therefore \quad 2 = x \ \text{ or } \ x = 2$

Check: LHS $= 5 - 3(-1 + 2) = 5 - 3 \times 1 = 2 = $ RHS   ✓

EXERCISE 4B.2

1 Solve for x:

  a $3(x + 2) + 2(x + 4) = 19$ **b** $2(x - 7) - 5(x + 1) = -7$
  c $3(x - 3) - 4(x - 5) = 2$ **d** $5(2x + 1) - 3(x - 1) = -6$
  e $2(3x - 2) + 7(2x + 1) = 13$ **f** $4(x + 4) + 3(5 - 2x) = 19$

2 Solve for x:

  a $5x - 5 = 4x + 1$ **b** $2x - 3 = 6 - x$ **c** $1 - 3x = 2x - 9$
  d $-4x = 8 - 2x$ **e** $9 - 5x = x + 6$ **f** $4x - 7 = x + 3$

3 Solve for x:

    a $6 - x + 3(1 - x) = 7 - 2x$
    b $8 - 5(3 - x) = 9 + x$

    c $6 + 7x - 2(3 - x) = 5x - 8$
    d $5(3x + 1) - 4x = x - 2$

4 Solve for x:

    a $5(2x - 1) + 2 = 10x - 3$
    b $2(9x - 1) = 6(3x + 1)$

    Comment on your solutions to **a** and **b**.

OTHER EXPANSIONS

Sometimes when more complicated equations are expanded and simplified, a linear equation results.

You will need to remember the expansion laws:

$$a(b + c) = ab + ac$$
$$(a + b)(c + d) = ac + ad + bc + bd$$
$$(a + b)^2 = a^2 + 2ab + b^2$$
$$(a - b)^2 = a^2 - 2ab + b^2$$
$$(a + b)(a - b) = a^2 - b^2$$

Example 8   ◀⬥ **Self Tutor**

Solve for x: $(x - 3)^2 = (4 + x)(2 + x)$

$(x - 3)^2 = (4 + x)(2 + x)$

$\therefore\ x^2 - 6x + 9 = 8 + 4x + 2x + x^2$ {expanding each side}

$\therefore\ x^2 - 6x + 9 - x^2 = 8 + 4x + 2x + x^2 - x^2$ {subtracting x^2 from both sides}

$\therefore\ -6x + 9 = 8 + 6x$

$\therefore\ -6x + 9 + 6x = 8 + 6x + 6x$ {adding $6x$ to both sides}

$\therefore\ 9 = 12x + 8$

$\therefore\ 9 - 8 = 12x + 8 - 8$ {subtracting 8 from both sides}

$\therefore\ 1 = 12x$

$\therefore\ \dfrac{1}{12} = \dfrac{12x}{12}$ {dividing both sides by 12}

$\therefore\ x = \dfrac{1}{12}$

EXERCISE 4B.3

1 Solve for x:

    a $x(x + 5) = (x - 4)(x - 3)$
    b $x(2x + 1) - 2(x + 1) = 2x(x - 1)$

    c $(x + 3)(x - 2) = (4 - x)^2$
    d $x^2 - 3 = (2 + x)(3 + x)$

    e $(x + 2)(2x - 1) = 2x(x + 3)$
    f $(x + 4)^2 = (x - 1)(x + 3)$

    g $(x + 3)(x - 3) = x(1 + x)$
    h $(x - 2)^2 = (x - 1)(x + 1)$

C   EQUATIONS INVOLVING FRACTIONS

For equations involving fractions, we write all fractions with the **lowest common denominator** (LCD).

For example: • In $\dfrac{2x}{3} = \dfrac{x}{4}$ the LCD is 12.   • In $\dfrac{3}{2x} = \dfrac{x}{4}$ the LCD is $4x$.

• In $\dfrac{x-7}{3} = \dfrac{x}{2x-1}$ the LCD is $3(2x-1)$.

Once the fractions are all written with the lowest common denominator, we can **equate the numerators**.

Example 9	◀)) Self Tutor

Solve for x: $\dfrac{2-x}{3} = \dfrac{x}{5}$

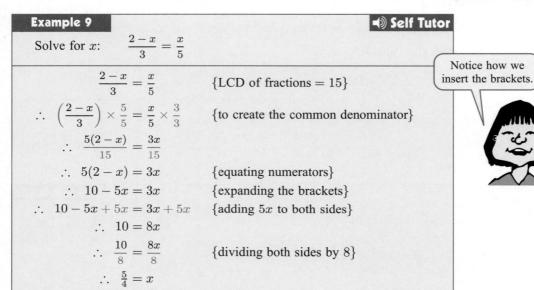

$$\frac{2-x}{3} = \frac{x}{5} \qquad \{\text{LCD of fractions} = 15\}$$

$$\therefore \left(\frac{2-x}{3}\right) \times \frac{5}{5} = \frac{x}{5} \times \frac{3}{3} \qquad \{\text{to create the common denominator}\}$$

$$\therefore \frac{5(2-x)}{15} = \frac{3x}{15}$$

$$\therefore 5(2-x) = 3x \qquad \{\text{equating numerators}\}$$

$$\therefore 10 - 5x = 3x \qquad \{\text{expanding the brackets}\}$$

$$\therefore 10 - 5x + 5x = 3x + 5x \qquad \{\text{adding } 5x \text{ to both sides}\}$$

$$\therefore 10 = 8x$$

$$\therefore \frac{10}{8} = \frac{8x}{8} \qquad \{\text{dividing both sides by 8}\}$$

$$\therefore \tfrac{5}{4} = x$$

Notice how we insert the brackets.

Example 10	◀)) Self Tutor

Solve for x: $\dfrac{3x+2}{1-2x} = \dfrac{1}{6}$

$$\frac{3x+2}{1-2x} = \frac{1}{6} \qquad \{\text{LCD of fractions} = 6(1-2x)\}$$

$$\therefore \left(\frac{3x+2}{1-2x}\right) \times \frac{6}{6} = \frac{1}{6} \times \left(\frac{1-2x}{1-2x}\right) \qquad \{\text{to create the common denominator}\}$$

$$\therefore \frac{6(3x+2)}{6(1-2x)} = \frac{(1-2x)}{6(1-2x)}$$

$$\therefore 6(3x+2) = 1 - 2x \qquad \{\text{equating numerators}\}$$

$$\therefore 18x + 12 = 1 - 2x \qquad \{\text{expanding the brackets}\}$$

$$\therefore 18x + 12 + 2x = 1 - 2x + 2x \qquad \{\text{adding } 2x \text{ to both sides}\}$$

$$\therefore 20x + 12 = 1$$

$$\therefore 20x + 12 - 12 = 1 - 12 \qquad \{\text{subtracting 12 from both sides}\}$$

$$\therefore 20x = -11$$

$$\therefore \frac{20x}{20} = \frac{-11}{20} \qquad \{\text{dividing both sides by 20}\}$$

$$\therefore x = -\tfrac{11}{20}$$

EXERCISE 4C

1 Solve for x:

a $\dfrac{x}{5} = \dfrac{2}{3}$

b $\dfrac{5}{6} = \dfrac{x}{5}$

c $\dfrac{x-3}{2} = \dfrac{1}{5}$

d $\dfrac{x}{4} = \dfrac{1+x}{3}$

e $\dfrac{2-x}{3} = \dfrac{8x}{5}$

f $\dfrac{2x-1}{5} = -\dfrac{3x}{7}$

g $\dfrac{1-3x}{4} = \dfrac{2+x}{3}$

h $\dfrac{7-x}{5} = \dfrac{3x+1}{8}$

i $\dfrac{3-2x}{5} = \dfrac{2+5x}{-3}$

2 Solve for x:

a $\dfrac{3}{x} = \dfrac{2}{5}$

b $\dfrac{2}{x} = \dfrac{1}{3}$

c $\dfrac{7}{x} = \dfrac{3}{4}$

d $\dfrac{3}{4x} = \dfrac{5}{3}$

e $\dfrac{5}{4x} = \dfrac{3}{2}$

f $\dfrac{2}{3x} = -\dfrac{4}{9}$

g $\dfrac{4}{x+1} = \dfrac{5}{3}$

h $\dfrac{3}{1-x} = \dfrac{2}{5}$

i $\dfrac{1}{5} = \dfrac{4}{3x+2}$

3 Solve for x: $\dfrac{4}{3x} = \dfrac{5}{4x}$ Comment on your answer.

4 Solve for x:

a $\dfrac{1}{x} = \dfrac{2}{x+1}$

b $\dfrac{2x-1}{1-x} = \dfrac{1}{2}$

c $\dfrac{3x+1}{x+2} = 4$

d $\dfrac{3x-2}{1-2x} = -\dfrac{1}{3}$

e $\dfrac{3}{2x-1} = \dfrac{5}{3x}$

f $\dfrac{1-5x}{4+x} = -\dfrac{3}{4}$

g $\dfrac{3-2x}{x+1} = -7$

h $\dfrac{4x+3}{1-2x} = \dfrac{3}{8}$

i $\dfrac{4}{3x+2} = \dfrac{7}{2-5x}$

D   SOLVING EQUATIONS USING TECHNOLOGY

You can use a graphics calculator to solve linear equations. For assistance you should refer to the **graphics calculator instructions** online.

GRAPHICS
CALCULATOR
INSTRUCTIONS

Example 11   ◀)) **Self Tutor**

Solve using technology: $4.6x - 8.9 = 7.2$

Casio fx-CG20

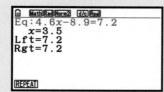

TI-84 Plus

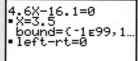

TI-nspire

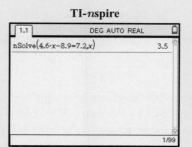

Using technology, $x = 3.5$

Alternatively, we can solve linear equations graphically. We graph the LHS and RHS of the equation on the same set of axes. The x-coordinate of the intersection point gives us the solution to the equation.

GRAPHICS CALCULATOR INSTRUCTIONS

Example 12   🔊 **Self Tutor**

Solve the equation $2.8x - 4.39 = 1.6$ graphically.

We graph $Y_1 = 2.8X - 4.39$ and $Y_2 = 1.6$ on the same set of axes, then find their point of intersection.

Casio fx-CG20

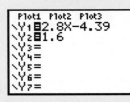

TI-84 Plus

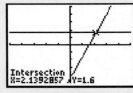

TI-*n*spire

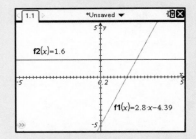

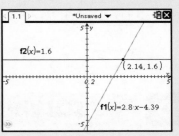

So, the solution is $x \approx 2.14$.

EXERCISE 4D

1 Use technology to solve the following:

    a $5.4x + 7.2 = 15.6$ **b** $0.05x - 9.6 = 3.5$

    c $23.24 - 13.08x = 8.94$ **d** $1234.32 + 37.56x = 259.04$

2 Use technology to solve the following graphically:

    a $\dfrac{3x + 2}{5} = -1$ **b** $5x + 3 = 2 - 8x$ **c** $\dfrac{2x + 3}{x - 4} = -5$

3 When w grams of weight are placed on a spring balance, the scale reads R mm. The reading is given by the rule $R = 0.4w + 5$.

    Find w when:

    a $R = 27$ **b** $R = 42$

4 In the United States of America, temperature is measured in degrees Fahrenheit (°F) rather than in degrees Celsius (°C). The rule showing the relationship between these two temperature scales is $F = 1.8C + 32$. What temperature in °C corresponds to a temperature of:

    a 40°F   **b** 0°F   **c** 200°F?

5 The total cost of sinking a bore is given by the rule $C = 15d + 350$ dollars where d is the depth in metres. How deep a bore can a farmer obtain for a cost of:

    a $2000   **b** $3200?

6 Solve:

    a $3x + 2 = 5x - 17$ **b** $3.6x - 1.8 = 2.7x + 4.1$

    c $3.56x + 13.67 = 1.05x + 39.97$ **d** $21.67 + 3.67x = 5.83x - 58.88$

E   PROBLEM SOLVING WITH LINEAR EQUATIONS

Many problems can be translated into **algebraic equations**. When problems are solved using algebra, we follow these steps:

> *Step 1:*   Determine what the unknown quantity is and use a letter or symbol to represent it.
>
> *Step 2:*   Decide which operations are involved.
>
> *Step 3:*   Translate the problem into an equation.
>
> *Step 4:*   Solve the equation by isolating the unknown.
>
> *Step 5:*   Check that your solution satisfies the original problem.
>
> *Step 6:*   Write your answer in sentence form.

Example 13   ◀) Self Tutor

When a number is doubled and then subtracted from 3, the result is -17. Find the number.

Let x be the number.

$\therefore$ $2x$ is the number doubled.

$\therefore$ $3 - 2x$ is this number subtracted from 3.

$$\begin{aligned} \text{So,} \quad 3 - 2x &= -17 \\ \therefore \quad 3 - 2x - 3 &= -17 - 3 \quad \text{\{subtracting 3 from both sides\}} \\ \therefore \quad -2x &= -20 \\ \therefore \quad x &= 10 \quad \text{\{dividing both sides by } -2\} \end{aligned}$$

So, the number is 10.   *Check*: $3 - 2 \times 10 = 3 - 20 = -17$ ✓

EXERCISE 4E

1 I take a certain number and multiply it by 5. I subtract the resulting product from 24 to get -11. What was my original number?

2 Doubling a certain number and then subtracting 5 gives the same result as subtracting 10 from the number and then multiplying by 7. Find the number.

3 Fayyad and Malik start with the same number. Fayyad divides the number by 3 then adds 3. Malik subtracts 7 from the number and then multiplies the result by 3. They now both have the same number. What number did they start with?

4 Jordana visits a furniture shop and sees a table she likes. She measures it to be 9 handspans and 4 cm long, but then she sees a label that says the table is 166 cm long. How wide is Jordana's handspan?

5 Farmer Giles walks down one side of his chicken coop and sees it is just 30 cm less than 8 paces. He walks along the next side, taking 15 paces to arrive 25 cm short of the end. He knows that the second side is twice as long as the first.

    a How long is Farmer Giles' pace?

    b What are the dimensions of the chicken coop?

Example 14　　　　　　　　　　　　　　　　　　　　　🔊 **Self Tutor**

Malikah's mum is presently four times as old as Malikah. In 6 years' time her mum will only be three times as old as Malikah is then. How old is Malikah now?

Let Malikah's present age be x years.

$\therefore$ her mother's present age is $4x$ years.

	Now	6 years' time
Malikah	x	$x + 6$
Mother	$4x$	$4x + 6$

So,　$4x + 6 = 3(x + 6)$　　　{her mum is three times as old}

$\therefore$　$4x + 6 = 3x + 18$

$\therefore$　$4x + 6 - 3x = 3x + 18 - 3x$

$\therefore$　$x + 6 = 18$

$\therefore$　$x = 12$　　　$\therefore$ Malikah's present age is 12 years.

---

6 Mira's father is presently three times as old as Mira. In 11 years' time her father will be twice as old as her. How old is Mira now?

7 At Ferenc's birth, his mother was 27 years old. At what age will Ferenc be 40% of his mother's age?

Example 15　　　　　　　　　　　　　　　　　　　　　🔊 **Self Tutor**

Carl has only 20 cent coins and 50 cent coins in his wallet. He has three more 50 cent coins than 20 cent coins, and their total value is $2.90. How many 20 cent coins does Carl have?

If Carl has x 20 cent coins then he has $(x + 3)$ 50 cent coins.

Coin	Number	Value
20 cent	x	$20x$ cents
50 cent	$x + 3$	$50(x + 3)$ cents

$\therefore$　$20x + 50(x + 3) = 290$　　　{equating values in cents}

$\therefore$　$20x + 50x + 150 = 290$

$\therefore$　$70x + 150 = 290$

$\therefore$　$70x = 140$

$\therefore$　$x = 2$　　　So, Carl has two 20 cent coins.

8 Wayne has a collection of 2 cent and 5 cent stamps. He has three times as many 2 cent stamps as 5 cent stamps, and the total value of the stamps is 66 cents. How many 5 cent stamps does Wayne have?

9 Louise has only 5 cent, 10 cent, and 20 cent coins in her purse. She has 30 coins in total, and she has two more 10 cent coins than 5 cent coins. If the total value of her coins is $3.80, how many 10 cent coins does she have?

10 Theresa sells lemonade for £1, juice for £1.50, and coffee for £2. On one day, the number of coffees she sells is twice the number of lemonades she sells, and 4 more than the number of juices she sells. If she earns a total of £74, how many lemonades does she sell?

F   FORMULA SUBSTITUTION

> A **formula** is an equation which connects two or more variables.
> The plural of formula is **formulae** or **formulas**.

In a formula it is common for one of the variables to be on one side of the equation and the other variable(s) and constants to be on the other side.

The variable on its own is called the **subject** of the formula.

If the formula contains two or more variables and we know the value of all but one of them, we can solve an equation to find the remaining variable.

> *Step 1:*   Write down the formula and state the values of the known variables.
>
> *Step 2:*   Substitute the known values into the formula to form a one variable equation.
>
> *Step 3:*   Solve the equation for the unknown variable.

Example 16   ◉ Self Tutor

The acceleration of a falling raindrop is given by $a = g - 1.96v$ m s^{-2} where $g = 9.8$ m s^{-2} is the gravitational constant and v is the speed of the raindrop.

Find: **a** the acceleration of the raindrop before it starts falling

b the acceleration of the raindrop when its speed reaches 3 m s^{-1}

c the speed of the raindrop for which it does not accelerate.

a $a = g - 1.96v$ where $g = 9.8$
and $v = 0$

$\therefore\ a = 9.8 - 1.96 \times 0$

$\therefore\ a = 9.8$ m s^{-2}

b $a = g - 1.96v$ where $g = 9.8$
and $v = 3$

$\therefore\ a = 9.8 - 1.96 \times 3$

$\therefore\ a = 3.92$ m s^{-2}

c $a = g - 1.96v$ where $a = 0$ and $g = 9.8$

$\therefore\ 0 = 9.8 - 1.96v$

$\therefore\ 1.96v = 9.8$

$\therefore\ v = \dfrac{9.8}{1.96} = 5$ m s^{-1}

EXERCISE 4F

1   The circumference C of a circle with diameter d is given by the formula $C = \pi d$ where $\pi \approx 3.14159$ is a constant. Find:

We use more than 3 significant figures in our working to ensure the answer is correct to at least this accuracy.

   a   the circumference of a circle with diameter 11.4 cm

   b   the diameter of a circle with circumference 250 cm

   c   the radius of a circle with circumference 100 metres.

2   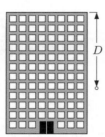   A tennis ball is dropped from the top of a tall building. The total distance it has fallen is given by the formula $D = \frac{1}{2}gt^2$ where D is the distance in metres and t is the time taken in seconds. $g = 9.8 \text{ m s}^{-2}$ is the gravitational constant.

   a   Find the total distance fallen in the first 3 seconds of fall.

   b   Find the height of the building, to the nearest metre, if the ball takes 5.13 seconds to reach the ground.

3   When a car travels d kilometres in time t hours, the average speed for the journey is given by $s = \dfrac{d}{t} \text{ km h}^{-1}$.   Find:

   a   the average speed of a car which travels 200 km in $2\frac{1}{2}$ hours

   b   the distance travelled by a car in $3\frac{1}{4}$ hours if its average speed is 80 km h^{-1}

   c   the time taken, to the nearest minute, for a car to travel 865 km at an average speed of 110 km h^{-1}.

4   The area of a circle of radius r is given by $A = \pi r^2$.   Find:

   a   the area of a circle of radius 5.6 cm

   b   the radius of a circular pond which has an area of 200 m².

5   The potential difference V across an R ohm resistor is given by $V = IR$ volts, where I is the current in amps flowing through the circuit. Find:

   a   the potential difference across a 6 ohm resistor if the current in the circuit is 0.08 amps

   b   the resistance in a circuit with current 0.2 amps if the potential difference is 12 volts.

6   The volume of a cylinder of radius r and height h is given by $V = \pi r^2 h$.   Find:

   a   the volume of a cylindrical tin can of radius 12 cm and height 17.5 cm

   b   the height of a cylinder of radius 4 cm if its volume is 80 cm³

   c   the radius, in mm, of copper wire with volume 100 cm³ and length 0.2 km.

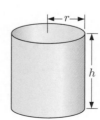

7

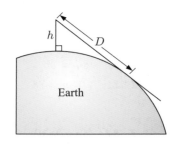

Earth

The formula $D = 3.56\sqrt{h}$ estimates the distance in kilometres to the horizon which is seen by a person with eye level h metres above the level of the sea.
Find:

   a the distance to the horizon when a person's eye level is 10 m above sea level

   b how far above sea level a person's eye must be for the horizon to be 30 km away.

8 The total surface area of a sphere of radius r is given by $A = 4\pi r^2$.   Find:

  a the total surface area of a sphere of radius 6.9 cm

  b the radius (in cm) of a spherical balloon which has a surface area of 1 m^2.

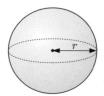

G   FORMULA REARRANGEMENT

Consider the formula $V = \frac{1}{3}\pi r^2 h$,   which gives the volume of a cone with radius r and height h.

We say that V is the **subject** of the formula because V is expressed in terms of the other variables r and h.

The formula can be **rearranged** to make **equivalent** formulae where the other variables are the subjects:

$$h = \frac{3V}{\pi r^2} \qquad\qquad r = \sqrt{\frac{3V}{\pi h}}$$

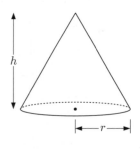

We rearrange formulae using the same methods which we used to solve equations. We perform **inverse operations** to isolate the variable we wish to make the subject.

Example 17	◀ᴺ) Self Tutor

Make y the subject of $3x - 7y = 22$.

$$3x - 7y = 22$$
$$\therefore\ 3x - 7y - 3x = 22 - 3x \qquad \{\text{subtracting } 3x \text{ from both sides}\}$$
$$\therefore\ -7y = 22 - 3x$$
$$\therefore\ 7y = 3x - 22 \qquad \{\text{multiplying both sides by } -1\}$$
$$\therefore\ \frac{7y}{7} = \frac{3x - 22}{7} \qquad \{\text{dividing both sides by } 7\}$$
$$\therefore\ y = \frac{3x - 22}{7}$$

EXERCISE 4G.1

1 Make y the subject of:

   a $x + 2y = 4$ **b** $2x + 6y = 7$ **c** $3x + 4y = 11$

   d $5x + 4y = 8$ **e** $7x + 2y = 20$ **f** $11x + 15y = 38$

2 Make y the subject of:

   a $x - 2y = 4$ **b** $2x - 6y = 7$ **c** $3x - 4y = -12$

   d $4x - 5y = 18$ **e** $7x - 6y = 42$ **f** $12x - 13y = -44$

3 Make x the subject of:

   a $a + x = b$ **b** $ax = b$ **c** $2x + a = d$

   d $c + x = t$ **e** $7x + 3y = d$ **f** $ax + by = c$

   g $mx - y = c$ **h** $c - 2x = p$ **i** $a - 3x = t$

   j $n - kx = 5$ **k** $a - bx = n$ **l** $p = a - nx$

Example 18   ◀⁾ **Self Tutor**

Make z the subject of $y = \dfrac{x}{z}$.

$$y = \frac{x}{z}$$

$$\therefore \quad y \times z = \frac{x}{z} \times z \quad \text{\{multiplying both sides by } z\}$$

$$\therefore \quad yz = x$$

$$\therefore \quad \frac{yz}{y} = \frac{x}{y} \quad \text{\{dividing both sides by } y\}$$

$$\therefore \quad z = \frac{x}{y}$$

---

4 Make x the subject of:

   a $a = \dfrac{x}{b}$ **b** $\dfrac{a}{x} = d$ **c** $p = \dfrac{2}{x}$

   d $\dfrac{x}{2} = n$ **e** $\dfrac{5}{x} = \dfrac{y}{z}$ **f** $\dfrac{m}{x} = \dfrac{x}{n}$

5 The equation of a straight line is $5x + 3y = 18$. Rearrange this formula into the form $y = mx + c$, and hence state the gradient m and the y-intercept c.

REARRANGEMENT AND SUBSTITUTION

In the previous section on formula substitution, the variables were replaced by numbers and then the equation was solved. However, often we need to substitute several values for the unknowns and solve the equation for each case. In this situation it is quicker to **rearrange** the formula **before substituting**.

Example 19   ◀》 **Self Tutor**

The circumference of a circle is given by $C = 2\pi r$, where r is the circle's radius. Rearrange this formula to make r the subject, and hence find the radius when the circumference is:

  a   10 cm   **b**   20 cm   **c**   50 cm.

$$2\pi r = C$$

$$\therefore \ r = \frac{C}{2\pi} \quad \{\text{dividing both sides by } 2\pi\}$$

a When $C = 10$, $r = \dfrac{10}{2\pi} \approx 1.59$ **b** When $C = 20$, $r = \dfrac{20}{2\pi} \approx 3.18$

$\therefore$ the radius is about 1.59 cm. $\therefore$ the radius is about 3.18 cm.

c When $C = 50$, $r = \dfrac{50}{2\pi} \approx 7.96$

$\therefore$ the radius is about 7.96 cm.

EXERCISE 4G.2

1   **a**   Make s the subject of the formula $R = 5s + 2t$.

    b   Find the value of s when:

        i $R = 16$ and $t = 3$ **ii** $R = 2$ and $t = 11$ **iii** $R = 8$ and $t = -2$

2   **a**   Make a the subject of the formula $K = \dfrac{d}{2ab}$.

    b   Find the value of a when:

        i $K = 112$, $d = 24$, $b = 2$ **ii** $K = 400$, $d = 72$, $b = 0.4$

3 When a car travels d kilometres in time t hours, the average speed s for the journey is given by the formula $s = \dfrac{d}{t}$ km h^{-1}.

    a   Make d the subject of the formula. Hence find the distance travelled by a car if:

        i   the average speed is 60 km h^{-1} and the time travelled is 3 hours

        ii the average speed is 80 km h^{-1} and the time travelled is $1\frac{1}{2}$ hours

        iii the average speed is 95 km h^{-1} and the time travelled is 1 h 20 min.

    b   Make t the subject of the formula. Hence find the time required for a car to travel:

        i   180 km at an average speed of 60 km h^{-1}

        ii 140 km at an average speed of 35 km h^{-1}

        iii 220 km at an average speed of 100 km h^{-1}.

4 The simple interest \$$I$ paid on an investment of \$$C$ is determined by the annual rate of interest r (as a percentage) and the duration of the investment, n years. The interest is given by the formula $I = \dfrac{Crn}{100}$.

    a   Make n the subject of the formula.

    b   Find the time required to generate \$1050 interest on an investment of \$6400 at an interest rate of 8% per annum.

    c   Find the time required for an investment of \$1000 to double given an interest rate of 10% per annum.

H LINEAR SIMULTANEOUS EQUATIONS

In some situations we may have several equations that must be true at the same time. We call these **simultaneous equations**.

To solve simultaneous equations we require values for the variables which satisfy each equation. These values are the **simultaneous solution** of the equations.

In this chapter we will consider systems of two linear simultaneous equations containing two unknowns. In these systems there will be infinitely many solutions which satisfy the first equation, and infinitely many solutions which satisfy the second equation. However, in general there will only be one solution which satisfies both equations at the same time.

INVESTIGATION   IMPORTING RACKETS

Kobeng imports two brands of racket for his store. In one shipment he buys x Asway rackets at \$40 each, and y Onex rackets at \$60 each.

In total Kobeng buys 50 rackets, so $x + y = 50$.

The total price is \$2640, so $40x + 60y = 2640$.

Therefore, to find out how many of each brand Kobeng buys, we need to solve simultaneously the equations $\begin{cases} x + y = 50 \\ 40x + 60y = 2640. \end{cases}$

What to do:

1 Click on the icon to open a spreadsheet. The first row displays all the possible **SPREADSHEET** values for x, from 0 to 50.

	A	B	C	D	E	F	G	H
1	Number of Asway rackets, x	0	1	2	3	4	5	....
2	Number of Onex rackets, y							
3	Total cost							

2 Kobeng buys 50 rackets in total, so $x + y = 50$, which means that $y = 50 - x$.
   Enter the formula $= 50\text{-B1}$ into cell **B2**, and fill the formula across to **AZ2**.

3 The total cost of x Asway rackets and y Onex rackets is $40x + 60y$ dollars.
   Enter the formula $= 40{*}\text{B1} + 60{*}\text{B2}$ into cell **B3**, and fill the formula across to **AZ3**.

4 Find the combination of rackets which results in a total cost of \$2640.

5 Verify that the values for x and y found in **4** satisfy both $x + y = 50$ and $40x + 60y = 2640$.

In the investigation we used trial and error to find a simultaneous solution to the system of equations. This method can be very tedious, however, so we need to consider other methods.

USING TECHNOLOGY

You can solve linear simultaneous equations using your graphics calculator. For instructions on how to do this, consult the **graphics calculator instructions** online.

GRAPHICS CALCULATOR INSTRUCTIONS

For the **TI-84 Plus**, you will need to download the application **Polysmlt 2** from
http://education.ti.com/educationportal/sites/US/productDetail/us_poly_83_84.html

Example 20	◄») Self Tutor

Use technology to solve: $\begin{cases} 2x - 3y = 4 \\ 3x + 2y = 19 \end{cases}$

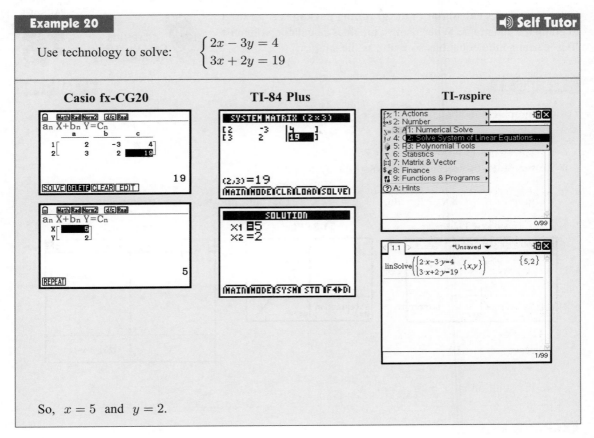

So, $x = 5$ and $y = 2$.

EXERCISE 4H.1

1 Use technology to solve these simultaneous equations:

a $\begin{cases} 3x + 4y = 1 \\ x - 2y = 7 \end{cases}$

b $\begin{cases} x + 4y = -2 \\ -3x + 2y = 13 \end{cases}$

c $\begin{cases} 6x + y = 13 \\ 2x - 3y = 16 \end{cases}$

d $\begin{cases} x + 3y = 1 \\ -3x + 7y = 21 \end{cases}$

e $\begin{cases} 1.4x - 2.3y = -1.3 \\ 5.7x - 3.4y = 12.6 \end{cases}$

f $\begin{cases} 3.6x - 0.7y = -11.37 \\ 4.9x + 2.7y = -1.23 \end{cases}$

2 Write each equation in the form $ax + by = c$, then use technology to solve the pair simultaneously. Round your answers to 3 significant figures.

a $\begin{cases} y = 2x + 3 \\ 3x - y = 1 \end{cases}$

b $\begin{cases} x = 2y + 1 \\ 4x - 3y = -6 \end{cases}$

c $\begin{cases} 3x + 5y = 3 \\ y = 2x - 7 \end{cases}$

d $\begin{cases} x = y - 1.5 \\ 5.8x - 4y = -6 \end{cases}$

e $\begin{cases} y = 4.5x - 4.75 \\ x = y + 1.3 \end{cases}$

f $\begin{cases} y = 5x \\ x = 12 - 3y \end{cases}$

3 Try to solve $\begin{cases} 0.2x + 0.9y = 5 \\ 0.6x + 2.7y = -3 \end{cases}$ using technology. Comment on your result.

GRAPHICAL METHOD

We can also solve linear simultaneous equations by graphing each of the equations. The coordinates of the **intersection point** gives us the simultaneous solution to the equations.

Either a **graphics calculator** or the **graphing package** can be used to graph the equations. When using a graphics calculator, you must first rearrange the equations so that y is the subject.

GRAPHING PACKAGE

GRAPHICS CALCULATOR INSTRUCTIONS

Example 21   ◀)) **Self Tutor**

Use graphical methods to solve: $\begin{cases} y = 3x - 2 \\ 2x + y = 13 \end{cases}$

We rearrange the second equation so the system is $\begin{cases} y = 3x - 2 \\ y = -2x + 13 \end{cases}$

We graph $Y_1 = 3X - 2$ and $Y_2 = -2X + 13$, and find the intersection point.

Casio fx-CG20	TI-84 Plus	TI-*n*spire

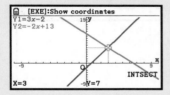 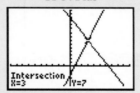 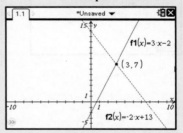

So, the solution is $x = 3$, $y = 7$.

EXERCISE 4H.2

1 Use graphical methods to solve:

a $\begin{cases} y = x - 2 \\ y = -2x + 10 \end{cases}$

b $\begin{cases} y = 3x + 6 \\ y = 2 - x \end{cases}$

c $\begin{cases} y = \frac{1}{2}x - 3 \\ y = \frac{9}{2} - 2x \end{cases}$

2 Use graphical methods to solve, rounding your answer to 3 significant figures where necessary:

a $\begin{cases} y = x - 7 \\ 2x + y = 5 \end{cases}$

b $\begin{cases} 3x + y = -6 \\ y = 2x + 4 \end{cases}$

c $\begin{cases} x - y = 2 \\ 2x + y = 7 \end{cases}$

d $\begin{cases} 4x + 2y = 1 \\ 3x + y = 2 \end{cases}$

e $\begin{cases} 5x - y = 3 \\ 2x + 3y = 9 \end{cases}$

f $\begin{cases} 4x + y = 0 \\ 7x + 5y = 2 \end{cases}$

3 Try to solve the following simultaneous equations using graphical methods. How many solutions does each pair have?

a $\begin{cases} y = 2x - 3 \\ 4x - 2y = 1 \end{cases}$

b $\begin{cases} y = 5 - x \\ 3x + 3y = 15 \end{cases}$

ALGEBRAIC METHODS

Linear simultaneous equations can also be solved algebraically. Although these methods are not required for this course, their study is recommended to enhance your understanding.

SOLUTION BY SUBSTITUTION

The method of **solution by substitution** is used when at least one equation is given with either x or y as the **subject** of the formula, or if it is easy to make x or y the subject.

Example 22	◀》 Self Tutor

Solve by substitution: $\begin{cases} y = 3 + x \\ 2x - 4y = -16 \end{cases}$

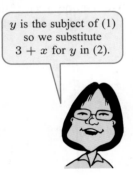

y is the subject of (1) so we substitute $3 + x$ for y in (2).

$$y = 3 + x \quad \text{.... (1)}$$
$$2x - 4y = -16 \quad \text{.... (2)}$$

Substituting (1) into (2) gives $2x - 4(3 + x) = -16$

$$\therefore \ 2x - 12 - 4x = -16$$
$$\therefore \ -2x = -4$$
$$\therefore \ x = 2$$

Substituting $x = 2$ into (1) gives $y = 3 + 2 = 5$

So, $x = 2$ and $y = 5$.

Check: In (2), $2 \times 2 - 4 \times 5 = 4 - 20 = -16$ ✓

EXERCISE 4H.3

1 Solve simultaneously by substitution:

a $\begin{cases} y = x - 3 \\ 2x + y = 12 \end{cases}$

b $\begin{cases} x = y - 1 \\ 4x - 3y = 0 \end{cases}$

c $\begin{cases} y = x + 6 \\ 3y + 2x = 13 \end{cases}$

d $\begin{cases} y = -2x \\ 3x - y = 10 \end{cases}$

e $\begin{cases} 3x - 5y = -9 \\ y = x + 3 \end{cases}$

f $\begin{cases} 2x = y \\ 2y - x = 1 \end{cases}$

2 a Try to solve using the method of substitution: $\begin{cases} y = 2x + 5 \\ y = 2x + 1 \end{cases}$

   b What is the simultaneous solution for the equations in a?

3 a Try to solve using the method of substitution: $\begin{cases} y = 2x + 5 \\ 2y = 4x + 10 \end{cases}$

   b How many simultaneous solutions do the equations in a have?

SOLUTION BY ELIMINATION

In problems where each equation has the form $ax + by = c$, **elimination** of one of the variables is preferred.

In this method we multiply each equation by a constant so that the coefficients of either x or y are the **same size** but **opposite in sign**.

We then **add the equations** to eliminate one variable.

Example 23
◀)) **Self Tutor**

Solve by elimination: $\begin{cases} 2x - 3y = 4 \\ 3x + 2y = 19 \end{cases}$

$$2x - 3y = 4 \quad \dots (1)$$
$$3x + 2y = 19 \quad \dots (2)$$

We multiply each equation by a constant so the coefficients of y will be the same size but opposite in sign.

$$4x - 6y = 8 \quad \{2 \times (1)\}$$
$$\underline{9x + 6y = 57} \quad \{3 \times (2)\}$$

Adding, $\quad 13x \qquad = 65$

$$\therefore \quad x = 5$$

Substituting $x = 5$ into (1), $\quad 2 \times 5 - 3y = 4$

$$\therefore \quad 10 - 3y = 4$$
$$\therefore \quad 6 = 3y$$
$$\therefore \quad 2 = y$$

So, $x = 5$ and $y = 2$.

Check: In (2), $3x + 2y = 3 \times 5 + 2 \times 2 = 15 + 4 = 19$ ✓

EXERCISE 4H.4

1 What equation results when the following are added vertically?

a $3x + 2y = 7$
$x - 2y = 8$

b $2x - y = 8$
$-2x + 3y = 4$

c $x - 5y = -3$
$4x + 5y = 13$

2 Solve using the method of elimination:

a $\begin{cases} 2x + y = 5 \\ x - y = 1 \end{cases}$

b $\begin{cases} 3x - 2y = 5 \\ -x + 2y = 1 \end{cases}$

c $\begin{cases} 2x + y = 8 \\ -2x + 3y = 0 \end{cases}$

d $\begin{cases} 2x + 5y = -1 \\ 3x - 5y = 11 \end{cases}$

e $\begin{cases} -2x - 2y = -5 \\ -8x + 2y = 0 \end{cases}$

f $\begin{cases} 2x - y = 3 \\ -2x - 5y = -1 \end{cases}$

3 Give the equation which results when both sides of:

a $x - y = 2$ are multiplied by 3

b $2x + y = -1$ are multiplied by -1

c $-x + 3y = 2$ are multiplied by 2

d $3x - 2y = 4$ are multiplied by 3.

4 Solve using the method of elimination:

a $\begin{cases} x + 2y = 4 \\ 3x + y = 7 \end{cases}$

b $\begin{cases} 3x + 2y = 3 \\ 5x - y = -8 \end{cases}$

c $\begin{cases} -x + 2y = 6 \\ 3x - 5y = -14 \end{cases}$

d $\begin{cases} 2x - 3y = 12 \\ 5x + 2y = 11 \end{cases}$

e $\begin{cases} x + 6y = 1 \\ -3x + 2y = 7 \end{cases}$

f $\begin{cases} 2x + 3y = 5 \\ 3x - 2y = 27 \end{cases}$

PROBLEM SOLVING WITH SIMULTANEOUS EQUATIONS

Many problems can be described using a pair of linear equations. We saw an example of this in the investigation on page **108** in which Kobeng was importing rackets.

You should follow these steps to solve problems involving simultaneous equations:

> *Step 1:*   Decide on the two unknowns, for example x and y. Do not forget the units.
>
> *Step 2:*   Write down **two** equations connecting x and y.
>
> *Step 3:*   Solve the equations simultaneously.
>
> *Step 4:*   Check your solutions with the original data given.
>
> *Step 5:*   Give your answer in sentence form.

Example 24   ◀》 **Self Tutor**

Find two numbers which have a sum of 37 and a difference of 11.

Let x and y be the unknown numbers, where $x > y$.

Then $x + y = 37$ .... (1)

   {'sum' means add}

and $x - y = 11$ .... (2)

   {'difference' means subtract}

We must find two equations containing two unknowns.

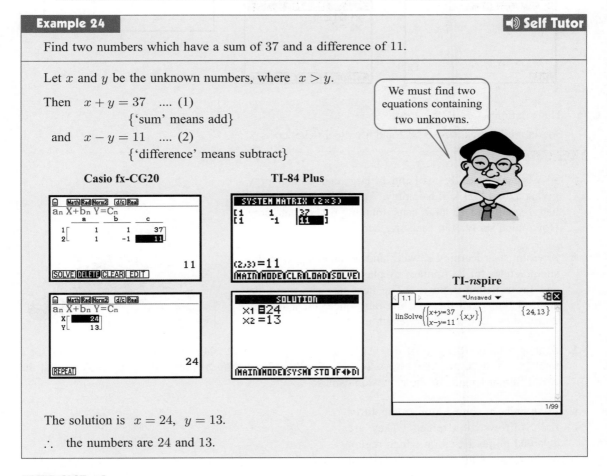

The solution is $x = 24$, $y = 13$.

∴   the numbers are 24 and 13.

EXERCISE 41

1 Two numbers have a sum of 58 and a difference of 22. Find the numbers.

2 The larger of two numbers is one more than double the smaller, and their sum is 82. Find the two numbers.

Example 25   ◆) **Self Tutor**

Two adults' tickets and three children's tickets to a baseball match cost $45, while three adults' and four children's tickets cost $64. Find the cost of each type of ticket.

Let x be the cost of an adult's ticket and y be the cost of a child's ticket.

So, $2x + 3y = 45$ and $3x + 4y = 64$

Casio fx-CG20	TI-84 Plus	TI-*n*spire
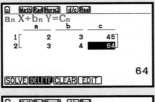 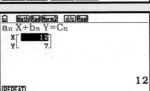	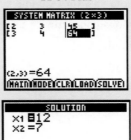 	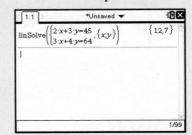

The solution is $x = 12$, $y = 7$.

So, an adult's ticket costs $12 and a child's ticket costs $7.

3 A hairdresser has 13 small and 14 large cans of hairspray, giving a total of 9 L of hairspray. At this time last year she had 4 small and 12 large cans, totalling 6 L of hairspray. How much spray is in each size can?

4 A violinist is learning a waltz and a sonatina. One day she practices for 33 minutes by playing the waltz 4 times and the sonatina 3 times. The next day she plays the waltz 6 times and the sonatina only once, for a total of 25 minutes. Determine the length of each piece.

5 A shop sells two lengths of extension cable. Tomasz buys 2 short cables and 5 long cables for a total length of 26 m. Alicja buys 24.3 m of cabling by getting 3 short and 4 long cables. Find the two different lengths of the extension cables.

6 In an archery competition, competitors fire 8 arrows at a target. They are awarded points based on which region of the target is hit. The results for two of the competitors are shown opposite. How many points are awarded for hitting the:

   a red   **b** blue region?

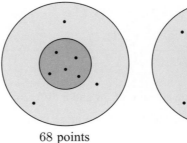
68 points

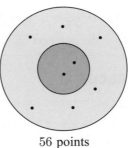
56 points

7 a Find the length of the longest side of this rectangle:

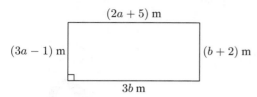

b Find the length of wire required to construct this pentagon:

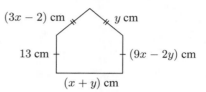

8 A hardware store sells 3 litre paint cans for £15 and 5 litre paint cans for £20. In one day the store sells 71 litres of paint, worth a total of £320. How many paint cans did the store sell?

9 A piano teacher charges $30 for a one hour lesson, and $50 for a two hour lesson. She works for 25 hours in one week, and earns $690. Determine how many two hour lessons she gave.

10 Kristen can run at 15 km h^{-1} and walk at 5 km h^{-1}. She completed a 42 km marathon in 4 hours. What distance did Kristen run during the marathon?

J QUADRATIC EQUATIONS

A **quadratic equation** in x is an equation which can be written in the form $ax^2 + bx + c = 0$ where a, b, and c are constants and $a \neq 0$.

The solutions of the equation are the values of x which make the equation true. We call these the **roots** of the equation, and they are also the **zeros** of the quadratic expression $ax^2 + bx + c$.

SOLUTION OF $x^2 = k$

Just as for linear equations, we can perform operations on both sides of a quadratic equation so as to maintain the balance.

Many quadratic equations can hence be rearranged into the form $x^2 = k$.

If k is positive then $\sqrt{k}$ exists such that $(\sqrt{k})^2 = k$ and $(-\sqrt{k})^2 = k$.

Thus the solutions are $x = \pm\sqrt{k}$.

> $\pm\sqrt{k}$ is read as 'plus or minus the square root of k'

If $x^2 = k$ then $\begin{cases} x = \pm\sqrt{k} & \text{if } k > 0 \\ x = 0 & \text{if } k = 0 \\ \text{there are no real solutions if } k < 0. \end{cases}$

Example 26   ◀) **Self Tutor**

Solve for x: **a** $3x^2 - 1 = 8$ **b** $5 - 2x^2 = 11$

a $3x^2 - 1 = 8$
$\therefore \ 3x^2 = 9$ $\{ +1 \text{ to both sides}\}$
$\therefore \ \ x^2 = 3$ $\{ \div \text{ both sides by 3}\}$
$\therefore \ \ x = \pm\sqrt{3}$

b $5 - 2x^2 = 11$
$\therefore \ -2x^2 = 6$ $\{ -5 \text{ from both sides}\}$
$\therefore \ \ x^2 = -3$ $\{ \div \text{ both sides by } -2\}$
which has no real solutions as x^2 cannot be negative.

We can apply this same method of solution whenever there is a perfect square on the left hand side.

Example 27
🔊 Self Tutor

Solve for x:

a $(x+3)^2 = 36$

b $(x-4)^2 = 7$

For equations of the form $(x \pm a)^2 = k$ we do not need to expand the brackets.

a $(x+3)^2 = 36$

$\therefore \; x+3 = \pm\sqrt{36}$

$\therefore \; x+3 = \pm 6$

$\therefore \; x = -3 \pm 6$

$\therefore \; x = 3 \text{ or } -9$

b $(x-4)^2 = 7$

$\therefore \; x-4 = \pm\sqrt{7}$

$\therefore \; x = 4 \pm \sqrt{7}$

EXERCISE 4J.1

1 Solve for x:

a $x^2 = 4$

b $3x^2 = 48$

c $4x^2 = 4$

d $5x^2 = 35$

e $2x^2 = -10$

f $6x^2 = 0$

g $4x^2 - 5 = 15$

h $7 - 3x^2 = 19$

2 Solve for x:

a $(x-3)^2 = 16$

b $(x+1)^2 = 9$

c $(x+4)^2 = -25$

d $(x-2)^2 = 10$

e $(x+4)^2 = 13$

f $(x-7)^2 = 0$

g $(2x-3)^2 = 25$

h $\frac{1}{2}(3x+1)^2 = 7$

THE NULL FACTOR LAW

We have seen that a linear equation such as $2x + 3 = 11$ will usually have *one* solution.
In contrast, a quadratic equation may have *two*, *one*, or *zero* solutions.

Here are some simple quadratic equations which clearly show the truth of this statement:

Equation	$ax^2 + bx + c = 0$ *form*	Solutions	Number of solutions
$(x+2)(x-2) = 0$	$x^2 + 0x - 4 = 0$	$x = 2 \text{ or } x = -2$	**two**
$(x-2)^2 = 0$	$x^2 - 4x + 4 = 0$	$x = 2$	**one**
$x^2 = -4$	$x^2 + 0x + 4 = 0$	none as x^2 is always $\geqslant 0$	**zero**

The **Null Factor law** states:

When the product of two (or more) numbers is zero then at least one of them must be zero.
So, if $ab = 0$ then $a = 0$ or $b = 0$.

Example 28
🔊 Self Tutor

Solve for x using the Null Factor law:

a $3x(x-5) = 0$

b $(x-4)(3x+7) = 0$

a $3x(x-5) = 0$

$\therefore \; 3x = 0 \text{ or } x-5 = 0$

$\therefore \; x = 0 \text{ or } 5$

b $(x-4)(3x+7) = 0$

$\therefore \; x-4 = 0 \text{ or } 3x+7 = 0$

$\therefore \; x = 4 \text{ or } 3x = -7$

$\therefore \; x = 4 \text{ or } -\frac{7}{3}$

EXERCISE 4J.2

1 Solve for the unknown using the Null Factor law:

   a $3x = 0$ **b** $a \times 8 = 0$ **c** $-7y = 0$

   d $ab = 0$ **e** $2xy = 0$ **f** $a^2 = 0$

2 Solve for x using the Null Factor law:

   a $x(x - 5) = 0$ **b** $2x(x + 3) = 0$ **c** $(x + 1)(x - 3) = 0$

   d $3x(7 - x) = 0$ **e** $-2x(x + 1) = 0$ **f** $4(x + 6)(2x - 3) = 0$

   g $(2x + 1)(2x - 1) = 0$ **h** $11(x + 2)(x - 7) = 0$ **i** $-6(x - 5)(3x + 2) = 0$

   j $x^2 = 0$ **k** $4(5 - x)^2 = 0$ **l** $-3(3x - 1)^2 = 0$

SOLUTION USING TECHNOLOGY

You can use your graphics calculator to solve quadratic equations.

The method for doing this is more complicated than for solving linear equations because there may be more than one solution.

GRAPHICS CALCULATOR INSTRUCTIONS

TI-84 Plus users will again need to use the **Polysmlt 2** application.

Example 29   **◀ Self Tutor**

Use technology to solve $\quad 2x^2 + 4x = 7$.

$$2x^2 + 4x = 7$$
$$\therefore \ 2x^2 + 4x - 7 = 0$$

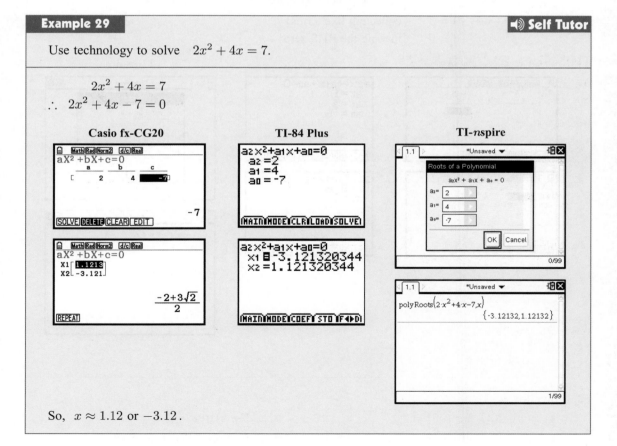

So, $x \approx 1.12$ or -3.12.

EXERCISE 4J.3

1 Use technology to solve:

    a $x^2 - 5x + 6 = 0$ **b** $x^2 + 9x + 14 = 0$

    c $x^2 - 8x + 16 = 0$ **d** $2x^2 - 9x + 4 = 0$

    e $8x^2 + 10x - 3 = 0$ **f** $4x^2 + x - 8 = 0$

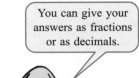

You can give your answers as fractions or as decimals.

2 Use technology to solve:

    a $x^2 + 6x = 7$ **b** $4x^2 + 4x = 15$

    c $10x^2 + 63 = 53x$ **d** $-3x^2 + 12x = 10$

    e $x = 8 - 2x^2$ **f** $6 = 2x - 5x^2$

Example 30   **◄)) Self Tutor**

Solve for x: $3(x - 1) + x(x + 2) = 3$

$3(x - 1) + x(x + 2) = 3$

$\therefore \; 3x - 3 + x^2 + 2x = 3$ {expanding the brackets}

$\therefore \; x^2 + 5x - 3 = 3$ {collecting like terms}

$\therefore \; x^2 + 5x - 6 = 0$ {making the RHS zero}

Casio fx-CG20	TI-84 Plus	TI-*n*spire

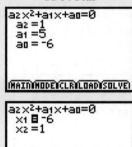

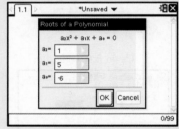

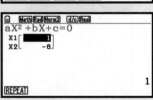

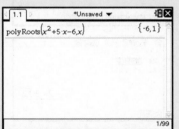

$\therefore \; x = -6$ or 1

---

3 Solve for x:

    a $x(x + 5) + 2(x + 6) = 0$ **b** $x(1 + x) + x = 3$

    c $(x - 1)(x + 9) = 5x$ **d** $3x(x + 2) - 5(x - 3) = 18$

    e $4x(x + 1) = -1$ **f** $2x(x - 6) = x - 25$

Example 31   ◀) **Self Tutor**

Solve for x: $3x + \dfrac{2}{x} = -7$

$$3x + \frac{2}{x} = -7$$

$\therefore \; x\left(3x + \dfrac{2}{x}\right) = -7x$ {multiplying both sides by x}

$\therefore \; 3x^2 + 2 = -7x$ {expanding the brackets}

$\therefore \; 3x^2 + 7x + 2 = 0$ {making the RHS = 0}

Casio fx-CG20	TI-84 Plus	TI-*n*spire
	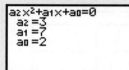	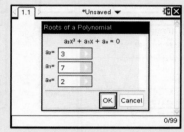
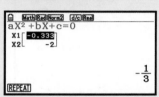		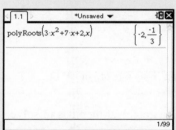

$\therefore \quad x = -2$ or $-\frac{1}{3}$

4 Solve for x:

a $4x - \dfrac{15}{x} = 17$

b $6x - 5 = \dfrac{6}{x}$

c $\dfrac{5}{x} = 8 - 2x$

d $\dfrac{x-1}{4} = \dfrac{3}{x}$

e $\dfrac{x-5}{x} = \dfrac{x+15}{5}$

f $\dfrac{x}{x+4} = \dfrac{1}{x+3}$

Example 32   ◀)) **Self Tutor**

Use graphical methods to solve $8x^2 + x - 2 = 9$.

We graph $Y_1 = 8X^2 + X - 2$ and $Y_2 = 9$ on the same set of axes, and find where the graphs intersect.

Casio fx-CG20	**TI-84 Plus**	**TI-nspire**
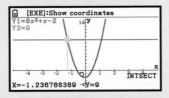	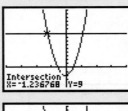	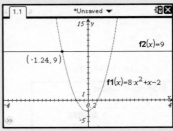
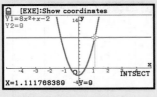	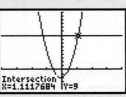	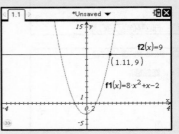

So, $x \approx -1.24$ or 1.11 .

5 Use graphical methods to solve:

    a $x^2 - 4x + 11 = 16$ **b** $x^2 - 4x + 11 = 7$ **c** $x^2 - 4x + 11 = 3$

    d $10x^2 + 19x - 6 = 9$ **e** $-3x^2 + 6x + 1 = 0$ **f** $4x^2 - 3x - 13 = -7$

6 Use graphical methods to find the roots of the following equations:

    a $3x^2 - 10x - 8 = 0$ **b** $-x^2 - 7x + 4 = 2.5$

    c $x^2 + 8x + 3 = x$

7 Use graphical methods to find the zeros of the following expressions:

    a $x^2 - 7x - 10$ **b** $16x^2 + 8x + 1$

    c $-3x^2 - 1.5x + 6$ **d** $\frac{9}{2}x^2 - 4x + \frac{2}{7}$

> The *zeros* of the expression $ax^2 + bx + c$ are the solutions or roots of $ax^2 + bx + c = 0$.

THE QUADRATIC FORMULA (EXTENSION)

We have seen how to use technology to find solutions of quadratic equations. However, in many cases the solutions are not *exact* but rather are approximations found by rounding decimals.

If we want to find *exact* solutions we can use the **quadratic formula**.

$$\text{If}\quad ax^2 + bx + c = 0\quad \text{then}\quad x = \frac{-b \pm \sqrt{b^2 - 4ac}}{2a}.$$

Example 33   ◀) **Self Tutor**

Solve for x: **a** $x^2 - 2x - 6 = 0$ **b** $2x^2 + 3x - 6 = 0$

a $x^2 - 2x - 6 = 0$ has
     $a = 1, \ b = -2, \ c = -6$

$\therefore \ x = \dfrac{-(-2) \pm \sqrt{(-2)^2 - 4(1)(-6)}}{2(1)}$

$\therefore \ x = \dfrac{2 \pm \sqrt{4 + 24}}{2}$

$\therefore \ x = \dfrac{2 \pm \sqrt{28}}{2}$

$\therefore \ x = \dfrac{2 \pm 2\sqrt{7}}{2}$

$\therefore \ x = 1 \pm \sqrt{7}$

b $2x^2 + 3x - 6 = 0$ has
     $a = 2, \ b = 3, \ c = -6$

$\therefore \ x = \dfrac{-3 \pm \sqrt{3^2 - 4(2)(-6)}}{2(2)}$

$\therefore \ x = \dfrac{-3 \pm \sqrt{9 + 48}}{4}$

$\therefore \ x = \dfrac{-3 \pm \sqrt{57}}{4}$

EXERCISE 4J.4

1 Use the quadratic formula to solve exactly for x:

  a $x^2 - 4x - 3 = 0$ **b** $x^2 + 6x + 7 = 0$ **c** $x^2 + 1 = 4x$

  d $x^2 + 4x = 1$ **e** $x^2 - 4x + 2 = 0$ **f** $2x^2 - 2x - 8 = 0$

  g $(3x + 1)^2 = -2x$ **h** $(x + 3)(2x + 1) = 9$ **i** $(3x + 2)(4 - x) = 3$

2 Use the quadratic formula to solve exactly for x:

  a $(x + 2)(x - 1) = 2 - 3x$ **b** $(2x + 1)^2 = 3 - x$ **c** $(x - 2)^2 = 1 + x$

  d $\dfrac{x - 1}{2 - x} = 2x + 1$ **e** $x - \dfrac{1}{x} = 1$ **f** $2x - \dfrac{1}{x} = 3$

K   PROBLEM SOLVING WITH QUADRATICS

When solving some problems algebraically, a quadratic equation results. We are generally only interested in any **real solutions**. If the resulting quadratic equation has no real roots then the problem has no real solution.

Any answer we obtain must be checked to see if it is reasonable. For example:

- if we are finding a length then it must be positive and we reject any negative solutions
- if we are finding 'how many people are present' then clearly the answer must be an integer.

We employ the following general problem solving method:

Step 1:   If the information is given in words, translate it into algebra using a pronumeral such as x. Write down the resulting equation.

Step 2:   Solve the equation by a suitable method.

Step 3:   Examine the solutions carefully to see if they are acceptable.

Step 4:   Give your answer in a sentence.

HISTORICAL NOTE   BABYLONIAN ALGEBRA

The mathematics used by the **Babylonians** was recorded on clay
tablets in cuneiform. One such tablet which has been preserved
is called *Plimton 322*, written around 1600 BC.

The Ancient Babylonians were able to solve difficult equations
using the rules we use today, such as transposing terms,
multiplying both sides by like quantities to remove fractions, and
factorisation.

They could, for example, add $4xy$ to $(x-y)^2$ to obtain $(x+y)^2$.

This was all achieved without the use of letters for unknown quantities. However, they often used
words for the unknown.

Consider the following example from about 4000 years ago:

Problem: *"I have subtracted the side of my square from the area and the
result is 870. What is the side of the square?"*

Solution: Take half of 1, which is $\frac{1}{2}$, and multiply $\frac{1}{2}$ by $\frac{1}{2}$ which is $\frac{1}{4}$;

add this to 870 to get $870\frac{1}{4}$. This is the square of $29\frac{1}{2}$.

Now add $\frac{1}{2}$ to $29\frac{1}{2}$ and the result is 30, the side of the square.

Using our modern symbols, the equation is $x^2 - x = 870$ and the solution is

$$x = \sqrt{\left(\tfrac{1}{2}\right)^2 + 870} + \tfrac{1}{2} = 30$$

Example 34   ◀)) Self Tutor

A rectangle has length 3 cm longer than its width. Its area is 42 cm². Find its width.

If the width is x cm then the length is $(x+3)$ cm.

$$\therefore \ x(x+3) = 42 \qquad \{\text{equating areas}\}$$
$$\therefore \ x^2 + 3x - 42 = 0$$
$$\therefore \ x \approx -8.15 \text{ or } 5.15 \quad \{\text{using technology}\}$$

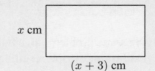

We reject the negative solution as lengths are positive.

So, the width ≈ 5.15 cm.

EXERCISE 4K

1 Two integers differ by 12 and the sum of their squares is 74. Find the integers.

2 The sum of a number and its reciprocal is $5\frac{1}{5}$. Find the number.

3 The sum of a natural number and its square is 210. Find the number.

4 The product of two consecutive even numbers is 360. Find the numbers.

5 The product of two consecutive odd numbers is 255. Find the numbers.

6 The number of diagonals of an n-sided polygon is given by the formula $D = \frac{n}{2}(n-3)$.
A polygon has 90 diagonals. How many sides does it have?

7 The length of a rectangle is 4 cm longer than its width. Find its width given that its area is 26 cm^2.

8 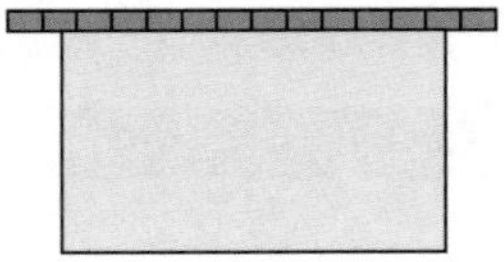

A rectangular pig pen is built against an existing brick fence. 24 m of fencing was used to enclose 70 m^2.
Find the dimensions of the pen.

Example 35 **Self Tutor**

Is it possible to bend a 12 cm length of wire to form the shorter sides of a right angled triangle with area 20 cm^2?

Suppose the wire is bent x cm from one end.

The area $A = \frac{1}{2}x(12-x)$ cm^2

$\therefore \frac{1}{2}x(12-x) = 20$

$\therefore x(12-x) = 40$

$\therefore 12x - x^2 - 40 = 0$

$\therefore x^2 - 12x + 40 = 0$

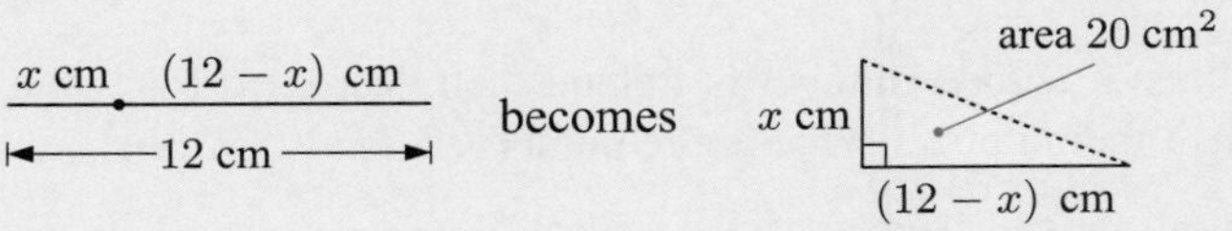

Using technology, there are no real solutions, indicating this situation is impossible.

9 Is it possible to bend a 20 cm length of wire into the shape of a rectangle which has an area of 30 cm^2?

10 A rectangular box has a square base, and its height is 1 cm longer than the length of each side of its base.

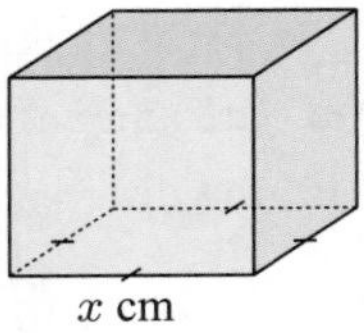

- **a** Suppose each side of its base has length x cm. Show that the total surface area of the box is given by $A = 6x^2 + 4x$ cm^2.
- **b** If the total surface area is 240 cm^2, find the dimensions of the box.

11 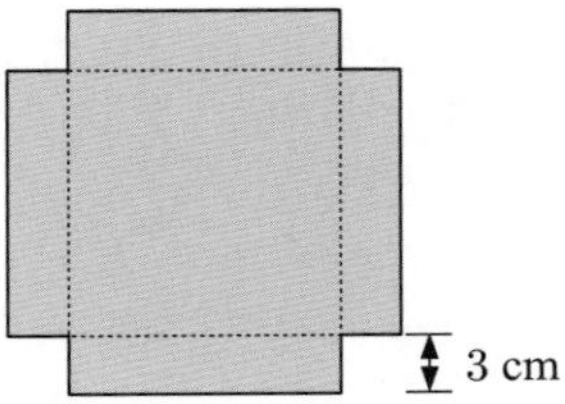

An open box can hold 80 cm^3. It is made from a square piece of tinplate with 3 cm squares cut from each of its 4 corners. Find the dimensions of the original piece of tinplate.

DEMO

12 A rectangular swimming pool is 12 m long by 6 m wide. It is surrounded by a pavement of uniform width, the area of the pavement being $\frac{7}{8}$ of the area of the pool.

- **a** If the pavement is x m wide, show that the area of the pavement is $4x^2 + 36x$ m^2.
- **b** Hence, show that $4x^2 + 36x - 63 = 0$.
- **c** How wide is the pavement?

13 Two trains travel a 160 km track each day. The express travels 10 km h^{-1} faster and takes 30 minutes less time than the normal train. Find the speed of the express.

14 A uniform concrete path is paved around a 30 m by 40 m rectangular lawn. The concrete has area one quarter of the area of the lawn. Find the width of the path.

REVIEW SET 4A

1 If $r = 2$, $s = -5$, and $t = -1$, find the value of:

    a $(rs)^2$
    b $\dfrac{t - 2r}{3s}$
    c $\sqrt{t + 5r}$

2 Solve for x:
  a $2(x - 3) + 5(1 - x) = 2$
  b $(x - 5)(x + 4) = (x - 2)^2$

3 Solve for x:
  a $\dfrac{6 - 5x}{4x + 3} = -2$
  b $\dfrac{1}{x} = \dfrac{3}{x + 8}$

4 Solve the following using technology:

    a $3.75x + 2.663 = 1.7255$
    b $\dfrac{3 - 2x}{x + 5} = -1$

5 When a certain number is trebled then decreased by 1, the result is twice as much as 5 more than the number. What is the number?

6 A post office has two lengths of mailing tube, 45 cm and 75 cm. They have 15 more short tubes than long tubes, and if the tubes were laid end to end they would total 1995 cm in length. How many 75 cm tubes does the post office have?

7 Solve for x:
  a $\begin{cases} -2x + 5y = -3 \\ 3x + 4y = 16 \end{cases}$
  b $\begin{cases} x - 8y = 1 \\ 6x - 2y = -17 \end{cases}$

8 The amount of heat Q Joules needed to warm up m kilograms of water by $T°C$ is given by $Q = 4186mT$. Find:

  a the amount of heat needed to warm up 6.7 kg of water by $8°C$

  b the difference in temperature when 4 kg of water is heated up with 20 000 Joules.

9 Make y the subject of:

    a $4x - 3y = 28$
    b $cy + d = k$
    c $\dfrac{p}{y} = q$

10 Solve for x:
  a $(x - 2)^2 = 25$
  b $x(x - 4) - (x - 6) = 0$

11 Solve for x by first eliminating the algebraic fractions:

    a $\dfrac{4}{x} = \dfrac{x}{7}$
    b $\dfrac{x + 1}{x + 3} = \dfrac{x}{2}$

12 The width of a rectangle is 7 cm less than its length, and its area is 260 cm^2. Find the dimensions of the rectangle.

13 Seven adults' tickets and eight children's tickets to an exhibition cost £255, while three adults' tickets and twenty three children's tickets cost £305. Find the cost of a child's ticket.

REVIEW SET 4B

1 If $a = 3$, $b = -4$, and $c = 7$, find the value of:

   a $b^2 - c^2$ **b** $\dfrac{3a + 4b}{c(b - 1)}$ **c** $\sqrt{b(a - c)}$

2 Solve for x:

   a $x - 14 = 6$ **b** $\dfrac{4x - 9}{2} = 8$ **c** $2x - 9 = 5(x + 1)$

3 Solve for x: **a** $\dfrac{2}{x} = \dfrac{8}{7}$ **b** $\dfrac{x + 6}{-4} = \dfrac{x - 1}{3}$

4 Use technology to solve the following:

   a $3.98k - 5.89 = 12.816$ **b** $\dfrac{12a - 5}{a + 5} = 1$

5 If the current price of bread dropped by 44 cents, 9 loaves of bread would cost as much as 7 do now. What is the current price of bread?

6 The population density of a region with population N and area A km^2 is given by $D = \dfrac{N}{A}$ people per square kilometre.

   a Find the population density of Liechtenstein, which has around 35 500 people living in 160 km^2.

   b India has a population density of approximately 357 people per square kilometre. Its population is about 1 170 000 000 people. How big is India?

7 Solve simultaneously: **a** $\begin{cases} x + 3y = 7 \\ y = x + 5 \end{cases}$ **b** $\begin{cases} 6x - 2y = 26 \\ 2x + 3y = 5 \end{cases}$

8 A coconut shy at the village fair offers three throws for £1, or seven throws for £2. In one hour, 187 throws are made, and the attendant takes £57. How many people bought three throws?

9 Solve for x:

   a $x^2 + 5x = 24$ **b** $2x^2 - 18 = 0$

   c $8x^2 + 2x - 3 = 0$

10 Solve for x:

   a $(x + 3)^2 = 5x + 29$ **b** $2x^2 - 108 = 6x$

11 Solve for x graphically:

   a $x^2 + 6x - 2 = 0$ **b** $-3x^2 + 5x + 14 = 0$

12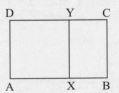
ABCD is a rectangle in which $AB = 21$ cm.
The square AXYD is removed and the remaining rectangle has area 80 cm^2.
Find the length BC.

13 When the square of a number is increased by 10, the result is seven times the original number. Find the number.

REVIEW SET 4C

1 If $p = -3$, $q = 4$, and $r = -2$, find the value of:

    a $p^2 q$
        b $\dfrac{3p - 2r}{q}$
        c $\sqrt{\dfrac{25q}{(p + r)^2}}$

2 Solve for x: **a** $3(x - 2) = 4(2 - x)$ **b** $(x - 3)^2 = (x - 1)^2$

3 Make w the subject of: **a** $5q - 2w = 12$ **b** $\dfrac{3t}{2w} = s$

4 The profit P of a business that sells all n items it produces is given by $P = Sn - Cn$, where S is the selling price and C is the cost price of each item.

    a Make n the subject of the formula.

    b Veronika is a jeweller. She imports watches for €205 and sells them for €215. How many must she sell to make €970 profit?

    c Rearrange the formula to make S the subject.

    d Veronika also aims to make €360 from selling earrings. She estimates that she can sell 75 pairs of earrings, with production costs of €24.50 per pair. At what price should she sell the earrings?

5 Solve simultaneously: **a** $\begin{cases} x = 2y - 4 \\ -3x + 2y = -1 \end{cases}$ **b** $\begin{cases} 6x + y = 22 \\ 4x + 3y = -4 \end{cases}$

6 A machine tests car batteries for faults. A functional battery takes 2 minutes to test, but a faulty battery requires 5 minutes to detect and repair. In an 83 minute session, 37 batteries were tested. How many were faulty?

7 Find the lengths of the sides of the rectangle:

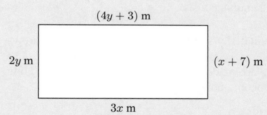

8 Solve for x:

    a $2x^2 - 5x = 0$ **b** $x^2 - 12 = 4x$ **c** $4x^2 - 5x = 6$

9 Solve for x:

    a $(x + 3)^2 = 36$ **b** $x(x + 4) + 2(x + 5) = 5$ **c** $3x(x - 2) = 2 - 11x$

10 Richard has an elder sister who is twice his age, and a younger sister who is two years younger than him. If the product of his sisters' ages is 70, how old is Richard?

11 Iain throws a ball into the air. Its height above the ground after x seconds is $2 + 4x - 4.9x^2$ metres. How long does it take for the ball to hit the ground?

12 During a 65 km ride, I cycled 7 km per hour faster than my sister. I finished 45 minutes ahead of her. What was my speed?

13 A football club was counting gate receipts from their last home game. They know that there were 250 more adults than children at the game, and the total value of tickets sold was €29 030. If a child's ticket was €7, and an adult's ticket was €12, how many adults and how many children attended?

Chapter 5

Sequences and series

Syllabus reference: 1.7, 1.8, 1.9

$$S_n = \frac{2}{2}\left(2 \times 20 + (30-1) \times\right)$$

OPENING PROBLEM

Vicki has 30 days to train for a swimming competition.   Arith

She swims 20 laps on the first day, then each day after that she swims two more laps than the previous day. So, she swims 22 laps on the second day, 24 laps on the third day, and so on.

Things to think about:

a How many laps does Vicki swim on:
   i the tenth day   **ii** the final day?

b How many laps does Vicki swim in total?

To help understand problems like the **Opening Problem**, we need to study **sequences** and their sums which are called **series**.

A   NUMBER SEQUENCES

In mathematics it is important that we can:
- **recognise** a pattern in a set of numbers,
- **describe** the pattern in words, and
- **continue** the pattern.

A list of numbers where there is a pattern is called a **number sequence**.

The numbers in the sequence are said to be its **members** or its **terms**.

For example: 3, 7, 11, 15, ...   form a number sequence.

The first term is 3, the second term is 7, the third term is 11, and so on.

We can describe this pattern in words:
   "The sequence starts at 3 and each term is 4 more than the previous one."

Thus, the fifth term is 19 and the sixth term is 23.

Example 1   ◀)) Self Tutor

Describe the sequence: 14, 17, 20, 23, ...   and write down the next two terms.

The sequence starts at 14, and each term is 3 more than the previous term.

The next two terms are 26 and 29.

EXERCISE 5A

1 Write down the first four terms of the sequence if you start with:
   a 4 and add 9 each time   **b** 45 and subtract 6 each time
   c 2 and multiply by 3 each time   **d** 96 and divide by 2 each time.

2 For each of the following write a description of the sequence and find the next 2 terms:
   a 8, 16, 24, 32, ...   **b** 2, 5, 8, 11, ...   **c** 36, 31, 26, 21, ...
   d 96, 89, 82, 75, ...   **e** 1, 4, 16, 64, ...   **f** 2, 6, 18, 54, ...
   g 480, 240, 120, 60, ...   **h** 243, 81, 27, 9, ...   **i** 50 000, 10 000, 2000, 400, ...

3 Describe the following number patterns and write down the next 3 terms:

    a 1, 4, 9, 16, ...
    b 1, 8, 27, 64, ...
    c 2, 6, 12, 20, ...

4 Find the next two terms of:

    a 95, 91, 87, 83, ...
    b 5, 20, 80, 320, ...
    c 1, 16, 81, 256, ...

    d 16, 8, 4, 2, ...
    e 2, 3, 5, 7, 11, ...
    f 2, 4, 7, 11, ...

                            1 2 3 4 5

B   THE GENERAL TERM OF A NUMBER SEQUENCE

Sequences may be defined in one of the following ways:

- listing the first few terms and assuming that the pattern represented continues indefinitely
- giving a description in words
- using a formula which represents the **general term** or **nth term**.

Consider the illustrated tower of bricks. The first row has three bricks, the second row has four bricks, and the third row has five bricks.

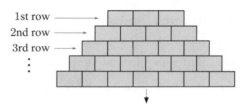

1st row
2nd row
3rd row

If u_n represents the number of bricks in row n (from the top) then $u_1 = 3$, $u_2 = 4$, $u_3 = 5$, $u_4 = 6$, ...

This sequence can be specified by:

- **listing terms**   3, 4, 5, 6, ...

- **using words**   "The top row has three bricks and each successive row under it has one more brick."

- **using an explicit formula** $u_n = n + 2$ is the **general term** or **nth term** formula for $n = 1, 2, 3, 4, 5, ...$

                    Check: $u_1 = 1 + 2 = 3$ ✓ $u_2 = 2 + 2 = 4$ ✓
                              $u_3 = 3 + 2 = 5$ ✓

- **a pictorial or graphical representation**
  Early members of a sequence can be graphed with each represented by a dot.
  The dots *must not* be joined because n must be an integer.

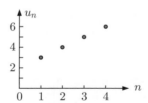

THE GENERAL TERM

The **general term** or **nth term** of a sequence is represented by a symbol with a subscript, for example u_n, T_n, t_n, or A_n. The general term is defined for $n = 1, 2, 3, 4, 5, 6, ...$

$\{u_n\}$ represents the sequence that can be generated by using u_n as the nth term.

The general term u_n is a function where $n \mapsto u_n$, and the domain is $n \in \mathbb{Z}^+$.

For example, $\{2n + 1\}$ generates the sequence 3, 5, 7, 9, 11, ...

You can use technology to help generate sequences from a formula.

GRAPHICS CALCULATOR INSTRUCTIONS

EXERCISE 5B

1 A sequence is defined by $u_n = 3n - 2$. Find:

   a u_1 **b** u_5 **c** u_{27}

2 Consider the sequence defined by $u_n = 2n + 5$.

   a Find the first four terms of the sequence.   **b** Display these members on a graph.

3 List the first *five* terms of the sequence:

   a $\{2n\}$ **b** $\{2n + 2\}$ **c** $\{2n - 1\}$ **d** $\{2n - 3\}$

   e $\{2n + 3\}$ **f** $\{2n + 11\}$ **g** $\{3n + 1\}$ **h** $\{4n - 3\}$

4 List the first *five* terms of the sequence:

   a $\{2^n\}$ **b** $\{3 \times 2^n\}$ **c** $\{6 \times (\frac{1}{2})^n\}$ **d** $\{(-2)^n\}$

5 List the first *five* terms of the sequence $\{15 - (-2)^n\}$.

6 List the terms of these sequences:

   a start with 5 and add 3 each time   **b** $\{2 + 3n\}$

   c start with 100 and take 7 each time   **d** $\{107 - 7n\}$

   e start with 5 and multiply successively by 2   **f** $\{5 \times 2^{n-1}\}$

   g start with 48 and multiply successively by $\frac{1}{2}$ **h** $\{48 \times (\frac{1}{2})^{n-1}\}$

   What do you notice about your answers?

RESEARCH   THE FIBONACCI SEQUENCE

Leonardo Pisano Bigollo, known commonly as Fibonacci, was born in Pisa around 1170 AD. He is best known for the **Fibonacci sequence** 0, 1, 1, 2, 3, 5, 8, 13, 21, ... which starts with 0 and 1, and then each subsequent member of the sequence is the sum of the preceding two members.

1 Where do we see the Fibonacci sequence in nature?

2 Can we write a formula for the general u_n term of the Fibonacci sequence? How else can the Fibonacci sequence be described using symbols?

C   ARITHMETIC SEQUENCES

An **arithmetic sequence** is a sequence in which each term differs from the previous one by the same fixed number.

It can also be referred to as an **arithmetic progression**.

For example:

- the tower of bricks in the previous section forms an arithmetic sequence where the difference between terms is 1

- 2, 5, 8, 11, 14, ... is arithmetic as $5 - 2 = 8 - 5 = 11 - 8 = 14 - 11 = ...$

- 31, 27, 23, 19, ... is arithmetic as $27 - 31 = 23 - 27 = 19 - 23 = ...$

ALGEBRAIC DEFINITION

> $\{u_n\}$ is **arithmetic** $\Leftrightarrow$ $u_{n+1} - u_n = d$ for all positive integers n where d is a constant called the **common difference**.

The symbol $\Leftrightarrow$ is read as 'if and only if'. It means that:

- if $\{u_n\}$ is arithmetic then $u_{n+1} - u_n$ is a constant
- if $u_{n+1} - u_n$ is a constant then $\{u_n\}$ is arithmetic.

THE NAME 'ARITHMETIC'

If a, b and c are any consecutive terms of an arithmetic sequence then

$$b - a = c - b \qquad \text{\{equating common differences\}}$$
$$\therefore \quad 2b = a + c$$
$$\therefore \quad b = \frac{a + c}{2}$$

So, the middle term is the **arithmetic mean** of the terms on either side of it.

THE GENERAL TERM FORMULA

Suppose the first term of an arithmetic sequence is u_1 and the common difference is d.

Then $u_2 = u_1 + d$, $u_3 = u_1 + 2d$, $u_4 = u_1 + 3d$,   and so on.

Hence $u_n = u_1 + \underbrace{(n - 1)}\,d$

term number   one less than the term number

> For an **arithmetic sequence** with **first term u_1** and **common difference d** the **general term** or **nth term** is $u_n = u_1 + (n - 1)d$.

Example 2   ◀) **Self Tutor**

Consider the sequence   2, 9, 16, 23, 30, ...

a Show that the sequence is arithmetic.
b Find a formula for the general term u_n.
c Find the 100th term of the sequence.
d Is   i 828   ii 2341   a term of the sequence?

---

a $9 - 2 = 7$ The difference between successive terms is constant.
    $16 - 9 = 7$ So, the sequence is arithmetic, with $u_1 = 2$ and $d = 7$.
    $23 - 16 = 7$
    $30 - 23 = 7$

b $u_n = u_1 + (n - 1)d$ c If $n = 100$,
    $\therefore \ u_n = 2 + 7(n - 1)$ $u_{100} = 7(100) - 5$
    $\therefore \ u_n = 7n - 5$ $= 695$

d   i   Let $u_n = 828$

$\therefore$ $7n - 5 = 828$

$\therefore$ $7n = 833$

$\therefore$ $n = 119$

$\therefore$ 828 is a term of the sequence,
and in fact is the 119th term.

ii   Let $u_n = 2341$

$\therefore$ $7n - 5 = 2341$

$\therefore$ $7n = 2346$

$\therefore$ $n = 335\frac{1}{7}$

But n must be an integer, so
2341 cannot be a term.

EXERCISE 5C

1   Find the 10th term of each of the following arithmetic sequences:

    a   19, 25, 31, 37, ...
    b   101, 97, 93, 89, ...
    c $8, 9\frac{1}{2}, 11, 12\frac{1}{2}$, ...

2   Find the 15th term of each of the following arithmetic sequences:

    a   31, 36, 41, 46, ...
    b   5, −3, −11, −19, ...
    c $a, a + d, a + 2d, a + 3d$, ...

3   Consider the arithmetic sequence   6, 17, 28, 39, 50, ...

    a   Explain why the sequence is arithmetic.
    b   Find the formula for its general term.
    c   Find its 50th term.
    d   Is 325 a member?
    e   Is 761 a member?

4   Consider the arithmetic sequence   87, 83, 79, 75, ...

    a   Explain why the sequence is arithmetic.
    b   Find the formula for its general term.
    c   Find the 40th term.
    d   Which term of the sequence is −297?

5   A sequence is defined by $u_n = 3n - 2$.

    a   Prove that the sequence is arithmetic.   **Hint:** Find $u_{n+1} - u_n$.
    b   Find u_1 and d.
    c   Find the 57th term.
    d   What term of the sequence is the last term smaller than 450?

6   A sequence is defined by $u_n = \dfrac{71 - 7n}{2}$.

    a   Prove that the sequence is arithmetic.
    b   Find u_1 and d.
    c   Find u_{75}.
    d   For what values of n are the terms of the sequence less than −200?

Example 3   ◀) Self Tutor

Find k given that $3k + 1$, k, and -3 are consecutive terms of an arithmetic sequence.

Since the terms are consecutive, $k - (3k + 1) = -3 - k$ {equating differences}

$\therefore$ $k - 3k - 1 = -3 - k$

$\therefore$ $-2k - 1 = -3 - k$

$\therefore$ $-1 + 3 = -k + 2k$

$\therefore$ $k = 2$

or   Since the middle term is the arithmetic mean of the terms on either side of it,

$$k = \frac{(3k + 1) + (-3)}{2}$$

$\therefore$ $2k = 3k - 2$

$\therefore$ $k = 2$

7 Find k given the consecutive arithmetic terms:

     a $32, k, 3$ **b** $k, 7, 10$ **c** $k + 1, 2k + 1, 13$

     d $k - 1, 2k + 3, 7 - k$ **e** $2k + 7, 3k + 5, 5k - 4$ **f** $2k + 18, -2 - k, 2k + 2$

8 Find k given the consecutive terms of an arithmetic sequence:

     a $k, k^2, k^2 + 6$ **b** $4k - k^2, 3k, 3$ **c** $5, k, k^2 - 8$

Example 4   ◀)) Self Tutor

Find the general term u_n for an arithmetic sequence with $u_3 = 8$ and $u_8 = -17$.

$u_3 = 8$ $\therefore$ $u_1 + 2d = 8$ .... (1)   {using $u_n = u_1 + (n - 1)d$}

$u_8 = -17$ $\therefore$ $u_1 + 7d = -17$ .... (2)

We now solve (1) and (2) simultaneously using technology:

TI-*n*spire

Casio fx-CG20   **TI-84 Plus**

 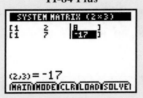 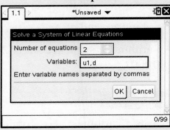

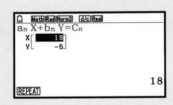 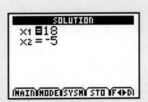 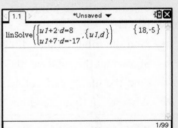

$\therefore$ $u_1 = 18$ and $d = -5$

Now $u_n = u_1 + (n - 1)d$

$\therefore$ $u_n = 18 - 5(n - 1)$ *Check*:

$\therefore$ $u_n = 18 - 5n + 5$ $u_3 = 23 - 5(3)$ $u_8 = 23 - 5(8)$

$\therefore$ $u_n = 23 - 5n$ $= 23 - 15$ $= 23 - 40$

                                        $= 8$ ✓ $= -17$ ✓

---

9 Find the general term u_n for an arithmetic sequence with:

     a $u_7 = 41$ and $u_{13} = 77$ **b** $u_5 = -2$ and $u_{12} = -12\frac{1}{2}$

     c   seventh term 1 and fifteenth term -39

     d   eleventh and eighth terms being -16 and $-11\frac{1}{2}$ respectively.

Example 5   ◀)) **Self Tutor**

Insert four numbers between 3 and 12 so that all six numbers are in arithmetic sequence.

Suppose the common difference is d.

∴   the numbers are   3, $3 + d$, $3 + 2d$, $3 + 3d$, $3 + 4d$, and 12

$$\therefore \quad 3 + 5d = 12$$
$$\therefore \quad 5d = 9$$
$$\therefore \quad d = \tfrac{9}{5} = 1.8$$

So, the sequence is   3, 4.8, 6.6, 8.4, 10.2, 12.

10   **a**   Insert three numbers between 5 and 10 so that all five numbers are in arithmetic sequence.

   b   Insert six numbers between -1 and 32 so that all eight numbers are in arithmetic sequence.

11   Consider the arithmetic sequence $36, 35\tfrac{1}{3}, 34\tfrac{2}{3}, ...$

   a   Find u_1 and d.   **b**   Which term of the sequence is -30?

12   An arithmetic sequence starts 23, 36, 49, 62, ...   What is the first term of the sequence to exceed 100 000?

Example 6   ◀)) **Self Tutor**

Ryan is a cartoonist. His comic strip has just been bought by a newspaper, so he sends them the 28 comic strips he has drawn so far. Each week after the first he mails 3 more comic strips to the newspaper.

   a   Find the total number of comic strips sent after 1, 2, 3, and 4 weeks.
   b   Show that the total number of comic strips sent after n weeks forms an arithmetic sequence.
   c   Find the number of comic strips sent after 15 weeks.
   d   When does Ryan send his 120th comic strip?

   a   *Week 1*:   28 comic strips
      Week 2: $28 + 3 = 31$ comic strips
      Week 3: $31 + 3 = 34$ comic strips
      Week 4: $34 + 3 = 37$ comic strips

   b   Every week, Ryan sends 3 comic strips, so the difference between successive weeks is always 3. We have an arithmetic sequence with $u_1 = 28$ and common difference $d = 3$.

   c $u_n = u_1 + (n - 1)d$
   $ = 28 + (n - 1) \times 3$ $\therefore \quad u_{15} = 25 + 3 \times 15$
   $ = 25 + 3n$ $\phantom{\therefore \quad u_{15}} = 70$

   After 15 weeks Ryan has sent 70 comic strips.

   d   We want to find n such that $u_n = 120$
   $$\therefore \quad 25 + 3n = 120$$
   $$\therefore \quad 3n = 95$$
   $$\therefore \quad n = 31\tfrac{2}{3}$$

   Ryan sends the 120th comic strip in the 32nd week.

13 A luxury car manufacturer sets up a factory for a new model. In the first month only 5 cars are produced. After this, 13 cars are assembled every month.

   a List the total number of cars that have been made in the factory by the end of each of the first six months.

   b Explain why the total number of cars made after n months forms an arithmetic sequence.

   c How many cars are made in the first year?

   d How long is it until the 250th car is manufactured? $\longrightarrow$ *Find n*

14 Valéria joins a social networking website. After 1 week she has 34 online friends. At the end of 2 weeks she has 41 friends, after 3 weeks she has 48 friends, and after 4 weeks she has 55 friends.

   a Show that Valéria's number of friends forms an arithmetic sequence.

   b Assuming the pattern continues, find the number of online friends Valéria will have after 12 weeks.

   c After how many weeks will Valéria have 150 online friends?

15 A farmer feeds his cattle herd with hay every day in July. The amount of hay in his barn at the end of day n is given by the arithmetic sequence $u_n = 100 - 2.7n$ tonnes.

   a Write down the amount of hay in the barn on the first three days of July.

   b Find and interpret the common difference.

   c Find and interpret u_{25}.

   d How much hay is in the barn at the beginning of August?

D   GEOMETRIC SEQUENCES

> A sequence is **geometric** if each term can be obtained from the previous one by multiplying by the same non-zero constant.
>
> A geometric sequence can also be referred to as a **geometric progression**.

For example: 2, 10, 50, 250, ... is a geometric sequence as each term can be obtained by multiplying the previous term by 5.

Notice that $\frac{10}{2} = \frac{50}{10} = \frac{250}{50} = 5$, so each term divided by the previous one gives the same constant.

ALGEBRAIC DEFINITION

> $\{u_n\}$ is **geometric** $\quad\Leftrightarrow\quad \dfrac{u_{n+1}}{u_n} = r$ for all positive integers n where r is a constant called the **common ratio**.

For example:
   - 2, 10, 50, 250, ...   is geometric with $r = 5$.
   - 2, -10, 50, -250, ...   is geometric with $r = -5$.

THE NAME 'GEOMETRIC'

If a, b and c are any consecutive terms of a geometric sequence then $\dfrac{b}{a} = \dfrac{c}{b}$.

$\therefore$ $b^2 = ac$ and so $b = \pm\sqrt{ac}$ where $\sqrt{ac}$ is the **geometric mean** of a and c.

THE GENERAL TERM FORMULA

Suppose the first term of a geometric sequence is u_1 and the common ratio is r.

Then $u_2 = u_1 r$, $u_3 = u_1 r^2$, $u_4 = u_1 r^3$,   and so on.

Hence $u_n = u_1 r^{n-1}$

term number   The power of r is one less than the term number.

> For a **geometric sequence** with **first term** u_1 and **common ratio** r,
> the **general term** or **nth term** is $u_n = u_1 r^{n-1}$.

Example 7
◀)) **Self Tutor**

Consider the sequence $8, 4, 2, 1, \frac{1}{2}, \,....$

a Show that the sequence is geometric.   **b** Find the general term u_n.

c Hence, find the 12th term as a fraction.

---

a $\dfrac{4}{8} = \dfrac{1}{2}$ $\dfrac{2}{4} = \dfrac{1}{2}$ $\dfrac{1}{2} = \dfrac{1}{2}$ $\dfrac{\frac{1}{2}}{1} = \dfrac{1}{2}$

Assuming the pattern continues, consecutive terms have a common ratio of $\frac{1}{2}$.

∴   the sequence is geometric with $u_1 = 8$ and $r = \frac{1}{2}$.

b $u_n = u_1 r^{n-1}$

∴ $u_n = 8 \left(\frac{1}{2}\right)^{n-1}$ *or* $u_n = 2^3 \times (2^{-1})^{n-1}$

$\qquad\qquad\qquad\qquad\qquad\qquad = 2^3 \times 2^{-n+1}$

$\qquad\qquad\qquad\qquad\qquad\qquad = 2^{3+(-n+1)}$

$\qquad\qquad\qquad\qquad\qquad\qquad = 2^{4-n}$

c $u_{12} = 8 \times \left(\frac{1}{2}\right)^{11}$

$\qquad\quad = \frac{1}{256}$

EXERCISE 5D.1

1 For the geometric sequence with first two terms given, find b and c:

    a $2, 6, b, c, \,....$ **b** $10, 5, b, c, \,....$ **c** $12, -6, b, c, \,....$

2 Find the 6th term in each of the following geometric sequences:

    a $3, 6, 12, 24, \,....$ **b** $2, 10, 50, \,....$ **c** $512, 256, 128, \,....$

3 Find the 9th term in each of the following geometric sequences:

    a $1, 3, 9, 27, \,....$ **b** $12, 18, 27, \,....$ **c** $\frac{1}{16}, -\frac{1}{8}, \frac{1}{4}, -\frac{1}{2}, \,....$ **d** $a, ar, ar^2, \,....$

4 Consider the geometric sequence $5, 10, 20, 40, \,....$

    a Find the first term u_1 and common ratio r for the sequence.

    b Find the general term u_n.   **c** Hence find the 15th term of the sequence.

5 Consider the geometric sequence $12, -6, 3, -\frac{3}{2}, \,....$

    a Find the first term u_1 and common ratio r for the sequence.

    b Find the general term u_n.

    c Hence find the 13th term of the sequence as a fraction.

6 Show that the sequence $8, -6, 4.5, -3.375, \ldots$ is geometric. Hence find the 10th term as a decimal.

7 Show that the sequence $8, 4\sqrt{2}, 4, 2\sqrt{2}, \ldots$ is geometric. Hence find, in simplest form, the general term u_n.

Example 8 ◀)) **Self Tutor**

$k - 1$, $2k$, and $21 - k$ are consecutive terms of a geometric sequence. Find k.

Since the terms are geometric, $\quad \dfrac{2k}{k-1} = \dfrac{21-k}{2k} \qquad$ {equating rs}

$$\therefore \ 4k^2 = (21-k)(k-1)$$
$$\therefore \ 4k^2 = 21k - 21 - k^2 + k$$
$$\therefore \ 5k^2 - 22k + 21 = 0$$

TI-*n*spire

Casio fx-CG20   **TI-84 Plus**

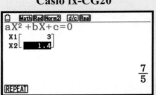

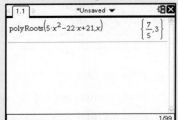

$$\therefore \ k = \tfrac{7}{5} \text{ or } 3 \quad \{\text{using technology}\}$$

Check: If $k = \tfrac{7}{5}$ the terms are: $\ \tfrac{2}{5}, \tfrac{14}{5}, \tfrac{98}{5}.$ ✓ $\{r = 7\}$

If $k = 3$ the terms are: $\ 2, 6, 18.$ ✓ $\{r = 3\}$

---

8 Find k given that the following are consecutive terms of a geometric sequence:

a $7, k, 28$ **b** $k, 3k, 20 - k$ **c** $k, k + 8, 9k$

Example 9 ◀)) **Self Tutor**

A geometric sequence has $u_2 = -6$ and $u_5 = 162$. Find its general term.

$$u_2 = u_1 r = -6 \quad \ldots \text{ (1)}$$
and $\quad u_5 = u_1 r^4 = 162 \quad \ldots \text{ (2)}$

Now $\quad \dfrac{u_1 r^4}{u_1 r} = \dfrac{162}{-6} \qquad \{(2) \div (1)\}$

$$\therefore \ r^3 = -27$$
$$\therefore \ r = \sqrt[3]{-27}$$
$$\therefore \ r = -3$$

Using (1), $\quad u_1(-3) = -6$
$$\therefore \ u_1 = 2$$
Thus $\quad u_n = 2 \times (-3)^{n-1}.$

---

9 Find the general term u_n of the geometric sequence which has:

a $u_4 = 24$ and $u_7 = 192$ **b** $u_3 = 8$ and $u_6 = -1$

c $u_7 = 24$ and $u_{15} = 384$ **d** $u_3 = 5$ and $u_7 = \tfrac{5}{4}$

Example 10   ◄)) **Self Tutor**

Find the first term of the sequence $6, 6\sqrt{2}, 12, 12\sqrt{2}, \ldots.$ which exceeds 1400.

The sequence is geometric with $u_1 = 6$ and $r = \sqrt{2}$

$$\therefore \ u_n = 6 \times (\sqrt{2})^{n-1}.$$

We need to find n such that $u_n > 1400$.

Using a graphics calculator with $Y_1 = 6 \times (\sqrt{2})^\wedge(X - 1)$,   we view a *table of values*:

Casio fx-CG20	**TI-84 Plus**	**TI-*n*spire**
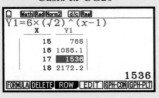	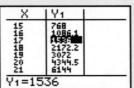	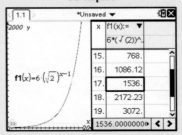

The first term to exceed 1400 is $u_{17} = 1536$.

10 **a** Find the first term of the geometric sequence $2, 6, 18, 54, \ldots.$ which exceeds $10\,000$.

    b Find the first term of the geometric sequence $4, 4\sqrt{3}, 12, 12\sqrt{3}, \ldots.$ which exceeds 4800.

    c Find the first term of the geometric sequence $12, 6, 3, 1.5, \ldots.$ which is less than 0.0001.

GEOMETRIC SEQUENCE PROBLEMS

Problems of **growth and decay** involve repeated multiplications by a constant number. We can therefore model the situations using geometric sequences.

In these problems we will often obtain an equation which we need to solve for n. We can do this using the equation solver on our calculator.

GRAPHICS CALCULATOR INSTRUCTIONS

Example 11   ◄)) **Self Tutor**

The initial population of rabbits on a farm was 50.
The population increased by 7% each week.

    a How many rabbits were present after:

        i 15 weeks   **ii** 30 weeks?

    b How long would it take for the population to reach 500?

There is a fixed percentage increase each week, so the population forms a geometric sequence.

$u_1 = 50$ and $r = 1.07$

$u_2 = 50 \times 1.07 =$ the population after 1 week

    a   **i** $u_{n+1} = u_1 \times r^n$ **ii** $u_{31} = 50 \times (1.07)^{30}$

           $\therefore \ u_{16} = 50 \times (1.07)^{15}$ ≈ 380.61

                 ≈ 137.95 There were 381 rabbits.

           There were 138 rabbits.

b $u_{n+1} = u_1 \times (1.07)^n$ after n weeks

So, we need to find when $50 \times (1.07)^n = 500$.

Casio fx-CG20	TI-84 Plus	TI-*n*spire

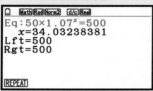

So, it would take approximately 34.0 weeks.

EXERCISE 5D.2

1 A nest of ants initially contains 500 individuals.   The population is increasing by 12% each week.

    a How many ants will there be after:

       i 10 weeks   **ii** 20 weeks?

    b Use technology to find how many weeks it will take for the ant population to reach 2000.

2

A herd of 32 deer is to be left unchecked on a large island off the coast of Alaska. It is estimated that the size of the herd will increase each year by 18%.

    a Estimate the size of the herd after:

       i 5 years   **ii** 10 years.

    b How long will it take for the herd size to reach 5000?

3 A film club initially had 300 members. However, its membership has since decreased by 6% each year.

    a How many members did the film club have after 5 years?

    b How long does it take for the number of members to drop to 150?

4 An endangered species of marsupials has a population of 178. However, with a successful breeding program it is expected to increase by 32% each year.

    a Find the expected population size after: **i** 10 years   **ii** 25 years.

    b How long will it take for the population to reach 10 000?

5 The animal *Eraticus* is endangered. At the time it was first studied, the population in one colony was 555. The population has been steadily decreasing at 4.5% per year.

    a Find the population of the colony after 12 years.

    b How long will it take for the population to decline to 50?

E   SERIES

A **series** is the addition of the terms of a sequence.

For the sequence $\{u_n\}$ the corresponding series is $u_1 + u_2 + u_3 + ...$

The **sum** of a series is the result when we perform the addition.

Given a series which includes the first n terms of a sequence, its sum is
$S_n = u_1 + u_2 + u_3 + ... + u_n$.

ARITHMETIC SERIES

An **arithmetic series** is the addition of successive terms of an arithmetic sequence.

For example: $21, 23, 25, 27, ..., 49$ is an arithmetic sequence.

$21 + 23 + 25 + 27 + ... + 49$ is an arithmetic series.

SUM OF AN ARITHMETIC SERIES

If the first term is u_1 and the common difference is d, the terms are $u_1, \ u_1 + d, \ u_1 + 2d, \ u_1 + 3d$, and so on.

Suppose that u_n is the final term of an arithmetic series.

So, $S_n = u_1 + (u_1 + d) + (u_1 + 2d) + ... + (u_n - 2d) + (u_n - d) + u_n$
But $S_n = u_n + (u_n - d) + (u_n - 2d) + ... + (u_1 + 2d) + (u_1 + d) + u_1$ {reversing them}

Adding these two expressions vertically we get

$$2S_n = \underbrace{(u_1 + u_n) + (u_1 + u_n) + (u_1 + u_n) + ... + (u_1 + u_n) + (u_1 + u_n) + (u_1 + u_n)}_{n \text{ of these}}$$

$\therefore \quad 2S_n = n(u_1 + u_n)$

$\therefore \quad S_n = \dfrac{n}{2}(u_1 + u_n)$ where $u_n = u_1 + (n-1)d$

The sum of an arithmetic series with n terms is

$$S_n = \frac{n}{2}(u_1 + u_n) \qquad or \qquad S_n = \frac{n}{2}(2u_1 + (n-1)d).$$

Example 12   ◀) **Self Tutor**

Find the sum of $4 + 7 + 10 + 13 + ...$ to 50 terms.

The series is arithmetic with $u_1 = 4$, $d = 3$ and $n = 50$.

Now $S_n = \dfrac{n}{2}(2u_1 + (n-1)d)$

$\therefore \quad S_{50} = \dfrac{50}{2}(2 \times 4 + 49 \times 3)$

$\qquad \quad = 3875$

Example 13

◀)) **Self Tutor**

Find the sum of $-6 + 1 + 8 + 15 + ... + 141$.

The series is arithmetic with $u_1 = -6$, $d = 7$ and $u_n = 141$.

First we need to find n.

$$\text{Now}\quad u_n = 141$$
$$\therefore \quad u_1 + (n-1)d = 141$$
$$\therefore \quad -6 + 7(n-1) = 141$$
$$\therefore \quad 7(n-1) = 147$$
$$\therefore \quad n-1 = 21$$
$$\therefore \quad n = 22$$

Using $S_n = \dfrac{n}{2}(u_1 + u_n)$,

$$S_{22} = \tfrac{22}{2}(-6 + 141)$$
$$= 11 \times 135$$
$$= 1485$$

EXERCISE 5E.1

1 Find the sum $1 + 5 + 9 + 13 + 17 + 21 + 25$

    a by simple addition
    b using $S_n = \dfrac{n}{2}(u_1 + u_n)$

    c using $S_n = \dfrac{n}{2}(2u_1 + (n-1)d)$

2 An arithmetic series has seven terms. The first term is 5 and the last term is 53. Find the sum of the series.

3 An arithmetic series has eleven terms. The first term is 6 and the last term is -27. Find the sum of the series.

4 Find the sum of:

    a $7 + 9 + 11 + 13 + ...$ to 10 terms
    b $3 + 7 + 11 + 15 + ...$ to 20 terms

    c $\frac{1}{2} + 3 + 5\frac{1}{2} + 8 + ...$ to 50 terms
    d $100 + 93 + 86 + 79 + ...$ to 40 terms

    e $(-31) + (-28) + (-25) + (-22) + ...$ to 15 terms

    f $50 + 48\frac{1}{2} + 47 + 45\frac{1}{2} + ...$ to 80 terms

5 Consider the arithmetic sequence   9, 15, 21, ..., 69, 75.

    a Find the common difference d.
    b Find the number of terms in the sequence.

    c Find the sum of the terms in the sequence.

6 Find the sum of:

    a $5 + 8 + 11 + 14 + ... + 101$
    b $50 + 49\frac{1}{2} + 49 + 48\frac{1}{2} + ... + (-20)$

    c $8 + 10\frac{1}{2} + 13 + 15\frac{1}{2} + ... + 83$

7 A soccer stadium has 25 sections of seating. Each section has 44 rows of seats, with 22 seats in the first row, 23 in the second row, 24 in the third row, and so on. How many seats are there in:

    a row 44
    b each section
    c the whole stadium?

8 Find the sum of:

    a the first 50 multiples of 11
    b the multiples of 7 between 0 and 1000

    c the integers between 1 and 100 which are not divisible by 3.

9 Answer the **Opening Problem** on page **128**.

Example 14

An arithmetic sequence has first term 8 and common difference 2. The sum of the terms of the sequence is 170. Find the number of terms in the sequence.

The sequence is arithmetic with $u_1 = 8$ and $d = 2$.

Now $S_n = 170$, so $\dfrac{n}{2}(2u_1 + (n-1)d) = 170$

$$\therefore \quad \frac{n}{2}(16 + 2(n-1)) = 170$$

$$\therefore \quad 8n + n(n-1) = 170$$

$$\therefore \quad n^2 + 7n - 170 = 0$$

TI-nspire

Casio fx-CG20	TI-84 Plus	
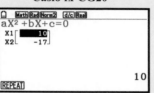		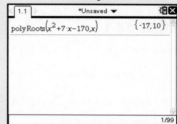

$\therefore \quad n = -17$ or 10 {technology}

But $n > 0$, so $n = 10$

$\therefore \quad$ there are 10 terms in the sequence.

---

10 An arithmetic sequence has first term 4 and common difference 6. The sum of the terms of the sequence is 200. Find the number of terms in the sequence.

11 An arithmetic sequence has $u_1 = 7$ and $S_2 = 17$.

    a Find the common difference of the sequence.   **b** Find n such that $S_n = 242$.

12 Consider the arithmetic sequence 13, 21, 29, 37, ... Find the least number of terms required for the sum of the sequence terms to exceed 1000.

13

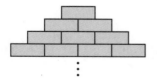

A bricklayer builds a triangular wall with layers of bricks as shown. If the bricklayer uses 171 bricks, how many layers did he build?

14 Three consecutive terms of an arithmetic sequence have a sum of 12 and a product of -80. Find the terms.

    Hint: Let the terms be $x - d$, x and $x + d$.

GEOMETRIC SERIES

> A **geometric series** is the addition of successive terms of a geometric sequence.

For example: $1, 2, 4, 8, 16, ..., 1024$ is a geometric sequence.

$1 + 2 + 4 + 8 + 16 + ... + 1024$ is a geometric series.

If we are adding the first n terms of a geometric sequence, we say we have a **finite geometric series**.

If we are adding all of the terms in a geometric sequence which goes on and on forever, we say we have an **infinite geometric series**.

SUM OF A FINITE GEOMETRIC SERIES

If the first term is u_1 and the common ratio is r, then the terms are: $u_1, u_1 r, u_1 r^2, u_1 r^3, ...$

So, $S_n = u_1 + u_1 r + u_1 r^2 + u_1 r^3 + ... + u_1 r^{n-2} + u_1 r^{n-1}$

$\qquad\qquad\quad \uparrow \qquad \uparrow \qquad \uparrow \qquad\qquad \uparrow \qquad\quad \uparrow$

$\qquad\qquad\quad u_2 \qquad u_3 \qquad u_4 \qquad\quad u_{n-1} \qquad u_n$

> For a finite geometric series with $r \neq 1$,
> $$S_n = \frac{u_1(r^n - 1)}{r - 1} \quad or \quad S_n = \frac{u_1(1 - r^n)}{1 - r}.$$

The proof of this result is not required for this course.

In the case $r = 1$ we have a sequence in which all terms are the same, so $S_n = u_1 n$.

Example 15   ◀)) **Self Tutor**

Find the sum of $2 + 6 + 18 + 54 + ...$ to 12 terms.

The series is geometric with $u_1 = 2$, $r = 3$, and $n = 12$.

$$S_n = \frac{u_1(r^n - 1)}{r - 1}$$

$$\therefore \; S_{12} = \frac{2(3^{12} - 1)}{3 - 1}$$

$$= 531\,440$$

Example 16   ◀)) **Self Tutor**

Find a formula for S_n for the first n terms of
$9 - 3 + 1 - \frac{1}{3} + ...$

The series is geometric with $u_1 = 9$ and $r = -\frac{1}{3}$

$$S_n = \frac{u_1(1 - r^n)}{1 - r} = \frac{9(1 - (-\frac{1}{3})^n)}{\frac{4}{3}}$$

$$\therefore \; S_n = \frac{27}{4}(1 - (-\frac{1}{3})^n)$$

> This answer cannot be simplified as we do not know if n is odd or even.

EXERCISE 5E.2

1 Find the sum $3 + 6 + 12 + 24 + 48$

    a by simple addition
                        b using $S_n = \dfrac{u_1(r^n - 1)}{r - 1}$

2 Find the sum of the following series:

    a $2 + 6 + 18 + 54 + ...$ to 8 terms
        b $5 + 10 + 20 + 40 + ...$ to 10 terms

    c $12 + 6 + 3 + 1.5 + ...$ to 10 terms
        d $\sqrt{7} + 7 + 7\sqrt{7} + 49 + ...$ to 12 terms

    e $6 - 3 + 1\frac{1}{2} - \frac{3}{4} + ...$ to 15 terms
        f $1 - \frac{1}{\sqrt{2}} + \frac{1}{2} - \frac{1}{2\sqrt{2}} + ...$ to 20 terms

3 Find a formula for S_n for the first n terms of:

    a $\sqrt{3} + 3 + 3\sqrt{3} + 9 + ...$
        b $12 + 6 + 3 + 1\frac{1}{2} + ...$

    c $0.9 + 0.09 + 0.009 + 0.0009 + ...$
        d $20 - 10 + 5 - 2\frac{1}{2} + ...$

4 Each year a salesperson is paid a bonus of \$2000 which is banked into the same account. It earns a fixed rate of interest of 6% p.a. with interest being paid annually. The total amount in the account at the end of each year is calculated as follows:

$$A_0 = 2000$$
$$A_1 = A_0 \times 1.06 + 2000$$
$$A_2 = A_1 \times 1.06 + 2000 \quad \text{and so on.}$$

    a Show that $A_2 = 2000 + 2000 \times 1.06 + 2000 \times (1.06)^2$.

    b Show that $A_3 = 2000[1 + 1.06 + (1.06)^2 + (1.06)^3]$.

    c Find the total bank balance after 10 years, assuming there are no fees or charges.

Example 17   🔊 Self Tutor

A geometric sequence has first term 5 and common ratio 2. The sum of the first n terms of the sequence is 635. Find n.

The sequence is geometric with $u_1 = 5$ and $r = 2$.

$$\therefore \; S_n = \frac{u_1(r^n - 1)}{r - 1}$$
$$= \frac{5(2^n - 1)}{2 - 1}$$
$$= 5(2^n - 1)$$

To find n such that $S_n = 635$,   we use a table of values with $Y_1 = 5 \times (2^{\wedge}X - 1)$:

Casio fx-CG20	TI-84 Plus	TI-nspire
	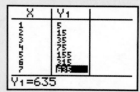	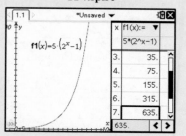

So, $S_7 = 635$ and $\therefore \; n = 7$.

5 A geometric sequence has first term 6 and common ratio 1.5. The sum of the first n terms of the sequence is 79.125. Find n.

6 Consider the geometric sequence 160, 80, 40, 20, ...

    a Find, in decimal form, the 8th term of the sequence.

    b Find the sum of the first 8 terms of the sequence.

    c Find the least number of terms required for the sum of the sequence terms to exceed 319.9.

THEORY OF KNOWLEDGE

The sequence of odd numbers 1, 3, 5, 7, ... is defined by $u_n = 2n - 1$, $n = 1, 2, 3, 4, ...$

Consider the following sums of the first few terms of the sequence:

$$\begin{aligned}
S_1 &= & 1 &= 1 = 1^2 \\
S_2 &= & 1 + 3 &= 4 = 2^2 \\
S_3 &= & 1 + 3 + 5 &= 9 = 3^2 \\
S_4 &= & 1 + 3 + 5 + 7 &= 16 = 4^2 \\
S_5 &= 1 + 3 + 5 + 7 + 9 &= 25 = 5^2
\end{aligned}$$

This suggests that: "the sum of the first n odd numbers is n^2".

But is this enough to *prove* that the statement is true for all positive integers n?

In this case we can prove that the sum of the first n odd numbers is n^2 using the sum of an arithmetic sequence formula:

$$\begin{aligned}
\text{Since} \quad u_1 = 1 \quad \text{and} \quad u_n = 2n - 1, \quad S_n &= \frac{n}{2}(u_1 + u_n) \\
&= \frac{n}{2}(1 + 2n - 1) \\
&= n^2
\end{aligned}$$

1 Can we prove that a statement is true in all cases by checking that it is true for some specific cases?

2 How do we know when we have proven a statement to be true?

There are many **conjectures** in mathematics. These are statements which we *believe* to be true, but have not proven.

Occasionally, incorrect statements have been thought to be true after a few specific cases were tested.

The Swiss mathematician **Leonhard Euler** (1707 - 1783) stated that $n^2 + n + 41$ is a prime number for any positive integer n.

In other words, he claimed that the sequence $u_n = n^2 + n + 41$ generates prime numbers.

We observe that: $u_1 = 1^2 + 1 + 41 = 43$ which is prime

                $u_2 = 2^2 + 2 + 41 = 47$ which is prime

                $u_3 = 3^2 + 3 + 41 = 53$ which is prime.

In fact, $n^2 + n + 41$ is prime for all positive integers n from 1 to 40.

Leonhard Euler

However, $u_{41} = 41^2 + 41 + 41 = 43 \times 41$ which is divisible by 41.

Suppose we place n points around a circle such that when we connect each point with every other point, no three lines intersect at the same point. We then count the number of regions that the circle is divided into.

The first five cases are shown below:

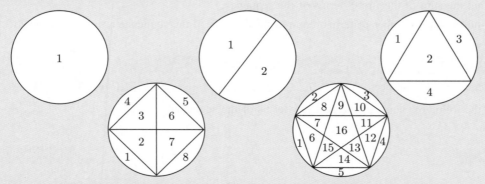

From these cases we *conjecture* that for n points, the circle is divided into 2^{n-1} regions.

Draw the case $n = 6$ and see if the conjecture is true!

3 Is it reasonable for a mathematician to assume a conjecture is true until it has been formally proven?

F   COMPOUND INTEREST

When money is deposited in a bank, it will usually earn **compound interest**.

After a certain amount of time called the **period**, the bank adds money to the account which is a percentage of the money already in there. The amount added is called the **interest**.

It is called *compound* interest because the interest generated in one period will itself earn more interest in the next period.

COMPOUND INTEREST

Suppose you invest $1000 in the bank. You leave the money in the bank for 3 years, and are paid an interest rate of 10% per annum (p.a). The interest is added to your investment each year, so the total value *increases*.

per annum means each year

The percentage increase each year is 10%, so at the end of the year you will have $100\% + 10\% = 110\%$ of the value at its start. This corresponds to a *multiplier* of 1.1 .

After one year your investment is worth $\$1000 \times 1.1 = \$1100$.

After two years it is worth
$$\$1100 \times 1.1$$
$$= \$1000 \times 1.1 \times 1.1$$
$$= \$1000 \times (1.1)^2 = \$1210$$

After three years it is worth
$$\$1210 \times 1.1$$
$$= \$1000 \times (1.1)^2 \times 1.1$$
$$= \$1000 \times (1.1)^3 = \$1331$$

We have a geometric sequence with first term 1000 and common ratio 1.1.

If the money is left in your account for n years it will amount to $\$1000 \times (1.1)^n$.

THE COMPOUND INTEREST FORMULA

For interest compounding annually, $FV = PV \times \left(1 + \dfrac{r}{100}\right)^n$

where: FV is the **future value** or final balance
PV is the **present value** or amount originally invested
r is the **interest rate per year**
n is the **number of years**

Example 18
◄》 Self Tutor

$\$5000$ is invested for 4 years at 7% p.a. compound interest, compounded annually. What will it amount to at the end of this period? Give your answer to the nearest cent.

$PV = 5000$
$r = 7$
$n = 4$

$$FV = PV \times \left(1 + \frac{r}{100}\right)^n$$
$$= 5000 \times \left(1 + \frac{7}{100}\right)^4$$
$$\approx 6553.98$$

The investment amounts to $\$6553.98$.

DIFFERENT COMPOUNDING PERIODS

Interest can be compounded more than once per year. Interest is commonly compounded:

- half-yearly (2 times per year)   • quarterly (4 times per year)   • monthly (12 times per year).

For interest compounding k times per year, $FV = PV \times \left(1 + \dfrac{r}{100k}\right)^{kn}$

Example 19
◄》 Self Tutor

Calculate the final balance of a $\$10\,000$ investment at 6% p.a. where interest is compounded quarterly for two years.

$PV = 10\,000$
$r = 6$
$n = 2$
$k = 4$
$\therefore \ kn = 8$

$$FV = PV \times \left(1 + \frac{r}{100k}\right)^{kn}$$
$$= 10\,000 \times \left(1 + \frac{6}{400}\right)^8$$
$$\approx 11\,264.93$$

The final balance is $\$11\,264.93$.

INTEREST EARNED

The **interest earned** is the difference between the original balance and the final balance.

$$\text{Interest} = FV - PV$$

Example 20   ◀) **Self Tutor**

How much interest is earned if €8800 is placed in an account that pays $4\frac{1}{2}\%$ p.a. compounded monthly for $3\frac{1}{2}$ years?

$PV = 8800, \quad r = 4.5, \quad n = 3.5, \quad k = 12$

$$\therefore \; kn = 12 \times 3\tfrac{1}{2} = 42$$

Now $\quad FV = PV \times \left(1 + \dfrac{r}{100k}\right)^{kn}$

$$= 8800 \times \left(1 + \frac{4.5}{1200}\right)^{42}$$

$$\approx 10\,298.08$$

The interest earned $= FV - PV$

$$= 10\,298.08 - 8800$$

$$= 1498.08$$

The interest earned is €1498.08.

EXERCISE 5F.1

1   Find the final value of a compound interest investment of $6000 after 3 years at 5% p.a., with interest compounded annually.

2   Luisa invests £15 000 into an account which pays 8% p.a. compounded annually. Find:

    a   the value of her account after 2 years   **b**   the total interest earned after 2 years.

3   Yumi places 880 000 yen in a fixed term investment account which pays 6.5% p.a. compounded annually.

    a   How much will she have in her account after 6 years?

    b   What interest has she earned over this period?

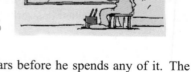

4   Ali places £9000 in a savings account that pays 8% p.a. compounded quarterly. How much will she have in the account after 5 years?

5   How much interest would be earned on a deposit of $2500 at 5% p.a. compounded half yearly for 4 years?

6   Jai recently inherited $92 000. He decides to invest it for 10 years before he spends any of it. The three banks in his town offer the following terms:

    Bank A: $5\frac{1}{2}\%$ p.a. compounded yearly.

    Bank B: $5\frac{1}{4}\%$ p.a. compounded quarterly.

    Bank C: 5% p.a. compounded monthly.

Which bank offers Jai the greatest interest on his inheritance?

USING A GRAPHICS CALCULATOR FOR COMPOUND INTEREST PROBLEMS

Most graphics calculators have an in-built **finance program** that can be used to investigate financial scenarios. This is called a **TVM Solver**, where **TVM** stands for **time value of money**.

To access the TVM Solver:

Casio fx-CG20

Select **Financial** from the Main Menu, then press
[F2] : **Compound Interest**.

TI-84 Plus

Press [APPS] , then select **1 : Finance...** and
1 : TVM Solver... .

TI-nspire

From the Calculator application, press [menu] , then
select **8 : Finance > 1 : Finance Solver...** .

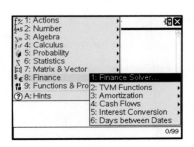

The TVM Solver can be used to find any variable if all the other variables are given. For the **TI-84 Plus**, the abbreviations used are:

- N represents the **number of time periods**
- $I\%$ represents the **interest rate per year**
- PV represents the **present value** of the investment
- PMT represents the **payment each time period**
- FV represents the **future value** of the investment
- P/Y is the **number of payments per year**
- C/Y is the **number of compounding periods per year**
- PMT : END BEGIN   lets you choose between the payments at the end of a time period or at the beginning of a time period. Most interest payments are made at the end of the time periods.

The abbreviations used by the other calculator models are similar, and can be found in the **graphics calculator instructions** online.

**GRAPHICS
CALCULATOR
INSTRUCTIONS**

Example 21

🔊 **Self Tutor**

Holly invests 15 000 UK pounds in an account that pays 4.25% p.a. compounded monthly. How much is her investment worth after 5 years?

To answer this using the TVM function on the calculator, first set up the TVM screen. The initial investment is considered as an outgoing and is entered as a negative value.

There are $5 \times 12 = 60$ month periods.

TI-*n*spire

Casio fx-CG20

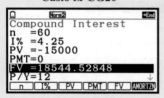

TI-84 Plus

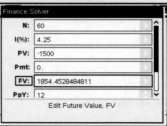

Holly's investment is worth 18 544.53 UK pounds after 5 years.

In IB examinations, a correct list of entries for the TVM Solver will be awarded the method mark.

For the previous example you would write:

$$N = 60$$
$$I = 4.25$$
$$PV = -15\,000$$
$$C/Y = 12$$
$$\Rightarrow \quad FV = 18\,544.53$$

So, Holly's investment is worth £18 544.53.

Example 22

🔊 **Self Tutor**

How much does Halena need to deposit into an account to collect $50 000 at the end of 3 years if the account is paying 5.2% p.a. compounded quarterly?

Set up the TVM screen as shown.
There are $3 \times 4 = 12$ quarter periods.

TI-*n*spire

Casio fx-CG20

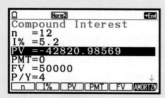

TI-84 Plus

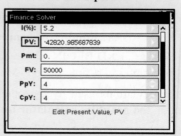

Thus, $42 821 needs to be deposited.

EXERCISE 5F.2

1 Use technology to check your answer to **Exercise 5F.1**, question **4**.

2 If I deposit £6000 in a bank account that pays 5% p.a. compounded monthly, how much will I have in my account after 2 years?

3 When my child was born I deposited $2000 in a bank account paying 4% p.a. compounded half-yearly. How much will my child receive on her 18th birthday?

4 Calculate the compound interest earned on an investment of €13 000 for 4 years if the interest rate is 7% p.a. compounded quarterly.

5 Calculate the amount you would need to invest now in order to accumulate 250 000 yen in 5 years' time, if the interest rate is 4.5% p.a. compounded monthly.

6 You would like to buy a car costing $23 000 in two years' time. Your bank account pays 5% p.a. compounded half-yearly. How much do you need to deposit now in order to be able to buy your car in two years?

7 You have just won the lottery and decide to invest the money. Your accountant advises you to deposit your winnings in an account that pays 6.5% p.a. compounded annually. After four years your winnings have grown to €102 917.31. How much did you win in the lottery?

Example 23   ◀)) **Self Tutor**

For how long must Magnus invest €4000 at 6.45% p.a. compounded half-yearly for it to amount to €10 000?

Set up the TVM screen as shown. We then need to find n, the number of periods required.

Casio fx-CG20	TI-84 Plus	TI-*n*spire

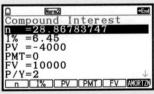

$n \approx 28.9$, so 29 half-years are required, or 14.5 years.

---

8 Your parents give you $8000 to buy a car, but the car you want costs $9200. You deposit the $8000 into an account that pays 6% p.a. compounded monthly. How long will it be before you have enough money to buy the car you want?

9 A couple inherited €40 000 and deposited it in an account paying $4\frac{1}{2}$% p.a. compounded quarterly. They withdrew the money as soon as they had over €45 000. How long did they keep the money in that account?

10 A business deposits £80 000 in an account that pays $5\frac{1}{4}$% p.a. compounded monthly. How long will it take before they double their money?

Example 24   ◄⑴ **Self Tutor**

Iman deposits $5000 in an account that compounds interest monthly. 2.5 years later the account totals $6000. What annual rate of interest was paid?

Set up the TVM screen as shown. In this case $n = 2.5 \times 12 = 30$ months.

Casio fx-CG20   **TI-84 Plus**   **TI-nspire**

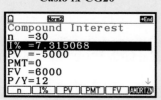

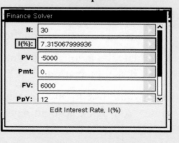

An annual interest rate of 7.32% p.a. is required.

11 An investor purchases rare medals for $10 000 and hopes to sell them 3 years later for $15 000. What must the annual increase in the value of the medals be over this period, in order for the investor's target to be reached?

12 I deposited €5000 into an account that compounds interest monthly, and $3\frac{1}{2}$ years later the account totals €6165. What annual rate of interest did the account pay?

13 A young couple invests their savings of 900 000 yen in an account where the interest is compounded annually. Three years later the account balance is 1 049 322 yen. What interest rate has been paid?

G   DEPRECIATION

Assets such as computers, cars, and furniture lose value as time passes. This is due to wear and tear, technology becoming old, fashions changing, and other reasons. We say that they **depreciate** over time.

Depreciation is the loss in value of an item over time.

Suppose a truck is bought for $36 000, and depreciates at 25% each year.

Each year, the truck is worth $100\% - 25\% = 75\%$ of its previous value.

We therefore have a geometric sequence with initial value $36 000 and common ratio 0.75 .

After 1 year, the value is $36 000 \times 0.75 = \$27\,000$
After 2 years, the value is $36 000 \times 0.75^2 = \$20\,250$
After n years, the value is $36 000 \times 0.75^n$.

When calculating depreciation, the **annual multiplier** is $\left(1 + \dfrac{r}{100}\right)$, where r is the *negative* annual depreciation rate as a percentage.

The **depreciation formula** is $FV = PV \times \left(1 + \dfrac{r}{100}\right)^n$

where FV is the **future value** after n time periods
PV is the **original purchase value**
r is the **depreciation rate per period** and r is **negative**
n is the **number of periods**.

Example 25 Self Tutor

An industrial dishwasher was purchased for £2400 and depreciated at 15% each year.

a Find its value after six years.   b By how much did it depreciate?

a $PV = 2400$

$r = -15$

$n = 6$

Now $FV = PV \times \left(1 + \dfrac{r}{100}\right)^n$

$= 2400 \times (1 - 0.15)^6$

$= 2400 \times (0.85)^6$

≈ 905.16

So, after 6 years the value is £905.16.

b Depreciation $= £2400 - £905.16 = £1494.84$

Example 26 ◀) Self Tutor

A vending machine bought for $15 000 is sold 3 years later for $9540. Calculate its annual rate of depreciation.

Set up the TVM screen with $N = 3$, $PV = -15\,000$, $PMT = 0$, $FV = 9540$, $P/Y = 1$, $C/Y = 1$.

TI-*n*spire

Casio fx-CG20

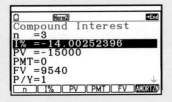

TI-84 Plus

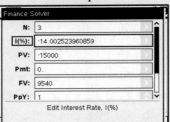

The annual depreciation rate is 14.0%.

EXERCISE 5G

1 A lathe, purchased by a workshop for €2500, depreciates by 20% each year. Find the value of the lathe after 3 years.

2 A tractor was purchased for €110 000, and depreciates at 25% p.a. for 5 years.

   a Find its value at the end of this period.   b By how much did it depreciate?

3 a I buy a laptop for ¥87 500 and keep it for 3 years. During this time it depreciates at an annual rate of 30%. What will its value be after 3 years?

   b By how much has the laptop depreciated?

4 A printing press costing £250 000 was sold 4 years later for £80 000. At what yearly rate did it depreciate in value?

5 A 4-wheel-drive vehicle was purchased for $45 000 and sold for $28 500 after 2 years and 3 months. Find its annual rate of depreciation.

REVIEW SET 5A

1 Identify the following sequences as arithmetic, geometric, or neither:

    a $7, -1, -9, -17, ...$ **b** $9, 9, 9, 9, ...$ **c** $4, -2, 1, -\frac{1}{2}, ...$

    d $1, 1, 2, 3, 5, 8, ...$ **e** the set of all multiples of 4 in ascending order.

2 Find k if $3k$, $k - 2$, and $k + 7$ are consecutive terms of an arithmetic sequence.

3 Show that $28, 23, 18, 13, ...$ is an arithmetic sequence. Hence find u_n and the sum S_n of the first n terms in simplest form.

4 Find k given that 4, k, and $k^2 - 12$ are consecutive terms of a geometric sequence.

5 Determine the general term of a geometric sequence given that its sixth term is $\frac{16}{3}$ and its tenth term is $\frac{256}{3}$.

6 Insert six numbers between 23 and 9 so that all eight numbers are in arithmetic sequence.

7 Find the 8th term of each of the following sequences:

    a $5, 1, \frac{1}{5}, ...$ **b** $-11, -8\frac{1}{2}, -6, ...$ **c** $a, a - d, a - 2d, ...$

8 At the start of the dry season, Yafiah's 3000 L water tank is full. She uses 183 L of water each week to water her garden.

    a Find the amount of water left in the tank after 1, 2, 3, and 4 weeks.

    b Explain why the amount of water left in the tank after n weeks forms an arithmetic sequence.

    c When does Yafiah's tank run out of water?

9 Find the sum of:

    a $14 + 11 + 8 + ... + (-55)$ **b** $3 + 15 + 75 + ...$ to 10 terms

10 Consider the arithmetic sequence $12, 19, 26, 33, ...$

    a Find the 8th term of the sequence.

    b Find the sum of the first 10 terms of the sequence.

    c The sum of the first n terms is 915. Find the value of n.

11 Val receives a \$285 000 superannuation payment when she retires. She finds the following investment rates are offered:

    Bank A :   6% p.a. compounded quarterly   *Bank B* : $5\frac{3}{4}$% p.a. compounded monthly.

    Compare the interest that would be received from these banks over a ten year period. In which bank should Val deposit her superannuation?

12 Sven sells his stamp collection and deposits the proceeds of \$8700 in a term deposit account for nine months. The account pays $9\frac{3}{4}$% p.a. compounded monthly. How much interest will he earn over this period?

13   **a** Find the future value of a truck which is purchased for \$135 000 and depreciates at 15% p.a. for 5 years.

    b By how much does it depreciate?

14 Ena currently has £7800, and wants to buy a car valued at £9000. She puts her money in an account paying 4.8% p.a. compounded quarterly. When will she be able to buy the car?

REVIEW SET 5B

1 A sequence is defined by $u_n = 6(\frac{1}{2})^{n-1}$.

    a Prove that the sequence is geometric.   **b** Find u_1 and r.

    c Find the 16th term to 3 significant figures.

2 Consider the sequence $24, 23\frac{1}{4}, 22\frac{1}{2}, ..., -36$. Find:

    a the number of terms in the sequence.   **b** the value of u_{35} for the sequence.

    c the sum of the terms in the sequence.

3 Find the sum of:

    a $3 + 9 + 15 + 21 + ...$ to 23 terms   **b** $24 + 12 + 6 + 3 + ...$ to 12 terms.

4 List the first five terms of the sequence:

    a $\{(\frac{1}{3})^n\}$ **b** $\{12 + 5n\}$ **c** $\left\{\frac{4}{n+2}\right\}$

5 **a** What will an investment of €6000 at 7% p.a. compound interest amount to after 5 years?

    b What part of this is interest?

6 Find the first term of the sequence $24, 8, \frac{8}{3}, \frac{8}{9}, ...$ which is less than 0.001.

7 A geometric sequence has $u_6 = 24$ and $u_{11} = 768$.

    a Determine the general term of the sequence.   **b** Hence find u_{17}.

    c Find the sum of the first 15 terms.

8 The nth term of a sequence is given by the formula $u_n = 4n - 7$.

    a Find the value of u_{10}.

    b Write down an expression for $u_{n+1} - u_n$ and simplify it.

    c Hence explain why the sequence is arithmetic.

    d Evaluate $u_{15} + u_{16} + u_{17} + ... + u_{30}$.

9 **a** Determine the number of terms in the sequence $128, 64, 32, 16, ..., \frac{1}{512}$.

    b Find the sum of these terms.

10 For the geometric sequence $180, 60, 20, ...,$ find:

    a the common ratio for this sequence.   **b** the 6th term of the sequence.

    c the least number of terms required for the sum of the terms to exceed 269.9.

11 Before leaving overseas on a three year trip to India, I leave a sum of money in an account that pays 6% p.a. compounded half-yearly. When I return from the trip, there is €5970.26 in my account. How much interest has been added since I have been away?

12 Megan deposits £3700 in an account paying interest compounded monthly for two years. If she ends up with £4072, what rate of interest did Megan receive?

13 Kania purchases office equipment valued at $17 500.

    a At the end of the first year, the value of the equipment is $15 312.50. Find the rate of depreciation.

    b If the value of the equipment continued to depreciate at the same rate, what would it be worth after $3\frac{1}{2}$ years?

REVIEW SET 5C

1 A sequence is defined by $u_n = 68 - 5n$.

    a Prove that the sequence is arithmetic.   **b** Find u_1 and d.

    c Find the 37th term of the sequence.

    d State the first term of the sequence which is less than -200.

2   **a** Show that the sequence $3, 12, 48, 192, ...$ is geometric.

    b Find u_n and hence find u_9.

3 Find the general term of the arithmetic sequence with $u_7 = 31$ and $u_{15} = -17$.
Hence, find the value of u_{34}.

4 Consider the sequence $24, a, 6, ...$

    Find the value of a if the sequence is: **a** arithmetic   **b** geometric.

5 Find the 10th term of the sequence:

    a $32, 25, 18, 11, ...$ **b** $\frac{1}{81}, \frac{1}{27}, \frac{1}{9}, \frac{1}{3}, ...$

6 There were originally 3000 koalas on Koala Island. Since then, the population of koalas on the island has increased by 5% each year.

    a How many koalas were on the island after 3 years?

    b How long will it take for the population to exceed 5000?

7 Find the formula for u_n, the general term of:

    a $86, 83, 80, 77, ...$ **b** $\frac{3}{4}, 1, \frac{7}{6}, \frac{9}{7}, ...$ **c** $100, 90, 81, 72.9, ...$

    Hint: One of these sequences is neither arithmetic nor geometric.

8 Find the first term of the sequence $5, 10, 20, 40, ...$ which exceeds $10\,000$.

9 $-1, k, k^2 - 7$ are consecutive terms of an arithmetic sequence. Find k.

10 Each year, a school manages to use only 90% as much paper as the previous year. In the year 2000, they used $700\,000$ sheets of paper.

    a Find how much paper the school used in the years 2001 and 2002.

    b How much paper did the school use in total in the decade from 2000 to 2009?

11 Find the final value of a compound interest investment of €8000 after 7 years at 3% p.a. with interest compounded annually.

12 Ned would like to have £15 000 in 3 years' time to install a swimming pool. His bank pays 4.5% p.a. interest, compounded half-yearly. How much does Ned need to deposit now?

13 A motorbike, purchased for £2300, was sold for £1300 after 4 years. Calculate the average annual rate of depreciation.

Chapter 6

Descriptive statistics

Syllabus reference: 2.1, 2.2, 2.3, 2.4, 2.5, 2.6

OPENING PROBLEM

A farmer is investigating the effect of a new organic fertiliser on his crops of peas. He has divided a small garden into two equal plots and planted many peas in each. Both plots have been treated the same except that fertiliser has been used on one but not the other.

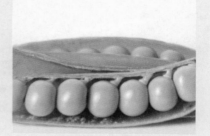

A random sample of 150 pods is harvested from each plot at the same time, and the number of peas in each pod is counted. The results are:

Without fertiliser

4 6 5 6 5 6 4 6 4 9 5 3 6 8 5 4 6 8 6 5 6 7 4 6 5 2 8 6 5 6 5 5 5 4 4 4 6 7 5 6
7 5 5 6 4 8 5 3 7 5 3 6 4 7 5 6 5 7 5 7 6 7 5 4 7 5 5 5 6 6 5 6 7 5 8 6 8 6 7 6
6 3 7 6 8 3 3 4 4 7 6 5 6 4 5 7 3 7 7 6 7 7 4 6 6 5 6 7 6 3 4 6 6 3 7 6 7 6 8 6
6 6 6 4 7 6 6 5 3 8 6 7 6 8 6 7 6 6 6 8 4 4 8 6 6 2 6 5 7 3

With fertiliser

6 7 7 4 9 5 5 5 8 9 8 9 7 7 5 8 7 6 6 7 9 7 7 7 8 9 3 7 4 8 5 10 8 6 7 6 7 5 6 8
7 9 4 4 9 6 8 5 8 7 7 4 7 8 10 6 10 7 7 7 9 7 7 8 6 8 6 8 7 4 8 6 8 7 3 8 7 6 9 7
6 9 7 6 8 3 9 5 7 6 8 7 9 7 8 4 8 7 7 6 6 8 6 3 8 5 8 7 6 7 4 9 6 6 6 8 4 7 8
9 7 7 4 7 5 7 4 7 6 4 6 7 7 6 7 8 7 6 6 7 8 6 7 10 5 13 4 7 11

Things to think about:

- Can you state clearly the problem that the farmer wants to solve?
- How has the farmer tried to make a fair comparison?
- How could the farmer make sure that his selection was at random?
- What is the best way of organising this data?
- What are suitable methods of displaying the data?
- Are there any abnormally high or low results and how should they be treated?
- How can we best describe the most typical pod size?
- How can we best describe the spread of possible pod sizes?
- Can the farmer make a reasonable conclusion from his investigation?

Statistics is the study of data collection and analysis. In a statistical investigation we collect information about a group of individuals, then analyse this information to draw conclusions about those individuals.

Statistics are used every day in many professions including:

- medical research to measure the effectiveness of different treatment options for a particular medical condition
- psychology for personality testing
- manufacturing to aid in quality control
- politics to determine the popularity of a political party
- sport to monitor team or player performances
- marketing to assess consumer preferences and opinions.

You should already be familiar with these words which are commonly used in statistics:

- **Population**   A defined collection of individuals or objects about which we want to draw conclusions.
- **Census**   The collection of information from the **whole population**.
- **Sample**   A subset of the population which we want to collect information from. It is important to choose a sample at **random** to avoid **bias** in the results.
- **Survey**   The collection of information from a **sample**.
- **Data** (singular **datum**)   Information about individuals in a population.
- **Parameter**   A numerical quantity measuring some aspect of a population.
- **Statistic**   A quantity calculated from data gathered from a sample. It is usually used to estimate a population parameter.

TYPES OF DATA

When we collect data, we measure or observe a particular feature or **variable** associated with the population. The variables we observe are described as either categorical or numerical.

CATEGORICAL VARIABLES

A **categorical variable** describes a particular quality or characteristic.

The data is divided into **categories**, and the information collected is called **categorical data**.

Some examples of categorical data are:

- *computer operating system*:   the categories could be Windows, Macintosh, or Linux.
- *gender*:   the categories are male and female.

QUANTITATIVE OR NUMERICAL VARIABLES

A **quantitative variable** has a numerical value. The information collected is called **numerical data**.

Quantitative variables can either be **discrete** or **continuous**.

A **quantitative discrete variable** takes exact number values and is often a result of **counting**.

Some examples of quantitative discrete variables are:

- *the number of apricots on a tree*:   the variable could take the values 0, 1, 2, 3, ... up to 1000 or more.
- *the number of players in a game of tennis*:   the variable could take the values 2 or 4.

A **quantitative continuous variable** can take any numerical value within a certain range. It is usually a result of **measuring**.

Some examples of quantitative continuous variables are:

- *the times taken to run a* 100 *m race*:   the variable would likely be between 9.8 and 25 seconds.

- *the distance of each hit in baseball*:   the variable could take values from 0 m to 100 m.

Example 1   ◀)) **Self Tutor**

Classify these variables as categorical, quantitative discrete, or quantitative continuous:

  a the number of heads when 3 coins are tossed
  b the brand of toothpaste used by the students in a class
  c the heights of a group of 15 year old children.

---

  a The value of the variable is obtained by counting the number of heads. The result can only be one of the values 0, 1, 2 or 3. It is a quantitative discrete variable.
  b The variable describes the brands of toothpaste. It is a categorical variable.
  c This is a numerical variable which can be measured. The data can take any value between certain limits, though when measured we round off the data to an accuracy determined by the measuring device. It is a quantitative continuous variable.

EXERCISE 6A

1 Classify the following variables as categorical, quantitative discrete, or quantitative continuous:

  a the number of brothers a person has
  b the colours of lollies in a packet
  c the time children spend brushing their teeth each day
  d the height of trees in a garden
  e the brand of car a person drives
  f the number of petrol pumps at a service station
  g the most popular holiday destinations
  h the scores out of 10 in a diving competition
  i the amount of water a person drinks each day
  j the number of hours spent per week at work
  k the average temperatures of various cities
  l the items students ate for breakfast before coming to school
  m the number of televisions in each house.

2 For each of the variables in **1**:

  - if the variable is categorical, list some possible categories for the variable
  - if the variable is quantitative, give the possible values or range of values the variable may take.

B | SIMPLE QUANTITATIVE DISCRETE DATA

ORGANISATION OF DATA

There are several different ways we can organise and display quantitative discrete data. One of the simplest ways to organise the data is using a **frequency table**.

For example, consider the **Opening Problem** in which the quantitative discrete variable is *the number of peas in a pod*. For the data *without fertiliser* we count the data systematically using a **tally**.

The **frequency** of a data value is the number of times that value occurs in the data set.

The **relative frequency** of a data value is the frequency divided by the total number of recorded values. It indicates the proportion of results which take that value.

Number of peas in a pod	Tally	Frequency	Relative frequency
1		0	0
2	||	2	0.013
3	ﾊﾄ ﾊﾄ |	11	0.073
4	ﾊﾄ ﾊﾄ ﾊﾄ ||||	19	0.127
5	ﾊﾄ ﾊﾄ ﾊﾄ ﾊﾄ ﾊﾄ ||||	29	0.193
6	ﾊﾄ ﾊﾄ ﾊﾄ ﾊﾄ ﾊﾄ ﾊﾄ ﾊﾄ ﾊﾄ ﾊﾄ ﾊﾄ ﾊﾄ |	51	0.34
7	ﾊﾄ ﾊﾄ ﾊﾄ ﾊﾄ ﾊﾄ	25	0.167
8	ﾊﾄ ﾊﾄ ||	12	0.08
9	|	1	0.007
Total		150	

A tally column is not essential for a frequency table, but is useful in the counting process for large data sets.

DISPLAY OF DATA

Quantitative discrete data is displayed using a **column graph**. For this graph:

- the range of data values is on the horizontal axis
- the frequency of data values is on the vertical axis
- the column widths are equal and the column height represents frequency
- there are gaps between columns to indicate the data is discrete.

A column graph for *the number of peas in a pod without fertiliser* is shown alongside.

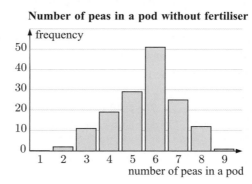

Number of peas in a pod without fertiliser

The **mode** of a data set is the most frequently occurring value. On a column graph the mode will have the highest column. In this case the mode is 6 peas in a pod.

THEORY OF KNOWLEDGE

Statistics are often used to give the reader a misleading impression of what the data actually means. In some cases this happens by accident through mistakes in the statistical process. Often, however, it is done deliberately in an attempt to persuade the reader to believe something.

Even simple things like the display of data can be done so as to create a false impression. For example, the two graphs below show the profits of a company for the first four months of the year.

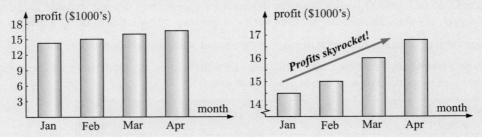

Both graphs accurately display the data, but on one graph the vertical axis has a break in its scale which can give the impression that the increase in profits is much larger than it really is. The comment 'Profits skyrocket!' encourages the reader to come to that conclusion without looking at the data more carefully.

1 Given that the data is presented with mathematical accuracy in both graphs, would you say the author in the second case has lied?

When data is collected by sampling, the choice of a biased sample can be used to give misleading results. There is also the question of whether outliers should be considered as genuine data, or ignored and left out of statistical analysis.

2 In what other ways can statistics be used to deliberately mislead the target audience?

The use of statistics in science and medicine has been widely debated, as companies employ scientific 'experts' to back their claims. For example, in the multi-billion dollar tobacco industry, huge volumes of data have been collected which claim that smoking leads to cancer and other harmful effects. However, the industry has sponsored other studies which deny these claims.

There are many scientific articles and books which discuss the uses and misuses of statistics. For example:

- *Surgeons General's reports on smoking and cancer: uses and misuses of statistics and of science*, R J Hickey and I E Allen, Public Health Rep. 1983 Sep-Oct; **98**(5): 410-411.

- *Misusage of Statistics in Medical Researches*, I Ercan, B Yazici, Y Yang, G Ozkaya, S Cangur, B Ediz, I Kan, 2007, European Journal of General Medicine, 4(3),127-133.

- *Sex, Drugs, and Body Counts: The Politics of Numbers in Global Crime and Conflict*, P Andreas and K M Greenhill, 2010, Cornell University Press.

3 Can we trust statistical results published in the media and in scientific journals?

4 What role does ethics have to play in mathematics?

DESCRIBING THE DISTRIBUTION OF A DATA SET

Many data sets show **symmetry** or **partial symmetry** about the mode.

If we place a curve over the column graph we see that this curve shows symmetry. We have a **symmetrical distribution** of the data.

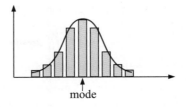

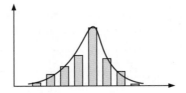

Comparing the *peas in a pod without fertiliser* data with the symmetrical distribution, we can see it has been 'stretched' on the left or negative side of the mode. We say the data is **negatively skewed**.

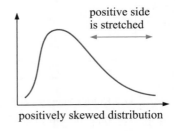

The descriptions we use are:

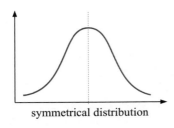

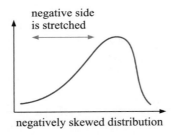

OUTLIERS

Outliers are data values that are either much larger or much smaller than the general body of data. Outliers appear separated from the body of data on a column graph.

For example, suppose the farmer in the **Opening Problem** found one pod without fertiliser that contained 13 peas. The data value 13 would be considered an outlier since it is much larger than the other data in the sample.

While knowledge of outliers is not examinable, it may be useful for statistically based projects.

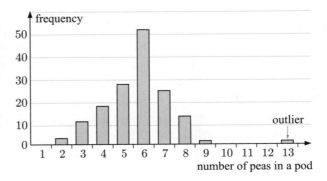

Example 2   ◀) **Self Tutor**

30 children attended a library holiday programme. Their year levels at school were:

    8   7   6   7   7   7   9   7   7   11   8   10   8   8   9
    10   7   7   8   8   8   8   7   6   6   6   6   9   6   9

a Record this information in a frequency table. Include a column for relative frequency.

b Construct a column graph to display the data.

c What is the modal year level of the children?

d Describe the shape of the distribution. Are there any outliers?

e What percentage of the children were in year 8 or below?

f What percentage of the children were above year 9?

a

Year level	Tally	Frequency	Relative frequency
6	卌 |	6	0.2
7	卌 ||||	9	0.3
8	卌 |||	8	0.267
9	||||	4	0.133
10	||	2	0.067
11	|	1	0.033
	Total	30	

b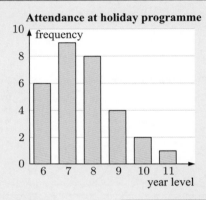

c The modal year level is year 7.

d The distribution of children's year levels is positively skewed. There are no outliers.

Due to rounding, the relative frequencies will not always appear to add to *exactly* 1.

e $\frac{6+9+8}{30} \times 100\% \approx 76.7\%$ were in year 8 or below.

   or the sum of the relative frequencies is $0.2 + 0.3 + 0.267 = 0.767$
   ∴ 76.7% were in year 8 or below.

f $\frac{2+1}{30} \times 100\% = 10\%$ were above year 9.

   or $0.067 + 0.033 = 0.1$ ∴ 10% were above year 9.

EXERCISE 6B

1 In the last football season, the Flames scored the following numbers of goals in each game:

    2   0   1   4   0   1   2   1   1   0   3   1
    3   0   1   1   6   2   1   3   1   2   0   2

a What is the variable being considered here?

b Explain why the data is discrete.

c Construct a frequency table to organise the data. Include a column for relative frequency.

d Draw a column graph to display the data.

e What is the modal score for the team?

    f Describe the distribution of the data. Are there any outliers?

    g In what percentage of games did the Flames fail to score?

2 Prince Edward High School prides itself on the behaviour of
its students. However, from time to time they do things they
should not, and as a result are placed on detention. The studious
school master records the number of students on detention each
week throughout the year:

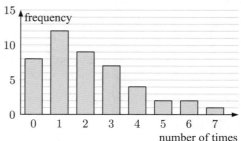

        0 2 1 5 0 1 4 2 3 1
        4 3 0 2 9 2 1 5 0 3
        6 4 2 1 5 1 0 2 1 4
        3 1 2 0 4 3 2 1 2 3

    a Construct a column graph to display the data.

    b What is the modal number of students on detention in a week?

    c Describe the distribution of the data, including the presence of outliers.

    d In what percentage of weeks were more than 4 students on detention?

3 While watching television, Joan recorded the number of commercials in each break. She obtained
these results:

        5 7 6 4 6 5 6 7 5 8
        7 6 9 8 7 6 6 9 6 7
        6 4 7 5 8 7 6 8 7 8
        5 6 9 7

    a Construct a frequency table to organise the data.

    b Draw a column graph to display the data.

    c Find the mode of the data.

    d Describe the distribution of the data. Are there any outliers?

    e What percentage of breaks contained at least 6 commercials?

4 A random sample of people were asked "How many times did you eat at a restaurant last week?"
A column graph was used to display the results.

    a How many people were surveyed?

    b Find the mode of the data.

    c How many people surveyed did not eat at a
restaurant at all last week?

    d What percentage of people surveyed ate at a
restaurant more than three times last week?

    e Describe the distribution of the data.

5 Consider *the number of peas in a pod with fertiliser* in the **Opening Problem**.

    a Construct a frequency table to organise the data.

    b Draw a column graph to display the data.

    c Describe fully the distribution of the data.

    d Is there evidence to suggest that the fertiliser increases the number of peas in each pod?

    e Is it reasonable to say that using the fertiliser will increase the farmer's profits?

C   GROUPED QUANTITATIVE DISCRETE DATA

A local kindergarten is concerned about the number of vehicles passing by between 8:45 am and 9:00 am. Over 30 consecutive week days they recorded data:

27, 30, 17, 13, 46, 23, 40, 28, 38, 24, 23, 22, 18, 29, 16,
35, 24, 18, 24, 44, 32, 52, 31, 39, 32,   9, 41, 38, 24, 32

In situations like this there are many different data values with very low frequencies. This makes it difficult to study the data distribution. It is more statistically meaningful to group the data into **class intervals** and then compare the frequency for each class.

For the data given we use class intervals of width 10. The frequency table is shown opposite.

We see the **modal class**, or class with the highest frequency, is from 20 to 29 cars.

Number of cars	Tally	Frequency
0 to 9	|	1
10 to 19	‖‖	5
20 to 29	‖‖ ‖‖	10
30 to 39	‖‖ ||||	9
40 to 49	||||	4
50 to 59	|	1
	Total	30

We can construct a **column graph** for grouped discrete data in the same way as before.

Vehicles passing kindergarten between 8:45 am and 9:00 am

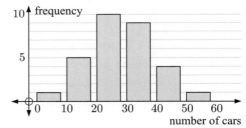

DISCUSSION

- If we are given a set of raw data, how can we efficiently find the lowest and highest data values?

- If the data values are grouped in classes on a frequency table or column graph, do we still know what the highest and lowest values are?

EXERCISE 6C

1   Arthur catches the train to school from a busy train station. Over the course of 30 days he counts the number of people waiting at the station when the train arrives.

17   25   32   19   45   30   22   15   38   8
21   29   37   25   42   35   19   31   26   7
22   11   27   44   24   22   32   18   40   29

    a   Construct a tally and frequency table for this data using class intervals 0 - 9, 10 - 19, ..., 40 - 49.

    b   On how many days were there less than 10 people at the station?

    c   On what percentage of days were there at least 30 people at the station?

 d Draw a column graph to display the data.

 e Find the modal class of the data.

2 A selection of businesses were asked how many employees they had.   A column graph was constructed to display the results.

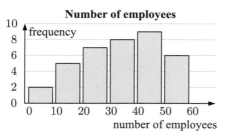

Number of employees

 a How many businesses were surveyed?

 b Find the modal class.

 c Describe the distribution of the data.

 d What percentage of businesses surveyed had less than 30 employees?

 e Can you determine the highest number of employees a business had?

3 A city council does a survey of the number of houses per street in a suburb.

42	15	20	6	34	19	8	5	11	38	56	23	24	24
35	47	22	36	39	18	14	44	25	6	34	35	28	12
27	32	36	34	30	40	32	12	17	6	37	32		

 a Construct a frequency table for this data using class intervals 0 - 9, 10 - 19, ..., 50 - 59.

 b Hence draw a column graph to display the data.

 c Write down the modal class.

 d What percentage of the streets contain at least 20 houses?

D   QUANTITATIVE CONTINUOUS DATA

When we measure data that is **continuous**, we cannot write down an exact value. Instead we write down an approximation which is only as accurate as the measuring device.

Since no two data values will be *exactly* the same, it does not make sense to talk about the frequency of particular values. Instead we group the data into **class intervals** of **equal width**. We can then talk about the frequency of each class interval.

A special type of graph called a **frequency histogram** or just **histogram** is used to display grouped continuous data. This is similar to a column graph, but the 'columns' are joined together and the values at the edges of the column indicate the boundaries of each class interval.

The **modal class**, or class of values that appears most often, is easy to identify from a frequency histogram.

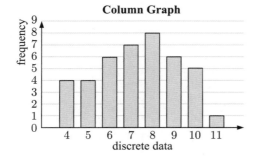

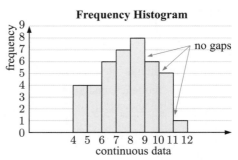

INVESTIGATION 1   CHOOSING CLASS INTERVALS

When dividing data values into intervals, the choice of how many intervals to use, and   **DEMO**
hence the width of each class, is important.

What to do:

1 Click on the icon to experiment with various data sets and the number of classes.
How does the number of classes alter the way we can interpret the data?

2 Write a brief account of your findings.

As a rule of thumb we use approximately $\sqrt{n}$ classes for a data set of n individuals. For very large
sets of data we use more classes rather than less.

Example 3   ◀) Self Tutor

A sample of 20 juvenile lobsters was randomly selected from a tank containing several hundred.
The length of each lobster was measured in cm, and the results were:

$$\begin{array}{cccccccccc} 4.9 & 5.6 & 7.2 & 6.7 & 3.1 & 4.6 & 6.0 & 5.0 & 3.7 & 7.3 \\ 6.0 & 5.4 & 4.2 & 6.6 & 4.7 & 5.8 & 4.4 & 3.6 & 4.2 & 5.4 \end{array}$$

Organise the data using a frequency table, and hence graph the data.

The variable 'the length of a lobster' is *continuous* even though
lengths have been rounded to the nearest mm.

The shortest length is 3.1 cm and the longest is 7.3 cm, so we
will use class intervals of width 1 cm.

Length (l cm)	Frequency
$3 \leqslant l < 4$	3
$4 \leqslant l < 5$	6
$5 \leqslant l < 6$	5
$6 \leqslant l < 7$	4
$7 \leqslant l < 8$	2

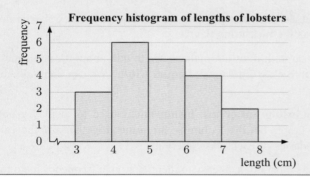

The modal class
$4 \leqslant l < 5$ cm occurs
most frequently.

EXERCISE 6D

1 A frequency table for the heights of a volleyball squad is given
alongside.

a Explain why 'height' is a continuous variable.

b Construct a frequency histogram for the data. Carefully
mark and label the axes, and include a heading for the
graph.

c What is the modal class? Explain what this means.

d Describe the distribution of the data.

Height (H cm)	Frequency
$170 \leqslant H < 175$	1
$175 \leqslant H < 180$	8
$180 \leqslant H < 185$	9
$185 \leqslant H < 190$	11
$190 \leqslant H < 195$	9
$195 \leqslant H < 200$	3
$200 \leqslant H < 205$	3

2 For the following data, state whether a frequency histogram or a column graph should be used, and draw the appropriate graph.

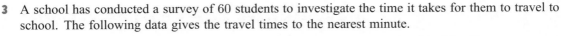

[120 , 130) means the same as $120 \leqslant h < 130$.

a The number of matches in 30 match boxes:

Number of matches per box	47	49	50	51	52	53	55
Frequency	1	1	9	12	4	2	1

b The heights of 25 hockey players (to the nearest cm):

Height (h cm)	[120, 130)	[130, 140)	[140, 150)	[150, 160)	[160, 170)
Frequency	1	2	7	14	1

3 A school has conducted a survey of 60 students to investigate the time it takes for them to travel to school. The following data gives the travel times to the nearest minute.

```
12  15  16   8  10  17  25  34  42  18  24  18  45  33  38
45  40   3  20  12  10  10  27  16  37  45  15  16  26  32
35   8  14  18  15  27  19  32   6  12  14  20  10  16  14
28  31  21  25   8  32  46  14  15  20  18   8  10  25  22
```

a Is travel time a discrete or continuous variable?

b Construct a frequency table for the data using class intervals $0 \leqslant t < 10$, $10 \leqslant t < 20$, ...,
$40 \leqslant t < 50$.

c Hence draw a histogram to display the data.

d Describe the distribution of the data.

e What is the modal travelling time?

4 A group of 25 young athletes participated in a javelin throwing competition. They achieved the following distances in metres:

```
17.6   25.7   21.3   30.9   13.0   31.6   22.3   28.3    7.4
38.4   19.1   24.0   40.0   16.2   42.9   31.9   28.1   41.8
13.6   27.4   33.7    9.2   23.3   39.8   25.1
```

a Choose suitable class intervals to group the data.

b Organise the data in a frequency table.

c Draw a frequency histogram to display the data.

d Find the modal class.

e What percentage of athletes threw the javelin 30 m or further?

5 A plant inspector takes a random sample of six month old seedlings from a nursery and measures their heights. The results are shown in the table.

a Represent the data on a frequency histogram.

b How many of the seedlings are 400 mm or more?

c What percentage of the seedlings are between 350 and 400 mm?

d The total number of seedlings in the nursery is 1462. Estimate the number of seedlings which measure:

   i less than 400 mm   **ii** between 375 and 425 mm.

Height (h mm)	Frequency
$300 \leqslant h < 325$	12
$325 \leqslant h < 350$	18
$350 \leqslant h < 375$	42
$375 \leqslant h < 400$	28
$400 \leqslant h < 425$	14
$425 \leqslant h < 450$	6

6 The weights, in grams, of 50 laboratory rats are given below.

261	133	173	295	265	142	140	271	185	251
166	100	292	107	201	234	239	159	153	263
195	151	156	117	144	189	234	171	233	182
165	122	281	149	152	289	168	260	256	156
239	203	101	268	241	217	254	240	214	221

  a Choose suitable class intervals to group the data.

  b Organise the data in a frequency table.

  c Draw a frequency histogram to display the data.

  d What percentage of the rats weigh less than 200 grams?

E   MEASURING THE CENTRE OF DATA

We can get a better understanding of a data set if we can locate its **middle** or **centre**, and also get an indication of its **spread** or **dispersion**. Knowing one of these without the other is often of little use.

There are *three statistics* that are used to measure the **centre** of a data set. These are the **mode**, the **mean**, and the **median**.

THE MODE

For ungrouped discrete numerical data, the **mode** is the most frequently occuring value in the data set.

For grouped numerical data, we talk about a **modal class**, which is the class that occurs most frequently.

If a set of scores has two modes we say it is **bimodal**. If there are more than two modes, we do not use mode as a measure of the centre.

THE MEAN

The **mean** of a data set is the statistical name for its arithmetic average.

$$\text{mean} = \frac{\textbf{sum of all data values}}{\textbf{the number of data values}}$$

The mean gives us a single number which indicates a centre of the data set. It is usually not a member of the data set.

For example, a mean test mark of 73% tells us that there are several marks below 73% and several above it. 73% is at the centre, but it does not necessarily mean that one of the students scored 73%.

We denote the mean for an entire **population** by μ, which we read as "mu".

However, in many cases we do not have data for all of the population, and so the exact value of μ is unknown. Instead we obtain data from a **sample** of the population and use the mean of the sample, $\overline{x}$, as an *approximation* for μ.

Suppose x is a numerical variable and there are n data values in the sample. We let x_i be the ith data value from the sample of values $\{x_1, x_2, x_3, ..., x_n\}$.

The mean of the sample is $\overline{x} = \dfrac{x_1 + x_2 + ... + x_n}{n} = \dfrac{\sum\limits_{i=1}^{n} x_i}{n}$

where $\sum\limits_{i=1}^{n} x_i$ means the **sum** of all n data values, $x_1 + x_2 + ... + x_n$.

THE MEDIAN

> The **median** is the *middle value* of an ordered data set.

An ordered data set is obtained by listing the data, usually from smallest to largest.

The median splits the data in halves. Half of the data are less than or equal to the median, and half are greater than or equal to it.

For example, if the median mark for a test is 73% then you know that half the class scored less than or equal to 73%, and half scored greater than or equal to 73%.

For an **odd number** of data, the median is one of the original data values.

For an **even number** of data, the median is the average of the two middle values, and may not be in the original data set.

> If there are n data values, find $\dfrac{n+1}{2}$. The median is the $\left(\dfrac{n+1}{2}\right)$th data value.

For example:

If $n = 13$, $\dfrac{n+1}{2} = \dfrac{13+1}{2} = 7$, so the median = 7th ordered data value.

DEMO

If $n = 14$, $\dfrac{n+1}{2} = \dfrac{14+1}{2} = 7.5$, so the median = average of the 7th and 8th ordered data values.

Example 4 ◀⑴ Self Tutor

Find the   **i** mean   **ii** mode   **iii** median   of the following data sets:

a 3, 6, 5, 6, 4, 5, 5, 6, 7   **b** 13, 12, 15, 13, 18, 14, 16, 15, 15, 17

a **i** mean $= \dfrac{3+6+5+6+4+5+5+6+7}{9} = \dfrac{47}{9} \approx 5.22$

   ii The scores 5 and 6 occur most frequently, so the data set is bimodal with modes 5 and 6.

   iii Listing the set in order of size: 3, 4, 5, 5, 5, 6, 6, 6, 7 $\quad$ {as $n = 9$, $\dfrac{n+1}{2} = 5$}

$\qquad\qquad\qquad\qquad\qquad\qquad$ ↑
$\qquad\qquad\qquad\qquad\qquad$ middle score

   ∴ the median is 5.

b **i** mean $= \dfrac{13+12+15+13+18+14+16+15+15+17}{10} = \dfrac{148}{10} = 14.8$

   ii The score 15 occurs most frequently, so the mode is 15.

   iii Listing the set in order of size:

$\qquad\qquad$ 12, 13, 13, 14, 15, 15, 15, 16, 17, 18 $\qquad$ {as $n = 10$, $\dfrac{n+1}{2} = 5.5$}

$\qquad\qquad\qquad\qquad\qquad$ ↑
$\qquad\qquad\qquad\qquad$ middle scores

   The median is the average of the two middle scores, which is $\dfrac{15+15}{2} = 15$.

Technology can be used to help find the statistics of a data set. Click on the appropriate icon to obtain instructions for your calculator or run software online.

GRAPHICS CALCULATOR INSTRUCTIONS

STATISTICS PACKAGE

Example 5   ◆) **Self Tutor**

A teenager recorded the time (in minutes per day) he spent playing computer games over a 2 week holiday period: 121, 65, 45, 130, 150, 83, 148, 137, 20, 173, 56, 49, 104, 97.

Using technology to assist, determine the mean and median daily game time the teenager recorded.

Casio fx-CG20

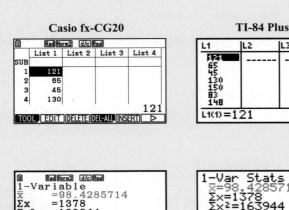

TI-84 Plus

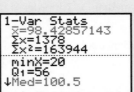

TI-nspire

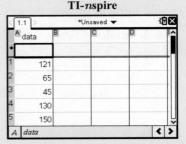

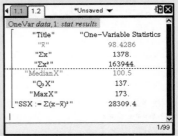

The mean $\overline{x} \approx 98.4$ minutes, and the median $= 100.5$ minutes.

EXERCISE 6E.1

1 Phil kept a record of the number of cups of coffee he drank each day for 15 days:
$$2, 3, 1, 1, 0, 0, 4, 3, 0, 1, 2, 3, 2, 1, 4$$
Without using technology, find the   **a** mode   **b** median   **c** mean   of the data.

2 The sum of 7 scores is 63. What is their mean?

3 Find the   **i** mean   **ii** median   **iii** mode   for each of the following data sets:

a 2, 3, 3, 3, 4, 4, 4, 5, 5, 5, 5, 6, 6, 6, 6, 6, 7, 7, 8, 8, 8, 9, 9

b 10, 12, 12, 15, 15, 16, 16, 17, 18, 18, 18, 18, 19, 20, 21

c 22.4, 24.6, 21.8, 26.4, 24.9, 25.0, 23.5, 26.1, 25.3, 29.5, 23.5

4 Consider the two data sets: *Data set A*:   3, 4, 4, 5, 6, 6, 7, 7, 7, 8, 8, 9, 10

Data set B: 3, 4, 4, 5, 6, 6, 7, 7, 7, 8, 8, 9, 15

a Find the mean of both data set A and data set B.

b Find the median of both data set A and data set B.

c Explain why the mean of data set A is less than the mean of data set B.

d Explain why the median of data set A is the same as the median of data set B.

5 The scores obtained by two ten-pin bowlers over a 10 game series are:

    Gordon: 160,   175,   142,   137,   151,   144,   169,   182,   175,   155
    Ruth: 157,   181,   164,   142,   195,   188,   150,   147,   168,   148

Who had the higher mean score?

6 A bakery keeps a record of how many pies and pasties they sell each day for a month.

Pies									Pasties							
62	76	55	65	49	78	71	82		37	52	71	59	63	47	56	68
79	47	60	72	58	82	76	67		43	67	38	73	54	55	61	49
50	61	70	85	77	69	48	74		50	48	53	39	45	60	46	51
63	56	81	75	63	74	54			38	57	41	72	50	44	76	

a Using technology to assist, find the:

    i mean number of pies and pasties sold   **ii** median number of pies and pasties sold.

b Which bakery item was more popular? Explain your answer.

7 A bus and tram travel the same route many times during the day. The drivers counted the number of passengers on each trip one day, as listed below.

Bus								Tram					
30	43	40	53	70	50	63		58	68	43	45	70	79
41	38	21	28	23	43	48		38	23	30	22	63	73
20	26	35	48	41	33			25	35	60	53		

a Using technology, calculate the mean and median number of passengers for both the Bus and Tram data.

b Comment on which mode of transport is more popular. Explain your answer.

8 A basketball team scored 43, 55, 41, and 37 points in their first four matches.

a What is the mean number of points scored for the first four matches?

b What score will the team need to shoot in their next match so that they maintain the same mean score?

c The team scores only 25 points in the fifth match. Find the mean number of points scored for the five matches.

d The team then scores 41 points in their sixth and final match. Will this increase or decrease their previous mean score? What is the mean score for all six matches?

Example 6   ◀ᴥ **Self Tutor**

If 6 people have a mean mass of 53.7 kg, find their total mass.

$$\frac{\text{sum of masses}}{6} = 53.7 \text{ kg}$$

$\therefore$ the total mass $= 53.7 \times 6 = 322.2$ kg.

---

9 This year, the mean monthly sales for a clothing store have been \$15 467. Calculate the total sales for the store for the year.

10 While on an outback safari, Bill drove an average of 262 km per day for a period of 12 days. How far did Bill drive in total while on safari?

11 Towards the end of the season, a netballer had played 14 matches and had thrown an average of 16.5 goals per game. In the final two matches of the season she threw 21 goals and 24 goals. Find the netballer's new average.

12 Find x if 5, 9, 11, 12, 13, 14, 17, and x have a mean of 12.

13 Find a given that 3, 0, a, a, 4, a, 6, a, and 3 have a mean of 4.

14 Over the complete assessment period, Aruna averaged 35 out of 40 marks for her maths tests. However, when checking her files, she could only find 7 of the 8 tests. For these she scored 29, 36, 32, 38, 35, 34, and 39. How many marks out of 40 did she score for the eighth test?

15 A sample of 10 measurements has a mean of 15.7 and a sample of 20 measurements has a mean of 14.3. Find the mean of all 30 measurements.

16 The mean and median of a set of 9 measurements are both 12. Seven of the measurements are 7, 9, 11, 13, 14, 17, and 19. Find the other two measurements.

17 Jana took seven spelling tests, each with twelve words, but she could only find the results of five of them. These were 9, 5, 7, 9, and 10. She asked her teacher for the other two results and the teacher said that the mode of her scores was 9 and the mean was 8. Given that Jana knows her worst result was a 5, find the two missing results.

INVESTIGATION 2   EFFECTS OF OUTLIERS

We have seen that an **outlier** or **extreme value** is a value which is much greater than, or much less than, the other values.

Your task is to examine the effect of an outlier on the three measures of central tendency.

What to do:

1 Consider the set of data: 4, 5, 6, 6, 6, 7, 7, 8, 9, 10. Calculate:
   a the mean   **b** the mode   **c** the median.

2 We now introduce the extreme value 100 to the data, so the data set is now:
   4, 5, 6, 6, 6, 7, 7, 8, 9, 10, 100.   Calculate:
   a the mean   **b** the mode   **c** the median.

3 Comment on the effect that the extreme value has on:
   a the mean   **b** the mode   **c** the median.

4 Which of the three measures of central tendency is most affected by the inclusion of an outlier?

5 Discuss with your class when it would not be appropriate to use a particular measure of the centre of a data set.

CHOOSING THE APPROPRIATE MEASURE

The mean, mode, and median can all be used to indicate the centre of a set of numbers. The most appropriate measure will depend upon the type of data under consideration. When selecting which one to use for a given set of data, you should keep the following properties in mind.

Mode:	• gives the most usual value
	• only takes common values into account
	• not affected by extreme values
Mean:	• commonly used and easy to understand
	• takes all values into account
	• affected by extreme values
Median:	• gives the halfway point of the data
	• only takes middle values into account
	• not affected by extreme values

For example:

- A shoe store is investigating the sizes of shoes sold over one month. The mean shoe size is not very useful to know, but the mode shows at a glance which size the store most commonly has to restock.

- On a particular day a computer shop makes sales of $900, $1250, $1000, $1700, $1140, $1100, $1495, $1250, $1090, and $1075. Here the mode is meaningless, the median is $1120, and the mean is $1200. The mean is the best measure of centre as the salesman can use it to predict average profit.

- When looking at real estate prices, the mean is distorted by the few sales of very expensive houses. For a typical house buyer, the median will best indicate the price they should expect to pay in a particular area.

EXERCISE 6E.2

1 The selling prices of the last 10 houses sold in a certain district were as follows:

$146 400, $127 600, $211 000, $192 500,
$256 400, $132 400, $148 000, $129 500,
$131 400, $162 500

a Calculate the mean and median selling prices and comment on the results.

b Which measure would you use if you were:
  i a vendor wanting to sell your house
  ii looking to buy a house in the district?

2 The annual salaries of ten office workers are: $23 000, $46 000, $23 000, $38 000, $24 000,
$23 000, $23 000, $38 000, $23 000, $32 000

a Find the mean, median, and modal salaries of this group.

b Explain why the mode is an unsatisfactory measure of the middle in this case.

c Is the median a satisfactory measure of the middle of this data set?

3 The following raw data is the daily rainfall, to the nearest millimetre, for a month:
  3, 1, 0, 0, 0, 0, 0, 2, 0, 0, 3, 0, 0, 0, 7, 1, 1, 0, 3, 8, 0, 0, 0, 42, 21, 3, 0, 3, 1, 0, 0

a Using technology, find the mean, median, and mode of the data.

b Give a reason why the median is not the most suitable measure of centre for this set of data.

c Give a reason why the mode is not the most suitable measure of centre for this set of data.

d   Are there any outliers in this data set?

e   On some occasions outliers are removed because they must be due to errors in observation or calculation. If the outliers in the data set were accurately found, should they be removed before finding the measures of the middle?

MEASURES OF THE CENTRE FROM OTHER SOURCES

When the same data appears several times we often summarise the data in table form.

Consider the data in the given table:

We can find the measures of the centre directly from the table.

The mode

The data value 7 has the highest frequency.

The mode is therefore 7.

The mean

Data value (x)	Frequency (f)	Product (fx)
3	1	$1 \times 3 = 3$
4	1	$1 \times 4 = 4$
5	3	$3 \times 5 = 15$
6	7	$7 \times 6 = 42$
7	15	$15 \times 7 = 105$
8	8	$8 \times 8 = 64$
9	5	$5 \times 9 = 45$
Total	$\sum f = 40$	$\sum fx = 278$

Adding a 'Product' column to the table helps to add all scores.

For example, there are 15 data of value 7 and these add to $15 \times 7 = 105$.

Remembering that the mean $= \dfrac{\text{sum of all data values}}{\text{the number of data values}}$, we find

$$\overline{x} = \frac{f_1 x_1 + f_2 x_2 + \ldots + f_k x_k}{f_1 + f_2 + \ldots + f_k} = \frac{\sum\limits_{i=1}^{k} f_i x_i}{n} \quad \text{where } n = \sum\limits_{i=1}^{k} f_i \text{ is the total number of data,}$$

and k is the number of *different* data values.

This formula is often abbreviated as $\overline{x} = \dfrac{\sum fx}{\sum f}$.

In this case the mean $= \dfrac{278}{40} = 6.95$.

The median

Since $\dfrac{n+1}{2} = \dfrac{41}{2} = 20.5$, the median is the average of the 20th and 21st data values.

In the table, the blue numbers show us accumulated values, or the **cumulative frequency**.

We can see that the 20th and 21st data values (in order) are both 7s.

Data value	Frequency	Cumulative frequency
3	1	1 ⸺ 1 number is 3
4	1	2 ⸺ 2 numbers are 4 or less
5	3	5 ⸺ 5 numbers are 5 or less
6	7	12 ⸺ 12 numbers are 6 or less
7	15	27 ⸺ 27 numbers are 7 or less
8	8	35 ⸺ 35 numbers are 8 or less
9	5	40 ⸺ all numbers are 9 or less
Total	40	

$\therefore$ the median $= \dfrac{7+7}{2} = 7$.

Example 7

The table shows the number of aces served by tennis players in their first sets of a tournament.

Number of aces	1	2	3	4	5	6
Frequency	4	11	18	13	7	2

Determine the:

a mean   **b** median   **c** mode   for this data.

Number of aces (x)	Frequency (f)	Product (fx)	Cumulative frequency
1	4	4	4
2	11	22	15
3	18	54	33
4	13	52	46
5	7	35	53
6	2	12	55
Total	$\sum f = 55$	$\sum fx = 179$	

In this case $\dfrac{\sum fx}{\sum f}$ is short for $\dfrac{\sum\limits_{i=1}^{6} f_i x_i}{\sum\limits_{i=1}^{6} f_i}$.

a
$$\overline{x} = \frac{\sum fx}{\sum f}$$
$$= \frac{179}{55}$$
$$\approx 3.25 \text{ aces}$$

b There are 55 data values, so $n = 55$. $\dfrac{n+1}{2} = 28$, so the median is the 28th data value.

From the cumulative frequency column, the data values 16 to 33 are 3 aces.

∴ the 28th data value is 3 aces.

∴ the median is 3 aces.

c Looking down the frequency column, the highest frequency is 18. This corresponds to 3 aces, so the mode is 3 aces.

POTTS

© Jim Russell, General Features Pty Ltd.

The publishers acknowledge the late Mr Jim Russell, General Features for the reproduction of this cartoon.

We can use a graphics calculator to find the measures of centre of grouped data, by entering the data in two lists. We need to adjust the commands we give the calculator so that the calculator uses both the scores and the corresponding frequency values.

GRAPHICS CALCULATOR INSTRUCTIONS

Example 8   ◄)) **Self Tutor**

Use technology to find the mean and median of the tennis data in **Example 7**.

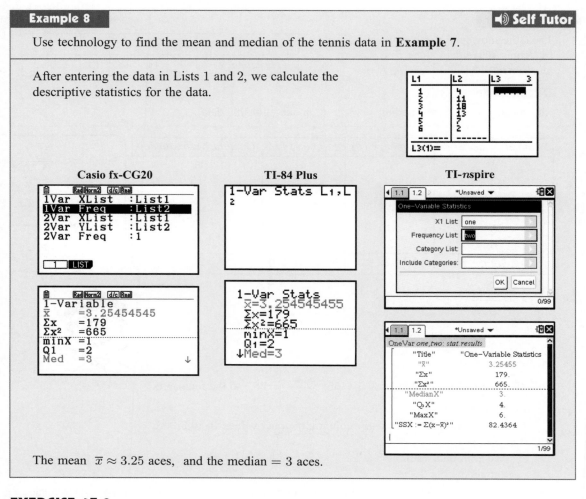

After entering the data in Lists 1 and 2, we calculate the descriptive statistics for the data.

The mean $\overline{x} \approx 3.25$ aces, and the median = 3 aces.

EXERCISE 6E.3

1 The table alongside shows the results when 3 coins were tossed simultaneously 30 times.

Calculate the:

   a mode   **b** median   **c** mean.

Number of heads	Frequency
0	4
1	12
2	11
3	3
Total	30

2 Families at a school in Australia were surveyed, and the number of children in each family recorded. The results of the survey are shown alongside.

   a Using technology, calculate the:

       i mean   **ii** mode   **iii** median.

   b The average Australian family has 2.2 children. How does this school compare to the national average?

   c The data set is skewed. Is the skewness positive or negative?

   d How has the skewness of the data affected the measures of its centre?

Number of children	Frequency
1	5
2	28
3	15
4	8
5	2
6	1
Total	59

3 The following frequency table records the number of phone calls made in a day by 50 fifteen-year-olds.

Number of phone calls	Frequency
0	5
1	8
2	13
3	8
4	6
5	3
6	3
7	2
8	1
11	1

a For this data, find the:
  i mean   **ii** median   **iii** mode.
b Construct a column graph for the data and show the position of the mean, median, and mode on the horizontal axis.
c Describe the distribution of the data.
d Why is the mean larger than the median for this data?
e Which measure of centre would be the most suitable for this data set?

4 A company claims that their match boxes contain, on average, 50 matches per box. On doing a survey, the Consumer Protection Society recorded the following results:

Number in a box	Frequency
47	5
48	4
49	11
50	6
51	3
52	1
Total	30

a Use technology to calculate the:
  i mode   **ii** median   **iii** mean.
b Do the results of this survey support the company's claim?
c In a court for 'false advertising', the company won their case against the Consumer Protection Society. Suggest how they did this.

5 Consider again the **Opening Problem** on page **158**.
a Use a frequency table for the *Without fertiliser* data to find the:
  i mean   **ii** mode   **iii** median number of peas per pod.
b Use a frequency table for the *With fertiliser* data to find the:
  i mean   **ii** mode   **iii** median number of peas per pod.
c Which of the measures of centre is appropriate to use in a report on this data?
d Has the application of fertiliser significantly improved the number of peas per pod?

DATA IN CLASSES

When information has been gathered in classes, we use the **midpoint** or **mid-interval value** of the class to represent all scores within that interval.

We are assuming that the scores within each class are evenly distributed throughout that interval. The mean calculated is an **approximation** of the true value, and we cannot do better than this without knowing each individual data value.

INVESTIGATION 3   MID-INTERVAL VALUES

When mid-interval values are used to represent all scores within that interval, what effect will this have on estimating the mean of the grouped data?

Consider the following table which summarises the marks received by students for a physics examination out of 50. The exact results for each student have been lost.

Marks	Frequency
0 - 9	2
10 - 19	31
20 - 29	73
30 - 39	85
40 - 49	28

What to do:

1 Suppose that all of the students scored the lowest possible result in their class interval, so 2 students scored 0, 31 students scored 10, and so on.

  Calculate the mean of these results, and hence complete:

  "The mean score of students in the physics examination must be *at least* ...."

2 Now suppose that all of the students scored the highest possible result in their class interval. Calculate the mean of these results, and hence complete:

  "The mean score of students in the physics examination must be *at most* ...."

3 We now have two extreme values between which the actual mean must lie.

  Now suppose that all of the students scored the mid-interval value in their class interval. We assume that 2 students scored 4.5, 31 students scored 14.5, and so on.

  a Calculate the mean of these results.

  b How does this result compare with lower and upper limits found in **1** and **2**?

  c Copy and complete:

  "The mean score of students in the physics examination was approximately ...."

Example 9   ◀) Self Tutor

Estimate the mean of the following *ages of bus drivers* data, to the nearest year:

Age (yrs)	21 - 25	26 - 30	31 - 35	36 - 40	41 - 45	46 - 50	51 - 55
Frequency	11	14	32	27	29	17	7

Age (yrs)	Frequency (f)	Midpoint (x)	fx
21 - 25	11	23	253
26 - 30	14	28	392
31 - 35	32	33	1056
36 - 40	27	38	1026
41 - 45	29	43	1247
46 - 50	17	48	816
51 - 55	7	53	371
Total	$\sum f = 137$		$\sum fx = 5161$

$$\overline{x} = \frac{\sum fx}{\sum f}$$

$$= \frac{5161}{137}$$

$$\approx 37.7$$

∴ the mean age of the drivers is about 38 years.

or we can find the same result using technology:

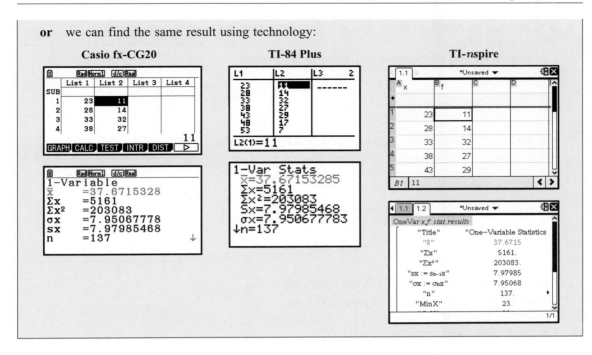

| Casio fx-CG20 | TI-84 Plus | TI-*nspire* |

EXERCISE 6E.4

1 50 students sit for a mathematics test. Given the results in the table, estimate the mean score.

Score	0 - 9	10 - 19	20 - 29	30 - 39	40 - 49
Frequency	2	5	7	27	9

2 The table shows the petrol sales in one day by a number of city service stations.

a How many service stations were involved in the survey?

b Estimate the total amount of petrol sold for the day by the service stations.

c Find the approximate mean sales of petrol for the day.

Petrol sold, L (litres)	Frequency
$2000 \leqslant L < 3000$	4
$3000 \leqslant L < 4000$	4
$4000 \leqslant L < 5000$	9
$5000 \leqslant L < 6000$	14
$6000 \leqslant L < 7000$	23
$7000 \leqslant L < 8000$	16

3 Following is a record of the number of points Chloe scored in her basketball matches.

$$15 \quad 8 \quad 6 \quad 10 \quad 0 \quad 9 \quad 2 \quad 16 \quad 11 \quad 14 \quad 13 \quad 17 \quad 16 \quad 12 \quad 13 \quad 12 \quad 10$$
$$3 \quad 13 \quad 5 \quad 18 \quad 14 \quad 19 \quad 4 \quad 15 \quad 15 \quad 19 \quad 19 \quad 14 \quad 6 \quad 11 \quad 8 \quad 9 \quad 3$$
$$9 \quad 7 \quad 15 \quad 19 \quad 12 \quad 17 \quad 14$$

a Find the mean number of points per match.

b Estimate the mean by grouping the data into the intervals:

    i 0 - 4, 5 - 9, 10 - 14, 15 - 19   **ii** 0 - 3, 4 - 7, 8 - 11, 12 - 15, 16 - 19

c Comment on the accuracy of your answers from **a** and **b**.

4   Kylie pitched a softball 50 times. The speeds of her pitches are shown in the table.

Use technology to estimate the mean speed of her pitches.

Speed (km h^{-1})	Frequency
80 - < 85	8
85 - < 90	14
90 - < 95	22
95 - < 100	6

5   The table shows the sizes of land blocks on a suburban street. Use technology to estimate the mean land block size.

Land size (m^2)	Frequency
[500, 600)	5
[600, 700)	11
[700, 800)	23
[800, 900)	14
[900, 1000)	9

6   This frequency histogram illustrates the results of an aptitude test given to a group of people seeking positions in a company.

a   How many people sat for the test?

b   Estimate the mean score for the test.

c   What fraction of the people scored less than 100 for the test?

d   If the top 20% of the people are offered positions in the company, estimate the minimum mark required.

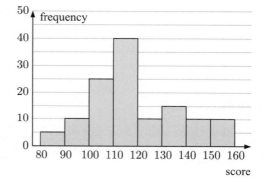

F   MEASURING THE SPREAD OF DATA

To accurately describe a distribution we need to measure both its **centre** and its **spread** or **dispersion**.

The distributions shown have the same mean, but clearly they have different spreads. The A distribution has most scores close to the mean whereas the C distribution has the greatest spread.

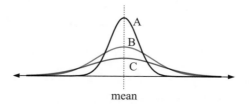

We will examine three different measures of spread: the **range**, the **interquartile range (IQR)**, and the **standard deviation**.

THE RANGE

The **range** is the difference between the maximum (largest) and the minimum (smallest) data value.

Example 10   ◀) **Self Tutor**

A library surveys 20 borrowers each day from Monday to Friday, and records the number who are not satisfied with the range of reading material. The results are: 3 7 6 8 11.

The following year the library receives a grant that enables the purchase of a large number of books. The survey is then repeated and the results are: 2 3 5 4 6.

Find the range of data in each survey.

The range is the maximum minus the minimum data value.

For the first survey, the range is $11 - 3 = 8$.

For the second survey, the range is $6 - 2 = 4$.

The **range** is not considered to be a particularly reliable measure of spread as it uses only two data values. It may be influenced by extreme values or outliers.

THE QUARTILES AND THE INTERQUARTILE RANGE

The median divides the ordered data set into two halves and these halves are divided in half again by the **quartiles**.

The middle value of the lower half is called the **lower quartile** or **25th percentile**. One quarter or 25% of the data have values less than or equal to the lower quartile. 75% of the data have values greater than or equal to the lower quartile.

The middle value of the upper half is called the **upper quartile** or **75th percentile**. One quarter or 25% of the data have values greater than or equal to the upper quartile. 75% of the data have values less than or equal to the upper quartile.

The **interquartile range** is the range of the middle half or 50% of the data.

> **interquartile range = upper quartile − lower quartile**

The data set is thus divided into quarters by the lower quartile (Q_1), the median (Q_2), and the upper quartile (Q_3).

So, the interquartile range,   **IQR = $Q_3 - Q_1$.**

Example 11   ◀) **Self Tutor**

For the data set: 7, 3, 1, 7, 6, 9, 3, 8, 5, 8, 6, 3, 7, 1, 9   find the:

  a median   **b** lower quartile   **c** upper quartile   **d** interquartile range.

The ordered data set is: ~~1,~~ ~~1,~~ 3, 3, 3, 5, ~~6,~~ 6, ~~7, 7, 7, 8, 8, 9, 9~~   (15 of them)

  a As $n = 15$, $\dfrac{n+1}{2} = 8$ ∴   the median = 8th data value = 6

  b/c As the median is a data value we now ignore it and split the remaining data into two:

lower	upper	
1 1 3 3 3 5 6	7 7 7 8 8 9 9	Q_1 = median of lower half = 3
		Q_3 = median of upper half = 8

  d IQR $= Q_3 - Q_1 = 8 - 3 = 5$

Example 12	◄)) Self Tutor

For the data set: 6, 4, 9, 15, 5, 13, 7, 12, 8, 10, 4, 1, 13, 1, 6, 4, 5, 2, 8, 2   find:

  a   the median   **b** Q_1 **c** Q_3 **d**   the IQR.

The ordered data set is:

$$\cancel{1}\ \cancel{1}\ \cancel{2}\ \cancel{2}\ \cancel{4}\ \cancel{4}\ \cancel{4}\ \cancel{5}\ \cancel{5}\ 6\ 6\ \cancel{7}\ \cancel{8}\ \cancel{8}\ \cancel{9}\ \cancel{10}\ \cancel{12}\ \cancel{13}\ \cancel{13}\ \cancel{15}$$ (20 of them)

  a   As $n = 20$, $\dfrac{n+1}{2} = 10.5$

        $\therefore$ the median $= \dfrac{\text{10th value } + \text{ 11th value}}{2} = \dfrac{6+6}{2} = 6$

  b/c   As we have an even number of data values, we split the data into two:

$$\overbrace{1\ 1\ 2\ 2\ 4\ 4\ 4\ 5\ 5\ 6}^{\text{lower}}\ \overbrace{6\ 7\ 8\ 8\ 9\ 10\ 12\ 13\ 13\ 15}^{\text{upper}}$$

        $\therefore$ $Q_1 = \dfrac{4+4}{2} = 4$, $Q_3 = \dfrac{9+10}{2} = 9.5$

  d $\begin{aligned} \text{IQR} &= Q_3 - Q_1 \\ &= 9.5 - 4 \\ &= 5.5 \end{aligned}$

EXERCISE 6F

1 For each of the following data sets, make sure the data is ordered and then find:

    i   the median   **ii**   the upper and lower quartiles

    iii   the range   **iv**   the interquartile range.

  a   2, 3, 3, 3, 4, 4, 4, 5, 5, 5, 5, 6, 6, 6, 6, 6, 7, 7, 8, 8, 8, 9, 9

  b   10, 12, 15, 12, 24, 18, 19, 18, 18, 15, 16, 20, 21, 17, 18, 16, 22, 14

  c   21.8, 22.4, 23.5, 23.5, 24.6, 24.9, 25, 25.3, 26.1, 26.4, 29.5

2 The times spent (in minutes) by 20 people waiting in a queue at a bank for a teller were:

  3.4 2.1 3.8 2.2 4.5 1.4 0   0   1.6 4.8
  1.5 1.9 0   3.6 5.2 2.7 3.0 0.8 3.8 5.2

  a   Find the median waiting time and the upper and lower quartiles.

  b   Find the range and interquartile range of the waiting times.

  c   Copy and complete the following statements:

    i   "50% of the waiting times were greater than ...... minutes."

    ii   "75% of the waiting times were less than ...... minutes."

    iii   "The minimum waiting time was ...... minutes and the maximum waiting time was ...... minutes. The waiting times were spread over ...... minutes."

Example 13   ◄)) **Self Tutor**

Consider the data set:
20, 31, 4, 17, 26, 9, 29, 37, 13, 42, 20, 18, 25, 7, 14, 3, 23, 16, 29, 38, 10, 33, 29

Use technology to find the:

a   range   b   interquartile range.

GRAPHICS
CALCULATOR
INSTRUCTIONS

TI-*n*spire

Casio fx-CG20

```
      Rad Norm2 d/c Real
1-Variable
n     =23
minX =3
Q1    =13
Med   =20
Q3    =29
maxX  =42
```

TI-84 Plus

```
1-Var Stats
↑n=23
 minX=3
 Q₁=13
 Med=20
 Q₃=29
 maxX=42
```

1.1 1.2	*Unsaved ▼	
"σx := σnX"	10.838	
"n"	23.	▶
"MinX"	3.	
"Q₁X"	13.	
"MedianX"	20.	
"Q₂X"	29.	
"MaxX"	42.	
"SSX := Σ(x−x̄)²"	2701.65	

1/99

a   range = maximum − minimum
       $= 42 - 3$
       $= 39$

b   IQR $= Q_3 - Q_1$
       $= 29 - 13$
       $= 16$

---

3 For the data set given, find using technology:

a   the minimum value   b   the maximum value

c   the median   d   the lower quartile

e   the upper quartile   f   the range

g   the interquartile range.

15	22	19	8	14	11
12	25	20	10	9	16
24	21	15	12	28	13
26	19	11	14	6	18
22	14	13	20	25	10

4 The heights of 20 ten year olds were recorded in centimetres:

109   111   113   114   114   118   119   122   122   124
124   126   128   129   129   131   132   135   138   138

a   Using technology, find the:
    i   median height   ii   upper and lower quartiles of the data.

b   Copy and complete the following statements:
    i   "Half of the children are no more than ...... cm tall."
    ii   "75% of the children are no more than ...... cm tall."

c   Find the: i   range   ii   interquartile range for the height of the ten year olds.

d   Copy and complete: "The middle 50% of the children have heights spread over ...... cm."

5 Revisit the **Opening Problem** on page **158**.

a   For the *Without fertiliser* data, find:
    i   the range   ii   the median   iii   the lower quartile
    iv   the upper quartile   v   the interquartile range.

b   Repeat a for the *With fertiliser* data.

c   Consider again the questions posed in the **Opening Problem**. Amend your solutions where appropriate.

G   BOX AND WHISKER PLOTS

A **box and whisker plot** or simply **boxplot** is a visual display of some of the descriptive statistics of a data set. It shows:

- the minimum value
- the lower quartile (Q_1)
- the median (Q_2)   These five numbers form the
- the upper quartile (Q_3)   **five-number summary** of the data set.
- the maximum value

For the data set in **Example 13** on page **185**, the five-number summary and boxplot are:

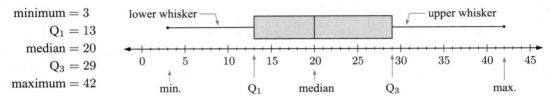

minimum $= 3$
$Q_1 = 13$
median $= 20$
$Q_3 = 29$
maximum $= 42$

The rectangular box represents the 'middle' half of the data set.

The lower whisker represents the 25% of the data with smallest values.

The upper whisker represents the 25% of the data with greatest values.

INTERPRETING A BOXPLOT

A set of data with a **symmetric distribution** will have a symmetric boxplot.

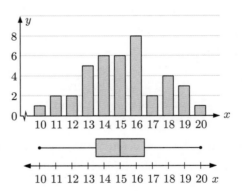

The whiskers of the boxplot are the same length and the median line is in the centre of the box.

A set of data which is **positively skewed** will have a positively skewed boxplot.

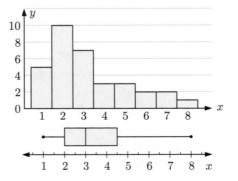

The right whisker is longer than the left whisker and the median line is to the left of the box.

A set of data which is **negatively skewed** will have a negatively skewed boxplot.

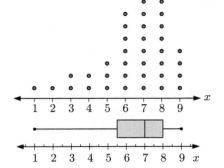

The left whisker is longer than the right whisker and the median line is to the right of the box.

Click on the icons to explore boxplots further.

GAME

STATISTICS PACKAGE

Example 14   ◀) **Self Tutor**

Consider the data set: 8 2 3 9 6 5 3 2 2 6 2 5 4 5 5 6

a Construct the five-number summary for this data.

b Draw a boxplot.

c Find the: i range   ii interquartile range of the data.

d Find the percentage of data values less than 3.

---

a The ordered data set is:

   2 2 2 2 3 3 4 5 | 5 5 5 6 6 6 8 9   {16 data values}

   $Q_1 = 2.5$ median $= 5$ $Q_3 = 6$

   So the 5-number summary is: $\begin{cases} \text{minimum} = 2 & Q_1 = 2.5 \\ \text{median} = 5 & Q_3 = 6 \\ \text{maximum} = 9 \end{cases}$

b

   ```
           |----------|------------|
     0   1   2   3   4   5   6   7   8   9   10
   ```

c i range $=$ maximum $-$ minimum   ii IQR $= Q_3 - Q_1$

      $= 9 - 2$ $= 6 - 2.5$

      $= 7$ $= 3.5$

d 25% of the data values are less than 3.

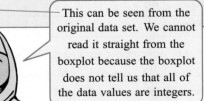

This can be seen from the original data set. We cannot read it straight from the boxplot because the boxplot does not tell us that all of the data values are integers.

EXERCISE 6G.1

1 The boxplot below summarises the points scored by a basketball team.

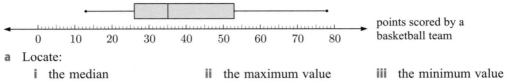

points scored by a basketball team

  a Locate:
- **i** the median
- **ii** the maximum value
- **iii** the minimum value
- **iv** the upper quartile
- **v** the lower quartile.

  b Calculate: **i** the range   **ii** the interquartile range.

2 The boxplot below summarises the class results for a test out of 100 marks.

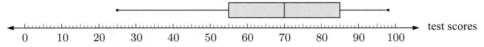

test scores

  a Copy and complete the following statements about the test results:
- **i** The highest mark scored for the test was ...., and the lowest mark was ....
- **ii** Half of the class scored a mark greater than or equal to ....
- **iii** The top 25% of the class scored at least .... marks for the test.
- **iv** The middle half of the class had scores between .... and .... for this test.

  b Find the range of the data set.

  c Find the interquartile range of the data set.

  d Estimate the mean mark for these test scores.

3 For the following data sets:
- **i** construct a 5-number summary
- **ii** draw a boxplot
- **iii** find the range
- **iv** find the interquartile range.

  a 3, 4, 5, 5, 5, 6, 6, 6, 7, 7, 8, 8, 9, 10

  b 3, 7, 0, 1, 4, 6, 8, 8, 8, 9, 7, 5, 6, 8, 7, 8, 8, 2, 9

  c 23, 44, 31, 33, 26, 17, 30, 35, 47, 31, 51, 47, 20, 31, 28, 49, 26, 49

4 Enid examines a new variety of bean and counts the number of beans in 33 pods. Her results were:

    5, 8, 10, 4, 2, 12, 6, 5, 7, 7, 5, 5, 5, 13, 9, 3, 4, 4, 7, 8, 9, 5, 5, 4, 3, 6, 6, 6, 6, 9, 8, 7, 6

  a Find the median, lower quartile, and upper quartile of the data set.

  b Find the interquartile range of the data set.

  c Draw a boxplot of the data set.

5 Ranji counts the number of bolts in several boxes and tabulates the data as follows:

Number of bolts	33	34	35	36	37	38	39	40
Frequency	1	5	7	13	12	8	0	1

  a Find the five-number summary for this data set.

  b Find the   **i** range   **ii** IQR   for this data set.

  c Draw a boxplot of the data set.

  d Are there any outliers in this data?

An outlier is more than $1.5 \times$ IQR from the nearest quartile.

PARALLEL BOXPLOTS

A parallel boxplot enables us to make a *visual comparison* of the distributions of two data sets. We can easily compare descriptive statistics such as their median, range, and interquartile range.

Example 15 ◀» **Self Tutor**

A hospital is trialling a new anaesthetic drug and has collected data on how long the new and old drugs take before the patient becomes unconscious. They wish to know which drug acts faster and which is more reliable.

Old drug times (s):	8, 12, 9, 8, 16, 10, 14, 7, 5, 21,
	13, 10, 8, 10, 11, 8, 11, 9, 11, 14

New drug times (s):	8, 12, 7, 8, 12, 11, 9, 8, 10, 8,
	10, 9, 12, 8, 8, 7, 10, 7, 9, 9

Prepare a parallel boxplot for the data sets and use it to compare the two drugs for speed and reliability.

The 5-number summaries are:

For the old drug: $\min_x = 5$ For the new drug: $\min_x = 7$

$Q_1 = 8$ $Q_1 = 8$

median $= 10$ median $= 9$

$Q_3 = 12.5$ $Q_3 = 10$

$\max_x = 21$ $\max_x = 12$

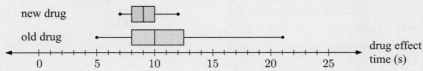

Using the median, 50% of the time the new drug takes 9 seconds or less, compared with 10 seconds for the old drug. We conclude that the new drug is generally a little quicker.

Comparing the spread:

range for old drug $= 21 - 5$	range for new drug $= 12 - 7$
$= 16$	$= 5$
IQR $= Q_3 - Q_1$	IQR $= Q_3 - Q_1$
$= 12.5 - 8$	$= 10 - 8$
$= 4.5$	$= 2$

The new drug times are less 'spread out' than the old drug times. They are more predictable or reliable.

EXERCISE 6G.2

1   The following side-by-side boxplots compare the times students in years 9 and 12 spend on homework.

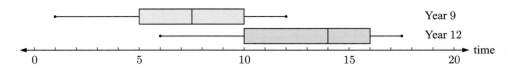

a   Copy and complete:

Statistic	Year 9	Year 12
minimum		
Q_1		
median		
Q_3		
maximum		

b   For each group, determine the:

   i   range   ii   interquartile range.

c   Are the following true or false, or is there not enough information to tell?

   i   On average, Year 12 students spend about twice as much time on homework as Year 9 students.

   ii   Over 25% of Year 9 students spend less time on homework than all Year 12 students.

2   The amounts of money withdrawn from an ATM were recorded on a Friday and a Saturday. The results are displayed on the parallel boxplot alongside.

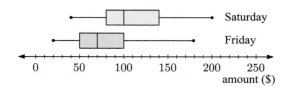

a   Find the five-number summary for each set of data.

b   For each data set, determine the

   i   range   ii   interquartile range.

3   After the final examination, two classes studying the same subject compiled this parallel boxplot to show their results.

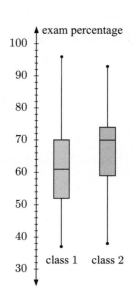

a   In which class was:

   i   the highest mark   ii   the lowest mark

   iii   there a larger spread of marks?

b   Find the interquartile range of class 1.

c   Find the range of class 2.

d   If students who scored at least 70% received an achievement award, what percentage of students received an award in:

   i   class 1   ii   class 2?

e   Describe the distribution of marks in:

   i   class 1   ii   class 2.

f   Copy and complete:

The students in class ...... generally scored higher marks.

The marks in class ...... were more varied.

4 Below are the durations, in minutes, of Paul and Redmond's last 25 mobile phone calls.

   Paul: 1.7, 2.0, 3.9, 3.4, 0.9, 1.4, 2.5, 1.1, 5.1, 4.2, 1.5, 2.6, 0.8,
                    4.0, 1.5, 1.0, 2.9, 3.2, 2.5, 0.8, 1.8, 3.1, 6.9, 2.3, 1.2

   Redmond: 2.0, 4.8, 1.2, 7.5, 3.2, 5.7, 3.9, 0.2, 2.7, 6.8, 3.4, 5.2, 3.2,
                    7.2, 1.7, 11.5, 4.0, 2.4, 3.7, 4.2, 10.7, 3.0, 2.0, 0.9, 5.7

   a Find the five-number summary for each of the data sets.
   b Display the data in a parallel boxplot.
   c Compare and comment on the distributions of the data.

5 Shane and Brett play in the same cricket team and are fierce but friendly rivals when it comes to bowling. During a season the number of wickets taken in each innings by the bowlers was:

Shane: 1 6 2 0 3 4 1 4 2 3 0 3 2 4 3 4 3 3
           3 4 2 4 3 2 3 3 0 5 3 5 3 2 4 3 4 3

Brett: 7 2 4 8 1 3 4 2 3 0 5 3 5 2 3 1 2 0
           4 3 4 0 3 3 0 2 5 1 1 2 2 5 1 4 0 1

   a Is the variable discrete or continuous?
   b Enter the data into a graphics calculator or statistics package.
   c Produce a vertical column graph for each data set.
   d Describe the shape of each distribution.
   e Compare the measures of the centre of each distribution.
   f Compare the spreads of each distribution.
   g Obtain a side-by-side boxplot.
   h What conclusions can be drawn from the data?

6 A manufacturer of light globes claims that their new design has a 20% longer life than those they are presently selling. Forty of each globe are randomly selected and tested. Here are the results to the nearest hour:

	103	96	113	111	126	100	122	110	84	117	103	113	104	104
Old type:	111	87	90	121	99	114	105	121	93	109	87	118	75	111
	87	127	117	131	115	116	82	130	113	95	108	112		

	146	131	132	160	128	119	133	117	139	123	109	129	109	131
New type:	191	117	132	107	141	136	146	142	123	144	145	125	164	125
	133	124	153	129	118	130	134	151	145	131	133	135		

   a Is the variable discrete or continuous?
   b Enter the data into a graphics calculator or statistics package.
   c Compare the measures of centre and spread.
   d Obtain a side-by-side boxplot.
   e Describe the shape of each distribution.
   f What conclusions, if any, can be drawn from the data?

OUTLIERS (EXTENSION)

We have seen that **outliers** are extraordinary data that are separated from the main body of the data.

A commonly used test to identify outliers involves the calculation of upper and lower boundaries:

> - **The upper boundary = upper quartile + 1.5 × IQR.**
>   Any data larger than the upper boundary is an outlier.
> - **The lower boundary = lower quartile − 1.5 × IQR.**
>   Any data smaller than the lower boundary is an outlier.

Outliers are marked with an asterisk on a boxplot. It is possible to have more than one outlier at either end.

Each whisker extends to the last value that is not an outlier.

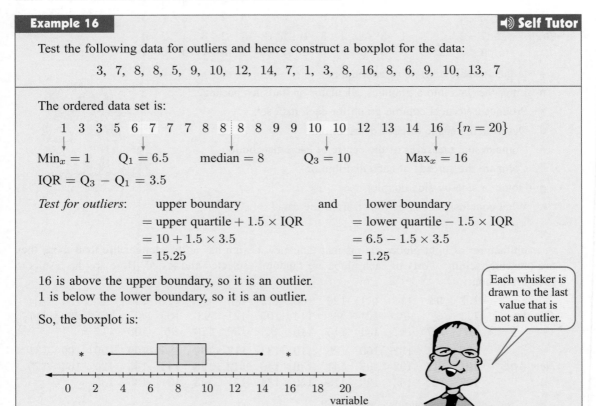

| Example 16 | ◀) Self Tutor |

Test the following data for outliers and hence construct a boxplot for the data:

$$3, \ 7, \ 8, \ 8, \ 5, \ 9, \ 10, \ 12, \ 14, \ 7, \ 1, \ 3, \ 8, \ 16, \ 8, \ 6, \ 9, \ 10, \ 13, \ 7$$

The ordered data set is:

$$1 \quad 3 \quad 3 \quad 5 \quad 6 \quad 7 \quad 7 \quad 7 \quad 8 \quad 8 \mid 8 \quad 8 \quad 9 \quad 9 \quad 10 \quad 10 \quad 12 \quad 13 \quad 14 \quad 16 \quad \{n = 20\}$$

$\text{Min}_x = 1 \qquad Q_1 = 6.5 \qquad \text{median} = 8 \qquad Q_3 = 10 \qquad \text{Max}_x = 16$

$\text{IQR} = Q_3 - Q_1 = 3.5$

Test for outliers:

upper boundary	and	lower boundary
= upper quartile + 1.5 × IQR		= lower quartile − 1.5 × IQR
= 10 + 1.5 × 3.5		= 6.5 − 1.5 × 3.5
= 15.25		= 1.25

16 is above the upper boundary, so it is an outlier.
1 is below the lower boundary, so it is an outlier.

So, the boxplot is:

> Each whisker is drawn to the last value that is not an outlier.

EXERCISE 6G.3

1   A set of data has a lower quartile of 31.5, a median of 37, and an upper quartile of 43.5.

   a   Calculate the interquartile range for this data set.

   b   Calculate the boundaries that identify outliers.

   c   The smallest values of the data set are 13 and 20. The largest values are 52 and 55. Which of these would be outliers?

   d   Draw a boxplot of the data set.

2 James goes bird watching for 25 days. The number of birds he sees each day are:

$$12, 5, 13, 16, 8, 10, 12, 18, 9, 11, 14, 14, 22, 9, 10, 7, 9, 11, 13, 7, 10, 6, 13, 3, 8$$

    a Find the median, lower quartile, and upper quartile of the data set.

    b Find the interquartile range of the data set.

    c What are the lower and upper boundaries for outliers?

    d Are there any outliers?

    e Draw a boxplot of the data set.

H   CUMULATIVE FREQUENCY GRAPHS

Sometimes, in addition to finding the median, it is useful to know the number or proportion of scores that lie above or below a particular value. In such situations we can construct a **cumulative frequency distribution table** and use a graph called a **cumulative frequency graph** to represent the data.

The cumulative frequencies are plotted and the points joined by a smooth curve. This differs from an ogive or cumulative frequency polygon where two points are joined by straight lines.

PERCENTILES

> A **percentile** is the score below which a certain percentage of the data lies.

For example:
- the 85th percentile is the score below which 85% of the data lies.
- If your score in a test is the 95th percentile, then 95% of the class have scored less than you.

> Notice that:
> - the **lower quartile (Q_1)** is the 25th percentile
> - the **median (Q_2)** is the 50th percentile
> - the **upper quartile (Q_3)** is the 75th percentile.

A cumulative frequency graph provides a convenient way to find percentiles.

Example 17   ◀» **Self Tutor**

The data shows the results of the women's marathon at the 2008 Olympics, for all competitors who finished the race.

    a Construct a cumulative frequency distribution table.

    b Represent the data on a cumulative frequency graph.

    c Use your graph to estimate the:

        i median finishing time

        ii number of competitors who finished in less than 2 hours 35 minutes

        iii percentage of competitors who took more than 2 hours 39 minutes to finish

        iv time taken by a competitor who finished in the top 20% of runners completing the marathon.

Finishing time t	Frequency
2 h 26 $\leqslant t <$ 2 h 28	8
2 h 28 $\leqslant t <$ 2 h 30	3
2 h 30 $\leqslant t <$ 2 h 32	9
2 h 32 $\leqslant t <$ 2 h 34	11
2 h 34 $\leqslant t <$ 2 h 36	12
2 h 36 $\leqslant t <$ 2 h 38	7
2 h 38 $\leqslant t <$ 2 h 40	5
2 h 40 $\leqslant t <$ 2 h 48	8
2 h 48 $\leqslant t <$ 2 h 56	6

a

Finishing time t	Frequency	Cumulative frequency
2 h 26 $\leqslant t <$ 2 h 28	8	8
2 h 28 $\leqslant t <$ 2 h 30	3	11
2 h 30 $\leqslant t <$ 2 h 32	9	20
2 h 32 $\leqslant t <$ 2 h 34	11	31
2 h 34 $\leqslant t <$ 2 h 36	12	43
2 h 36 $\leqslant t <$ 2 h 38	7	50
2 h 38 $\leqslant t <$ 2 h 40	5	55
2 h 40 $\leqslant t <$ 2 h 48	8	63
2 h 48 $\leqslant t <$ 2 h 56	6	69

$8 + 3 = 11$ competitors completed the marathon in less than 2 hours 30 minutes.

50 competitors completed the marathon in less than 2 hours 38 minutes.

b

Cumulative frequency graph of marathon runners' times

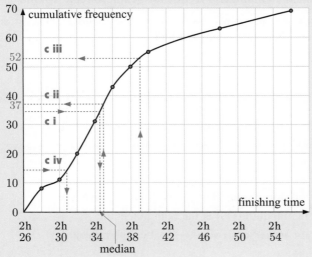

The cumulative frequency gives a *running total* of the number of runners finishing by a given time.

c **i** The median is estimated using the 50th percentile. As 50% of 69 is 34.5, we start with the cumulative frequency of 34.5 and find the corresponding time.
The median is approximately 2 hours 34.5 min.

ii There are approximately 37 competitors who took less than 2 h 35 min to complete the race.

iii There are $69 - 52 = 17$ competitors who took more than 2 hours 39 min.
So $\frac{17}{69} \approx 26.4\%$ took more than 2 hours 39 min.

iv The time taken is estimated using the 20th percentile. As 20% of 69 is 13.8, we find the time corresponding to a cumulative frequency of approximately 14.
The top 20% of competitors took less than 2 hours 31 minutes.

Another way to calculate percentiles is to add a separate scale to a cumulative frequency graph.   On the graph alongside, the cumulative frequency is read from the axis on the left side, and each value corresponds to a percentile on the right side.

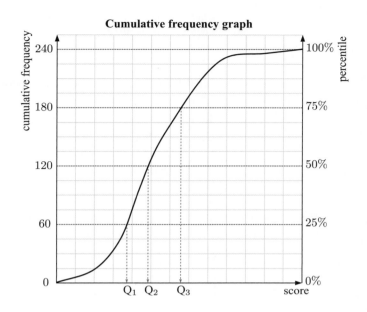

Cumulative frequency graph

EXERCISE 6H

1   The examination scores of a group of students are shown in the table. Draw a cumulative frequency graph for the data and use it to find:

   a the median examination mark

   b how many students scored less than 65 marks

   c how many students scored between 50 and 70 marks

   d how many students failed, given that the pass mark was 45

   e the credit mark, given that the top 16% of students were awarded credits.

Score	Frequency
$10 \leqslant x < 20$	2
$20 \leqslant x < 30$	5
$30 \leqslant x < 40$	7
$40 \leqslant x < 50$	21
$50 \leqslant x < 60$	36
$60 \leqslant x < 70$	40
$70 \leqslant x < 80$	27
$80 \leqslant x < 90$	9
$90 \leqslant x < 100$	3

2   A botanist has measured the heights of 60 seedlings and has presented her findings on the cumulative frequency graph below.

   a How many seedlings have heights of 5 cm or less?

   b What percentage of seedlings are taller than 8 cm?

   c Find the median height.

   d Find the interquartile range for the heights.

   e Copy and complete:
   "90% of the seedlings are shorter than ......"

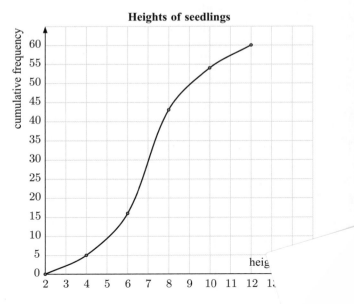

Heights of seedlings

3 The following table summarises the age groups of car drivers involved in accidents in a city for a given year. Draw a cumulative frequency graph for the data and use it to estimate:

Age (in years)	Number of accidents
$16 \leqslant x < 20$	59
$20 \leqslant x < 25$	82
$25 \leqslant x < 30$	43
$30 \leqslant x < 35$	21
$35 \leqslant x < 40$	19
$40 \leqslant x < 50$	11
$50 \leqslant x < 60$	24
$60 \leqslant x < 80$	41

   a the median age of the drivers involved in accidents

   b the percentage of drivers involved in accidents who had an age of 23 or less

   c the probability that a driver involved in an accident is:

      i aged 27 years or less   **ii** aged 27 years.

4 The following data shows the lengths of 30 trout caught in a lake during a fishing competition. The measurements were rounded down to the next centimetre.

31 38 34 40 24 33 30 36 38 32 35 32 36 27 35
40 34 37 44 38 36 34 33 31 38 35 36 33 33 28

   a Construct a cumulative frequency table for trout lengths, x cm, using the intervals $24 \leqslant x < 27$, $27 \leqslant x < 30$, and so on.

   b Draw a cumulative frequency graph for the data.

   c Hence estimate the median length.

   d Use the original data to find its median and compare your answer with **c**. Comment on your results.

5 The following cumulative frequency graph displays the performance of 80 competitors in a cross-country race.

Cross-country race times

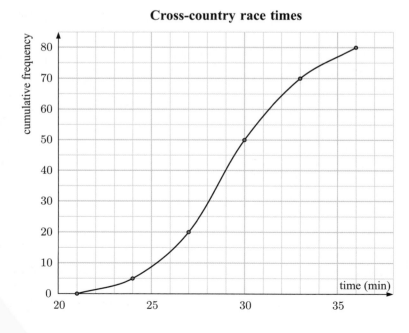

Find:

   a the lower quartile time

   b the median

   c the upper quartile

   d the interquartile range

   e an estimate of the 40th percentile.

6 The table shows the lifetimes of a sample of electric light globes.

Draw a cumulative frequency graph for the data and use it to estimate:

  a the median life of a globe

  b the percentage of globes which had a life of 2700 hours or less

  c the number of globes which had a life between 1500 and 2500 hours.

Life (hours)	Number of globes
$0 \leqslant l < 500$	5
$500 \leqslant l < 1000$	17
$1000 \leqslant l < 2000$	46
$2000 \leqslant l < 3000$	79
$3000 \leqslant l < 4000$	27
$4000 \leqslant l < 5000$	4

7 The following frequency distribution was obtained by asking 50 randomly selected people to measure the lengths of their feet. Their answers were given to the nearest centimetre.

Foot length (cm)	20	21	22	23	24	25	26	27	28	29	30
Frequency	1	1	0	3	5	13	17	7	2	0	1

  a Between what limits are scores rounded to 20 cm?

  b Rewrite the frequency table to show the data in class intervals like the one found in **a**.

  c Hence draw a cumulative frequency graph for the data.

  d Estimate: **i** the median foot length

  ii the number of people with foot length 26 cm or more.

I STANDARD DEVIATION

The problem with using the range and the IQR as measures of spread or dispersion of scores is that both of them only use two values in their calculation. Some data sets have their spread characteristics hidden when the range or IQR are quoted, and so we need a better way of describing spread.

The **standard deviation** of a distribution takes into account the **deviation** of **each score** from the mean. It is therefore a good measure of the **dispersion** of the data.

Consider a data set of n values: $x_1, x_2, x_3, x_4, ..., x_n,$ with mean $\overline{x}$.

$$\text{For a data set of } n \text{ values,} \quad s_n = \sqrt{\dfrac{\sum\limits_{i=1}^{n}(x_i - \overline{x})^2}{n}} \quad \text{is called the \textbf{standard deviation}.}$$

Notice in this formula that:

- $(x_i - \overline{x})^2$ is a measure of how far x_i deviates from $\overline{x}$.

- If $\sum\limits_{i=1}^{n}(x_i - \overline{x})^2$ is small, it will indicate that most of the data values are close to $\overline{x}$.

- Dividing by n gives an indication of how far, on average, the data is from the mean.

- The square root is used to correct the units.

The standard deviation is a **non-resistant** measure of spread. This is due to its dependence on the mean of the sample and because extreme data values will give large values for $(x_i - \overline{x})^2$. It is only a use~ measure if the distribution is close to symmetrical. The IQR and percentiles are more approp. for measuring spread if the distribution is considerably skewed.

INVESTIGATION 4   STANDARD DEVIATION

A group of 5 students is chosen from each of three schools, to test their ability to solve puzzles.

The 15 students are each given a series of puzzles and two hours to solve as many as they can individually.

The results were: School A: 7, 7, 7, 7, 7
                          School B: 5, 6, 7, 8, 9
                          School C: 3, 5, 7, 9, 11

What to do:

1   Show that the mean and median for each school is 7.

2   Given the mean $\overline{x} = 7$ for each group, complete a table like the one following, for each school:

School A

Score (x_i)	Deviation ($x_i - \overline{x}$)	Square of deviation ($x_i - \overline{x})^2$
7		
7		
7		
7		
7		
Sum		

3   Calculate the standard deviation $\sqrt{\dfrac{\sum (x_i - \overline{x})^2}{n}}$ for each group.

Check that your results match the following table:

School	Mean	Standard deviation
A	7	0
B	7	$\sqrt{2}$
C	7	$\sqrt{8}$

4   Use the table above to compare the performances of the different schools.

5   A group of 5 students from a higher year level at school C are given the same test. They each score 2 more than the students in the lower year group, so their scores are: 5, 7, 9, 11, 13.

   a   Find the mean and standard deviation for this set.

   b   Comment on the effect of adding 2 to each member of a data set.

6   A group of 5 teachers from B decide to show their students how clever they are. They complete twice as many puzzles as each of their students, so their scores are: 10, 12, 14, 16, 18.

   a   Find the mean and standard deviation for this set.

   b   Comment on the effect of doubling each member of a data set.

In this course you are only expected to use technology to calculate standard deviation. However, we present both methods in the following example so you can see how it works!

 **GRAPHICS CALCULATOR INSTRUCTIONS**

 STATISTICS PACKAGE   **SPREADSHEET**

Example 18   ◀)) **Self Tutor**

Calculate the standard deviation of the data set: 2, 5, 4, 6, 7, 5, 6.

$$\overline{x} = \frac{2+5+4+6+7+5+6}{7} = 5$$

$$s = \sqrt{\frac{\sum(x-\overline{x})^2}{n}}$$

$$= \sqrt{\frac{16}{7}} \approx 1.51$$

Score (x)	$x - \overline{x}$	$(x - \overline{x})^2$
2	-3	9
4	-1	1
5	0	0
5	0	0
6	1	1
6	1	1
7	2	4
35		16

Make sure you always use the standard deviation of the **population** as highlighted in the screenshots.

The following screendumps indicate the result when we calculate the standard deviation for this data set:

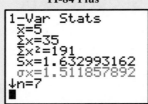

Casio fx-CG20   TI-84 Plus   TI-*n*spire

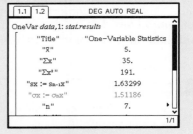

EXERCISE 61.1

1   Use technology to find the standard deviation of the following data sets:

   a   5, 8, 6, 9, 6, 6, 4, 7   **b**   22, 19, 28, 20, 15, 27, 23, 26, 32, 26, 21, 30

2   A company recorded the following weekly petrol usage (in litres) by its salespersons:

   62, 40, 52, 48, 64, 55, 44, 75, 40, 68, 60, 42, 70, 49, 56

   Use technology to find the mean and standard deviation of this data.

3   The weights of a group of cooking chickens in kilograms are:

   1.5, 1.8, 1.7, 1.4, 1.7, 1.8, 2.0, 1.5, 1.6, 1.6, 1.9, 1.7, 1.4, 1.7, 1.8, 2.0

   Use technology to find the mean and standard deviation of weights.

4   The heights in cm of seven junior footballers are: 179, 164, 159, 171, 168, 168, 174.

   a   Find the mean and standard deviation for this group.

   b   When measured one year later, each footballer had grown by exactly 5 cm. Find the new mean and standard deviation.

   c   Comment on your results in general terms.

5   The weights of ten young turkeys to the nearest 0.1 kg are:
0.8, 1.1, 1.2, 0.9, 1.2, 1.2, 0.9, 0.7, 1.0, 1.1

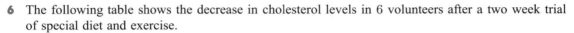

    a Find the mean and standard deviation for the weights of the turkeys.

    b After being fed a special diet for one month, the weights of the turkeys doubled. Find the new mean and standard deviation.

    c Comment on your results.

6   The following table shows the decrease in cholesterol levels in 6 volunteers after a two week trial of special diet and exercise.

Volunteer	A	B	C	D	E	F
Decrease in cholesterol	0.8	0.6	0.7	0.8	0.4	2.8

    a Find the standard deviation of the data.

    b Which of the data values is an outlier?

    c Recalculate the standard deviation with the outlier removed.

    d Discuss the effect of an extreme value on the standard deviation.

STANDARD DEVIATION FOR GROUPED DATA

For **continuous** data, or data that has been grouped in **classes**, we use the **mid-interval values** to represent all data in that interval.

GRAPHICS CALCULATOR INSTRUCTIONS

Example 19   ◀) **Self Tutor**

Use technology to estimate the standard deviation for this distribution of examination scores:

Mark	Frequency	Mark	Frequency
0 - 9	1	50 - 59	16
10 - 19	1	60 - 69	24
20 - 29	2	70 - 79	13
30 - 39	4	80 - 89	6
40 - 49	11	90 - 99	2

In order to estimate the standard deviation of already grouped data, the mid-interval values are used to represent all data in that interval.

We then use technology to estimate the standard deviation.

Class interval	Mid-interval value	Frequency	Class interval	Mid-interval value	Frequency
0 - 9	4.5	1	50 - 59	54.5	16
10 - 19	14.5	1	60 - 69	64.5	24
20 - 29	24.5	2	70 - 79	74.5	13
30 - 39	34.5	4	80 - 89	84.5	6
40 - 49	44.5	11	90 - 99	94.5	2

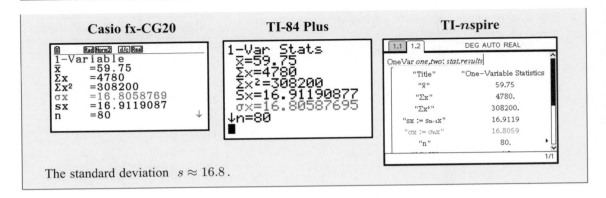

The standard deviation $s \approx 16.8$.

EXERCISE 61.2

1   The workers at a factory were asked how many children they had. The results are shown in the table below.

Number of children	0	1	2	3	4	5	6	7
Frequency	14	18	13	5	3	2	2	1

Find the mean and standard deviation of the data.

2   The ages of squash players at the Junior National Squash Championship are given below.

Age	11	12	13	14	15	16	17	18
Frequency	2	1	4	5	6	4	2	1

Find the mean and standard deviation of the ages.

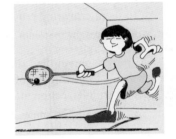

3   The local Health and Fitness Centre recorded the following number of clients per week during the last year:

Calculate the average number of clients per week and the standard deviation from this number.

Number of clients	Frequency
36	2
39	5
44	9
45	11
46	15
48	5
50	4
52	1
Total	52

4   The lengths of 30 randomly selected 12-day old babies were measured and the following data obtained:

Length (cm)	[40, 42)	[42, 44)	[44, 46)	[46, 48)	[48, 50)	[50, 52)	[52, 54)
Frequency	1	1	3	7	11	5	2

Estimate the mean length and the standard deviation of the lengths.

5 The weekly wages (in dollars) of 200 steel workers are given alongside.

Estimate the mean and the standard deviation of the data.

Wage ($)	Number of workers
360 - 369.99	17
370 - 379.99	38
380 - 389.99	47
390 - 399.99	57
400 - 409.99	18
410 - 419.99	10
420 - 429.99	10
430 - 439.99	3

6 The hours worked last week by 40 employees of a local clothing factory were as follows:

```
38  40  46  32  41  39  44  38  40  42  38  40  43  41
47  36  38  39  34  40  48  30  49  40  40  43  45  36
35  39  42  44  48  36  38  42  46  38  39  40
```

Since the data is continuous, we use the intervals 29.5 - 33.5, 33.5 - 37.5, ... for the cumulative frequency graph.

a Calculate the mean and standard deviation for this data.

b Now group the data into classes 30 - 33, 34 - 37, and so on. Calculate the mean and standard deviation using these groups. Examine any differences in the two sets of answers.

c Draw a cumulative frequency graph for the data and determine its interquartile range.

d Represent this data on a boxplot.

7 A traffic survey by the highways department revealed that the following numbers of vehicles passed through a suburban intersection in 15 minute intervals during the day.

a Estimate the mean and the standard deviation for the data.

b Draw a cumulative frequency graph of the data and determine its interquartile range.

Number of vehicles	Frequency
1 - 5	4
6 - 10	16
11 - 15	22
16 - 20	28
21 - 25	14
26 - 30	9
31 - 35	5
36 - 40	2

COMPARING THE SPREAD OF TWO DATA SETS

We have seen how the **mean** of two data sets is a useful comparison of their centres. To compare the spread or dispersion of two data sets we can use their **standard deviations**.

Example 20   ◄) **Self Tutor**

The following exam results were recorded by two classes of students studying Spanish:

Class A: 64 69 74 67 78 88 76 90 89 84 83 87 78 80 95 75 55 78 81
Class B: 94 90 88 81 86 96 92 93 88 72 94 61 87 90 97 95 77 77 82 90

Compare the results of the two classes including their spread.

Class A:

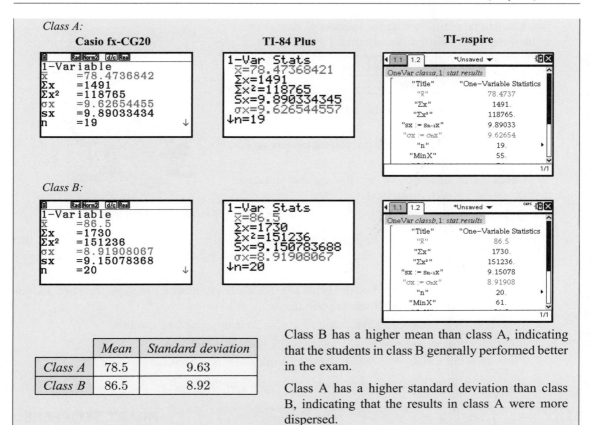

Class B:

	Mean	*Standard deviation*
Class A	78.5	9.63
Class B	86.5	8.92

Class B has a higher mean than class A, indicating that the students in class B generally performed better in the exam.

Class A has a higher standard deviation than class B, indicating that the results in class A were more dispersed.

EXERCISE 61.3

1   The column graphs show two distributions:

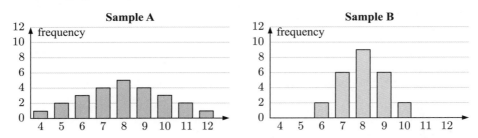

a   By looking at the graphs, which distribution appears to have wider spread?

b   Find the mean of each sample.

c   Find the standard deviation of each sample. Comment on your answers.

2   The number of points scored by Andrew and Brad in the last 8 basketball matches are shown below.

Points by Andrew	23	17	31	25	25	19	28	32
Points by Brad	9	29	41	26	14	44	38	43

a   Find the mean and standard deviation of the number of points scored by each player.

b   Which of the two players is more consistent?

3 Two baseball coaches compare the number of runs scored by their teams in their last ten matches:

Rockets	0	10	1	9	11	0	8	5	6	7
Bullets	4	3	4	1	4	11	7	6	12	5

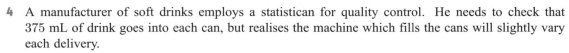

  a Show that each team has the same mean and range of runs scored.

  b Which team's performance do you suspect is more variable over the period?

  c Check your answer to **b** by finding the standard deviation for each distribution.

  d Does the range or the standard deviation give a better indication of variability?

4 A manufacturer of soft drinks employs a statistican for quality control. He needs to check that 375 mL of drink goes into each can, but realises the machine which fills the cans will slightly vary each delivery.

  a Would you expect the standard deviation for the whole production run to be the same for one day as it is for one week? Explain your answer.

  b If samples of 125 cans are taken each day, what measure would be used to:

    i check that an average of 375 mL of drink goes into each can

    ii check the variability of the volume of drink going into each can?

  c What is the significance of a low standard deviation in this case?

INVESTIGATION 5   HEART STOPPERS

A new drug is claimed to lower the cholesterol level in humans. To test this claim, a heart specialist enlisted the help of 50 of his patients.

The patients agreed to take part in an experiment in which 25 of them would be randomly allocated to take the new drug and the other 25 would take an identical looking pill that was actually a *placebo* with no effect.

All participants had their cholesterol level measured before starting the course of pills, with the following results:

  7.1 8.2 8.4 6.5 6.5 7.1 7.2 7.1 6.1 6.0 8.5 5.0 6.3 6.7 7.3 8.9 6.2
  6.3 7.1 8.4 7.4 7.6 7.5 6.6 8.1 6.2 6.2 7.0 8.1 8.4 6.4 7.6 8.6 7.5
  7.9 6.2 6.8 7.5 6.0 5.0 8.3 7.9 6.7 7.3 6.0 7.4 7.4 8.6 6.5 7.6

Two months later, the cholesterol levels of the participants were again measured, but this time they were divided into two groups.

The cholesterol levels of the 25 participants who took the drug were:

      4.8 5.6 4.7 4.2 4.8 4.6 4.8 5.2 4.8 5.0 4.7 5.1 4.7
      4.4 4.7 4.9 6.2 4.7 4.7 4.4 5.6 3.2 4.4 4.6 5.2

The cholesterol levels of the 25 participants who took the placebo were:

      7.0 8.4 8.8 6.1 6.6 7.6 6.5 7.9 6.2 6.8 7.5 6.0 8.2
      5.7 8.3 7.9 6.7 7.3 6.1 7.4 8.4 6.6 6.5 7.6 6.1

What to do:

1 Use the data to complete the table:

Cholesterol level	Before the experiment	25 participants taking the drug	25 participants taking the placebo
$4.0 \leqslant l < 4.5$			
$4.5 \leqslant l < 5.0$			
$5.0 \leqslant l < 5.5$			
$5.5 \leqslant l < 6.0$			
$\vdots$			
$8.5 \leqslant l < 9.0$			

STATISTICS PACKAGE

2 Produce histograms showing the cholesterol levels of the three groups in the table.

3 Calculate the mean and standard deviation for each group in the table.

4 Write a report presenting your findings.

PROJECT IDEAS

You should now have enough knowledge to be able to conduct your own statistical investigation.

1 Choose a problem or issue that you find interesting. Find a question that you can investigate, making sure that you can find useful data for it. Some ideas to get you started can be found by clicking on the icon alongside.

PROJECT IDEAS

2 Think about how you will organise and display your data when you have collected it.

3 Discuss your question and plans for analysis with your teacher, and make changes to the problem or your research plan if necessary.

4 Collect your data, making sure that it is randomly selected, and that you have enough to make a fair conclusion. Use technology to produce appropriate graphs or statistical calculations. In your analysis, you may need to consider:

- Is the data categorical, quantitative discrete, or quantitative continuous?
- Do you need to group any of the data?
- Are there any outliers? If so, are they legitimate data?
- Should you find measures for the centre or spread? If so, which ones should you use?

5 Write a report of your investigation as a newspaper article, a slideshow presentation, or a word processed document. Your report should include:

- an explanation of the problem you researched
- a simple description of your method of investigation
- the analysis you carried out including raw data and any summary statistics, graphs, or tables that you produced
- your conclusion, with the reasons you came to that decision
- a discussion of any flaws in your method that might weaken your conclusion.

REVIEW SET 6A

1 Classify the following data as categorical, quantitative discrete, or quantitative continuous:

   a the number of pages in a daily newspaper

   b the maximum daily temperature in the city

   c the manufacturer of a television

   d the preferred football code

   e the position taken by a player on a lacrosse field

   f the time it takes to run one kilometre

   g the length of people's feet

   h the number of goals shot by a soccer player

   i the cost of a bicycle.

2 The data below are the lengths, in metres, of yachts competing in a sailing race.

     14.7   14.1   21.6   16.2   15.7   12.8   10.1   13.9   14.4   13.0

     11.7   14.6   17.2   13.4   12.1   11.3   13.1   21.6   23.5   16.4

     14.4   15.8   12.6   19.7   18.0   16.2   27.4   21.9   14.4   12.4

   a Produce a frequency histogram of the data.

   b Find the   **i** median   **ii** range   of the yacht lengths.

   c Comment on the skewness of the data.

3 Find a given that the data set   2, a, 5, 4, 1, 2, 3, 5   has a mean of 3.

4 The column graph shows the marks out of 20 that were scored for a test.

   a Describe the distribution of the data.

   b What percentage of the students scored 13 or more marks?

   c What percentage of the students scored less than 5 marks?

   d Explain why we cannot display the data in this graph in a box and whisker plot.

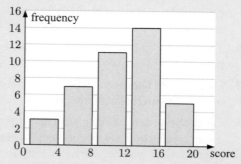

5 Draw a box and whisker plot for the data: 11, 12, 12, 13, 14, 14, 15, 15, 15, 16, 17, 17, 18.

6 120 people caught whooping cough in an outbreak. The times for them to recover were recorded and the results were used to produce the cumulative frequency graph shown.

   Estimate:

   a the median

   b the interquartile range.

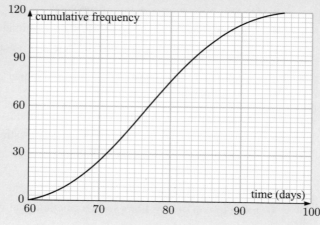

7 Find, using your calculator, the mean and standard deviation of these sets of data:

    a 117, 129, 105, 124, 123, 128, 131, 124, 123, 125, 108

    b 6.1, 5.6, 7.2, 8.3, 6.6, 8.4, 7.7, 6.2

8 Consider this set of data:

$$19, 7, 22, 15, 14, 10, 8, 28, 14, 18, 31, 13, 18, 19, 11, 3, 15, 16, 19, 14$$

    a Find the 5-number summary for the data.   **b** Find the range and IQR of the data.

    c Draw a boxplot of the data set.

REVIEW SET 6B

1 A sample of lamp-posts was surveyed for the following data. Classify the data as categorical, quantitative discrete, or quantitative continuous:

    a the diameter of the lamp-post measured 1 metre from its base

    b the material from which the lamp-post is made

    c the location of the lamp-post (inner, outer, North, South, East, or West)

    d the height of the lamp-post

    e the time since the last inspection

    f the number of inspections since installation

    g the condition of the lamp-post (very good, good, fair, unsatisfactory).

2 The data below are the distances in metres that Thabiso threw a baseball:

71.2	65.1	68.0	71.1	74.6	68.8	83.2	85.0	74.5	87.4
84.3	77.0	82.8	84.4	80.6	75.9	89.7	83.2	97.5	82.9
90.5	85.5	90.7	92.9	95.6	85.5	64.6	73.9	80.0	86.5

    a Determine the highest and lowest value for the data set.

    b Determine: **i** the mean   **ii** the median.

    c Choose between 6 and 12 groups into which all the data values can be placed.

    d Prepare a frequency distribution table.

    e Draw a frequency histogram for the data.

3 Consider the following distribution of continuous grouped data:

Scores (x)	$0 \leqslant x < 10$	$10 \leqslant x < 20$	$20 \leqslant x < 30$	$30 \leqslant x < 40$	$40 \leqslant x < 50$
Frequency	1	13	27	17	2

    a Construct a cumulative frequency graph for the data.

    b Estimate the:

        i median   **ii** interquartile range   **iii** mean   **iv** standard deviation.

4 The daily profits of a shop over the last 20 days, in pounds, are:

| 324 | 348 | 352 | 366 | 346 | 329 | 375 | 353 | 336 | 368 |
| 336 | 375 | 356 | 358 | 353 | 311 | 365 | 376 | 343 | 331 |

    a Find the: **i** median   **ii** lower quartile   **iii** upper quartile.

    b Find the interquartile range of the data set.

    c Find the mean and standard deviation of the daily profits.

5 This cumulative frequency curve shows the times taken for 200 students to travel to school by bus.

   a Estimate how many of the students spent between 10 and 20 minutes travelling to school.

   b 30% of the students spent more than m minutes travelling to school. Estimate the value of m.

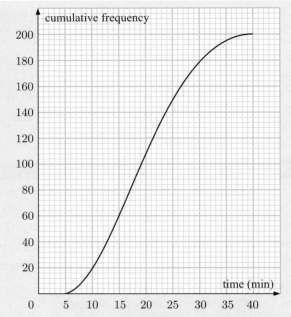

6 The playing time, in minutes, of CDs in a shop is shown alongside.

   a Estimate the mean and standard deviation of the playing time.

   b Draw a histogram to present this data.

   c Comment on the shape of the distribution.

Playing time (minutes)	Number of CDs
$30 \leqslant t < 35$	5
$35 \leqslant t < 40$	13
$40 \leqslant t < 45$	17
$45 \leqslant t < 50$	29
$50 \leqslant t < 55$	27
$55 \leqslant t < 60$	18
$60 \leqslant t < 65$	7

7 Find the range, lower quartile, upper quartile, and standard deviation for the following data:

120, 118, 132, 127, 135, 116, 122, 128.

8 A confectioner claims to sell an average of 30 liquorice allsorts per bag. The results from a survey of bags are shown in the table below.

Number of allsorts	27	28	29	30	31	32
Frequency	23	29	41	37	22	32

   a Find the mean and standard deviation for this data.

   b Is the confectioner's claim justified?

REVIEW SET 6C

1 A set of 14 data is: 6, 8, 7, 7, 5, 7, 6, 8, 6, 9, 6, 7, p, q.
The mean and mode of the set are both 7.
Find p and q.

2 The winning margins in 100 rugby games were recorded as follows:

Margin (points)	1 - 10	11 - 20	21 - 30	31 - 40	41 - 50
Frequency	13	35	27	18	7

Draw a column graph to present this information.

3 The table alongside shows the number of patrons visiting an art gallery on various days.

Estimate the mean number of patrons per day.

Number of patrons	*Frequency*
250 - 299	14
300 - 349	34
350 - 399	68
400 - 449	72
450 - 499	54
500 - 549	23
550 - 599	7

4 The parallel boxplots show the 100 metre sprint times for the members of two athletics squads.

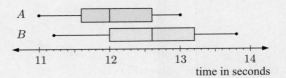

time in seconds

a Determine the 5-number summaries for both A and B.

b Determine: **i** the range   **ii** the interquartile range   for each group.

c Copy and complete:

  i We know the members of squad ...... generally ran faster because ......

  ii We know the times in squad ...... are more varied because ......

5 The supermarket bills for a number of families was recorded in the table given.

Estimate the mean bill and the standard deviation of the bills.

Bill (€)	*Frequency*
70 - 79.99	27
80 - 89.99	32
90 - 99.99	48
100 - 109.99	25
110 - 119.99	37
120 - 129.99	21
130 - 139.99	18
140 - 149.99	7

6 An examination worth 100 marks was given to 800 biology students. The cumulative frequency graph for the students' results is shown on the following page.

a Find the number of students who scored 45 marks or less for the test.

b Find the median score.

c Between what values do the middle 50% of test results lie?

d Find the interquartile range of the data.

e What percentage of students obtained a mark of 55 or more?

f If a 'distinction' is awarded to the top 10% of students, what score is required to receive this honour?

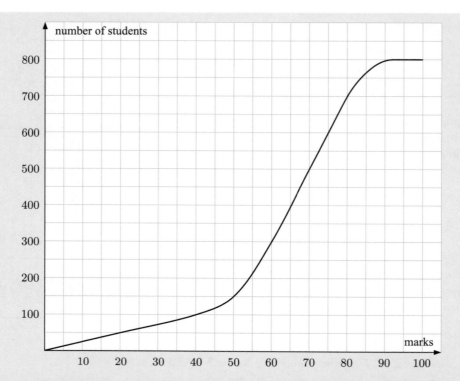

7 The number of peanuts in a jar varies slightly from jar to jar. Samples of 30 jars were taken for each of two brands X and Y, and the number of peanuts in each jar was recorded.

Brand X					
871	885	878	882	889	885
916	913	886	905	907	898
874	904	901	894	897	899
908	901	898	894	895	895
910	904	896	893	903	888

Brand Y					
909	906	913	891	898	901
894	894	928	893	924	892
927	907	901	900	907	913
921	904	903	896	901	895
917	903	910	903	909	904

a Copy and complete this table:

	Brand X	Brand Y
min		
Q_1		
median		
Q_3		
max		
IQR		

b Display the data on a parallel boxplot.

c Comment on which brand:

   i has more peanuts per jar

  ii has a more consistent number of peanuts per jar.

Chapter 7

Sets and Venn diagrams

Syllabus reference: 1.1, 3.5

OPENING PROBLEM

A city has three football teams in the national league: A, B, and C.

In the last season, 20% of the city's population saw team A play, 24% saw team B, and 28% saw team C. Of these, 4% saw both A and B, 5% saw both A and C, and 6% saw both B and C. 1% saw all three teams play.

Things to think about:

a Writing out all of this information in sentences is very complicated. How can we represent this information more simply on a diagram?

b What percentage of the population:

   i saw only team A play

   ii saw team A *or* team B play but not team C

   iii did not see any of the teams play?

A   SETS

SET NOTATION

> A **set** is a collection of numbers or objects.

For example, the set of all digits which we use to write numbers is $\{0, 1, 2, 3, 4, 5, 6, 7, 8, 9\}$.

Notice how the ten digits have been written within the brackets "{" and "}", and how they are separated by commas.

We usually use capital letters to represent sets, so we can refer to the set easily.

For example, if V is the set of all vowels, then $V = \{a, e, i, o, u\}$.

> The numbers or objects in a set are called the **elements** or **members** of the set.

We use the symbol $\in$ to mean *is an element of* and $\notin$ to mean *is not an element of.*

So, for the set $A = \{1, 2, 3, 4, 5, 6, 7\}$ we can say $4 \in A$ but $9 \notin A$.

> The set $\{\ \}$ or $\varnothing$ is called the **empty set** and contains no elements.

SPECIAL NUMBER SETS

The following is a list of some special number sets you should be familiar with:

> $\mathbb{N} = \{0, 1, 2, 3, 4, 5, 6, 7, ...\}$ is the set of all **natural** or **counting numbers**.
>
> $\mathbb{Z} = \{0, \pm 1, \pm 2, \pm 3, \pm 4, ...\}$ is the set of all **integers**.
>
> $\mathbb{Z}^{+} = \{1, 2, 3, 4, 5, 6, 7, ...\}$ is the set of all **positive integers**.
>
> $\mathbb{Z}^{-} = \{-1, -2, -3, -4, -5, ...\}$ is the set of all **negative integers**.

$\mathbb{Q}$ is the set of all **rational numbers**, or numbers which can be written in the form $\frac{p}{q}$ where p and q are integers and $q \neq 0$.

$\mathbb{R}$ is the set of all **real numbers**, which are all numbers which can be placed on the number line.

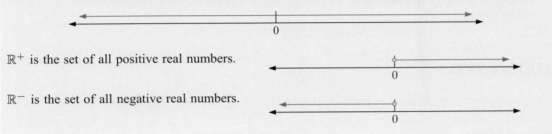

$\mathbb{R}^+$ is the set of all positive real numbers.

$\mathbb{R}^-$ is the set of all negative real numbers.

COUNTING ELEMENTS OF SETS

The number of elements in set A is written $n(A)$.

For example, the set $A = \{2, 3, 5, 8, 13, 21\}$ has 6 elements, so we write $n(A) = 6$.

A set which has a finite number of elements is called a **finite set**.

For example: $A = \{2, 3, 5, 8, 13, 21\}$ is a finite set.
$\varnothing$ is also a finite set, since $n(\varnothing) = 0$.

Infinite sets are sets which have infinitely many elements.

For example, the set of positive integers $\{1, 2, 3, 4, ...\}$ does not have a largest element, but rather keeps on going forever. It is therefore an infinite set.

In fact, the sets $\mathbb{N}$, $\mathbb{Z}$, $\mathbb{Z}^+$, $\mathbb{Z}^-$, $\mathbb{Q}$, and $\mathbb{R}$ are all infinite sets.

SUBSETS

Suppose P and Q are two sets. P is a **subset** of Q if every element of P is also an element of Q. We write $P \subseteq Q$.

For example, $\{2, 3, 5\} \subseteq \{1, 2, 3, 4, 5, 6\}$ as every element in the first set is also in the second set.

We say P is a **proper subset** of Q if P is a subset of Q but is *not equal to Q*. We write $P \subset Q$.

UNION AND INTERSECTION

If P and Q are two sets then

- $P \cap Q$ is the **intersection** of P and Q, and consists of all elements which are in **both P and Q**.
- $P \cup Q$ is the **union** of P and Q, and consists of all elements which are in P **or** Q.

Every element in P and every element in Q is found in $P \cup Q$.

For example:

DEMO

- If $P = \{1, 3, 4\}$ and $Q = \{2, 3, 5\}$ then $P \cap Q = \{3\}$ and $P \cup Q = \{1, 2, 3, 4, 5\}$
- The set of integers is made up of the set of negative integers, zero, and the set of positive integers.

$$\mathbb{Z} = (\mathbb{Z}^- \cup \{0\} \cup \mathbb{Z}^+)$$

DISJOINT SETS

Two sets are **disjoint** or **mutually exclusive** if they have no elements in common.

Example 1	◀) **Self Tutor**

$M = \{2, 3, 5, 7, 8, 9\}$ and $N = \{3, 4, 6, 9, 10\}$

a True or false? **i** $4 \in M$ **ii** $6 \notin M$

b List the sets: **i** $M \cap N$ **ii** $M \cup N$

c Is **i** $M \subseteq N$ **ii** $\{9, 6, 3\} \subseteq N$?

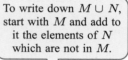

To write down $M \cup N$, start with M and add to it the elements of N which are not in M.

a **i** 4 is not an element of M, so $4 \in M$ is false.

 ii 6 is not an element of M, so $6 \notin M$ is true.

b **i** $M \cap N = \{3, 9\}$ since 3 and 9 are elements of both sets.

 ii Every element which is in either M or N is in the union of M and N.

 $\therefore$ $M \cup N = \{2, 3, 4, 5, 6, 7, 8, 9, 10\}$

c **i** No. Not every element of M is an element of N.

 ii Yes, as 9, 6, and 3 are also in N.

EXERCISE 7A

1 Write using set notation:

 a 5 is an element of set D **b** 6 is not an element of set G

 c d is not an element of the set of all English vowels

 d $\{2, 5\}$ is a subset of $\{1, 2, 3, 4, 5, 6\}$ **e** $\{3, 8, 6\}$ is not a subset of $\{1, 2, 3, 4, 5, 6\}$.

2 Find **i** $A \cap B$ **ii** $A \cup B$ for:

 a $A = \{6, 7, 9, 11, 12\}$ and $B = \{5, 8, 10, 13, 9\}$

 b $A = \{1, 2, 3, 4\}$ and $B = \{5, 6, 7, 8\}$

 c $A = \{1, 3, 5, 7\}$ and $B = \{1, 2, 3, 4, 5, 6, 7, 8, 9\}$

3 Write down the number of elements in the following sets:

 a $A = \{0, 3, 5, 8, 14\}$ **b** $B = \{1, 4, 5, 8, 11, 13\}$ **c** $A \cap B$ **d** $A \cup B$

4 True or false?

 a $\mathbb{Z}^+ \subseteq \mathbb{N}$ **b** $\mathbb{N} \subset \mathbb{Z}$ **c** $\mathbb{N} = \mathbb{Z}^+$ **d** $\mathbb{Z}^- \subseteq \mathbb{Z}$

 e $\mathbb{Q} \subset \mathbb{Z}$ **f** $\{0\} \subseteq \mathbb{Z}$ **g** $\mathbb{Z} \subseteq \mathbb{Q}$ **h** $\mathbb{Z}^+ \cup \mathbb{Z}^- = \mathbb{Z}$

5 Describe the following sets as either finite or infinite:

    a the set of counting numbers between 10 and 20

    b the set of counting numbers greater than 5

    c the set of all rational numbers $\mathbb{Q}$

    d the set of all rational numbers between 0 and 1.

6 True or false?

    a $127 \in \mathbb{N}$ **b** $\frac{138}{279} \in \mathbb{Q}$ **c** $3\frac{1}{7} \notin \mathbb{Q}$ **d** $-\frac{4}{11} \in \mathbb{Q}$

7 Which of these pairs of sets are disjoint?

    a $A = \{3, 5, 7, 9\}$ and $B = \{2, 4, 6, 8\}$ **b** $P = \{3, 5, 6, 7, 8, 10\}$ and $Q = \{4, 9, 10\}$

8 True or false? If R and S are two non-empty sets and $R \cap S = \varnothing$ then R and S are disjoint.

9 $\{a\}$ has two subsets, $\varnothing$ and $\{a\}$. $\{a, b\}$ has four subsets: $\varnothing$, $\{a\}$, $\{b\}$, and $\{a, b\}$.

    a List the subsets of   **i** $\{a, b, c\}$ **ii** $\{a, b, c, d\}$ and hence state the number of subsets for each.

    b Copy and complete: "If a set has n elements then it has ...... subsets."

B   INTERVAL NOTATION

To avoid having to list all members of a set, we often use a general description of its members. For example:

- $A = \{x \mid -2 \leqslant x \leqslant 4, \ x \in \mathbb{Z}\}$ reads "the set of all x such that x is an integer between -2 and 4, including -2 and 4."

    └── such that
    └── the set of all

We can represent A on a number line as:

A is a finite set, and $n(A) = 7$.

- $B = \{x \mid -2 \leqslant x < 4, \ x \in \mathbb{R}\}$ reads "the set of all real x such that x is greater than or equal to -2 and less than 4."

We represent B on a number line as:

a filled in circle indicates -2 is included   an open circle indicates 4 is not included

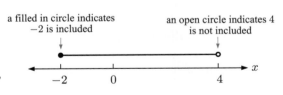

B is an infinite set, and $n(B) = \infty$.

We could also write $B = \{x \mid -2 \leqslant x < 4\}$, in which case we would *assume* that $x \in \mathbb{R}$.

Example 2   ◄⑴ **Self Tutor**

Suppose $A = \{x \mid 3 < x \leqslant 10, \ x \in \mathbb{Z}\}$.

    a Write down the meaning of the interval notation.

    b List the elements of set A.   **c** Find $n(A)$.

    a The set of all x such that x is an integer between 3 and 10, including 10.

    b $A = \{4, 5, 6, 7, 8, 9, 10\}$ **c** There are 7 elements, so $n(A) = 7$.

EXERCISE 7B

1 Explain whether the following sets are finite or infinite:

    a $\{x \mid -2 \leqslant x \leqslant 1, \ x \in \mathbb{Z}\}$ **b** $\{x \mid -2 \leqslant x \leqslant 1, \ x \in \mathbb{R}\}$

    c $\{x \mid x \geqslant 5, \ x \in \mathbb{Z}\}$ **d** $\{x \mid 0 \leqslant x \leqslant 1, \ x \in \mathbb{Q}\}$

2 For the following sets:

    i write down the meaning of the interval notation

    ii if possible, list the elements of A **iii** find $n(A)$.

    a $A = \{x \mid -1 \leqslant x \leqslant 7, \ x \in \mathbb{Z}\}$ **b** $A = \{x \mid -2 < x < 8, \ x \in \mathbb{N}\}$

    c $A = \{x \mid 0 \leqslant x \leqslant 1, \ x \in \mathbb{R}\}$ **d** $A = \{x \mid 5 \leqslant x \leqslant 6, \ x \in \mathbb{Q}\}$

3 Write in interval notation:

    a the set of all integers between -100 and 100

    b the set of all real numbers greater than 1000

    c the set of all rational numbers between 2 and 3, including 2 and 3.

4 State whether $A \subseteq B$:

    a $A = \varnothing, \ B = \{2, 5, 7, 9\}$ **b** $A = \{2, 5, 8, 9\}, \ B = \{8, 9\}$

    c $A = \{x \mid 2 \leqslant x \leqslant 3, \ x \in \mathbb{R}\}, \ B = \{x \mid x \in \mathbb{R}\}$

    d $A = \{x \mid 3 \leqslant x \leqslant 9, \ x \in \mathbb{Q}\}, \ B = \{x \mid 0 \leqslant x \leqslant 10, \ x \in \mathbb{R}\}$

    e $A = \{x \mid -10 \leqslant x \leqslant 10, \ x \in \mathbb{Z}\}, \ B = \{z \mid 0 \leqslant z \leqslant 5, \ z \in \mathbb{Z}\}$

    f $A = \{x \mid 0 \leqslant x \leqslant 1, \ x \in \mathbb{Q}\}, \ B = \{y \mid 0 < y \leqslant 2, \ y \in \mathbb{Q}\}$

C   COMPLEMENTS OF SETS

UNIVERSAL SETS

Suppose we are only interested in the natural numbers from 1 to 20, and we want to consider subsets of this set. We say the set $U = \{x \mid 1 \leqslant x \leqslant 20, \ x \in \mathbb{N}\}$ is the *universal set* in this situation.

> The symbol U is used to represent the **universal set** under consideration.

COMPLEMENTARY SETS

> The **complement** of A, denoted A', is the set of all elements of U which are *not* in A.

For example, if the universal set $U = \{1, 2, 3, 4, 5, 6, 7, 8\}$, and the set $A = \{1, 3, 5, 7, 8\}$, then the complement of A is $A' = \{2, 4, 6\}$.

Three obvious relationships are observed connecting A and A'. These are:

- $A \cap A' = \varnothing$ as A' and A have no common members.
- $A \cup A' = U$ as all elements of A and A' combined make up U.
- $n(A) + n(A') = n(U)$

For example, $\mathbb{Q} \cap \mathbb{Q}' = \varnothing$ and $\mathbb{Q} \cup \mathbb{Q}' = \mathbb{R}$.

Example 3   ◀)) **Self Tutor**

Find C' given that:

  a $U = \{$all positive integers$\}$ and $C = \{$all even integers$\}$

  b $C = \{x \mid x \geqslant 2, \; x \in \mathbb{Z}\}$ and $U = \mathbb{Z}$

  a $C' = \{$all odd integers$\}$ **b** $C' = \{x \mid x \leqslant 1, \; x \in \mathbb{Z}\}$

Example 4   ◀)) **Self Tutor**

Suppose $U = \{x \mid -5 \leqslant x \leqslant 5, \; x \in \mathbb{Z}\}$, $A = \{x \mid 1 \leqslant x \leqslant 4, \; x \in \mathbb{Z}\}$, and
$B = \{x \mid -3 \leqslant x < 2, \; x \in \mathbb{Z}\}$.   List the elements of these sets:

  a A **b** B **c** A' **d** B'

  e $A \cap B$ **f** $A \cup B$ **g** $A' \cap B$ **h** $A' \cup B'$

  a $A = \{1, 2, 3, 4\}$ **b** $B = \{-3, -2, -1, 0, 1\}$

  c $A' = \{-5, -4, -3, -2, -1, 0, 5\}$ **d** $B' = \{-5, -4, 2, 3, 4, 5\}$

  e $A \cap B = \{1\}$ **f** $A \cup B = \{-3, -2, -1, 0, 1, 2, 3, 4\}$

  g $A' \cap B = \{-3, -2, -1, 0\}$

  h $A' \cup B' = \{-5, -4, -3, -2, -1, 0, 2, 3, 4, 5\}$

EXERCISE 7C

1   Find the complement of C given that:

    a $U = \{$letters of the English alphabet$\}$ and $C = \{$vowels$\}$

    b $U = \{$integers$\}$ and $C = \{$negative integers$\}$

    c $U = \mathbb{Z}$ and $C = \{x \mid x \leqslant -5, \; x \in \mathbb{Z}\}$

    d $U = \mathbb{Q}$ and $C = \{x \mid x \leqslant 2 \text{ or } x \geqslant 8, \; x \in \mathbb{Q}\}$

2   Suppose $U = \{x \mid 0 \leqslant x \leqslant 8, \; x \in \mathbb{Z}\}$, $A = \{x \mid 2 \leqslant x \leqslant 7, \; x \in \mathbb{Z}\}$, and
                $B = \{x \mid 5 \leqslant x \leqslant 8, \; x \in \mathbb{Z}\}$.   List the elements of:

    a A **b** A' **c** B **d** B'

    e $A \cap B$ **f** $A \cup B$ **g** $A \cap B'$

3   Suppose P and Q' are subsets of U. $n(U) = 15$, $n(P) = 6$, and $n(Q') = 4$.   Find:

    a $n(P')$ **b** $n(Q)$

4   True or false?

    a   If $n(U) = a$ and $n(A) = b$ where $A \subseteq U$, then $n(A') = b - a$.

    b   If Q is a subset of U then $Q' = \{x \mid x \notin Q, \; x \in U\}$.

5   Suppose $U = \{x \mid 0 < x \leqslant 12, \; x \in \mathbb{Z}\}$, $A = \{x \mid 2 \leqslant x \leqslant 7, \; x \in \mathbb{Z}\}$,
           $B = \{x \mid 3 \leqslant x \leqslant 9, \; x \in \mathbb{Z}\}$, and $C = \{x \mid 5 \leqslant x \leqslant 11, \; x \in \mathbb{Z}\}$.

    List the elements of:

    a B' **b** C' **c** A' **d** $A \cap B$

    e $(A \cap B)'$ **f** $A' \cap C$ **g** $B' \cup C$ **h** $(A \cup C) \cap B'$

Example 5   ◆) **Self Tutor**

Suppose $U = \{\text{positive integers}\}$, $P = \{\text{multiples of 4 less than 50}\}$, and
$Q = \{\text{multiples of 6 less than 50}\}$.

  a List P and Q.   **b** Find $P \cap Q$.   **c** Find $P \cup Q$.

  d Verify that $n(P \cup Q) = n(P) + n(Q) - n(P \cap Q)$.

---

  a $P = \{4, 8, 12, 16, 20, 24, 28, 32, 36, 40, 44, 48\}$
      $Q = \{6, 12, 18, 24, 30, 36, 42, 48\}$

  b $P \cap Q = \{12, 24, 36, 48\}$

  c $P \cup Q = \{4, 6, 8, 12, 16, 18, 20, 24, 28, 30, 32, 36, 40, 42, 44, 48\}$

  d $n(P \cup Q) = 16$ and $n(P) + n(Q) - n(P \cap Q) = 12 + 8 - 4 = 16$
      So, $n(P \cup Q) = n(P) + n(Q) - n(P \cap Q)$ is verified.

---

6 Suppose $U = \mathbb{Z}^+$, $P = \{\text{prime numbers} < 25\}$, and $Q = \{2, 4, 5, 11, 12, 15\}$.

  a List P.   **b** Find $P \cap Q$.   **c** Find $P \cup Q$.

  d Verify that $n(P \cup Q) = n(P) + n(Q) - n(P \cap Q)$.

7 Suppose $U = \mathbb{Z}^+$, $P = \{\text{factors of 28}\}$, and $Q = \{\text{factors of 40}\}$.

  a List P and Q.   **b** Find $P \cap Q$.   **c** Find $P \cup Q$.

  d Verify that $n(P \cup Q) = n(P) + n(Q) - n(P \cap Q)$.

8 Suppose $U = \mathbb{Z}^+$, $M = \{\text{multiples of 4 between 30 and 60}\}$, and
     $N = \{\text{multiples of 6 between 30 and 60}\}$.

  a List M and N.   **b** Find $M \cap N$.   **c** Find $M \cup N$.

  d Verify that $n(M \cup N) = n(M) + n(N) - n(M \cap N)$.

9 Suppose $U = \mathbb{Z}$, $R = \{x \mid -2 \leqslant x \leqslant 4, \ x \in \mathbb{Z}\}$, and $S = \{x \mid 0 \leqslant x < 7, \ x \in \mathbb{Z}\}$.

  a List R and S.   **b** Find $R \cap S$.   **c** Find $R \cup S$.

  d Verify that $n(R \cup S) = n(R) + n(S) - n(R \cap S)$.

10 Suppose $U = \mathbb{Z}$, $C = \{y \mid -4 \leqslant y \leqslant -1, y \in \mathbb{Z}\}$, and $D = \{y \mid -7 \leqslant y < 0, y \in \mathbb{Z}\}$.

  a List C and D.   **b** Find $C \cap D$.   **c** Find $C \cup D$.

  d Verify that $n(C \cup D) = n(C) + n(D) - n(C \cap D)$.

11 Suppose $U = \mathbb{Z}^+$, $P = \{\text{factors of 12}\}$, $Q = \{\text{factors of 18}\}$, and $R = \{\text{factors of 27}\}$.

  a List the sets P, Q, and R.

  b Find: **i** $P \cap Q$ **ii** $P \cap R$ **iii** $Q \cap R$

             iv $P \cup Q$ **v** $P \cup R$ **vi** $Q \cup R$

  c Find: **i** $P \cap Q \cap R$ **ii** $P \cup Q \cup R$

12 Suppose $U = \mathbb{Z}^+$, $A = \{$multiples of 4 less than 40$\}$,

   $B = \{$multiples of 6 less than 40$\}$, and $C = \{$multiples of 12 less than 40$\}$.

   a List the sets A, B and C.

   b Find: **i** $A \cap B$ **ii** $B \cap C$ **iii** $A \cap C$

      iv $A \cap B \cap C$ **v** $A \cup B \cup C$

   c Verify that

   $n(A \cup B \cup C) = n(A) + n(B) + n(C) - n(A \cap B) - n(B \cap C) - n(A \cap C) + n(A \cap B \cap C).$

13 Suppose $U = \mathbb{Z}^+$, $A = \{$multiples of 6 less than 31$\}$,

      $B = \{$factors of 30$\}$, and $C = \{$primes $< 30\}$.

   a List the sets A, B, and C.

   b Find: **i** $A \cap B$ **ii** $B \cap C$ **iii** $A \cap C$

      iv $A \cap B \cap C$ **v** $A \cup B \cup C$

   c Verify that

   $n(A \cup B \cup C) = n(A) + n(B) + n(C) - n(A \cap B) - n(B \cap C) - n(A \cap C) + n(A \cap B \cap C).$

D   VENN DIAGRAMS

Venn diagrams are often used to represent sets of objects, numbers, or things.

> A **Venn diagram** consists of a universal set U represented by a rectangle.
>
> Sets within the universal set are usually represented by circles.

For example:

- This Venn diagram shows set A within the universal set U.
  A', the complement of A, is the shaded region outside the circle.

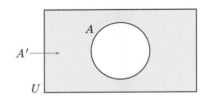

- The sets $U = \{2, 3, 5, 7, 8\}$, $A = \{2, 7, 8\}$, and $A' = \{3, 5\}$ are represented by:

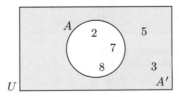

SUBSETS

If $B \subseteq A$ then every element of B is also in A.

The circle representing B is placed within the circle representing A.

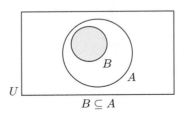

$B \subseteq A$

INTERSECTION

$A \cap B$ consists of all elements common to both A and B.

It is the shaded region where the circles representing A and B overlap.

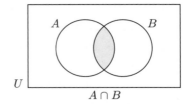

UNION

$A \cup B$ consists of all elements in A or B or both.

It is the shaded region which includes both circles.

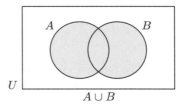

DISJOINT OR MUTUALLY EXCLUSIVE SETS

Disjoint sets do not have common elements.

They are represented by non-overlapping circles.

For example, if $A = \{2, 3, 8\}$ and $B = \{4, 5, 9\}$
  then $A \cap B = \varnothing$.

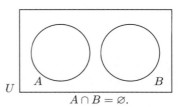

Example 6   ◀) **Self Tutor**

Suppose $U = \{1, 2, 3, 4, 5, 6, 7, 8\}$.   Illustrate on a Venn diagram the sets:

  a $A = \{1, 3, 6, 8\}$ and $B = \{2, 3, 4, 5, 8\}$

  b $A = \{1, 3, 6, 7, 8\}$ and $B = \{3, 6, 8\}$.

  a $A \cap B = \{3, 8\}$

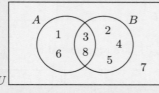

  b $A \cap B = \{3, 6, 8\}$, $B \subseteq A$

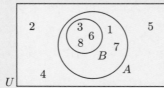

Example 7   ◀) **Self Tutor**

Suppose $U = \{1, 2, 3, 4, 5, 6, 7, 8, 9\}$.   Illustrate on a Venn diagram the sets $A = \{2, 4, 8\}$ and $B = \{1, 3, 5, 9\}$.

$A \cap B = \varnothing$

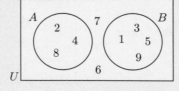

Since A and B are disjoint, their circles are separated.

EXERCISE 7D

1   Represent sets A and B on a Venn diagram, given:

   a $U = \{2, 3, 4, 5, 6, 7\}$, $A = \{2, 4, 6\}$,   and $B = \{5, 7\}$

   b $U = \{2, 3, 4, 5, 6, 7\}$, $A = \{2, 4, 6\}$,   and $B = \{3, 5, 7\}$

   c $U = \{1, 2, 3, 4, 5, 6, 7\}$, $A = \{2, 4, 5, 6\}$,   and $B = \{1, 4, 6, 7\}$

   d $U = \{3, 4, 5, 7\}$, $A = \{3, 4, 5, 7\}$,   and $B = \{3, 5\}$

2   Suppose $U = \{x \mid 1 \leqslant x \leqslant 10,\ x \in \mathbb{Z}\}$, $A = \{\text{odd numbers} < 10\}$,   and $B = \{\text{primes} < 10\}$.

   a   List sets A and B.
   b   Find $A \cap B$ and $A \cup B$.

   c   Represent the sets A and B on a Venn diagram.

3   Suppose $U = \{x \mid 1 \leqslant x \leqslant 9,\ x \in \mathbb{Z}\}$, $A = \{\text{factors of } 6\}$,   and $B = \{\text{factors of } 9\}$.

   a   List sets A and B.
   b   Find $A \cap B$ and $A \cup B$.

   c   Represent the sets A and B on a Venn diagram.

4   Suppose $U = \{\text{even numbers between 0 and 30}\}$,
   $P = \{\text{multiples of 4 less than 30}\}$,   and
   $Q = \{\text{multiples of 6 less than 30}\}$.

   a   List sets P and Q.
   b   Find $P \cap Q$ and $P \cup Q$.

   c   Represent the sets P and Q on a Venn diagram.

5   Suppose $U = \{x \mid x \leqslant 30,\ x \in \mathbb{Z}^{+}\}$, $R = \{\text{primes less than 30}\}$,   and
   $S = \{\text{composites less than 30}\}$.

   a   List sets R and S.
   b   Find $R \cap S$ and $R \cup S$.

   c   Represent the sets R and S on a Venn diagram.

6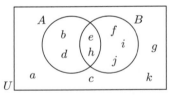

List the elements of set:

   a A
   b B
   c A'

   d B'
   e $A \cap B$
   f $A \cup B$

   g $(A \cup B)'$
   h $A' \cup B'$

7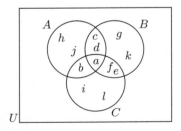

This Venn diagram consists of three overlapping circles A, B, and C.

   a   List the letters in set:

   i A
   ii B
   iii C

   iv $A \cap B$
   v $A \cup B$
   vi $B \cap C$

   vii $A \cap B \cap C$
   viii $A \cup B \cup C$

   b   Find:

   i $n(A \cup B \cup C)$

   ii $n(A) + n(B) + n(C) - n(A \cap B) - n(A \cap C) - n(B \cap C) + n(A \cap B \cap C)$

   c   What do you notice about your answers in **b**?

E   VENN DIAGRAM REGIONS

We can use shading to show various sets on a Venn diagram.
For example, for two intersecting sets A and B:

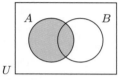
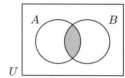
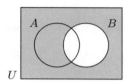
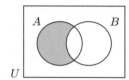

A is shaded $A \cap B$ is shaded B' is shaded $A \cap B'$ is shaded

---

Example 8	◀) Self Tutor

Shade the following regions for two intersecting sets A and B:

   a $A \cup B$ **b** $A' \cap B$ **c** $(A \cap B)'$

a 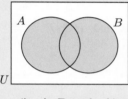   **b** 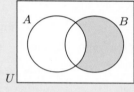   **c**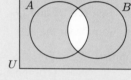

  (in A, B, or both)   (outside A, intersected with B)   (outside $A \cap B$)

EXERCISE 7E

1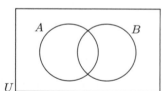

On separate Venn diagrams, shade regions for:

  a $A \cap B$ **b** $A \cap B'$
  c $A' \cup B$ **d** $A \cup B'$
  e $(A \cap B)'$ **f** $(A \cup B)'$

PRINTABLE VENN DIAGRAMS (OVERLAPPING)

2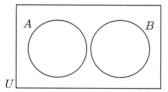

Suppose A and B are two disjoint sets. Shade on separate Venn diagrams:

  a A **b** B **c** A'
  d B' **e** $A \cap B$
  f $A \cup B$ **g** $A' \cap B$
  h $A \cup B'$ **i** $(A \cap B)'$

PRINTABLE VENN DIAGRAMS (DISJOINT)

3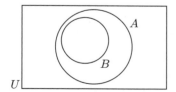

Suppose $B \subseteq A$, as shown in the given Venn diagram. Shade on separate Venn diagrams:

  a A **b** B **c** A'
  d B' **e** $A \cap B$
  f $A \cup B$ **g** $A' \cap B$
  h $A \cup B'$ **i** $(A \cap B)'$

PRINTABLE VENN DIAGRAMS (SUBSET)

4

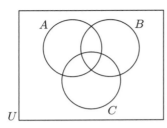

This Venn diagram consists of three intersecting sets. Shade on separate Venn diagrams:

a A	**b** B'
c $B \cap C$	**d** $A \cup B$
e $A \cap B \cap C$	**f** $A \cup B \cup C$
g $(A \cap B \cap C)'$	**h** $(A \cup B) \cap C$
i $(B \cap C) \cup A$	

PRINTABLE VENN DIAGRAMS (3 SETS)

Click on the icon to practise shading regions representing various subsets. You can practise with both two and three intersecting sets.

VENN DIAGRAMS

F   NUMBERS IN REGIONS

We have seen that there are four regions on a Venn diagram which contains two overlapping sets A and B.

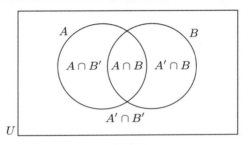

There are many situations where we are only interested in the **number of elements** of U that are in each region. We do not need to show all the elements on the diagram, so instead we write the number of elements in each region in brackets.

For example, the Venn diagram opposite shows there are 4 elements in both sets A and B, and 3 elements in neither set A nor B.

Every element in U belongs in only one region of the Venn diagram. So, in total there are $7 + 4 + 6 + 3 = 20$ elements in the universal set U.

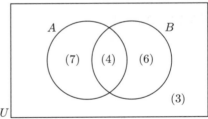

Example 9   ◀) **Self Tutor**

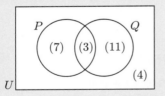

In the Venn diagram given, (3) means that there are 3 elements in the set $P \cap Q$. How many elements are there in:

a P	**b** Q'
c $P \cup Q$	**d** P, but not Q
e Q, but not P	**f** neither P nor Q?

a $n(P) = 7 + 3 = 10$	**b** $n(Q') = 7 + 4 = 11$
c $n(P \cup Q) = 7 + 3 + 11 = 21$	**d** $n(P,$ but not $Q) = 7$
e $n(Q,$ but not $P) = 11$	**f** $n($neither P nor $Q) = 4$

Venn diagrams allow us to easily visualise identities such as

$$n(A \cap B') = n(A) - n(A \cap B)$$
$$n(A' \cap B) = n(B) - n(A \cap B)$$

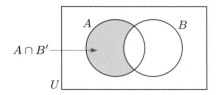

EXERCISE 7F

1

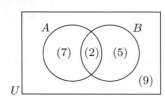

In the Venn diagram given, (2) means that there are 2 elements in the set $A \cap B$. How many elements are there in:

a B
b A'
c $A \cup B$
d A, but not B
e B, but not A
f neither A nor B?

2

Give the number of elements in:

a X'
b $X \cap Y$
c $X \cup Y$
d X, but not Y
e Y, but not X
f neither X nor Y.

3

In the Venn diagram given, (a) means that there are a elements in the shaded region.
Notice that $n(A) = a + b$.
Find:

a $n(B)$ **b** $n(A')$ **c** $n(A \cap B)$
d $n(A \cup B)$ **e** $n((A \cap B)')$ **f** $n((A \cup B)')$

4

The Venn diagram shows that $n(P \cap Q) = a$ and $n(P) = 3a$.

a Find:
   i $n(Q)$ **ii** $n(P \cup Q)$
   iii $n(Q')$ **iv** $n(U)$

b Find a if:
   i $n(U) = 29$ **ii** $n(U) = 31$
Comment on your results.

5

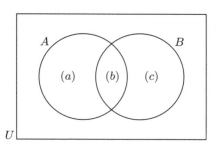

Use the Venn diagram to show that:
$$n(A \cup B) = n(A) + n(B) - n(A \cap B)$$

Example 10   ◀)) **Self Tutor**

Given $n(U) = 30$, $n(A) = 14$, $n(B) = 17$, and $n(A \cap B) = 6$, find:

a $n(A \cup B)$ 　　　　　　　　　　b $n(A, \text{ but not } B)$

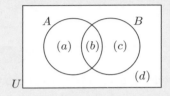

We see that　$b = 6$　　$\{\text{as }n(A \cap B) = 6\}$
$a + b = 14$　　$\{\text{as }n(A) = 14\}$
$b + c = 17$　　$\{\text{as }n(B) = 17\}$
$a + b + c + d = 30$　　$\{\text{as }n(U) = 30\}$

$\therefore\ b = 6,\ a = 8,\ \text{and }c = 11$
$\therefore\ 8 + 6 + 11 + d = 30$
$\therefore\ d = 5$

a $n(A \cup B) = a + b + c = 25$ 　　　b $n(A, \text{ but not } B) = a = 8$

6　Given $n(U) = 26$, $n(A) = 11$, $n(B) = 12$, and $n(A \cap B) = 8$, find:
　　a $n(A \cup B)$ 　　　　　　　　b $n(B, \text{ but not } A)$

7　Given $n(U) = 32$, $n(M) = 13$, $n(M \cap N) = 5$, and $n(M \cup N) = 26$, find:
　　a $n(N)$ 　　　　　　　　　　b $n((M \cup N)')$

8　Given $n(U) = 50$, $n(S) = 30$, $n(R) = 25$, and $n(R \cup S) = 48$, find:
　　a $n(R \cap S)$ 　　　　　　　　b $n(S, \text{ but not } R)$

G ┃ PROBLEM SOLVING WITH VENN DIAGRAMS

In this section we use Venn diagrams to illustrate real world situations. We can solve problems by considering the number of elements in each region.

Example 11   ◀)) **Self Tutor**

A squash club has 27 members. 19 have black hair, 14 have brown eyes, and 11 have both black hair and brown eyes.

a Place this information on a Venn diagram.

b Hence find the number of members with:
　i black hair or brown eyes
　ii black hair, but not brown eyes.

a Let Bl represent the black hair set and Br represent the brown eyes set.

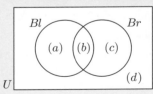

$a + b + c + d = 27$　　$\{\text{total members}\}$
$a + b = 19$　　$\{\text{black hair}\}$
$b + c = 14$　　$\{\text{brown eyes}\}$
$b = 11$　　$\{\text{black hair and brown eyes}\}$
$\therefore\ a = 8,\ c = 3,\ d = 5$

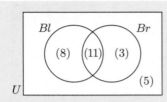

b   **i** $n(Bl \cup Br) = 8 + 11 + 3 = 22$

22 members have black hair or brown eyes.

ii $n(Bl \cap Br') = 8$

8 members have black hair, but not brown eyes.

Example 12   ◄)) **Self Tutor**

A platform diving squad of 25 has 18 members who dive from 10 m and 17 who dive from 4 m. How many dive from both platforms?

Let T represent those who dive from 10 m and
F represent those who dive from 4 m.

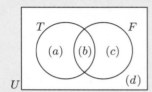

$d = 0$ {as all divers in the squad must dive
from at least one of the platforms}

$a + b = 18$

$b + c = 17$ ∴ $a = 8$, $b = 10$, $c = 7$

$a + b + c = 25$

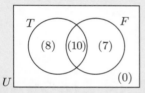

$n(\text{both } T \text{ and } F) = n(T \cap F)$
$= 10$

10 members dive from both platforms.

EXERCISE 7G

1 Pelé has 14 cavies as pets. Five have long hair and 8 are brown. Two are both brown and have long hair.

    a Place this information on a Venn diagram.

    b Hence find the number of cavies that:

       i   do not have long hair

      ii   have long hair and are not brown

     iii   are neither long-haired nor brown.

2

During a 2 week period, Murielle took her umbrella with her on 8 days. It rained on 9 days, and Murielle took her umbrella on five of the days when it rained.

    a Display this information on a Venn diagram.

    b Hence find the number of days that:

       i   Murielle did not take her umbrella and it rained

      ii   Murielle did not take her umbrella and it did not rain.

3 A badminton club has 31 playing members. 28 play singles and 16 play doubles. How many play both singles and doubles?

4 In a factory, 56 people work on the assembly line. 47 work day shifts and 29 work night shifts. How many work both day shifts and night shifts?

Example 13   ◀» **Self Tutor**

A city has three football teams in the national league: A, B, and C.

In the last season, 20% of the city's population saw team A play, 24% saw team B, and 28% saw team C. Of these, 4% saw both A and B, 5% saw both A and C, and 6% saw both B and C. 1% saw all three teams play.

Using a Venn diagram, find the percentage of the city's population which:

  a saw only team A play

  b saw team A or team B play but not team C

  c did not see any of the teams play.

We construct the Venn diagram in terms of percentages.

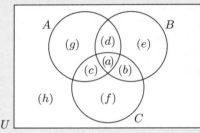

Using the given information,

$$a = 1 \qquad \{1\% \text{ saw all three teams play}\}$$
$$a + d = 4 \qquad \{4\% \text{ saw } A \text{ and } B\}$$
$$a + b = 6 \qquad \{6\% \text{ saw } B \text{ and } C\}$$
$$a + c = 5 \qquad \{5\% \text{ saw } A \text{ and } C\}$$

$$\therefore \quad d = 3, \quad b = 5, \quad \text{and} \quad c = 4$$

In total, 20% saw team A play,
so $g + 1 + 4 + 3 = 20$ $\therefore$ $g = 12$

24% saw team B play,
so $e + 1 + 5 + 3 = 24$ $\therefore$ $e = 15$

28% saw team C play,
so $f + 1 + 5 + 4 = 28$ $\therefore$ $f = 18$

In total we cover 100% of the population, so $h = 42$.

  a $n(\text{saw } A \text{ only}) = 12\%$ {shaded}

  b $n(A \text{ or } B, \text{ but not } C)$
      $= 12\% + 3\% + 15\%$
      $= 30\%$

  c $n(\text{saw none of the teams}) = 42\%$

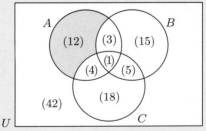

5 In a year group of 63 students, 22 study Biology, 26 study Chemistry, and 25 study Physics. 18 study both Physics and Chemistry, 4 study both Biology and Chemistry, and 3 study both Physics and Biology. 1 studies all three subjects.

    a Display this information on a Venn diagram.

    b How many students study:

        i Biology only   **ii** Physics or Chemistry

        iii none of Biology, Physics, or Chemistry   **iv** Physics but not Chemistry?

6 36 students participated in the mid-year adventure trip. 19 students went paragliding, 21 went abseiling, and 16 went white water rafting. 7 went abseiling and rafting, 8 went paragliding and rafting, and 11 went paragliding and abseiling. 5 students did all three activities. Find the number of students who:

    a went paragliding or abseiling

    b only went white water rafting

    c did not participate in any of the activities mentioned

    d did exactly two of the activities mentioned.

7 There are 32 students in the woodwind section of the school orchestra. 11 students can play the flute, 15 can play the clarinet, and 12 can play the saxophone. 2 can play the flute and the saxophone, 2 can play the flute and the clarinet, and 6 can play the clarinet and the saxophone. 1 student can play all three instruments. Find the number of students who can play:

    a none of the instruments mentioned   **b** only the saxophone

    c the saxophone and the clarinet, but not the flute

    d only one of the clarinet, saxophone, or flute.

8 In a particular region, most farms have livestock and crops. A survey of 21 farms showed that 15 grow crops, 9 have cattle, and 11 have sheep. 4 have sheep and cattle, 7 have cattle and crops, and 8 have sheep and crops. 3 have cattle, sheep, and crops. Find the number of farms with:

    a only crops   **b** only animals   **c** exactly one type of animal, and crops.

REVIEW SET 7A

1 If $S = \{x \mid 2 < x \leqslant 7, \ x \in \mathbb{Z}\}$:

    a list the elements of S **b** find $n(S)$.

2 Determine whether $A \subseteq B$ for the following sets:

    a $A = \{2, 4, 6, 8\}$ and $B = \{x \mid 0 < x < 10, \ x \in \mathbb{Z}\}$

    b $A = \varnothing$ and $B = \{x \mid 2 < x < 3, \ x \in \mathbb{R}\}$

    c $A = \{x \mid 2 < x \leqslant 4, \ x \in \mathbb{Q}\}$ and $B = \{x \mid 0 \leqslant x < 4, \ x \in \mathbb{R}\}$

    d $A = \{x \mid x < 3, \ x \in \mathbb{R}\}$ and $B = \{x \mid x \leqslant 4, \ x \in \mathbb{R}\}$

3 Find the complement of X given that:

    a $U = \{\text{the 7 colours of the rainbow}\}$ and $X = \{\text{red, indigo, violet}\}$

    b $U = \{x \mid -5 \leqslant x \leqslant 5, \ x \in \mathbb{Z}\}$ and $X = \{-4, -1, 3, 4\}$

    c $U = \{x \mid x \in \mathbb{Q}\}$ and $X = \{x \mid x < -8, \ x \in \mathbb{Q}\}$

4 On separate Venn diagrams like the one alongside, shade:

   a N' **b** $M \cap N$ **c** $M \cap N'$

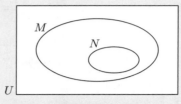

5 Let $U = \{$the letters in the English alphabet$\}$, $A = \{$the letters in "springbok"$\}$, and $B = \{$the letters in "waterbuck"$\}$.

   a Find: **i** $A \cup B$ **ii** $A \cap B$ **iii** $A \cap B'$

   b Write a description for each of the sets in **a**.

   c Show U, A, and B on a Venn diagram.

6 Let $U = \{x \mid x \leqslant 30, \ x \in \mathbb{Z}^+\}$, $P = \{$factors of 24$\}$, and $Q = \{$factors of 30$\}$.

   a List the elements of: **i** P **ii** Q **iii** $P \cap Q$ **iv** $P \cup Q$

   b Illustrate the sets P and Q on a Venn diagram.

7 A school has 564 students. During Term 1, 229 of them were absent for at least one day due to sickness, and 111 students missed some school because of family holidays. 296 students attended every day of Term 1.

   a Display this information on a Venn diagram.

   b Find how many students:

      i missed school for both illness and holidays

      ii were away for holidays but not sickness

      iii were absent during Term 1 for any reason.

8 The main courses at a restaurant all contain rice or onion. Of the 23 choices, 17 contain onion and 14 contain rice. How many dishes contain both rice and onion?

9 38 students were asked what life skills they had. 15 could swim, 12 could drive, and 23 could cook. 9 could cook and swim, 5 could swim and drive, and 6 could drive and cook. There was 1 student who could do all three. Find the number of students who:

   a could only cook

   b could not do any of these things

   c had exactly two life skills.

10 Consider the sets $U = \{x \mid x \leqslant 10, \ x \in \mathbb{Z}^+\}$, $P = \{$odd numbers less than 10$\}$, and $Q = \{$even numbers less than 11$\}$.

   a List the sets P and Q.   **b** What can be said about sets P and Q?

   c Illustrate sets P and Q on a Venn diagram.

REVIEW SET 7B

1 True or false?

   a $\mathbb{N} \subset \mathbb{Q}$ **b** $0 \in \mathbb{Z}^+$ **c** $0 \in \mathbb{Q}$ **d** $\mathbb{R} \subseteq \mathbb{Q}$ **e** $\mathbb{Z}^+ \cap \mathbb{Z}^- = \{0\}$

2   **a**   Write in interval notation:
   i   the real numbers between 5 and 12
   ii   the integers between -4 and 7, including -4
   iii   the natural numbers greater than 45.

   b   Which sets in **a** are finite and which are infinite?

3   List the subsets of $\{1, 3, 5\}$.

4   Let $U = \{x \mid 0 < x < 10, \ x \in \mathbb{Z}\}$, $A = \{\text{the even integers between 0 and 9}\}$,   and
   $B = \{\text{the factors of 8}\}$.

   a   List the elements of: **i** A **ii** $A \cap B$ **iii** $(A \cup B)'$
   b   Represent this information on a Venn diagram.

5 S and T are disjoint sets. $n(S) = s$ and $n(T) = t$.   Find:
   a $S \cap T$ **b** $n(S \cup T)$

6   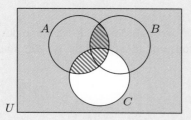   Give an expression for the region shaded in:
   a   blue   **b**   red.

7   In a car club, 13 members drive a manual and 15 members have a sunroof on their car. 5 have manual cars with a sunroof, and 4 have neither.
   a   Display this information on a Venn diagram.
   b   How many members:
   i   are in the club   **ii**   drive a manual car without a sunroof
   iii   do not drive a manual?

8   All attendees of a camp left something at home. 11 forgot to bring their towel, and 23 forgot their hat. Of the 30 campers, how many had neither a hat nor a towel?

9   Consider the sets $U = \{x \mid x \leqslant 40, \ x \in \mathbb{Z}^+\}$, $A = \{\text{factors of 40}\}$,   and
   $B = \{\text{factors of 20}\}$.

   a   List the sets A and B.   **b**   What can be said about sets A and B?
   c   Illustrate sets A and B on a Venn diagram.

10   At a conference, the 58 delegates speak many different languages. 28 speak Arabic, 27 speak Chinese, and 39 speak English. 12 speak Arabic and Chinese, 16 speak both Chinese and English, and 17 speak Arabic and English. 2 speak all three languages. How many delegates speak:

   a   Chinese only
   b   none of these languages
   c   neither Arabic nor Chinese?

Chapter 8

Logic

Syllabus reference: 3.1, 3.2, 3.3, 3.4

Contents:

OPENING PROBLEM

On Saint Patrick's Day, the students in a class are all encouraged to wear green clothes to school.

Brogan   Eamonn   Padraig   Sean

Things to think about:

For each of these statements, list the students for which the statement is true:

 a I am wearing a green shirt.

 b I am not wearing a green shirt.

 c I am wearing a green shirt and green pants.

 d I am wearing a green shirt or green pants.

 e I am wearing a green shirt or green pants, but not both.

Mathematical logic deals with the conversion of worded statements into symbols, and how we can apply rules of deduction to them. The concept was originally suggested by **G W Leibniz** (1646-1716).

George Boole (1815-1864) introduced the symbols which we use for analysis.   Other important contributors to the field include Bertrand Russell, Augustus DeMorgan, David Hilbert, John Venn, Giuseppe Peano, and Gottlob Frege.

Mathematical arguments require basic **definitions** and **axioms**, which are simple statements that we accept without proof. Logical reasoning is then essential to building clear rules based upon these definitions.

G W Leibniz

A   PROPOSITIONS

Propositions are statements which may be true or false.

Questions are not propositions.

Comments or opinions that are subjective, for example, 'Green is a nice colour' are also not propositions since they are not definitely true or false.

Propositions may be **indeterminate**. For example, 'your father is 50 years old' would not have the same answer (true or false) for all people.

The **truth value** of a proposition is whether it is true or false.

Example 1

◀》 **Self Tutor**

Which of the following statements are propositions? If they are propositions, are they true, false, or indeterminate?

a $20 \div 4 = 80$

b $25 \times 8 = 200$

c Where is my pen?

d Your eyes are blue.

a This is a proposition. It is false as $20 \div 4 = 5$.

b This is a proposition and is true.

c This is a question, so is not a proposition.

d This is a proposition. It is indeterminate, as the statement is true for some people and false for other people.

PROPOSITION NOTATION

We represent propositions by letters such as p, q, and r.

For example, p: It always rains on Tuesdays.

q: $37 + 9 = 46$

r: x is an even number.

NEGATION

The **negation** of a proposition p is "not p", and is written as $\neg p$.
The truth value of $\neg p$ is the opposite of the truth value of p.

For example:

- The negation of p: It is raining is $\neg p$: It is not raining.
- The negation of p: Tim has brown hair is $\neg p$: Tim does not have brown hair.

From these examples, we can see that $\neg p$ is $\begin{cases} \text{false when } p \text{ is true} \\ \text{true when } p \text{ is false.} \end{cases}$

This information can be represented in a **truth table**. The first column contains the possible truth values for p, and the second column contains the corresponding values for $\neg p$.

p	$\neg p$
T	F
F	T

EXERCISE 8A.1

1 Which of the following statements are propositions? If they are propositions, are they true, false, or indeterminate?

a $11 - 5 = 7$

b $12 \in \{\text{odd numbers}\}$

c $\frac{3}{4} \in \mathbb{Q}$

d $2 \notin \mathbb{Q}$

e A hexagon has 6 sides.

f $37 \in \{\text{prime numbers}\}$

g How tall are you?

h All squares are rectangles.

i Is it snowing?

j A rectangle is not a parallelogram.

k Your brother is 13.

l Do you like dramatic movies?

m Joan sings loudly.

n You were born in China.

o Alternate angles are equal.

p Parallel lines eventually meet.

2 For each of the following propositions:

    i write down the negation   **ii** indicate if the proposition or its negation is true.

a p: All rectangles are parallelograms.   **b** m: $\sqrt{5}$ is an irrational number.

c r: 7 is a rational number.   **d** q: $23 - 14 = 12$

e r: $52 \div 4 = 13$

f s: The difference between two odd numbers is always even.

g t: The product of consecutive integers is always even.

h u: All obtuse angles are equal.   **i** p: All trapeziums are parallelograms.

j q: If a triangle has two equal angles it is isosceles.

3 Find the negation of these propositions for $x, y \in \mathbb{R}$:

a $x < 5$ **b** $x \geqslant 3$ **c** $y < 8$ **d** $y \leqslant 10$

4 For the two propositions r and s given:

    i Is s the negation of r?

    ii If s is not the negation of r, give the correct negation of r.

a r: Kania scored more than 60%. s: Kania scored less than 60%.

b r: Dea has less than two sisters. s: Dea has at least two sisters.

c r: Fari is at soccer practice. s: Fari is at music practice.

d r: I have been to Canada. s: I have never been to Canada.

e r: I drank black tea today. s: I drank white tea today.

Example 2	◀)) **Self Tutor**
Find the negation of: **a** x is a dog for $x \in \{$dogs, cats$\}$ **b** $x \geqslant 2$ for $x \in \mathbb{N}$ **c** $x \geqslant 2$ for $x \in \mathbb{Z}$.	**a** x is a cat. **b** $x \in \{0, 1\}$ **c** $x < 2$ for $x \in \mathbb{Z}$

---

5 Find the negation of:

a $x \geqslant 5$ for $x \in \mathbb{Z}^+$ **b** $x \geqslant 0$ for $x \in \mathbb{Z}$

c x is a cow for $x \in \{$horses, sheep, cows, goats, deer$\}$

d x is a male student for $x \in \{$students$\}$ **e** x is a female student for $x \in \{$females$\}$.

NEGATION AND VENN DIAGRAMS

Many propositions contain a variable. The proposition may be true for some values of the variable, and false for others.

We can use a **Venn diagram** to represent these propositions and their negations.

For example, consider p: x is greater than 10.

  U is the **universal set** of all the values that the variable x may take.

  P is the **truth set** of the proposition p, or the set of values of $x \in U$ for which p is true.

  P' is the truth set of $\neg p$.

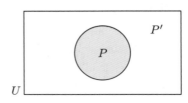

Example 3
◀) **Self Tutor**

Consider $U = \{x \mid 0 < x < 10, \ x \in \mathbb{N}\}$ and proposition p: x is a prime number.

Find the truth sets of p and $\neg p$, and display them on a Venn diagram.

If P is the truth set of p then $P = \{2, 3, 5, 7\}$.

The truth set of $\neg p$ is $P' = \{1, 4, 6, 8, 9\}$

The Venn diagram representation is:

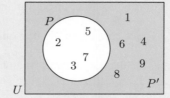

EXERCISE 8A.2

1 Find the truth sets of these statements, and display **a** and **b** on a Venn diagram:
   a p: x is a multiple of 3, for $U = \{x \mid 20 < x < 30, \ x \in \mathbb{Z}\}$
   b p: x is an even number, for $U = \{x \mid 1 < x \leqslant 10, \ x \in \mathbb{Z}\}$
   c p: x is a factor of 42, for $U = \mathbb{Z}$.

2 Suppose $U = \{$students in Year 11$\}$, $M = \{$students who study music$\}$, and $O = \{$students who play in the orchestra$\}$.
   Draw a Venn diagram to represent the statements:
   a All music students play in the school orchestra.
   b None of the orchestral students study music.
   c No-one in the orchestra does not study music.

3 **a** Represent $U = \{x \mid 5 < x < 15, \ x \in \mathbb{N}\}$ and p: $x < 9$ on a Venn diagram.
   b List the truth set of $\neg p$.

4 **a** Represent $U = \{x \mid x < 10, \ x \in \mathbb{N}\}$ and p: x is a multiple of 2 on a Venn diagram.
   b List the truth set of $\neg p$.

B   COMPOUND PROPOSITIONS

Compound propositions are statements which are formed using connectives such as **and** and **or**.

CONJUNCTION

When two propositions are joined using the word **and**, the new proposition is the **conjunction** of the original propositions.

If p and q are propositions, $p \wedge q$ is used to denote their conjunction.

For example: p: Eli had soup for lunch

q: Eli had a pie for lunch

$p \wedge q$: Eli had soup and a pie for lunch.

$p \wedge q$ is only true if Eli had both soup *and* a pie for lunch, which means that both p and q are true.

If either of p or q is not true, or both p and q are not true, then $p \wedge q$ is not true.

> A conjunction is true only when both original propositions are true.

The truth table for the conjunction "p and q" is:

p	q	$p \wedge q$
T	T	T
T	F	F
F	T	F
F	F	F

$p \wedge q$ is true when both p and q are true.

$p \wedge q$ is false whenever one or both of p and q are false.

The first 2 columns list the possible combinations for p and q.

We can use Venn diagrams to represent conjunctions.

Suppose P is the truth set of p, and
Q is the truth set of q.

The truth set of $p \wedge q$ is $P \cap Q$, the region where both p **and** q are true.

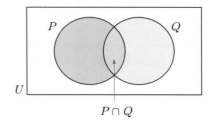

$P \cap Q$

EXERCISE 8B.1

1   Write $p \wedge q$ for the following pairs of propositions:

   a p: Ted is a doctor, q: Shelly is a dentist.

   b p: x is greater than 15, q: x is less than 30.

   c p: It is windy, q: It is raining.

   d p: Kim has brown hair, q: Kim has blue eyes.

2   For the following pairs of propositions p and q, determine whether $p \wedge q$ is true or false:

   a p: 5 is an odd number, q: 5 is a prime number.

   b p: A square has four sides, q: A triangle has five sides.

   c p: $39 < 27$, q: $16 > 23$

   d p: 3 is a factor of 12, q: 4 is a factor of 12.

   e p: $5 + 8 = 12$, q: $6 + 9 = 15$.

3   For $U = \{x \mid 1 \leqslant x \leqslant 12, \ x \in \mathbb{Z}\}$, consider the propositions
p: x is even and q: x is less than 7.

   a   Illustrate the truth sets for p and q on a Venn diagram like the one alongside.

   b   Use your Venn diagram to find the truth set of $p \wedge q$.

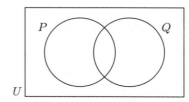

DISJUNCTION

When two propositions are joined by the word **or**, the new proposition is the **disjunction** of the original propositions.

If p and q are propositions, $p \lor q$ is used to denote their disjunction.

For example:

p: Frank played tennis today
q: Frank played golf today
$p \lor q$: Frank played tennis or golf today.

$p \lor q$ is true if Frank played tennis or golf *or both* today.

So, $p \lor q$ is true if p or q or both are true.

A disjunction is true when one or both propositions are true.

Alternatively, we can say that

A disjunction is only false if both propositions are false.

The truth table for the disjunction "p or q" is:

p	q	$p \lor q$
T	T	T
T	F	T
F	T	T
F	F	F

$p \lor q$ is true if p or q or both are true.

$p \lor q$ is only false if both p and q are false.

If P and Q are the truth sets for propositions p and q respectively, then the truth set for $p \lor q$ is $P \cup Q$, the region where p or q or both are true.

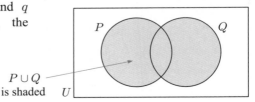

$P \cup Q$
is shaded

EXCLUSIVE DISJUNCTION

The **exclusive disjunction** is true when **only one** of the propositions is true.

The exclusive disjunction of p and q is written $p \veebar q$.

We can describe $p \veebar q$ as "p or q, but not both", or "exactly one of p and q".

For example:

p: Sally ate cereal for breakfast
q: Sally ate toast for breakfast
$p \veebar q$: Sally ate cereal or toast, but not both, for breakfast.

The truth table for the exclusive disjunction $p \veebar q$ is:

p	q	$p \veebar q$
T	T	F
T	F	T
F	T	T
F	F	F

$p \veebar q$ is true if exactly one of p and q is true.

$p \veebar q$ is false if p and q are both true or both false.

If P and Q are the truth sets for propositions p and q respectively, then the truth set for $p \veebar q$ is the region shaded, where exactly one of p and q is true.

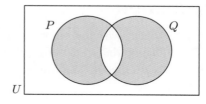

EXERCISE 8B.2

1 Write the disjunction $p \vee q$ for the following pairs of propositions:

  a p: Tim owns a bicycle, q: Tim owns a scooter.

  b p: x is a multiple of 2, q: x is a multiple of 5.

  c p: Dana studies Physics, q: Dana studies Chemistry.

2 For the following propositions, determine whether $p \vee q$ is true or false:

  a p: 24 is a multiple of 4, q: 24 is a multiple of 6.

  b p: There are $100°$ in a right angle, q: There are $180°$ on a straight line.

  c p: $-8 > -5$, q: $5 < 0$

  d p: The mean of 5 and 9 is 7, q: The mean of 8 and 14 is 10.

3 Write the exclusive disjunction $p \veebar q$ for the following pairs of propositions:

  a p: Meryn will visit Japan next year, q: Meryn will visit Singapore next year.

  b p: Ann will invite Kate to her party, q: Ann will invite Tracy to her party.

  c p: x is a factor of 56, q: x is a factor of 40.

4 For the following pairs of propositions a and b, determine whether the exclusive disjunction $a \veebar b$ is true or false:

  a a: 23 is a prime number, b: 29 is a prime number.

  b a: 15 is even, b: 15 is a multiple of 3.

  c a: $4.5 \in \mathbb{Z}$, b: $-8 \in \mathbb{N}$

  d a: $2^3 \times 2^4 = 2^7$, b: $(2^8)^6 = 2^{42}$

5 Consider r: Kelly is a good driver, and s: Kelly has a good car.
Write in symbolic form:

  a Kelly is not a good driver

  b Kelly is a good driver and has a good car

  c Kelly does not have a good car and is not a good driver

  d Kelly has a good car or Kelly is a good driver.

6 Consider x: Sergio would like to go swimming tomorrow, and
          y: Sergio would like to go bowling tomorrow.
Write in symbolic form:

  a Sergio would not like to go swimming tomorrow

  b Sergio would like to go swimming and bowling tomorrow

  c Sergio would like to go swimming or bowling tomorrow

  d Sergio would not like to go both swimming and bowling tomorrow

  e Sergio would like either to go swimming or go bowling tomorrow, but not both.

7 For each of the following, define appropriate propositions and then write in symbolic form:

  a Phillip likes icecream and jelly.

  b Phillip likes icecream or Phillip does not like jelly.

  c x is both greater than 10 and a prime number.

  d Tuan can go to the mountains or the beach, but not both.

  e The computer is not on.

  f Angela does not have a watch but does have a mobile phone.

  g Maya studied one of Spanish or French.

  h I can hear thunder or an aeroplane.

8 If $p \vee q$ is true and $p \veebar q$ is false, determine the truth values of p and q.

9 For $U = \{x \mid 1 \leqslant x \leqslant 20, \ x \in \mathbb{Z}\}$, consider the propositions

  p: x is a multiple of 3, and q: x is an odd number.

  a Illustrate the truth sets for p and q on a Venn diagram.

  b Use your Venn diagram to find the truth set for:

  i $\neg q$ **ii** $p \vee q$ **iii** $p \wedge q$ **iv** $p \veebar q$

10 For $U = \{x \mid 1 \leqslant x \leqslant 12, \ x \in \mathbb{Z}\}$, consider the propositions p: x is prime, and q: x is a factor of 12.

  a Illustrate the truth sets for p and q on a Venn diagram.

  b Write down the meaning of:

  i $p \wedge q$ **ii** $p \vee q$ **iii** $p \veebar q$

  c Use your Venn diagram to find the truth sets for:

  i $p \wedge q$ **ii** $p \vee q$ **iii** $p \veebar q$

11 Read the description of Ed's day:

"Ed slept in, then had pancakes for breakfast. He went to the gym in the morning, then ate a sandwich for lunch. He played golf in the afternoon, and had steak for dinner."

Consider the following propositions:

p: Ed got out of bed early	q: Ed ate pancakes for breakfast
r: Ed ate steak for lunch	s: Ed ate steak for dinner
t: Ed ate fish for dinner	u: Ed went to the gym
v: Ed went to the movies	w: Ed played golf.

Determine whether the following are true or false:

  a p **b** s **c** $q \wedge u$ **d** $p \vee w$

  e $r \vee s$ **f** $r \wedge s$ **g** $r \veebar s$ **h** $t \vee v$

12 For each of the following propositions, write the corresponding set notation, and illustrate on a Venn diagram:

  a $p \vee q$ **b** $\neg p \vee q$ **c** $p \veebar q$ **d** $\neg p \wedge \neg q$

Example 4   ◄» **Self Tutor**

Let P be the truth set of proposition p and Q be the truth set of proposition q.
Use mathematical logic to express the following shaded regions in terms of p and q:

a
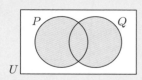
b
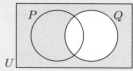
c
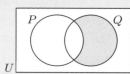

a The shaded region is $P \cup Q$, which is the region in P or Q or both.
   So, p or q or both are true, which is $p \vee q$.

b The shaded region is Q', which is the region not in Q.
   So, q is not true, which is $\neg q$.

c The shaded region is $P' \cap Q$, which is the region in Q but not in P.
   So, p is not true and q is true, which is $\neg p \wedge q$.

13 Let P be the truth set of proposition p and Q be the truth set of proposition q. Use mathematical
logic to express the following shaded regions in terms of p and q:

a
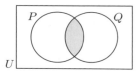
b
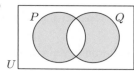
c
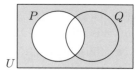

14 Consider a: The captain is male   and b: The captain is old.
Let A be the truth set of a and B be the truth set of b.
Interpret each of the following Venn diagrams:

a
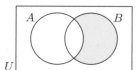
b
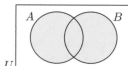
c

C   TRUTH TABLES AND LOGICAL EQUIVALENCE

The truth tables for negation, conjunction, disjunction, and exclusive disjunction can be summarised in
one table.

p	q	Negation $\neg p$	Conjunction $p \wedge q$	Disjunction $p \vee q$	Exclusive disjunction $p \veebar q$
T	T	F	T	T	F
T	F	F	F	T	T
F	T	T	F	T	T
F	F	T	F	F	F

We can use these rules to construct truth tables for more complicated propositions.

Example 5
🔊 **Self Tutor**

Construct a truth table for $p \lor \neg q$.

We start by listing all the possible combinations for p and q:

p	q	$\neg q$	$p \lor \neg q$
T	T		
T	F		
F	T		
F	F		

We then use the negation rule on the q column to find $\neg q$:

p	q	$\neg q$	$p \lor \neg q$
T	T	F	
T	F	T	
F	T	F	
F	F	T	

Finally, we use the disjunction rule on the p and $\neg q$ columns to find $p \lor \neg q$:

p	q	$\neg q$	$p \lor \neg q$
T	T	F	T
T	F	T	T
F	T	F	F
F	F	T	T

We can use graphics calculators to construct truth tables. We use 1 to represent *true*, and 0 to represent *false*. The screenshots below show how to construct the truth table for $p \lor \neg q$ as in **Example 5**:

GRAPHICS CALCULATOR INSTRUCTIONS

TI-*n*spire

Casio fx-CG20   **TI-84 Plus**

TAUTOLOGY AND LOGICAL CONTRADICTION

A compound proposition is a **tautology** if all the values in its truth table column are **true**.

A compound proposition is a **logical contradiction** if all the values in its truth table column are **false**.

Example 6
🔊 **Self Tutor**

Show that $p \lor \neg p$ is a tautology.

The truth table is:

p	$\neg p$	$p \lor \neg p$
T	F	T
F	T	T

All the values in the $p \lor \neg p$ column are true, so $p \lor \neg p$ is a tautology.

For any proposition p, either p is true or $\neg p$ is true. So, $p \lor \neg p$ is **always** true.

Example 7 ◀) **Self Tutor**

Show that $(\neg q \wedge p) \wedge (q \vee \neg p)$ is a logical contradiction.

The truth table is:

p	q	$\neg p$	$\neg q$	$(\neg q \wedge p)$	$(q \vee \neg p)$	$(\neg q \wedge p) \wedge (q \vee \neg p)$
T	T	F	F	F	T	F
T	F	F	T	T	F	F
F	T	T	F	F	T	F
F	F	T	T	F	T	F

All the values in the final column are false, so $(\neg q \wedge p) \wedge (q \vee \neg p)$ is a logical contradiction.

LOGICAL EQUIVALENCE

Two propositions are **logically equivalent** if they have the same truth table column.

Example 8 ◀) **Self Tutor**

Show that $\neg(p \wedge q)$ and $\neg p \vee \neg q$ are logically equivalent.

The truth table for $\neg(p \wedge q)$ is:

p	q	$p \wedge q$	$\neg(p \wedge q)$
T	T	T	F
T	F	F	T
F	T	F	T
F	F	F	T

The truth table for $\neg p \vee \neg q$ is:

p	q	$\neg p$	$\neg q$	$\neg p \vee \neg q$
T	T	F	F	F
T	F	F	T	T
F	T	T	F	T
F	F	T	T	T

Since the truth table columns for $\neg(p \wedge q)$ and $\neg p \vee \neg q$ are identical, $\neg(p \wedge q)$ and $\neg p \vee \neg q$ are logically equivalent.

So, $\neg(p \wedge q) = \neg p \vee \neg q$.

EXERCISE 8C.1

1 Construct a truth table for the following propositions:
 a $\neg p \wedge q$ **b** $\neg(p \veebar q)$ **c** $\neg p \vee \neg q$ **d** $p \vee p$

2 For the following propositions:
 i construct a truth table
 ii determine whether the proposition is a tautology, a logical contradiction, or neither.
 a $\neg p \wedge \neg q$ **b** $(p \vee q) \vee \neg p$ **c** $p \wedge (p \veebar q)$ **d** $(p \wedge q) \wedge (p \veebar q)$

3 a Explain why $p \wedge \neg p$ is always false.
 b Use a truth table to show that $p \wedge \neg p$ is a logical contradiction.

4   Use truth tables to establish the following logical equivalences:

   a $\neg(\neg p) = p$ **b** $p \wedge p = p$ **c** $p \vee (\neg p \wedge q) = p \vee q$

   d $\neg(p \veebar q) = p \veebar \neg q$ **e** $\neg(q \vee \neg p) = \neg q \wedge (p \vee q)$ **f** $\neg p \veebar (p \vee q) = p \vee \neg q$

5   **a**   Construct a truth table for $(\neg p \wedge q) \vee (p \wedge \neg q)$.

   b   Use the truth table summary on page **240** to identify a proposition logically equivalent to $(\neg p \wedge q) \vee (p \wedge \neg q)$.

6   **a**   Consider the propositions p: I like apples and q: I like bananas.
      Write the meaning of:

      i $p \vee q$ **ii** $\neg(p \vee q)$ **iii** $\neg p$ **iv** $\neg p \wedge \neg q$

   b   Use truth tables to show that $\neg(p \vee q)$ and $\neg p \wedge \neg q$ are logically equivalent.

7   **a**   Complete the truth table below:

p	q	$p \veebar q$	$q \wedge (p \veebar q)$	$(p \veebar q) \vee p$
T	T			
T	F			
F	T			
F	F			

   b   Consider the propositions p: $-3 \leqslant x \leqslant 7$ and q: $x \geqslant 2$.
      Find the values of x which make the following propositions true:

      i $p \veebar q$ **ii** $q \wedge (p \veebar q)$ **iii** $(p \veebar q) \vee p$

8   Explain why:

   a   any two tautologies are logically equivalent

   b   any two logical contradictions are logically equivalent.

9   What can be said about:

   a   the negation of a logical contradiction

   b   the negation of a tautology

   c   the disjunction of a tautology and any other statement?

TRUTH TABLES FOR THREE PROPOSITIONS

When three propositions are under consideration, we usually denote them p, q, and r.

The possible combinations of the truth values for p, q, and r are listed systematically in the table alongside.

p	q	r
T	T	T
T	T	F
T	F	T
T	F	F
F	T	T
F	T	F
F	F	T
F	F	F

Example 9	◀) Self Tutor

Construct a truth table for the compound proposition $(p \vee q) \wedge r$.

To find $(p \vee q) \wedge r$, we first find $p \vee q$.
We then find the conjunction of $p \vee q$ and r.

p	q	r	$p \vee q$	$(p \vee q) \wedge r$
T	T	T	T	T
T	T	F	T	F
T	F	T	T	T
T	F	F	T	F
F	T	T	T	T
F	T	F	T	F
F	F	T	F	F
F	F	F	F	F

EXERCISE 8C.2

1 Construct truth tables for these compound statements:

   a $\neg p \vee (q \wedge r)$ **b** $(p \vee \neg q) \wedge r$ **c** $(p \vee q) \vee (p \wedge \neg r)$

2 Determine whether the following propositions are tautologies, logical contradictions, or neither:

   a $(p \vee q) \vee \neg(r \wedge p)$ **b** $(p \veebar r) \wedge \neg q$ **c** $(q \wedge r) \wedge \neg(p \vee q)$

3 **a** Consider the propositions p: Jake owns a phone
                                q: Jake owns a TV
                                r: Jake owns a laptop.

   Write down the meaning of:

    i $p \wedge q$ **ii** $(p \wedge q) \wedge r$ **iii** $q \wedge r$ **iv** $p \wedge (q \wedge r)$

   b Use truth tables to show that $(p \wedge q) \wedge r = p \wedge (q \wedge r)$.

4 Use truth tables to show that $(p \vee q) \vee r$ and $p \vee (q \vee r)$ are logically equivalent.

5 **a** Consider the propositions p: Mary will study Mathematics next year
                                q: Mary will study French next year
                                r: Mary will study German next year.

   Write down the meaning of:

    i $q \vee r$ **ii** $p \wedge (q \vee r)$ **iii** $p \wedge q$ **iv** $p \wedge r$ **v** $(p \wedge q) \vee (p \wedge r)$

   b Use truth tables to show that $p \wedge (q \vee r) = (p \wedge q) \vee (p \wedge r)$.

6 **a** Use truth tables to show that $p \vee (q \wedge r) = (p \vee q) \wedge (p \vee r)$.

   b Consider the Venn diagram alongside, where P, Q, and R are the truth sets of p, q, and r respectively. On separate Venn diagrams, shade the truth set for:

    i $p \vee (q \wedge r)$
    ii $(p \vee q) \wedge (p \vee r)$

   Comment on your results.

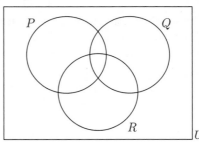

D   IMPLICATION AND EQUIVALENCE

IMPLICATION

If two propositions can be linked with "If .... then ....", then we have an **implication**.

The implicative statement "if p then q" is written $p \Rightarrow q$ and reads "p implies q".

p is called the **antecedent** and q is called the **consequent**.

For example: Given p: Kato has a TV set, and q: Kato can watch TV,

we have $p \Rightarrow q$: If Kato has a TV set, then Kato can watch TV.

THE TRUTH TABLE FOR IMPLICATION

Consider p: It will rain on Saturday, and q: The Falcons will win.

The implicative statement is $p \Rightarrow q$: If it rains on Saturday, then the Falcons will win.

To establish the truth table for $p \Rightarrow q$, we consider each of the possible combinations of p and q in turn:

p	q	Scenario	$p \Rightarrow q$
T	T	It rains on Saturday, and the Falcons win. This is consistent with the implicative statement.	T
T	F	It rains on Saturday, but the Falcons do not win. This is inconsistent with the implicative statement.	F
F	T	It does not rain on Saturday, and the Falcons win. This is consistent with the implicative statement, as no claim has been made regarding the outcome if it does not rain.	T
F	F	It does not rain on Saturday, and the Falcons do not win. Again, this is consistent with the implicative statement as no claim has been made regarding the outcome if it does not rain.	T

So, the truth table for $p \Rightarrow q$ is:

p	q	$p \Rightarrow q$
T	T	T
T	F	F
F	T	T
F	F	T

$p \Rightarrow q$ is only false if
p is true but q is false.

EQUIVALENCE

If two propositions are linked with ".... if and only if ....", then we have an **equivalence**.

The equivalence "p if and only if q" is written $p \Leftrightarrow q$.

$p \Leftrightarrow q$ is logically equivalent to the conjunction of the implications $p \Rightarrow q$ and $q \Rightarrow p$.

Consider p: I will pass the exam, and q: The exam is easy.

We have $p \Rightarrow q$: *If* I pass the exam, *then* the exam is easy.

$q \Rightarrow p$: *If* the exam is easy, *then* I will pass it.

$p \Leftrightarrow q$: I will pass the exam *if and only if* the exam is easy.

THE TRUTH TABLE FOR EQUIVALENCE

We can find the truth table for $p \Leftrightarrow q$ by constructing the truth table of its logical equivalent $(p \Rightarrow q) \wedge (q \Rightarrow p)$:

p	q	$p \Rightarrow q$	$q \Rightarrow p$	$(p \Rightarrow q) \wedge (q \Rightarrow p)$
T	T	T	T	T
T	F	F	T	F
F	T	T	F	F
F	F	T	T	T

So, the truth table for **equivalence** $p \Leftrightarrow q$ is:

p	q	$p \Leftrightarrow q$
T	T	T
T	F	F
F	T	F
F	F	T

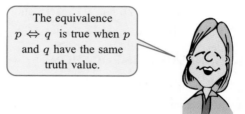

The equivalence $p \Leftrightarrow q$ is true when p and q have the same truth value.

EXERCISE 8D

1 In the following implicative statements, state the antecedent and the consequent.

  a If I miss the bus, then I will walk to school.

  b If the temperature is low enough, then the lake will freeze.

  c If $x > 20$, then $x > 10$.

  d If you jump all 8 hurdles, then you may win the race.

2 For the following propositions, write down the implicative statement $p \Rightarrow q$:

  a p: The sun is shining, q: I will go swimming

  b p: x is a multiple of 6, q: x is even

  c p: There are eggs in the fridge, q: Jan will bake a cake.

3 For the following propositions p and q:

  i write down the equivalence $p \Leftrightarrow q$

  ii state whether the equivalence is true or false.

  a p: Rome is the capital of Italy, q: Paris is the capital of France

  b p: $2x + 3 = 10$ is an expression, q: $2x + 3$ is an expression

  c p: Cows have nine legs, q: Horses have five heads.

4 Consider the propositions p: It is raining and q: There are puddles forming. Write the following statements in symbols:

  a If it is raining then puddles are forming.

  b If puddles are forming then it is raining.

  c Puddles are not forming.

  d It is not raining.

  e If it is not raining, then puddles are not forming.

  f If it is raining, then puddles are not forming.

  g If there are no puddles, then it is raining.

  h It is raining if and only if there are puddles forming.

5 Construct truth tables for:

    a $p \Rightarrow \neg q$ **b** $\neg q \Rightarrow \neg p$ **c** $(p \wedge q) \Rightarrow p$ **d** $q \wedge (p \Rightarrow q)$

    e $p \Leftrightarrow \neg q$ **f** $(p \Leftrightarrow q) \wedge \neg p$ **g** $p \Rightarrow (p \wedge \neg q)$ **h** $(p \Rightarrow q) \Rightarrow \neg p$

6 By examining truth tables, show that:

    a $p \veebar q = \neg(p \Leftrightarrow q)$ **b** $\neg p \Rightarrow q = p \vee q$

    c $q \Rightarrow (p \veebar q) = \neg(p \wedge q)$ **d** $p \Leftrightarrow q = (p \wedge q) \vee (\neg p \wedge \neg q)$

7 Which of these forms are logically equivalent to the negation of $q \Rightarrow p$?

    A $p \Rightarrow q$ **B** $\neg q \Rightarrow p$ **C** $q \Rightarrow \neg p$ **D** $\neg(\neg p \Rightarrow \neg q)$

8 Determine whether the following are logical contradictions, tautologies, or neither:

    a $p \Rightarrow (\neg p \wedge q)$ **b** $(p \wedge q) \Rightarrow (p \vee q)$ **c** $(p \Rightarrow \neg q) \vee (\neg p \Rightarrow q)$

E   CONVERSE, INVERSE, AND CONTRAPOSITIVE

THE CONVERSE

> The **converse** of the statement $p \Rightarrow q$ is the statement $q \Rightarrow p$.

The converse has truth table:

p	q	$q \Rightarrow p$
T	T	T
T	F	T
F	T	F
F	F	T

Example 10   ◀) **Self Tutor**

For p: the triangle is isosceles, and q: two angles of the triangle are equal, state $p \Rightarrow q$ and its converse $q \Rightarrow p$.

$p \Rightarrow q$:   If the triangle is isosceles, then two of its angles are equal.

$q \Rightarrow p$:   If two angles of the triangle are equal, then the triangle is isosceles.

THE INVERSE

> The **inverse** statement of $p \Rightarrow q$ is the statement $\neg p \Rightarrow \neg q$.

The inverse has truth table:

p	q	$\neg p$	$\neg q$	$\neg p \Rightarrow \neg q$
T	T	F	F	T
T	F	F	T	T
F	T	T	F	F
F	F	T	T	T

This is the same truth table as $q \Rightarrow p$, so the converse and inverse of an implication are logically equivalent.

THE CONTRAPOSITIVE

> The **contrapositive** of the statement $p \Rightarrow q$ is the statement $\neg q \Rightarrow \neg p$.

The **contrapositive** has truth table:

p	q	$\neg q$	$\neg p$	$\neg q \Rightarrow \neg p$
T	T	F	F	T
T	F	T	F	F
F	T	F	T	T
F	F	T	T	T

The truth table for $\neg q \Rightarrow \neg p$ is the same as that for $p \Rightarrow q$, so the implication and its contrapositive are logically equivalent.

For example, consider p: Sam is in the library and q: Sam is reading.

Implication $p \Rightarrow q$	If Sam is in the library, then Sam is reading.
Converse $q \Rightarrow p$	If Sam is reading, then Sam is in the library.
Inverse $\neg p \Rightarrow \neg q$	If Sam is not in the library, then Sam is not reading.
Contrapositive $\neg q \Rightarrow \neg p$	If Sam is not reading, then Sam is not in the library.

logically equivalent

The implication and the converse are *not* logically equivalent since, for example, the implication allows for the possibility that Sam is reading in the classroom, but the converse does not.

Example 11	◀ᴐ **Self Tutor**

Write down the contrapositive of: "All teachers drive blue cars".

This statement is the same as "if a person is a teacher, then he or she drives a blue car".

This has the form $p \Rightarrow q$ with p: A person is a teacher and q: A person drives a blue car.

The contrapositive $\neg q \Rightarrow \neg p$ is "If a person does not drive a blue car, then the person is not a teacher."

EXERCISE 8E

1 Write the converse and inverse for:

   a If Nicole is wearing a jumper, then she is warm.

   b If two triangles are similar, then they are equiangular.

   c If $2x^2 = 12$, then $x = \pm\sqrt{6}$.

   d If Alex is in the playground, then he is having fun.

   e If a triangle is equilateral, then its three sides are equal in length.

2 Write down the contrapositives of these statements:

   a If a person is fair and clever then the person is a doctor.

   b All rose bushes have thorns.

    c All umpires make correct decisions all the time.

    d All good soccer players have good kicking skills.

    e Liquids always take the shape of the container in which they are placed.

3   **a** State the contrapositive of: "All high school students study Mathematics."

    b Suppose the statement in **a** is true. What, if anything, can be deduced about:

        i Keong, who is a high school student

        ii Tamra, who does not study Mathematics

        iii Eli, who studies English and Mathematics?

4 Write down the contrapositive of:

    a x is divisible by 3 $\Rightarrow$ x^2 is divisible by 9

    b x is a number ending in 2 $\Rightarrow$ x is even

    c PQRS is a rectangle $\Rightarrow$ PQ $\parallel$ SR and PS $\parallel$ QR

    d KLM is an equilateral triangle $\Rightarrow$ $\widehat{\text{KML}}$ measures $60°$.

5 Consider p: A house has at least 3 windows and q: A house has a chimney.   We construct the implication $p \Rightarrow q$: If a house has at least 3 windows, then it has a chimney.

    a For this implication, write down the:

        i converse   **ii** inverse   **iii** contrapositive.

    b Determine the truth values for the implication, converse, inverse, and contrapositive for each of these houses:

    i    **ii**    **iii**

6 W represents all weak students and E represents all Year 11 students.

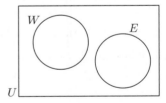

    a Copy and complete:

        i No weak students are ....

        ii No Year 11 students are ....

    b Copy and complete:

        i If $x \in W$ then ....   **ii** If $x \in E$ then ....

    c What is the relationship between the implications in **b**?

F   VALID ARGUMENTS

An **argument** is made up of a set of propositions, called the **premise**, that leads to a conclusion. An argument is usually indicated by a word such as 'therefore' or 'hence'.

A simple example of an argument is:

    If George is at the beach, then he is getting sunburnt.

    George is at the beach.

    Therefore, George is getting sunburnt.

We set out arguments by separating the premise and the conclusion with a horizontal line.

$$\begin{array}{r}
\text{If George is at the beach, then he is getting sunburnt.} \\
\text{George is at the beach.}
\end{array} \Big\} \text{ premise}$$

$$\text{George is getting sunburnt.} \ \} \text{ conclusion}$$

We can test whether the logic applied in our argument is valid by expressing the argument in terms of propositions.

If we have p: George is at the beach,
and q: George is getting sunburnt,
then the argument becomes:

$$\left. \begin{array}{c} p \Rightarrow q \\ p \end{array} \right\} \text{ premise}$$

$$q \ \} \text{ conclusion}$$

So, from the propositions $p \Rightarrow q$ and p, we are implying the conclusion q. We can write this argument in logical form as $(p \Rightarrow q) \wedge p \Rightarrow q$.

To determine whether this argument is valid, we construct a truth table for this proposition, and see whether it is a tautology.

p	q	$p \Rightarrow q$	$(p \Rightarrow q) \wedge p$	$(p \Rightarrow q) \wedge p \Rightarrow q$
T	T	T	T	T
T	F	F	F	T
F	T	T	F	T
F	F	T	F	T

We have a tautology, so our argument is valid. The conclusion we have made follows logically from the premise.

Example 12   ◀ঠ Self Tutor

Determine the validity of the following argument:

> If a triangle has three sides, then $2 + 4 = 7$.
> $2 + 4 = 7$
> Hence, a triangle has three sides.

We have p: A triangle has three sides and q: $2 + 4 = 7$

The argument is: $\left. \begin{array}{c} p \Rightarrow q \\ q \end{array} \right\} \text{ premise}$

$$p \ \} \text{ conclusion}$$

We can write this in logical form as $(p \Rightarrow q) \wedge q \Rightarrow p$.

p	q	$p \Rightarrow q$	$(p \Rightarrow q) \wedge q$	$(p \Rightarrow q) \wedge q \Rightarrow p$
T	T	T	T	T
T	F	F	F	T
F	T	T	T	F
F	F	T	F	T

Since we do **not** have a tautology, the argument is not valid.

> The validity of an argument is not related to the actual truth values of the propositions within it.

IMPORTANT: Proposition q is clearly false. However, this does not affect the validity of the argument. Logic is not concerned with whether the premise is true or false, but rather with what can be validly concluded from the premise.

EXERCISE 8F.1

1   Consider the following argument:

> Lucy will have to work today if and only if Paul is sick.
> Paul is not sick.
> Therefore, Lucy will not have to work today.

a   Write down the premise and conclusion of this argument in terms of the propositions
p: Lucy will have to work today and q: Paul is sick.

b   Write the argument in logical form.

c   Construct a truth table to show that the argument is valid.

2   **a**   Write the following arguments in logical form:

i $p \Rightarrow q$	**ii** $p \vee q$	**iii** $p \vee q$	**iv** $p \Rightarrow q$	**v** $p \Rightarrow q$
$\neg q$	$\neg p$	p	$\neg p$	$q \Rightarrow p$
$\neg p$	q		$\neg q$	p

b   Construct truth tables for each part in **a**. Which of the arguments are valid?

3   Determine the validity of the following arguments written in logical form:

a $(p \wedge q) \Rightarrow p$

b $(p \Rightarrow q) \wedge \neg q \Rightarrow p$

c $(p \Rightarrow q) \wedge (q \Rightarrow p) \Rightarrow (p \Leftrightarrow q)$

d $(p \wedge \neg q) \Rightarrow (\neg p \vee q)$

4   Use p: x is prime and q: x is odd to show that the following are valid arguments:

a   If x is prime, then x is odd.
x is prime or odd.
Hence, x is odd.

b x is prime or odd, but not both.
x is not odd.
Therefore, x is prime.

5   Consider the following argument: Don has visited Australia or New Zealand.
Don has visited New Zealand.
Therefore, Don has not visited Australia.

a   Use a truth table to show that this argument is invalid.

b   Describe the scenario which demonstrates that the argument is invalid.

6   Determine the validity of the following arguments:

a   Tan went to the movies or the theatre last night, but not both.
Tan did not go to the movies.
Therefore, Tan went to the theatre.

b   If x is a multiple of 4, then x is even.
Hence, if x is even, then x is a multiple of 4.

c   London is in China if and only if 20 is a multiple of 5.
20 is a multiple of 5.
Therefore, London is in China.

d x is a factor of 30 or 50.
Hence, x is a factor of 50.

e   If the sequence is not geometric, then the sequence is arithmetic.
Therefore, the sequence is arithmetic or geometric.

f   All students like chips.
Melanie likes chips.
Hence, Melanie is a student.

INVESTIGATION   **SYLLOGISMS**

A **syllogism** is an argument consisting of three lines. The third line is supposed to be the logical conclusion from the first two lines.

Example 1:   *Example 2*:

If I had wings like a seagull I could fly.   If I had wings like a seagull I could fly.
I have wings like a seagull.   I can fly.
Therefore, I can fly.   Therefore, I have wings like a seagull.

The arguments in these examples can be written as:

$$\text{\textit{Example 1}:} \quad \frac{\begin{array}{c} p \Rightarrow q \\ p \end{array}}{q} \qquad\qquad \text{\textit{Example 2}:} \quad \frac{\begin{array}{c} p \Rightarrow q \\ q \end{array}}{p}$$

What to do:

1 Use truth tables to show that the first example is a valid argument, and the second is invalid.

2 Consider this syllogism: All cows have four legs.
                                      Wendy is not a cow.
                                      Hence, Wendy does not have four legs.

We see it is comprised of two propositions, p: x is a cow, and
                                             q: x has four legs.

Write the argument in logical form and show that it is invalid.

3 Test the validity of the following syllogisms:

   a All prime numbers greater than two are odd. 15 is odd.
          Hence, 15 is a prime number.

   b All mathematicians are clever. Jules is not clever.
          Therefore, Jules is not a mathematician.

   c All rabbits eat grass. Peter is a rabbit.
          Therefore, Peter eats grass.

4 Give the third line of the following syllogisms to reach a correct conclusion.

   a All cats have fur.   **b** Students who waste   **c** All emus cannot fly.
          Jason is a cat.   time fail.   Meredith can fly.
          Therefore, ...   Takuma wastes time.   Therefore, ...
                                             Hence, ...

ARGUMENTS WITH THREE PROPOSITIONS

Example 13 ◀) **Self Tutor**

Determine the validity of the following argument:

> If x is a natural number, then x is an integer.
> If x is an integer, then x is rational.
> Therefore, if x is a natural number, then x is rational.

We have p: x is a natural number, q: x is an integer, and r: x is rational.

The argument is written as

$$p \Rightarrow q$$
$$\underline{q \Rightarrow r}$$
$$p \Rightarrow r$$

We can write this in logical form as $(p \Rightarrow q) \wedge (q \Rightarrow r) \Rightarrow (p \Rightarrow r)$.

p	q	r	$p \Rightarrow q$	$q \Rightarrow r$	$(p \Rightarrow q) \wedge (q \Rightarrow r)$	$p \Rightarrow r$	$(p \Rightarrow q) \wedge (q \Rightarrow r)$ $\Rightarrow (p \Rightarrow r)$
T	T	T	T	T	T	T	T
T	T	F	T	F	F	F	T
T	F	T	F	T	F	T	T
T	F	F	F	T	F	F	T
F	T	T	T	T	T	T	T
F	T	F	T	F	F	T	T
F	F	T	T	T	T	T	T
F	F	F	T	T	T	T	T

The logical form of the argument is a tautology, so the argument is valid.

EXERCISE 8F.2

1 Consider the propositions p: It is sunny, q: I am warm, and r: I feel happy.
   Write the following arguments in words.

   a $(p \wedge q) \Rightarrow r$ **b** $p \wedge \neg q \Rightarrow \neg r$ **c** $q \wedge r \Rightarrow p$

2 Which, if any, of the following arguments are valid?

   A $p \Rightarrow q$
   $\quad\;\; q \Rightarrow r$
   $\quad\;\; \overline{(q \wedge r)}$

   B $\dfrac{(p \wedge q) \vee r}{p \vee r}$

   C $(p \wedge q) \Rightarrow r$
   $\qquad\qquad\quad\; \dfrac{p}{r}$

3 **a** Show that the argument $p \Rightarrow q$ is invalid.
   $\qquad\qquad\qquad\qquad\quad\; q \Rightarrow r$
   $\qquad\qquad\qquad\qquad\;\; \overline{p \Rightarrow \neg r}$

   b What truth values of p, q, and r lead to an invalid argument?

4 If I do not like a subject then I do not work hard. If I do not work hard then I fail. I passed, therefore I must like the subject.

    a Identify the propositions p, q, and r.   **b** Write the above argument in logical form.

    c Is the conclusion a result of valid reasoning?

5 Determine the validity of this argument:

    If Jeremy is on the basketball team, then he is tall and fast.

    Jeremy is tall and he is not on the basketball team.

    Therefore, Jeremy is not fast.

REVIEW SET 8A

1 Which of the following are propositions? If they are propositions, state whether they are true, false, or indeterminate.

    a Sheep have four legs.   **b** Do giraffes have four legs?

    c Alicia is good at Mathematics.   **d** I think my favourite team will win.

    e Vicki is very clever.   **f** There are 7 days in a week.

    g Put your shoes on.   **h** All cows are brown.

    i $a^2 + b^2 = c^2$

    j The opposite sides of a parallelogram are equal in length.

2 Consider the propositions p: x is an even number, and q: x is divisible by 3. Write the following in words:

    a $\neg p$ **b** $p \vee q$ **c** $p \veebar q$ **d** $p \Rightarrow q$

    e $\neg p \wedge q$ **f** $\neg p \veebar q$ **g** $p \Rightarrow \neg q$ **h** $\neg p \Rightarrow \neg q$

3 Consider the propositions p: x is a prime number, and q: x is a multiple of 7.
Write the following in symbolic language:

    a If x is a prime number then x is a multiple of 7.

    b x is not a prime number.

    c x is a multiple of 7 and not a prime number.

    d x is either a prime number or a multiple of 7, but not both.

    e x is neither a prime number nor a multiple of 7.

  In each case, write down a number that satisfies the statement.

4 Write the implication $p \Rightarrow q$, the inverse, converse, and contrapositive of the following propositions in both words and symbols.

    a p: I love swimming.   **b** p: I like food.

       q: I live near the sea. q: I eat a lot.

5 Represent the truth sets of the following on Venn diagrams:

    a $p \veebar q$ **b** $\neg(p \vee q)$ **c** $\neg p \wedge q$

    d $\neg p$ **e** $\neg p \vee q$ **f** $\neg(p \wedge q \wedge r)$

6 For the propositions p: x is a factor of 12, and q: x is an odd number < 10, list the truth sets of:

    a p **b** q **c** $p \wedge q$ **d** $p \vee q$

7 Use truth tables to determine the validity of the following arguments:

a $p \Rightarrow q$

$\dfrac{\neg p}{\neg q}$

b $p \vee q$

$\dfrac{\neg q}{\neg p}$

c $p \Rightarrow q$

$q \Rightarrow r$

$\overline{ r \vee q }$

REVIEW SET 8B

1 Consider the propositions p: x is a multiple of 4, $18 < x < 30$
  q: x is a factor of 24,
  and r: x is an even number, $18 < x < 30$.

a List the truth sets of p, q, and r.

b List the truth sets of: **i** $p \wedge q$ **ii** $q \wedge r$ **iii** $p \wedge r$ **iv** $p \wedge q \wedge r$

2 Find negations for the following:

a Eddy is good at football.   **b** The maths class includes more than 10 boys.

c The writing is illegible.   **d** Ali owns a new car.

3 Write the following statements as implications:

a All birds have two legs.   **b** Snakes are not mammals.

c No rectangle has five sides.   **d** This equation has no real solutions.

4 'Positive' and 'negative' are defined as follows:
  x is positive $\Leftrightarrow$ $x > 0$ x is negative $\Leftrightarrow$ $x < 0$

a Is zero positive or negative?

b What is the negation of 'x is negative' when $x \in \{$rational numbers$\}$?

5 Let P, Q, and R be the truth sets of propositions p, q, and r respectively.
Write the following as compound propositions in terms of p, q, and r:

a
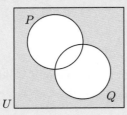

b
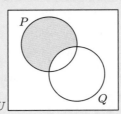

c
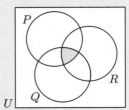

6 Which of the following pairs are logically equivalent?

a $p \Rightarrow q$ and $\neg q \Rightarrow \neg p$ **b** $\neg(p \wedge q)$ and $\neg p \vee \neg q$

c $p \Leftrightarrow q$ and $(p \wedge q) \wedge \neg q$ **d** $\neg p \Rightarrow \neg q$ and $q \Rightarrow p$

7 Express the following in logical form. Determine whether or not the argument is valid.

a If the sun is shining I will wear my shorts. The sun is shining. Therefore, I will wear shorts.

b All teachers work hard. Marty is not a teacher. Therefore Marty does not work hard.

REVIEW SET 8C

1 Find the negation of:

  a $x \leqslant 3$ for $x \in \mathbb{Z}$

  b x is a comb, for $x \in \{$brush, comb, hairclip, bobby pin$\}$

  c x is a tall woman for $x \in \{$women$\}$.

2 For $U = \{x \mid 1 \leqslant x \leqslant 20,\ x \in \mathbb{Z}\}$, consider the propositions

        p: x is an even number and q: x is a square number.

  a Illustrate the truth sets for p and q on a Venn diagram.

  b Use your Venn diagram to find the truth set for:

    i $p \wedge q$ **ii** $\neg p \vee q$ **iii** $\neg(p \veebar q)$

3 Write down, in words, the inverse, converse, and contrapositive for the implication: "The diagonals of a rhombus are equal in length."

4 Consider the propositions p: cakes are sweet and q: cakes are full of sultanas. Write each of the following using logic symbols:

  a If cakes are not sweet then they are not full of sultanas.

  b If cakes are not sweet then they are full of sultanas.

  c Cakes are full of sultanas and they are not sweet.

  d Cakes are not sweet or they are full of sultanas.

5 Consider the propositions:

  p: The plane leaves from gate 5. q: The plane leaves from gate 2.

  r: The plane does not leave this morning.

  a Write the following logic statement in words: $p \Rightarrow (\neg r \wedge \neg q)$

  b Write in symbols: The plane leaves this morning if and only if it leaves from gate 2 or from gate 5.

6 Construct truth tables for the following and state whether the statements are tautologies, logical contradictions, or neither:

  a $(p \Rightarrow q) \wedge q \Rightarrow p$ **b** $(p \wedge q) \wedge \neg(p \vee q)$ **c** $\neg p \Leftrightarrow q$

  d $(p \vee \neg q) \Rightarrow q$ **e** $(\neg p \vee q) \Rightarrow r$ **f** $p \wedge q \Rightarrow q$

7 Express the following in logical form. Determine whether or not the argument is valid.

  a If Fred is a dog he has fur. If Fred has fur he has a cold nose. Fred is a dog. Hence, Fred has a cold nose.

  b If Viv is a judge, she wears a robe or a wig. Viv does not wear a wig, nor is she a judge. Therefore, Viv does not wear a robe.

Chapter **9**

Probability

Syllabus reference: 3.5, 3.6, 3.7

Contents:

OPENING PROBLEM

Consider the following game:

You first roll a die. If the result is less than 3, you randomly select a ball from bag A. Otherwise, you randomly select a ball from bag B.

You win if the ball is red, and lose if the ball is blue.

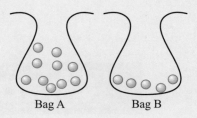

Bag A   Bag B

Things to think about:

a What is the probability that the die will give a result less than 3?

b If bag B is selected, what is the probability that the ball selected will be red?

c Are you more likely to win or lose this game?

In the field of **probability theory** we use mathematics to describe the **chance** or **likelihood** of an event happening.

We apply probability theory in physical and biological sciences, economics, politics, sport, life insurance, quality control, production planning, and a host of other areas.

We assign to every event a number which lies between 0 and 1 inclusive. We call this number a **probability**.

> An **impossible** event which has 0% chance of happening is assigned a probability of 0.
>
> A **certain** event which has 100% chance of happening is assigned a probability of 1.
>
> All other events can be assigned a probability between 0 and 1.

The number line below shows how we could interpret different probabilities:

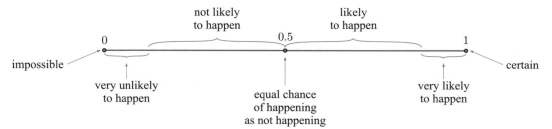

The assigning of probabilities is usually based on either:

- observing the results of an experiment (experimental probability),   or
- using arguments of symmetry (theoretical probability).

HISTORICAL NOTE

In the late 17th century, English mathematicians compiled and analysed mortality tables which showed the number of people who died at different ages. From these tables they could estimate the probability that a person would be alive at a future date. This led to the establishment of the first life-insurance company in 1699.

EXPERIMENTAL PROBABILITY

In experiments involving chance we use the following terms to talk about what we are doing and the results we obtain:

- The **number of trials** is the total number of times the experiment is repeated.
- The **outcomes** are the different results possible for one trial of the experiment.
- The **frequency** of a particular outcome is the number of times that this outcome is observed.
- The **relative frequency** of an outcome is the frequency of that outcome expressed as a fraction or percentage of the total number of trials.

For example, when a small plastic cone was tossed into the air 279 times it fell on its *side* 183 times and on its *base* 96 times. We say:

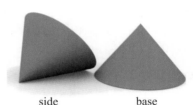

side   base

- the number of trials is 279
- the outcomes are *side* and *base*
- the frequencies of *side* and *base* are 183 and 96 respectively
- the relative frequencies of *side* and *base* are $\frac{183}{279} \approx 0.656$ and $\frac{96}{279} \approx 0.344$ respectively.

  In the absence of any further data, the relative frequency of each event is our best estimate of the probability of that event occurring.

Experimental probability = relative frequency.

In this case, Experimental P(side) ≈ 0.656 and Experimental P(base) ≈ 0.344.

The larger the number of trials, the more confident we are that the estimated probability will be accurate.

INVESTIGATION 1   TOSSING DRAWING PINS

If a drawing pin tossed in the air finishes we say it has finished on its *back*. If it

finishes we say it has finished on its *side*.

If two drawing pins are tossed simultaneously, the possible results are:

two backs   *back and side*   *two sides*

What to do:

1 Obtain two drawing pins of the same shape and size. Toss the pair 80 times and record the outcomes in a table.

2 Obtain relative frequencies (experimental probabilities) for each of the three events.

3 Pool your results with four other people and so obtain experimental probabilities from 400 tosses. The other people must have pins with the same shape and size.

4 Which gives the more reliable probability estimates, your results or the whole group's? Explain your answer.

In some situations, for example in the **Investigation** above, experimentation is the only way of obtaining probabilities.

EXERCISE 9A.1

1 When a batch of 145 paper clips was dropped onto 6 cm by 6 cm squared paper, it was observed that 113 fell completely inside squares and 32 finished up on the grid lines. Find, to 2 decimal places, the experimental probability of a clip falling:

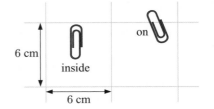

a inside a square   **b** on a line.

2

Length	Frequency
0 - 19	17
20 - 39	38
40 - 59	19
60+	4

Jose surveyed the length of TV commercials (in seconds). Find, to 3 decimal places, the experimental probability that a randomly chosen TV commercial will last:

a 20 to 39 seconds   **b** more than a minute

c between 20 and 59 seconds (inclusive).

3 Betul records the number of phone calls she receives over a period of consecutive days.

a For how many days did the survey last?

b Estimate Betul's chances of receiving:

i no phone calls on one day

ii 5 or more phone calls on a day

iii less than 3 phone calls on a day.

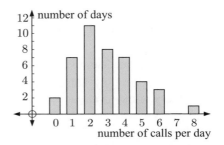

4 Pat does a lot of travelling in her car, and she keeps records on how often she fills her car with petrol. The table alongside shows the frequencies of the number of days between refills. Estimate the likelihood that:

a there is a four day gap between refills

b there is at least a four day gap between refills.

Days between refills	Frequency
1	37
2	81
3	48
4	17
5	6
6	1

DISCUSSION

- When we perform an experiment, are the results always the same?
- Why does the number of trials we perform affect the accuracy of the experimental probabilities we obtain?

INVESTIGATION 2   COIN TOSSING EXPERIMENTS

The coins of most currencies have two distinct faces, usually referred to as 'heads' and 'tails'. When we toss a coin in the air, we expect it to finish on a head or tail with equal likelihood.

In this investigation the coins do not have to be all the same type.

What to do:

1 Toss *one coin* 40 times. Record the number of heads in each trial, in a table:

Result	Tally	Frequency	Relative frequency
1 head			
0 head			

2 Toss *two coins* 60 times. Record the number of heads in each trial, in a table.

Result	Tally	Frequency	Relative frequency
2 heads			
1 head			
0 head			

3 Toss *three coins* 80 times. Record the number of heads in each trial, in a table.

Result	Tally	Frequency	Relative frequency
3 heads			
2 heads			
1 head			
0 head			

4 Share your results for **1**, **2**, and **3** with several other students. Comment on any similarities and differences.

5 Pool your results and find new relative frequencies for tossing one coin, two coins, and three coins.

6 Click on the icon to examine a coin tossing simulation.

Set it to toss one coin 10 000 times.

Run the simulation ten times, each time recording the relative frequency for each possible result. Comment on these results. Do your results agree with what you expected?

COIN TOSSING

7 Experiment with the simulation for *two coins* and then *three coins*.

From the previous **Investigation** you should have observed that, when tossing two coins, there are roughly twice as many 'one head' results as there are 'no heads' or 'two heads'.

The explanation for this is best seen using two different coins where you could get:

two heads	one head	one head	no heads

We should expect the ratio two heads : one head : no heads to be 1 : 2 : 1. However, due to chance, there will be variations from this when we look at experimental results.

INVESTIGATION 3   DICE ROLLING EXPERIMENTS

WORKSHEET

You will need: At least one normal six-sided die with numbers 1 to 6 on its faces.   Several dice would be useful to speed up the experimentation.

What to do:

1   List the possible outcomes for the uppermost face when the die is rolled.

2   Consider the possible outcomes when the die is rolled 60 times.
    Copy and complete the following table of your **expected results**:

Outcome	Expected frequency	Expected relative frequency
1		
2		
⋮		
6		

3   Roll the die 60 times. Record the results in a table like the one shown:

Outcome	Tally	Frequency	Relative frequency
1			
2			
⋮			
6			
Total		60	1

4   Pool as much data as you can with other students.

   a   Look at similarities and differences from one set to another.

   b   Summarise the overall pooled data in one table.

   c   Compare your results with your expectation in **2**.

SIMULATION

5   Use the die rolling simulation online to roll the die 10 000 times. Repeat this 10 times. On each occasion, record your results in a table like that in **3**. Do your results further confirm your expected results?

6   The different possible results when a pair of dice is rolled are shown alongside.
    There are 36 possible outcomes.
    Notice that three of the outcomes, {1, 3}, {2, 2}, and {3, 1}, give a sum of 4.

Using the illustration above, copy and complete the table of **expected results**:

Sum	2	3	4	5	6	7	8	9	10	11	12
Fraction of total			$\frac{3}{36}$								
Fraction as decimal			0.083								

7 If a pair of dice is rolled 150 times, how many of each result (2, 3, 4, ..., 12) would you expect to get? Extend the table in **6** by adding another row and writing your **expected frequencies** within it.

8 Toss two dice 150 times. Record the *sum of the two numbers* for each toss in a table.

WORKSHEET

Sum	Tally	Frequency	Relative frequency
2			
3			
4			
⋮			
12			
	Total	150	1

9 Pool as much data as you can with other students and find the overall relative frequency of each sum.

10 Use the two dice simulation online to roll the pair of dice 10 000 times. Repeat this 10 times and on each occasion record your results in a table like that in **8**. Are your results consistent with your expectations?

SIMULATION

ESTIMATING PROBABILITIES FROM DATA

Statistical information can be used to calculate probabilities in many situations.

Example 1   ◀》 **Self Tutor**

Short-Term Visitors to Australia

Main reason for journey	April 2011	May 2011	June 2011
Convention/conference	8300	14 800	8800
Business	27 200	33 900	32 000
Visiting friends/relatives	77 500	52 700	59 900
Holiday	159 300	119 300	156 500
Employment	4200	4300	5500
Education	9800	7900	12 500
Other	35 200	28 000	33 200
Total	321 500	260 900	308 300

The table shows the number of short-term visitors coming to Australia in the period April - June 2011, and the main reason for their visit.

a Find the probability that a person who visited in June was on holiday.

b Find the probability that a person coming to Australia arrived in May.

c Lars arrived in Australia in April, May, or June 2011. He came to visit his brother. What is the probability that he arrived in April?

a $P(\text{on holiday in June}) = \dfrac{156\,500}{308\,300}$ ◀—— number on holiday in June
◀—— total number for June

≈ 0.508

b There were $321\,500 + 260\,900 + 308\,300 = 890\,700$ short-term visitors during the three months.

$\therefore$ $P(\text{arrived in May}) = \dfrac{260\,900}{890\,700} \approx 0.293$

c $77\,500 + 52\,700 + 59\,900 = 190\,100$ people came to Australia to visit friends or relatives during this period.

$\therefore$ $P(\text{arrived in April}) = \dfrac{77\,500}{190\,100}$ ◀—— number visiting friends or relatives in April
◀—— total number visiting friends or relatives over April, May, and June

≈ 0.408

EXERCISE 9A.2

1 The table shows data from a survey conducted at five schools on the rate of smoking amongst 15 year old students.

School	Number of 15 year olds		Number of smokers	
	Male	Female	Male	Female
A	45	51	10	11
B	36	42	9	6
C	52	49	13	13
D	28	33	9	10
E	40	39	7	4
Total	201	214	48	44

    a Find the probability that a randomly chosen female 15 year old student at school **C** is a smoker.

    b Find the probability that a randomly chosen 15 year old student at school **E** is *not* a smoker.

    c If a 15 year old is chosen at random from the five schools, what is the probability that he or she is a smoker?

2 The table describes complaints received by the Telecommunications Ombudsman concerning internet services over a four year period.

Reason	2006/07	2007/08	2008/09	2009/10
Access	585	1127	2545	1612
Billing	1822	2102	3136	3582
Contracts	242	440	719	836
Credit control	3	44	118	136
Customer Service	12	282	1181	1940
Disconnection	n/a	n/a	n/a	248
Faults	86	79	120	384
Privacy	93	86	57	60
Provision	173	122	209	311
Total	3015	4282	8085	9109

Find the probability that a complaint received:

    a in 2008/09 was about customer service

    b at any time during the 4 year period was related to billing

    c in 2009/10 did *not* relate to either billing or faults.

3 The table provides data on the average daily maximum temperatures in Auburn during summer. You may assume that there are 28 days in February.

Summer Temperatures in Auburn	Month		
	Dec	*Jan*	*Feb*
Mean days max. $\geqslant 40°$ C	0.3	1.2	0.7
Mean days max. $\geqslant 35°$ C	3.0	5.8	5.3
Mean days max. $\geqslant 30°$ C	9.4	12.3	12.6

  a Find the probability that on a February day in Auburn, the maximum temperature will:

   i be 35°C or higher

   ii be less than 30°C.

  b Find the probability that on any summer day in Auburn, the temperature will be 30°C or higher.

  c It is a 40°C summer day in Auburn. Find the probability that the month is January.

B   SAMPLE SPACE

> A **sample space** U is the set of all possible outcomes of an experiment. It is also referred to as the **universal set** U.

There are a variety of ways of representing or illustrating sample spaces, including:

- lists
- tables of outcomes
- 2-dimensional grids
- Venn diagrams
- tree diagrams

We will use tables and Venn diagrams later in the chapter.

LISTING OUTCOMES

Example 2	◀ Self Tutor

List the sample space of possible outcomes for:

  a tossing a coin

  b rolling a die.

  a When a coin is tossed, there are 2 possible outcomes.

    ∴ sample space = {H, T}

  b When a die is rolled, there are 6 possible outcomes.

    ∴ sample space = {1, 2, 3, 4, 5, 6}

2-DIMENSIONAL GRIDS

When an experiment involves more than one operation we can still use listing to illustrate the sample space. However, a grid is often more efficient. Each point on the grid represents one of the outcomes.

Example 3	◀ Self Tutor

Using a 2-dimensional grid, illustrate the possible outcomes when 2 coins are tossed.

Each of the points on the grid represents one of the possible outcomes:
{HH, HT, TH, TT}

TREE DIAGRAMS

The sample space in **Example 3** could also be represented by a tree diagram. The advantage of tree diagrams is that they can be used when more than two operations are involved.

Example 4   ◀ѕ) **Self Tutor**

Illustrate, using a tree diagram, the possible outcomes for:

  a tossing two coins

  b drawing two marbles from a bag containing many red, green, and yellow marbles.

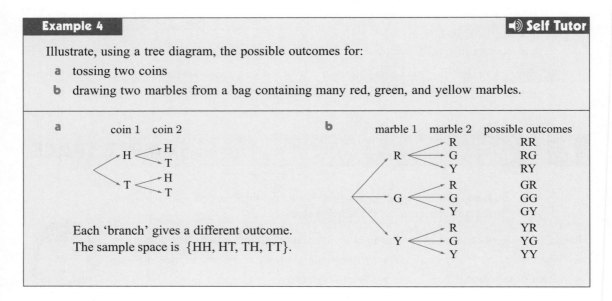

a

Each 'branch' gives a different outcome.
The sample space is {HH, HT, TH, TT}.

EXERCISE 9B

1 List the sample space for the following:

  a twirling a square spinner labelled A, B, C, D

  b the sexes of a 2-child family

  c the order in which 4 blocks A, B, C, and D can be lined up

  d the 8 different 3-child families.

2 Illustrate on a 2-dimensional grid the sample space for:

  a simultaneously rolling a die and tossing a coin

  b rolling two dice

  c rolling a die and spinning a spinner with sides A, B, C, D

  d twirling two square spinners, one labelled A, B, C, D and the other 1, 2, 3, 4.

3 Illustrate on a tree diagram the sample space for:

  a simultaneously tossing a 5-cent and a 10-cent coin

  b tossing a coin and twirling an equilateral triangular spinner labelled A, B, and C

  c twirling two equilateral triangular spinners labelled 1, 2, and 3, and X, Y, and Z

  d drawing two tickets from a hat containing a number of pink, blue, and white tickets.

C ▍ THEORETICAL PROBABILITY

Consider the **octagonal spinner** alongside.

Since the spinner is symmetrical, when it is spun the arrowed marker could finish with equal likelihood on any of the sections marked 1 to 8.

The likelihood of obtaining the outcome 4 would be:

$$1 \text{ chance in } 8, \qquad \tfrac{1}{8}, \qquad 12\tfrac{1}{2}\%, \qquad \text{or} \qquad 0.125 \,.$$

This is a **mathematical** or **theoretical** probability and is based on what we theoretically expect to occur. It is the chance of that event occurring in any trial of the experiment.

If we are interested in the event of getting a result of *6 or more* from one spin of the octagonal spinner, there are three favourable results (6, 7, or 8) out of the eight possible results. Since each of these is equally likely to occur, $P(6 \text{ or more}) = \tfrac{3}{8}$.

> We read $\tfrac{3}{8}$ as "3 chances in 8".

In general, for an event A containing **equally likely** possible results, the probability of A occurring is

$$P(A) = \frac{\text{the number of members of the event } A}{\text{the total number of possible outcomes}} = \frac{n(A)}{n(U)} \,.$$

Example 5   ◄)) Self Tutor

A ticket is *randomly selected* from a basket containing 3 green, 4 yellow, and 5 blue tickets. Determine the probability of getting:

a a green ticket	**b** a green or yellow ticket
c an orange ticket	**d** a green, yellow, or blue ticket.

There are $3 + 4 + 5 = 12$ tickets which could be selected with equal chance.

a $P(G)$	**b** $P(G \text{ or } Y)$	**c** $P(O)$	**d** $P(G, Y, \text{ or } B)$
$= \tfrac{3}{12}$	$= \tfrac{3+4}{12}$	$= \tfrac{0}{12}$	$= \tfrac{3+4+5}{12}$
$= \tfrac{1}{4}$	$= \tfrac{7}{12}$	$= 0$	$= 1$

From **Example 5**, notice that:

- In **c** an orange result cannot occur. The calculated probability is 0 because the event has *no chance of occurring*.

- In **d** the outcome of a green, yellow, or blue is certain to occur. It is 100% likely so the theoretical probability is 1.

Events which have *no chance of occurring* or probability 0, or are *certain to occur* or probability 1, are two extremes.

For any event A, $\mathbf{0 \leqslant P(A) \leqslant 1.}$

Example 6   ◀) **Self Tutor**

An ordinary 6-sided die is rolled once. Determine the chance of:

  a getting a 6   **b** not getting a 6   **c** getting a 1 or 2   **d** not getting a 1 or 2

The sample space of possible outcomes is $\{1, 2, 3, 4, 5, 6\}$.

a	**b**	**c**	**d**
$P(6)$	$P(\text{not a } 6)$	$P(1 \text{ or } 2)$	$P(\text{not a } 1 \text{ or } 2)$
$= \frac{1}{6}$	$= P(1, 2, 3, 4, \text{ or } 5)$	$= \frac{2}{6}$	$= P(3, 4, 5, \text{ or } 6)$
	$= \frac{5}{6}$		$= \frac{4}{6}$

COMPLEMENTARY EVENTS

In **Example 6** notice that
$$P(6) + P(\text{not getting a } 6) = 1 \quad \text{and that}$$
$$P(1 \text{ or } 2) + P(\text{not getting a } 1 \text{ or } 2) = 1.$$

This is no surprise as *getting a 6* and *not getting a 6* are **complementary events** where one of them **must occur**.

> Two events are **complementary** if exactly one of the events *must* occur.
> If A is an event, then A' is the complementary event of A, or 'not A'.
> $$P(A) + P(A') = 1$$

EXERCISE 9C.1

1 A marble is randomly selected from a box containing 5 green, 3 red, and 7 blue marbles. Determine the probability that the marble is:

  a red   **b** green   **c** blue

  d not red   **e** neither green nor blue   **f** green or red.

2 A carton of a dozen eggs contains eight brown eggs.
The rest are white.

  a How many white eggs are there in the carton?

  b Find the probability that an egg selected at random is:

    i brown   **ii** white.

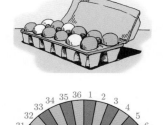

3 A dart board has 36 sectors labelled 1 to 36. Determine
the probability that a dart thrown at the centre of the board
will hit:

  a a multiple of 4

  b a number between 6 and 9 inclusive

  c a number greater than 20

  d 9   **e** a multiple of 13

  f an odd number that is a multiple of 3

  g a multiple of 4 and 6   **h** a multiple of 4 or 6.

4 What is the probability that a randomly chosen person has his or her next birthday:

  a on a Tuesday   **b** on a weekend   **c** in July   **d** in January or February?

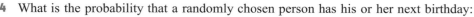

5 a List the six different orders in which Antti, Kai, and Neda may sit in a row.

  b If the three of them sit randomly in a row, determine the probability that:

  i Antti sits in the middle   **ii** Antti sits at the left end

  iii Antti does not sit at the right end   **iv** Kai and Neda are seated together.

6 a List the 8 possible 3-child families according to the gender of the children. For example, GGB means *"the first is a girl, the second is a girl, the third is a boy"*.

  b Assuming that each of these is equally likely to occur, determine the probability that a randomly selected 3-child family consists of:

  i all boys   **ii** all girls   **iii** boy then girl then girl

  iv two girls and a boy   **v** a girl for the eldest   **vi** at least one boy.

7 a List, in systematic order, the 24 different orders in which four people A, B, C, and D may sit in a row.

  b Determine the probability that when the four people sit at random in a row:

  i A sits on one of the end seats

  ii B sits on one of the two middle seats

  iii A and B are seated together

  iv A, B, and C are seated together, not necessarily in that order.

USING GRIDS TO FIND PROBABILITIES

Two-dimensional grids can give us excellent visual displays of sample spaces. We can use them to count favourable outcomes and so calculate probabilities.

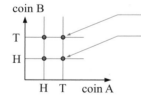

This point represents 'a tail from coin A' and 'a tail from coin B'.

This point represents 'a tail from coin A' and 'a head from coin B'.

There are four members of the sample space.

Example 7   ◀ᵛ **Self Tutor**

Use a two-dimensional grid to illustrate the sample space for tossing a coin and rolling a die simultaneously. From this grid determine the probability of:

  a tossing a head   **b** getting a tail and a 5   **c** getting a tail or a 5.

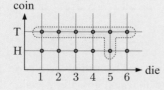

There are 12 members in the sample space.

  a P(head) $= \frac{6}{12} = \frac{1}{2}$

  b P(tail and a '5') $= \frac{1}{12}$

  c P(tail or a '5') $= \frac{7}{12}$ {the enclosed points}

Example 8   ◀) **Self Tutor**

There are two square spinners, each with 1, 2, 3, and 4 on their edges. The spinners are twirled simultaneously. Draw a two-dimensional grid of the possible outcomes. Use your grid to determine the probability of getting:

a a 3 with each spinner
b a 3 and a 1
c an even result with each spinner.

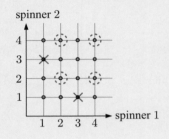

There are 16 members in the sample space.

a P(a 3 with each spinner) $= \frac{1}{16}$

b P(a 3 and a 1) $= \frac{2}{16}$ {crossed points}
$$= \frac{1}{8}$$

c P(an even result with each spinner)
$$= \frac{4}{16} \quad \{\text{circled points}\}$$
$$= \frac{1}{4}$$

EXERCISE 9C.2

1 Draw the grid of the sample space when a 5-cent and a 10-cent coin are tossed simultaneously. Hence determine the probability of getting:

a two heads
b two tails
c exactly one head
d at least one head.

2 A coin and a pentagonal spinner with sectors 1, 2, 3, 4, and 5 are tossed and spun respectively.

a Draw a grid to illustrate the sample space of possible outcomes.
b How many outcomes are possible?
c Use your grid to determine the chance of getting:
　　i a tail and a 3　　　　　　　　**ii** a head and an even number
　　iii an odd number　　　　　　　**iv** a head or a 5.

3 A pair of dice is rolled. The 36 different possible results are illustrated in the 2-dimensional grid.
Use the grid to determine the probability of getting:

a two 3s
b a 5 and a 6
c a 5 or a 6
d at least one 6
e exactly one 6
f no sixes.

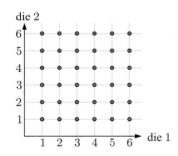

DISCUSSION

Three children have been experimenting with a coin, tossing it in the air and recording the outcomes. They have done this 10 times and have recorded 10 tails. Before the next toss they make the following statements:

Jackson:　　"It's got to be a head next time!"

Sally: "No, it always has an equal chance of being a head or a tail. The coin cannot remember what the outcomes have been."

Amy: "Actually, I think it will probably be a tail again, because I think the coin must be biased. It might be weighted so it is more likely to give a tail."

Discuss the statements of each child. Who do you think is correct?

TABLES OF OUTCOMES

In many board games, the players are required to roll two dice simultaneously. The results of the rolls are added together to determine how many squares the player moves.

We can represent the possible outcomes of a player's turn using a two-dimensional grid in which the sum of the dice is written at each grid-point. We call this a **table of outcomes**.

Example 9   ◀)) **Self Tutor**

Draw a table of outcomes to display the possible results when two dice are rolled and the scores are added together.

Hence, determine the probability that the sum of the dice is 7.

die 2

6	7	8	9	10	11	12
5	6	7	8	9	10	11
4	5	6	7	8	9	10
3	4	5	6	7	8	9
2	3	4	5	6	7	8
1	2	3	4	5	6	7
	1	2	3	4	5	6	die 1

Of the 36 possible combinations of scores from the two dice, six have the sum 7.

$\therefore$ the probability $= \frac{6}{36} = \frac{1}{6}$

EXERCISE 9C.3

1 **a** Draw a table of outcomes to display the possible results when two dice are rolled and the scores are added together.

  b Hence determine the probability that the sum of the dice is:
     i 11   **ii** 8 or 9   **iii** less than 6.

2 **a** Draw a table of outcomes to display the possible results when two dice are rolled, and the smaller number is subtracted from the larger number.

  b Hence determine the probability that the resulting value is:
     i 0   **ii** 2   **iii** greater than 3.

3 The spinners alongside are spun, and the scores are multiplied together.

  a Draw a table of outcomes to display the possible results.

  b Hence determine the probability that the result is:

     i 6   **ii** less than 5   **iii** odd.

D   COMPOUND EVENTS

Consider the following problem:

Box X contains 2 blue and 2 green balls. Box Y contains 1 white and 3 red balls. A ball is randomly selected from each of the boxes. Determine the probability of getting "a blue ball from X *and* a red ball from Y".

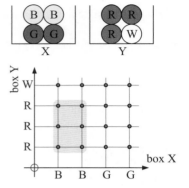

By illustrating the sample space on the two-dimensional grid shown, we can see that 6 of the 16 possibilities are blue from X and red from Y. Each of the outcomes is equally likely, so

P(blue from X **and** red from Y) $= \frac{6}{16}$.

In this section we look for a quicker method for finding the probability of two events both occurring.

INVESTIGATION 4   PROBABILITIES OF COMPOUND EVENTS

The purpose of this investigation is to find a rule for calculating P(*A and B*) for two events *A* and *B*.

Suppose a coin is tossed and a die is rolled at the same time. The result of the coin toss will be called outcome *A*, and the result of the die roll will be outcome *B*.

What to do:

1 Copy and complete, using a 2-dimensional grid if necessary:

	P(A and B)	P(A)	P(B)
P(a head and a 4)			
P(a head and an odd number)			
P(a tail and a number larger than 1)			
P(a tail and a number less than 3)			

2 What is the connection between P(A and B), P(A), and P(B)?

From **Investigation 4** it seems that:

If A and B are two events for which the occurrence of each one does not affect the occurrence of the other, then   P(A **and** B) = P(A) × P(B).

Before we can formalise this as a rule, however, we need to distinguish between **independent** and **dependent** events.

INDEPENDENT EVENTS

Events are **independent** if the occurrence of either of them does not affect the probability that the others occur.

Consider again the example on the previous page. Suppose we happen to choose a blue ball from box X. This does not affect the outcome when we choose a ball from box Y. So, the two events "a blue ball from X" and "a red ball from Y" are independent.

If A and B are **independent events** then $P(A \text{ and } B) = P(A) \times P(B)$.

This rule can be extended for any number of independent events.

For example: If A, B, and C are all **independent events**, then
$P(A \text{ and } B \text{ and } C) = P(A) \times P(B) \times P(C)$.

Example 10
🔊 Self Tutor

A coin and a die are tossed and rolled simultaneously. Determine the probability of getting a head and a 3 without using a grid.

$P(\text{a head and a 3}) = P(H) \times P(3)$ {events are physically independent}

$\phantom{P(\text{a head and a 3})} = \tfrac{1}{2} \times \tfrac{1}{6}$

$\phantom{P(\text{a head and a 3})} = \tfrac{1}{12}$

EXERCISE 9D.1

1 Rob and Kerry each roll a die. Determine the probability that:

  a Rob rolls a 4 and Kerry rolls a 2

  b Rob rolls an odd number and Kerry rolls a number greater than 4

  c they both roll a number greater than 1.

2 A coin is tossed 3 times. Determine the probability of getting the following sequences of results:

  a head then head then head   **b** tail then head then tail.

3 A school has two photocopiers. On any one day, machine A has an 8% chance of malfunctioning and machine B has a 12% chance of malfunctioning. Determine the probability that on any one day both machines will:

  a malfunction   **b** work effectively.

4 A couple would like 4 children, none of whom will be adopted. They will be disappointed if the children are not born in the order boy, girl, boy, girl. Determine the probability that they will be:

  a happy with the order of arrival   **b** unhappy with the order of arrival.

5 Two marksmen fire at a target simultaneously. Jiri hits the target 70% of the time and Benita hits it 80% of the time. Determine the probability that:

  a they both hit the target   **b** they both miss the target

  c Jiri hits but Benita misses   **d** Benita hits but Jiri misses.

6

An archer hits a circular target with each arrow fired, and hits the bullseye on average 2 out of every 5 shots. If 3 arrows are fired at the target, determine the probability that the bullseye is hit:

  a every time

  b the first two times, but not on the third shot

  c on no occasion.

DEPENDENT EVENTS

Suppose a hat contains 5 red and 3 blue tickets. One ticket is randomly chosen, its colour is noted, and it is then put aside. A second ticket is then randomly selected. What is the chance that it is red?

If the first ticket was red, $P(\text{second is red}) = \frac{4}{7}$ —— 4 reds remaining
—— 7 to choose from

If the first ticket was blue, $P(\text{second is red}) = \frac{5}{7}$ —— 5 reds remaining
—— 7 to choose from

So, the probability of the second ticket being red *depends* on what colour the first ticket was. We therefore have **dependent events**.

> Two or more events are **dependent** if they are **not independent**.
>
> **Dependent** events are events for which the occurrence of one of the events *does affect* the occurrence of the other event.

For compound events which are dependent, a similar product rule applies to that for independent events:

> If A and B are dependent events then
>
> $P(A \textbf{ then } B) = P(A) \times P(B \text{ given that } A \text{ has occurred}).$

Example 11   ◀️) **Self Tutor**

A box contains 4 red and 2 yellow tickets. Two tickets are randomly selected from the box one by one *without* replacement. Find the probability that:

a both are red   **b** the first is red and the second is yellow.

a   P(both red)
= P(first selected is red *and* second is red)
= P(first selected is red) × P(second is red given that the first is red)
= $\frac{4}{6} \times \frac{3}{5}$ —— If a red is drawn first, 3 reds remain out of a total of 5.
= $\frac{2}{5}$ —— 4 reds out of a total of 6 tickets

b   P(first is red *and* second is yellow)
= P(first is red) × P(second is yellow given that the first is red)
= $\frac{4}{6} \times \frac{2}{5}$ —— If a red is drawn first, 2 yellows remain out of a total of 5.
= $\frac{4}{15}$ —— 4 reds out of a total of 6 tickets

EXERCISE 9D.2

1 A bin contains 12 identically shaped chocolates of which 8 are strawberry creams. If 3 chocolates are selected simultaneously from the bin, determine the probability that:

> Drawing three chocolates *simultaneously* implies there is no replacement.

a they are all strawberry creams

b none of them are strawberry creams.

Example 12

A hat contains tickets with the numbers 1, 2, 3, ..., 19, 20 printed on them. If 3 tickets are drawn from the hat, without replacement, determine the probability that they are all prime numbers.

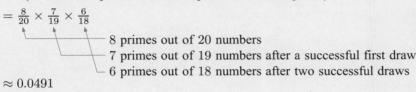

In each fraction the numerator is the number of outcomes in the event. The denominator is the total number of possible outcomes.

$\{2, 3, 5, 7, 11, 13, 17, 19\}$ are primes.

$\therefore$ there are 20 numbers of which 8 are primes.

$\therefore$ P(3 primes)

= P(1st drawn is prime *and* 2nd is prime *and* 3rd is prime)

= $\frac{8}{20} \times \frac{7}{19} \times \frac{6}{18}$

⌐ 8 primes out of 20 numbers

⌐ 7 primes out of 19 numbers after a successful first draw

└ 6 primes out of 18 numbers after two successful draws

≈ 0.0491

---

2 A box contains 7 red and 3 green balls. Two balls are drawn one after another from the box without replacement. Determine the probability that:

   a both are red   **b** the first is green and the second is red.

3 A lottery has 100 tickets which are placed in a barrel. Three tickets are drawn at random from the barrel, without replacement, to decide 3 prizes. If John has 3 tickets in the lottery, determine his probability of winning:

   a first prize   **b** first and second prize   **c** all 3 prizes   **d** none of the prizes.

4 A hat contains 7 names of players in a tennis squad including the captain and the vice captain. If a team of 3 is chosen at random by drawing the names from the hat, determine the probability that it does *not* contain:

   a the captain   **b** the captain or the vice captain.

5 Two students are chosen at random from a group of two girls and five boys. Find the probability that the two students chosen will be:

   a two boys   **b** the eldest two students.

E   TREE DIAGRAMS

Tree diagrams can be used to illustrate sample spaces if the alternatives are not too numerous. Once the sample space is illustrated, the tree diagram can be used for determining probabilities.

Consider two archers firing simultaneously at a target.

Li has probability $\frac{3}{4}$ of hitting a target and Yuka has probability $\frac{4}{5}$.

The tree diagram for this information is:

H = hit   M = miss

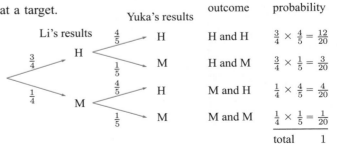

	outcome	probability
H and H		$\frac{3}{4} \times \frac{4}{5} = \frac{12}{20}$
H and M		$\frac{3}{4} \times \frac{1}{5} = \frac{3}{20}$
M and H		$\frac{1}{4} \times \frac{4}{5} = \frac{4}{20}$
M and M		$\frac{1}{4} \times \frac{1}{5} = \frac{1}{20}$
	total	1

Notice from the tree diagram that:

- The probabilities for hitting and missing are marked on the branches.
- There are *four* alternative branches, each showing a particular outcome.
- All outcomes are represented.
- The probability of each outcome is obtained by **multiplying** the probabilities along its branch.

Example 13   ◀)) **Self Tutor**

Carl is not having much luck lately. His car will only start 80% of the time and his motorbike will only start 60% of the time.

  a Draw a tree diagram to illustrate this situation.

  b Use the tree diagram to determine the chance that:

    i both will start   **ii** Carl can only use his car.

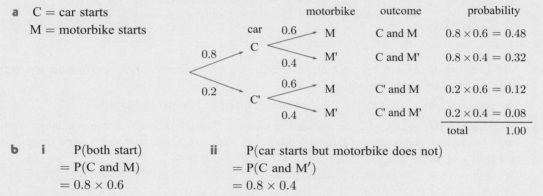

	motorbike	outcome	probability
a C = car starts			
M = motorbike starts	M	C and M	$0.8 \times 0.6 = 0.48$
	M'	C and M'	$0.8 \times 0.4 = 0.32$
	M	C' and M	$0.2 \times 0.6 = 0.12$
	M'	C' and M'	$0.2 \times 0.4 = 0.08$
		total	1.00

b **i**   P(both start)

       = P(C and M)

       = 0.8×0.6

       = 0.48

  ii P(car starts but motorbike does not)

       = P(C and M')

       = 0.8×0.4

       = 0.32

If there is more than one outcome in an event then we need to **add** the probabilities of these outcomes.

Example 14   ◀)) **Self Tutor**

Two boxes each contain 6 petunia plants that are not yet flowering. Box A contains 2 plants that will have purple flowers and 4 plants that will have white flowers. Box B contains 5 plants that will have purple flowers and 1 plant that will have white flowers. A box is selected by tossing a coin, and one plant is removed at random from it. Determine the probability that it will have purple flowers.

Box A

P	W	W
W	P	W

Box B

P	P	P
W	P	P

P(purple flowers)

= P(A and P) + P(B and P)

= $\frac{1}{2} \times \frac{2}{6} + \frac{1}{2} \times \frac{5}{6}$ {branches marked ✓}

= $\frac{7}{12}$

flower

box $\frac{2}{6}$ → P ✓

$\frac{1}{2}$ A

    $\frac{4}{6}$ → W

$\frac{1}{2}$ B

    $\frac{5}{6}$ → P ✓

    $\frac{1}{6}$ → W

EXERCISE 9E

1   Of the students in a class playing musical instruments, 60%
are female. 20% of the females and 30% of the males play
the violin.

    a   Copy and complete the tree diagram.

    b   What is the probability that a randomly selected
student:

       i   is male and does not play the violin

      ii   plays the violin?

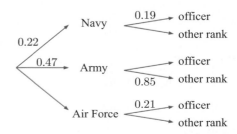

2   **a**   Copy and complete this tree diagram about
people in the armed forces.

    b   What is the probability that a member of the
armed forces:

       i   is an officer

      ii   is not an officer in the navy

     iii   is not an army or air force officer?

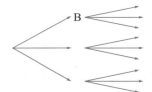

3   Suppose this spinner
is spun twice.

    a   Copy and complete the branches on the tree
diagram shown.

    b   Find the probability that black appears on both spins.

    c   Find the probability that yellow appears on both spins.

    d   Find the probability that different colours appear on the two spins.

    e   Find the probability that black appears on either spin.

4   The probability of rain tomorrow is estimated to be $\frac{1}{5}$. If it does rain, Mudlark will start favourite in
the horse race, with probability $\frac{1}{2}$ of winning. If it is fine, he only has a 1 in 20 chance of winning.
Display the sample space of possible results of the horse race on a tree diagram. Hence determine
the probability that Mudlark will win tomorrow.

5   Machine A makes 40% of the bottles produced at a factory. Machine B makes the rest. Machine
A spoils 5% of its product, while Machine B spoils only 2%. Using an appropriate tree diagram,
determine the probability that the next bottle inspected at this factory is spoiled.

6   Jar A contains 2 white and 3 red discs. Jar B contains 3 white and 1 red disc. A jar is chosen at
random by the flip of a coin, and one disc is taken at random from it. Determine the probability
that the disc is red.

7   The English Premier League consists of 20 teams. Tottenham is currently in 8th place on the table.
It has 20% chance of winning and 50% chance of losing against any team placed above it. If a team
is placed below it, Tottenham has a 50% chance of winning and a 30% chance of losing. Find the
probability that Tottenham will draw its next game.

8 Three bags contain different numbers of blue and red marbles.

A bag is selected using a die which has three A faces, two B faces, and one C face. One marble is then selected randomly from the bag.

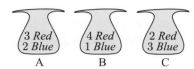

Determine the probability that the marble is:

   a blue   **b** red.

F   SAMPLING WITH AND WITHOUT REPLACEMENT

Suppose we have a large group of objects. If we select one of the objects at random and inspect it for particular features, then this process is known as **sampling**.

If the object is put back in the group before an object is chosen again, we call it **sampling with replacement**.

If the object is put to one side, we call it **sampling without replacement**.

Sampling is commonly used in the quality control of industrial processes.

Sometimes the inspection process makes it impossible to return the object to the large group. For example:

- To see if a chocolate is hard or soft-centred, we need to bite it or squeeze it.
- To see if an egg contains one or two yolks, we need to break it open.
- To see if an object is correctly made, we may need to pull it apart.

Consider a box containing 3 red, 2 blue, and 1 yellow marble. If we sample two marbles, we can do this either:

- **with replacement** of the first before the second is drawn, or
- **without replacement** of the first before the second is drawn.

Examine how the tree diagrams differ:

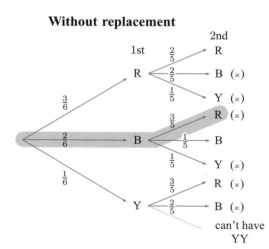

The highlighted branch represents a blue marble with the first draw and a red marble with the second draw. We write this as BR.

Notice that:
- with replacement
  $$P(\text{two reds}) = \tfrac{3}{6} \times \tfrac{3}{6} = \tfrac{1}{4}$$
- without replacement
  $$P(\text{two reds}) = \tfrac{3}{6} \times \tfrac{2}{5} = \tfrac{1}{5}$$

Example 15

A box contains 3 red, 2 blue and 1 yellow marble. Find the probability of getting two different colours:

a if replacement occurs   b if replacement does not occur.

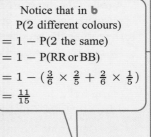

Notice that in **b**
P(2 different colours)
$= 1 - $ P(2 the same)
$= 1 - $ P(RR or BB)
$= 1 - (\frac{3}{6} \times \frac{2}{5} + \frac{2}{6} \times \frac{1}{5})$
$= \frac{11}{15}$

To answer this question we use the tree diagram on page **278**.

a   P(two different colours)

= P(RB or RY or BR or BY or YR or YB)   {ticked ones ✓}

$= \frac{3}{6} \times \frac{2}{6} + \frac{3}{6} \times \frac{1}{6} + \frac{2}{6} \times \frac{3}{6} + \frac{2}{6} \times \frac{1}{6} + \frac{1}{6} \times \frac{3}{6} + \frac{1}{6} \times \frac{2}{6}$

$= \frac{11}{18}$

b   P(two different colours)

= P(RB or RY or BR or BY or YR or YB)   {crossed ones ×}

$= \frac{3}{6} \times \frac{2}{5} + \frac{3}{6} \times \frac{1}{5} + \frac{2}{6} \times \frac{3}{5} + \frac{2}{6} \times \frac{1}{5} + \frac{1}{6} \times \frac{3}{5} + \frac{1}{6} \times \frac{2}{5}$

$= \frac{11}{15}$

Example 16

A bag contains 5 red and 3 blue marbles. Two marbles are drawn simultaneously from the bag. Determine the probability that at least one is red.

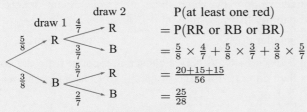

P(at least one red)

= P(RR or RB or BR)

$= \frac{5}{8} \times \frac{4}{7} + \frac{5}{8} \times \frac{3}{7} + \frac{3}{8} \times \frac{5}{7}$

$= \frac{20+15+15}{56}$

$= \frac{25}{28}$

Alternatively,   P(at least one red)

$= 1 - $ P(no reds)   {complementary events}

$= 1 - $ P(BB)   and so on.

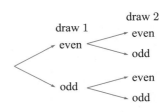

Drawing *simultaneously* is the same as sampling *without* replacement.

EXERCISE 9F

1 Two marbles are drawn in succession from a box containing 2 purple and 5 green marbles. Determine the probability that the two marbles are different colours if:

a the first is replaced   b the first is *not* replaced.

2 5 tickets numbered 1, 2, 3, 4, and 5 are placed in a bag. Two tickets are taken from the bag without replacement.

a Complete the tree diagram by writing the probabilities on the branches.

b Determine the probability that:

i both are odd   ii both are even

iii one is odd and the other is even.

3 A die has 4 faces showing A, and 2 faces showing B. Jar A contains 3 red and 2 green tickets. Jar B contains 3 red and 7 green tickets.

A roll of the die is used to select either jar A or jar B. Once a jar has been selected, two tickets are randomly selected from it without replacement. Determine the probability that:

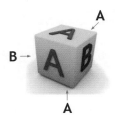

    a both are green   **b** they are different in colour.

4 Marie has a bag of sweets which are all identical in shape. The bag contains 6 orange drops and 4 lemon drops. She selects one sweet at random, eats it, and then takes another at random.

    a Determine the probability that:

        i both sweets are orange drops   **ii** both sweets are lemon drops

        iii the first is an orange drop and the second is a lemon drop

        iv the first is a lemon drop and the second is an orange drop.

    b Add your answers in **a**. Explain why the total must be 1.

5 A bag contains four red and two blue marbles. Three marbles are selected simultaneously. Determine the probablity that:

    a all are red   **b** only two are red   **c** at least two are red.

6 Bag A contains 3 red and 2 white marbles. Bag B contains 4 red and 3 white marbles. One marble is randomly selected from A and its colour noted. If it is red, 2 reds are added to B. If it is white, 2 whites are added to B. A marble is then selected from B. What is the chance that the marble selected from B is white?

7 A man holds two tickets in a 100-ticket lottery in which there are two winning tickets. If no replacement occurs, determine the probability that he will win:

    a both prizes   **b** neither prize   **c** at least one prize.

8 A container holds 3 red, 7 white, and 2 black balls. A ball is chosen at random from the container and is not replaced. A second ball is then chosen. Find the probability of choosing one white and one black ball in any order.

INVESTIGATION 5   SAMPLING SIMULATION

When balls enter the 'sorting' chamber shown they hit a metal rod and may go left or right. This movement continues as the balls fall from one level of rods to the next. The balls finally come to rest in collection chambers at the bottom of the sorter.

This sorter looks very much like a tree diagram rotated through 90°.

Click on the icon to open the simulation. Notice that the sliding bar will alter the probabilities of balls going to the left or right at each rod.

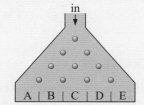

What to do:

1 To simulate the results of tossing two coins, set the bar to 50% and the sorter as shown.

Run the simulation 200 times and repeat this process four more times. Record each set of results. What do you notice about the results?

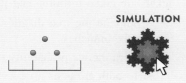

SIMULATION

2 A bag contains 7 blue and 3 red marbles. Two marbles are randomly selected from the bag, the first being *replaced* before the second is drawn.

Since $P(\text{blue}) = \frac{7}{10} = 70\%$,   set the bar to 70%.

a Run the simulation a large number of times. Use the results to estimate the probability of getting:

   i two blues   **ii** one blue   **iii** no blues.

b The following tree diagram shows the theoretical probabilities for the different outcomes:

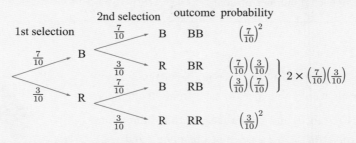

   i Do the theoretical probabilities agree with the experimental results above?

   ii Write down the algebraic expansion of $(a + b)^2$.

   iii Substitute $a = \frac{7}{10}$ and $b = \frac{3}{10}$ in the $(a + b)^2$ expansion. What do you notice?

3 From the bag of 7 blue and 3 red marbles, *three* marbles are randomly selected *with replacement*. Set the sorter to 3 levels and the bar to 70%.

a Run the simulation a large number of times to obtain the experimental probabilities of getting:

   i three blues   **ii** two blues   **iii** one blue   **iv** no blues.

b Use a tree diagram showing 1st selection, 2nd selection, and 3rd selection to find theoretical probabilities for this experiment.

c Show that $(a + b)^3 = a^3 + 3a^2b + 3ab^2 + b^3$. Substitute $a = \frac{7}{10}$ and $b = \frac{3}{10}$ and compare your results with **a** and **b**.

G   EXPECTATION

Consider the following problem:

   A die is to be rolled 120 times. On how many occasions should we *expect* the result to be a "six"?

In order to answer this question we must first consider all possible outcomes of rolling the die. The possibilities are 1, 2, 3, 4, 5, and 6, and each of these is equally likely to occur.

Therefore, we would expect $\frac{1}{6}$ of them to be a "six".

$\frac{1}{6}$ of 120 is 20, so we expect 20 of the 120 rolls of the die to yield a "six".

However, this does not mean that we always *will* get 20 sixes when we roll a die 120 times.

If there are n trials of an experiment, and an event has probability p of occurring in each of the trials, then the number of times we **expect** the event to occur is np.

Example 17
◄)) **Self Tutor**

Each time a footballer kicks for goal he has a $\frac{3}{4}$ chance of being successful.

In a particular game he has 12 kicks for goal. How many goals would you expect him to score?

$p = \text{P(goal)} = \frac{3}{4}$

∴   the expected number of goals is $np = 12 \times \frac{3}{4} = 9$

EXERCISE 9G.1

1 A goalkeeper has probability $\frac{3}{10}$ of saving a penalty attempt. How many goals would he expect to save from 90 attempts?

2 A cube with 4 red faces and 2 blue faces is rolled three times.
  a On any roll, what is the chance of obtaining a red?
  b For the three rolls, how many times would you expect to roll a red?

3 **a** If 3 coins are tossed, what is the chance that they all fall heads?
  b If the 3 coins are tossed 200 times, on how many occasions would you expect them all to fall heads?

4 During the snow season there is a $\frac{3}{7}$ probability of snow falling on any particular day. If Udo skis for five weeks, on how many days could he expect to see snow falling?

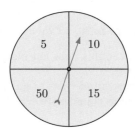

5 If two dice are rolled simultaneously 180 times, on how many occasions would you expect to get a double?

6 In a random survey of her electorate, politician A discovered the residents' voting intentions in relation to herself and her two opponents B and C. The results are indicated alongside:

A	B	C
165	87	48

  a Estimate the probability that a randomly chosen voter in the electorate will vote for:
    i A   **ii** B   **iii** C.
  b If there are 7500 people in the electorate, how many of these would you expect to vote for:
    i A   **ii** B   **iii** C?

EXPECTED VALUE

When the spinner alongside is spun, players are awarded the resulting number of points. On average, how many points can we *expect* to be awarded per spin?

For every 4 spins, we would on average expect each score to be spun once. The total score would be $50 + 15 + 10 + 5 = 80$,   which is an average of $\frac{80}{4} = 20$ points per spin.

Alternatively, we can say that on a given spin, the probability of each score is $\frac{1}{4}$, so the expected score for one spin is

$\frac{1}{4} \times 50 + \frac{1}{4} \times 15 + \frac{1}{4} \times 10 + \frac{1}{4} \times 5 = 20$ points.

> It is impossible to score 20 points on any given spin, but over many spins we *expect* an average score of 20 points per spin.

For an experiment with outcomes $x_1, x_2, x_3, ..., x_n$ and associated probabilities $p_1, p_2, ..., p_n$, the **expectation** or **expected value** from the experiment is given by

Expected value $= x_1 p_1 + x_2 p_2 + ... + x_n p_n$

$\qquad\qquad\quad = \sum x_i p_i$

Example 18 | ◄ Self Tutor

A magazine store recorded the number of magazines purchased by its customers in one week. 23% purchased one magazine, 38% purchased two, 21% purchased three, 13% purchased four, and 5% purchased five.

Find the average number of magazines purchased by customers over a long period.

The probability table is:

x	1	2	3	4	5
p_i	0.23	0.38	0.21	0.13	0.05

The expected value $= \sum x_i p_i$

$\qquad\qquad\qquad\qquad = 1(0.23) + 2(0.38) + 3(0.21) + 4(0.13) + 5(0.05)$

$\qquad\qquad\qquad\qquad = 2.39$

Over a long period, the average number of magazines purchased per customer is 2.39.

EXERCISE 9G.2

1 When the spinner alongside is spun, players are awarded the resulting number of points. On average, how many points can we expect to be awarded per spin?

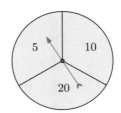

2 When Ernie goes fishing, he catches either 0, 1, 2, or 3 fish, with the probabilities shown.
On average, how many fish would you expect Ernie to catch per fishing trip?

Number of fish	0	1	2	3
Probability	0.17	0.28	0.36	0.19

3 Each time Pam visits the library, she borrows either 1, 2, 3, 4, or 5 books, with the probabilities shown alongside.

Number of books	1	2	3	4	5
Probability	0.16	0.15	0.25	0.28	0.16

On average, how many books does Pam borrow per visit?

4   Lachlan selects a ball from a bag containing 5 red balls, 2 green balls, and 1 white ball.

He is then allowed to take lollies from a lolly jar. The number of lollies is determined by the colour of the ball as shown in the table.

Find the average number of lollies Lachlan would expect to receive.

Colour	Number of lollies
Red	4
Green	6
White	10

5   When ten-pin bowler Jenna bowls her first bowl of a frame, she always knocks down at least 8 pins.

$\frac{1}{3}$ of the time she knocks down 8 pins, and $\frac{2}{5}$ of the time she knocks down 9 pins.

   a   Find the probability that she knocks down all 10 pins on the first bowl.

   b   On average, how many pins does Jenna expect to knock down with her first bowl?

FAIR GAMES

In gambling, we say that the **expected gain** of the player from each game is the expected return or payout from the game, minus the amount it costs to play.

The game will be **fair** if the expected gain is zero.

Example 19   ◀)) **Self Tutor**

In a game of chance, a player spins a square spinner labelled 1, 2, 3, 4. The player wins the amount of money shown in the table alongside, depending on which number comes up. Determine:

Number	1	2	3	4
Winnings	$1	$2	$5	$8

   a   the expected return for one spin of the spinner

   b   the expected *gain* of the player if it costs $5 to play each game

   c   whether the game is fair.

   a   Each outcome is equally likely, so the probability for each outcome is $\frac{1}{4}$.

   The expected return from one spin $= \frac{1}{4} \times 1 + \frac{1}{4} \times 2 + \frac{1}{4} \times 5 + \frac{1}{4} \times 8 = \$4$.

   b   Since it costs $5 to play the game, the expected gain $=$ expected return $-$ \$5

   $$= \$4 - \$5$$
   $$= -\$1$$

   c   Since the expected gain is not zero, the game is not fair. In particular, since the expected gain is $-\$1$, we expect the player to lose $1 on average with each spin.

EXERCISE 9G.3

1   A dice game costs $2 to play. If an odd number is rolled, the player receives $3. If an even number is rolled, the player receives $1.

Determine whether the game is fair.

2 A man rolls a normal six-sided die. He wins the number of euros (€) shown on the uppermost face.

  a Find the expected return from one roll of the die.

  b Find the expected *gain* of the man if it costs €4 to play the game. Would you advise the man to play several games?

3 A roulette wheel has 18 red numbers, 18 black numbers, and 1 green number. Each number has an equal chance of occurring. I place a bet of $2 on red. If a red is spun, I receive my $2 back plus another $2. Otherwise I lose my $2.

  a Calculate the expected gain from this bet.

  b If this bet was made 100 times, what is the overall expected result?

4 A person plays a game with a pair of coins. If two heads appear then £10 is won. If a head and a tail appear then £3 is won. If two tails appear then £1 is won. It costs £5 to play the game. Find the expected gain for this game.

5 A person selects a disc from a bag containing 10 black discs, 4 blue discs, and 1 gold disc. They win $1 for a black disc, $5 for a blue disc, and $20 for the gold disc. The game costs $4 to play.

  a Calculate the expected gain for this game, and hence show that the game is not fair.

  b To make the game fair, the prize money for selecting the gold disc is increased. Find the new prize money for selecting the gold disc.

6 In a fundraising game 'Lucky 11', a player selects 3 cards, without replacing them, from a box containing 5 red, 4 blue, and 3 green cards. The player wins $11 if the cards drawn are all the same colour, or are one of each colour.

If the organiser of the game wants to make an average of $1 per game, how much should they charge to play it?

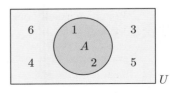

H   PROBABILITIES FROM VENN DIAGRAMS

Venn diagrams are a useful way of representing the events in a sample space. These diagrams usually consist of a rectangle which represents the complete sample space U, and circles within it which represent particular events.

Venn diagrams can be used to solve certain types of probability questions and also to establish a number of probability laws.

When we roll an ordinary die, the sample space or universal set is $U = \{1, 2, 3, 4, 5, 6\}$.

Suppose the event A is "*a number less than 3*". The two outcomes 1 and 2 satisfy this event, so we can write $A = \{1, 2\}$.

The Venn diagram alongside illustrates the event A within the universal set U.

$n(U) = 6$ and $n(A) = 2$, so $P(A) = \dfrac{n(A)}{n(U)} = \dfrac{2}{6} = \dfrac{1}{3}$.

Example 20   ◀ᴈ **Self Tutor**

The Venn diagram alongside represents the set U of all children
in a class. Each dot represents a student. The event E shows
all those students with blue eyes. Determine the probability that
a randomly selected child:

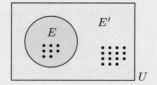

  a has blue eyes   **b** does not have blue eyes.

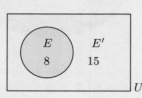

$$n(U) = 23, \quad n(E) = 8$$

  a $\text{P(blue eyes)} = \dfrac{n(E)}{n(U)} = \dfrac{8}{23}$

  b $\text{P(not blue eyes)} = \dfrac{n(E')}{n(U)} = \dfrac{15}{23}$

    or $\text{P(not blue)} = 1 - \text{P(blue eyes)} = 1 - \dfrac{8}{23} = \dfrac{15}{23}$

Example 21   ◀ᴈ **Self Tutor**

In a class of 30 students, 19 study Physics, 17 study Chemistry, and 15 study both of these subjects.
Display this information on a Venn diagram and hence determine the probability that a randomly
selected class member studies:

  a both subjects   **b** at least one of the subjects

  c Physics but not Chemistry   **d** exactly one of the subjects

  e neither subject

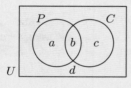

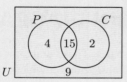

Let P represent the event of 'studying Physics'
and C represent the event of 'studying Chemistry'.

Now $a + b = 19$ {as 19 study Physics}

                 $b + c = 17$ {as 17 study Chemistry}

                      $b = 15$ {as 15 study both}

    $a + b + c + d = 30$ {as there are 30 in the class}

$\therefore \quad b = 15, \ a = 4, \ c = 2, \ d = 9.$

  a P(studies both)   **b** P(studies at least one subject)   **c** $\text{P}(P$ but not $C)$

      $= \dfrac{15}{30}$ or $\dfrac{1}{2}$ $= \dfrac{4+15+2}{30}$ $= \dfrac{4}{30}$

                           $= \dfrac{7}{10}$ $= \dfrac{2}{15}$

  d P(studies exactly one)   **e** P(studies neither)

      $= \dfrac{4+2}{30}$ $= \dfrac{9}{30}$

      $= \dfrac{1}{5}$ $= \dfrac{3}{10}$

EXERCISE 9H

1 The Venn diagram alongside represents the set U of sheep in a pen. Each dot represents a sheep. The event B shows the sheep with black wool.

Determine the probability that a randomly selected sheep:

   a has black wool   **b** does not have black wool.

2 The Venn diagram alongside illustrates the number of students in a particular class who study Chemistry (C) and History (H). Determine the probability that a randomly chosen student studies:

   a both subjects   **b** at least one of the subjects

   c only Chemistry.

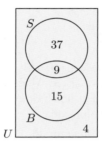

3 In a survey at an alpine resort, people were asked whether they liked skiing (S) or snowboarding (B). Use the Venn diagram to determine the probability that a randomly chosen person:

   a liked both activities

   b liked neither activity

   c liked exactly one activity.

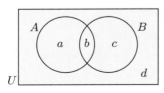

4 In a class of 40 students, 19 play tennis, 20 play netball, and 8 play neither of these sports. A student is randomly chosen from the class. Determine the probability that the student:

   a plays tennis   **b** does not play netball

   c plays at least one of the sports   **d** plays one and only one of the sports

   e plays netball but not tennis.

5 50 married men were asked whether they gave their wife flowers or chocolates for her last birthday. The results were: 31 gave chocolates, 12 gave flowers, and 5 gave both chocolates and flowers. If one of the married men was chosen at random, determine the probability that he gave his wife:

   a chocolates or flowers   **b** chocolates but not flowers

   c neither chocolates nor flowers.

6 The medical records for a class of 30 children showed that 24 previously had measles, 12 previously had measles and mumps, and 26 previously had at least one of measles or mumps. If one child from the class is selected at random, determine the probability that he or she has had:

   a mumps   **b** mumps but not measles   **c** neither mumps nor measles.

7

From the Venn diagram, $\quad P(A) = \dfrac{a+b}{a+b+c+d}$.

   a Use the Venn diagram to find:

      i $P(B)$ **ii** $P(A \text{ and } B)$ **iii** $P(A \text{ or } B)$ **iv** $P(A) + P(B) - P(A \text{ and } B)$

   b What is the connection between $P(A \text{ or } B)$ and $P(A) + P(B) - P(A \text{ and } B)$?

8 In the Venn diagram, U is the set of all 60 members of a club.

The members indicate their liking for Chinese (C), Italian (I), and Thai (T) food.

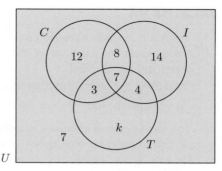

   a Find the value of k.

   b A randomly chosen member is asked about their preferences. Find the probability that the member likes:

     i only Italian   **ii** Italian and Thai

     iii none of these foods   **iv** at least one of these foods

     v all of these foods   **vi** Chinese and Italian, but not Thai

     vii Thai or Italian   **viii** exactly one of these foods.

9 As a group bonding project, 50 delegates at a European conference were asked what languages they had conversations in at lunch time. The data collected is summarised alongside.

Languages	Delegates
English only	17
French only	7
Spanish only	12
English and French only	3
English and Spanish only	6
French and Spanish only	4
English, French, and Spanish	1

   a Construct a Venn diagram to display the information.

   b Determine the probability that a randomly selected delegate had a conversation in:

     i English   **ii** French

     iii Spanish, but not in English

     iv French, but not in Spanish   **v** French, and also in English.

10 The Venn diagram opposite indicates the types of program a group of 40 individuals watched on television last night.

M represents movies, S represents sport, and D represents drama.

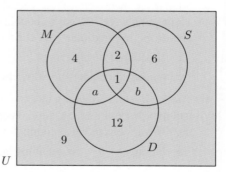

   a Given that 10 people watched a movie last night, calculate a and b.

   b Find the probability that one of these individuals, selected at random, watched:

     i sport   **ii** drama and sport   **iii** a movie but not sport

     iv drama but not a movie   **v** drama or a movie.

I   LAWS OF PROBABILITY

THE ADDITION LAW

In the previous exercise we showed that:

For two events A and B,

$$P(A \cup B) = P(A) + P(B) - P(A \cap B).$$

$A \cup B$ means A **or** B and $A \cap B$ means A **and** B

This is known as the **addition law of probability**, and can also be written as

P(**either** A **or** B) = P(A) + P(B) − P(**both** A **and** B).

Example 22   ◀) **Self Tutor**

If $P(A) = 0.6$, $P(A \cup B) = 0.7$, and $P(A \cap B) = 0.3$, find $P(B)$.

$$P(A \cup B) = P(A) + P(B) - P(A \cap B)$$
$$\therefore \quad 0.7 = 0.6 + P(B) - 0.3$$
$$\therefore \quad P(B) = 0.4$$

or

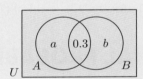

Using a Venn diagram with the probabilities on it,

$a + 0.3 = 0.6$ and $a + b + 0.3 = 0.7$
$\therefore \quad a = 0.3$ $\therefore \quad a + b = 0.4$
                                              $\therefore \quad 0.3 + b = 0.4$
                                              $\therefore \quad b = 0.1$

$\therefore \quad P(B) = 0.3 + b = 0.4$

MUTUALLY EXCLUSIVE OR DISJOINT EVENTS

If A and B are **mutually exclusive** events then $P(A \cap B) = 0$
and so the addition law becomes $P(A \cup B) = P(A) + P(B)$.

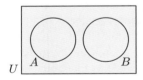

Example 23   ◀) **Self Tutor**

Of the 31 people on a bus tour, 7 were born in Scotland (S), and 5 were born in Wales (W).
  a Are S and W mutually exclusive events?
  b If a member of the tour is chosen at random, find the probability that he or she was born in:
     i Scotland   **ii** Wales   **iii** Scotland or Wales.

  a A person cannot be born in both Scotland and Wales, so S and W are mutually exclusive.
  b **i** $P(S) = \frac{7}{31}$ **ii** $P(W) = \frac{5}{31}$
     iii $P(S \cup W) = P(S) + P(W)$ {mutually exclusive events}
              $= \frac{7}{31} + \frac{5}{31} = \frac{12}{31}$

EXERCISE 9I

1 If $P(A) = 0.4$, $P(A \cup B) = 0.9$,   and $P(A \cap B) = 0.1$,   find $P(B)$.

2 If $P(X) = 0.6$, $P(Y) = 0.5$,   and $P(X \cup Y) = 0.9$,   find $P(X \cap Y)$.

3 A and B are mutually exclusive events.
If $P(B) = 0.45$ and $P(A \cup B) = 0.8$,   find $P(A)$.

4 Tickets numbered 1 to 15 are placed in a hat, and one ticket is chosen at random. Let A be the event that the number drawn is greater than 11, and B be the event that the number drawn is less than 8.

   a Are A and B mutually exclusive?

   b Find: **i** $P(A)$ **ii** $P(B)$ **iii** $P(A \cup B)$.

5 A class consists of 25 students.
      11 students are fifteen years old (F).
      12 students are sixteen years old (S).
      8 students own a dog (D).
      7 students own a cat (C).
      4 students do not own any pets (N).

A student is chosen at random. If possible, find:

   a $P(F)$ **b** $P(S)$ **c** $P(D)$ **d** $P(C)$ **e** $P(N)$

   f $P(F \cup S)$ **g** $P(F \cup D)$ **h** $P(C \cup N)$ **i** $P(C \cup D)$ **j** $P(D \cup N)$

J   CONDITIONAL PROBABILITY

If we have two events A and B, then

> $A \mid B$ is used to represent that "A occurs knowing that B has occurred".
> $A \mid B$ is read as "A given B".

Example 24   ◀⑴ **Self Tutor**

In a class of 25 students, 14 like pizza and 16 like iced coffee. One student likes neither and 6 students like both. One student is randomly selected from the class. What is the probability that the student:

   a likes pizza   **b** likes pizza given that he or she likes iced coffee?

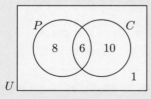

The Venn diagram of the situation is shown.

   a Of the 25 students, 14 like pizza.
      $\therefore$ $P(\text{pizza}) = \frac{14}{25}$

   b Of the 16 who like iced coffee, 6 like pizza.
      $\therefore$ $P(\text{pizza} \mid \text{iced coffee}) = \frac{6}{16}$

> If A and B are events then $P(A \mid B) = \dfrac{P(A \cap B)}{P(B)}$.

Proof:

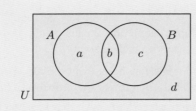

$$P(A \mid B) = \frac{b}{b+c} \quad \{\text{Venn diagram}\}$$

$$= \frac{\frac{b}{(a+b+c+d)}}{\frac{b+c}{(a+b+c+d)}}$$

$$= \frac{P(A \cap B)}{P(B)}$$

It follows that $\mathbf{P(A \cap B) = P(A \mid B)\,P(B)}$ or $\mathbf{P(A \cap B) = P(B \mid A)\,P(A)}$.

Example 25   ◀⑴ **Self Tutor**

In a class of 40 students, 34 like bananas, 22 like pineapple, and 2 dislike both fruits. A student is randomly selected. Find the probability that the student:

  a likes both fruits   **b** likes at least one fruit

  c likes bananas given that he or she likes pineapple

  d dislikes pineapple given that he or she likes bananas.

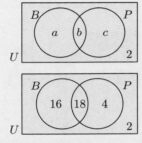

B represents students who like bananas.
P represents students who like pineapple.

We are given that $\quad a + b = 34$
$$b + c = 22$$
$$a + b + c = 38$$

$\therefore \quad c = 38 - 34 = 4 \quad$ and so $\quad b = 18$
$$\text{and} \quad a = 16$$

  a P(likes both)   **b** P(likes at least one)   **c** $P(B \mid P)$ **d** $P(P' \mid B)$

$\quad = \frac{18}{40} \qquad\qquad\qquad = \frac{38}{40} \qquad\qquad\qquad\quad = \frac{18}{22} \qquad\qquad = \frac{16}{34}$

$\quad = \frac{9}{20} \qquad\qquad\qquad = \frac{19}{20} \qquad\qquad\qquad\quad = \frac{9}{11} \qquad\qquad = \frac{8}{17}$

EXERCISE 9J

1 In a group of 50 students, 40 study Mathematics, 32 study Physics, and each student studies at least one of these subjects.

  a Use a Venn diagram to find how many students study both subjects.

  b If a student from this group is randomly selected, find the probability that he or she:

    i studies Mathematics but not Physics

    ii studies Physics given that he or she studies Mathematics.

2 In a group of 40 boys, 23 have dark hair, 18 have brown eyes, and 26 have dark hair, brown eyes, or both. One of the boys is selected at random. Determine the probability that he has:

  a dark hair and brown eyes   **b** neither dark hair nor brown eyes

  c dark hair but not brown eyes   **d** brown eyes given that he has dark hair.

Example 26   ◀》 **Self Tutor**

The top shelf in a cupboard contains 3 cans of pumpkin soup and 2 cans of chicken soup. The bottom shelf contains 4 cans of pumpkin soup and 1 can of chicken soup.

Lukas is twice as likely to take a can from the bottom shelf as he is from the top shelf. Suppose Lukas takes one can of soup without looking at the label. Determine the probability that it:

a   is chicken   **b**   was taken from the top shelf given that it is chicken.

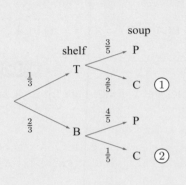

a   P(soup is chicken)

$$= \tfrac{1}{3} \times \tfrac{2}{5} + \tfrac{2}{3} \times \tfrac{1}{5} \quad \{\text{paths } ① \text{ and } ②\}$$

$$= \tfrac{4}{15}$$

b   P(top shelf | chicken)

$$= \frac{\text{P(top shelf and chicken)}}{\text{P(chicken)}}$$

$$= \frac{\tfrac{1}{3} \times \tfrac{2}{5}}{\tfrac{4}{15}} \quad \longleftarrow \text{ path } ①$$

$$= \tfrac{1}{2}$$

---

3 50 students went bushwalking. 23 were sunburnt, 22 were bitten by ants, and 5 were both sunburnt and bitten by ants. Determine the probability that a randomly selected student:

   a escaped being bitten

   b was either bitten or sunburnt

   c was neither bitten nor sunburnt

   d was bitten, given that he or she was sunburnt

   e was sunburnt, given that he or she was not bitten.

4 400 families were surveyed. It was found that 90% had a TV set and 60% had a computer. Every family had at least one of these items. One of these families is randomly selected, and it is found that they have a computer. Find the probability that it also has a TV set.

5 In a certain town, three newspapers are published. 20% of the population read A, 16% read B, 14% read C, 8% read A and B, 5% read A and C, 4% read B and C, and 2% read all 3 newspapers. A person is selected at random. Use a Venn diagram to help determine the probability that the person reads:

   a none of the papers   **b** at least one of the papers

   c exactly one of the papers   **d** either A or B

   e A, given that the person reads at least one paper

   f C, given that the person reads either A or B or both.

6 Urn A contains 2 red and 3 blue marbles, and urn B contains 4 red and 1 blue marble. Peter selects an urn by tossing a coin, and takes a marble from that urn.

   a Determine the probability that it is red.

   b Given that the marble is red, what is the probability that it came from B?

7 The probability that Greta's mother takes her shopping is $\frac{2}{5}$. When Greta goes shopping with her mother she gets an icecream 70% of the time. When Greta does not go shopping with her mother she gets an icecream 30% of the time.
Determine the probability that:

   a Greta's mother buys her an icecream when shopping

   b Greta went shopping with her mother, given that her mother buys her an icecream.

8 On a given day, machine A has a 10% chance of malfunctioning and machine B has a 7% chance of the same. Given that at least one of the machines malfunctioned today, what is the chance that machine B malfunctioned?

9 On any day, the probability that a boy eats his prepared lunch is 0.5. The probability that his sister eats her lunch is 0.6. The probability that the girl eats her lunch given that the boy eats his is 0.9. Determine the probability that:

   a both eat their lunch   **b** the boy eats his lunch given that the girl eats hers

   c at least one of them eats their lunch.

10 The probability that a randomly selected person has cancer is 0.02. The probability that he or she reacts positively to a test which detects cancer is 0.95 if he or she has cancer, and 0.03 if he or she does not. Determine the probability that a randomly tested person:

   a reacts positively   **b** has cancer given that he or she reacts positively.

11 A group of teenagers were surveyed on which of three types of computer games they play. The results are shown in the Venn diagram.
A represents those who play arcade games.
S represents those who play sports games.
R represents those who play role-playing games.
Find the probability that a randomly selected member of the group plays:

   a arcade games but not role-playing games

   b sports games and arcade games

   c role-playing games or sports games

   d sports games, given that he or she plays arcade games

   e role-playing games, given that he or she plays arcade games

   f arcade games, given that he or she does *not* play sports games.

12 In a team of 30 judo players, 13 have won a match by throwing (T), 12 have won by hold-down (H), and 13 have won by points decision (P). 2 have won matches by all three methods. 5 have won matches by throwing and hold-down. 4 have won matches by hold-down and points decision. 3 have won matches by throwing and points decision.

   a Draw a Venn diagram to display this information.

   b Find:

      i $P(T \cap H)$ **ii** $P(P)$ **iii** $P(H \mid P)$

      iv $P(T \cup P)$ **v** $P(T \mid H')$ **vi** $P((T \cap P) \mid H)$

K   INDEPENDENT EVENTS

A and B are **independent events** if the occurrence of each one of them does not affect the probability that the other occurs.

This means that $P(A \mid B) = P(A \mid B') = P(A)$.

$\Leftrightarrow$ means 'if and only if'.

Using $P(A \cap B) = P(A \mid B)\, P(B)$ we see that

A and B are **independent events** $\Leftrightarrow$ $P(A \cap B) = P(A)\, P(B)$.

Example 27   ◀ Self Tutor

Suppose $P(A) = \frac{1}{2}$ and $P(B) = \frac{1}{3}$. Find $P(A \cup B)$ if:

a A and B are mutually exclusive   **b** A and B are independent.

a   If A and B are mutually exclusive, $A \cap B = \varnothing$ and so $P(A \cap B) = 0$

$\therefore \ \ P(A \cup B) = P(A) + P(B) - P(A \cap B)$

$= \frac{1}{2} + \frac{1}{3} - 0$

$= \frac{5}{6}$

b   If A and B are independent, $P(A \cap B) = P(A)\, P(B) = \frac{1}{2} \times \frac{1}{3} = \frac{1}{6}$

$\therefore \ \ P(A \cup B) = \frac{1}{2} + \frac{1}{3} - \frac{1}{6}$

$= \frac{2}{3}$

Example 28   ◀ Self Tutor

Suppose $P(A) = \frac{2}{5}$, $P(B \mid A) = \frac{1}{3}$, and $P(B \mid A') = \frac{1}{4}$, find: **a** $P(B)$ **b** $P(A \cap B')$

$P(B \mid A) = \dfrac{P(B \cap A)}{P(A)}$ so $P(B \cap A) = P(B \mid A)\, P(A) = \frac{1}{3} \times \frac{2}{5} = \frac{2}{15}$

Similarly, $P(B \cap A') = P(B \mid A')\, P(A') = \frac{1}{4} \times \frac{3}{5} = \frac{3}{20}$

$\therefore$ the Venn diagram is:

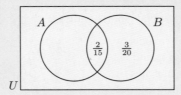

a $P(B) = \frac{2}{15} + \frac{3}{20} = \frac{17}{60}$

b $P(A \cap B') = P(A) - P(A \cap B)$

$= \frac{2}{5} - \frac{2}{15}$

$= \frac{4}{15}$

EXERCISE 9K

1 $P(R) = 0.4$, $P(S) = 0.5$, and $P(R \cup S) = 0.7$.   Are R and S independent events?

2 $P(A) = \frac{2}{5}$, $P(B) = \frac{1}{3}$, and $P(A \cup B) = \frac{1}{2}$.

   a Find: **i** $P(A \cap B)$ **ii** $P(B \mid A)$ **iii** $P(A \mid B)$

   b Are A and B independent events?

3 $P(X) = 0.5$, $P(Y) = 0.7$, and X and Y are independent events. Determine the probability of the occurrence of:

    a   both X and Y **b** X or Y **c**   neither X nor Y

    d X but not Y **e** X given that Y occurs.

4 The probabilities that A, B, and C can solve a particular problem are $\frac{3}{5}$, $\frac{2}{3}$, and $\frac{1}{2}$ respectively. If they all try, determine the probability that at least one of the group solves the problem.

5 A and B are independent events. Prove that A' and B' are also independent events.

6 Suppose $P(A \cap B) = 0.1$ and $P(A \cap B') = 0.4$. Find $P(A \cup B')$ given that A and B are independent.

THEORY OF KNOWLEDGE

Modern probability theory began in 1653 when gambler Chevalier de Mere contacted mathematician **Blaise Pascal** with a problem on how to divide the stakes when a gambling game is interrupted during play. Pascal involved **Pierre de Fermat**, a lawyer and amateur mathematician, and together they solved the problem. In the process they laid the foundations upon which the laws of probability were formed.

Blaise Pascal   *Pierre de Fermat*

Agner Krarup Erlang

Applications of probability are now found from quantum physics to medicine and industry.

The first research paper on **queueing theory** was published in 1909 by the Danish engineer **Agner Krarup Erlang** who worked for the Copenhagen Telephone Exchange. In the last hundred years this theory has become an integral part of the huge global telecommunications industry, but it is equally applicable to modelling car traffic right down to queues at your local supermarket.

Statistics and probability are used extensively to predict the behaviour of the global stock market. For example, American mathematician **Edward Oakley Thorp** developed and applied hedge fund techniques for the financial markets in the 1960s.

On the level of an individual investor, money is put into the stock market if there is a good probability that the value of the shares will increase. This investment has risk, however, as witnessed recently with the Global Financial Crisis of 2008-2009.

    1   In what ways can mathematics model the world without using functions?

    2   How does a knowledge of probability theory affect decisions we make?

    3   Do ethics play a role in the use of mathematics?

REVIEW SET 9A

1 List the different orders in which 4 people A, B, C, and D could line up. If they line up at random, determine the probability that:

    a A is next to C

    b there is exactly one person between A and C.

2 Given $P(A) = m$ is the probability of event A occurring in any given trial:

    a Write $P(A')$ in terms of m.

    b State the range of possible values for m.

3 A coin is tossed and a square spinner labelled A, B, C, D, is twirled. Determine the probability of obtaining:

    a a head and consonant

    b a tail and C

    c a tail or a vowel.

4 The probability that a man will be alive in 25 years is $\frac{3}{5}$, and the probability that his wife will be alive is $\frac{2}{3}$. Assuming these events are independent, determine the probability that in 25 years:

    a both will be alive

    b at least one will be alive

    c only the wife will be alive.

5 Given $P(Y) = 0.35$ and $P(X \cup Y) = 0.8$, and that X and Y are mutually exclusive events, find:

    a $P(X \cap Y)$

    b $P(X)$

    c the probability that X occurs or Y occurs, but not both X and Y.

6 What is meant by: **a** independent events   **b** mutually exclusive events?

7 Graph the sample space of all possible outcomes when a pair of dice is rolled and the sum on their faces is found. Hence determine the probability of getting:

    a a sum of 7 or 11

    b a sum of at least 8.

8 The probability that a tomato seed will germinate is 0.87. If a market gardener plants 5000 seeds, how many are expected to germinate?

9 In a group of 40 students, 22 study Economics, 25 study Law, and 3 study neither of these subjects. Determine the probability that a randomly chosen student studies:

    a both Economics and Law

    b at least one of these subjects

    c Economics given that he or she studies Law.

10 The probability that a particular salesman will leave his sunglasses behind in any store is $\frac{1}{5}$. Suppose the salesman visits two stores in succession and leaves his sunglasses behind in one of them. What is the probability that the salesman left his sunglasses in the first store?

REVIEW SET 9B

1 Two dice are rolled and the results are multiplied together.

    a Draw a table of outcomes to display the possible results.

    b Hence determine the probability that the resulting value is:

        i 12   **ii** greater than 17   **iii** a square number.

2 Niklas and Rolf play tennis with the winner being the first to win two sets. Niklas has a 40% chance of beating Rolf in any set. Draw a tree diagram showing the possible outcomes and hence determine the probability that Niklas will win the match.

3 A group of businesses were asked whether they had increased or decreased their number of employees in the last year.

Number of employees	Decreased	Stayed the same	Increased
1-4	26	168	25
5-9	19	41	3
10-19	23	9	7
20-99	20	2	14
100-499	6	0	6
500+	14	0	19
Total	108	220	74

  a Find the probability that a business with 10-19 employees grew in the previous year.

  b Find the probability that a business that increased in size had 10-99 employees.

  c Find the probability that a randomly selected business decreased in size over the previous year.

4 If I buy 4 tickets in a 500 ticket lottery, and the prizes are drawn without replacement, determine the probability that I will win:

  a the first 3 prizes
  b at least one of the first 3 prizes.

5 The students in a school are all vaccinated against measles. 48% of the students are males, of whom 16% have an allergic reaction to the vaccine. 35% of the girls also have an allergic reaction. A student is randomly chosen from the school. Find the probability that the student:

  a has an allergic reaction

  b is female given that a reaction occurs.

6 On any one day, there is a 25% chance of rain and 36% chance of being windy.

  a Draw a tree diagram showing the probabilities of wind or rain on a particular day.

  b Hence determine the probability that on a particular day there will be:
    i rain and wind
    ii rain or wind.

  c What assumption have you made in your answers?

7 Divers A, B, and C have a 10%, 20%, and 30% chance of independently finding an artefact in a shipwreck. If they all dive separately, what is the probability that the artefact is found?

8 There were 42 staff members in the common room at morning tea today.
Their selection of biscuits is illustrated in the Venn diagram alongside.
A is the set of staff who ate a chocolate biscuit.
B is the set of staff who ate a cookie.
C is the set of staff who ate a cream biscuit.
Find the probability that a randomly selected staff member ate:

  a a chocolate biscuit
  b a chocolate biscuit and a cookie
  c a chocolate biscuit or a cookie
  d exactly one type of biscuit
  e exactly two types of biscuit
  f a cream biscuit but not a cookie
  g a cookie, given that he or she ate a chocolate biscuit
  h a cream biscuit, given that he or she ate a cookie.

9   A soccer team scores up to 4 goals in each game they play, with the probabilities shown.
How many goals are they expected to score per match?

Number of goals	0	1	2	3	4
Probability	0.29	0.35	0.27	0.07	0.02

REVIEW SET 9C

1   List, in systematic order, the possible sexes of a 4-child family. Hence determine the probability that a randomly selected 4-child family has two children of each sex.

2   A bag contains 3 red, 4 yellow and 5 blue marbles. Two marbles are randomly selected from the bag without replacement. What is the probability that:

  a both are blue   **b** they have the same colour

  c at least one is red   **d** exactly one is yellow?

3   An art gallery has 25 rooms. 17 contain sculptures, 19 contain paintings and only the cloak room contains neither. If a visitor enters a room at random, determine the probability that it contains:

  a both paintings and sculptures   **b** only one type of art

  c paintings given that there are no sculptures.

4   An urn contains three red balls and six blue balls.

  a A ball is drawn at random and found to be blue. What is the probability that a second draw with no replacement will also produce a blue ball?

  b Two balls are drawn without replacement and the second is found to be red. What is the probability that the first ball was also red?

5   An automatic gate has a 95% chance of working on any particular day. Find the probability that it will be working on at least one of the next two days.

6   Jon goes cycling on three random mornings each week. When he goes cycling he has eggs for breakfast 70% of the time. When he does not go cycling he has eggs for breakfast 25% of the time. Determine the probability that Jon:

  a has eggs for breakfast   **b** goes cycling, given that he had eggs for breakfast.

7 $P(X) = \frac{1}{4}$, $P(Y') = \frac{1}{6}$, and $P(X \cup Y) = \frac{7}{8}$. Are X and Y independent events?

8   A survey of 50 families found that 13 owned a caravan, 10 owned a holiday house, and 30 owned a tent. 6 had a caravan and a tent only, 7 had a holiday house and a tent only, and 1 had a caravan and a holiday house only. 1 family owned all three. With the aid of a Venn diagram, determine the probability that a randomly selected family owns:

  a a caravan only

  b exactly two types of holiday accommodation

  c none of these things.

Chapter 10

The normal distribution

Syllabus reference: 4.1

Contents:

OPENING PROBLEM

A salmon breeder catches hundreds of adult fish. He is interested in the distribution of the *weight of an adult salmon, W*. He records their weights in a frequency table with class intervals $3 \leqslant w < 3.1$ kg, $3.1 \leqslant w < 3.2$ kg, $3.2 \leqslant w < 3.3$ kg, and so on.

The mean weight was 4.73 kg, and the standard deviation was 0.53 kg.

A frequency histogram of the data was bell-shaped and symmetric about the mean.

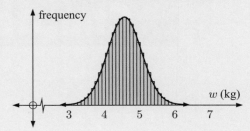

Things to think about:

  a Can we use the mean and standard deviation only to estimate the proportion of salmon whose weight is:

    i greater than 6 kg   **ii** between 4 kg and 6 kg?

  b How can we find the weight:

    i which 90% of salmon are less than   **ii** which 25% of salmon are more than?

A **continuous random variable** is a variable which can take any real value within a certain range. We usually denote random variables by a capital letter such as X. Individual measurements of this variable are denoted by the corresponding lower case letter x.

For a continuous variable X, the probability that X is *exactly* equal to a particular value is zero. So, $P(X = a) = 0$ for all a.

For example, the probability that an egg will weigh *exactly* 72.9 g is zero.

If you were to weigh an egg on scales that weigh to the nearest 0.1 g, a reading of 72.9 g means the weight lies somewhere between 72.85 g and 72.95 g. No matter how accurate your scales are, you can only ever know the weight of an egg within a range.

So, for a continuous variable we can only talk about the probability that an event lies in an **interval**, and:

$$P(a \leqslant X \leqslant b) = P(a < X \leqslant b) = P(a \leqslant X < b) = P(a < X < b).$$

A   THE NORMAL DISTRIBUTION

The normal distribution is the most important distribution for a continuous random variable. Many naturally occurring phenomena have a distribution that is normal, or approximately normal. Some examples are:

- physical attributes of a population such as height, weight, and arm length
- crop yields
- scores for tests taken by a large population

Once a normal model has been established, we can use it to make predictions about a distribution and to answer other relevant questions.

HOW A NORMAL DISTRIBUTION ARISES

Consider the oranges picked from an orange tree. They do not all have the same weight. The variation may be due to several factors, including:

- genetics
- different times when the flowers were fertilised
- different amounts of sunlight reaching the leaves and fruit
- different weather conditions such as the prevailing winds.

The result is that most of the fruit will have weights close to the mean, while fewer oranges will be *much* heavier or *much* lighter.

This results in a **bell-shaped distribution** which is symmetric about the mean.

A TYPICAL NORMAL DISTRIBUTION

A large sample of cockle shells was collected and the maximum width of each shell was measured. Click on the video clip icon to see how a histogram of the data is built up. Then click on the demo icon to observe the effect of changing the class interval lengths for normally distributed data.

THE NORMAL DISTRIBUTION CURVE

Although all normal distributions have the same general bell-shaped curve, the exact location and shape of the curve is determined by the **mean μ** and **standard deviation σ** of the variable.

For example, we can say that:

- The height of trees in a park is normally distributed with mean 10 metres and standard deviation 3 metres.

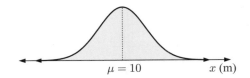

- The time it takes Sean to get to school is normally distributed with mean 15 minutes and standard deviation 1 minute.

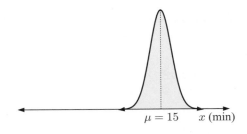

Notice that the normal curve is always symmetric about the vertical line $x = \mu$.

If a continuous variable X is normally distributed with mean μ and standard deviation σ, we write $X \sim N(\mu, \sigma^2)$.

Click on the icon to explore the normal probability density function and how it changes when μ and σ are altered.

We say that μ and σ are the **parameters** of the distribution.

DEMO

INVESTIGATION 1   STANDARD DEVIATION

The purpose of this investigation is to find the proportions of normal distribution data which lie within σ, 2σ, and 3σ of the mean.

What to do:

1   Click on the icon to start the demonstration in Microsoft® Excel.

DEMO

2   Take a random sample of size $n = 1000$ from a normal distribution.

3   Find the sample mean $\overline{x}$ and standard deviation s.

4   Find:

   a $\overline{x} - s$ and $\overline{x} + s$ **b** $\overline{x} - 2s$ and $\overline{x} + 2s$ **c** $\overline{x} - 3s$ and $\overline{x} + 3s$

5   Count all values between:

   a $\overline{x} - s$ and $\overline{x} + s$ **b** $\overline{x} - 2s$ and $\overline{x} + 2s$ **c** $\overline{x} - 3s$ and $\overline{x} + 3s$

6   Determine the percentage of data values in these intervals.

7   Repeat the procedure several times. Hence suggest the proportions of normal distribution data which lie within:

   a σ **b** 2σ **c** 3σ from the mean.

For a normal distribution with mean μ and standard deviation σ, the proportional breakdown of where the random variable could lie is shown below.

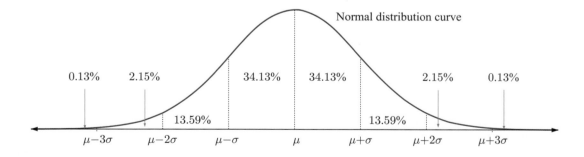

Notice that:
- $\approx 68.26\%$ of values lie between $\mu - \sigma$ and $\mu + \sigma$
- $\approx 95.44\%$ of values lie between $\mu - 2\sigma$ and $\mu + 2\sigma$
- $\approx 99.74\%$ of values lie between $\mu - 3\sigma$ and $\mu + 3\sigma$.

We can use these proportions to find the probability that the value of a normally distributed variable will lie within a particular range.

Example 1   🔊 **Self Tutor**

The chest measurements of 18 year old male footballers are normally distributed with a mean of 95 cm and a standard deviation of 8 cm.

  a Find the percentage of footballers with chest measurements between:

    i 87 cm and 103 cm   **ii** 103 cm and 111 cm

  b Find the probability that the chest measurement of a randomly chosen footballer is between 87 cm and 111 cm.

  a   **i** We need the percentage between
      $\mu - \sigma$ and $\mu + \sigma$.
      ∴ about 68.3% of footballers have a
      chest measurement between 87 cm
      and 103 cm.

    ii We need the percentage between
      $\mu + \sigma$ and $\mu + 2\sigma$.
      ∴ about 13.6% of footballers have a
      chest measurement between 103 cm
      and 111 cm.

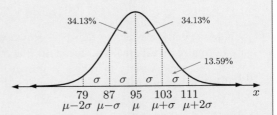

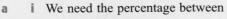

  b We need the percentage between
    $\mu - \sigma$ and $\mu + 2\sigma$.
    This is $2(34.13\%) + 13.59\%$
           $\approx 81.9\%$.
    So, the probability is ≈ 0.819.

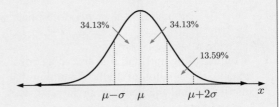

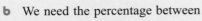

EXERCISE 10A

1 Explain why it is likely that the distributions of the following variables will be normal:

  a the volume of soft drink in cans

  b the diameter of bolts immediately after manufacture.

2 State the probability that a randomly selected, normally distributed value lies between:

  a σ below the mean and σ above the mean

  b the mean and the value 2σ above the mean.

3 The mean height of players in a basketball competition is 184 cm. If the standard deviation is 5 cm, what percentage of them are likely to be:

  a taller than 189 cm   **b** taller than 179 cm

  c between 174 cm and 199 cm   **d** over 199 cm tall?

4 The mean average rainfall of Claudona for August is 48 mm with a standard deviation of 6 mm. Over a 20 year period, how many times would you expect there to be less than 42 mm of rainfall during August in Claudona?

5 The weights of babies born at Prince Louis Maternity Hospital last year averaged 3.0 kg with a standard deviation of 200 grams. If there were 545 babies born at this hospital last year, estimate the number that weighed:

  a less than 3.2 kg   **b** between 2.8 kg and 3.4 kg.

6 The height of male students in a university is normally distributed with mean 170 cm and standard deviation 8 cm.

   a Find the percentage of male students whose height is:

      i between 162 cm and 170 cm   **ii** between 170 cm and 186 cm.

   b Find the probability that a randomly chosen student from this group has a height:

      i between 178 cm and 186 cm   **ii** less than 162 cm

      iii less than 154 cm   **iv** greater than 162 cm.

7 Suppose $X \sim N(16, 3^2)$. Find:

   a $P(13 \leqslant X \leqslant 16)$ **b** $P(X \leqslant 13)$ **c** $P(X \geqslant 22)$

8 When a specific variety of radish is grown without fertiliser, the weights of the radishes produced are normally distributed with mean 40 g and standard deviation 10 g.

When the same variety of radish is grown in the same way but with fertiliser added, the weights of the radishes produced are also normally distributed, but with mean 140 g and standard deviation 40 g.

Determine the proportion of radishes grown:

   a without fertiliser with weights less than 50 grams

   b with fertiliser with weights less than 60 grams

   c **i** with and   **ii** without fertiliser with weights between 20 and 60 g

   d **i** with and   **ii** without fertiliser with weights greater than 60 g.

9 A bottle filling machine fills an average of 20 000 bottles a day with a standard deviation of 2000. Assuming that production is normally distributed and the year comprises 260 working days, calculate the approximate number of working days on which:

   a under 18 000 bottles are filled

   b over 16 000 bottles are filled

   c between 18 000 and 24 000 bottles (inclusive) are filled.

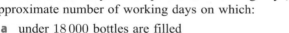

B   PROBABILITIES USING A CALCULATOR

Using the properties of the normal probability density function, we have considered probabilities in regions of width σ either side of the mean.

To find probabilities more generally we use technology.

Suppose $X \sim N(10, 2.3^2)$, so X is normally distributed with mean 10 and standard deviation 2.3.

How do we find $P(8 \leqslant X \leqslant 11)$?

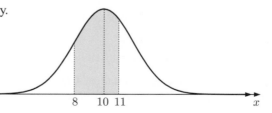

Click on the icon to find instructions for these processes.

GRAPHICS
CALCULATOR
INSTRUCTIONS

Example 2

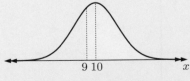)) **Self Tutor**

If $X \sim N(10, 2.3^2)$, find these probabilities:

a $P(8 \leqslant X \leqslant 11)$ **b** $P(X \leqslant 12)$ **c** $P(X > 9)$.   Illustrate your results.

X is normally distributed with mean 10 and standard deviation 2.3.

a Using a **Casio fx-CG20**:

From the STATISTICS menu, press [F5] **(DIST)** [F1] **(NORM)** [F2] **(Ncd)**

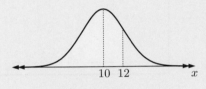 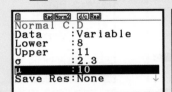 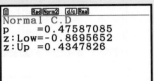

$\therefore \quad P(8 \leqslant X \leqslant 11) \approx 0.476$

b Using a **TI-84 Plus**:

Press [2nd] [VARS] **(DISTR)** **2 : normalcdf (** :

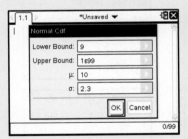 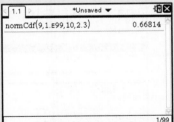

$\therefore \quad P(X \leqslant 12) \approx 0.808$

c Using a **TI-nspire**:

From the calculator application, press [menu] **6 : Statistics** > **5 : Distributions** > **2 : normalcdf...** :

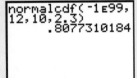

$\therefore \quad P(X > 9) \approx 0.668$

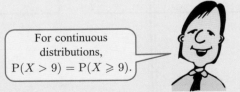

For continuous distributions, $P(X > 9) = P(X \geqslant 9)$.

Example 3   ◀) **Self Tutor**

In 1972 the heights of rugby players were approximately normally distributed with mean 179 cm and standard deviation 7 cm. Find the probability that a randomly selected player in 1972 was:

a at least 175 cm tall   **b** between 170 cm and 190 cm.

If X is the height of a player then X is normally distributed with $\mu = 179$, $\sigma = 7$.

a

Casio fx-CG20	TI-84 Plus	TI-*nspire*

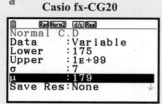  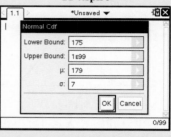

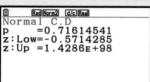  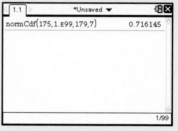

$$P(X \geqslant 175) \approx 0.716 \quad \text{\{using technology\}}$$

b

Casio fx-CG20	TI-84 Plus	TI-*nspire*

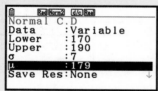  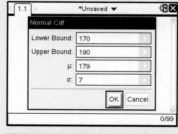

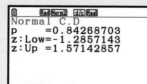 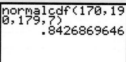 

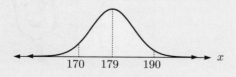

$$P(170 < X < 190) \approx 0.843 \quad \text{\{using technology\}}$$

EXERCISE 10B

1 X is a random variable that is distributed normally with mean 70 and standard deviation 4. Find:

   a $P(70 \leqslant X \leqslant 74)$ **b** $P(68 \leqslant X \leqslant 72)$ **c** $P(X \leqslant 65)$

It is helpful to sketch the normal distribution and shade the area of interest.

2 X is a random variable that is distributed normally with mean 60 and standard deviation 5. Find:

   a $P(60 \leqslant X \leqslant 65)$ **b** $P(62 \leqslant X \leqslant 67)$

   c $P(X \geqslant 64)$ **d** $P(X \leqslant 68)$

   e $P(X \leqslant 61)$ **f** $P(57.5 \leqslant X \leqslant 62.5)$

3 X is a random variable that is distributed normally with mean 32 and standard deviation 6. Find:

   a $P(25 \leqslant X \leqslant 30)$ **b** $P(X > 27)$ **c** $P(22 \leqslant X \leqslant 28)$

   d $P(X \leqslant 30.9)$ **e** $P(X < 23.8)$ **f** $P(22.1 < X < 32.1)$

4 Suppose $X \sim N(37, 7^2)$.

   a Use technology to find $P(X > 40)$.

   b Hence find $P(37 \leqslant X \leqslant 40)$ without technology.

5 A manufacturer makes nails which are supposed to be 50 mm long. In reality, the length L of the nails is normally distributed with mean 50.2 mm and standard deviation 0.93 mm. Find:

   a $P(L \geqslant 50)$ **b** $P(L \leqslant 51)$ **c** $P(49 \leqslant L \leqslant 50.5)$

6 A machine produces metal bolts. The lengths of these bolts have a normal distribution with mean 19.8 cm and standard deviation 0.3 cm. If a bolt is selected at random from the machine, find the probability that it will have a length between 19.7 cm and 20 cm.

7 Max's customers put money for charity into a collection box in his shop. The average weekly collection is approximately normally distributed with mean $40 and standard deviation $6.

   a In a randomly chosen week, find the probability of Max collecting:

      i between $30.00 and $50.00   **ii** at most $32.00.

   b In a 52 week year, in how many weeks would Max expect to collect at least $45.00?

8 Eels are washed onto a beach after a storm. Their lengths have a normal distribution with mean 41 cm and standard deviation 5.5 cm.

   a If an eel is randomly selected, find the probability that it is at least 50 cm long.

   b Find the proportion of eels measuring between 40 cm and 50 cm long.

   c How many eels from a sample of 200 would you expect to measure at least 45 cm in length?

9 The speed of cars passing the supermarket is normally distributed with mean 56.3 km h^{-1} and standard deviation 7.4 km h^{-1}. Find the probability that a randomly selected car has speed:

  a between 60 and 75 km h^{-1} **b** at most 70 km h^{-1} **c** at least 60 km h^{-1}.

C   QUANTILES OR k-VALUES

Consider a population of crabs where the length of a shell, X mm, is normally distributed with mean 70 mm and standard deviation 10 mm.

A biologist wants to protect the population by allowing only the largest 5% of crabs to be harvested. He therefore asks the question: "95% of the crabs have lengths less than what?".

To answer this question we need to find k such that $P(X \leqslant k) = 0.95$.

The number k is known as a **quantile**, and in this case the 95% quantile.

When finding quantiles we are given a probability and are asked to calculate the corresponding measurement. This is the *inverse* of finding probabilities, and we use the **inverse normal function** on our calculator.

GRAPHICS CALCULATOR INSTRUCTIONS

Example 4   ◄ﬁ **Self Tutor**

If $X \sim N(23.6,\ 3.1^2)$, find k for which $P(X < k) = 0.95$.

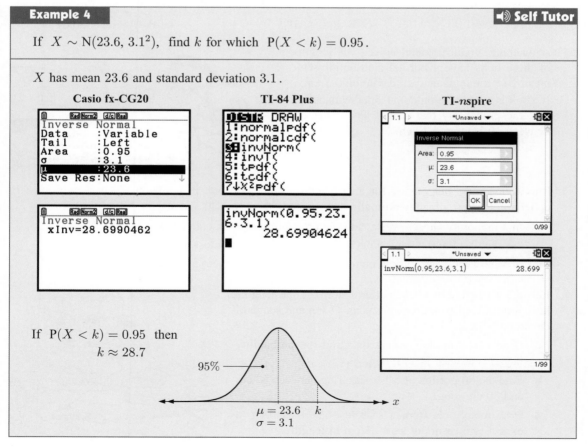

To perform inverse normal calculations on most calculator models, we must enter the area to the *left* of k.

If $P(X \geqslant k) = p$,   then $P(X \leqslant k) = 1 - p$.

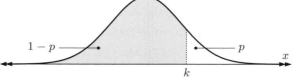

A university professor determines that 80% of this year's History candidates should pass the final examination. The examination results were approximately normally distributed with mean 62 and standard deviation 12. Find the lowest score necessary to pass the examination.

Let X denote the final examination result, so $X \sim N(62, 12^2)$.

We need to find k such that $P(X \geqslant k) = 0.8$

$\therefore$ $P(X \leqslant k) = 0.2$

Casio fx-CG20	TI-84 Plus	TI-*n*spire
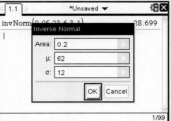	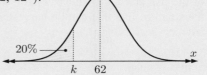	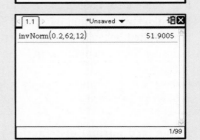

$\therefore$ $k \approx 51.9$ {using technology}

So, the minimum pass mark is 52.

EXERCISE 10C

1   Suppose $X \sim N(20, 3^2)$.   Illustrate with a sketch and find k such that:

    a $P(X \leqslant k) = 0.348$ **b** $P(X \leqslant k) = 0.878$ **c** $P(X \leqslant k) = 0.5$

2   Suppose $X \sim N(38.7, 8.2^2)$.   Illustrate with a sketch and find k such that:

    a $P(X \leqslant k) = 0.9$ **b** $P(X \geqslant k) = 0.8$

3 Suppose $X \sim N(30, 5^2)$ and $P(X \leqslant a) = 0.57$.

    a Using a diagram, determine whether a is greater or less than 30.

    b Use technology to find a.

    c Without using technology, find: **i** $P(X \geqslant a)$ **ii** $P(30 \leqslant X \leqslant a)$

4 Given that $X \sim N(23, 5^2)$, find a such that:

    a $P(X < a) = 0.378$ **b** $P(X \geqslant a) = 0.592$ **c** $P(23 - a < X < 23 + a) = 0.427$

5 The students of Class X sat a Physics test. The average score was 46 with a standard deviation of 25. The teacher decided to award an A to the top 7% of the students in the class. Assuming that the scores were normally distributed, find the lowest score that would achieve an A.

6 The lengths of a fish species are normally distributed with mean 35 cm and standard deviation 8 cm. The fisheries department has decided that the smallest 10% of the fish are not to be harvested. What is the size of the smallest fish that can be harvested?

7 The lengths of screws produced by a machine are normally distributed with mean 75 mm and standard deviation 0.1 mm. If a screw is too long it is automatically rejected. If 1% of screws are rejected, what is the length of the smallest screw to be rejected?

8 The weights of cabbages sold at a market are normally distributed with mean 1.6 kg and standard deviation 0.3 kg.

    a One wholesaler buys the heaviest 10% of cabbages. What is the minimum weight cabbage he buys?

    b Another buyer chooses cabbages with weights in the lower quartile. What is the heaviest cabbage this person buys?

9 The volumes of cool drink in bottles filled by a machine are normally distributed with mean 503 mL and standard deviation 0.5 mL. 1% of the bottles are rejected because they are underfilled, and 2% are rejected because they are overfilled; otherwise they are kept for retail. What range of volumes is in the bottles that are kept?

INVESTIGATION 2   THE STANDARD NORMAL DISTRIBUTION (z-DISTRIBUTION)

The **standard normal distribution** or **Z-distribution** is the normal distribution with mean 0 and standard deviation 1. We write $Z \sim N(0, 1)$.

Every normal X-distribution can be **transformed** into the Z-distribution using the transformation

$$z = \frac{x - \mu}{\sigma}$$

    subtracting μ shifts the mean to 0

    dividing by σ scales the standard deviation to 1

No matter what the parameters μ and σ of the X-distribution are, we always end up with the same Z-distribution.

The transformation $z = \frac{x - \mu}{\sigma}$ can be used to calculate the z-scores for any value in the X-distribution. The z-score tells us how many standard deviations the value is from the mean.

What to do:

1 Use your calculator to find:

    a $P(0 \leqslant z \leqslant 1)$ **b** $P(1 \leqslant z \leqslant 2)$ **c** $P(1 \leqslant z \leqslant 3)$

Have you seen these values before?

2 The percentages scored in an exam are normally distributed with mean 70% and standard deviation 10%.

    a Victoria scored 90% for the exam. Calculate her z-score and explain what it means.

    b Ethan scored 55% for the exam. Calculate his z-score and explain what it means.

3 The table shows Emma's midyear exam results. The exam results for each subject are normally distributed with the mean μ and standard deviation σ shown in the table.

Subject	Emma's score	μ	σ
English	48	40	4.4
Mandarin	81	60	9
Geography	84	55	18
Biology	68	50	20
Maths	84	50	15

    a Find the z-score for each of Emma's subjects.

    b Arrange Emma's subjects from 'best' to 'worst' in terms of the z-scores.

USING THE Z-DISTRIBUTION

The Z-distribution is useful when finding an unknown mean or standard deviation for a normal distribution.

For example, suppose X is normally distributed with mean 40, and $P(X \leqslant 45) = 0.9$.

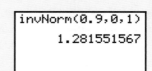

We can find the standard deviation as follows:

$$P(X \leqslant 45) = 0.9$$

$$\therefore \ P\left(\frac{X - \mu}{\sigma} \leqslant \frac{45 - \mu}{\sigma}\right) = 0.9 \quad \{\text{transforming to the } Z\text{-distribution}\}$$

$$\therefore \ P\left(Z \leqslant \frac{45 - \mu}{\sigma}\right) = 0.9 \quad \{Z = \frac{X - \mu}{\sigma}\}$$

$$\therefore \ \frac{45 - \mu}{\sigma} \approx 1.28 \quad \{\text{technology}\}$$

$$\therefore \ \frac{5}{\sigma} \approx 1.28 \quad \{\mu = 40\}$$

$$\therefore \ \sigma \approx 3.90$$

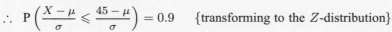
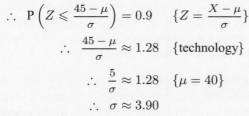

```
invNorm(0.9,0,1)
        1.281551567
```

What to do:

1 The IQs of students at school are normally distributed with a standard deviation of 15. If 20% of students have an IQ higher than 125, find the mean IQ of students at school.

2 The distances an athlete jumps are normally distributed with mean 5.2 m. If 15% of the jumps by this athlete are less than 5 m, what is the standard deviation?

3 The weekly income of a bakery is normally distributed with a mean of $6100. If 85% of the time the weekly income exceeds $6000, what is the standard deviation?

4 The arrival times of buses at a depot are normally distributed with standard deviation 5 minutes. If 10% of the buses arrive before 3:55 pm, find the mean arrival time of buses at the depot.

REVIEW SET 10A

1 The average height of 17 year old boys is normally distributed with mean 179 cm and standard deviation 8 cm. Calculate the percentage of 17 year old boys whose heights are:

    a more than 195 cm   **b** between 163 cm and 195 cm

    c between 171 cm and 187 cm.

2 The contents of cans of a certain brand of soft drink are normally distributed with mean 377 mL and standard deviation 4.2 mL.

    a Find the percentage of cans with contents:

        i less than 368.6 mL   **ii** between 372.8 mL and 389.6 mL.

    b Find the probability that a randomly selected can has contents between 377 mL and 381.2 mL.

3 Suppose $X \sim N(150, 12^2)$. Find:

    a $P(138 \leqslant X \leqslant 162)$ **b** $P(126 \leqslant X \leqslant 174)$

    c $P(X \leqslant 147)$ **d** $P(X \geqslant 135)$

4 The length of steel rods produced by a machine is normally distributed with a standard deviation of 3 mm. It is found that 2% of all rods are less than 25 mm long. Find the mean length of rods produced by the machine.

5 The distribution curve shown corresponds to $X \sim N(\mu, \sigma^2)$.

Area A = Area $B = 0.2$.

    a Find μ and σ.

    b Calculate:

        i $P(X \leqslant 35)$ **ii** $P(23 \leqslant X \leqslant 30)$

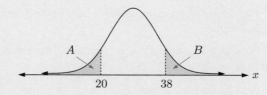

6 Let X be the weight in grams of bags of sugar filled by a machine. Bags less than 500 grams are considered underweight.

Suppose that $X \sim N(503, 2^2)$.

    a What proportion of bags are underweight?

    b Bags weighing more than 507 grams are considered overweight. If the machine fills 6000 bags in one day, how many bags would you expect to be overweight?

7 In a competition to see who could hold their breath underwater the longest, the times were normally distributed with a mean of 150 seconds and standard deviation 12 seconds. The top 15% of contestants go through to the finals. What time is required to advance to the finals?

REVIEW SET 10B

1 State the probability that a randomly selected, normally distributed value lies between:

    a σ above the mean and 2σ above the mean

    b the mean and σ above the mean.

2 A random variable X is normally distributed with mean 20.5 and standard deviation 4.3. Find:

    a $P(X \geqslant 22)$ **b** $P(18 \leqslant X \leqslant 22)$ **c** k such that $P(X \leqslant k) = 0.3$.

3  A bottle shop sells on average 2500 bottles per day with a standard deviation of 300 bottles. Assuming that the number of bottles is normally distributed, calculate the percentage of days when:

    a less than 1900 bottles are sold

    b more than 2200 bottles are sold

    c between 2200 and 3100 bottles are sold.

4 X is a random variable which is distributed normally with $\mu = 55$ and $\sigma = 7$. Find:

    a $P(48 \leqslant X \leqslant 55)$ **b** $P(X \leqslant 41)$

    c $P(X \geqslant 60)$ **d** $P(53 \leqslant X \leqslant 57)$

5 The life of a Xenon-brand battery is normally distributed with mean 33.2 weeks and standard deviation 2.8 weeks.

    a Find the probability that a randomly selected battery will last at least 35 weeks.

    b For how many weeks can the manufacturer expect the batteries to last before 8% of them fail?

6 A recruiting agency tests the typing speed of its workers. The results are normally distributed with a mean of 40 words per minute and standard deviation of 16.7 words per minute.

If the slowest 10% of typists are enrolled in a typing skills course, what range of speeds are enrolled?

7 In summer, Alison goes for a walk after school when the temperature is suitable. The temperature at that time is normally distributed with mean 25.4°C and standard deviation 4.8°C. Alison finds it too hot for walking 13% of the time, and too cold 5% of the time. Find Alison's range of suitable walking temperatures.

REVIEW SET 10C

1 X is a random variable that is normally distributed with mean 80 and standard deviation 14. Find:

    a $P(75 \leqslant X \leqslant 85)$ **b** $P(X > 90)$ **c** $P(X < 77)$

2 Suppose $X \sim N(16, 5^2)$.

    a Find $P(X < 13)$.

    b Without using technology, find:

        i $P(X \geqslant 13)$ **ii** $P(13 \leqslant X \leqslant 16)$

3 The daily energy intake of Canadian adults is normally distributed with mean 8700 kJ and standard deviation 1000 kJ.

What proportion of Canadian adults have a daily energy intake which is:

    a greater than 8000 kJ   **b** less than 7500 kJ

    c between 9000 and 10 000 kJ?

4 Suppose $X \sim N(30, 8^2)$. Illustrate with a sketch and find k such that:

    a $P(X \leqslant k) = 0.1$ **b** $P(X \geqslant k) = 0.6$

5 The weights of suitcases at an airport are normally distributed with a mean of 17 kg and standard deviation 3.4 kg.

   a Find the probability that a randomly selected suitcase weighs between 10 kg and 15 kg.

   b 300 suitcases are presented for check-in over a one hour period. How many of these suitcases would you expect to be lighter than 20 kg?

   c 3.9% of the suitcases are rejected because they exceed the maximum weight limit. Find the maximum weight limit.

6 Suppose X is normally distributed with mean 25 and standard deviation 7. We also know that $P(X > k) = 0.4$.

   a Using a diagram, determine whether k is greater or less than 25.

   b Use technology to find k.

7 The times that participants take to complete a fun-run are normally distributed with mean 65 minutes and standard deviation 9 minutes.

   a Find the probability that a randomly selected person takes more than 80 minutes to complete the fun-run.

   b A total of 5000 people participate in the fun-run.

     i How many of these people will complete the fun-run in less than one hour?

     ii Simon is the 1000th person to complete the fun-run. How long does Simon take?

Chapter 11

Two variable statistics

Syllabus reference: 4.2, 4.3, 4.4

OPENING PROBLEM

At a junior tournament, a group of young athletes throw a discus. The *age* and *distance thrown* are recorded for each athlete.

Athlete	A	B	C	D	E	F	G	H	I	J	K	L
Age (years)	12	16	16	18	13	19	11	10	20	17	15	13
Distance thrown (m)	20	35	23	38	27	47	18	15	50	33	22	20

Things to think about:

a Do you think the distance an athlete can throw is related to the person's age?

b What happens to the distance thrown as the age of the athlete increases?

c How could you graph the data to more clearly see the relationship between the variables?

d How can we *measure* the relationship between the variables?

Statisticians are often interested in how two variables are **related**.

For example, in the **Opening Problem**, we want to know how a change in the *age* of the athlete will affect the *distance* the athlete can throw.

We can observe the relationship between the variables by plotting the data on a **scatter diagram**. We place the independent variable *age* on the horizontal axis, and the dependent variable *distance* on the vertical axis.

We then plot each data value as a point on the scatter diagram. For example, the red point represents athlete H, who is 10 years old and threw the discus 15 metres.

From the general shape formed by the dots, we can see that as the *age* increases, so does the *distance thrown*.

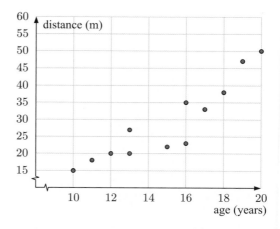

A   CORRELATION

Correlation refers to the relationship or association between two variables.

There are several characteristics we consider when describing the correlation between two variables: direction, linearity, strength, outliers, and causation.

DIRECTION

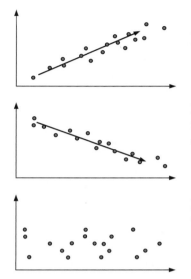

For a generally *upward* trend, we say that the correlation is **positive**. An increase in the independent variable means that the dependent variable generally increases.

For a generally *downward* trend, we say that the correlation is **negative**. An increase in the independent variable means that the dependent variable generally decreases.

For *randomly scattered* points, with no upward or downward trend, we say there is **no correlation**.

LINEARITY

We determine whether the points follow a **linear** trend, or in other words approximately form a straight line.

These points are roughly linear.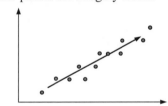

These points do not follow a linear trend.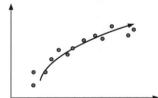

STRENGTH

We want to know how closely the data follows a pattern or trend. The strength of correlation is usually described as either strong, moderate, or weak.

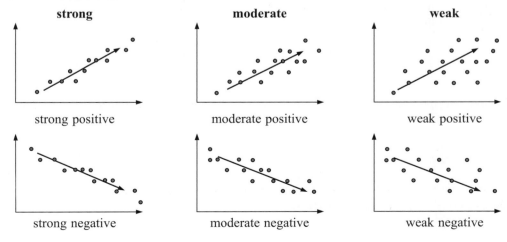

OUTLIERS

We observe and investigate any **outliers**, or isolated points which do not follow the trend formed by the main body of data.

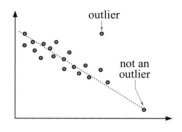

If an outlier is the result of a recording or graphing error, it should be discarded. However, if the outlier proves to be a genuine piece of data, it should be kept.

For the scatter diagram for the data in the **Opening Problem**, we can say that there is a strong positive correlation between *age* and *distance thrown*. The relationship appears to be linear, with no outliers.

CAUSATION

Correlation between two variables does not necessarily mean that one variable *causes* the other.

Consider the following:

1   The *arm length* and *running speed* of a sample of young children were measured, and a strong, positive correlation was found to exist between the variables.

Does this mean that short arms cause a reduction in running speed or that a high running speed causes your arms to grow long? This would clearly be nonsense.

Rather, the strong, positive correlation between the variables is attributed to the fact that both *arm length* and *running speed* are closely related to a third variable, *age*. Up to a certain age, both *arm length* and *running speed* increase with *age*.

2   The number of television sets sold in Ballarat and the number of stray dogs collected in Bendigo were recorded over several years and a strong positive correlation was found between the variables. Obviously the number of television sets sold in Ballarat was not influencing the number of stray dogs collected in Bendigo. Both variables have simply been increasing over the period of time that their numbers were recorded.

If a change in one variable *causes* a change in the other variable then we say that a **causal relationship** exists between them.

For example, in the **Opening Problem** there is a causal relationship in which increasing the *age* of an athlete increases the *distance thrown*.

In cases where this is not apparent, there is no justification, based on high correlation alone, to conclude that changes in one variable cause the changes in the other.

EXERCISE 11A

1 For each of the scatter diagrams below, describe the relationship between the variables. Consider the direction, strength, and linearity of the relationship, as well as the presence of outliers.

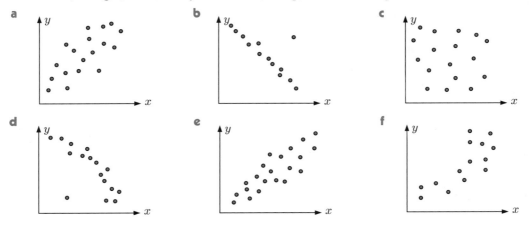

2 The scores awarded by two judges at an ice skating competition are shown in the table.

Competitor	P	Q	R	S	T	U	V	W	X	Y
Judge A	5	6.5	8	9	4	2.5	7	5	6	3
Judge B	6	7	8.5	9	5	4	7.5	5	7	4.5

a Construct a scatter diagram for this data with Judge A's scores on the horizontal axis and Judge B's scores on the vertical axis.

b Copy and complete the following comments about the scatter diagram:

There appears to be ......, ..., ... correlation between Judge A's scores and Judge B's scores. This means that as Judge A's scores increase, Judge B's scores ......

You can use technology to draw scatter diagrams.

GRAPHICS CALCULATOR INSTRUCTIONS

c Would it be reasonable to conclude that an increase in Judge A's scores *causes* an increase in Judge B's scores?

3 The results of a group of students for a Maths test and an Art essay are compared:

Student	A	B	C	D	E	F	G	H	I	J
Maths test	64	67	69	70	73	74	77	82	84	85
Art essay	85	82	80	82	72	71	70	71	62	66

This data is called **bivariate** data because *two* variables are recorded for each individual.

a Construct a scatter diagram for the data. Make the scales on both axes from 60 to 90.

b Describe the relationship between the Mathematics and Art marks.

4 Choose the scatter diagram which would best illustrate the relationship between the variables x and y.

  a $x =$ the number of apples bought by customers, $y =$ the total cost of apples

  b $x =$ the number of pushups a student can perform in one minute,
    $y =$ the time taken for the student to run 100 metres

  c $x =$ the height of people, $y =$ the weight of people

  d $x =$ the distance a student travels to school, $y =$ the height of the student's uncle

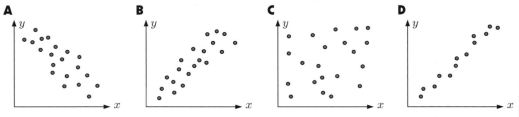

5 The scatter diagram shows the marks obtained by students in a test out of 50 marks, plotted against the number of hours each student studied for the test.

  a Describe the correlation between the variables.

  b How should the outlier be treated? Explain your answer.

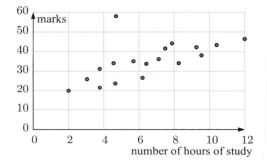

6 The following pairs of variables were measured and a strong positive correlation between them was found. Discuss whether a causal relationship exists between the variables. If not, suggest a third variable to which they may both be related.

  a The lengths of one's left and right feet.

  b The damage caused by a fire and the number of firemen who attend it.

  c Company expenditure on advertising, and sales.

  d The height of parents and the height of their adult children.

  e The number of hotels and the number of churches in rural towns.

B   MEASURING CORRELATION

In the previous section, we classified the strength of the correlation between two variables as either strong, moderate, or weak. We observed the points on a scatter diagram, and made a judgement as to how clearly the points formed a linear relationship.

However, this method can be quite inaccurate, so it is important to get a more precise measure of the strength of linear correlation between two variables. We achieve this using **Pearson's product-moment correlation coefficient** r.

For a set of n data given as ordered pairs (x_1, y_1), (x_2, y_2), (x_3, y_3), ..., (x_n, y_n),

Pearson's correlation coefficient is $\quad r = \dfrac{\sum(x - \overline{x})(y - \overline{y})}{\sqrt{\sum(x - \overline{x})^2 \sum(y - \overline{y})^2}}$

where $\overline{x}$ and $\overline{y}$ are the means of the x and y data respectively, and $\sum$ means the sum over all the data values.

You are not required to learn this formula. Instead, we use technology to find the value of r.

The values of r range from -1 to $+1$.

GRAPHICS CALCULATOR INSTRUCTIONS

The **sign** of r indicates the **direction** of the correlation.

- A positive value for r indicates the variables are **positively correlated**.
  An increase in one of the variables will result in an increase in the other.
- A negative value for r indicates the variables are **negatively correlated**.
  An increase in one of the variables will result in a decrease in the other.

The **size** of r indicates the **strength** of the correlation.

- A value of r close to $+1$ or -1 indicates strong correlation between the variables.
- A value of r close to zero indicates weak correlation between the variables.

The following table is a guide for describing the strength of linear correlation using r.

Positive correlation			Negative correlation		
$r = 1$	perfect positive correlation		$r = -1$	perfect negative correlation	
$0.95 \leqslant r < 1$	very strong positive correlation		$-1 < r \leqslant -0.95$	very strong negative correlation	
$0.87 \leqslant r < 0.95$	strong positive correlation		$-0.95 < r \leqslant -0.87$	strong negative correlation	
$0.5 \leqslant r < 0.87$	moderate positive correlation		$-0.87 < r \leqslant -0.5$	moderate negative correlation	
$0.1 \leqslant r < 0.5$	weak positive correlation		$-0.5 < r \leqslant -0.1$	weak negative correlation	
$0 \leqslant r < 0.1$	no correlation		$-0.1 < r \leqslant 0$	no correlation	

| **Example 1** | ◀) **Self Tutor** |

The Department of Road Safety wants to know if there is any association between *average speed* in the metropolitan area and the *age of drivers*. They commission a device to be fitted in the cars of drivers of different ages.

The results are shown in the scatter diagram.
The r-value for this association is $+0.027$.
Describe the association.

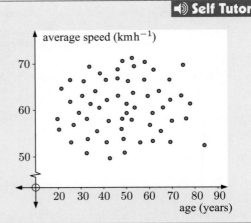

As r is close to zero, there is no correlation between the two variables.

We observe this in the graph as the points are randomly scattered.

EXERCISE 11B.1

1 In a recent survey, the Department of International Commerce compared the *size of a company* with its *export earnings*. A scatter diagram of their data is shown alongside. The corresponding value of r is 0.556.
Describe the association between the variables.

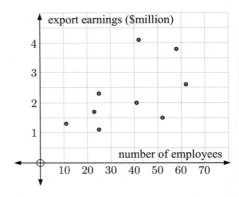

2 Match each scatter diagram with the correct value of r.

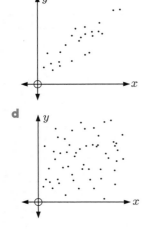

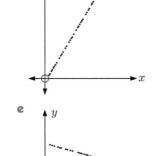

A $r = 1$ **B** $r = 0.6$ **C** $r = 0$ **D** $r = -0.7$ **E** $r = -1$

Example 2

◄) **Self Tutor**

The Botanical Gardens have been trying out a new chemical to control the number of beetles infesting their plants. The results of one of their tests are shown in the table.

a Draw a scatter diagram of the data.

b Determine Pearson's correlation coefficient r.

c Describe the correlation between the *quantity of chemical* and the *number of surviving lawn beetles*.

Sample	Quantity of chemical (g)	Number of surviving beetles
A	2	11
B	5	6
C	6	4
D	3	6
E	9	3

We first enter the data into separate lists:

Casio fx-CG20

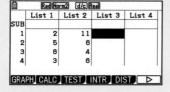

TI-84 Plus

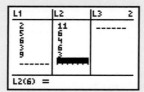

TI-*n*spire

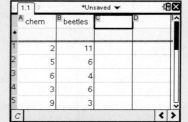

a

Casio fx-CG20

TI-84 Plus

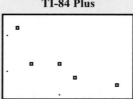

TI-*n*spire

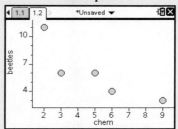

b

Casio fx-CG20

TI-84 Plus

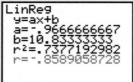

TI-*n*spire

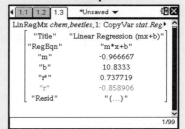

So, $r \approx -0.859$.

c There is a moderate, negative correlation between the *quantity of chemical used* and the *number of surviving beetles*.

In general, the more chemical that is used, the fewer beetles that survive.

3 For the following data sets:

    i draw a scatter diagram of the data

    ii calculate Pearson's correlation coefficient r

    iii describe the linear correlation between X and Y.

a

X	1	2	3	4	5	6
Y	3	2	5	5	9	6

b

X	3	8	5	14	19	10	16
Y	17	12	15	6	1	10	4

c

X	3	6	11	7	5	6	8	10	4
Y	2	8	8	4	7	9	11	1	5

4 A selection of students were asked how many phone calls and text messages they had received the previous day. The results are shown below.

Student	A	B	C	D	E	F	G	H
Phone calls received	4	7	1	0	3	2	2	4
Text messages received	6	9	2	2	5	8	4	7

    a Draw a scatter diagram of the data.

    b Calculate r.

    c Describe the linear correlation between *phone calls received* and *text messages received*.

5 Consider the **Opening Problem** on page **316**.

    a Calculate r for this data.

    b Hence describe the association between the variables.

6 A basketballer takes 20 shots from each of ten different positions marked on the court. The table below shows how far each position is from the goal, and how many shots were successful:

Position	A	B	C	D	E	F	G	H	I	J
Distance from goal (x m)	2	5	3.5	6.2	4.5	1.5	7	4.1	3	5.6
Successful shots (y)	17	6	10	5	8	18	6	8	13	9

    a Draw a scatter diagram of the data.

    b Do you think r will be positive or negative?

    c Calculate the value of r.

    d Describe the linear correlation between these variables.

    e Copy and complete:

    As the distance from goal increases, the number of successful shots generally ......

    f Is there a causal relationship between these variables?

CALCULATING r BY HAND (EXTENSION)

In examinations you are expected to calculate r using technology.

However, calculating r using the formula $r = \dfrac{\sum(x - \overline{x})(y - \overline{y})}{\sqrt{\sum(x - \overline{x})^2 \sum(y - \overline{y})^2}}$ may help you understand how this coefficient works.

Example 3   ◀》 **Self Tutor**

Sue investigates how the volume of water in a pot affects the time it takes to boil on the stove. The results are given in the table.

Find and interpret Pearson's correlation coefficient between the two variables.

Pot	Volume $(x$ L$)$	Time to boil $(y$ min$)$
A	1	3
B	2	5
C	4	7
D	5	9

	x	y	$x - \overline{x}$	$y - \overline{y}$	$(x - \overline{x})(y - \overline{y})$	$(x - \overline{x})^2$	$(y - \overline{y})^2$
	1	3	-2	-3	6	4	9
	2	5	-1	-1	1	1	1
	4	7	1	1	1	1	1
	5	9	2	3	6	4	9
Totals:	12	24			14	10	20

$$\therefore \quad \overline{x} = \frac{\sum x}{n} \qquad\qquad \overline{y} = \frac{\sum y}{n} \qquad\qquad r = \frac{\sum(x - \overline{x})(y - \overline{y})}{\sqrt{\sum(x - \overline{x})^2 \sum(y - \overline{y})^2}}$$

$$= \frac{12}{4} \qquad\qquad\qquad = \frac{24}{4} \qquad\qquad\qquad = \frac{14}{\sqrt{10 \times 20}}$$

$$= 3 \qquad\qquad\qquad\quad = 6 \qquad\qquad\qquad\quad \approx 0.990$$

There is a very strong correlation between the *volume of water* and the *time for the water to boil*. As the volume of water increases, so does the time required.

EXERCISE 11B.2

1 The table below includes 4 data points.

	x	y	$x - \overline{x}$	$y - \overline{y}$	$(x - \overline{x})(y - \overline{y})$	$(x - \overline{x})^2$	$(y - \overline{y})^2$
	2	10					
	4	7					
	7	5					
	11	2					
Totals:							

a Find $\overline{x}$ and $\overline{y}$.   **b** Copy and complete the table.   **c** Calculate r.

2 For each of the following graphs, evaluate $r = \dfrac{\sum(x - \overline{x})(y - \overline{y})}{\sqrt{\sum(x - \overline{x})^2 \sum(y - \overline{y})^2}}$ and comment on its value.

a
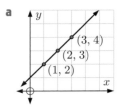

b
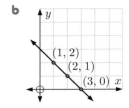

c
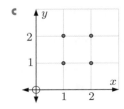

3 A teacher asked 5 students how much time they spent preparing a speech. The results are shown in the table, along with the grade awarded to the student.

  a Draw a scatter diagram to illustrate this data.

  b Evaluate r using the formula

  $$r = \frac{\sum(x - \overline{x})(y - \overline{y})}{\sqrt{\sum(x - \overline{x})^2 \sum(y - \overline{y})^2}}$$

  c Hence describe the strength and direction of the linear correlation between *preparation time* and the *grade awarded*.

Student	Preparation time (x hours)	Grade (y%)
A	5	95
B	4.5	80
C	7	90
D	1	65
E	3	75

THE COEFFICIENT OF DETERMINATION r^2 (EXTENSION)

To help describe the correlation between two variables, we can also calculate the **coefficient of determination** r^2. This is simply the square of Pearson's correlation coefficient r, and as such the direction of correlation is eliminated.

Given a set of bivariate data, we can find r^2 using our calculator in the same way we find r.

Alternatively, if r is already known, we can simply square this value.

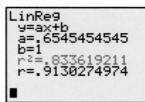

```
LinReg
 y=ax+b
 a=.6545454545
 b=1
 r²=.833619211
 r=.9130274974
■
```

INTERPRETATION OF THE COEFFICIENT OF DETERMINATION

If there is a causal relationship then r^2 indicates the degree to which change in the independent variable explains change in the dependent variable.

For example, an investigation into many different brands of muesli found that there is strong positive correlation between the variables *fat content* and *kilojoule content*. It was found that $r \approx 0.862$ and $r^2 \approx 0.743$.

An interpretation of this r^2 value is:

 —— dependent variable   independent variable ——

74.3% of the variation in *kilojoule content* of muesli can be explained by the variation in *fat content* of muesli.

If 74.3% of the variation in *kilojoule content* of muesli can be explained by the *fat content* of muesli, then we can assume that the other $100\% - 74.3\% = 25.7\%$ of the variation in *kilojoule content* of muesli can be explained by other factors.

Example 4   ◀) Self Tutor

At a father-son camp, the heights of the fathers and their sons were measured.

Father's height (x cm)	175	183	170	167	179	180	183	185	170	181	185
Son's height (y cm)	167	178	158	162	171	167	180	177	152	164	172

  a Draw a scatter diagram of the data.

  b Calculate r^2 for the data and interpret its value.

a

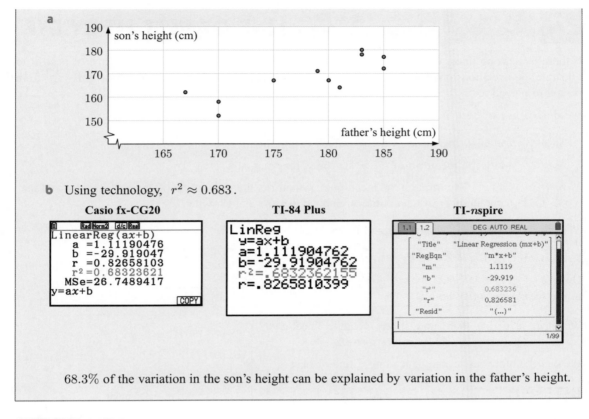

b   Using technology, $r^2 \approx 0.683$.

| Casio fx-CG20 | TI-84 Plus | TI-nspire |

68.3% of the variation in the son's height can be explained by variation in the father's height.

EXERCISE 11B.3

1   From an investigation at an aquatic centre, the coefficient of determination for the variables *number of visitors* and *maximum temperature* is found to be 0.578 . Complete the following interpretation of the coefficient of determination:

...... % of the variation in the ...... can be explained by the variation in ......

2   An investigation has found the association between the variables *time spent gambling* and *money lost* has an r value of 0.4732 . Find the coefficient of determination and interpret its meaning.

3   For a group of children a product-moment correlation coefficient of -0.365 is found between the variables *heart rate* and *age*. Find the coefficient of determination and interpret its meaning.

4   A sample of 8 tyres was taken to examine the association between the *tread depth* and the *number of kilometres travelled*.

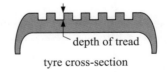

depth of tread

tyre cross-section

Kilometres (x thousand)	14	17	24	34	35	37	38	39
Tread depth (y mm)	5.7	6.5	4.0	3.0	1.9	2.7	1.9	2.3

a   Draw a scatter diagram of the data.

b   Calculate r^2 for the data and interpret its meaning.

C   LINE OF BEST FIT BY EYE

If there is a strong linear correlation between two variables X and Y, we can draw a line of best fit to illustrate their relationship. The line formed is called a **line of best fit by eye**. This line will vary from person to person.

We draw a line of best fit connecting variables X and Y as follows:

Step 1:   Calculate the mean of the X values $\overline{x}$, and the mean of the Y values $\overline{y}$.

Step 2:   Mark the **mean point** $(\overline{x}, \overline{y})$ on the scatter diagram.

Step 3:   Draw a line through the mean point which fits the trend of the data, and so that about the same number of data points are above the line as below it.

Consider again the data from the **Opening Problem**:

Athlete	A	B	C	D	E	F	G	H	I	J	K	L
Age (years)	12	16	16	18	13	19	11	10	20	17	15	13
Distance thrown (m)	20	35	23	38	27	47	18	15	50	33	22	20

We have seen that there is a strong positive linear correlation between *age* and *distance thrown*.

We can therefore model the data using a line of best fit.

The mean point is $(15, 29)$, so we draw our line of best fit through $(15, 29)$.

We can use the line of best fit to estimate the value of y for any given value of x, and vice versa.

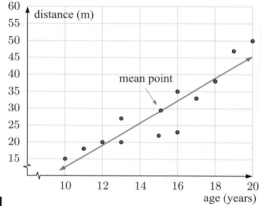

INTERPOLATION AND EXTRAPOLATION

Consider the data in the scatter diagram alongside. The data with the highest and lowest values are called the **poles**.

A line of best fit has been drawn so we can predict the value of one variable for a given value of the other.

If we predict a y value for an x value **in between** the poles, we say we are **interpolating** in between the poles.

If we predict a y value for an x value **outside** the poles, we say we are **extrapolating** outside the poles.

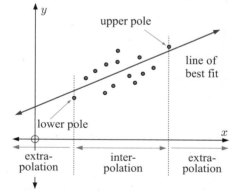

The accuracy of an interpolation depends on how linear the original data was. This can be gauged by the correlation coefficient and by ensuring that the data is randomly scattered around the line of best fit.

The accuracy of an extrapolation depends not only on how linear the original data was, but also on the assumption that the linear trend will continue past the poles. The validity of this assumption depends greatly on the situation we are looking at.

For example, using our line of best fit from the **Opening Problem** data, the age of 14 is within the range of ages already supplied. It is reasonable to predict that a 14 year old will be able to throw the discus 26 m.

However, it is unreasonable to predict that a 30 year old will throw the discus 78 m. The age of 30 is outside the range of values already supplied, and it is unlikely that the linear trend shown in the data will continue up to the age of 30.

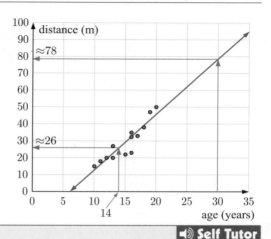

Example 5   ◀ッ **Self Tutor**

On a hot day, six cars were left in the sun in a car park. The length of time each car was left in the sun was recorded, as well as the temperature inside the car at the end of the period.

Car	A	B	C	D	E	F
Time x (min)	50	5	25	40	15	45
Temperature y (°C)	47	28	36	42	34	41

  a Calculate $\overline{x}$ and $\overline{y}$.

  b Draw a scatter diagram for the data.

  c Plot the mean point $(\overline{x}, \overline{y})$ on the scatter diagram. Draw a line of best fit through this point.

  d Predict the temperature of a car which has been left in the sun for:

    i 35 minutes   **ii** 75 minutes.

  e Comment on the reliability of your predictions in **d**.

  a $\overline{x} = \dfrac{50 + 5 + 25 + 40 + 15 + 45}{6} = 30,$ $\overline{y} = \dfrac{47 + 28 + 36 + 42 + 34 + 41}{6} = 38$

  b, c

  d   **i** When $x = 35$, $y \approx 40$.

        The temperature of a car left in the sun for 35 minutes will be approximately 40°C.

     ii When $x = 75$, $y \approx 55$.

        The temperature of a car left in the sun for 75 minutes will be approximately 55°C.

> **e** The prediction in **d i** is reliable, as the data appears linear, and this is an interpolation.
> The prediction in **d ii** may be unreliable, as it is an extrapolation, and the linear trend displayed by the data may not continue beyond the 50 minute mark.

EXERCISE 11C

1 Fifteen students were weighed, and their pulse rates were measured:

Weight (x kg)	61	52	47	72	62	79	57	45	67	71	80	58	51	43	55
Pulse rate (y beats per min)	65	59	54	74	69	87	61	59	70	69	75	60	56	53	58

   a Draw a scatter diagram for the data.   **b** Calculate r.

   c Describe the relationship between *weight* and *pulse rate*.

   d Calculate the mean point $(\overline{x}, \overline{y})$.

   e Plot the mean point on the scatter diagram, and draw a line of best fit through the mean point.

   f Estimate the pulse rate of a student who weighs 65 kg. Comment on the reliability of your estimate.

2 To investigate whether speed cameras have an impact on road safety, data was collected from several cities. The number of speed cameras in operation was recorded for each city, as well as the number of accidents over a 7 day period.

Number of speed cameras (x)	7	15	20	3	16	17	28	17	24	25	20	5	16	25	15	19
Number of car accidents (y)	48	35	31	52	40	35	28	30	34	19	29	42	31	21	37	32

   a Construct a scatter diagram to display the data.

   b Calculate r for the data.

   c Describe the relationship between the *number of speed cameras* and the *number of car accidents*.

   d Plot the mean point $(\overline{x}, \overline{y})$ on the scatter diagram, and draw a line of best fit through the mean point.

   e Where does your line cut the y-axis? Interpret what this answer means.

3 The trunk widths and heights of the trees in a garden were recorded:

Trunk width (x cm)	35	47	72	40	15	87	20	66	57	24	32
Height (y m)	11	18	24	12	3	30	22	21	17	5	10

   a Draw a scatter diagram of the data.

   b Which of the points is an outlier?

   c How would you describe the tree represented by the outlier?

   d Calculate the mean point $(\overline{x}, \overline{y})$.

   e Plot the mean point on the scatter diagram, and draw a line of best fit through the mean point.

   f Predict the height of a tree with trunk width 120 cm. Comment on the reliability of your prediction.

D
LINEAR REGRESSION

The problem with drawing a line of best fit by eye is that the line drawn will vary from one person to another. Instead, we use a method known as **linear regression** to find the equation of the line which best fits the data. The most common method is the method of 'least squares'.

THE LEAST SQUARES REGRESSION LINE

Consider the set of points alongside.

For any line we draw to model the points, we can find the vertical distances d_1, d_2, d_3, ... between each point and the line.

We can then square each of these distances, and find their sum $d_1^2 + d_2^2 + d_3^2 + ...$

If the line is a good fit for the data, most of the distances will be small, and so will the sum of their squares.

The **least squares regression line** is the line which makes this sum as small as possible.

The demonstration alongside allows you to experiment with various data sets. Use trial and error to find the least squares regression line for each set.

In practice, rather than finding the regression line by experimentation, we use a **calculator** or **statistics package**.

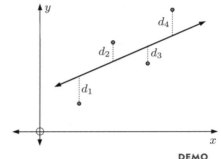

DEMO

STATISTICS PACKAGE

GRAPHICS CALCULATOR INSTRUCTIONS

Example 6
◄ᴗ **Self Tutor**

The annual income and average weekly grocery bill for a selection of families is shown below:

Income (x thousand pounds)	55	36	25	47	60	64	42	50
Grocery bill (y pounds)	120	90	60	160	190	250	110	150

a Construct a scatter diagram to illustrate the data.

b Use technology to find the least squares regression line.

c Estimate the weekly grocery bill for a family with an annual income of £95 000. Comment on whether this estimate is likely to be reliable.

a
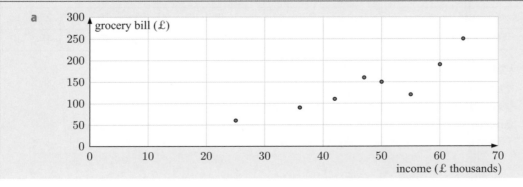

b

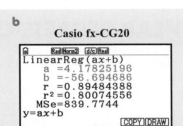

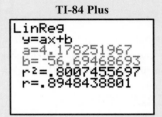

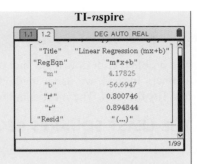

Using technology, the line of best fit is $y \approx 4.18x - 56.7$

c When $x = 95$, $y \approx 4.18(95) - 56.7 \approx 340$

So, we expect a family with an income of £95 000 to have a weekly grocery bill of approximately £340.

This is an extrapolation, however, so the estimate may not be reliable.

EXERCISE 11D

1 A newspaper reports starting salaries for recently graduated university students which depend on whether they hold a Bachelor degree or a PhD.

Field	Bachelor degree (x)	PhD (y)
Chemical engineer	38 250	48 750
Computer coder	41 750	68 270
Electrical engineer	38 250	56 750
Sociologist	32 750	38 300
Applied mathematician	43 000	72 600
Accountant	38 550	46 000

   a Draw a scatter diagram for the data.

   b Determine r.

   c Describe the association between *starting salaries for Bachelor degrees* and *starting salaries for PhDs*.

   d Find the equation of the line of best fit.

   e The starting salary for an economist with a Bachelor degree is $40 000.

     i Predict the starting salary for an economist with a PhD.

     ii Comment on the reliability of your prediction.

2 Steve wanted to see whether there was any relationship between the temperature when he leaves for work in the morning, and the time it takes to get to work.

He collected data over a 14 day period:

Temperature (x °C)	25	19	23	27	32	35	29	27	21	18	16	17	28	34
Time (y min)	35	42	49	31	37	33	31	47	42	36	45	33	48	39

   a Draw a scatter diagram of the data.

   b Calculate r.

   c Describe the relationship between the variables.

   d Is it reasonable to try to find a line of best fit for this data? Explain your answer.

3 The table below shows the price of petrol and the number of customers per hour for sixteen petrol stations.

Petrol price (x cents per litre)	105.9	106.9	109.9	104.5	104.9	111.9	110.5	112.9
Number of customers (y)	45	42	25	48	43	15	19	10

Petrol price (x cents per litre)	107.5	108.0	104.9	102.9	110.9	106.9	105.5	109.5
Number of customers (y)	30	23	42	50	12	24	32	17

  a Calculate r for the data.

  b Describe the relationship between the *petrol price* and the *number of customers*.

  c Use technology to find the line of best fit.

  d Interpret the gradient of this line.

  e Estimate the number of customers per hour for a petrol station which sells petrol at 115.9 cents per litre.

  f Comment on the validity of your estimate in **e**.

4 The table below contains information about the *maximum speed* and *maximum altitude obtainable* or *ceiling* for nineteen World War II fighter planes. The maximum speed is given in thousands of km/h, and the ceiling is given in km.

max. speed	ceiling	max. speed	ceiling	max. speed	ceiling
0.46	8.84	0.68	10.66	0.67	12.49
0.42	10.06	0.72	11.27	0.57	10.66
0.53	10.97	0.71	12.64	0.44	10.51
0.53	9.906	0.66	11.12	0.67	11.58
0.49	9.448	0.78	12.80	0.70	11.73
0.53	10.36	0.73	11.88	0.52	10.36
0.68	11.73				

  a Draw a scatter diagram for this data.   **b** Calculate r.

  c Describe the association between *maximum speed* (x) and *ceiling* (y).

  d Use technology to find the line of best fit.

  e Estimate the ceiling for a fighter plane with a maximum speed of 600 km/h.

5 A group of children were asked the number of hours they spent exercising and watching television each week.

Exercise (x hours per week)	4	1	8	7	10	3	3	2
Television (y hours per week)	12	24	5	9	1	18	11	16

  a Draw a scatter diagram for the data.   **b** Calculate r.

  c Describe the correlation between *time exercising* and *time watching television*.

  d Find the equation of the least squares line of best fit.

  e Give an interpretation of the gradient and the y-intercept of this line.

  f Another child exercises for 5 hours each week. Estimate how long he spends watching television each week.

6 The yield of pumpkins on a farm depends on the quantity of fertiliser used.

Fertiliser (x g m^{-2})	4	13	20	26	30	35	50
Yield (y kg)	1.8	2.9	3.8	4.2	4.7	5.7	4.4

a Draw a scatter diagram of the data and identify the outlier.

b Calculate the correlation coefficient:

    i with the outlier included   **ii** without the outlier.

c Calculate the equation of the least squares regression line:

    i with the outlier included   **ii** without the outlier.

d If you wish to estimate the yield when 15 g m^{-2} of fertiliser is used, which regression line from **c** should be used?

e Can you explain what may have caused the outlier?

E   THE χ^2 TEST OF INDEPENDENCE

This table shows the results of a sample of 400 randomly selected adults classified according to *gender* and *regular exercise*.

We call this a 2 × 2 **contingency table**.

	Regular exercise	No regular exercise	sum
Male	110	106	216
Female	98	86	184
sum	208	192	400

We may be interested in how the variables *gender* and *regular exercise* are related. The variables may be **dependent**, for example females may be more likely to exercise regularly than males. Alternatively, the variables may be **independent**, which means the gender of a person has no effect on whether they exercise regularly.

The **chi-squared** or χ^2 **test** is used to determine whether two variables from the same sample are independent.

CALCULATING χ^2

To test whether *gender* and *regular exercise* are independent, we first consider only the sum values of the contingency table. We then calculate the values we would *expect* to obtain if the variables were independent.

	Regular exercise	No regular exercise	sum
Male			216
Female			184
sum	208	192	400

For example, if *gender* and *regular exercise* were independent, then

$$\text{P}(\textit{male} \cap \textit{regular exercise}) = \text{P}(\textit{male}) \times \text{P}(\textit{regular exercise})$$

$$= \frac{216}{400} \times \frac{208}{400}$$

So, in a sample of 400 adults, we would expect

$$400 \times \left(\frac{216}{400} \times \frac{208}{400} \right) = \frac{216 \times 208}{400} = 112.32 \text{ to be male and exercise regularly.}$$

We can perform similar calculations for each cell to complete an **expected frequency table**. This displays the values we would expect to obtain if the variables were independent.

For each cell, we multiply the row sum by the column sum, then divide by the total.

	Regular exercise	No regular exercise	sum
Male	$\dfrac{216 \times 208}{400} = 112.32$	$\dfrac{216 \times 192}{400} = 103.68$	216
Female	$\dfrac{184 \times 208}{400} = 95.68$	$\dfrac{184 \times 192}{400} = 88.32$	184
sum	208	192	400

The χ^2 test examines the difference between the **observed** values we obtained from our sample, and the **expected** values we have calculated.

$$\chi^2_{calc} = \sum \frac{(f_o - f_e)^2}{f_e} \qquad \text{where } f_o \text{ is an observed frequency} \\ \text{and } f_e \text{ is an expected frequency.}$$

If the variables are independent, the observed and expected values will be very similar. This means that the values of $(f_o - f_e)$ will be small, and hence χ^2_{calc} will be small.

If the variables are not independent, the observed values will differ significantly from the expected values. The values of $(f_o - f_e)$ will be large, and hence χ^2_{calc} will be large.

For our example on *gender* and *regular exercise*, our χ^2 calculation is

f_o	f_e	$f_o - f_e$	$(f_o - f_e)^2$	$\dfrac{(f_o - f_e)^2}{f_e}$
110	112.32	-2.32	5.3824	0.0479
106	103.68	2.32	5.3824	0.0519
98	95.68	2.32	5.3824	0.0563
86	88.32	-2.32	5.3824	0.0609
			Total	0.2170

In this case, $\chi^2_{calc} \approx 0.217$, which is very small.

This indicates that *gender* and *regular exercise* are independent.

USING TECHNOLOGY

You can also use your calculator to find χ^2_{calc}. You must first enter the contingency table as a matrix.

Using a Casio fx-CG20:

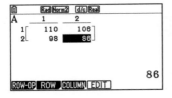

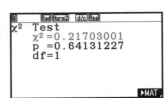

Using a TI-84 Plus:

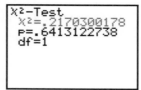

Using a TI-*n*spire:

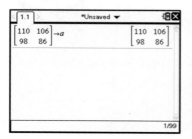

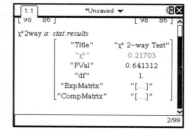

Consult the **graphics calculator instructions** for more detailed help.

GRAPHICS
CALCULATOR
INSTRUCTIONS

EXERCISE 11E.1

1 Construct an expected frequency table for the following contingency tables:

a

	Likes chicken	Dislikes chicken	sum
Likes fish			60
Dislikes fish			40
sum	75	25	100

b

	Drove to work	Cycled to work	Public transport	sum
Male				44
Female				36
sum	46	14	20	80

c

	Junior school	Middle school	High school	sum
Plays sport	35	59	71	165
Does not play sport	23	27	35	85
sum	58	86	106	250

d

	Wore hat and sunscreen	Wore hat or sunscreen	Wore neither	sum
Sunburnt	3	5	13	
Not sunburnt	36	17	1	
sum				

2 Consider the contingency table:

	Pass Maths test	Fail Maths test	sum
Male	24	26	50
Female	36	14	50
sum	60	40	100

a Construct an expected frequency table.

b Interpret the value in the top left corner of the expected frequency table.

c Calculate χ^2_{calc} by copying and completing this table:

f_o	f_e	$f_o - f_e$	$(f_o - f_e)^2$	$\dfrac{(f_o - f_e)^2}{f_e}$
24				
26				
36				
14				
			Total	

3 For the following contingency tables:

    i construct the expected frequency table   **ii** find χ^2_{calc} without using technology.

a

	Likes football	Dislikes football	sum
Male	21	5	26
Female	7	17	24
sum	28	22	50

b

	Full-time job	Part-time job	Unemployed	sum
Left handed	19	12	9	
Right handed	141	128	91	
sum				

c

	Age 18 - 29	30 - 39	40+
Married	10	16	21
Single	15	12	10

d

Visits Museum \ Visits Art Gallery	Often	Rarely	Never
Often	56	33	22
Rarely	29	42	37
Never	20	31	40

Check your answers using your calculator. They may differ slightly due to rounding.

FORMAL TEST FOR INDEPENDENCE

We have seen that a small value of χ^2 indicates that two variables are independent, while a large value of χ^2 indicates that the variables are not independent.

We will now consider a more formal test which determines *how large* χ^2 must be for us to conclude the variables are not independent. This is known as the **critical value** of χ^2.

The critical value of χ^2 depends on:

- the **size** of the contingency table, measured by **degrees of freedom**
- the **significance level** used.

DEGREES OF FREEDOM

In a contingency table, the number of **degrees of freedom (df)** is the number of values which are free to vary.

Consider the 2×2 contingency table alongside, with the sum values given.

The value in the top left corner is free to vary, as it can take many possible values, one of which is 9. However, once we set this value, the remaining values are *not* free to vary, as they are determined by the row and column sums.

So, the number of degrees of freedom is 1, which is $(2-1) \times (2-1)$.

	A_1	A_2	sum
B_1			12
B_2			8
sum	15	5	20

	A_1	A_2	sum
B_1	9	3	12
B_2	6	2	8
sum	15	5	20

In a 3×3 contingency table, we can choose $(3-1) \times (3-1) = 4$ values before the remaining values are not free to vary.

	C_1	C_2	C_3	sum
D_1				12
D_2				8
D_3				13
sum	13	9	11	33

	C_1	C_2	C_3	sum
D_1	5	3	4	12
D_2	2	4	2	8
D_3	6	2	5	13
sum	13	9	11	33

The row and column numbers do not include sums.

For a contingency table which has r rows and c columns,
$$\mathbf{df} = (r-1)(c-1).$$

SIGNIFICANCE LEVEL

As the χ^2 value gets larger, it becomes increasingly unlikely that the variables involved are independent. The **significance level** indicates the minimum acceptable probability that the variables are independent.

We usually use either 10%, 5%, or 1% for the significance level.

For a given significance level and degrees of freedom, the table alongside gives the **critical value** of χ^2, above which we conclude the variables are not independent.

For example, at a 5% significance level with $df = 1$, the critical value is 3.84. This means that at a 5% significance level, the departure between the observed and expected values is too great if $\chi^2_{calc} > 3.84$.

Likewise, at a 1% significance level with $df = 7$, the departure between the observed and expected values is too great if $\chi^2_{calc} > 18.48$.

Degrees of	Significance level		
freedom (df)	10%	5%	1%
1	2.71	3.84	6.63
2	4.61	5.99	9.21
3	6.25	7.81	11.34
4	7.78	9.49	13.28
5	9.24	11.07	15.09
6	10.64	12.59	16.81
7	12.02	14.07	18.48
8	13.36	15.51	20.09
9	14.68	16.92	21.67
10	15.99	18.31	23.21

Click on the icon for a more detailed table of
critical values.

**CRITICAL
VALUES**

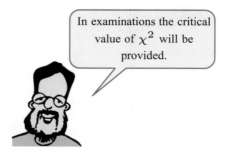

In examinations the critical
value of χ^2 will be
provided.

Important: In order for χ^2 to be distributed appropriately, the sample size n must be sufficiently large.
Generally, n is sufficiently large if no values in the expected value table are less than 5.

THE p-VALUE

When finding χ^2 on your calculator, a **p-value** is also provided. This can be used, together with the
χ^2 value and the critical value, to determine whether or not to accept that the variables are independent.

> For a given contingency table, the **p-value** is the probability of obtaining observed values as far or
> further from the expected values, assuming the variables are independent.

If the p-value is smaller than the significance level, then it is sufficiently unlikely that we would have
obtained the observed results if the variables had been independent. We therefore conclude that the
variables are not independent.

It is not always essential to use the p-value when testing for independence, as we can perform the test
by simply comparing χ^2_{calc} with the critical value. However, the p-value does give a more meaningful
measure of how likely it is that the variables are independent.

THE FORMAL TEST FOR INDEPENDENCE

Step 1:   State H_0 called the **null hypothesis**. This is a statement that the two variables being
considered are independent.
State H_1 called the **alternative hypothesis**. This is a statement that the two variables being
considered are not independent.

Step 2:   State the **rejection inequality** $\chi^2_{calc} > k$ where k is the **critical value** of χ^2.

Step 3:   Construct the expected frequency table.

Step 4:   Use technology to find χ^2_{calc}.

Step 5:   We either reject H_0 or do not reject H_0, depending on the result of the rejection inequality.

Step 6:   We could also use a **p-value** to help us with our decision making.
For example, at a 5% significance level: If $p < 0.05$, we reject H_0.
If $p > 0.05$, we do not reject H_0.

We write 'we do not reject H_0'
rather than 'we accept H_0' because
if we perform the test again with a
different level of significance, we
may then have reason to reject H_0.

Example 7

◀ഃ **Self Tutor**

A survey was given to randomly chosen high school students from years 9 to 12 on possible changes to the school's canteen.

The contingency table shows the results.

At a 5% significance level, test whether the student's *canteen preference* depends on the year group.

	Year group			
	9	10	11	12
change	7	9	13	14
no change	14	12	9	7

H_0 is that *year group* and *canteen preference* are independent.
H_1 is that *year group* and *canteen preference* are not independent.

$df = (2-1)(4-1) = 3$ and the significance level is 5% or 0.05.

$\therefore$ the critical value is 7.81   {from the table of critical values}

We reject H_0 if $\chi^2_{calc} > 7.81$.

The 2×4 contingency table is:

	Year group				
	9	10	11	12	*sum*
C	7	9	13	14	43
C'	14	12	9	7	42
sum	21	21	22	21	85

The expected frequency table is:

	Year group			
	9	10	11	12
C	10.6	10.6	11.1	10.6
C'	10.4	10.4	10.9	10.4

Casio fx-CG20

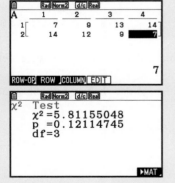

TI-84 Plus

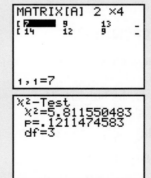

TI-nspire

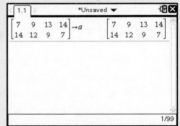

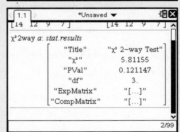

Using technology, $\chi^2_{calc} \approx 5.81$, which is < 7.81.

Therefore, we do not reject H_0.

$p \approx 0.121$ which is > 0.05, providing further evidence to not reject H_0.

We conclude that at a 5% level of significance, the variables *year group* and *canteen preference* are independent.

EXERCISE 11E.2

1   This contingency table shows the responses of a randomly chosen sample of adults regarding the person's weight and whether they have *diabetes*.

At a 5% significance level, the critical value of χ^2 is 5.99.

Test at a 5% level whether there is a link between *weight* and suffering *diabetes*.

	Weight		
	light	*medium*	*heavy*
Diabetic	11	19	26
Non-diabetic	79	68	69

2   The table opposite shows the way in which a random sample of people intend to vote in the next election.

   a   For a 10% significance level, what is the critical value of χ^2?

	Age of voter		
	18 to 35	36 to 59	60+
Party A	85	95	131
Party B	168	197	173

   b   Test at a 10% level whether there is any association between the *age of a voter* and the *party they wish to vote for*.

3   Noah wanted to find out whether there is a relationship between a person's *gender* and their *favourite season*. He sampled 100 people, and obtained the results alongside.

At a 1% significance level, the critical value for this test is 11.34.

Favourite season

	Summer	Autumn	Winter	Spring
Male	8	11	6	20
Female	12	17	10	16

Test, at a 1% level, whether the variables *gender* and *favourite season* are independent.

4   The guests staying at a hotel are asked to provide their *reason for travelling*, and to *rate* the hotel on a scale from Poor to Excellent. The results are shown below.

		Rating			
		Poor	Fair	Good	Excellent
Reason for	*Business*	27	25	20	8
travelling	*Holiday*	9	17	24	30

   a   Show that, at a 5% significance level, the variables *reason for travelling* and *rating* are dependent.

   b   By examining the contingency table, describe how a guest's *rating* is affected by their *reason for travelling*.

5   The hair and eye colours of 150 randomly selected individuals are shown in the table below.

		Hair colour			
		Blond	Black	Brunette	Red
Eye colour	*Blue*	14	10	21	5
	Brown	11	32	20	12
	Green	5	2	14	4

At a 5% significance level, the critical value for χ^2 is 12.59.

Test, at a 5% level, whether there is an association between *hair colour* and *eye colour*.

6 Hockey player Julie wondered whether the position you played affected your likelihood of being injured. She asked a random sample of hockey players what position they played, and what injuries they had sustained in the last year.

		Forward	Midfielder	Defender	Goalkeeper
				Position	
	No injury	23	18	24	7
Injury type	Mild injury	14	34	23	11
	Serious injury	10	16	13	7

Test, at a 10% significance level, whether the variables *position* and *injury type* are independent.

LIMITATIONS OF THE χ^2 TEST (EXTENSION)

There are two situations in which the χ^2 test may be unreliable:

1 Any of the expected frequencies are less than 5.
This can be resolved by **combining data**.

2 The degrees of freedom is 1.
This can be resolved using **Yates' continuity correction**.

These situations may arise in internal assessment tasks, but you will not be required to deal with them in examinations.

COMBINING DATA

The χ^2 test may be unreliable if any of the expected frequency values are less than 5.

Consider the contingency table alongside.

For this contingency table, $\chi^2 \approx 8.52$.

For a 5% significance level and df $= 3$, the critical value is 7.81.

Watch TV

	Rarely	Sometimes	Often	Very often
Male	12	15	10	8
Female	22	21	11	1

Since $\chi^2_{calc} > 7.81$, we would reject H_0, and conclude that *gender* and *television watching* are dependent.

However, on inspecting the expected frequency table, there are two expected frequencies which are less than 5. This indicates that our conclusion may not be reliable.

Watch TV

	Rarely	Sometimes	Often	Very often
Male	15.3	16.2	9.45	4.05
Female	18.7	19.8	11.55	4.95

We can improve the reliability of this test by **combining** rows or columns so that there are no cells with expected frequency less than 5. In this case we combine the *often* and *very often* columns to produce:

Watch TV

	Rarely	Sometimes	Often/Very often
Male	12	15	18
Female	22	21	12

The expected frequency table is now:

Watch TV

	Rarely	*Sometimes*	*Often/Very often*
Male	15.3	16.2	13.5
Female	18.7	19.8	16.5

Now $\chi^2_{calc} \approx 4.18$, and for a 5% level with df $= 2$, the critical value is 5.99.

Since $\chi^2_{calc} < 5.99$, we now conclude that the variables are independent. This is different from our original conclusion.

EXERCISE 11E.3

1 Consider the contingency table alongside:

- **a** Construct the expected frequency table.
- **b** Are any of the expected frequencies less than 5?
- **c** Combine the data so that none of the cells have an expected frequency less than 5.

Own a pet?

		Yes	*No*
Age	0 - 19	5	3
	20 - 29	32	22
	30 - 49	42	58
	50+	39	34

2 The following table is a result of a major investigation considering the two factors of *intelligence level* and *cigarette smoking.*

Intelligence level

	low	*average*	*high*	*very high*
Non smoker	279	386	96	2
Medium level smoker	123	201	58	5
Heavy smoker	100	147	64	2

- **a** Test at a 1% level whether there is a link between *intelligence level* and *cigarette smoking.*
- **b** Construct the expected frequency table.
- **c** Combine appropriate columns so that none of the expected frequencies is less than 5.
- **d** Perform this test again at a 1% level. Is your conclusion the same as in **a**?

YATES' CONTINUITY CORRECTION

The χ^2 test may also be unreliable if the number of degrees of freedom is 1. This occurs when we have a 2×2 contingency table.

To improve the reliability of the χ^2 test for 2×2 contingency tables, we can apply **Yates' continuity correction**. We use a modified formula to find χ^2_{calc}.

If df $= 1$, we use

$$\chi^2_{calc} = \sum \frac{(|f_o - f_e| - 0.5)^2}{f_e}$$

where $|f_o - f_e|$ is the **absolute value** or **modulus** of $f_o - f_e$.

Example 8   ◄)) **Self Tutor**

80 people were surveyed to find whether they enjoyed surfing and skiing. The results are shown alongside.

Test, at a 1% level, whether there is an association between *enjoying surfing* and *enjoying skiing*.

		Enjoy surfing?	
		Yes	No
Enjoy skiing?	Yes	17	15
	No	8	40

H_0: The variables *enjoying surfing* and *enjoying skiing* are independent.

H_1: The variables *enjoying surfing* and *enjoying skiing* are not independent.

At a 1% level with df $= 1$, the critical value is 6.63. So, we reject H_0 if $\chi^2_{calc} > 6.63$.

The 2×2 contingency table is:

Enjoy surfing?

		Yes	No	sum
Enjoy skiing?	Yes	17	15	32
	No	8	40	48
	sum	25	55	80

The expected frequency table is:

Enjoy surfing?

		Yes	No
Enjoy skiing?	Yes	10	22
	No	15	33

We will now find χ^2_{calc} using Yates' continuity correction:

f_o	f_e	$f_o - f_e$	$|f_o - f_e|$	$|f_o - f_e| - 0.5$	$(|f_o - f_e| - 0.5)^2$	$\dfrac{(|f_o - f_e| - 0.5)^2}{f_e}$
17	10	7	7	6.5	42.25	4.225
15	22	-7	7	6.5	42.25	1.920
8	15	-7	7	6.5	42.25	2.817
40	33	7	7	6.5	42.25	1.280
					Total	10.242

So, $\chi^2_{calc} \approx 10.2$

Since $\chi^2_{calc} > 6.63$, we reject H_0 and conclude that, at a 1% significance level, *enjoying surfing* and *enjoying skiing* are dependent.

EXERCISE 11E.4

1 Horace claims that he can predict the outcome of a coin toss. To test this, he tosses a coin 200 times, and tries to guess the outcome of each toss. The results are shown alongside.

		Result	
		Heads	Tails
Guess	Heads	54	50
	Tails	41	55

   a Construct the expected frequency table.

   b Use Yates' continuity correction to find χ^2_{calc}.

   c The critical value at a 5% level with df $= 1$ is 3.84. Test whether Horace's *guess* and the *result* are independent.

   d Comment on the validity of Horace's claim.

In examinations, the number of degrees of freedom will always be greater than 1, so Yates' continuity correction will not be required.

2 The practical test for a motorbike licence differs in France and Germany. An inquiry into the two systems yielded the following results for randomly selected candidates.

A chi-squared test at a 10% significance level is used to investigate whether the result of a motorbike test is independent of the country where it took place.

		Result	
		Pass	*Fail*
Country	*France*	56	29
	Germany	176	48

  a Construct the expected frequency table.

  b Write down the critical value of the chi-squared test statistic.

  c Using Yates' continuity correction, find the chi-squared value for this data.

  d What conclusion can be drawn from this chi-squared test?

THEORY OF KNOWLEDGE

In the previous exercise we saw examples of data which was non-linear, but for which we could *transform* the variables so a linear model could be used.

In other situations we can use quadratic or trigonometric functions to model data.

  1 Can all data be modelled by a known mathematical function?

  2 How reliable is mathematics in predicting real-world phenomena?

The **Lotka-Volterra predator-prey model** was developed independently by **Alfred Lotka** (1880 - 1949) and **Vito Volterra** (1860 - 1940). The model is used to predict the populations of two species of animals over time, where one species is a predator of the other.

Alfred Lotka

  3 Is the Lotka-Volterra model defined by nature or by man?

  4 Is nature governed by mathematics, or are we imposing our own creation upon it?

REVIEW SET 11A

1 Thomas rode for an hour each day for eleven days. He recorded the number of kilometres he rode along with the temperature that day.

Temperature (T °C)	32.9	33.9	35.2	37.1	38.9	30.3	32.5	31.7	35.7	36.3	34.7
Distance (d km)	26.5	26.7	24.4	19.8	18.5	32.6	28.7	29.4	23.8	21.2	29.7

  a Using technology, construct a scatter diagram of the data.

  b Find and interpret Pearson's correlation coefficient for the two variables.

  c Find the equation of the least squares regression line.

  d How hot must it get before Thomas does not ride at all?

2 The contingency table below shows the results of motor vehicle accidents in relation to whether the traveller was wearing a seat belt.

	Serious injury	Permanent disablement	Death
Wearing a belt	189	104	58
Not wearing a belt	83	67	46

At a 5% level with df = 2, the critical value is 5.99. Test at a 5% level whether *wearing of a seat belt* and *severity of injury* are independent factors.

3 A craft shop sells canvasses in a variety of sizes. The table below shows the area and price of each canvas type.

Area (x cm^2)	100	225	300	625	850	900
Price ($y)	6	12	13	24	30	35

  a Construct a scatter diagram for the data.   **b** Calculate r.

  c Describe the correlation between *area* and *price*.

  d Find the equation of the least squares regression line.

  e Draw the line of best fit on your scatter diagram.

  f Estimate the price of a canvas with area 1200 cm^2. Is your estimate likely to be reliable?

4 A clothing store recorded the length of time customers were in the store and the amount of money they spent.

Time (min)	8	18	5	10	17	11	2	13	18	4	11	20	23	22	17
Money (€)	40	78	0	46	72	86	0	59	33	0	0	122	90	137	93

  a Draw a scatter diagram of the data.   **b** Calculate the mean point.

  c Plot the mean point on your diagram and draw a line of best fit through the mean point.

  d Describe the relationship between *time in the store* and *money spent*.

  e Estimate the amount of money spent by a person who is in the store for 15 minutes. Comment on the reliability of your estimation.

5 A drinks vendor varies the price of Supa-fizz on a daily basis. He records the number of sales of the drink as shown:

Price (p)	$2.50	$1.90	$1.60	$2.10	$2.20	$1.40	$1.70	$1.85
Sales (s)	389	450	448	386	381	458	597	431

  a Produce a scatter diagram for the data.

  b Are there any outliers? If so, should they be included in the analysis?

  c Calculate the least squares regression line.

  d Do you think the least squares regression line would give an accurate prediction of sales if Supa-fizz was priced at 50 cents? Explain your answer.

6 Eight identical flower beds contain petunias. The different beds were watered different numbers of times each week, and the number of flowers each bed produced was recorded in the table below:

Number of waterings (n)	0	1	2	3	4	5	6	7
Flowers produced (f)	18	52	86	123	158	191	228	250

a Which is the independent variable?

b Calculate the equation of the least squares regression line.

c Is it likely that a causal relationship exists between these two variables? Explain your answer.

d Plot the least squares regression line on a scatter diagram of the data.

e Violet has two beds of petunias. One she waters five times a fortnight ($2\frac{1}{2}$ times a week), and the other ten times a week.

    i How many flowers can she expect from each bed?

    ii Which is the more reliable estimate?

7 Examine the following contingency table for the independence of factors P and Q.

Use a χ^2 test:

a at a 5% level of significance

b at a 1% level of significance.

	Q_1	Q_2	Q_3	Q_4
P_1	19	23	27	39
P_2	11	20	27	35
P_3	26	39	21	30

REVIEW SET 11B

1 The following table gives the average number of children for different family incomes.

Income (I thousand $)	20	25	30	35	40	50	60	70	90
Number of children, n	4.2	3.4	3.2	2.9	2.7	2.5	2.3	2.1	1.9

a Construct an appropriate graph to display the data.

b Find r.

c Find the equation of the line of best fit.

d Estimate the average number of children for a family income of:

    i $45 000   **ii** $140 000

e Comment on the reliability of your estimates.

2 For the following pairs of variables, discuss:

    i whether the correlation between the variables is likely to be positive or negative

    ii whether a causal relationship exists between the variables.

a *price of tickets* and *number of tickets sold*

b *ice cream sales* and *number of drownings*.

3 The table shows the responses to a survey about whether the city speed limit should be increased.

Test at a 10% level whether there is any association between the *age of a driver* and *increasing the speed limit*.

	Age of driver		
	18 to 30	31 to 54	55+
Increase	234	169	134
No increase	156	191	233

4 The following table shows the results from a major investigation considering the two factors *intelligence level* and *business success*.

		Intelligence level			
		Low	Average	High	Very high
Business success	No success	35	30	41	25
	Low success	28	41	26	29
	Success	35	24	41	56
	High success	52	38	63	72

At a 1% level with df $= 9$, the critical value is 21.67. Test at a 1% level whether there is a link between *intelligence level* and *business success*.

5 Safety authorities advise drivers to travel three seconds behind the car in front of them. This provides the driver with a greater chance of avoiding a collision if the car in front has to brake quickly or is itself involved in an accident.

A test was carried out to find out how long it would take a driver to bring a car to rest from the time a red light was flashed. It involved one driver in the same car under the same test conditions.

Speed (v km h^{-1})	10	20	30	40	50	60	70	80	90
Stopping time (t s)	1.23	1.54	1.88	2.20	2.52	2.83	3.15	3.45	3.83

a Produce a scatter diagram of the data.

b Find the linear model which best fits the data.

c Hence estimate the stopping time for a speed of: **i** 55 km h^{-1} **ii** 110 km h^{-1}

d Interpret the vertical intercept of the model.

6 Two supervillains, Silent Predator and the Furry Reaper, terrorise Metropolis by abducting fair maidens (most of whom happen to be journalists). The superhero Superman believes that they are collaborating, alternatively abducting fair maidens so as not to compete with each other for ransom money. He plots their abduction rate below, in dozens of maidens.

Silent Predator (p)	4	6	5	9	3	5	8	11	3	7	7	4
Furry Reaper (r)	13	10	11	8	11	9	6	6	12	7	10	8

a Plot the data on a scatter diagram with Silent Predator on the horizontal axis.

b Find the least squares regression line.

c Calculate r, and hence describe the strength of Silent Predator and Furry Reaper's relationship. Is there any evidence to support Superman's suspicions?

d Estimate the number of the Furry Reaper's abductions when the Silent Predator's were 6 dozen.

e Why is the model inappropriate when the Furry Reaper abducts more than 20 dozen maidens?

f Calculate the p- and r-intercepts of the regression line. What do these values represent?

g If Superman is faced with a choice of capturing one supervillain but not the other, which should he choose?

Chapter **12**

Pythagoras' theorem

Contents:

OPENING PROBLEM

Joy has a hiking stick which collapses down to 55 cm in length. She wants to pack it in a small suitcase which is 45 cm × 30 cm × 30 cm.

a Will the hiking stick fit flat in the bottom of the case?

b Can Joy fit the hiking stick in the case?

We see 90° angles or **right angles** every day in buildings, boxes, books, and many other places. For thousands of years the construction of right angles has been an important skill. An example of this is the great pyramids of Egypt.

In this chapter we look at **Pythagoras' theorem** which relates to right angles in triangles. We can use this rule to find unknown side lengths in figures known to have right angles, and also to test for right angles.

A   PYTHAGORAS' THEOREM

A **right angled triangle** is a triangle which has a right angle as one of its angles.

The side opposite the right angle is called the **hypotenuse**, and is the longest side of the triangle. The other two sides are called the **legs** of the triangle.

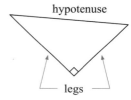

Pythagoras' theorem states:

> In a right angled triangle with legs a and b,
> and hypotenuse c,
>
> $$a^2 + b^2 = c^2$$

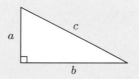

If we know the lengths of any two sides of a right angled triangle, we can use Pythagoras' theorem to find the third side.

Example 1	◀) Self Tutor

Find the length of the hypotenuse in the triangle shown.

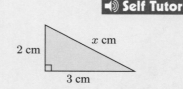

> If $x^2 = k$, then $x = \pm\sqrt{k}$. We reject $-\sqrt{k}$ as lengths must be positive!

The hypotenuse is opposite the right angle and has length x cm.

$$\therefore \quad x^2 = 3^2 + 2^2 \quad \text{\{Pythagoras\}}$$
$$\therefore \quad x^2 = 9 + 4$$
$$\therefore \quad x^2 = 13$$
$$\therefore \quad x = \sqrt{13} \quad \text{\{as } x > 0\}$$

So, the hypotenuse is $\sqrt{13}$ cm long.

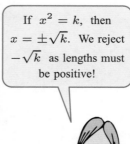

ACCURACY OF ANSWERS

In **Example 1**, the solution $\sqrt{13}$ in surd form is exact, and is acceptable since it is irrational. If the answer was $\sqrt{16}$, you would be expected to simplify it to 4.

Answers given in surd form may not always be practical in real contexts. For example, if we needed to draw a line $\sqrt{13}$ centimetres long using a ruler, we would approximate the value to 3.6 cm using a calculator.

Within all IB Mathematics courses, final answers should be given either exactly or correct to 3 significant figures. Rounding to 3 significant figures should only occur at the end of a calculation and not at intermediate steps.

EXERCISE 12A

1 Find the length of the hypotenuse in the following right angled triangles.
   Where appropriate, leave your answer in surd (square root) form.

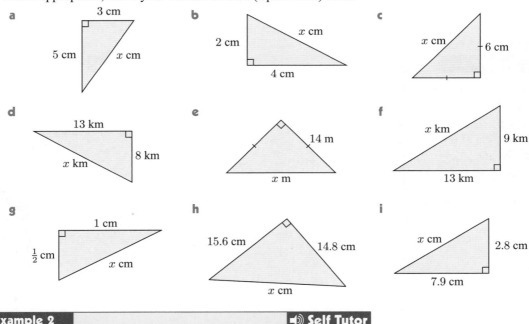

a 3 cm, 5 cm, x cm
b 2 cm, x cm, 4 cm
c x cm, 6 cm
d 13 km, 8 km, x km
e 14 m, x m
f x km, 9 km, 13 km
g 1 cm, $\frac{1}{2}$ cm, x cm
h 15.6 cm, 14.8 cm, x cm
i x cm, 2.8 cm, 7.9 cm

Example 2   ◀) **Self Tutor**

Find the length of the third side of the given triangle.

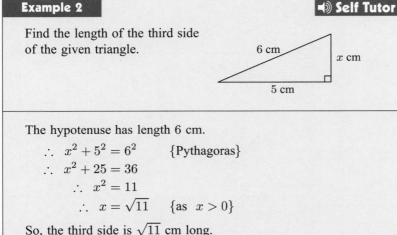

6 cm, x cm, 5 cm

The hypotenuse has length 6 cm.

$\therefore \ x^2 + 5^2 = 6^2$ {Pythagoras}
$\therefore \ x^2 + 25 = 36$
$\therefore \ \ x^2 = 11$
$\therefore \ \ x = \sqrt{11}$ {as $x > 0$}

So, the third side is $\sqrt{11}$ cm long.

2   Find the length of the third side of the following right angled triangles.
Where appropriate, leave your answer in surd (square root) form.

a

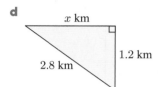

6 cm, 10 cm, x cm

b

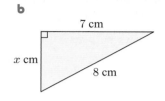

7 cm, x cm, 8 cm

c

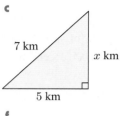

7 km, x km, 5 km

d

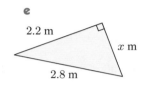

x km, 1.2 km, 2.8 km

e

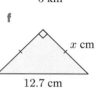

2.2 m, x m, 2.8 m

f

x cm, 12.7 cm

Example 3   ◀) **Self Tutor**

Find x in the following:

$\sqrt{10}$ cm, 2 cm, x cm

The hypotenuse has length x cm.

$$\therefore \ x^2 = 2^2 + (\sqrt{10})^2 \quad \{\text{Pythagoras}\}$$
$$\therefore \ x^2 = 4 + 10$$
$$\therefore \ x^2 = 14$$
$$\therefore \ x = \pm\sqrt{14}$$

But $x > 0$, so $x = \sqrt{14}$.

Remember that
$(\sqrt{a})^2 = a$.

---

3   Find x in the following:

a

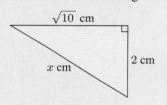

2 cm, x cm, $\sqrt{3}$ cm

b

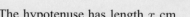

$\sqrt{5}$ cm, x cm, $\sqrt{3}$ cm

c

2 m, x m, $\sqrt{11}$ m

d

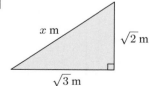

x m, $\sqrt{2}$ m, $\sqrt{3}$ m

e

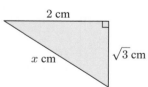

x cm, $\sqrt{10}$ cm

f

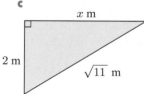

x m, $\sqrt{7}$ m, $\sqrt{15}$ m

Example 4

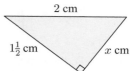 Self Tutor

Solve for x:

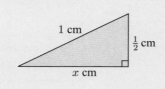

1 cm
$\frac{1}{2}$ cm
x cm

$$x^2 + \left(\tfrac{1}{2}\right)^2 = 1^2 \qquad \{\text{Pythagoras}\}$$
$$\therefore \ x^2 + \tfrac{1}{4} = 1$$
$$\therefore \ x^2 = \tfrac{3}{4}$$
$$\therefore \ x = \pm\sqrt{\tfrac{3}{4}}$$
$$\therefore \ x = \sqrt{\tfrac{3}{4}} \qquad \{\text{as} \ x > 0\}$$

4 Solve for x:

a

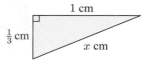

1 cm
$\frac{1}{3}$ cm
x cm

b

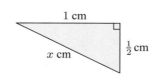

1 cm
$\frac{1}{2}$ cm
x cm

c

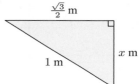

2 cm
$1\frac{1}{2}$ cm
x cm

d

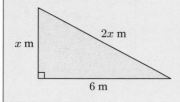

x cm
$\frac{1}{2}$ cm
$\frac{3}{4}$ cm

e

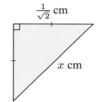

$\frac{1}{\sqrt{2}}$ cm
x cm

f

$\frac{\sqrt{3}}{2}$ m
1 m
x m

Example 5

Self Tutor

Find the value of x:

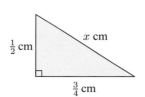

$2x$ m
x m
6 m

$$(2x)^2 = x^2 + 6^2 \quad \{\text{Pythagoras}\}$$
$$\therefore \ 4x^2 = x^2 + 36$$
$$\therefore \ 3x^2 = 36$$
$$\therefore \ x^2 = 12$$
$$\therefore \ x = \pm\sqrt{12}$$
$$\therefore \ x = \sqrt{12} \qquad \{\text{as} \ x > 0\}$$

The use of brackets here is essential.

5 Find the value of x:

a

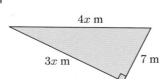

12 cm
x cm
$2x$ cm

b

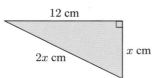

13 cm
$2x$ cm
$3x$ cm

c

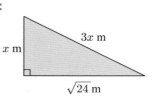

$3x$ m
x m
$\sqrt{24}$ m

d

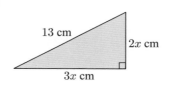

$4x$ m
$3x$ m
7 m

e

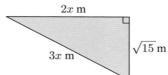

$2x$ m
$3x$ m
$\sqrt{15}$ m

f

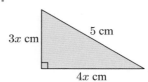

5 cm
$3x$ cm
$4x$ cm

Example 6   ◀) **Self Tutor**

Find the value of any unknowns:

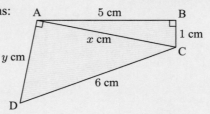

The intermediate answer $\sqrt{26}$ cm is left in exact form so we do not lose accuracy.

In $\triangle ABC$, the hypotenuse is x cm long.

$$\therefore \ x^2 = 5^2 + 1^2 \quad \{\text{Pythagoras}\}$$
$$\therefore \ x^2 = 26$$
$$\therefore \ x = \sqrt{26} \quad \{\text{as } x > 0\}$$

In $\triangle ACD$, the hypotenuse is 6 cm long.

$$\therefore \ y^2 + (\sqrt{26})^2 = 6^2 \quad \{\text{Pythagoras}\}$$
$$\therefore \ y^2 + 26 = 36$$
$$\therefore \ y^2 = 10$$
$$\therefore \ y = \sqrt{10} \quad \{\text{as } y > 0\}$$

6 Find the value of any unknowns:

a

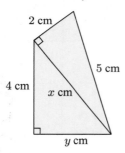

b

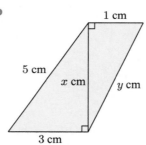

c

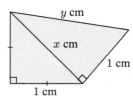

7 Find x:

a

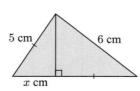

b

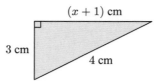

8 Find the length AC:

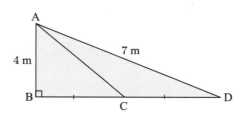

9 In the following figures, draw additional lines to complete right angled triangles. Apply Pythagoras' theorem to find the unknown distance AB.

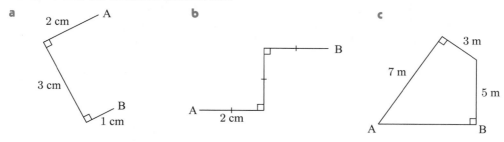

| **B** | **RIGHT ANGLES IN GEOMETRY** |

There are many geometric figures which involve right angles. It is important to recognise these because it tells us when we can apply Pythagoras' theorem.

A **rectangle** is a quadrilateral in which all four angles are right angles.

We can form right angled triangles by drawing in a **diagonal** of the rectangle.

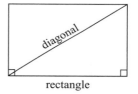

A **rhombus** is a quadrilateral which has sides equal in length. Its diagonals bisect each other at right angles.

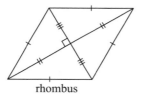

A **square** is both a rectangle *and* a rhombus, so contains many right angles.

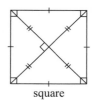

An **isosceles triangle** has two sides which are equal in length. The altitude bisects the base at right angles.

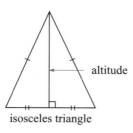

An **equilateral triangle** has all three sides equal in length. The altitude bisects the base at right angles.

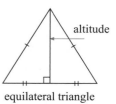

To solve problems involving geometric figures:

- Draw a neat diagram showing the information given.
- Use a symbol such as x to represent the unknown length.
- Identify a right angled triangle to which you can apply Pythagoras' theorem.
- Solve the equation which results from Pythagoras' theorem.
- Specify an exact answer or round to 3 significant figures.
- If appropriate, write the answer in sentence form.

Example 7   ◀)) **Self Tutor**

The longer side of a rectangle is 12 cm and its diagonal is 13 cm. Find:

a the length of the shorter side   **b** the area of the rectangle.

a
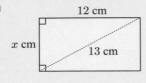

Let the shorter side be x cm.

$\therefore \ x^2 + 12^2 = 13^2$ {Pythagoras}

$\therefore \ x^2 + 144 = 169$

$\therefore \ x^2 = 25$

$\therefore \ x = 5$ {as $x > 0$}

So, the shorter side is 5 cm long.

b Area = length × width

= 12 × 5

= 60 cm^2

EXERCISE 12B.1

1 Find the lengths of the diagonals of these rectangles:

a
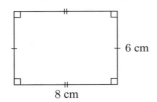

6 cm

8 cm

b

3 m

2 Find the lengths of the diagonals of a 12 mm × 16 mm rectangle.

3 The shorter side of a rectangle is 5 mm, and its diagonal is 11 mm. Find:

a the length of the longer side   **b** the area of the rectangle.

4 The longer side of a rectangle is three times the length of the shorter side. The diagonal has length $\sqrt{1000}$ m. Find the exact dimensions of the rectangle.

Example 8   ◀)) **Self Tutor**

A rhombus has diagonals of length 6 cm and 8 cm. Find the length of its sides.

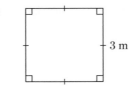

The diagonals of a rhombus *bisect at right angles*.

Let each side be x cm long.

$\therefore \ x^2 = 3^2 + 4^2$ {Pythagoras}

$\therefore \ x^2 = 9 + 16$

$\therefore \ x^2 = 25$

$\therefore \ x = 5$ {as $x > 0$}

So, the sides are 5 cm long.

5 A rhombus has diagonals of length 2 cm and 4 cm. Find the length of its sides in surd form.

6 Find the side length of a square with diagonals 18 cm long.

7 A rhombus has sides of length 8 m. Its shorter diagonal is 10 m long. Find:

  a the length of the longer diagonal   **b** the area of the rhombus.

Example 9   🔊 **Self Tutor**

  a Find the altitude of an equilateral triangle with sides 6 m long.

  b Hence find the area of the triangle.

a
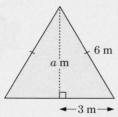

Let the altitude be a m.

The altitude bisects the base at right angles.

$\therefore \;\; a^2 + 3^2 = 6^2 \quad$ {Pythagoras}

$\therefore \;\; a^2 + 9 = 36$

$\therefore \;\; a^2 = 27$

$\therefore \;\; a = \sqrt{27} \quad$ {as $a > 0$}

So, the altitude of the triangle is about 5.20 m long.

b Area $= \frac{1}{2} \times$ base $\times$ height

$= \frac{1}{2} \times 6 \times \sqrt{27}$

$\approx 15.6 \text{ m}^2$

---

8 An isosceles triangle has equal sides of length 6 cm. Its third side is 8 cm long. Find:

  a the altitude of the triangle   **b** the area of the triangle.

9 The base of an isosceles triangle is 6 cm long, and its area is 12 cm^2. Find the length of the two equal sides.

10 The altitude of an equilateral triangle is $2\sqrt{3}$ mm in length. Find the perimeter of the triangle.

INVESTIGATION 1   **RIGHT ANGLES IN GEOMETRIC FIGURES**

In this investigation we will discover how a right angle can be found within a common geometric figure.

What to do:

  1 Mark two points A and B about 10 cm apart on a piece of blank paper.

  2 Join A and B with a straight line.

  3 Place a set square on the paper so that A and B lie along the set square edges that are at right angles to each other. Mark the point where the right angle lies.

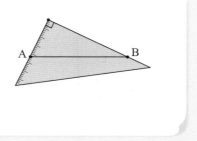

  4 Repeat step **3** 15 times, with the right angled corner at a different position each time. Make sure the hypotenuse of the set square is always on the same side of AB.

  5 If we continued this process, the **locus** of points would form a familiar shape. What is it?

  6 Let C be any point on the locus. Copy and complete: *"The angle ACB on a ..... is always a ......"*

CIRCLES (EXTENSION)

There are several situations where right angles are involved with circles.
The circle theorems which follow are not part of this course, but provide useful applications of Pythagoras' theorem.

ANGLE IN A SEMI-CIRCLE

In the previous investigation you should have found that:

> The angle in a semi-circle is always a right angle.

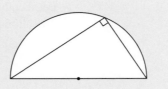

GEOMETRY PACKAGE

THE CHORD OF A CIRCLE

Consider the chord AB of a circle.

Since the radius of the circle is AO = BO, triangle ABO is isosceles.

Using the isosceles triangle theorem:

> The line drawn from the centre of a circle at right angles to a chord, bisects the chord.

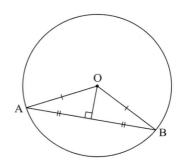

Example 10   ◀) **Self Tutor**

A circle of radius 8 cm has a chord of length 10 cm.
Find the shortest distance from the centre of the circle to the chord.

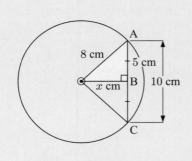

The shortest distance is the 'perpendicular distance'. The line drawn from the centre of a circle, at right angles to a chord, bisects the chord, so

$$AB = BC = 5 \text{ cm}$$

In $\triangle AOB$, $5^2 + x^2 = 8^2$ {Pythagoras}

$$\therefore \quad x^2 = 64 - 25 = 39$$
$$\therefore \quad x = \sqrt{39} \quad \{\text{as } x > 0\}$$
$$\therefore \quad x \approx 6.24$$

So, the shortest distance is 6.24 cm.

THE TANGENT TO A CIRCLE

A **tangent** to a circle touches the circle but does not cut it.

> The radius from the centre of a circle to the point of contact is at right angles to the tangent.

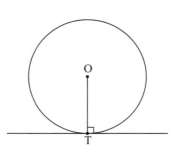

EXERCISE 12B.2

1 Consider the circle alongside with diameter PQ.

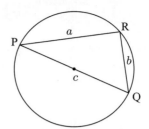

   a What is the measure of $P\widehat{R}Q$?

   b Write down an equation relating a, b, and c.

2 Find x:

a

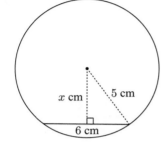

b

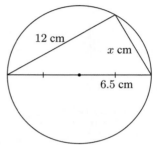

c

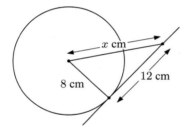

3 The chord of a circle is 8 cm long. The closest point of the chord to the centre of the circle is 3 cm away from it. Find the radius of the circle.

4 Find the radius of this semi-circle.

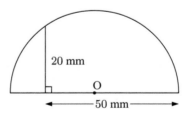

5 The doorway alongside is rectangular at the bottom with a semi-circular arch at the top.

   a Find the radius of the semi-circle.

   b Find the length of line segment AC.

   c Hence find the length of the line segment AB which passes through the circle's centre C.

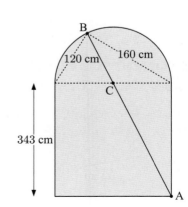

C   THE CONVERSE OF PYTHAGORAS' THEOREM

There are many situations in real life where we need to know whether an angle is a right angle. For example, to make sure that this flag pole is not leaning to one side, we need to determine whether triangle ABC is right angled at B.

If we know all the side lengths of a triangle, we can determine whether the triangle is right angled by using the **converse of Pythagoras' theorem**.

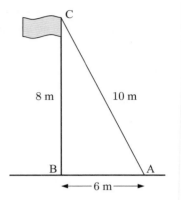

If a triangle has sides of length a, b, and c units and $a^2 + b^2 = c^2$, then the triangle is right angled.

GEOMETRY PACKAGE

Example 11   ◀)) Self Tutor

The dimensions marked on this triangle are correct, but the triangle is not drawn to scale. Is it a right angled triangle?

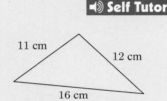

The two shorter sides have lengths 11 cm and 12 cm.

Now $11^2 + 12^2 = 121 + 144 = 265$

whereas $16^2 = 256$

Since $11^2 + 12^2 \neq 16^2$,   the triangle is not right angled.

EXERCISE 12C

1   The following figures are not drawn accurately. Which of the triangles are right angled?

a

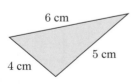

6 cm
5 cm
4 cm

b

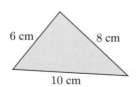

6 cm   8 cm
10 cm

c

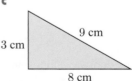

9 cm
3 cm
8 cm

d

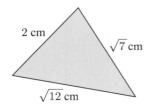

2 cm
$\sqrt{7}$ cm
$\sqrt{12}$ cm

e

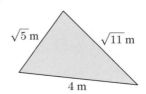

$\sqrt{5}$ m $\sqrt{11}$ m
4 m

f

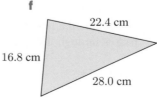

22.4 cm
16.8 cm
28.0 cm

2 The following triangles are not drawn accurately. If any of them is right angled, find the vertex where the right angle occurs.

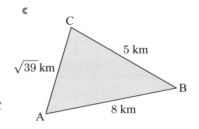

a

$\sqrt{2}$ cm, 1 cm, $\sqrt{3}$ cm with vertices A, B, C

b

5 m, 13 m, 12 m with vertices A, B, C

c

5 km, $\sqrt{39}$ km, 8 km with vertices C, A, B

3 Explain how the converse of Pythagoras' theorem can be used to test for right angled corners in a building frame.

INVESTIGATION 2   PYTHAGOREAN TRIPLES SPREADSHEET

A **Pythagorean triple** is a set of three integers which obeys the rule $a^2 + b^2 = c^2$.   **SPREADSHEET**

Well known Pythagorean triples include $\{3, 4, 5\}$, $\{5, 12, 13\}$, $\{7, 24, 25\}$, and $\{8, 15, 17\}$.

Formulae can be used to generate Pythagorean triples.

An example is $\{2n + 1, \; 2n^2 + 2n, \; 2n^2 + 2n + 1\}$ where n is a positive integer.

A spreadsheet can quickly generate sets of Pythagorean triples using such formulae.

What to do:

1 Open a new spreadsheet and enter the following:

	A	B	C	D
1	n	a	b	c
2	1	=2*A2+1	=2*A2^2+2*A2	=C2+1
3	=A2+1			
4	↓			
5		↓ fill down ↓		↓

   a in column A, the values of n for $n = 1, 2, 3, 4, 5, ...$

   b in column B, the values of $2n + 1$

   c in column C, the values of $2n^2 + 2n$

   d in column D, the values of $2n^2 + 2n + 1$.

2 Highlight the appropriate formulae and **fill down** to Row 11 to generate the first 10 sets of triples.

	A	B	C	D
1	n	a	b	c
2	1	3	4	5
3	2	5	12	13
4	3	7	24	25
5	4	9	40	41

3 Check that each set of numbers is indeed a triple by finding $a^2 + b^2$ and c^2.

4 Your final task is to prove that $\{2n+1, \; 2n^2+2n, \; 2n^2+2n+1\}$ will produce a Pythagorean triple for all positive integer values of n.

   Hint: Let $a = 2n + 1$, $b = 2n^2 + 2n$, and $c = 2n^2 + 2n + 1$, then simplify
$c^2 - b^2 = (2n^2 + 2n + 1)^2 - (2n^2 + 2n)^2$ using the *difference of two squares* factorisation.

D   PROBLEM SOLVING

Right angled triangles occur frequently in **problem solving**. Any time a right angle is present you should check whether Pythagoras' theorem can be used and whether it is beneficial.

Example 12   ◀ᴺ) **Self Tutor**

A rectangular gate is 3 m wide and has a 3.5 m diagonal. How high is the gate?

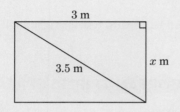

Let x m be the height of the gate.

Now $(3.5)^2 = x^2 + 3^2$ {Pythagoras}

$\therefore$ $12.25 = x^2 + 9$

$\therefore$ $3.25 = x^2$

$\therefore$ $x = \sqrt{3.25}$ {as $x > 0$}

$\therefore$ $x \approx 1.803$

The gate is about 1.80 m high.

EXERCISE 12D

1 Find, correct to 3 significant figures, the value of x in:

a   **b**   **c**

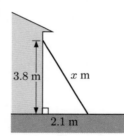

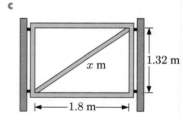

2 The size of a movie screen is the length across its diagonal. The largest screen in the world is at LG IMAX, Sydney, measuring 35.73 m across and 29.42 m high. What is its size?

Example 13   ◀ᴺ) **Self Tutor**

Bjorn suspects that the corner A of a
tennis court is not a right angle.
With a measuring tape he finds that
AB = 3.72 m, BC = 4.56 m, and
AC = 2.64 m.
Is Bjorn's suspicion correct?

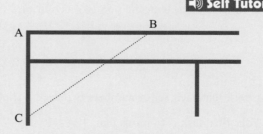

$$BC^2 = 4.56^2 \approx 20.8$$
$$\text{and}\quad AB^2 + AC^2 = 3.72^2 + 2.64^2 \approx 20.8 \quad \text{\{to 3 significant figures\}}$$

Within the limitations of accuracy of the measurements, the angle at A is a right angle.

3 A surveyor is trying to mark out a rectangle. She measures the sides to be 13.3 m and 17.9 m, and a diagonal to be 22.3 m. Is the angle between the sides a right angle?

4 After takeoff, an aeroplane climbs at a constant angle until it reaches an altitude of 12 000 m. If the flight distance reads 89 km, how far has the plane travelled across the land?

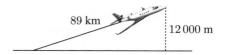

89 km

12 000 m

Example 14   🔊 **Self Tutor**

Kimi leaves point A and heads east for 5 km. He then heads south for 6 km. How far is he now from point A?

5 km N

A □ ⋯▸E

x km   6 km

S

$x^2 = 5^2 + 6^2$ {Pythagoras}

∴ $x^2 = 61$

∴ $x = \sqrt{61}$ {as $x > 0$}

∴ $x \approx 7.81$

So, Kimi is 7.81 km from A.

---

5 A schooner sails 46 km north then 74 km east.

  a Draw a fully labelled diagram of the ship's course.

  b How far is the ship from its starting point?

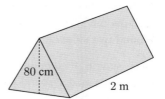

6 A runner is 22 km east and 15 km south of her starting point.

  a How far is she from her starting point?

  b How long would it take her to return to her starting point in a direct line if she can run at 10 km h^{-1}?

7 Find the length of roof truss AB.

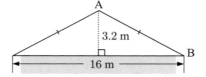

A

3.2 m

□   B

16 m

8 Rohan is building a rabbit hutch in the shape of an equilateral triangular prism.

  a If the height is 80 cm, how long are the sides of the triangle?

  b Find the area of ground covered by the rabbit hutch.

80 cm

2 m

9 Find the attic height AB.

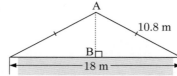

A

10.8 m

B□

18 m

Example 15   ◀) **Self Tutor**

A man and his son leave point A at the same time. The man cycles due east at 16 km h^{-1}. His son cycles due south at 20 km h^{-1}.

How far apart are they after 4 hours?

After 4 hours the man has travelled $4 \times 16 = 64$ km and his son has travelled $4 \times 20 = 80$ km.

Thus $x^2 = 64^2 + 80^2$ {Pythagoras}

$\therefore \quad x^2 = 4096 + 6400$

$\therefore \quad x^2 = 10\,496$

$\therefore \quad x = \sqrt{10\,496}$ {as $x > 0$}

$\therefore \quad x \approx 102.4$

They are about 102 km apart after 4 hours.

10   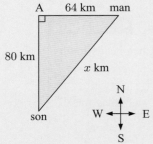   Captain Jack and Captain Will leave Bridgetown at the same time. Jack sails due east at a constant speed of 15 km h^{-1}, and Will sails due south at a constant speed of 19 km h^{-1}.

a   How far has each captain travelled after two hours?

b   Find the distance between them 2 hours after leaving Bridgetown.

11   A projector is 40 m from the middle of a screen which is 15 m high. How much further away from the projector is the top edge than the centre of the screen?

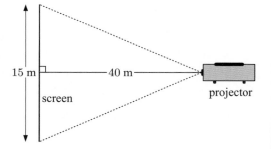

12   Julia walks to school across the diagonal of a rectangular field. The diagonal is 85 metres long. One side of the field is 42 m.

a   Find the length of the other side of the field.

b   By how much is it shorter to walk across the diagonal, than around two sides?

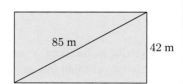

13   A power station P supplies two towns A and B with electricity. New underground power lines to each town are required. The towns are connected by a straight highway through A and B, and the power station is 42 km from this highway.

a   Find the length of power line required from P to each town.

b   Find the total cost of the new power line given that each kilometre will cost $2350.

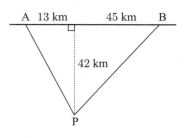

14

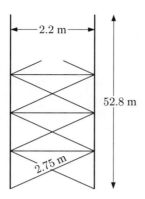

A steel frame office building has the framework section shown in the diagram. The vertical supports are 2.2 m apart and 52.8 m high. If the diagonal braces have length 2.75 m, how many are needed for this section?

15 The diagram shows various measurements of a field. Calculate the perimeter of the field to the nearest metre.

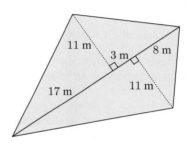

16

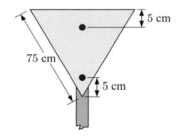

A traffic sign is an equilateral triangle with edges 75 cm long. It will be fixed to its post with bolts 5 cm in from the top and bottom of the sign. How far apart will the bolts be?

17 Queensville is 210 km north of Rosebank and 130 km west of Springfield. There is a highway direct from Rosebank to Springfield with speed limit 90 km h^{-1}, and a train line from Rosebank through Queensville to Springfield.

  a How long will it take to drive from Rosebank to Springfield, travelling at the speed limit the whole way?

  b If the train travels at an average of 135 km h^{-1}, how long does the Rosebank - Queensville - Springfield journey take?

  c Which option is quicker?

18

Police Officer Francisca has had her bicycle stolen. She walks north from the police station trying to find it. Officer Gisela also searches by travelling west of the station, and she goes at twice the speed because her bicycle wasn't stolen. After 2 hours, their walkie-talkies are just out of their 12 km range. How fast did each officer travel?

THEORY OF KNOWLEDGE

Pythagoras of Samos was an Ionian Greek philosopher and mathematician in the late 6th century BC. He was an influential teacher and leader of the group called the **Pythagoreans**, a secretive sect who believed that everything was related to mathematics and numbers.

Legend says that Pythagoras discovered his theorem while observing the tiled palace floor as he waited for an audience with the ruler Polycrates.

However, Pythagoras did not discover the theorem that bears his name. We know this because it was used previously by the Babylonians and Indians. In fact, there is no written evidence that Pythagoras proved or even used his theorem.

Pythagoras

Pythagoras' theorem can be proved geometrically by observing two different subdivisions of a square:

Proof: Suppose the square PQRS is subdivided in two different ways, as shown below. All of the triangles are right angled, and congruent to one another.

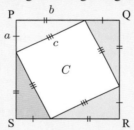

We see that area C = area A + area B

$$\therefore \quad c^2 = a^2 + b^2$$

There are over 400 known proofs of Pythagoras' theorem, most of which are algebraic. One of them is attributed to US President **James Abram Garfield**:

Proof:

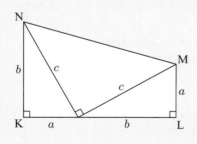

KLMN is a trapezium with area

$$= \left(\frac{a+b}{2}\right) \times (a+b)$$

$$= \frac{(a+b)^2}{2}$$

$$= \frac{a^2 + 2ab + b^2}{2} \quad \text{.... (1)}$$

However, by adding the areas of the three triangles, we see the area

$$= \tfrac{1}{2}ab + \tfrac{1}{2}ab + \tfrac{1}{2}c^2$$

$$= \frac{2ab + c^2}{2} \quad \text{.... (2)}$$

Comparing (1) and (2), we find $c^2 = a^2 + b^2$.

1 If something has not yet been proven, does that make it untrue?

2 Is the state of an idea being true or false dependent on our ability to prove it?

3 Can a logical argument without using symbols, be considered as mathematics?

4 In what other fields of human endeavour is it necessary to establish truth?

ACTIVITY   SHORTEST DISTANCE

A and B are two homesteads which are 4 km and 3 km away from a water pipeline. M and N are the nearest points on the pipeline to A and B respectively, and MN = 6 km. The cost of running a spur pipeline across country from the pipeline is $3000 per km, and the cost of a pump is $8000.

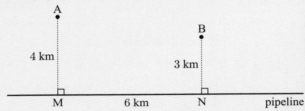

Your task is to determine the most economic way of pumping the water from the pipeline to A and B. Should you use two pumps located at M and N, or just one pump located somewhere between M and N? One pump would be satisfactory to pump sufficient water to meet the needs of both homesteads.

What to do:

1 Find the total cost of the pumps and pipelines if two pumps are used, one at M and the other at N.

2 Suppose one pump is used and it is located at P, the midpoint of MN.

   a Find PA and PB to the nearest metre.

   b Find the total cost of the pipeline and pump in this case.

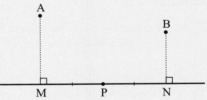

3   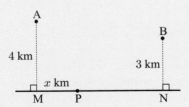

Suppose P is x km from M.

   a Show that PA + PB is given by $\sqrt{x^2 + 16} + \sqrt{x^2 - 12x + 45}$ km.

   b Use a **spreadsheet** to find PA + PB for $x = 0.1, 0.2, 0.3, ..., 5.9$.

4 Your spreadsheet could look like:

   a For what value of x is PA + PB least?

   b Use your spreadsheet to calculate the value of x that minimises PA + PB, correct to 3 decimal places.

5 Determine whether it is more economical to use two pumps at M and N, or one pump between M and N.

	A	B	C
	x-values	PA+PB	
1			
2	0.1	10.620	
3	0.2	10.535	
4	0.3	10.453	

E   THREE-DIMENSIONAL PROBLEMS

When we deal with three-dimensional objects, it is common to find right angled triangles. We can use Pythagoras' theorem in the normal way by looking for right angled triangles with two known lengths.

Michael's coffee mug is 90 mm high and 73 mm in diameter. It is filled to the brim with steaming hot coffee. Michael does not like sugar, but he always stirs in his milk. What is the minimum length stirrer Michael needs so that if he drops it in, it will not disappear in the coffee?

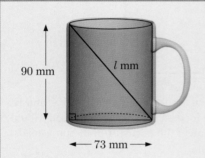

Let the stirrer have length l mm.

If the stirrer fits exactly in the mug, we have a right angled triangle.

By Pythagoras, $l^2 = 73^2 + 90^2$

$\therefore \ l = \sqrt{(73^2 + 90^2)}$ {as $l > 0$}

$\therefore \ l \approx 115.9$ mm

So, the stirrer must be at least 116 mm long.

EXERCISE 12E

1   An ice cream cone is 8 cm tall and its slant height is 10 cm. Find the radius of the circle at the top of the cone.

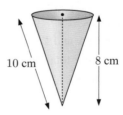

2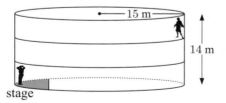

An actor stands at the back of the stage of Shakespeare's Globe theatre, which is cylindrical. How far must his voice reach so that he can be heard by the audience member furthest away from him?

3   A cylindrical soft drink can is 8 cm wide and 12 cm high, with a hole in the middle of the top for the straw. How long must the straw be so that all of the soft drink can be reached, and there is 2 cm of straw sticking out at the top?

4 A test tube consists of a cylindrical section which is 15 cm long, and a hemispherical end with diameter 3 cm. Find the direct distance from any point R on the rim of the test tube, to the bottom of the test tube B.

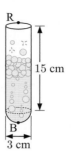

Example 17   ◀ᴐ **Self Tutor**

Skyways Airlines has the policy that passengers cannot carry on luggage with diagonal measurement of more than 56 cm. Katie's bag is 40 cm × 30 cm × 25 cm. Is she allowed to carry it on board the plane?

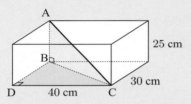

We first consider the distance BC across the base.

By Pythagoras, $BC^2 = 40^2 + 30^2$

Now triangle ABC is right angled at B.

> In many three-dimensional problems we need to use Pythagoras' theorem *twice*.

$\therefore \ AC^2 = AB^2 + BC^2$ {Pythagoras}

$\therefore \ AC^2 = 25^2 + 40^2 + 30^2$

$\therefore \ AC = \sqrt{(25^2 + 40^2 + 30^2)}$ {as $AC > 0$}

$\therefore \ AC \approx 55.9$ cm

So, Katie is allowed to carry her bag on the plane.

---

5 A cube has sides of length 2 cm. Find the length of a diagonal of the cube.

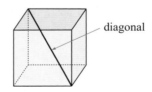
diagonal

6 A room is 6 m by 5 m and has a height of 3 m. Find the distance from a corner point on the floor to the opposite corner of the ceiling.

7 A cube has sides of length 2 m. B is at the centre of one face, and A is an opposite vertex. Find the direct distance from A to B.

8 Answer the **Opening Problem** on page **350**.

9 A parcel wrapped in string has the dimensions shown. M is the midpoint of AD, and N is the midpoint of CG. Find the distance between:

    a C and E   **b** F and M   **c** M and N.

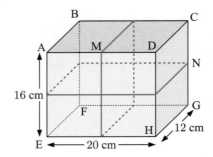

Example 18   ◀ϟ **Self Tutor**

A pyramid of height 40 m has a square base with edges 50 m long.

Determine the length of the slant edges.

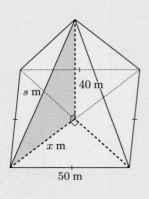

Let a slant edge have length s m.

Let half a diagonal have length x m.

Using

$$x^2 + x^2 = 50^2 \quad \text{\{Pythagoras\}}$$
$$\therefore \ 2x^2 = 2500$$
$$\therefore \ x^2 = 1250$$

Using

$$s^2 = x^2 + 40^2 \quad \text{\{Pythagoras\}}$$
$$\therefore \ s^2 = 1250 + 1600$$
$$\therefore \ s^2 = 2850$$
$$\therefore \ s = \sqrt{2850} \quad \text{\{as } s > 0\text{\}}$$
$$\therefore \ s \approx 53.4$$

So, each slant edge is about 53.4 m long.

---

10 The pyramid shown is 12 cm high, and has a rectangular base.

    a Find the distance AM.

    b Find the length AE of the slant edges.

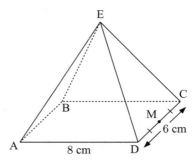

11 A camping tent is 2 metres wide, 3 metres long, and 1.5 metres high. It has been decorated with diagonal stripes as illustrated. Find the length of each stripe.

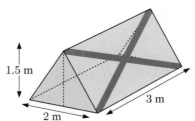

12

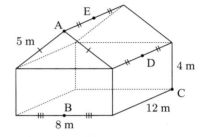

A square-based pyramid tent has a centre pole 1.6 m high, and edge poles 2.1 m long. What is the maximum possible height of a camper who sleeps along the edge of the tent?

13 For the structure alongside, find the distance between:

  a A and B   **b** A and C

  c B and E   **d** B and D

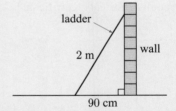

REVIEW SET 12A

1

How high is the roof above the walls in the roof structure shown?

2 A ladder is 2 m long. It leans against a wall so that it is 90 cm from the base of the wall.
How far up the wall does the ladder reach?

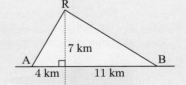

3

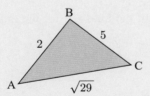

Show that this triangle is right angled and state which vertex is the right angle.

4 A softball diamond has sides of length 30 m. Determine the distance the catcher must throw the ball from the home base to reach second base.

5 A pyramid of height 30 m has a square base with edges 40 m long. Determine the length of the slant edges.

6 A reservoir R supplies two towns Alton and Barnsville with water. The pipelines from R to each town are being replaced to cope with increased demand. The towns are connected by a straight road. The reservoir is 7 km from this road.

  a Find the distances AR and BR to the nearest metre.

  b Find the total cost of the new pipelines given that each 100 m will cost €2550.

7

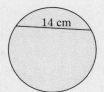

A pipe runs diagonally across a roof 2.8 m high, 27.7 m long, and 10.4 m wide. How long is the pipe?

8 Kate and Ric leave home at the same time. Kate walks north at 5 km h^{-1} and Ric walks west at 6.5 km h^{-1}.

   a How far do they each walk in 30 minutes?

   b How far apart are they at that time?

9

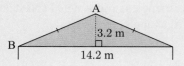

A 14 cm long cut is made across a circular pizza. The shortest distance from the cut to the centre of the pizza is 9 cm. Find the radius of the pizza.

REVIEW SET 12B

1 A graduation certificate has a validation thread across one diagonal and around the edges. How much thread is required for each certificate?

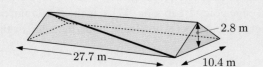

2

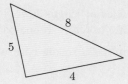

Find the length of the truss AB for the roof structure shown.

3 Is this triangle right angled?
Give evidence for your answer.

4 Will a 10 m long piece of timber fit in a rectangular shed of dimensions 8 m by 5 m by 3 m? Give evidence for your answer.

5

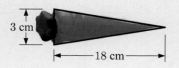

A carrot is 18 cm long with maximum diameter 3 cm. How long is a strip of its peel?

6

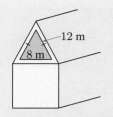

A chalet roof is shaped as shown. There is a triangular window at the front.

   a Find the height of the window.

   b Find the area of glass for the window.

7 In the local park there is a 50 m long slide running down the hill. From an overhead map, Nancy knows the slide covers a horizontal distance of 34 m. The platform of the slide is 1.5 m above the top of the hill. How high is the hill?

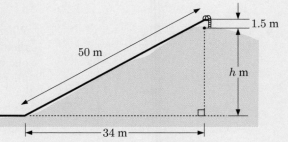

8 Eli thinks he has laid a rectangular slab of concrete for the floor of his toolshed. It measures 3.2 m long and 2.1 m wide. The diagonal measures 3.83 m. Check that Eli's concrete is rectangular.

9 A cubic iron grid has sides of length 10 m.
Find the length of a diagonal brace of the cube.

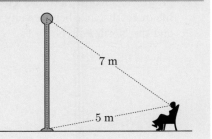

10 Find the length AC.

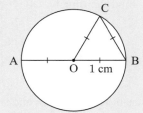

REVIEW SET 12C

1 As Margarita sits on the park bench, her eyes are 1 metre above the ground, 5 metres from the base of the lamp-post, and 7 metres from its top. Find the height of the lamp-post.

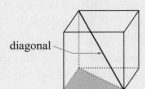

2

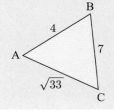

Show that the triangle alongside is right angled and state which vertex is the right angle.

3 Examine this tile pattern. Show that the sides of the largest square are twice as long as the sides of the smallest square.

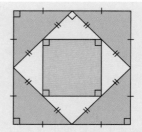

4

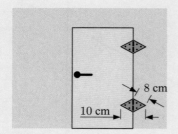

When a door is closed, its hinge is in the shape of a rhombus. The edges of the hinge are 8 cm long, and one of its diagonals is 10 cm long. Find the length of the other diagonal.

5 A soccer pitch is marked out on a field. To ensure it is rectangular, its dimensions are measured. It is 101.6 m long and 76.2 m wide, and the diagonal measures 127 m. Is the pitch rectangular?

6 Lisa leaves her friend's house and runs east for 900 m. She then turns south and runs until she arrives home. If Lisa's house is 1.5 km in a direct line from her friend's house, how far south did she run?

7 A rectangular box has the dimensions shown. B is an LED at the centre of the top face. Find the direct distance from A to B.

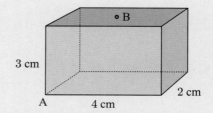

8 A symmetrical square-based pyramid has base edges 20 m and slant edges 25 m. Find the height of the pyramid.

9 A chord is 8 cm from the centre of a circle of radius 11 cm. Find the length of the chord.

10 A spherical world globe has a diameter of 30 cm. Find the direct distance between any point E on the equator and the North Pole N.

Chapter **13**

Coordinate geometry

Syllabus reference: 5.1

Contents:

OPENING PROBLEM

A city has two hospitals: Ridgehaven located at R(6, −9), and Sunport located at S(−8, 5).

Things to think about:

a Trish lives at T(4, 4). Which hospital is Trish closest to?

b Can you find the point midway between the hospitals?

c The city's planning council wants to define a 'boundary line' so that people will go to the hospital closest to them. Can you find the equation of this boundary line?

THEORY OF KNOWLEDGE

History shows that the two Frenchmen **René Descartes** and **Pierre de Fermat** arrived at the idea of **analytical geometry** at about the same time. Descartes' work *La Geometrie* was published first, in 1637, while Fermat's *Introduction to Loci* was not published until after his death.

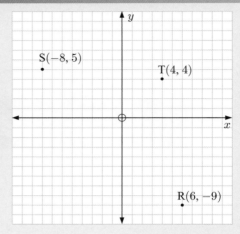

Pierre de Fermat

Today, they are considered the co-founders of this important branch of mathematics, which links algebra and geometry.

The initial approaches used by these mathematicians were quite opposite. Descartes began with a line or curve and then found the equation which described it. Fermat, to a large extent, started with an equation and investigated the shape of the curve it described.

René Descartes

Analytical geometry and its use of coordinates enabled **Isaac Newton** to later develop another important branch of mathematics called **calculus**. Newton humbly stated: *"If I have seen further than Descartes, it is because I have stood on the shoulders of giants."*

1 Are geometry and algebra two separate domains of knowledge?

2 Given that many mathematicians have contributed to the development of each major branch of mathematics, is it reasonable to say that mathematics *evolves*?

THE NUMBER PLANE

The position of any point in the **number plane** can be specified in terms of an **ordered pair** of numbers (x, y), where:

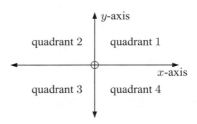

x is the **horizontal step** from a fixed point or **origin** O, and
y is the **vertical step** from O.

Once the origin O has been located, two perpendicular axes are drawn. The **x-axis** is horizontal and the **y-axis** is vertical. The axes divide the number plane into four **quadrants**.

The number plane is also known as either:

- the **2-dimensional plane**, or
- the **Cartesian plane**, named after **René Descartes**.

In the diagram, the point P is at (a, b).
a and b are referred to as the **coordinates** of P.
a is called the **x-coordinate**.
b is called the **y-coordinate**.

For example, the coordinates of the given points are:

$$A(4, 2)$$
$$B(0, 2)$$
$$C(-3, 1)$$
$$D(-1, 0)$$
$$E(1, -2).$$

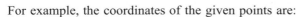

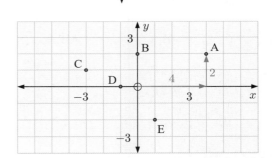

A. DISTANCE BETWEEN TWO POINTS

How can we find the distance d between points A$(1, 2)$ and B$(5, 4)$?

By drawing line segments AC and BC along the grid lines, we form a right angled triangle with hypotenuse AB.

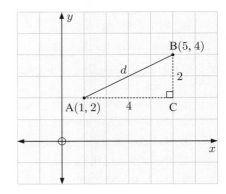

Using Pythagoras' theorem,

$$d^2 = 4^2 + 2^2$$
$$\therefore \ d^2 = 20$$
$$\therefore \ d = \sqrt{20} \qquad \{\text{as } d > 0\}$$

So, the distance between A and B is $\sqrt{20}$ units.

While this approach is effective, it is time-consuming because a diagram is needed.

To make the process quicker, we can develop a formula.

To go from A$(x_1,\ y_1)$ to B$(x_2,\ y_2)$, we find the

$$x\text{-step} = x_2 - x_1$$

and $y\text{-step} = y_2 - y_1.$

Using Pythagoras' theorem,

$$(AB)^2 = (x\text{-step})^2 + (y\text{-step})^2$$

$$\therefore\ \ AB = \sqrt{(x\text{-step})^2 + (y\text{-step})^2}$$

$$\therefore\ \ d = \sqrt{(x_2 - x_1)^2 + (y_2 - y_1)^2}.$$

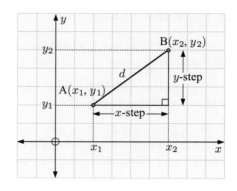

THE DISTANCE FORMULA

The distance d between two points $(x_1,\ y_1)$ and $(x_2,\ y_2)$ is given by

$$d = \sqrt{(x_2 - x_1)^2 + (y_2 - y_1)^2}.$$

Example 1	◀) Self Tutor

Find the distance between A$(6,\ 3)$ and B$(8,\ -2)$.

A$(6,\ 3)$ B$(8,\ -2)$ $AB = \sqrt{(8-6)^2 + (-2-3)^2}$

$\qquad\uparrow\ \uparrow\qquad\quad\uparrow\quad\ \uparrow$

$\quad x_1\ y_1\qquad\ x_2\ \ y_2$
$\qquad\qquad\qquad\qquad\ = \sqrt{2^2 + (-5)^2}$

$\qquad\qquad\qquad\qquad\ = \sqrt{4 + 25}$

$\qquad\qquad\qquad\qquad\ = \sqrt{29}$ units

The distance formula saves us having to graph the points each time we want to find a distance.

EXERCISE 13A

1   Find the distance from:

   a   A$(2,\ 6)$ to B$(3,\ 3)$

   c   M$(2,\ 4)$ to N$(-1,\ -3)$

   e   R$(3,\ -2)$ to S$(5,\ -2)$

   g   W$(-4,\ 0)$ to X$(0,\ 3)$

   b   C$(-2,\ 3)$ to D$(1,\ 5)$

   d   O$(0,\ 0)$ to P$(-2,\ 4)$

   f   T$(0,\ 3)$ to U$(2,\ -1)$

   h   Y$(-1,\ -4)$ to Z$(-3,\ 3)$.

2   On the map alongside, each grid unit represents 1 km.

   Find the distance between:

   a   the lighthouse and the tree

   b   the jetty and the lighthouse

   c   the well and the tree

   d   the lighthouse and the well.

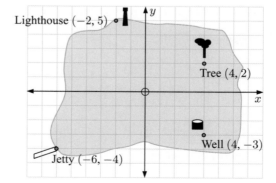

Example 2   ◀) **Self Tutor**

The points A(2, −1), B(5, 1), and C(0, 2) form a triangle ABC.

  a Use the distance formula to classify the triangle as equilateral, isosceles, or scalene.

  b Does the triangle have a right angle?

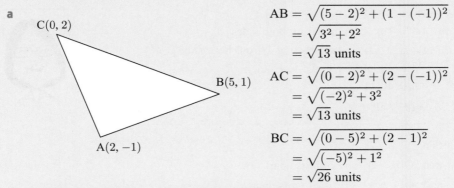

a

$$AB = \sqrt{(5-2)^2 + (1-(-1))^2}$$
$$= \sqrt{3^2 + 2^2}$$
$$= \sqrt{13} \text{ units}$$

$$AC = \sqrt{(0-2)^2 + (2-(-1))^2}$$
$$= \sqrt{(-2)^2 + 3^2}$$
$$= \sqrt{13} \text{ units}$$

$$BC = \sqrt{(0-5)^2 + (2-1)^2}$$
$$= \sqrt{(-5)^2 + 1^2}$$
$$= \sqrt{26} \text{ units}$$

Since AB = AC but not BC, triangle ABC is isosceles.

b $AB^2 + AC^2 = 13 + 13$
$$= 26$$
$$= BC^2$$

Using the converse of Pythagoras' theorem, triangle ABC is right angled.
The right angle is opposite the longest side, so the right angle is at A.

---

3 Use the distance formula to classify triangle ABC as either equilateral, isosceles, or scalene.

  a A(−1, 0), B(−2, 3), C(−5, 4)   **b** A(−2, −4), B(1, 4), C(2, −3)

  c A(0, 1), B(0, −1), C(−$\sqrt{3}$, 0)   **d** A(0, −4), B($\sqrt{3}$, 1), C(3$\sqrt{3}$, −5)

4 Use the distance formula to see if the following triangles are right angled. If they are, state the vertex where the right angle is.

  a A(1, −1), B(−1, 2), C(7, 3)   **b** A(−1, 2), B(3, 4), C(5, 0)

  c A(−2, 3), B(−5, 4), C(1, 2)   **d** A(5, 4), B(−4, 6), C(−3, 2)

5 Fully classify the triangles formed by the following points:

  a A(−4, 5), B(3, 4), C(8, −1)

  b A(2, −5), B(−2, 2), C(−4, −1)

  c A(−2, 1), B(−3, 4), C(1, 2)

  d A($\sqrt{3}$, −1), B(0, 2), C(−$\sqrt{3}$, −1)

Classify the triangles according to side length *and* the presence of a right angle.

Example 3   ◀)) **Self Tutor**

Find q given that P$(-2, 4)$ and Q$(-1, q)$ are $\sqrt{10}$ units apart.

From P to Q, the x-step $= -1 - (-2) = 1$

and the y-step $= q - 4$

$\therefore \quad \sqrt{1^2 + (q - 4)^2} = \sqrt{10}$

$\therefore \quad 1 + (q - 4)^2 = 10$ {squaring both sides}

$\therefore \quad (q - 4)^2 = 9$ {subtracting 1 from both sides}

$\therefore \quad q - 4 = \pm 3$ {if $X^2 = k$ then $X = \pm\sqrt{k}$}

$\therefore \quad q = 4 \pm 3$

$\therefore \quad q = 1$ or 7

This example has two possible solutions. Draw a diagram to see why this is so.

6   Find q given that:

   a P$(2, 1)$ and Q$(q, -3)$ are 5 units apart

   b P$(q, 6)$ and Q$(-2, 1)$ are $\sqrt{29}$ units apart

   c P(q, q) is $\sqrt{8}$ units from the origin

   d Q$(3, q)$ is equidistant from A$(-1, 5)$ and B$(6, 4)$.

7   Classify the triangle formed by the points A(a, b), B$(a, -b)$, and C$(1, 0)$ as scalene, isosceles, or equilateral.

B   **MIDPOINTS**

The point M halfway between points A and B is called the **midpoint** of line segment AB.

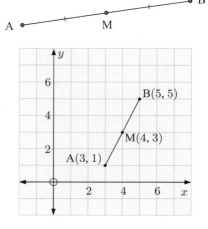

Consider the points A$(3, 1)$ and B$(5, 5)$. M is at $(4, 3)$ on the line segment connecting A and B.

Using the distance formula, we can see that

$\text{AM} = \sqrt{(4 - 3)^2 + (3 - 1)^2} = \sqrt{5}$ units, and

$\text{MB} = \sqrt{(5 - 4)^2 + (5 - 3)^2} = \sqrt{5}$ units.

So, M is the midpoint of AB.

The x-coordinate of M is the *average* of the x-coordinates of A and B.

The y-coordinate of M is the *average* of the y-coordinates of A and B.

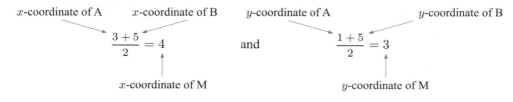

x-coordinate of A x-coordinate of B y-coordinate of A y-coordinate of B

$$\dfrac{3 + 5}{2} = 4 \qquad \text{and} \qquad \dfrac{1 + 5}{2} = 3$$

x-coordinate of M y-coordinate of M

THE MIDPOINT FORMULA

The coordinates of the midpoint of the line segment with endpoints (x_1, y_1) and (x_2, y_2) are

$$\left(\frac{x_1 + x_2}{2}, \frac{y_1 + y_2}{2} \right).$$

Example 4 ◀) **Self Tutor**

Given $A(-1, 3)$ and $B(5, -2)$, find the coordinates of the midpoint M of AB.

The x-coordinate of M	The y-coordinate of M
$= \dfrac{-1 + 5}{2}$	$= \dfrac{3 + (-2)}{2}$
$= \frac{4}{2}$	$= \frac{1}{2}$
$= 2$	$\therefore$ the midpoint of AB is M$(2, \frac{1}{2})$.

EXERCISE 13B

1 **a** Use the distance formula to check that:

  i M is the midpoint of AB

  ii N is the midpoint of CD.

b Use the midpoint formula to check your answers to **a**.

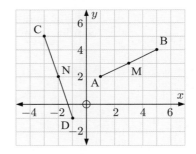

2

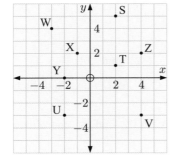

Using the diagram only, find the coordinates of the midpoint of the line segment:

a ST	**b** UV
c WX	**d** YZ
e SV	**f** UT
g YT	**h** TV

3 Find the coordinates of the midpoint of the line segment that joins:

  a $(2, 5)$ and $(4, 7)$ **b** $(1, 6)$ and $(4, 2)$

  c $(0, 3)$ and $(2, 0)$ **d** $(3, -2)$ and $(3, 2)$

  e $(-1, 4)$ and $(2, 2)$ **f** $(0, -3)$ and $(-2, 5)$

  g $(-4, -1)$ and $(3, -2)$ **h** $(1, 0)$ and $(-6, 8)$.

Example 5

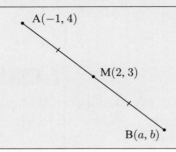

◀) **Self Tutor**

M is the midpoint of AB. If A is $(-1, 4)$ and M is $(2, 3)$, find the coordinates of B.

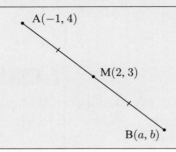

Let B have coordinates (a, b).

$$\therefore \quad \frac{a + (-1)}{2} = 2 \quad \text{and} \quad \frac{b + 4}{2} = 3$$

$$\therefore \quad a - 1 = 4 \quad \text{and} \quad b + 4 = 6$$

$$\therefore \quad a = 5 \quad \text{and} \quad b = 2$$

So, B is the point $(5, 2)$.

4 M is the midpoint of AB. Find the coordinates of B if:

   a A is $(1, 3)$ and M is $(2, -1)$

   b A is $(2, 1)$ and M is $(0, 2)$

   c A is $(-2, 1)$ and M is $(-1\frac{1}{2}, 3)$

   d A is $(3, -2)$ and M is $(3\frac{1}{2}, -2)$

   e A is $(0, 0)$ and M is $(2, -\frac{1}{2})$

   f A is $(-3, \frac{1}{2})$ and M is $(0, 0)$.

Example 6

◀) **Self Tutor**

M is the midpoint of AB. Use *equal steps* to find the coordinates of B, given A is $(-4, 3)$ and M is $(-1, 2)$.

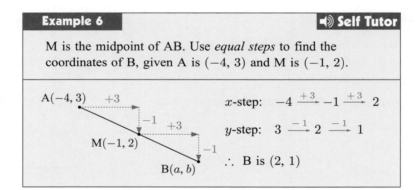

x-step: $-4 \xrightarrow{+3} -1 \xrightarrow{+3} 2$

y-step: $3 \xrightarrow{-1} 2 \xrightarrow{-1} 1$

$\therefore$ B is $(2, 1)$

5 Check your answers to **4a** and **4b** using equal steps.

6 P is the midpoint of IJ. Find the coordinates of I if:

   a P is $(2, -6)$ and J is $(4, -3)$

   b P is $(0, -2)$ and J is $(-5, 1)$.

7 PQ is the diameter of a circle, centre C. If P is $(4, -7)$ and Q is $(-2, -3)$, find the coordinates of C.

8 AB is a diameter of a circle, centre $(3\frac{1}{2}, -1)$. Given that B is $(2, 0)$, find the coordinates of A.

9 Torvald gets into a rowboat at A$(1, 2)$ on one side of a circular lake. He rows in a straight line towards the other side. He stops in the middle of the lake for a rest, at M$(-2, 3)$.

   a What are the coordinates of the point Torvald is aiming for?

   b If distances are in km, how much further does he have to row?

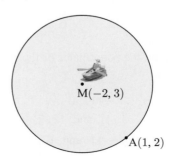

10

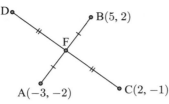

A flagpole at F is held by four wires pegged into the ground at A, B, C and D. Opposite pegs are the same distance away from the pole. Find the coordinates of D.

11 Molly the cat stands at $A(-1, -2)$, watching in fear as Susan and Sandra throw water balloons at each other. Susan is at $B(2, 3)$, and Sandra is at $C(0, 4)$. The two girls throw at the same time, and their balloons collide and explode midway between them. Units are given in metres.

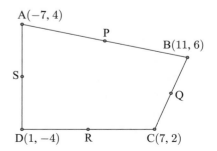

   a Find the coordinates of the explosion point.

   b How far is Molly from the explosion?

Example 7 ◀)) **Self Tutor**

Use midpoints to find the fourth vertex of the given parallelogram:

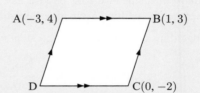

Since ABCD is a parallelogram, the diagonals bisect each other.

∴ the midpoint of DB is the same as the midpoint of AC.

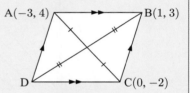

If D is (a, b), then $\dfrac{a+1}{2} = \dfrac{-3+0}{2}$ and $\dfrac{b+3}{2} = \dfrac{4+(-2)}{2}$

$$\therefore \quad a + 1 = -3 \quad \text{and} \quad b + 3 = 2$$
$$\therefore \quad a = -4 \quad \text{and} \quad b = -1$$

So, D is $(-4, -1)$.

---

12 Use midpoints to find the fourth vertex of the given parallelograms:

  a

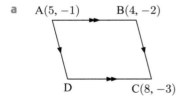

  b

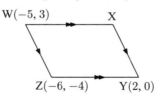

  c

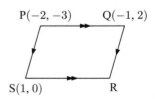

13 An inaccurate sketch of quadrilateral ABCD is given. P, Q, R, and S are the midpoints of AB, BC, CD, and DA respectively.

  a Find the coordinates of:

    i P   **ii** Q   **iii** R   **iv** S

  b Find the length of:

    i PQ   **ii** QR   **iii** RS   **iv** SP

  c What can be deduced about quadrilateral PQRS from **b**?

GRADIENT

Consider the following lines. Which do you think is steepest?

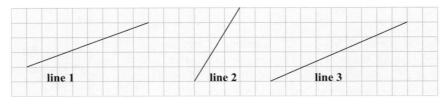

We can see that line 2 rises much faster than the other two lines, so line 2 is steepest. However, most people would find it hard to tell which of lines 1 and 3 is steeper just by looking at them. We therefore need a more precise way to measure the steepness of a line.

> The **gradient** of a line is a measure of its steepness.

To calculate the gradient of a line, we first choose any two distinct points on the line. We can move from one point to the other by making a positive **horizontal step** followed by a **vertical step**.

The gradient is calculated by dividing the vertical step by the horizontal step.

$$\text{The } \textbf{gradient} \text{ of a line} = \frac{\text{vertical step}}{\text{horizontal step}} \quad \text{or} \quad \frac{y\text{-step}}{x\text{-step}}.$$

If the line is sloping upwards, the vertical step will be positive.

So, lines like

   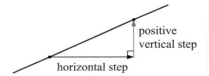

are upwards sloping and have **positive gradients**.

If the line is sloping downwards, the vertical step will be negative.

So, lines like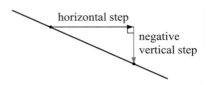

are downwards sloping and have **negative gradients**.

For lines with the same horizontal step, as the lines get steeper the vertical step increases. This results in a higher gradient.

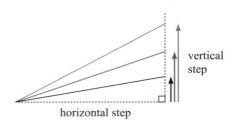

Example 8   🔊 **Self Tutor**

Find the gradient of each line segment:

a	gradient	b	gradient	c	gradient	d	gradient $= \frac{3}{0}$
	$= \frac{2}{1}$		$= \frac{-1}{3}$		$= \frac{0}{4}$		which is
	$= 2$		$= -\frac{1}{3}$		$= 0$		undefined

From **Example 8** we can see that:

- the gradient of **horizontal** lines is **0**
- the gradient of **vertical** lines is **undefined**.

EXERCISE 13C.1

1 Find the gradient of each line segment:

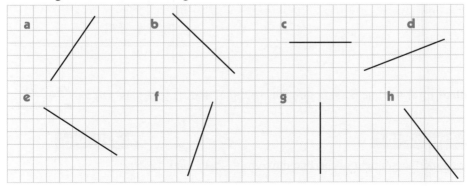

2 On grid paper, draw a line segment with gradient:

   a $\frac{3}{4}$ **b** -2 **c** 4 **d** $-\frac{1}{4}$ **e** 0 **f** $\frac{4}{7}$

3 Consider these line segments:

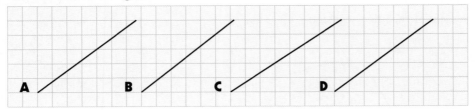

a Which two lines have the same gradient?   **b** Which line is steepest?

Example 9   ◀)) **Self Tutor**

Draw a line through $(1, 3)$ with gradient $-\frac{1}{2}$.

Plot the point $(1, 3)$.

The gradient $= \dfrac{y\text{-step}}{x\text{-step}} = \dfrac{-1}{2}$

$\therefore$ let y-step $= -1$, x-step $= 2$.

We use these steps to find another point and draw the line through these points.

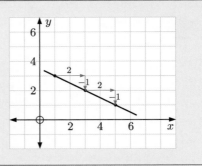

---

4 On the same set of axes, draw lines through $(2, 3)$ with gradients $\frac{1}{3}$, $\frac{3}{4}$, 2, and 4.

5 On the same set of axes, draw lines through $(-1, 2)$ with gradients 0, $-\frac{2}{5}$, -2, and -5.

THE GRADIENT FORMULA

If a line passes through $A(x_1, y_1)$ and $B(x_2, y_2)$, then the horizontal or x-step is $x_2 - x_1$, and the vertical or y-step is $y_2 - y_1$.

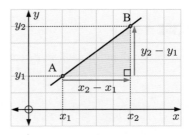

The **gradient** m of the line passing through (x_1, y_1) and (x_2, y_2) is $\quad m = \dfrac{y_2 - y_1}{x_2 - x_1}.$

Example 10   ◀)) **Self Tutor**

Find the gradient of the line through $(-2, 1)$ and $(2, 9)$.

$\underset{\substack{\uparrow \quad \uparrow \\ x_1 \; y_1}}{(-2, 1)} \quad \underset{\substack{\uparrow \quad \uparrow \\ x_2 \; y_2}}{(2, 9)}$

The gradient $m = \dfrac{y_2 - y_1}{x_2 - x_1} = \dfrac{9 - 1}{2 - (-2)}$

$\qquad = \dfrac{8}{4}$

$\qquad = 2$

EXERCISE 13C.2

1 Find the gradients of the line segments joining the following pairs of points:

    a $(1, 3)$ and $(6, 8)$ **b** $(-4, 5)$ and $(4, 3)$ **c** $(0, 0)$ and $(3, 5)$

    d $(5, 2)$ and $(2, 9)$ **e** $(1, -4)$ and $(-5, -2)$ **f** $(-3, 4)$ and $(2, 4)$

    g $(-6, 0)$ and $(0, -4)$ **h** $(-3, 5)$ and $(-3, 1)$ **i** $(-5, -8)$ and $(3, 4)$.

2 Find the gradient of line:

    a 1   **b** 2

    c 3   **d** 4

    e 5   **f** 6

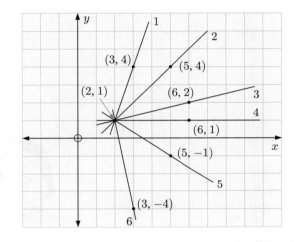

Example 11 ◀)) **Self Tutor**

Find a given that the line joining $P(a, -4)$ to $Q(1, 8)$ has gradient 3.

The gradient of PQ $= 3$, so $\dfrac{8 - (-4)}{1 - a} = 3$ {gradient formula}

$$\therefore \;\; 12 = 3(1 - a)$$
$$\therefore \;\; 12 = 3 - 3a$$
$$\therefore \;\; 3a = -9$$
$$\therefore \;\; a = -3$$

---

3 Find a given that the line joining:

    a $P(1, 5)$ to $Q(4, a)$ has gradient 2

    b $M(-2, a)$ to $N(0, -2)$ has gradient -4

    c $A(a, 8)$ to $B(-3, -4)$ has gradient $\frac{2}{3}$.

4 A line with gradient -2 passes through the point $(-1, 10)$. Determine where this line cuts the x-axis.

    Hint: A point on the x-axis has coordinates $(a, 0)$.

D   PARALLEL AND PERPENDICULAR LINES

PARALLEL LINES

The figure ABCD alongside is a trapezium, with AB parallel to DC.

DC has gradient $\frac{1}{3}$, and AB has gradient $\frac{3}{9} = \frac{1}{3}$.

Thus, AB and DC have the same gradient.

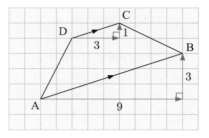

For lines l_1 and l_2 with gradients m_1 and m_2 respectively,

l_1 is parallel to $l_2 \Leftrightarrow m_1 = m_2$.

$\Leftrightarrow$ means "if and only if"

PERPENDICULAR LINES

The figure alongside is a square, so AB is perpendicular to BC.

AB has gradient $\frac{3}{2}$, and BC has gradient $\frac{-2}{3} = -\frac{2}{3}$.

The gradients are *negative reciprocals* of each other, and their product is $\frac{3}{2} \times -\frac{2}{3} = -1$.

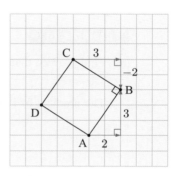

For non-vertical and non-horizontal lines l_1 and l_2 with gradients m_1 and m_2 respectively,

l_1 is perpendicular to $l_2 \Leftrightarrow m_1 \times m_2 = -1$.

Alternatively, we see that l_1 is perpendicular to l_2 if $m_1 = -\dfrac{1}{m_2}$.

Example 12	◀)) Self Tutor

If a line has gradient $\frac{2}{5}$, find the gradient of all lines:

  a parallel to the given line   **b** perpendicular to the given line.

  a The original line has gradient $\frac{2}{5}$, so the gradient of all parallel lines is also $\frac{2}{5}$.

  b The gradient of all perpendicular lines is $-\frac{5}{2}$.   {the negative reciprocal}

Example 13   ◀)) **Self Tutor**

Find t given that the line joining A$(1, 4)$ to B$(5, t)$ is perpendicular to a line with gradient $\frac{2}{3}$.

The gradient of AB $= -\dfrac{3}{2}$ {perpendicular to line with gradient $\frac{2}{3}$}

$\therefore \ \dfrac{t-4}{5-1} = -\dfrac{3}{2}$ {gradient formula}

$\therefore \ \dfrac{t-4}{4} = \dfrac{-6}{4}$ {writing fractions with equal denominators}

$\therefore \ t - 4 = -6$ {equating numerators}

$\therefore \ t = -2$

COLLINEAR POINTS

> Three or more points are **collinear** if they lie on the same straight line.

Consider the three collinear points A, B, and C, which all lie on the line l.

   gradient of AB = gradient of BC = gradient of l.

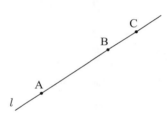

> Three points A, B, and C are **collinear** if:
>
>   gradient of AB = gradient of BC = gradient of AC

Example 14   ◀)) **Self Tutor**

Show that the points A$(-5, -3)$, B$(-1, -1)$, and C$(7, 3)$ are collinear.

The gradient of AB $= \dfrac{-1 - (-3)}{-1 - (-5)}$ The gradient of BC $= \dfrac{3 - (-1)}{7 - (-1)}$

$\qquad\qquad\qquad = \dfrac{2}{4} = \dfrac{1}{2}$ $\qquad\qquad\qquad = \dfrac{4}{8} = \dfrac{1}{2}$

AB and BC have equal gradients, and so A, B, and C are collinear.

EXERCISE 13D

1 Find the gradient of all lines   **i** parallel   **ii** perpendicular to a line with gradient:

   a $\frac{3}{4}$ **b** $\frac{1}{5}$ **c** 4 **d** -3 **e** $-\frac{3}{7}$ **f** $-4\frac{1}{2}$ **g** 0 **h** -1

2 The gradients of several pairs of lines are listed below.
   Which of the line pairs are perpendicular?

   a $2, \frac{1}{2}$ **b** $\frac{3}{5}, -\frac{3}{5}$ **c** $4, -\frac{1}{4}$ **d** $\frac{3}{4}, 1\frac{1}{3}$ **e** $-\frac{2}{5}, 2\frac{1}{2}$ **f** $-\frac{3}{8}, 2\frac{1}{3}$

3 Consider the line segments below.

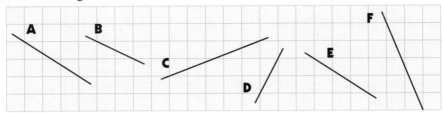

Identify any pairs of lines which are:

a parallel   **b** perpendicular.

4 Find t given that the line joining:

a C(2, 5) and D(4, t) is perpendicular to a line with gradient $\frac{1}{4}$

b X(-3, -1) and Y(t, 1) is perpendicular to a line with gradient $3\frac{1}{2}$.

5 Consider the points A(1, 2), B(-3, 0), C(5, 3), and D(3, k). Find k if:

a AB is parallel to CD   **b** AC is parallel to DB

c AB is perpendicular to CD   **d** AD is perpendicular to BC.

6 Consider the triangle ABC alongside.

a Find the length of each side. Hence, show that the triangle is right angled at B.

b Find the gradients of AB and BC. Hence verify that AB is perpendicular to BC.

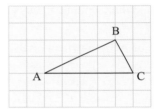

7 Determine whether the following sets of three points are collinear:

a A(-1, 7), B(1, 1), C(4, -8)   **b** P(-4, 2), Q(-1, 3), R(5, 6)

c R(-2, 1), S(4, 11), T(-5, -4)   **d** X(7, -5), Y(2, -1), Z(-6, 5)

8 Find n given that:

a A(-7, -8), B(-1, 1), and C(3, n) are collinear

b P(3, -11), Q(n, -2), and R(-5, 13) are collinear.

E   APPLICATIONS OF GRADIENT

We see gradients every day in the real world when we consider the slope of a hill or ramp.

The sign alongside indicates to drivers that the road ahead is steeply downhill. The gradient here has been presented as a percentage.

STEEP
DESCENT
12%

gradient $= -12\%$

$\qquad = -\frac{12}{100}$

$\qquad = -\frac{3}{25}$ ←— drop 3 m
$\qquad\qquad\quad$ ←— run 25 m

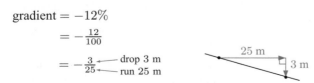

For every 25 metres we move horizontally, the road drops 3 metres vertically.

Example 15   ◀ᵖ) **Self Tutor**

The Oberon railway in Australia has a steep ascending section of track with gradient 4%.

a Interpret this gradient by writing it as a fraction in simplest form.

b If a train travels a horizontal distance of 500 metres at 4% gradient, what vertical distance will it climb?

a $4\% = \frac{4}{100} = \frac{1}{25}$

For every 25 metres we move horizontally, we rise 1 metre vertically.

b If the train travels 500 metres horizontally, it will rise $\frac{500}{25} = 20$ metres vertically.

Gradients are also important when we consider how quantities are related. If we draw the graph relating two quantities, the gradient of the line describes the **rate** at which one quantity changes relative to the other.

One of the most common examples of a rate is **speed**, which is the rate at which something is travelling.

For example, a cheetah sprinting after its prey can travel 20 m every second.

If we plot the distance the cheetah travels against the time taken, the gradient of the graph

$$= \frac{y\text{-step}}{x\text{-step}} = \frac{80}{4} = 20.$$

In comparison, the speed of the cheetah

$$= \frac{\text{distance travelled}}{\text{time taken}} = \frac{80 \text{ m}}{4 \text{ s}} = 20 \text{ m s}^{-1}.$$

So, the gradient of the graph gives the speed at which the cheetah is running.

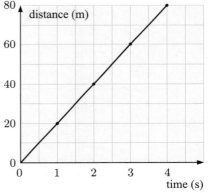

EXERCISE 13E

1 Interpret the following gradients by first writing them as fractions in simplest form:

    a 15% descent   **b** 2% ascent   **c** −55%   **d** 30%

2 The Lisbon Railway in Portugal ascends with a gradient of 13.5% in one section of the track.

    a Interpret this gradient.

    b What increase in altitude results from travelling 800 m horizontally?

3 A skateboard ramp has a constant gradient of 22%. Its base is 80 cm. How tall is the ramp?

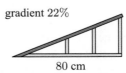

gradient 22%

80 cm

4

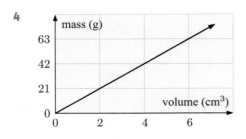

The graph alongside displays the mass of various volumes of silver.

    a Find the gradient of the line.

    b Interpret the gradient found in **a**.

    c   **i** What is the mass of 3 cm³ of silver?

        ii What is the volume of 100 g of silver?

5 A motorcyclist makes a day's journey and plots her progress on the graph alongside. Find:

   a the average speed for the whole trip

   b the average speed from

      i O to A   **ii** B to C

   c the time interval over which her average speed was greatest.

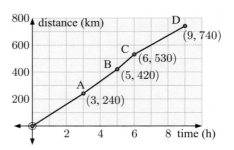

6

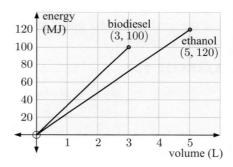

Harriet buys a car. Every 500 km she records how much she has spent on petrol and upkeep costs. She then plots the results on the graph shown.

   a How much did the car cost?

   b Find the gradient of AB. What does this represent?

   c Find the gradient of the straight line segment from A to D. What does this gradient mean?

7 The graphs alongside show the energy contained in different volumes of biodiesel and ethanol.

   a Find the gradient of each line.

   b Which type of fuel gives more energy per litre?

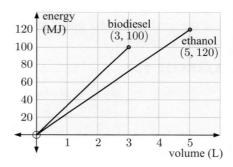

8 The graph alongside indicates the amount of tax paid for various incomes.

   a What does the value at A mean?

   b Find the gradients of the line segments AB and BC. What do these gradients indicate?

   c What do you expect to happen for people who earn more than $42 000 p.a.?

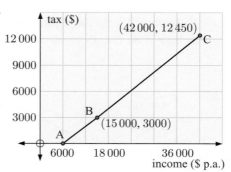

F | VERTICAL AND HORIZONTAL LINES

VERTICAL LINES

The graph opposite shows a vertical line passing through $(2, -1)$ and $(2, 3)$.

The gradient of the line is $\dfrac{3 - (-1)}{2 - 2} = \dfrac{4}{0}$ which is undefined.

All points on the line have x-coordinate 2, so the **equation** of the line is $x = 2$.

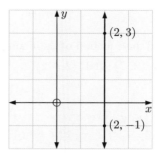

All **vertical** lines have equations of the form $x = a$ where a is a constant.

The gradient of a vertical line is **undefined**.

HORIZONTAL LINES

The graph opposite shows a horizontal line passing through $(-3, 1)$ and $(2, 1)$.

The gradient of the line is $\dfrac{1 - 1}{2 - (-3)} = \dfrac{0}{5} = 0$.

All points on the line have y-coordinate 1, so the **equation** of the line is $y = 1$.

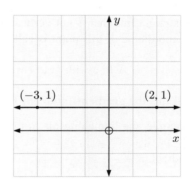

All **horizontal** lines have equations of the form $y = b$ where b is a constant.

The gradient of a horizontal line is **zero**.

EXERCISE 13F

1 Find the equations of the lines labelled **A** to **D**:

a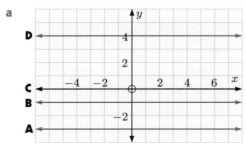

b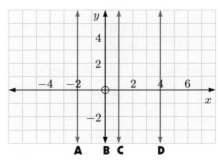

2 Identify as either a vertical or horizontal line and hence plot the graph of:

a $x = 1$ b $y = 2$ c $x = -4$ d $y = -2$

3 Find the equation of the:

    a horizontal line through $(3, -4)$

    c vertical line through $(-1, -3)$

    e x-axis

    b vertical line which cuts the x-axis at 5

    d horizontal line which cuts the y-axis at 2

    f y-axis.

4 Find the equation of the line passing through:

    a $(2, 2)$ and $(2, -2)$

    b $(2, -2)$ and $(-2, -2)$.

G   EQUATIONS OF LINES

> The **equation of a line** is an equation which connects the x and y values for every point on the line.

GRADIENT-INTERCEPT FORM

Every straight line that is not vertical will cut the y-axis at a single point.
The y-coordinate of this point is called the **y-intercept** of the line.

> A line with gradient m and y-intercept c has equation $y = mx + c.$

We call this the **gradient-intercept form** of the equation of a line.

For example, the line alongside has

    $\text{gradient} = \dfrac{y\text{-step}}{x\text{-step}} = \dfrac{-2}{3}$

    and its y-intercept is 2.

So, its equation is $y = -\frac{2}{3}x + 2.$

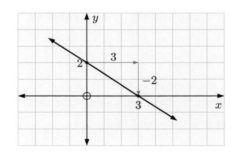

GENERAL FORM

Another way to write the equation of a line is using the **general form** $ax + by + d = 0.$

We can rearrange equations from gradient-intercept form into general form by performing operations on both sides of the equation.

For example: If $y = -\frac{2}{3}x + 2$

           then $3y = -2x + 6$ {multiplying both sides by 3}

         $\therefore$ $2x + 3y = 6$ {adding $2x$ to both sides}

      $\therefore$ $2x + 3y - 6 = 0$ {subtracting 6 from both sides}

        So, the line with gradient-intercept form $y = -\frac{2}{3}x + 2$
        has general form $2x + 3y - 6 = 0.$

FINDING THE EQUATION OF A LINE

In order to find the equation of a line, we need to know some information.

Suppose we know the gradient of the line is 2 and that the line passes through $(4, 1)$.

We suppose (x, y) is any point on the line.

The gradient between $(4, 1)$ and (x, y) is $\dfrac{y-1}{x-4}$, and this gradient must equal 2.

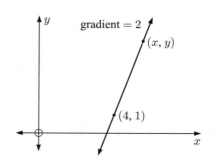

So, $\dfrac{y-1}{x-4} = 2$

$\quad \therefore \ y - 1 = 2(x - 4) \qquad$ {multiplying both sides by $(x - 4)$}

$\quad \therefore \ y - 1 = 2x - 8 \qquad$ {expanding the brackets}

$\quad \quad \therefore \ y = 2x - 7 \qquad$ {adding 1 to both sides}

This is the equation of the line in gradient-intercept form.

We can find the equation of a line if we know:

- its **gradient** and the **coordinates of any point** on the line, or
- the **coordinates of two distinct points** on the line.

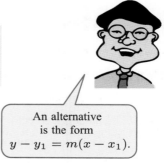

If a straight line has gradient m and passes through the point (x_1, y_1) then its equation is $\dfrac{y - y_1}{x - x_1} = m$.

> An alternative is the form $y - y_1 = m(x - x_1)$.

We can rearrange this equation into either gradient-intercept or general form.

Example 16   ◀》 Self Tutor

Find, in *gradient-intercept form*, the equation of the line through $(-1, 3)$ with a gradient of 5.

| The equation of the line is | *or* | The equation of the line is |

The equation of the line is
$y = mx + c$ where $m = 5$.

When $x = -1$, $y = 3$

$\quad \therefore \ 3 = 5(-1) + c$

$\quad \therefore \ 3 = c - 5$

$\quad \therefore \ c = 8$

Thus, $y = 5x + 8$ is the equation.

or

The equation of the line is

$\dfrac{y - 3}{x - (-1)} = 5$

$\therefore \ \dfrac{y - 3}{x + 1} = 5$

$\therefore \ y - 3 = 5(x + 1)$

$\therefore \ y - 3 = 5x + 5$

$\quad \therefore \ y = 5x + 8$

EXERCISE 13G.1

1 Find the equation of the line with:

    a gradient 1 and y-intercept -2

    b gradient -1 and y-intercept 4

    c gradient 2 and y-intercept 0

    d gradient $-\frac{1}{2}$ and y-intercept 3.

2 Find, in *gradient-intercept form*, the equation of the line through:

   a $(2, -5)$ with gradient 4

   b $(-1, -2)$ with gradient -3

   c $(7, -3)$ with gradient -5

   d $(1, 4)$ with gradient $\frac{1}{2}$

   e $(-1, 3)$ with gradient $-\frac{1}{3}$

   f $(2, 6)$ with gradient 0.

Example 17   ◀)) **Self Tutor**

Find, in *general form*, the equation of the line with gradient $\frac{3}{4}$ which passes through $(5, -2)$.

The equation of the line is $\dfrac{y - (-2)}{x - 5} = \dfrac{3}{4}$

$\therefore \quad \dfrac{y + 2}{x - 5} = \dfrac{3}{4}$

$\therefore \quad 4(y + 2) = 3(x - 5)$

$\therefore \quad 4y + 8 = 3x - 15$

$\therefore \quad 3x - 4y - 23 = 0$

---

3 Find, in *general form*, the equation of the line through:

   a $(2, 5)$ having gradient $\frac{2}{3}$

   b $(-1, 4)$ having gradient $\frac{3}{5}$

   c $(5, 0)$ having gradient $-\frac{1}{3}$

   d $(6, -2)$ having gradient $-\frac{2}{7}$

   e $(-3, -1)$ having gradient 4

   f $(5, -3)$ having gradient -2

   g $(4, -5)$ having gradient $-3\frac{1}{2}$

   h $(-7, -2)$ having gradient 6.

Example 18   ◀)) **Self Tutor**

Find the equation of the line which passes through the points A$(-1, 5)$ and B$(2, 3)$.

The gradient of the line is $\dfrac{3 - 5}{2 - (-1)} = \dfrac{-2}{3}$.

Using A, the equation is

$\dfrac{y - 5}{x - (-1)} = \dfrac{-2}{3}$

$\therefore \quad \dfrac{y - 5}{x + 1} = \dfrac{-2}{3}$

$\therefore \quad 3(y - 5) = -2(x + 1)$

$\therefore \quad 3y - 15 = -2x - 2$

$\therefore \quad 2x + 3y - 13 = 0$

or   Since $m = -\frac{2}{3}$, we have $y = -\frac{2}{3}x + c$.

Using A, we substitute $x = -1$, $y = 5$

$\therefore \quad 5 = -\frac{2}{3}(-1) + c$

$\therefore \quad 5 = \frac{2}{3} + c$

$\therefore \quad c = 5 - \frac{2}{3} = \frac{13}{3}$

$\therefore$ the equation is $y = -\frac{2}{3}x + \frac{13}{3}$

We would get the same equations using point B. Try it yourself.

4 Find, in *gradient-intercept form*, the equation of the line which passes through the points:

  a A$(2, 3)$ and B$(4, 8)$ **b** A$(0, 3)$ and B$(-1, 5)$

  c A$(-1, -2)$ and B$(4, -2)$ **d** C$(-3, 1)$ and D$(2, 0)$

  e P$(5, -1)$ and Q$(-1, -2)$ **f** R$(-1, -3)$ and S$(-4, -1)$.

5 Find, in *general form*, the equation of the line which passes through:

  a $(0, 1)$ and $(3, 2)$ **b** $(1, 4)$ and $(0, -1)$ **c** $(2, -1)$ and $(-1, -4)$

  d $(0, -2)$ and $(5, 2)$ **e** $(3, 2)$ and $(-1, 0)$ **f** $(-1, -1)$ and $(2, -3)$.

Example 19   ◀⬥ **Self Tutor**

Find the equation of the line with graph:

a 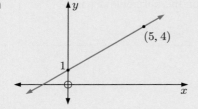   **b**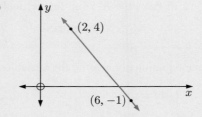

a Two points on the line are $(0, 1)$ and $(5, 4)$

  $\therefore$ the gradient $m = \dfrac{4 - 1}{5 - 0} = \dfrac{3}{5}$

  and the y-intercept $c = 1$

  The equation is $y = \dfrac{3}{5}x + 1$

  {gradient-intercept form}

b Two points on the line are $(2, 4)$ and $(6, -1)$

  $\therefore$ the gradient $m = \dfrac{-1 - 4}{6 - 2} = -\dfrac{5}{4}$

  As we do not know the y-intercept we use the general form.

  The equation is $\dfrac{y - 4}{x - 2} = -\dfrac{5}{4}$

  $\therefore \quad 4(y - 4) = -5(x - 2)$

  $\therefore \quad 4y - 16 = -5x + 10$

  $\therefore \quad 5x + 4y - 26 = 0$

---

6 Find the equations of the illustrated lines:

a 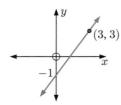   **b** 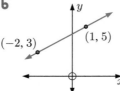   **c**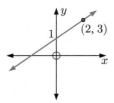

d 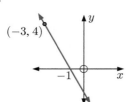   **e** 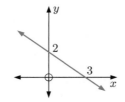   **f**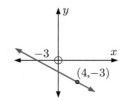

Example 20   ◀) **Self Tutor**

Find the equation connecting
the variables in:

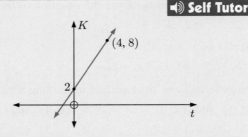

$(0, 2)$ and $(4, 8)$ lie on the straight line

∴   the gradient $m = \dfrac{8 - 2}{4 - 0} = \dfrac{6}{4} = \dfrac{3}{2}$,   and the y-intercept $c = 2$.

In this case K is on the vertical axis and t is on the horizontal axis.

∴   the equation is $K = \frac{3}{2}t + 2$.

7   Find the equation connecting the variables given:

a
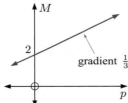

b
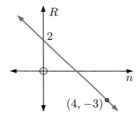

c
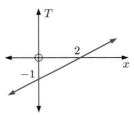

d
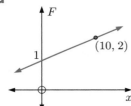

e
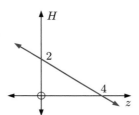

f
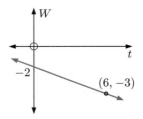

FINDING THE GRADIENT FROM AN EQUATION

When the equation of a line is written in gradient-intercept form, we can find the gradient by looking at the coefficient of x.

For equations in general form, one method of finding the gradient is to rearrange the equation first.

Example 21   ◀) **Self Tutor**

Find the gradient of the line $2x + 5y - 17 = 0$.

$$2x + 5y - 17 = 0$$
$$\therefore \; 5y = -2x + 17$$
$$\therefore \; y = -\tfrac{2}{5}x + \tfrac{17}{5}$$

So, the gradient is $-\frac{2}{5}$.

In the exercise you will learn a faster way of finding the gradient of a line with equation written in general form.

EXERCISE 13G.2

1 Find the gradient of the line with equation:

    a $y = 3x + 2$ **b** $y = 3 - 2x$ **c** $y = 0$

    d $x = 5$ **e** $y = \dfrac{2x + 1}{3}$ **f** $y = \dfrac{3 - 4x}{5}$

2 Find the gradient of the line with equation:

    a $3x + y - 7 = 0$ **b** $2x - 7y = 8$ **c** $2x + 7y - 8 = 0$

    d $3x - 4y = 11$ **e** $4x + 11y - 9 = 0$ **f** $7x - 9y = 63$

3   **a** Find the gradient of the line with equation $ax + by + d = 0$.

    b *Hence* find the gradient of the line with equation:

       i $2x + 5y + 1 = 0$ **ii** $3x - 2y = 0$ **iii** $5x + 4y - 10 = 0$

      iv $-x + 3y - 2 = 0$ **v** $-2x + y = -3$ **vi** $x - 4y = 6$

DOES A POINT LIE ON A LINE?

A point lies on a line if its coordinates satisfy the equation of the line.

Example 22	◀ᵈ) **Self Tutor**

Does $(3, -2)$ lie on the line with equation $5x - 2y = 20$?

Substituting $(3, -2)$ into $5x - 2y = 20$

$$\text{gives} \quad 5(3) - 2(-2) = 20$$

$$\text{or} \quad 19 = 20 \quad \text{which is false.}$$

$\therefore$ $(3, -2)$ does not lie on the line.

EXERCISE 13G.3

1   **a** Does $(3, 4)$ lie on the line with equation $3x - 2y - 1 = 0$?

    b Does $(-2, 5)$ lie on the line with equation $5x + 3y = -5$?

    c Does $(6, -\frac{1}{2})$ lie on the line with equation $3x - 8y - 22 = 0$?

    d Does $(8, -\frac{2}{3})$ lie on the line with equation $x - 9y = 14$?

2 Find k if:

    a $(3, 4)$ lies on the line with equation $x - 2y - k = 0$

    b $(1, 5)$ lies on the line with equation $4x - 2y = k$

    c $(1, 5)$ lies on the line with equation $6x + 7y = k$

    d $(-2, -3)$ lies on the line with equation $4x - 3y - k = 0$

3 Find a given that:

    a $(a, 3)$ lies on the line with equation $y = 2x - 1$

    b $(-2, a)$ lies on the line with equation $y = 1 - 3x$

    c $(a, 5)$ lies on the line with equation $y = 3x + 4$

4 A straight road is to pass through points A(5, 3) and B(1, 8).

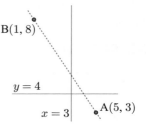

    a Find the point at which this road meets the road given by:

        i $x = 3$ **ii** $y = 4$

    b If we wish to refer to the points on road AB that are *between* A and B, how can we indicate this?

    c The road through A and B extends far into the distance in either direction. Does C(23, −20) lie on the road?

H   GRAPHING LINES

    GRAPHING LINES

Discuss the easiest way to graph a line when its equation is given in the form:

- $y = mx + c$ such as $y = 2x + 3$
- $ax + by + d = 0$ such as $2x + 3y - 12 = 0$.

GRAPHING FROM THE GRADIENT-INTERCEPT FORM

The easiest way to graph lines with equations given in gradient-intercept form is to use the y-intercept and one other point on the graph. The other point can be found by substitution or by using the gradient.

Example 23   ◀)) **Self Tutor**

Graph the line with equation $y = \frac{5}{2}x - 2$.

Method 1:

The y-intercept is −2.

When $x = 2$, $y = 5 - 2 = 3$

∴ $(0, -2)$ and $(2, 3)$ lie on the line.

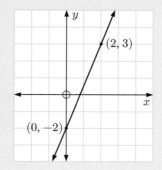

Method 2:

The y-intercept is −2

and the gradient $= \frac{5}{2}$ ◀—— y-step
                ◀—— x-step

We start at $(0, -2)$ and move to another point by moving across 2, then up 5.

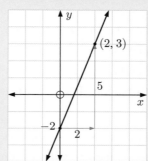

GRAPHING FROM THE GENERAL FORM

The easiest way to graph lines given in general form is to use the axes intercepts.

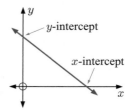

The x-intercept is found by letting $y = 0$.

The y-intercept is found by letting $x = 0$.

Example 24	◀) Self Tutor

Graph the line with equation $3x + 5y + 30 = 0$.

When $x = 0$, $5y + 30 = 0$
$$\therefore \quad y = -6$$

So, the y-intercept is -6.

When $y = 0$, $3x + 30 = 0$
$$\therefore \quad x = -10$$

So, the x-intercept is -10.

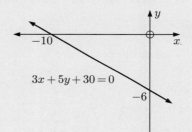

EXERCISE 13H.1

1 Draw the graph of the line with equation:

a $y = \frac{1}{2}x + 2$ **b** $y = 2x + 1$ **c** $y = -x + 3$

d $y = -3x + 2$ **e** $y = -\frac{1}{2}x$ **f** $y = -2x - 2$

g $y = \frac{3}{2}x$ **h** $y = \frac{2}{3}x + 2$ **i** $y = -\frac{3}{4}x - 1$

2 Use axes intercepts to sketch the graphs of:

a $x + 2y = 8$ **b** $4x + 3y - 12 = 0$ **c** $2x - 3y = 6$

d $3x - y - 6 = 0$ **e** $x + y = 5$ **f** $x - y = -5$

g $2x - y + 4 = 0$ **h** $9x - 2y = 9$ **i** $3x + 4y = -15$

ACTIVITY

Click on the icon to run a card game on straight lines.

CARD GAME

FINDING WHERE LINES MEET

When we graph two lines on the same set of axes, there are three possible situations which may occur:

Case 1:

Case 2: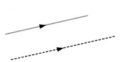

Case 3:

The lines meet in a single **point of intersection**.

The lines are **parallel** and **never meet**. There is no point of intersection.

The lines are **coincident**. There are infinitely many points of intersection.

We saw these situations in **Chapter 4** when we solved simultaneous equations. In general there was a single solution, but in some special cases there was either no solution or infinitely many solutions.

Example 25   ◄)) **Self Tutor**

Use graphical methods to find where the lines $x + y = 6$ and $2x - y = 6$ meet.

For $x + y = 6$:

when $x = 0$, $y = 6$
when $y = 0$, $x = 6$

x	0	6
y	6	0

For $2x - y = 6$:

when $x = 0$, $-y = 6$ $\therefore$ $y = -6$
when $y = 0$, $2x = 6$ $\therefore$ $x = 3$

x	0	3
y	-6	0

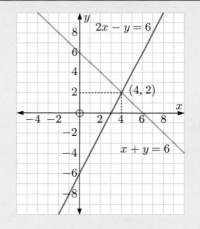

The graphs meet at $(4, 2)$.

Check: $4 + 2 = 6$ ✓ and $2 \times 4 - 2 = 6$ ✓

EXERCISE 13H.2

1 Use graphical methods to find the point of intersection of:

a $y = x - 3$
   $y = 1 - x$

b $x - y - 1 = 0$
   $y = 2x$

c $4x + 3y + 12 = 0$
   $x - 2y + 3 = 0$

d $3x + y + 3 = 0$
   $2x - 3y + 24 = 0$

e $3x + y = 9$
   $3x - 2y = -12$

f $x - 3y = -9$
   $2x - 3y = -12$

g $2x - y = 6$
   $x + 2y = 8$

h $y = 2x - 4$
   $2x - y - 2 = 0$

i $y = -x - 5$
   $2x + 2y = -10$

2 How many points of intersection do the following pairs of lines have?
   Explain your answer, but **do not** graph them.

a $3x + y - 5 = 0$
   $3x + y - 8 = 0$

b $3x + y + 5 = 0$
   $6x + 2y + 10 = 0$

c $3x - y + 5 = 0$
   $3x - y + k = 0$ where k is a constant.

Example 26

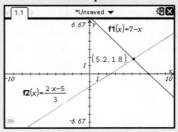

Self Tutor

Use technology to find the point of intersection of $y = 7 - x$ and $2x - 3y - 5 = 0$.

We must first rearrange the second equation so that y is the subject:

$$2x - 3y - 5 = 0$$
$$\therefore \quad 3y = 2x - 5$$
$$\therefore \quad y = \frac{2x - 5}{3}$$

We now plot $Y_1 = 7 - X$ and $Y_2 = \dfrac{2X - 5}{3}$ on the same set of axes.

Casio fx-CG20	TI-84 Plus	TI-nspire

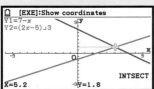 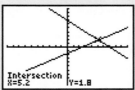

So, the point of intersection is $(5.2, 1.8)$.

---

3   Use technology to find the point of intersection of:

    a $y = x + 5$
        $x + 2y - 1 = 0$

    b $5x + 2y - 13 = 0$
        $y = 3x + 1$

    c $2x + y - 6 = 0$
        $4x - 3y - 5 = 0$

    d $7x + 3y + 3 = 0$
        $x - y - 4 = 0$

GRAPHICS CALCULATOR INSTRUCTIONS

GRAPHING PACKAGE

4   If you can, find the point(s) of intersection of the following using technology. Explain your results.

    a $y = 2x + 5$
        $2x - y - 2 = 0$

    b $4x - 3y + 6 = 0$
        $y = \frac{4}{3}x + 2$

5   A potter knows that if he makes x pots per day, his costs are $y = 200 + 4x$ pounds. His income from selling these pots is $y = 17x$ pounds.   He always sells all the pots he makes.

    a Graph these two equations using technology, and find their point of intersection.

    b What does this point represent?

6   5 oranges and 2 rockmelons cost me \$8.30, whereas 8 oranges and 1 rockmelon cost me \$8.00.

Let \$$x$ be the cost of an orange, and \$$y$ be the cost of a rockmelon.

    a Write two linear equations involving x and y.

    b Graph the two equations using technology, and find their point of intersection.

    c Explain the significance of this point.

ACTIVITY

Two candles are lit at the same time. The first candle is 20 cm long and burns at a rate of 2.5 mm per hour. The second candle is 24.5 cm long and burns at a rate of 3.5 mm per hour.

What to do:

1 Explain why the heights of the candles after t hours are given by $h_1 = 200 - 2.5t$ mm for the first candle and $h_2 = 245 - 3.5t$ mm for the second candle.

2 Use the equations in **1** to determine how long each candle will last.

3 Graph each equation on the same set of axes.

4 At what time will the candles have the same height?

5 If you want the candles to 'go out' together, which candle would you light first? How long after this would you light the other one?

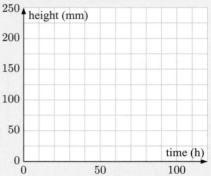

PERPENDICULAR BISECTORS

We have already seen that the **midpoint** M of the line segment AB is the point on the line segment that is halfway between A and B.

The **perpendicular bisector** of AB is the line which is perpendicular to AB, and which passes through its midpoint M.

The perpendicular bisector of AB is the set of all points which are the same distance from A and B. It divides the Cartesian plane into two regions: the set of points closer to A than to B, and the set of points closer to B than to A.

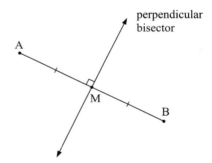

Example 27
◀)) **Self Tutor**

Find the equation of the perpendicular bisector of AB given $A(-1, 2)$ and $B(3, 4)$.

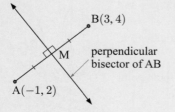

The midpoint M of AB is $\left(\dfrac{-1+3}{2}, \dfrac{2+4}{2} \right)$

or $M(1, 3)$.

The gradient of AB is $\dfrac{4-2}{3-(-1)} = \dfrac{2}{4} = \dfrac{1}{2}$

$\therefore$ the gradient of the perpendicular bisector is $-\dfrac{2}{1}$

{the negative reciprocal of $\frac{1}{2}$}

The equation of the perpendicular bisector is $\dfrac{y-3}{x-1} = -2$

$$\therefore \quad y-3 = -2(x-1)$$
$$\therefore \quad y-3 = -2x+2$$
$$\therefore \quad y = -2x+5$$

EXERCISE 13I

1 Find the equation of the perpendicular bisector of AB given:

   a A(3, −3) and B(1, −1)   **b** A(1, 3) and B(−3, 5)

   c A(3, 1) and B(−3, 6)   **d** A(4, −2) and B(4, 4).

2 Two post offices are located at P(3, 8) and Q(7, 2) on a Council map. Each post office services those houses which are closer to them than the other post office. Find the equation of the boundary between the regions.

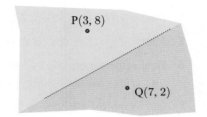

3 Answer the **Opening Problem** on page **376**.

4 The perpendicular bisector of a chord of a circle passes through the centre of the circle.

A circle passes through points P(1, 7), Q(−1, 5), and R(1, −1).

   a Find the equations of the perpendicular bisectors of PQ and QR.

   b Solve the equations in **a** simultaneously to find the centre of the circle.

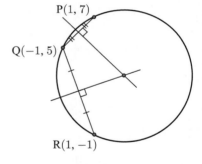

5 Triangle ABC has the vertices shown.

   a Find the coordinates of P, Q, and R, the midpoints of AB, BC, and AC respectively.

   b Find the equation of the perpendicular bisector of:

      i AB   **ii** BC   **iii** AC

   c Find the coordinates of X, the point of intersection of the perpendicular bisector of AB and the perpendicular bisector of BC.

   d Does the point X lie on the perpendicular bisector of AC?

   e What does your result from **d** suggest about the perpendicular bisectors of the sides of a triangle?

   f What is special about the point X in relation to the vertices of the triangle ABC?

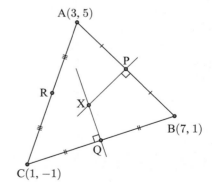

REVIEW SET 13A

1 **a** Find the distance between the points A$(-3, 2)$ and B$(1, 5)$.

 b Find the gradient of the line perpendicular to a line with gradient $\frac{3}{4}$.

 c Find the midpoint of the line segment joining C$(-3, 1)$ to D$(5, 7)$.

2 Find the axes intercepts and gradient of the line with equation $5x - 2y + 10 = 0$.

3 Determine the equation of the illustrated line:

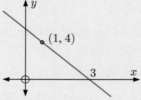

4 Find a given that P$(-3, 4)$, Q$(2, 6)$, and R$(5, a)$ are collinear.

5 Find c if $(-1, c)$ lies on the line with equation $3x - 2y + 7 = 0$.

6 Determine the equation of the line:

 a with gradient -3 and y-intercept 4   **b** which passes through $(-3, 4)$ and $(3, 1)$.

7 Use graphical methods to find the point of intersection of $y = 2x - 9$ and $x + 4y - 36 = 0$.

8 **a** Find the gradient of the line $y = -4x + 7$.

 b Line l is perpendicular to $y = -4x + 7$. What is its gradient?

 c l passes through the point $(-2, 1)$. Find the equation of l.

9 Use midpoints to find the fourth vertex of the given parallelogram:

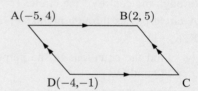

10 Find k given that $(-3, k)$ is 7 units away from $(2, 4)$.

11 A cable car descends with 16% gradient.

 a Interpret this gradient by writing it as a fraction in simplest form.

 b If the cable car travels 300 metres horizontally, how far does it drop vertically?

REVIEW SET 13B

1 Determine the midpoint of the line segment joining K$(3, 5)$ to L$(7, -2)$.

2 Find, in gradient-intercept form, the equation of the line through:

 a $(2, -1)$ with gradient -3 **b** $(3, -2)$ and $(-1, 4)$.

3 Find the gradient of each of the following lines:

a   **b**    **c**   **d**

4 Find where the following lines cut the axes:

a $y = -\frac{3}{2}x + 7$ **b** $5x - 3y - 12 = 0$

5 Does $(2, -5)$ lie on the line with equation $3x + 4y + 14 = 0$?

6 $3x + ky = 7$ and $y = 3 - 4x$ are the equations of two lines. Find k if the lines are:

a parallel   **b** perpendicular.

7 Use graphical methods to find where the line through A$(-5, 0)$ and B$(3, 10)$ meets the line with equation $3x + 2y - 7 = 0$.

8 Find the equation of the:

a horizontal line through $(-4, 3)$ **b** vertical line through $(-6, 1)$.

9 Find the equation of the perpendicular bisector of the line segment joining P$(7, -1)$ and Q$(-3, 5)$.

10 The illustrated circle has centre $(3, 2)$ and radius 5.

The points A$(8, 2)$ and B$(6, -2)$ lie on the circle.

   a Find the midpoint of chord AB.

   b Hence, find the equation of the perpendicular bisector of the chord.

   c Show that this perpendicular bisector passes through the centre $(3, 2)$.

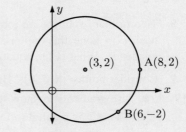

11 Farmer Huber has a triangular field with corners A$(-1, 1)$, B$(1, 5)$, and C$(5, 1)$. There are gates at M and N, the midpoints of AB and BC respectively. A straight path goes from M to N.

   a Use gradients to show that the path is parallel to AC.

   b Show that the path is half as long as the fenceline AC.

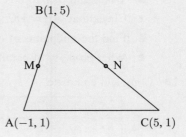

REVIEW SET 13C

1 Find, in general form, the equation of the line through:

a $(1, -5)$ with gradient $\frac{2}{3}$ **b** $(2, -3)$ and $(-4, -5)$.

2 $5x - 7y - 8 = 0$ and $3x + ky + 11 = 0$ are the equations of two lines. Find the value of k for which the lines are:

    a parallel   **b** perpendicular.

3 A point T on the y-axis is 3 units from the point A$(-1, 2)$. Find:

    a the possible coordinates of T

    b the equation of the line AT, given that T has a positive y-coordinate.

4 A truck driver plots his day's travel on the graph alongside.

    a Find the gradient of AB.

    b Find the gradient of OC.

    c Interpret your answers to **a** and **b**.

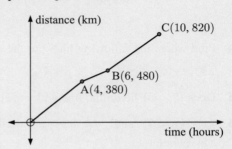

5 Fully classify triangle KLM for K$(-5, -2)$, L$(0, 1)$, and M$(3, -4)$.

6

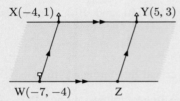

Navigation signs are posted on the bank of a river at W, X, and Y as shown alongside. The local council plans to place another sign at Z such that WXYZ is a parallelogram. Use midpoints to find the coordinates of Z.

7 Draw the graph of the line with equation:

    a $y = -\frac{1}{3}x + 4$ **b** $5x - 2y + 1 = 0$

8 Two primary schools are located at P$(5, 12)$ and Q$(9, 4)$ on a council map. The local council wishes to zone the region so that children must attend the closest school to their place of residence. What is the equation of the line that forms this boundary?

9 Consider points A$(6, 8)$, B$(14, 6)$, C$(-1, -3)$, and D$(-9, -1)$.

    a Use gradients to show that:

        i AB is parallel to DC   **ii** BC is parallel to AD.

    b What kind of figure is ABCD?

    c Check that AB $=$ DC and BC $=$ AD using the distance formula.

    d Find the midpoints of diagonals: **i** AC   **ii** BD.

    e What property of parallelograms has been checked in **d**?

> For figures named ABCD, the labelling is in cyclic order.

10 Copy and complete:

	Equation of line	Gradient	x-intercept	y-intercept
a	$5x - 2y - 10 = 0$			
b	$4x + 5y = 20$			
c	$y = -2x + 5$			
d	$x = 8$			
e	$y = 5$			
f	$x + y = 11$			

11 Consider the points A(1, 3), B(6, 3), C(3, −1), and D(−2, −1).

    a Use the distance formula to show that ABCD is a rhombus.

    b Find the midpoints of AC and BD.

    c Use gradients to show that AC and BD are perpendicular.

REVIEW SET 13D

1 For the points P(1, −3) and Q(−4, 0), find:

    a the distance between P and Q   **b** the gradient of PQ

    c the equation of the line passing through P and Q.

2 Fully classify triangle ABC for A(5, −1), B(−2, 3), and C(0, 8).

3 Find k if the line joining A(5, k) and B(2, 4) is perpendicular to the line with equation $x - 3y - 7 = 0$.

4 Use midpoints to find the fourth vertex K of parallelogram HIJK given H(3, 4), I(−3, −1), and J(4, 10).

5

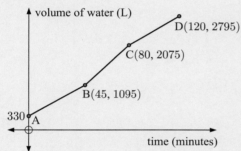

Jalen monitors the amount of water in his rainwater tank during a storm.

    a How much water was in the tank before the storm?

    b When was it raining hardest?

    c At what rate is the tank filling between C and D?

    d What is the average water collection rate during the whole storm?

6 Find c given that P(5, 9), Q(−2, c), and R(−5, 4) are collinear.

7 Find the gradient of the line with equation:

    a $y = \dfrac{4 - 3x}{2}$ **b** $5x + 3y + 6 = 0$

8 Find the equations linking the variables in these graphs:

    a

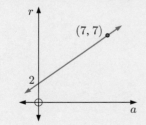

    b

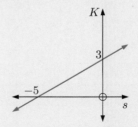

9 Find t if:

    a (−2, 4) lies on the line with equation $2x - 7y = t$

    b (3, t) lies on the line with equation $4x + 5y = -1$.

10 Consider P(1, 5), Q(5, 7), and R(3, 1).

   a Show that triangle PQR is isosceles.

   b Find the midpoint M of QR.

   c Use gradients to verify that PM is perpendicular to QR.

   d Illustrate what you have found in **a**, **b**, and **c**.

11 The Circular Gardens are bounded by East Avenue and Diagonal Road. Diagonal Road intersects North Street at C and East Avenue at D. Diagonal Rd is tangential to the Circular Gardens at B. X is at the centre of the Circular Gardens.

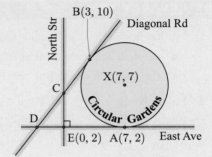

   a Find the equation of:

      i East Avenue   **ii** North Street

      iii Diagonal Road.

   b Where does Diagonal Road intersect:

      i East Avenue   **ii** North Street?

Chapter 14

Perimeter, area, and volume

Syllabus reference: 1.4, 5.5

Contents:

OPENING PROBLEM   BRICK EDGING

You are asked to quote on the supply and installation of bricks around a lawn. The bricks are expensive and are not returnable. Consequently, you need to accurately calculate how many are needed and what they will cost. You draw a rough sketch of what the house owner wants. You take it back to your office to do the calculations. The brick supplier tells you that each brick is 220 mm long and costs $4.70.

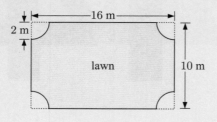
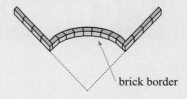

Things to think about:

a How far is it around the lawn?

b How many bricks will you need?

c What will be the cost of the bricks needed to do the job?

You may wish to set up a spreadsheet to handle the calculations. This is particularly useful for a company expecting dozens of similar jobs in the future.

In **Chapter 2** we saw that the **International System of Units** or **SI** has seven base units, three of which are used very frequently:

Base unit	Abbreviation	Used for measuring
metre	m	length
kilogram	kg	mass
second	s	time

Other units are derived in terms of the base units. Some of the common ones are shown below:

Unit	Abbreviation	Used for measuring
litre	L	capacity
tonne	t	heavy masses
square metre	m^2	area
cubic metre	m^3	volume
metres per second	$m\,s^{-1}$	speed
newton	N	force
joule	J	energy
watt	W	power

A | CONVERSION OF UNITS

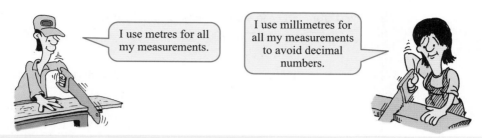

DISCUSSION

Discuss why we need to convert from one set of units to another.

When we work in the SI system, we often use units that are related to the base units by powers of ten. We use prefixes such as kilo, centi, and milli to indicate these units.

CONVERSION DIAGRAM

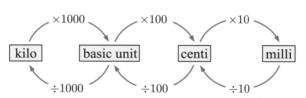

For example, to convert **milli**metres into **centi**metres we divide by 10.

When changing from smaller to larger units, **divide** by the conversion factor.

When changing from larger to smaller units, **multiply** by the conversion factor.

LENGTH CONVERSIONS

The following table shows the relationship between various **length units**:

1 km = 1000 m	1 m = 100 cm	1 cm = 10 mm	1 mm = $\frac{1}{10}$ cm
= 100 000 cm	= 1000 mm	= $\frac{1}{100}$ m	= $\frac{1}{1000}$ m
= 1 000 000 mm	= $\frac{1}{1000}$ km		

However, you may find it easier to use the following **conversion diagram**:

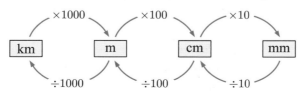

Example 1   ◀)) **Self Tutor**

Convert: **a** 16.73 m to cm   **b** 48 380 cm to km

a We convert from larger to smaller units, so we need to multiply.
$$16.73 \text{ m} = (16.73 \times 100) \text{ cm}$$
$$= 1673 \text{ cm}$$

b We convert from smaller to larger units, so we need to divide.
$$48 380 \text{ cm} = (48 380 \div 100 \div 1000) \text{ km}$$
$$= 0.4838 \text{ km}$$

MASS CONVERSIONS

1 t = 1000 kg
1 kg = 1000 g
1 g = 1000 mg

Example 2   ◀)) **Self Tutor**

Convert:

a 2.3 kg to grams   **b** 8 470 000 g to tonnes

a   2.3 kg   **b**   8 470 000 g
   $= (2.3 \times 1000)$ g $= (8 470 000 \div 1000 \div 1000)$ tonnes
   $= 2300$ g $= 8.47$ tonnes

EXERCISE 14A

1 Convert:
   a 8250 cm to m   **b** 295 mm to cm   **c** 6250 m to km
   d 73.8 m to cm   **e** 24.63 cm to m   **f** 9.761 m to km

2 Convert:
   a 413 cm to mm   **b** 3754 km to m   **c** 4.829 km to cm
   d 26.9 m to mm   **e** 0.47 km to cm   **f** 3.88 km to mm

3 I have 55 reels of garden hose, each containing 132 m of hose. How many kilometres of garden hose do I have?

4 Phyllis is a candlemaker. The wick of each of her candles is 27.5 cm. If Phyllis has 4.95 km of wick, how many candles can she make?

5 Convert:
   a 5.9 kg to g   **b** 2600 g to kg   **c** 3750 g to t
   d 15 kg to mg   **e** 4.8 t to g   **f** 1600 mg to kg
   g 1.7385 g to mg   **h** 46 218 g to t   **i** 0.0361 kg to mg

6 How many 6 gram nails can be made from 0.12 t of iron?

7 Dominic found that the average banana weight on his plantation was 138 grams. That year he exported 45 000 bananas.

   a How many tonnes of bananas did Dominic export?

   b If each truck carried 700 kg of bananas to the port, how many truck loads were required that year?

B   PERIMETER

PERIMETER

The **perimeter** of a figure is the distance around its boundary.

For a **polygon**, the perimeter is obtained by adding the lengths of all of its sides.

For a **circle**, the perimeter has a special name, the **circumference**.

Following is a summary of some **perimeter formulae**:

Shape	Formula	Shape	Formula
square l	$P = 4l$	rectangle w l	$P = 2l + 2w$ or $P = 2(l + w)$
polygon a b c d e	$P = a + b + c + d + e$	circle d r	$C = \pi d$ or $C = 2\pi r$

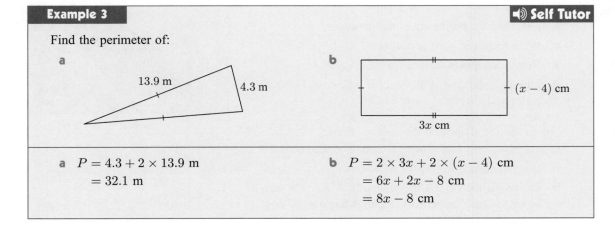

Example 3   ◀⅛ **Self Tutor**

Find the perimeter of:

a

13.9 m   4.3 m

b

$(x - 4)$ cm

$3x$ cm

a $P = 4.3 + 2 \times 13.9$ m
    $= 32.1$ m

b $P = 2 \times 3x + 2 \times (x - 4)$ cm
     $= 6x + 2x - 8$ cm
     $= 8x - 8$ cm

EXERCISE 14B

1 Find the perimeter of the following figures:

a

3.9 m

b

7 mm
3 mm
6 mm
12 mm

c

rectangle   0.8 km
2.3 km

d

17.2 cm

e

$(x - 1)$ cm

f

x m $2x$ m
$(x + 2)$ m

g

$5x$ km
$(3x + 2)$ km

h

$(2y - 5)$ cm

i

$(y + 1)$ cm

x km

2 A rectangular field 220 metres long and 300 metres wide is to be fenced.

    a Draw and label a diagram of the field.   **b** Find the total length of fencing required.

3 A sailing crew races around the course shown. The race is 4 laps long. What distance do they travel in total?

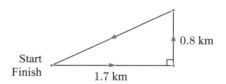

Start
Finish
0.8 km
1.7 km

4 A farmer wants to fence his private garden to keep out his sheep. The garden measures 26 m × 40 m. The fence has 5 strands of wire, and posts are placed every 2 metres. A gate occupies one of the 2 m gaps.

    a Calculate the perimeter of the garden.

    b What length of wire is needed?

    c How many posts are needed?

    d Find the total cost of the fence if wire costs €0.34 per metre and each post costs €11.95.

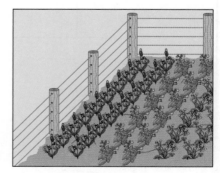

5 A room has the shape and dimensions shown. Skirting board was laid around the edge of the room.

    a How much skirting board was needed?

    b Skirting is sold in 2.4 metre lengths which can then be cut. If each length costs $2.48, what was the cost of the skirting board?

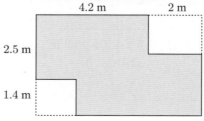

4.2 m   2 m
2.5 m
1.4 m

Example 4

Self Tutor

Find, to 3 significant figures, the perimeter of:

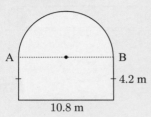

The diameter of semi-circle $d = 10.8$ m.

$\therefore$ the distance from A to B around the semi-circle

$$= \tfrac{1}{2}(\pi d)$$
$$= \tfrac{1}{2} \times \pi \times 10.8$$
$$\approx 16.96 \text{ m}$$

$\therefore \quad P \approx 10.8 + 2 \times 4.2 + 16.96 \text{ m}$
$$\approx 36.2 \text{ m}$$

6 Find, to 3 significant figures, the perimeter of:

a

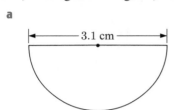

b

c

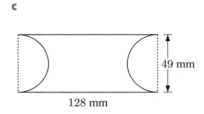

7 My bike wheels have a radius of 32 centimetres. When I ride to school the wheels complete 239 revolutions. How far do I live from my school?

8 Answer the **Opening Problem** on page **412**.

9 A netball court has the dimensions shown.

a Find the perimeter of the court.

b Find the total length of all the marked lines.

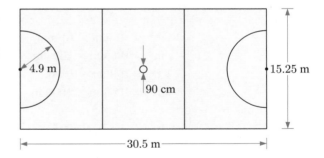

Example 5

Self Tutor

Find the radius of a circle with circumference 11.7 m.

$$C = 2\pi r$$
$$\therefore \quad 11.7 = 2 \times \pi \times r$$
$$\therefore \quad 11.7 \approx 6.283 \times r$$
$$\therefore \quad \frac{11.7}{6.283} \approx r \qquad \{\text{dividing both sides by } 6.283\}$$
$$\therefore \quad r \approx 1.86$$

$\therefore$ the radius is approximately 1.86 m.

You could use a graphics calculator to solve $2 \times \pi \times r = 11.7$

10 Find: **a** the diameter of a circular pond of circumference 37.38 m

   b the radius of a circular pond of circumference 32.67 m.

11 A conveyor belt 50 m long is used to carry objects a distance of 23 m. What depth is the recess needed to exactly contain the belt rollers?

 AREA

> The **area** of a closed figure is the number of square units it contains.

The relationships between the various units of area can be obtained using the conversions for length.

For example, since 1 cm = 10 mm,

$$1 \text{ cm} \times 1 \text{ cm} = 10 \text{ mm} \times 10 \text{ mm}$$

$$\therefore \ 1 \text{ cm}^2 = 100 \text{ mm}^2$$

AREA UNITS

The most common units of area are the squares of the length units:

- **square millimetres** (mm^2)
- **square metres** (m^2)
- **square centimetres** (cm^2)
- **square kilometres** (km^2).

For larger areas we must also use **hectares** (ha).

Area conversions are shown in the following table and conversion diagram:

$$\begin{aligned}
1 \text{ cm}^2 &= 10 \text{ mm} \times 10 \text{ mm} &&= 100 \text{ mm}^2 \\
1 \text{ m}^2 &= 100 \text{ cm} \times 100 \text{ cm} &&= 10\,000 \text{ cm}^2 \\
1 \text{ ha} &= 100 \text{ m} \times 100 \text{ m} &&= 10\,000 \text{ m}^2 \\
1 \text{ km}^2 &= 1000 \text{ m} \times 1000 \text{ m} &&= 1\,000\,000 \text{ m}^2 \text{ or } 100 \text{ ha}
\end{aligned}$$

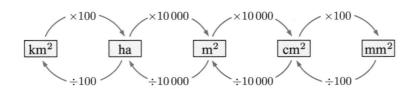

Example 6   ◀) **Self Tutor**

Convert: **a** 650 000 m^2 into ha   **b** 2.5 m^2 into mm^2

a We convert from smaller to larger units, so we need to divide.

$$650\,000 \text{ m}^2$$
$$= (650\,000 \div 10\,000) \text{ ha}$$
$$= 65 \text{ ha}$$

b We convert from larger to smaller units, so we need to multiply.

$$2.5 \text{ m}^2$$
$$= (2.5 \times 10\,000 \times 100) \text{ mm}^2$$
$$= 2\,500\,000 \text{ mm}^2$$

EXERCISE 14C.1

1 Convert:

a 560 cm^2 to m^2 **b** 4.8 km^2 to ha **c** 55 mm^2 to cm^2

d 0.13 km^2 to m^2 **e** $46\,170 \text{ mm}^2$ to m^2 **f** 7.21 ha to km^2

g 8.43 m^2 to km^2 **h** 0.0059 ha to m^2 **i** $9\,890\,000 \text{ cm}^2$ to km^2

2 **a** In my city there are around $56\,800$ houses built on 4800 hectares of land. Find, in square metres, the average lot size for a house.

b A glazing company manufactures glass in 9.9 m^2 sheets. It then cuts the sheets into 550 cm^2 panels. How many panels can be cut from each sheet?

AREA FORMULAE

The formulae for calculating the areas of the most commonly occurring shapes are given below:

Shape	*Figure*	*Formula*
Rectangle	width, length	**Area = length × width**
Triangle	height, base, base	**Area = $\frac{1}{2}$ × base × height** DEMO
Parallelogram	height, base	**Area = base × height** DEMO
Trapezium	a, h, b	**Area = $\left(\dfrac{a+b}{2}\right) \times h$** DEMO
Circle	r	**Area = πr^2** DEMO

Example 7   ◀)) **Self Tutor**

Find, to 3 significant figures, the areas of the following figures:

a

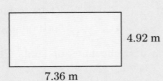

4.92 m

7.36 m

b

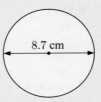

8.7 cm

a $A = lw$
$= 7.36 \times 4.92$
$\approx 36.2 \text{ m}^2$

b The diameter $d = 8.7$ cm,

so the radius $r = \dfrac{8.7}{2} = 4.35$ cm

Now $A = \pi r^2$
$\therefore \quad A = \pi \times (4.35)^2$
$\therefore \quad A \approx 59.4 \text{ cm}^2$

EXERCISE 14C.2

1 Find the area of:

   a a square cattle ranch with sides of length 16.72 km

   b a rectangular housing block which is 42.7 m by 21.3 m

   c a circular pond of radius 23.8 m

   d a triangular garden patch shown:

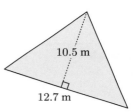

10.5 m

12.7 m

2 Write down and then simplify expressions for the areas of the following:

a

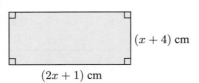

$(x + 4)$ cm

$(2x + 1)$ cm

b

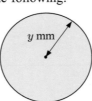

y mm

c

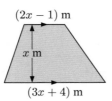

$(2x - 1)$ m

x m

$(3x + 4)$ m

d

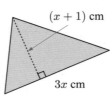

$(x + 1)$ cm

$3x$ cm

e

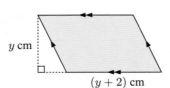

y cm

$(y + 2)$ cm

f

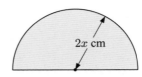

$2x$ cm

3 Write down and simplify expressions for the areas of the following figures. Note that some of the information given is unnecessary!

a

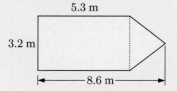

b

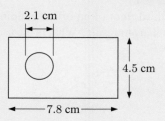

Example 8   ◀) **Self Tutor**

Calculate the shaded area:

a

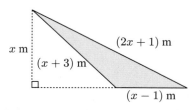

b

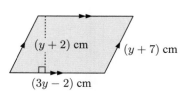

a The required area is the sum of

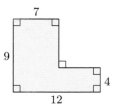 and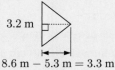

8.6 m − 5.3 m = 3.3 m

∴ the total area = area of rectangle + area of triangle
$$= 5.3 \times 3.2 + \tfrac{1}{2} \times 3.2 \times 3.3$$
$$\approx 22.2 \text{ m}^2$$

b Area = area of rectangle − area of circle
$$= 7.8 \times 4.5 - \pi \times \left(\tfrac{2.1}{2}\right)^2$$
$$\approx 31.6 \text{ cm}^2$$

---

4 Calculate the area of the following composite shapes. All measurements are given in cm.

a

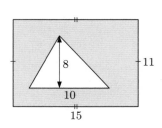

b

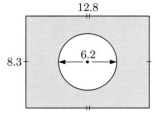

c

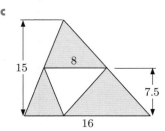

5 Calculate the area of the following shaded regions. All measurements are given in cm.

a

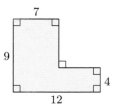

b

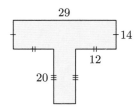

c

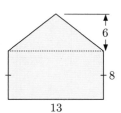

6 Find a formula for the area A of each shaded region:

a

b

c

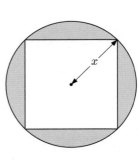

7 The third floor of an office building has the floorplan alongside. What is the usable floor space?

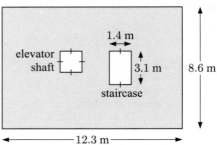

8 Pete's Pizza Bar sells 3 sizes of circular pizza. The small pizza is 15 cm across and costs €4.20. The medium size is 30 cm across and costs €9.60. The super size has a diameter of 35 cm and costs €14.00. Which of the pizzas gives the best value?

Hint: Calculate the price per square centimetre.

Example 9   ◆)) Self Tutor

A rectangular lawn is 12 m by 8 m. A 3.2 m square garden bed is dug within it. The remaining lawn is then reseeded from boxes of seed. Each box costs $8.50 and covers 18 m². Find:

a   the area of the lawn
b   the number of boxes of seed required
c   the total cost of the seed.

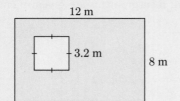

a   Area of lawn
= area of rectangle − area of square
= $(12 \times 8) - (3.2 \times 3.2)$ m²
= 85.76 m²
≈ 85.8 m²

b   Number of boxes

$= \dfrac{\text{area of lawn}}{\text{area covered by one box}}$

$= \dfrac{85.76 \text{ m}^2}{18 \text{ m}^2}$

≈ 4.76 boxes

∴   5 boxes of seeds are required.

c   Total cost
= number of boxes × cost of 1 box
= 5 × $8.50
= $42.50

9 Concrete slabs suitable for a driveway are sold in two sizes:

Type A: 0.6 m by 0.6 m
Type B: 0.6 m by 0.3 m.

Both types of slab cost $18.25 per square metre. A driveway is to be 2.4 m wide and 18 m long. The slabs are laid on sand which costs $18 per tonne. A tonne of sand covers 17.5 m^2 to the required depth. Sand must be purchased to a multiple of 0.2 of a tonne.

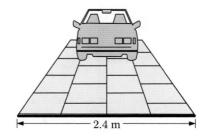

2.4 m

a Calculate the area of the driveway.

b Explain why you need 4 type B slabs for the pattern given in the diagram.

c How many type A slabs are needed?

d How much sand must be purchased?

e Find the total cost of the slabs and sand.

10 A cylindrical tank of base diameter 8 m and height 6 m requires a non-porous lining on its circular base and curved walls. The lining of the base costs $3.20 per m^2, and on the sides it costs $4.50 per m^2.

a Find the base radius. **b** Find the area of the base.

c Find the cost of lining the base.

d Explain why the area of the curved wall is given by $2\pi r \times h$ where r is the radius and h is the height.

e Find the area of the curved wall.

f Find the cost of lining the curved wall.

g Find the total cost of the lining to the nearest $10.

11 Your task is to design a rectangular duck enclosure of area 100 m^2. Wire netting must be purchased for three of the sides, as the fourth side is an existing barn wall. Naturally you wish to minimise the length of netting required to do the job, thereby minimising your costs.

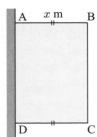

a If AB is x m long, find BC in terms of x.

b Explain why the required length of netting is given

by $L = 2x + \dfrac{100}{x}$ m.

c Use technology to find the value of x which will make L a minimum.

d Sketch the desired shape, showing the dimensions of the enclosure.

12 An industrial shed is being constructed with a total floor space of 600 m^2. It will be divided into three rectangular rooms of equal size. The walls will cost $60 per metre to build.

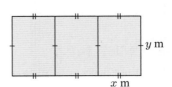

a Calculate the area of the shed in terms of x and y.

b Explain why $y = \dfrac{200}{x}$.

c Show that the total cost of the walls is given by $C = 360x + \dfrac{48\,000}{x}$ dollars.

d Use technology to find x (to the nearest cm) which will minimise the cost of the walls.

e Sketch the desired shape, showing all dimensions.

D   SURFACE AREA

> The **surface area** of a three-dimensional figure with plane faces is the sum of the areas of the faces.

So, if we collapse the figure into its net, the surface area is the area of the net.

For example, the surface area of

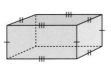 = the area of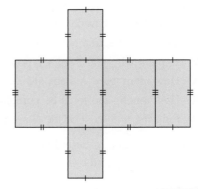

Example 10   ◀)) **Self Tutor**

Find the surface area of this square-based pyramid.

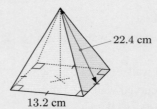

22.4 cm

13.2 cm

From the net of the pyramid shown alongside, we see that the figure has one square face with sides 13.2 cm, and four triangular faces with base 13.2 cm and height 22.4 cm.

∴   the total surface area

$= 13.2^2 + 4 \times \left(\frac{1}{2} \times 13.2 \times 22.4\right)$ cm^2

$= 765.6$ cm^2

≈ 766 cm^2

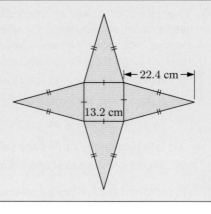

22.4 cm

13.2 cm

EXERCISE 14D.1

1 Find the total surface area of:

a
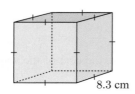
8.3 cm

b
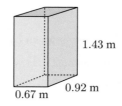
1.43 m
0.67 m   0.92 m

c
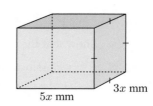
5x mm   3x mm

2 Find the total surface area of:

a

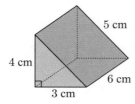

b

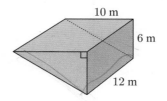

3 Draw each of the following and hence find its surface area:

a an ice cube with sides 2.5 cm

b a block of cheese measuring 14 cm by 8 cm by 3 cm

c a wooden wedge with a 3 cm by 4 cm by 5 cm right-triangular cross-section and length 8 cm.

4

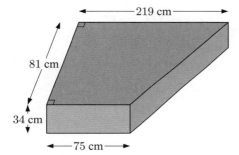

A harpsichord case has the dimensions shown.

a Find the area of the top and bottom surfaces.

b Find the area of each side of the case.

c If the timber costs $128 per square metre, find the cost of the timber to construct this case.

5 The diagram shows a room whose walls and ceiling need to be painted with two coats of paint. The door is 0.8 m by 2.2 m and the window is 183 cm by 91 cm. The door also has to be stained on *both* sides with two coats of stain. Use the following table to calculate the total cost of the stain and paint:

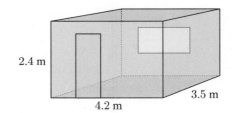

Type of paint	Size	Area covered	Cost per tin
wall paint	4 litres	16 m²	$32.45
	2 litres	8 m²	$20.80
wood stain	2 litres	10 m²	$23.60
(for doors)	1 litre	5 m²	$15.40

6 The **Taylor Prism** is a clay hexagonal prism with a historical record written on its sides. It was found by archaeologist Colonel Taylor in 1830. If the ancient Assyrians had written on all the surfaces, what surface area was available to write on?

Hint: Divide the hexagonal top and bottom into triangles and find their areas.

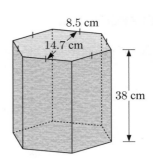

CYLINDERS, SPHERES, AND CONES

These objects have curved surfaces, but their surface area can still be calculated using formulae.

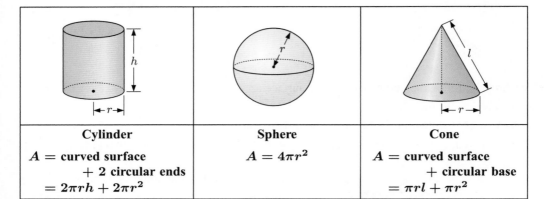

Cylinder	Sphere	Cone
A = **curved surface** $+$ **2 circular ends** $= 2\pi rh + 2\pi r^2$	$A = 4\pi r^2$	A = **curved surface** $+$ **circular base** $= \pi rl + \pi r^2$

Example 11   ◀)) **Self Tutor**

Find the outer surface area, to 1 decimal place, of:

a hollow top and bottom   **b**   **c**

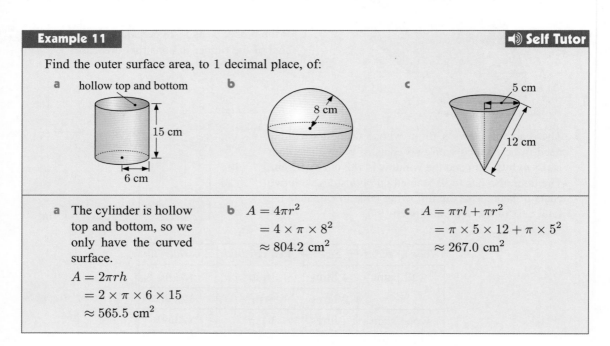

a The cylinder is hollow top and bottom, so we only have the curved surface.

$A = 2\pi rh$
$\quad = 2 \times \pi \times 6 \times 15$
$\quad \approx 565.5 \text{ cm}^2$

b $A = 4\pi r^2$
$\quad = 4 \times \pi \times 8^2$
$\quad \approx 804.2 \text{ cm}^2$

c $A = \pi rl + \pi r^2$
$\quad = \pi \times 5 \times 12 + \pi \times 5^2$
$\quad \approx 267.0 \text{ cm}^2$

EXERCISE 14D.2

1 Find, correct to 1 decimal place, the outer surface area of the following:

a   **b**   **c**

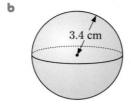
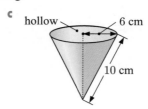

d

solid

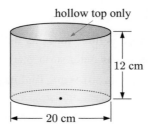

18 m

14 m

e

hollow top only

12 cm

20 cm

f

4.5 km

2 Find the total surface area of the solid hemisphere shown.

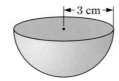

3 cm

3 Find the total surface area of these solids:

   a a cylinder with height $3x$ cm and base radius x cm

   b a sphere with radius $2x$ cm

   c a cone with radius $2x$ cm and slant height $4x$ cm

   d a cone with radius $3x$ cm and height $4x$ cm.

4 A new wharf has 24 cylindrical concrete pylons, each with diameter 0.6 m and length 10 m. The pylons will be coated with a salt resistant material.

   a Find the total surface area of one pylon.

   b Coating the pylons with the material costs £45.50 per m². Find the cost of coating one pylon.

   c Find the total cost of coating the 24 pylons.

10 m

0.6 m

5

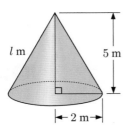

l m

5 m

2 m

A conical tent has base radius 2 m and height 5 m.

   a Find the slant height l, to 2 decimal places.

   b Find the area of canvas necessary to make the tent, including the base.

   c If canvas costs \$18 per m², find the cost of the canvas.

6 A spherical art piece has diameter 2 metres. Find:

   a the surface area of the sphere

   b the cost of painting the sphere given that each square metre will cost €38.50 for paint and labour.

Example 12
🔊 **Self Tutor**

The length of a hollow pipe is three times its radius.

a Write an expression for its outer surface area.

b If its outer surface area is 301.6 m², find its radius.

a Let the radius be x m, so the length is $3x$ m.

$$\begin{aligned} \text{Surface area} &= 2\pi rh \\ &= 2\pi x \times 3x \\ &= 6\pi x^2 \text{ m}^2 \end{aligned}$$

b The surface area is 301.6 m²

$$\therefore \ 6\pi x^2 = 301.6$$

$$\therefore \ x^2 = \frac{301.6}{6\pi}$$

$$\therefore \ x = \sqrt{\frac{301.6}{6\pi}} \quad \{\text{as } x > 0\}$$

$$\therefore \ x \approx 4.00$$

The radius of the pipe is 4 m.

7 The height of a hollow cylinder is the same as its diameter.

  a Write an expression for the outer surface area of the cylinder in terms of its radius r.

  b Find the height of the cylinder if its surface area is 91.6 m².

8 The slant height of a hollow cone is three times its radius.

  a Write an expression for the outer surface area of the cone in terms of its radius r.

  b Find the slant height if its surface area is 21.2 cm².

  c Hence find the height of the cone.

hollow

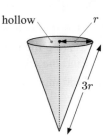

E   VOLUME

The **volume** of a solid is the amount of space it occupies. It is measured in cubic units.

UNITS OF VOLUME

The most common units of volume are the cubes of the units of length.

1 cm
1 cm   1 cm

$$\begin{aligned} 1 \text{ cm}^3 &= 10 \text{ mm} \times 10 \text{ mm} \times 10 \text{ mm} \\ &= 1000 \text{ mm}^3 \end{aligned}$$

$$\begin{aligned} 1 \text{ m}^3 &= 100 \text{ cm} \times 100 \text{ cm} \times 100 \text{ cm} \\ &= 1\,000\,000 \text{ cm}^3 \end{aligned}$$

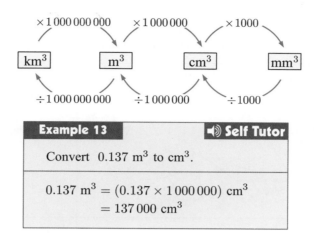

Example 13	◀)) Self Tutor

Convert 0.137 m^3 to cm^3.

$$0.137 \text{ m}^3 = (0.137 \times 1\,000\,000) \text{ cm}^3$$
$$= 137\,000 \text{ cm}^3$$

EXERCISE 14E.1

1 Rohit was convinced that $1 \text{ m}^3 = 1000 \text{ cm}^3$. Sarat told Rohit to go back to basics. He said that 1 m^3 is the volume of a 1 m by 1 m by 1 m box and $1 \text{ m} = 100 \text{ cm}$. Follow Sarat's instructions to show that $1 \text{ m}^3 = 1\,000\,000 \text{ cm}^3$.

2 Convert:

    a $39\,100\,000 \text{ cm}^3$ to m^3 **b** 0.51 cm^3 to mm^3 **c** $469\,000 \text{ cm}^3$ to m^3

    d 3.82 m^3 to cm^3 **e** 5.27 mm^3 to cm^3 **f** 0.0179 m^3 to cm^3

    g $692\,000 \text{ mm}^3$ to cm^3 **h** $183\,460\,000 \text{ mm}^3$ to m^3 **i** 0.0051 m^3 to cm^3

3 **a** A steel ball bearing has volume 0.27 cm^3. If the manufacturer has 1.35 m^3 of steel, how many ball bearings can be made?

    b There is about 5.5 cm^3 of aluminium in a soft drink can. A recycling depot collects $46\,291$ cans and melts them down, losing 15% of the metal in the process. How many cubic metres of aluminium do they now have?

UNIFORM SOLIDS

If the perpendicular cross-section of a solid is always the same shape and size all the way along the object, we call it a **solid of uniform cross-section**.

For all solids of uniform cross-section,

> **volume = length × area of cross-section**
> *or* $V = l \times A$

DEMO

In each of the following examples, A is the cross-sectional area and l is the length of the solid.

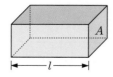

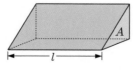

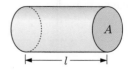

$V = l \times A$
  $= \text{length} \times \text{width} \times \text{height}$

$V = l \times A$

$V = l \times A$
  $= l \times \pi r^2$
  $= \pi r^2 l$

OTHER SOLIDS

The formulae for calculating the volume of some other common objects are shown below:

Object	Figure	Volume formula
Pyramids and cones	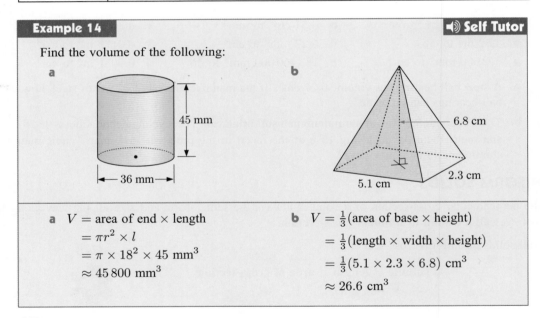	**Volume of a pyramid or cone** $= \frac{1}{3}($area of base $\times$ height$)$ **DEMO**
Spheres		**Volume of a sphere** $= \frac{4}{3}\pi r^3$

Example 14   ◀) **Self Tutor**

Find the volume of the following:

a

45 mm

36 mm

b

6.8 cm

5.1 cm   2.3 cm

a $V =$ area of end $\times$ length
$= \pi r^2 \times l$
$= \pi \times 18^2 \times 45$ mm^3
$\approx 45\,800$ mm^3

b $V = \frac{1}{3}($area of base $\times$ height$)$
$= \frac{1}{3}($length $\times$ width $\times$ height$)$
$= \frac{1}{3}(5.1 \times 2.3 \times 6.8)$ cm^3
≈ 26.6 cm^3

EXERCISE 14E.2

1 Calculate the volume of:

a

3.2 m   1.73 m^2

b

74.6 cm^2

5 cm

c

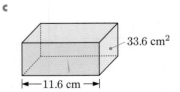

33.6 cm^2

11.6 cm

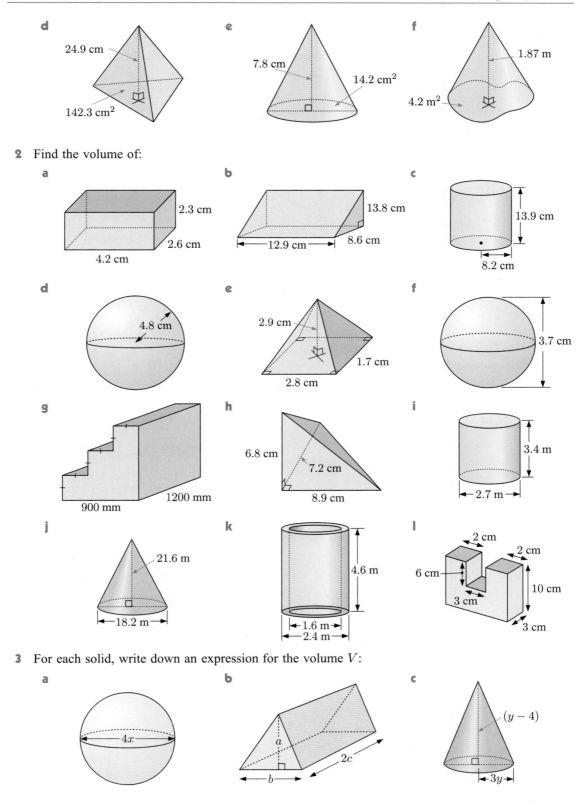

d 24.9 cm   142.3 cm²

e 7.8 cm   14.2 cm²

f 1.87 m   4.2 m²

2 Find the volume of:

a 2.3 cm, 2.6 cm, 4.2 cm

b 13.8 cm, 12.9 cm, 8.6 cm

c 13.9 cm, 8.2 cm

d 4.8 cm

e 2.9 cm, 1.7 cm, 2.8 cm

f 3.7 cm

g 900 mm, 1200 mm

h 6.8 cm, 7.2 cm, 8.9 cm

i 3.4 m, 2.7 m

j 21.6 m, 18.2 m

k 4.6 m, 1.6 m, 2.4 m

l 2 cm, 2 cm, 6 cm, 3 cm, 10 cm, 3 cm

3 For each solid, write down an expression for the volume V:

a $4x$

b a, b, $2c$

c $(y-4)$, $3y$

Example 15   ◀ Self Tutor

A box has a square base and its height is 12 cm. If the volume of the box is 867 cm³, find the length of the base.

Let the length be x cm.

volume = length × width × height

$\therefore\ 867 = x \times x \times 12$

$\therefore\ 12x^2 = 867$

$\therefore\ x^2 = \frac{867}{12}$

$\therefore\ x = \sqrt{\frac{867}{12}}$ {as $x > 0$}

$\therefore\ x = 8.5$

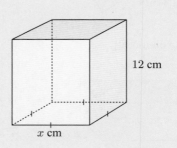

So, the length of the base is 8.5 cm.

---

4 **a** Find the length of the side of a cube if its volume is 2.52 cm³.

   b Find the height of a cylinder with base area 23.8 cm² and volume 142.8 cm³.

5 A concrete path 1 m wide and 10 cm deep is placed around a circular lighthouse of diameter 12 m.

   a Draw a plan view of the situation.

   b Find the surface area of the concrete.

   c Find the volume of concrete required to lay the path.

6 A circular cake tin has radius 20 cm and height 7 cm. When cake mix was added to the tin its height was 2 cm. After the cake was cooked it rose to 1.5 cm below the top of the tin.

   a Sketch these two situations.

   b Find the volume of the cake mix.

   c Find the volume of the cooked cake.

   d What was the percentage increase in the volume of the cake while it cooked?

Remember that percentage increase $= \dfrac{\text{increase}}{\text{original}} \times 100\%$

7 The Water Supply department uses huge concrete pipes to drain storm water away.

   a Find the external radius of a pipe.

   b Find the internal radius of a pipe.

   c Find the volume of concrete necessary to make one pipe.

0.05 m

2.5 m

1 m

8   A rectangular garage floor 9.2 m by 6.5 m is to be concreted to a depth of 120 mm.

   a   What volume of concrete is required?

   b   Concrete costs €135 per m^3, and is only supplied in multiples of 0.2 m^3. How much will it cost to concrete the floor?

9   Timber cutters need to calculate the volume of usable timber in a tree. They use the following approximation for the tree's volume:

$V \approx 0.06 \times g^2 \times l$ where V = volume (in m^3)

g = approximate girth (in m)

and l = usable length (in m).

   a   Estimate the volume of usable timber in a tree with an average girth of 3.8 m and usable length 9.9 m.

   b   For a cylinder with circumference g, show that $V = \frac{1}{4\pi} g^2 \times l$.

   c   Find the percentage difference between the volumes predicted by these two formulae.

   d   Explain this percentage difference.

10   I want to build a new rectangular garden which is 8.6 m by 2.4 m, and 15 cm deep. I decide to get some soil from the local garden supplier, loading it into my trailer which measures 2.2 m × 1.8 m × 60 cm. I fill the trailer to within 20 cm from the top.

   a   How many trailer loads of soil will I need?

   b   Each load of soil costs $27.30. What is the total cost of the soil?

   c   I decide to put bark on top of the soil in the garden. Each load covers 11 m^2 of garden bed.

     i   How many loads of bark will I need?

     ii   Each load of bark costs $17.95. What is the total cost of the bark?

   d   Calculate the total cost of establishing the garden.

11   1000 km of black plastic cylindrical water piping with internal diameter 13 mm and walls of thickness 2 mm is required for a major irrigation project. The piping is made from bulk plastic which weighs 2.3 tonnes per cubic metre. How many tonnes of black plastic are required for the project?

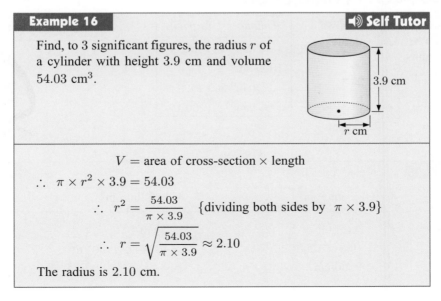

Example 16   ◀⬥ **Self Tutor**

Find, to 3 significant figures, the radius r of a cylinder with height 3.9 cm and volume 54.03 cm^3.

3.9 cm

r cm

V = area of cross-section × length

$\therefore \ \pi \times r^2 \times 3.9 = 54.03$

$\therefore \ r^2 = \dfrac{54.03}{\pi \times 3.9}$ {dividing both sides by $\pi \times 3.9$}

$\therefore \ r = \sqrt{\dfrac{54.03}{\pi \times 3.9}} \approx 2.10$

The radius is 2.10 cm.

12 Find:

    a   the height of a rectangular prism with base 5 cm by 3 cm and volume 40 cm³

    b   the side length of a cube of butter with volume 34.01 cm³

    c   the height of a glass cone with base diameter 24.6 cm and volume 706 cm³

    d   the radius of a spherical weather balloon with volume 73.62 m³

    e   the radius of a steel cylinder with height 4.6 cm and volume 43.75 cm³

    f   the base radius of a conical bin with height 6.2 m and volume 203.9 m³.

F   CAPACITY

> The **capacity** of a container is the quantity of fluid it is capable of holding.

CAPACITY UNITS

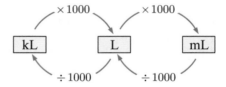

$$1000 \text{ mL} = 1 \text{ L}$$
$$1000 \text{ L} = 1 \text{ kL}$$

	Example 17		◀) Self Tutor

Convert: **a**   3.7 L into mL   **b**   57 620 L into kL

    a   3.7 L = (3.7 × 1000) mL   **b**   57 620 L = (57 620 ÷ 1000) kL
               = 3700 mL   = 57.62 kL

VOLUME-CAPACITY CONNECTION

Alongside is a table which shows the connection between volume and capacity units.

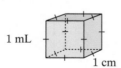

1 mL

1 cm

Volume	Capacity
1 cm³ ≡ 1 mL	
1000 cm³ ≡ 1 L	
1 m³ ≡ 1 kL	
1 m³ ≡ 1000 L	

≡ means 'is equivalent to'

	Example 18		◀) Self Tutor

Convert: **a**   9.6 L into cm³   **b**   3240 L into m³

    a   9.6 L   **b**   3240 L
           = (9.6 × 1000) cm³   = (3240 ÷ 1000) m³
           = 9600 cm³   = 3.24 m³

EXERCISE 14F

1   Convert:

    a 4.21 L into mL
    b 8.63 kL into L
    c 4600 mL into L

    d 56 900 L into kL
    e 3970 mL into kL
    f 0.012 kL into mL

2   **a**   A petrol station begins the week with 143 kL of petrol in its storage tanks. During the week, 2856 people fill up their car tanks, using an average of 35.8 L each. How much petrol is left at the station?

    b   A citrus oil producer sells oil in 200 mL bottles. How many bottles can be filled from a 372 L batch of citrus oil?

3   Convert:

    a 83 kL into m^3
    b 3200 mL into cm^3
    c 2300 cm^3 into L

    d 7154 m^3 into L
    e 0.46 kL into m^3
    f 4.6 kL into cm^3

Example 19   ◀)) **Self Tutor**

Find how many kL of water it takes to fill a 2.6 m by 3.1 m by 1.45 m tank.

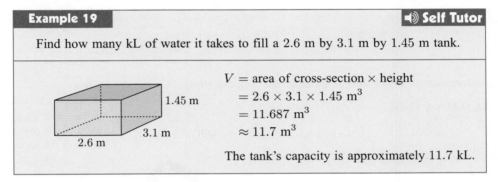

V = area of cross-section × height

$= 2.6 \times 3.1 \times 1.45$ m^3

$= 11.687$ m^3

≈ 11.7 m^3

The tank's capacity is approximately 11.7 kL.

---

4   Find the capacity (in kL) of the following tanks:

    a   **b**   **c**

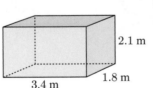
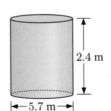
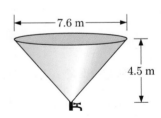

5   How many litres of soup will fit in this hemispherical pot?

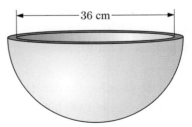

6   A dam wall is built at the narrow point of a river to create a small reservoir. When full, the reservoir has an average depth of 13 m, and has the shape shown in the diagram. Find the capacity of the reservoir.

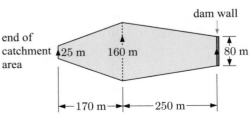

Example 20   ◀) **Self Tutor**

17.3 mm of rain falls on a flat rectangular shed roof of length 10 m and width 6.5 m. All of the water goes into a cylindrical tank with base diameter 4 m. By how many millimetres does the water level in the tank rise?

For the roof: The dimensions of the roof are in m, so we convert 17.3 mm to metres.

$$17.3 \text{ mm} = (17.3 \div 1000) \text{ m} = 0.0173 \text{ m}$$

The volume of water collected by the roof = area of roof × depth
$$= 10 \times 6.5 \times 0.0173 \text{ m}^3$$
$$= 1.1245 \text{ m}^3$$

For the tank: The volume added to the tank
= area of base × height
$$= \pi \times 2^2 \times h \text{ m}^3$$
$$\approx 12.566 \times h \text{ m}^3$$

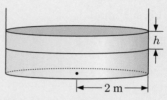

The volume added to the tank must equal the volume which falls on the roof, so

$$12.566 \times h \approx 1.1245$$

$$\therefore \ h \approx \frac{1.1245}{12.566} \quad \text{\{dividing both sides by 12.566\}}$$

$$\therefore \ h \approx 0.0895 \text{ m}$$

$\therefore$ the water level rises by about 89.5 mm.

We can store intermediate values in our calculator to preserve the accuracy of calculations.

**GRAPHICS
CALCULATOR
INSTRUCTIONS**

---

7   The base of a house has area 110 m². One night 12 mm of rain falls on the roof. All of the water goes into a tank of base diameter 4 m.

   a   Find the volume of water which fell on the roof.

   b   How many kL of water entered the tank?

   c   By how much did the water level in the tank rise?

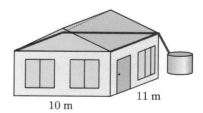

8   A conical wine glass has the dimensions shown.

   a   When the glass is 75% full, how many mL of wine does it contain?

   b   If the wine is poured into a cylinder of the same diameter, how high will it rise?

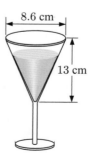

9 Jam is packed into cylindrical tins which are 4.5 cm in radius and 15 cm high. The mixing vat is also cylindrical with a cross-section of 1.2 m² and height of 4.1 m.

   a What is the capacity of jam in each tin?

   b What is the capacity of the mixing vat?

   c How many tins of jam could be filled from one vat?

   d If the jam is sold at €2.05 per tin, what is the value of one vat of jam?

10 The design department of a fish canning company wants to change the size of their cylindrical tins. The original tin is 15 cm high and 7.2 cm in diameter. The new tin is to have approximately the same volume, but its diameter will be 10 cm. How high must it be, to the nearest mm?

11 A fleet of trucks have containers with the shape illustrated. Wheat is transported in these containers, and its level must not exceed a mark 10 cm below the top. How many truck loads of wheat are necessary to fill a cylindrical silo with internal diameter 8 m and height 25 m?

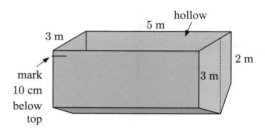

INVESTIGATION   MINIMISING MATERIAL

Your boss asks you to design a rectangular box-shaped container which is open at the top and contains exactly 1 litre of fluid. The base measurements must be in the ratio 2 : 1. She intends to manufacture millions of these containers and wishes to keep manufacturing costs to a minimum. She therefore insists that the least amount of material is used.

What to do:

1 The base is to be in the ratio 2 : 1, so we let the dimensions be x cm and $2x$ cm. The height is also unknown, so we let it be y cm. As the values of x and y vary, the container changes size.

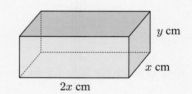

   Explain why:

   a the volume $V = 2x^2y$ **b** $2x^2y = 1000$ **c** $y = \dfrac{500}{x^2}$

2 Show that the surface area is given by $A = 2x^2 + 6xy$.

3 Design a **spreadsheet** which, for given values of $x = 1, 2, 3, 4, ...,$ calculates y and A

   or use a **graphics calculator** to graph A against x.

	A	B	C
1	x values	y values	A values
2	1	=500/A2^2	=2*A2^2+6*A2*B2
3	=A2+1		
4	↓	↓	fill down ↓

SPREADSHEET

4 Find the smallest value of A, and the value of x which produces it. Hence write down the dimensions of the box your boss desires.

G | **DENSITY (EXTENSION)**

Imagine two containers with capacity 1 kL. If one container was filled with concrete and the other container with feathers, which do you think would weigh more?

Obviously the container of concrete would have greater **mass** than the container of feathers. We say that concrete has a higher **density** than feathers.

> The **mass** of an object is the amount of matter it contains.

> **One gram** is the mass of one cubic centimetre of pure water at $4°C$.

DENSITY

> The **density** of a substance is its mass per unit volume.
> $$\text{density} = \frac{\text{mass}}{\text{volume}}$$

For example, the density of water is 1 g per 1 cm^3 or $\dfrac{1 \text{ g}}{1 \text{ cm}^3}$ or 1 g cm^{-3}.

Some common densities are shown in the following table:

Substance	Density ($g\,cm^{-3}$)
pine wood	0.65
paper	0.93
water	1.00
steel	7.82
lead	11.37
uranium	18.97

We can rearrange the formula for density to obtain

$$\textbf{mass} = \textbf{density} \times \textbf{volume} \qquad \text{and} \qquad \textbf{volume} = \frac{\textbf{mass}}{\textbf{density}}.$$

Example 21   ◀) **Self Tutor**

Find the density of a metal with mass 25 g and volume 4 cm^3.

$\text{Density} = \dfrac{\text{mass}}{\text{volume}}$

$= \dfrac{25 \text{ g}}{4 \text{ cm}^3}$

$= 6.25 \text{ g cm}^{-3}$

EXERCISE 14G

1 Find the density of:

    a a metal with mass 10 g and volume 2 cm^3

    b a substance with mass 2 g and volume 1.5 cm^3.

2 Find the density of:

    a a cube of chocolate with sides 2 cm and mass 18 g

    b a 15 cm by 8 cm by 4 cm rectangular block of metal with mass 9.6 kg.

3 What volume is occupied by a lump of metal with mass 3.62 kg and density 11.6 g cm^{-3}?

4 Find the mass of a 5 cm diameter sphere of a metal which has a density of 8.7 g cm^{-3}.

5 A gold ingot with the dimensions shown has mass 12.36 kg.
Determine the density of gold.

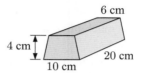

6 A rectangular block of metal has base 7 cm by 5 cm. The block has total mass 1285 g and the metal has density 7.5 g cm^{-3}. How high is the block?

7 Polystyrene spherical beads have an average diameter of 0.6 cm. The density of polystyrene is 0.15 g cm^{-3}. Estimate the total number of beads in a box of beads with total mass 8 kg.

8 Determine the total mass of stone required to build a square-based pyramid with all edges of length 200 m. The density of the stone is 2.25 tonnes per m^3.

H   HARDER APPLICATIONS

EXERCISE 14H

1 A feed silo is made out of sheet steel 3 mm thick using a hemisphere, a cylinder, and a cone.

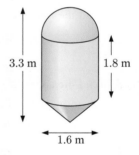

    a Explain why the height of the cone must be 70 cm, and hence find the *slant* height of the conical section.

    b Calculate the surface area of each of the three sections, and hence show that the total amount of steel used is about 15.7 square metres.

    c Show that the silo would hold about 5.2 cubic metres of grain when completely full.

    d Grain has a density of 0.68 g cm^{-3}, and the density of steel is 8 g cm^{-3}. Find the total weight of the silo when it is full.

2 When work has to be done on underground telephone cables, workers often use a small tent over the opening. This shelters them from bad weather and stops passers-by from absent-mindedly falling in on top of them. The cover is constructed from canvas, and this is supported by a tubular steel frame, as shown.

Use the measurements from the diagram to calculate:

    a the length of steel tubing needed to make the frame

    b the amount of room inside the tent in m^3

    c the amount of canvas in m^2 needed for the cover.

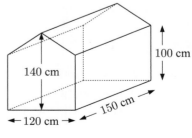

3 A ready mixed concrete tanker is to be constructed of steel as a cylinder with conical ends.

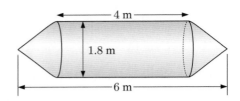

   a Calculate the total volume of concrete that can be held in the tanker.

   b How *long* would the tanker be if the ends were hemispheres instead of cones but the cylindrical section remained the same? Explain your reasoning.

   c How much more or less concrete would fit in the tanker if the ends were hemispheres instead of cones?

   d Show that the surface area of the tanker:

     i with conical ends is about 30 m²   **ii** with hemispherical ends is about 33 m².

   e Using the figures you have from **a** to **d**, discuss the advantages of each design. Overall, which do you think is the better design for the tanker? Give reasons for your answer.

REVIEW SET 14A

1 Convert: **a** 30.5 kg to t   **b** 0.093 kL to mL   **c** 8033 mm³ to cm³

2 Moana tiles her bathroom floor with 12 cm by 12 cm tiles. The area of the floor is 4.96 m². Determine how many tiles she will need, assuming 10% extra are required for tiles which must be cut.

3 Find, correct to 2 decimal places, the circumference of a circle of diameter 16.4 m.

4 An athletics track is to have a perimeter of 400 m and straights of 78 m.
Find the radius r of the circular 'bend'.

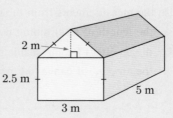

5 Find the area of:

   a a rectangular airport 3.4 km by 2.1 km

   b a semi-circular garden with radius 5.64 m.

6

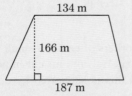

Find the area of the horse paddock shown alongside in:

   a square metres   **b** hectares.

7 A tool shed with the dimensions illustrated is to be painted with *two coats* of zinc-alum. Each litre of zinc-alum covers 5 m² and costs $8.25. It must be purchased in whole litres.

   a Find the area to be painted including the roof. Reduce your answer by 5% to allow for windows.

   b Find the total cost of the zinc-alum.

8 A fish farm has six netted cylindrical cages open at the top. The cylinders have depth 17 m and diameter 7.5 m. Find the area of netting required.

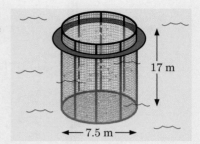

9 Calculate, correct to 3 significant figures, the volume of:

a

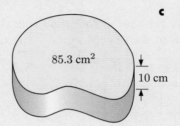

3.2 m   1.56 m²

b

85.3 cm²

10 cm

c

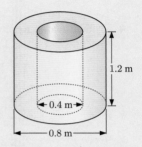

1.2 m

0.4 m

0.8 m

10 Tom has just had a load of sand delivered. The pile of sand is in the shape of a cone of radius 1.6 m and height 1.2 m. Find the volume of the sand.

11 A cylindrical drum for storing industrial waste has capacity 10 kL. If the height of the drum is 3 m, find its radius.

12 Frank wants to have a large concrete F outside his shop for advertising. He designs one to the dimensions shown.
What volume of concrete will Frank need?

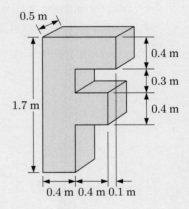

0.5 m

0.4 m

0.3 m

1.7 m

0.4 m

0.4 m 0.4 m 0.1 m

13 Find:

   a the density of a pebble with mass 19 g and volume 7 cm³

   b the volume of an oak log with density 710 kg m⁻³ and mass 1150 kg.

REVIEW SET 14B

1

1.6 m

2.4 m

A window has the design shown.
What length of wood is needed to build the frame?

2 Convert:

  a 23 L to m^3 **b** 5062 ha to km^2 **c** 0.534 g to mg

3

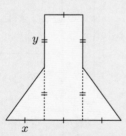

In the Cardone Gardens there is a 4 m diameter circular pond surrounded by a 1.5 m wide brick border. A chain fence is placed around the border with posts every 2 m.

  a Find the length of the chain required for the fence. Allow 10% extra for the sag in the chain.

  b How many posts are needed?

4 Louise wants to pave her new outdoor patio with slate tiles. The area to be covered is 4.8 m by 3.6 m. Louise has to decide between:

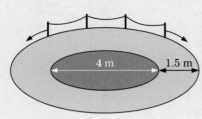

Style 1:   30 cm by 30 cm   *Style 2:*   40 cm by 20 cm
              costing \$4.55 per tile   costing \$3.95 per tile

  a Calculate the area to be paved.
  b Find the area of a single slate tile of each style.
  c Find the number of tiles needed for each style.
  d Compare the total cost of using the different styles. Which would be cheaper?

5 Find a formula for the area A of each shaded region:

  a   **b**   **c**

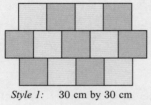

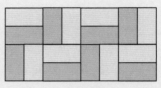

6 Find the outer surface area, to 1 decimal place, of:

  a   **b**   **c**

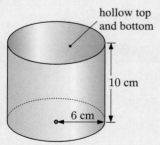

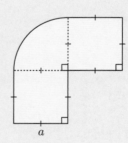

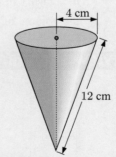

7 Fiona purchased 400 m^2 of plastic sheeting and needs to cut it into rectangles of area 500 cm^2. This can be done with no waste. How many rectangles can Fiona cut?

8 The hexagonal gazebo shown has wood panelling for the roof, floor, and part of five of the walls. Find the total surface area of wood panelling in the gazebo.

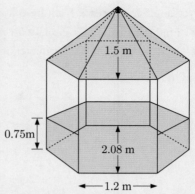

9 A manufacturer of spikes has 0.245 kL of molten iron. If each spike contains 15 mL of iron, how many spikes can be made?

10 A plastic beach ball has a radius of 27 cm. Find its volume.

11

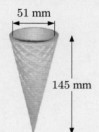

A gelateria sells gelato in cones with the dimensions opposite. The cone is filled completely, with a hemispherical scoop on top.

a Find the volume of gelato sold with each cone.

b How many cones can be sold from 10 L of gelato?

12 A rectangular shed has a roof of length 12 m and width 5.5 m. Rainfall from the roof runs into a cylindrical tank with base diameter 4.35 m. If 15.4 mm of rain falls, how many millimetres does the water level in the tank rise?

13 At the top of the Washington Monument, there is an aluminium square-based pyramid with base length 14.2 cm and height 22.6 cm. Aluminium has density 2.7 $g\,cm^{-3}$.

a Find the mass of the pyramid.

b The pyramid actually weighs about 2.8 kg. Suggest a reason for the difference in mass.

REVIEW SET 14C

1 Convert:

a 24.3 mm to m   **b** 0.032 m^3 to cm^3 **c** 845 mg to kg

2 Half a tonne of rubber is to be turned into 20 g erasers. How many erasers can be made?

3 A tourist walks all the way around the "Praça do Império", a large city square in Lisbon with sides 280 m long. How far did the tourist walk?

4 Write an expression for the perimeter of:

a

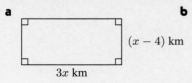

b

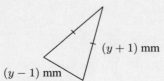

c

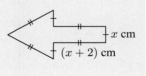

5 A rectangle measures 7.1 cm by 6.3 cm.

   a Find the radius of a circle with the same area.

   b Which has a shorter perimeter, and by how much?

6 Find the volume of:

  a

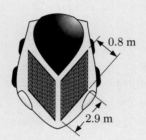

8.1 cm

4.4 cm

  b

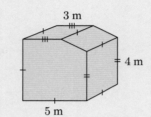

3 m

4 m

5 m

  c

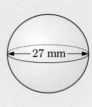

27 mm

7

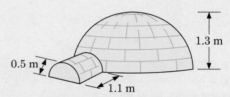

0.8 m

2.9 m

A solar powered car runs on two parallelogram-shaped solar panels. Find the area of panelling on the car.

8 Find the volume of the igloo alongside.

1.3 m

0.5 m

1.1 m

9 A kitchen bench is a rectangular prism measuring 3845 mm by 1260 mm by 1190 mm. It contains a rectangular sink which is 550 mm wide, 750 mm long, and 195 mm deep. Find the storage capacity of the bench in litres.

10 I am sending my sister some fragile objects inside a postal cylinder. The cylinder is 325 mm long and has diameter 40 mm. What area of bubble wrap do I need to line its inside walls?

11 500 dozen bottles of wine, each of capacity 750 mL, are to be filled from tanks of capacity 1000 L. How many tanks are needed?

12 Find:

   a the length of a triangular prism with end area 61 cm^2 and volume 671 cm^3

   b the radius of a circle of area 98 m^2

   c the height of a cone with base radius 5 cm and volume 288 cm^3.

13 A set of plastic cubic dice contains six 16 mm dice. The set weighs 23 g. Find the density of the plastic in g cm^{-3}.

Chapter 15

Trigonometry

Syllabus reference: 5.2, 5.3, 5.4

OPENING PROBLEM

A triangular sail is cut from a section of cloth. Two of the sides have lengths 4 m and 6 m as illustrated. The total area of the sail is 11.6 m², the maximum allowed for the boat to race in its class.

Things to think about:

a Can you find the size of the angle θ between the two sides of given length?

b Can you find the length of the third side?

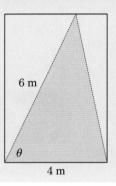

To answer the questions posed in the **Opening Problem**, we need to study **trigonometry**. This is the branch of mathematics which connects the angles and side lengths of triangles.

A   LABELLING RIGHT ANGLED TRIANGLES

The **hypotenuse (HYP)** of a right angled triangle is the side which is opposite the right angle. It is the longest side of the triangle.

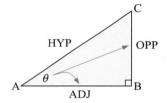

For the angle marked θ:

- BC is the side **opposite (OPP)** angle θ
- AB is the side **adjacent (ADJ)** to angle θ.

For the angle marked ϕ:

- AB is the side **opposite (OPP)** angle ϕ
- BC is the side **adjacent (ADJ)** to angle ϕ.

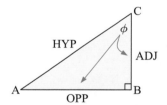

Example 1   ◀》 Self Tutor

For the triangle alongside, find the:

a hypotenuse
b side opposite α
c side adjacent to α
d side opposite β
e side adjacent to β.

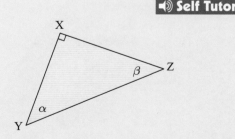

a The hypotenuse is the side opposite the right angle. This is side YZ.

b The side opposite α is XZ.   **c** The side adjacent to α is XY.

d The side opposite β is XY.   **e** The side adjacent to β is XZ.

EXERCISE 15A

1 For the triangles below, find the:

     i hypotenuse   **ii** side opposite α **iii** side adjacent to α.

a 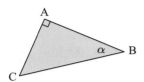   **b** 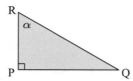   **c**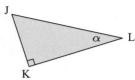

2 For the triangle alongside, find the length of the:

   a hypotenuse

   b side opposite θ

   c side adjacent to θ

   d side opposite ϕ

   e side adjacent to ϕ.

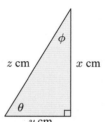

B   THE TRIGONOMETRIC RATIOS

Consider a right angled triangle with an angle θ. We label the sides OPP for the side opposite θ, ADJ for the side adjacent to θ, and HYP for the hypotenuse.

We define three **trigonometric ratios** which are the **sine**, **cosine**, and **tangent** of the angle θ, in terms of the side lengths.

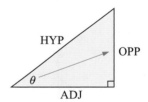

These ratios are:

$$\sin\theta = \frac{\text{OPP}}{\text{HYP}} \qquad \cos\theta = \frac{\text{ADJ}}{\text{HYP}} \qquad \tan\theta = \frac{\text{OPP}}{\text{ADJ}}$$

We use the trigonometric ratios as tools for finding side lengths and angles of right angled triangles.

FINDING TRIGONOMETRIC RATIOS

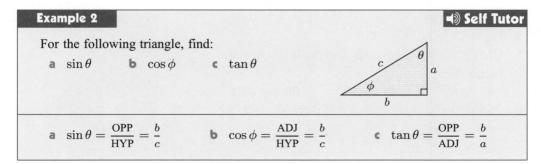

Example 2   ◀) **Self Tutor**

For the following triangle, find:

   a $\sin\theta$ **b** $\cos\phi$ **c** $\tan\theta$

a $\sin\theta = \dfrac{\text{OPP}}{\text{HYP}} = \dfrac{b}{c}$ **b** $\cos\phi = \dfrac{\text{ADJ}}{\text{HYP}} = \dfrac{b}{c}$ **c** $\tan\theta = \dfrac{\text{OPP}}{\text{ADJ}} = \dfrac{b}{a}$

EXERCISE 15B.1

1 For each of the following triangles, find:

      i $\sin\theta$ **ii** $\cos\theta$ **iii** $\tan\theta$

a
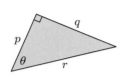

b
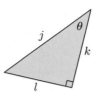

c
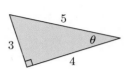

2 For each of the following triangles, find:

    i $\sin\theta$ **ii** $\cos\theta$ **iii** $\tan\theta$ **iv** $\sin\phi$ **v** $\cos\phi$ **vi** $\tan\phi$

a
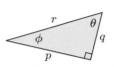

b
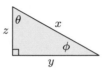

c
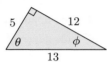

d
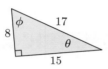

e
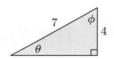

f
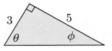

3 The right angled triangle alongside contains an angle of $56°$.

  a Use a ruler to measure the length of each side, to the nearest millimetre.

  b Hence estimate the value, to 2 decimal places, of:

      i $\sin 56°$ **ii** $\cos 56°$

      iii $\tan 56°$.

  c Check your answers using a calculator.

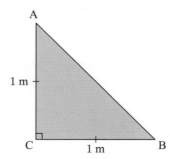

GRAPHICS CALCULATOR INSTRUCTIONS

4 Consider the right angled isosceles triangle ABC alongside.

  a Explain why $\widehat{ABC} = 45°$.

  b Use Pythagoras' theorem to find the length of AB.

  c Hence find:

      i $\sin 45°$ **ii** $\cos 45°$ **iii** $\tan 45°$.

  d Check your answers using a calculator.

INVESTIGATION 1   COMPLEMENTARY ANGLES

Two angles are **complementary** if their sum is 90°. We say that θ and $(90° - \theta)$ are   **PRINTABLE WORKSHEET**
complements of each other.

Your task is to determine if a relationship exists between the sines and cosines of an angle and its complement.

What to do:

1 With the aid of a calculator, complete a table like the one shown. Include some angles of your choice.

θ	$\sin \theta$	$\cos \theta$	$90° - \theta$	$\sin(90° - \theta)$	$\cos(90° - \theta)$
17°			73°		
38°					
59°					

2 Write down your observations from the table.

3 Use the figure alongside to prove that your observations are true for all angles θ where $0° < \theta < 90°$.

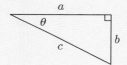

4 Investigate possible connections between $\tan \theta$ and $\tan(90° - \theta)$.

HISTORICAL NOTE

The origin of the term "sine" is quite fascinating. **Arbyabhata**, a Hindu mathematician who studied trigonometry in the 5th century AD, called the sine-leg of a circle diagram "ardha-jya" which means "half-chord". This was eventually shortened to "jya".

When Arab scholars later translated Arbyabhata's work into Arabic, they initially translated "jya" phonetically as "jiba". Since this meant nothing in Arabic, they very shortly began writing the word as "jaib", which has the same letters but means "cove" or "bay".

In 1150, **Gerardo of Cremona** translated this work into Latin. He replaced "jaib" with "sinus", which means "bend" or "curve" but was commonly used in Latin to refer to a bay or gulf on a coastline. The term "sine" that we use today comes from this Latin word.

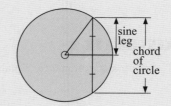

The term "cosine" comes from the fact that the cosine of an angle is equal to the sine of its complement. In 1620, **Edmund Gunter** introduced the abbreviated "co sinus" for "complementary sine".

FINDING SIDES

In a right angled triangle where we are given one other angle and the length of one of the sides, we can use the trigonometric ratios to find either of the remaining sides.

> *Step 1:*   Redraw the figure and mark on it HYP, OPP, ADJ relative to the given angle.
>
> *Step 2:*   Choose the correct trigonometric ratio and use it to construct an equation.
>
> *Step 3:*   Solve the equation to find the unknown.

Example 3   ◀)) **Self Tutor**

Find, to 3 significant figures, the unknown length in the
following triangles:

Make sure your
calculator is set to
degrees mode.

a
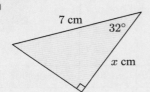
7 cm
32°
x cm

b
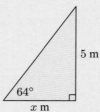
5 m
64°
x m

a
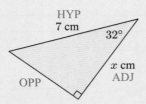
HYP
7 cm
32°
x cm
ADJ
OPP

The sides of interest are the *adjacent* side and the
hypotenuse, so we use the cosine ratio.

$$\cos 32° = \frac{x}{7} \qquad \{ \cos \theta = \frac{\text{ADJ}}{\text{HYP}} \}$$

$$\therefore \ 7 \times \cos 32° = x$$

$$\therefore \ x \approx 5.94 \qquad \textbf{TI-84 Plus}:$$

7 $\boxed{\times}$ $\boxed{\text{COS}}$ 32 $\boxed{\text{ENTER}}$

So, the side is about 5.94 cm long.

b

HYP
OPP
5 m
64°
x m
ADJ

The sides of interest are the *adjacent* side and the
opposite side, so we use the tangent ratio.

$$\tan 64° = \frac{5}{x} \qquad \{ \tan \theta = \frac{\text{OPP}}{\text{ADJ}} \}$$

$$\therefore \ x \times \tan 64° = 5$$

$$\therefore \ x = \frac{5}{\tan 64°}$$

$$\therefore \ x \approx 2.44 \qquad \textbf{Casio fx-CG20}:$$

5 $\boxed{\div}$ $\boxed{\text{tan}}$ 64 $\boxed{\text{EXE}}$

So, the side is about 2.44 m long.

EXERCISE 15B.2

1 Set up a trigonometric equation connecting the given angle and sides:

a

x
21°
k

b
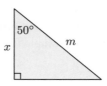
50°
x
m

c
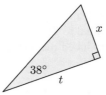
x
38°
t

d
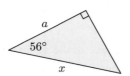
a
56°
x

e
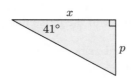
x
41°
p

f
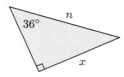
36°
n
x

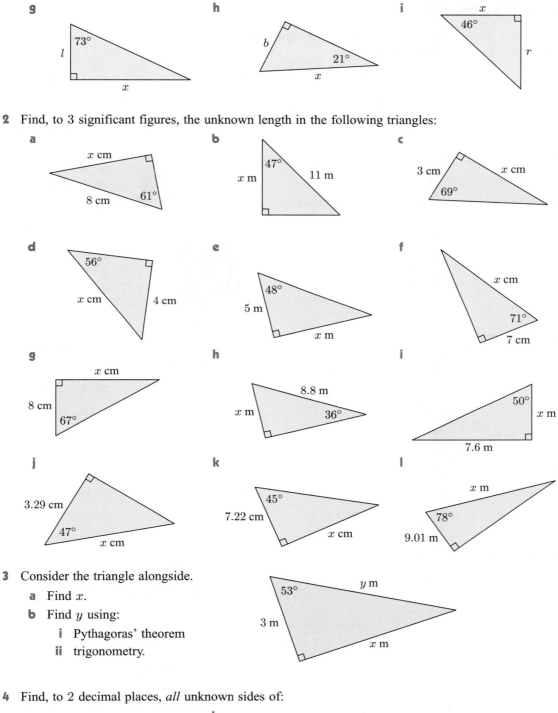

g 73°, l, x

h b, 21°, x

i x, 46°, r

2 Find, to 3 significant figures, the unknown length in the following triangles:

a x cm, 8 cm, 61°

b 47°, x m, 11 m

c 3 cm, x cm, 69°

d 56°, x cm, 4 cm

e 48°, 5 m, x m

f x cm, 71°, 7 cm

g x cm, 8 cm, 67°

h 8.8 m, x m, 36°

i 50°, x m, 7.6 m

j 3.29 cm, 47°, x cm

k 45°, 7.22 cm, x cm

l x m, 78°, 9.01 m

3 Consider the triangle alongside.
  a Find x.
  b Find y using:
    i Pythagoras' theorem
    ii trigonometry.

53°, y m, 3 m, x m

4 Find, to 2 decimal places, *all* unknown sides of:

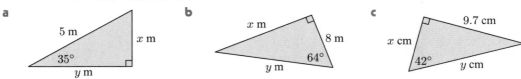

a 5 m, x m, 35°, y m

b x m, 8 m, 64°, y m

c 9.7 cm, x cm, 42°, y cm

FINDING ANGLES

If we know the lengths of two sides of a right angled triangle, we can find the size of its angles.

Suppose we want to find the size of angle θ in the triangle alongside.

We can see that $\sin \theta = \frac{2}{3}$, so we need to find the angle θ whose sine is $\frac{2}{3}$.

We say that θ is the **inverse sine** of $\frac{2}{3}$. We write $\theta = \sin^{-1}\left(\frac{2}{3}\right)$ and evaluate using our graphics calculator.

The **inverse cosine** and **inverse tangent** functions work in a similar way.

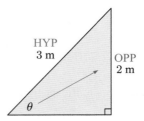

GRAPHICS CALCULATOR INSTRUCTIONS

$\sin^{-1}(x)$ is the angle with a sine of x.

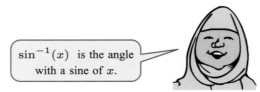

Example 4   ◀)) **Self Tutor**

Find, to 3 significant figures, the measure of the angle marked θ in:

a
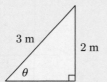

b
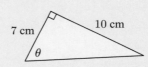

---

a
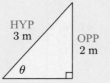

$\sin \theta = \frac{2}{3}$ $\left\{\sin \theta = \dfrac{\text{OPP}}{\text{HYP}}\right\}$

$\therefore \ \theta = \sin^{-1}\left(\frac{2}{3}\right)$

$\therefore \ \theta \approx 41.8°$ **TI-84 Plus**:

b
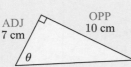

$\tan \theta = \frac{10}{7}$ $\left\{\tan \theta = \dfrac{\text{OPP}}{\text{ADJ}}\right\}$

$\therefore \ \theta = \tan^{-1}\left(\frac{10}{7}\right)$

$\therefore \ \theta \approx 55.0°$ **Casio fx-CG20**:

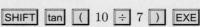

EXERCISE 15B.3

1 Find, to 3 significant figures, the measure of the angle marked θ in:

a
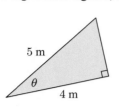
5 m
4 m
θ

b
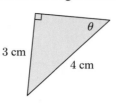
3 cm
4 cm
θ

c
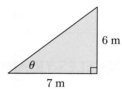
6 m
7 m
θ

d
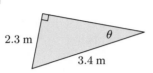
2.3 m
3.4 m
θ

e
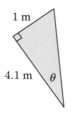
1 m
4.1 m
θ
θ

f
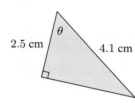
2.5 cm
4.1 cm
θ

g
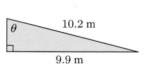
10.2 m
9.9 m
θ

h

2 cm
4 cm
θ

i

80 cm
1.1 m
θ

2 Consider the triangle alongside.

a Find θ, correct to 1 decimal place.

b Find ϕ using:

  i the angles in a triangle theorem

  ii trigonometry.

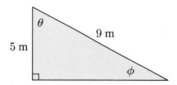
θ
9 m
5 m
ϕ

3 Find, to 1 decimal place, all unknown angles in:

a
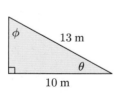
ϕ
13 m
θ
10 m

b
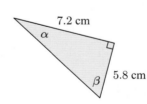
7.2 cm
α
β
5.8 cm

c
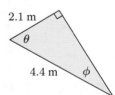
2.1 m
θ
4.4 m
ϕ

4 Try to find θ in the following. What conclusions can you draw?

a
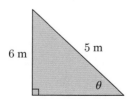
6 m
5 m
θ

b
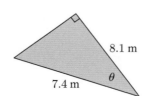
8.1 m
7.4 m
θ

c
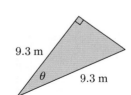
9.3 m
9.3 m
θ

C   USING TRIGONOMETRY IN GEOMETRIC FIGURES

We can use trigonometry to find unknown lengths and angles in special geometric figures which contain right angled triangles.

ISOSCELES TRIANGLES

To use trigonometry with isosceles triangles we draw the **perpendicular** from the apex to the base. This altitude **bisects** the base.

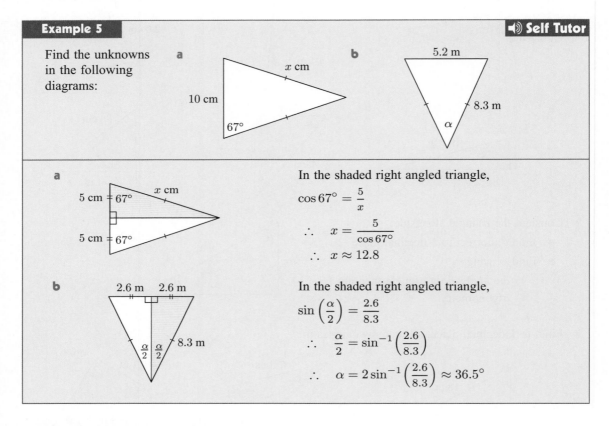

Example 5   ◄》 **Self Tutor**

Find the unknowns in the following diagrams:

a   In the shaded right angled triangle,

$$\cos 67° = \frac{5}{x}$$

$$\therefore \quad x = \frac{5}{\cos 67°}$$

$$\therefore \quad x \approx 12.8$$

b   In the shaded right angled triangle,

$$\sin\left(\frac{\alpha}{2}\right) = \frac{2.6}{8.3}$$

$$\therefore \quad \frac{\alpha}{2} = \sin^{-1}\left(\frac{2.6}{8.3}\right)$$

$$\therefore \quad \alpha = 2\sin^{-1}\left(\frac{2.6}{8.3}\right) \approx 36.5°$$

SPECIAL QUADRILATERALS

Right angled triangles can also be found in special quadrilaterals such as rectangles, rhombi, trapezia, and kites.

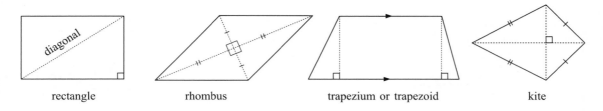

rectangle   rhombus   trapezium or trapezoid   kite

Example 6

🔊 **Self Tutor**

A rhombus has diagonals of length 10 cm and 6 cm.
Find the smaller angle of the rhombus.

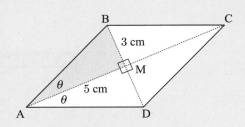

The diagonals of a rhombus bisect each other at right angles, so $AM = 5$ cm and $BM = 3$ cm.

In $\triangle ABM$, θ will be the smallest angle, as it is opposite the shortest side.

$$\tan \theta = \tfrac{3}{5}$$
$$\therefore \quad \theta = \tan^{-1}\left(\tfrac{3}{5}\right)$$
$$\therefore \quad \theta \approx 30.964°$$

The required angle is 2θ as the diagonals bisect the angles at each vertex.
So, the angle is about $61.9°$.

EXERCISE 15C.1

1 Find, correct to 3 significant figures, the unknowns in the following:

a

b

c

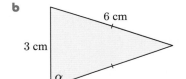

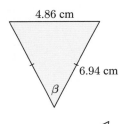

d

e

f

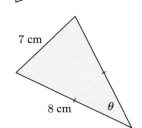

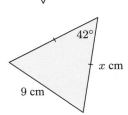

2 A rectangle is 9.2 m by 3.8 m. What angle does its diagonal make with its longer side?

3 The diagonal and the longer side of a rectangle make an angle of $43.2°$. If the longer side is 12.6 cm, find the length of the shorter side.

4 A rhombus has diagonals of length 12 cm and 7 cm. Find the larger angle of the rhombus.

5 The smaller angle of a rhombus measures $21.8°$ and the shorter diagonal has length 13.8 cm. Find the lengths of the sides of the rhombus.

6 A rectangular field is 20 metres longer than it is wide. When Patrick walks from one corner to the opposite corner, he makes an angle of $55°$ with the shorter side of the field. Find the width of the field.

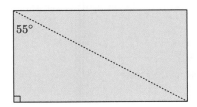

7 Find θ.

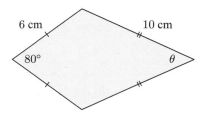

6 cm   10 cm

80° θ

Example 7   ◄ Self Tutor

Find x given:

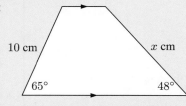

10 cm x cm

65°   48°

We draw perpendiculars AM and BN to DC, creating right angled triangles and the rectangle ABNM.

In $\triangle$ADM, $\sin 65° = \dfrac{y}{10}$

$\therefore \; y = 10\sin 65°$

In $\triangle$BCN, $\sin 48° = \dfrac{y}{x}$

$= \dfrac{10\sin 65°}{x}$

$\therefore \; x = \dfrac{10\sin 65°}{\sin 48°}$

≈ 12.2

To maintain accuracy during this calculation, we leave the value $y = 10\sin 65°$ in exact form.

A   B

10 cm y cm y cm x cm

65°   48°

D   M   N   C

8 **a** Find the value of x:

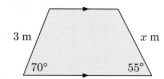

3 m x m

70°   55°

b Find the value of α:

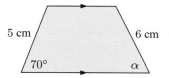

5 cm   6 cm

70° α

9 A stormwater drain has the shape illustrated. Determine angle β where the left hand side meets with the bottom of the drain.

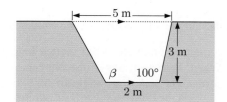

5 m

3 m

β 100°

2 m

CHORDS AND TANGENTS (EXTENSION)

Right angled triangles also occur in chord and tangent problems.

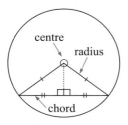

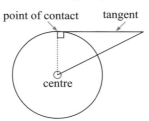

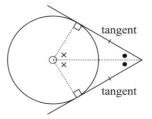

Example 8	◀) **Self Tutor**

A chord of a circle subtends an angle of $112°$ at its centre. Find the length of the chord if the radius of the circle is 6.5 cm.

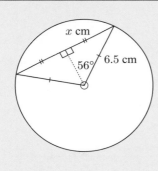

We complete an isosceles triangle and draw the line from the apex to the base.

For the $56°$ angle, HYP $= 6.5$ and OPP $= x$

$$\therefore \quad \sin 56° = \frac{x}{6.5}$$
$$\therefore \quad 6.5 \times \sin 56° = x$$
$$\therefore \quad x \approx 5.389$$
$$\therefore \quad 2x \approx 10.78$$

The chord is about 10.8 cm long.

EXERCISE 15C.2

1 Find the value of the unknown in:

a

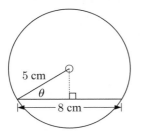

b

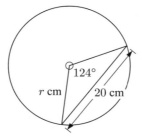

c

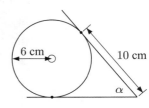

2 A chord of a circle subtends an angle of $89°$ at its centre. Find the length of the chord given that the circle's diameter is 11.4 cm.

3 A chord of a circle is 13.2 cm long and the circle's radius is 9.4 cm. Find the angle subtended by the chord at the centre of the circle.

4 Point P is 10 cm from the centre of a circle of radius 4 cm. Tangents are drawn from P to the circle. Find the angle between the tangents.

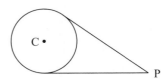

5 A circular clock has dots on its boundary which indicate the numbers 1 to 12. The dots representing 10 and 2 are 24 cm apart. Find the radius of the clock.

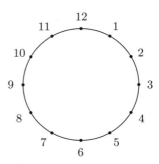

D   PROBLEM SOLVING USING TRIGONOMETRY

Trigonometry is a very useful branch of mathematics. **Heights** and **distances** which are very difficult or even impossible to measure can often be found using trigonometry.

ANGLES OF ELEVATION AND DEPRESSION

The angle between the horizontal and your line of sight to an object is called the **angle of elevation** if you are looking upwards, or the **angle of depression** if you are looking downwards.

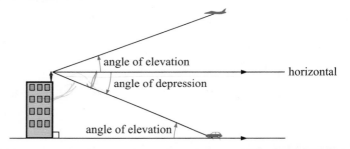

Example 9   ◀ Self Tutor

When measured from a point 12.4 m from its base, the angle of elevation to the top of a tree is 52°. Find the height of the tree.

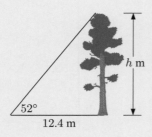

Let h be the tree's height in metres.

For the 52° angle, OPP $= h$ and ADJ $= 12.4$

$$\therefore \quad \tan 52° = \frac{h}{12.4}$$

$$\therefore \quad 12.4 \times \tan 52° = h$$

$$\therefore \quad h \approx 15.9$$

So, the tree is 15.9 m high.

EXERCISE 15D

1 When measured from a point 9.32 m from its base, the angle of elevation to the top of a flagpole is 63°. Find the height of the flagpole.

2 A hill is inclined at 18° to the horizontal. It runs down to the beach with constant gradient so its base is at sea level.

   a If I walk 1.2 km up the hill, what is my height above sea level?

   b If I am 500 metres above sea level, how far have I walked up the hill?

3

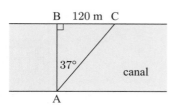

A surveyor standing at A notices two posts B and C on the opposite side of a canal. The posts are 120 m apart. If the angle of sight between the posts is 37°, how wide is the canal?

4 A train must climb a constant gradient of 5.5 m for every 200 m of track. Find the angle of incline.

5 **a** Find the angle of elevation to the top of a 56 m high building from point A, which is 113 m from its base.

   b What is the angle of depression from the top of the building to A?

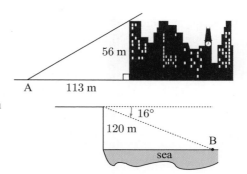

6 The angle of depression from the top of a 120 m high vertical cliff to a boat B is 16°.

How far is the boat from the base of the cliff?

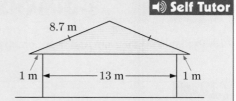

Example 10   ◀》 Self Tutor

A builder has designed the roof structure illustrated.   The pitch of the roof is the angle that the roof makes with the horizontal. Find the pitch of this roof.

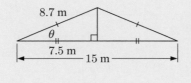

By constructing an altitude of the isosceles triangle, we form two right angled triangles. For angle θ, ADJ $= 7.5$ and HYP $= 8.7$

$$\therefore\quad \cos\theta = \frac{7.5}{8.7}$$

$$\therefore\quad \theta = \cos^{-1}\left(\frac{7.5}{8.7}\right)$$

$$\therefore\quad \theta \approx 30.45°$$

The pitch of the roof is approximately 30.5°.

---

7 Find θ, the pitch of the roof.

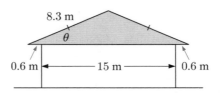

8

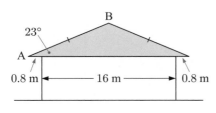

The pitch of the given roof is 23°. Find the length of the timber beam AB.

9 From an observer O, 200 m from a building, the angles of
elevation to the bottom and the top of a flagpole are 36°
and 38° respectively. Find the height of the flagpole.

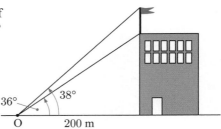

10 Kylie measures a 32° angle of elevation from a point on level ground to the top of a building
120 metres high. She walks towards the building until the angle of elevation is 45°. How far does
she walk?

11 The angle of depression from the top of a 150 m high cliff to a boat at sea is 7°. How much closer
to the cliff must the boat move for the angle of depression to become 19°?

12 A helicopter flies horizontally at 100 km h^{-1}. It takes 20 seconds for the helicopter to fly from
directly overhead to being at an angle of elevation of 60°. Find the height of the helicopter above
the ground.

E   3-DIMENSIONAL PROBLEM SOLVING

We can use Pythagoras' theorem and trigonometry to find unknown angles and lengths in 3-dimensional
figures.

Example 11   ◀) **Self Tutor**

A rectangular prism has the dimensions shown alongside.
Find the angle between the diagonal AB and the edge BC.

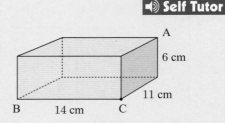

Consider the end of the prism containing A and C.
Let AC be x cm.

By Pythagoras, $x^2 = 6^2 + 11^2$

$\therefore\ x^2 = 157$

$\therefore\ x = \sqrt{157}$

The points A, B, and C form a triangle which is
right angled at $B\widehat{C}A$.

$$\tan\theta = \frac{\text{OPP}}{\text{ADJ}} = \frac{\sqrt{157}}{14}$$

$$\therefore\ \theta = \tan^{-1}\left(\frac{\sqrt{157}}{14}\right)$$

$$\therefore\ \theta \approx 41.8°$$

So, the required angle is 41.8°.

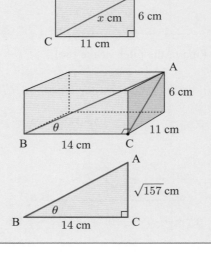

EXERCISE 15E.1

1 The cube shown has sides of length 13 cm. Find:

   a BD   **b** the angle FDB.

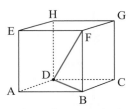

2

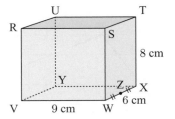

In the rectangular prism shown, Z is the midpoint of XW. Find:

   a VX   **b** the angle RXV

   c YZ   **d** the angle YZU.

3 An open cone has a vertical angle measuring $40°$ and a base radius of 30 cm. Find:

   a the height of the cone

   b the capacity of the cone in litres.

4

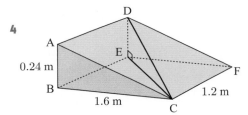

A wooden ramp is built as a triangular prism with supports DC and CE. Find:

   a the length of the supports

   b the angle between them.

5 Elizabeth is terrified of spiders. When she walks into a room, she notices one in the opposite corner of the room from where she is standing.

   a If Elizabeth is 1.6 m tall, how far is the spider from her head?

   b This type of spider can see up to an angle of $42°$ from the direction it is facing. This spider is facing a fly at F. Can it see Elizabeth?

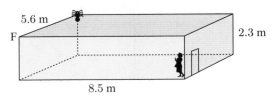

6 All edges of a square-based pyramid are 12 m in length.

   a Find the angle between a slant edge and a base diagonal.

   b Show that this angle is the same for any square-based pyramid with all edge lengths equal.

SHADOW LINES (PROJECTIONS)

Consider a wire frame in the shape of a cube as shown in the diagram alongside. Imagine a light source shining directly onto this cube from above.

The shadow cast by wire AG would be EG. This is called the **projection** of AG onto the base plane EFGH.

Similarly, the projection of BG onto the base plane is FG.

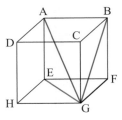

Example 12

🔊 Self Tutor

Find the shadow or projection of the following onto the base plane if a light is shone from directly above the rectangular prism:

a UP   **b** WP

c VP   **d** XP

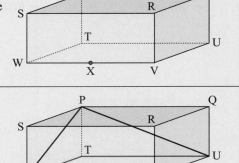

a The projection of UP onto the base plane is UT.

b The projection of WP onto the base plane is WT.

c The projection of VP onto the base plane is VT.

d The projection of XP onto the base plane is XT.

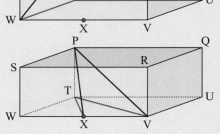

THE ANGLE BETWEEN A LINE AND A PLANE

> The angle between a line and a plane is the angle between the line and its projection on the plane.

Example 13

🔊 Self Tutor

Name the angle between the following line segments and the base plane EFGH of the rectangular prism:

a AH   **b** AG.

a The projection of AH onto the base plane EFGH is EH.

∴ the required angle is $\widehat{AHE}$.

b The projection of AG onto the base plane EFGH is EG.

∴ the required angle is $\widehat{AGE}$.

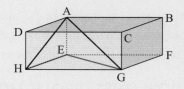

Example 14 ◀) **Self Tutor**

Find the angle between the following line segments and the base plane EFGH of the rectangular prism:

a DG   b BH

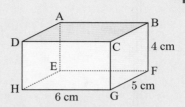

a The required angle is $D\widehat{G}H$.

$$\therefore \quad \tan\theta = \frac{\text{OPP}}{\text{ADJ}} = \frac{4}{6}$$

$$\therefore \quad \theta = \tan^{-1}\left(\frac{4}{6}\right)$$

$$\therefore \quad \theta \approx 33.69°$$

$\therefore$ the angle is about $33.7°$.

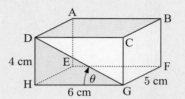

b The required angle is $B\widehat{H}F$.

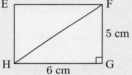

By Pythagoras,
$$(HF)^2 = 6^2 + 5^2 \text{ cm}^2$$
$$\therefore \quad (HF)^2 = 61 \text{ cm}^2$$
$$\therefore \quad HF = \sqrt{61} \text{ cm}$$

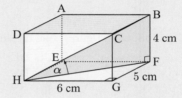

$$\tan\alpha = \frac{\text{OPP}}{\text{ADJ}} = \frac{4}{\sqrt{61}}$$

$$\therefore \quad \alpha = \tan^{-1}\left(\frac{4}{\sqrt{61}}\right)$$

$$\therefore \quad \alpha \approx 27.12°$$

$\therefore$ the angle is about $27.1°$.

EXERCISE 15E.2

1 Find the projections of the following onto the base planes of the given figures:

a
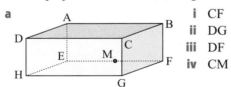

  i CF
  ii DG
  iii DF
  iv CM

b
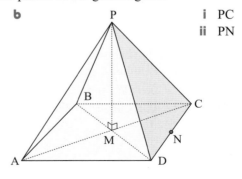

  i PC
  ii PN

c
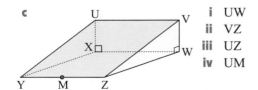

  i UW
  ii VZ
  iii UZ
  iv UM

2 For each of the following figures, name the angle between the given line segment and the base plane:

a

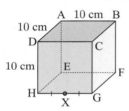

i DE
ii CE
iii AG
iv BX

b

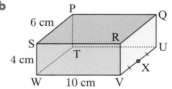

i PY
ii QW
iii QX
iv YQ

c

i AQ
ii AY

3 For each of the following figures, find the angle between the given line segments and the base plane:

a

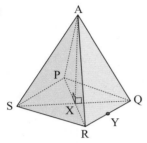

i DE
ii DF
iii DX
iv AX

b

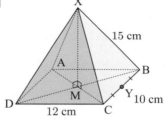

i PU
ii PV
iii SX

c

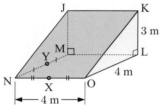

i KO
ii JX
iii KY

d

i XD
ii XY

4 Roberto is flying his kite with the aid of a southerly wind. He has let out 54 m of string, and the kite is at an angle of elevation of 37°. His friend Geraldo stands to the west, 95 m away.

a How far is Geraldo from the kite?

b What is the kite's angle of elevation from Geraldo?

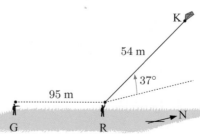

AREAS OF TRIANGLES

F

If we know the base and height measurements of a triangle, we can calculate the area using
area $= \frac{1}{2}$ base $\times$ height.

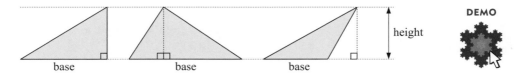

DEMO

In many cases we do not know the height of the triangle. However, if we have sufficient other information, we can find the area of the triangle using trigonometry.

INVESTIGATION 2   THE AREA OF AN ISOSCELES TRIANGLE

In the diagram alongside, θ is the *included angle* between the sides of equal length.

In this investigation we seek a formula for the area of an isosceles triangle which involves two side lengths and the included angle between them.

At the same time we will discover a useful property of **sine**.

What to do:

1 Consider the equilateral triangle alongside.

   a Find the triangle's altitude using Pythagoras.

   b Find the area of the triangle using geometry.

   c Find the size of θ.

   d Use your calculator to evaluate $1 \times 1 \times \sin\theta$.
   What do you notice?

2 Now consider the isosceles triangle alongside.

   a Find the triangle's altitude using Pythagoras.

   b Find the area of the triangle using geometry.

   c Find the size of θ using right angled trigonometry.

   d Use your calculator to evaluate $1 \times 1 \times \sin\theta$.
   What do you notice?

   e Use your results from **1 d** and **2 d** to show that $\sin 120° = \sin 60°$.

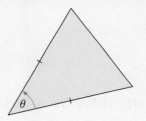

3

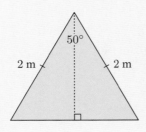

For the triangle alongside:

   a Use right angled trigonometry to find the altitude and base length of the triangle.

   b Find the area of the triangle using geometry.

   c Use your calculator to evaluate $2 \times 2 \times \sin 50°$. What do you notice?

4

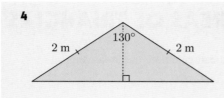

For the triangle alongside:

a Use right angled trigonometry to find the altitude and base length of the triangle.

b Find the area of the triangle using geometry.

c Use your calculator to evaluate $2 \times 2 \times \sin 130°$. What do you notice?

d Use your results from **3c** and **4c** to show that $\sin 130° = \sin 50°$.

You should have discovered that the area of an isosceles triangle is half of the **product** of its equal sides and the sine of the included angle between them.

You should also have discovered that

$$\sin 60° = \sin 120° = \sin(180° - 60°)$$
and $\quad \sin 50° = \sin 130° = \sin(180° - 50°).$

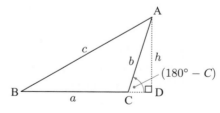

> Experiment using your calculator to satisfy yourself that this is true.

This leads us to the general conclusion

$$\sin \theta = \sin(180° - \theta)$$

THE AREA OF A TRIANGLE FORMULA

Suppose triangle ABC has angles of size A, B, and C, and the sides opposite these angles are labelled a, b, and c respectively.

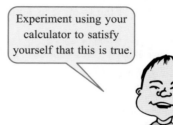

Any triangle that is not right angled must be either acute or obtuse. In either case we construct a perpendicular from A to D on BC (extended if necessary).

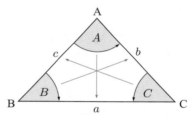

Using right angled trigonometry:

$$\sin C = \frac{h}{b} \qquad\qquad \sin(180° - C) = \frac{h}{b}$$
$$\therefore \ h = b \sin C \qquad\qquad \therefore \ h = b \sin(180° - C)$$
$$\therefore \ h = b \sin C$$

So, area $= \frac{1}{2}ah$ gives $\boxed{A = \frac{1}{2}ab \sin C.}$

Using different altitudes we can show that the area is also $\frac{1}{2}bc \sin A$ or $\frac{1}{2}ac \sin B$.

Given the lengths of two sides of a triangle and the included angle between them, the area of the triangle is

> *a half of the product of two sides and the sine of the included angle.*

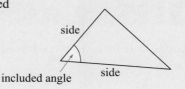

side
included angle   side

Example 15   ◀) **Self Tutor**

Find the area of triangle ABC:

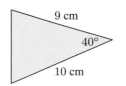

A
8.4 cm
31°
C
11.7 cm   B

Area $= \frac{1}{2}ac\sin B$

$ = \frac{1}{2} \times 11.7 \times 8.4 \times \sin 31°$

$ \approx 25.3 \text{ cm}^2$

EXERCISE 15F

1 Find the area of:

a

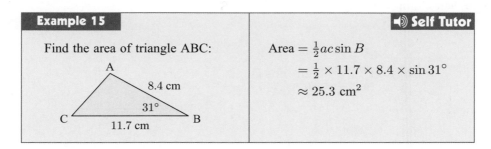

9 cm
40°
10 cm

b

31 km
82°
25 km

c

10.2 cm
125°
6.4 cm

2 If triangle ABC has area 150 cm², find the value of x:

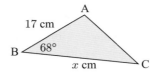

A
17 cm
B   68°
x cm   C

3 Calculate the area of:

   a an isosceles triangle with equal sides of length 21 cm and an included angle of 49°

   b an equilateral triangle with sides of length 57 cm.

4 A parallelogram has adjacent sides of length 4 cm and 6 cm. If the included angle measures 52°, find the area of the parallelogram.

5 A rhombus has sides of length 12 cm and an angle of 72°. Find its area.

6

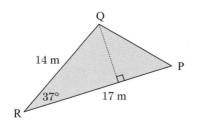

Q
14 m
P
37°   17 m
R

   a Find the area of triangle PQR to 3 decimal places.

   b Hence, find the length of the altitude from Q to RP.

G | THE COSINE RULE

The **cosine rule** involves the sides and angles of any triangle. The triangle does not need to contain a right angle.

In any $\triangle ABC$ with sides a, b, and c units in length, and opposite angles A, B, and C respectively:

$$a^2 = b^2 + c^2 - 2bc\cos A$$
$$\text{or } \quad b^2 = a^2 + c^2 - 2ac\cos B$$
$$\text{or } \quad c^2 = a^2 + b^2 - 2ab\cos C$$

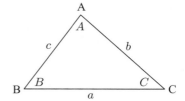

The following proof of the cosine rule is not examinable, but is included for completeness:

Proof:

We will develop the formula $\quad a^2 = b^2 + c^2 - 2bc\cos A \quad$ for both an acute and an obtuse triangle.

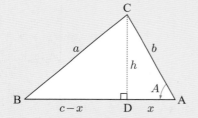 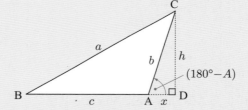

In both triangles we draw a perpendicular line from C to meet AB (extended if necessary) at D.

Let $AD = x$ and let $CD = h$.

In both cases, applying Pythagoras' theorem to $\triangle ADC$ gives $\quad h^2 + x^2 = b^2 \quad$ .... (1)

Applying Pythagoras' theorem to $\triangle BCD$ gives:

$a^2 = h^2 + (c-x)^2$	$a^2 = h^2 + (c+x)^2$
$\therefore \quad a^2 = h^2 + c^2 - 2cx + x^2$	$\therefore \quad a^2 = h^2 + c^2 + 2cx + x^2$
$\therefore \quad a^2 = b^2 + c^2 - 2cx \quad$ {using (1)}	$\therefore \quad a^2 = b^2 + c^2 + 2cx \quad$ {using (1)}

In $\triangle ADC$: $\quad \cos A = \dfrac{x}{b}$

$\therefore \quad b\cos A = x$

$\therefore \quad a^2 = b^2 + c^2 - 2bc\cos A$

$\cos(180° - A) = \dfrac{x}{b}$

$\therefore \quad b\cos(180° - A) = x$

But $\quad \cos(180° - A) = -\cos A$

$\therefore \quad -b\cos A = x$

$\therefore \quad a^2 = b^2 + c^2 - 2bc\cos A$

The other variations of the cosine rule can be developed by rearranging the vertices of $\triangle ABC$.

Notice that if $A = 90°$ then $\cos A = 0$ and $a^2 = b^2 + c^2 - 2bc\cos A$ reduces to $a^2 = b^2 + c^2$, which is Pythagoras' theorem.

THEORY OF KNOWLEDGE

Trigonometry appears to be one of the most useful disciplines of mathematics, having great importance in building and engineering. Its study has been driven by the need to solve real world problems throughout history.

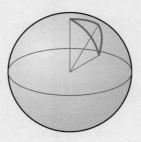

The study of trigonometry began when Greek, Babylonian, and Arabic astronomers needed to calculate the positions of stars and planets. These early mathematicians considered the trigonometry of spherical triangles, which are triangles on the surface of a sphere.

Trigonometric functions were developed by Hipparchus around 140 BC, and then by Ptolemy and Menelaus around 100 AD.

Around 500 AD, Hindu mathematicians published a table called the *Aryabhata*. It was a table of lengths of half chords, which are the lengths $AM = r \sin x$ in the diagram. This is trigonometry of triangles in a plane, as we study in schools today.

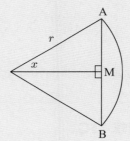

1   How do society and culture affect mathematical knowledge?

2   Should congruence and similarity, or the work of Pythagoras, be considered part of modern trigonometry?

3   Is the angle sum of a triangle always equal to $180°$?

USING THE COSINE RULE

If we know the length of **two sides** of a triangle and the size of the **included angle** between them, we can use the cosine rule to find the third side.

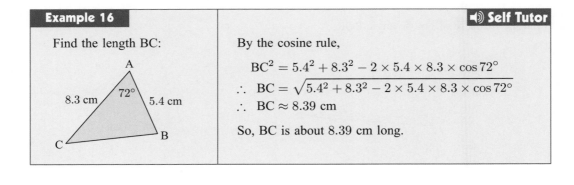

| **Example 16** | ◀) **Self Tutor** |

Find the length BC:

By the cosine rule,

$$BC^2 = 5.4^2 + 8.3^2 - 2 \times 5.4 \times 8.3 \times \cos 72°$$

$$\therefore \quad BC = \sqrt{5.4^2 + 8.3^2 - 2 \times 5.4 \times 8.3 \times \cos 72°}$$

$$\therefore \quad BC \approx 8.39 \text{ cm}$$

So, BC is about 8.39 cm long.

If we know all **three sides** of a triangle, we can rearrange the cosine rule formulae to find any of the angles:

$$\cos A = \frac{b^2 + c^2 - a^2}{2bc} \qquad \cos B = \frac{c^2 + a^2 - b^2}{2ca} \qquad \cos C = \frac{a^2 + b^2 - c^2}{2ab}$$

We use the **inverse** cosine ratio $\cos^{-1}$ to evaluate the angle.

Example 17   ◀) **Self Tutor**

In triangle ABC, AB = 7 cm, BC = 5 cm, and CA = 8 cm.
Find the measure of angle BCA.

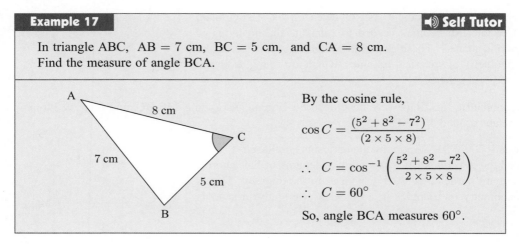

By the cosine rule,

$$\cos C = \frac{(5^2 + 8^2 - 7^2)}{(2 \times 5 \times 8)}$$

$$\therefore \quad C = \cos^{-1}\left(\frac{5^2 + 8^2 - 7^2}{2 \times 5 \times 8}\right)$$

$$\therefore \quad C = 60°$$

So, angle BCA measures 60°.

EXERCISE 15G

1 Find the length of the remaining side in the given triangle:

a

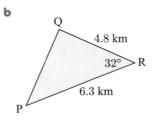

b

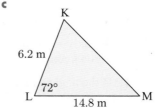

c

2 Find the measure of all angles of:

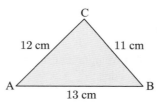

3 Find the measure of obtuse angle PQR:

a

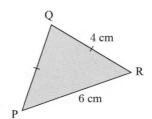

b

4   **a**   Find the smallest angle of a triangle with sides 11 cm, 13 cm, and 17 cm.

   b   Find the largest angle of a triangle with sides 4 cm, 7 cm, and 9 cm.

The smallest angle is opposite the shortest side.

5   **a**   Find $\cos \theta$ but not θ.

   b   Find the value of x.

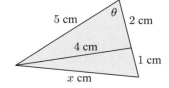

6   Find the value of θ:

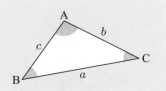

H   THE SINE RULE

The **sine rule** is a set of equations which connects the lengths of the sides of any triangle with the sines of the angles of the triangle. The triangle does not have to be right angled for the sine rule to be used.

> In any triangle ABC with sides a, b, and c units in length, and opposite angles A, B, and C respectively,
>
> $$\frac{\sin A}{a} = \frac{\sin B}{b} = \frac{\sin C}{c} \quad or \quad \frac{a}{\sin A} = \frac{b}{\sin B} = \frac{c}{\sin C}.$$
>
>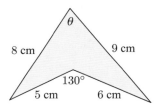

Proof: The area of any triangle ABC is given by $\frac{1}{2}bc\sin A = \frac{1}{2}ac\sin B = \frac{1}{2}ab\sin C$.

Dividing each expression by $\frac{1}{2}abc$ gives $\dfrac{\sin A}{a} = \dfrac{\sin B}{b} = \dfrac{\sin C}{c}$.

The sine rule is used to solve problems involving triangles, given:

• **two angles** and **one side**   • **two sides** and a **non-included** angle.

FINDING SIDES

If two angles of a triangle are known, we can always find the third angle as the three angles must add to $180°$. Therefore if **two angles** and **one side** of a triangle are known, the sine rule can be used to determine the lengths of the other sides.

Example 18   ◀) Self Tutor

Find the length of BC correct to three significant figures.

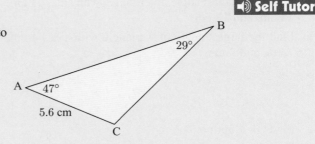

Let BC be a cm long.

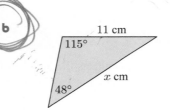

Using the sine rule, $\dfrac{a}{\sin 47°} = \dfrac{5.6}{\sin 29°}$

$$\therefore \quad a = \frac{5.6 \times \sin 47°}{\sin 29°}$$

$$\therefore \quad a \approx 8.45$$

$\therefore$ BC is about 8.45 cm long.

EXERCISE 15H.1

1 Find the value of x:

a

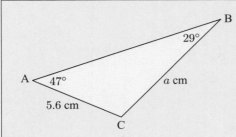

b

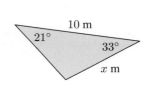

c

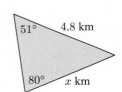

d

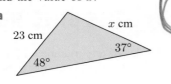

e

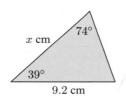

f

2 In triangle ABC, find:

  a a if $A = 63°$, $B = 49°$, and $b = 18$ cm

  b b if $A = 82°$, $C = 25°$, and $c = 34$ cm

  c c if $B = 21°$, $C = 48°$, and $a = 6.4$ cm.

> The angles of a triangle add to $180°$.

3 Find the lengths of the remaining sides of triangle PQR.

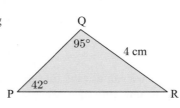

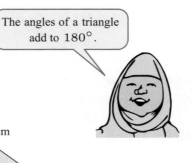

FINDING ANGLES

If two sides and a non-included angle are known in a triangle, the sine rule can be used to determine the size of the other angles.

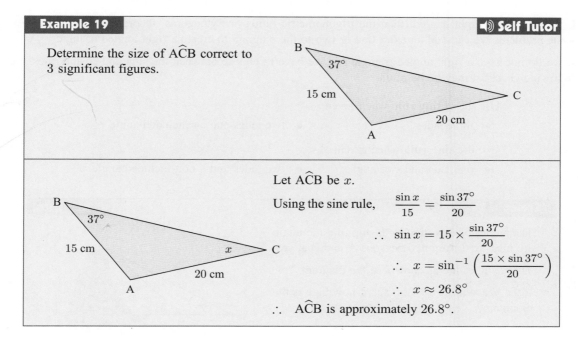

Example 19   ◀» **Self Tutor**

Determine the size of $\widehat{ACB}$ correct to 3 significant figures.

Let $\widehat{ACB}$ be x.

Using the sine rule, $\dfrac{\sin x}{15} = \dfrac{\sin 37°}{20}$

$\therefore \quad \sin x = 15 \times \dfrac{\sin 37°}{20}$

$\therefore \quad x = \sin^{-1}\left(\dfrac{15 \times \sin 37°}{20}\right)$

$\therefore \quad x \approx 26.8°$

$\therefore \quad \widehat{ACB}$ is approximately $26.8°$.

EXERCISE 15H.2

1 Find the value of x:

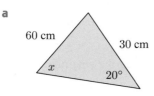
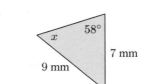

2 A triangle has vertices A, B, and C with opposite side lengths a, b, and c respectively. Find:

a $\widehat{BAC}$ if $\widehat{ABC} = 45°$, $a = 8$ cm, and $b = 11$ cm

b $\widehat{ABC}$ if $a = 32$ cm, $b = 23$ cm, and $\widehat{BAC} = 42°$

c $\widehat{ACB}$ if $c = 30$ m, $b = 36$ m, and $\widehat{ABC} = 37°$.

3 Unprepared for class, Mr Whiffen asks his students to determine the size of x in the diagram shown.

a Show that Mr Whiffen's question cannot be solved.

b Explain what this means about the triangle Mr Whiffen created.

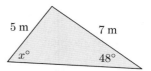

USING THE SINE AND COSINE RULES

If we are given a problem involving a triangle, we must first decide which rule to use.

If the triangle is right angled, then the trigonometric ratios or Pythagoras' theorem can be used. For some problems we can add an extra line or two to the diagram to create a right angled triangle.

If we do not have a right angled triangle and we have to choose between the sine and cosine rules, the following checklist may be helpful:

Use the **cosine rule** when given:
- three sides
- two sides and an included angle.

Use the **sine rule** when given:
- one side and two angles
- two sides and a non-included angle.

Example 20   ◀)) Self Tutor

The angles of elevation to the top of a mountain are measured from two beacons A and B at sea.

These angles are as shown on the diagram.

If the beacons are 1473 m apart, how high is the mountain?

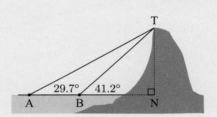

Let the height of the mountain be h m and the distance BT be x m.

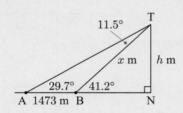

$A\widehat{T}B = 41.2° - 29.7°$ {exterior angle of $\triangle$}
$\qquad\quad = 11.5°$

We find x in $\triangle ABT$ using the sine rule:

$$\frac{x}{\sin 29.7°} = \frac{1473}{\sin 11.5°}$$

$$\therefore \quad x = \frac{1473}{\sin 11.5°} \times \sin 29.7°$$

$$\approx 3660.62$$

In $\triangle BNT$, $\sin 41.2° = \frac{h}{x} \approx \frac{h}{3660.62}$

$$\therefore \quad h \approx \sin 41.2° \times 3660.62$$

$$\therefore \quad h \approx 2410$$

So, the mountain is about 2410 m high.

EXERCISE 15I

1 Rodrigo takes a sighting to the top of the flagpole from point P. He then moves 20 metres further away from the flagpole to point Q and takes a second sighting. The information is shown in the diagram. How high is the flagpole?

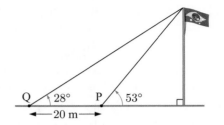

2

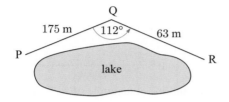

A park ranger walks along a trail from P to Q and then to R.

What is the distance in a straight line from P to R?

3 A golfer played his tee shot 220 m to point A. His ball was then 165 m from the green. The distance from tee to green is 340 m. Determine the number of degrees the golfer was off line with his tee shot.

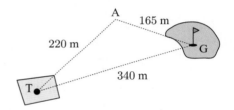

4 Two yachts P and Q are anchored at different locations at sea. A beacon at B determines that P and Q are 24 km and 21 km away respectively. The yacht at Q measures B and P to be 53° apart. What angle would the yacht at P measure between B and Q?

5 A football goal is 5 metres wide. When a player is 26 metres from one goal post and 23 metres from the other, he shoots for goal. What is the angle of view of the goals that the player sees?

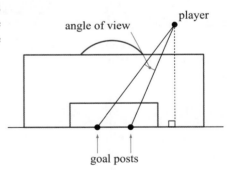

6 A tower 42 metres high stands on top of a hill. From a point some distance from the base of the hill, the angle of elevation to the top of the tower is 13.2° and the angle of elevation to the bottom of the tower is 8.3°. Find the height of the hill.

7 A large property needs to be sprayed with insecticide prior to being used for agriculture. An incomplete sketch of the property is shown.

    a Calculate angle EFG.

    b Determine the cost of spraying the property if insecticide costs £400 per square kilometre.

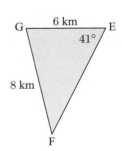

8 From the foot of a building I have to look upwards at an angle of 22° to sight the top of a tree. From the top of the building, 150 metres above ground level, I have to look down at an angle of 50° below the horizontal to sight the tree top.

    a How high is the tree?   **b** How far from the building is this tree?

9 Two observation posts are 12 km apart at A and B. A third observation post C is located such that angle CAB is 42° and angle CBA is 67°. Find the distance of C from both A and B.

10 Stan and Olga are considering buying a sheep farm. A surveyor has supplied them with the given accurate sketch. Find the area of the property, giving your answer in:

    a km²   **b** hectares.

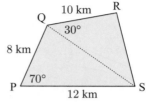

11 Thabo and Palesa start at point A. They each walk in a straight line at an angle of 120° to each other. Thabo walks at 6 km h⁻¹ and Palesa walks at 8 km h⁻¹. How far apart are they after 45 minutes?

12 The cross-section of the kerbing for a driverless-bus roadway is shown opposite. The metal strip is inlaid into the concrete and is used to control the direction and speed of the bus. Find the width of the metal strip.

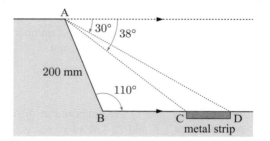

J   THE AMBIGUOUS CASE (EXTENSION)

The problem of finding angles using the sine rule can be complicated because there may be two possible answers. We call this situation the **ambiguous case**.

DEMO

INVESTIGATION 3   THE AMBIGUOUS CASE

You will need a blank sheet of paper, a ruler, a protractor, and a compass for the tasks that follow. In each task you will be required to construct triangles from given information. You could also do this using a computer package such as 'The Geometer's Sketchpad'.

Task 1: Draw AB = 10 cm. At A construct an angle of 30°. Using B as the centre, draw an arc of a circle of radius 6 cm. Let the arc intersect the ray from A at C. How many different positions may C have, and therefore how many different triangles ABC may be constructed?

Task 2: As before, draw AB = 10 cm and construct a 30° angle at A. This time draw an arc of radius 5 cm centred at B. How many different triangles are possible?

Task 3: Repeat, but this time draw an arc of radius 3 cm centred at B. How many different triangles are possible?

Task 4: Repeat, but this time draw an arc of radius 12 cm centred at B. How many different triangles are possible now?

You should have discovered that when you are given two sides and a non-included angle, there are a number of different possibilities. You could get two triangles, one triangle, or it may be impossible to draw any triangles at all from the given data.

Example 21 🔊 **Self Tutor**

Find the measure of angle C in triangle ABC if $AC = 7$ cm, $AB = 11$ cm, and angle B measures $25°$.

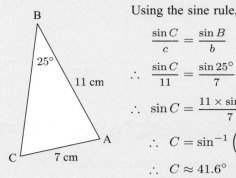

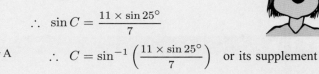

Using the sine rule,

$$\frac{\sin C}{c} = \frac{\sin B}{b}$$

$$\therefore \quad \frac{\sin C}{11} = \frac{\sin 25°}{7}$$

$$\therefore \quad \sin C = \frac{11 \times \sin 25°}{7}$$

$$\therefore \quad C = \sin^{-1}\left(\frac{11 \times \sin 25°}{7}\right) \quad \text{or its supplement}$$

$$\therefore \quad C \approx 41.6° \quad \text{or} \quad 180° - 41.6° \quad \{\text{as } C \text{ may be obtuse}\}$$

$$\therefore \quad C \approx 41.6° \quad \text{or} \quad 138.4°$$

Supplementary angles add up to $180°$.

$\therefore$ C measures $41.6°$ if angle C is acute, or $138.4°$ if angle C is obtuse.

In this case there is insufficient information to determine the actual shape of the triangle.

Sometimes there is information in the question which enables us to **reject** one of the answers.

Example 22 🔊 **Self Tutor**

Find the measure of angle L in triangle KLM given that angle LKM measures $56°$, $LM = 16.8$ m, and $KM = 13.5$ m.

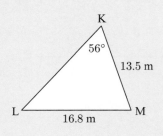

$$\frac{\sin L}{13.5} = \frac{\sin 56°}{16.8} \quad \{\text{by the sine rule}\}$$

$$\therefore \quad \sin L = \frac{13.5 \times \sin 56°}{16.8}$$

$$\therefore \quad L = \sin^{-1}\left(\frac{13.5 \times \sin 56°}{16.8}\right) \quad \text{or its supplement}$$

$$\therefore \quad L \approx 41.8° \quad \text{or} \quad 180° - 41.8°$$

$$\therefore \quad L \approx 41.8° \quad \text{or} \quad 138.2°$$

We reject $L \approx 138.2°$, since $138.2° + 56° > 180°$ which is impossible.
$\therefore$ $L \approx 41.8°$.

EXERCISE 15J

1 Triangle ABC has angle $B = 40°$, $b = 8$ cm, and $c = 11$ cm. Find the two possible values for angle C.

2 In triangle PQR, angle Q measures $34°$, $PR = 10$ cm, and $QR = 7$ cm. Find the measure of angle P.

3 In triangle ABC, find the measure of:

   a angle A if $a = 13.8$ cm, $b = 16.5$ cm, and $A\widehat{B}C = 43°$

   b angle B if $b = 27.9$ m, $c = 20.4$ m, and $A\widehat{C}B = 36°$

   c angle C if $a = 7.7$ km, $c = 8.1$ km, and $B\widehat{A}C = 71°$.

4 Is it possible to have a triangle with the measurements shown? Explain your answer.

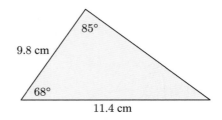

REVIEW SET 15A

1

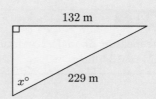

For the triangle alongside, find:

   a the hypotenuse

   b the side adjacent to ϕ

   c $\sin\theta$

   d $\tan\phi$

2 Find the value of x:

   a

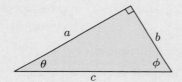

   b

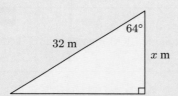

3 Find the measure of all unknown sides and angles in triangle CDE:

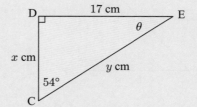

4 Find θ, the pitch of the roof.

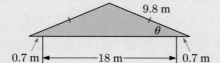

5 Determine the area of the triangle:

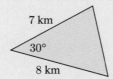

6 Two identical buildings stand opposite each other, as shown alongside. Find the angle of depression from A to B.

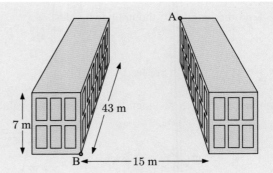

7 Determine the value of x:

a

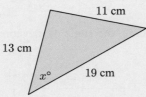

b

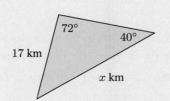

8 Find the unknown side and angles:

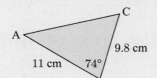

9 Find the area of quadrilateral ABCD:

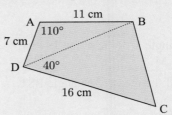

10 Paul 'puts' a shot put from the front of a throwing circle with diameter 2.135 m. It only just lands inside the 40° throwing boundaries.

The official measurement goes from the shot to the nearest point of the throwing circle, and reads 17.64 m.

How far did Paul actually put the shot?

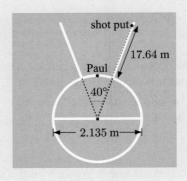

REVIEW SET 15B

1 Find $\sin \theta$, $\cos \theta$, and $\tan \theta$ for the triangle:

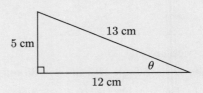

2   Find the lengths of the unknown sides:

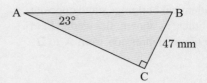

3   Find, correct to two significant figures, the value of x in:

a

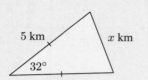

b

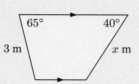

c

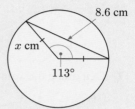

4   From a point 120 m horizontally from the base of a building, the angle of elevation to the top of the building is 34°. Find the height of the building.

5   For the rectangular prism shown, find the angle that:

   a   AH makes with HG

   b   DF makes with the base plane EFGH.

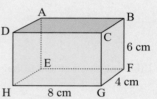

6   Triangle LMN has area 184 mm², angle LMN = 20°, and MN is 34 mm long. Find the length of LM.

7   Find the measure of angle RST.

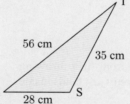

8   Jason's sketch of his father's triangular vegetable patch is shown alongside. Find:

   a   the length of the fence AB.

   b   the area of the patch in hectares.

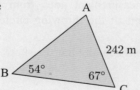

9   A vertical tree is growing on the side of a hill with gradient 10° to the horizontal. From a point 50 m downhill from the tree, the angle of elevation to the top of the tree is 18°. Find the height of the tree.

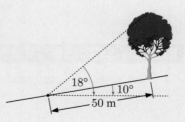

10   Find the measure of:

   a   angle D in triangle DEF if $d = 35$ m, $e = 40$ m, and $\hat{DEF} = 61°$

   b   angle J in triangle IJK if $i = 5.9$ cm, $j = 8.2$ cm, and $\hat{JIK} = 37°$.

REVIEW SET 15C

1 Use your calculator to find, correct to 4 decimal places:

    a $\cos 74°$ **b** $\sin 132°$ **c** $\tan 97°$.

2 Find the value of x in the following:

    a
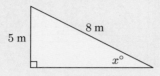

    b
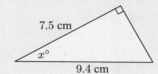

3 Find the measure of all unknown sides and angles in triangle KLM:

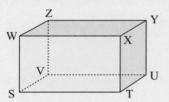

4 A rhombus has diagonals of length 15 cm and 8 cm. Find the larger angle of the rhombus.

5 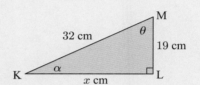 For the rectangular prism shown, name:

    a the projection of ZS onto the base plane STUV

    b the angle between XS and the base plane

    c the angle between UW and the base plane.

6 The figure alongside is a square-based pyramid. Find:

    a $A\hat{D}M$ **b** $A\hat{C}D$.

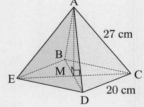

7 Anke and Lucas are considering buying a block of land. The land agent supplies them with the given accurate sketch. Find the area of the property, giving your answer in:

    a m^2 **b** hectares.

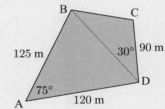

8 From point A, the angle of elevation to the top of a tall building is $20°$. On walking 80 m towards the building, the angle of elevation is now $23°$. How tall is the building?

9 Towns A, B, and C are connected by straight roads.

    a Find the length of the road from A to B.

    b A new road is to be constructed from C to M, the midpoint of AB. Find the length of this road.

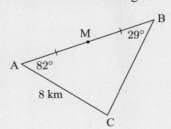

10 Soil contractor Frank was given the following dimensions over the telephone:

The triangular garden plot ABC has angle CAB measuring 44°. AC is 8 m long and BC is 6 m long. Soil to a depth of 10 cm is required.

a Explain why Frank needs extra information from his client.

b What is the maximum volume of soil that may be needed if his client is unable to supply the necessary information?

Chapter **16**

Functions

Syllabus reference: 6.1, 6.2

A   RELATIONS AND FUNCTIONS

The charges for parking a car in a short-term car park at an airport are shown in the table below. The total charge is *dependent* on the length of time t the car is parked.

Car park charges	
Time t (hours)	*Charge*
0 - 1 hours	$5.00
1 - 2 hours	$9.00
2 - 3 hours	$11.00
3 - 6 hours	$13.00
6 - 9 hours	$18.00
9 - 12 hours	$22.00
12 - 24 hours	$28.00

Looking at this table we might ask: How much would be charged for *exactly* one hour? Would it be $5 or $9?

To avoid confusion, we could adjust the table or draw a graph. We indicate that 2 - 3 hours really means a time over 2 hours up to and including 3 hours, by writing $2 < t \leqslant 3$ hours.

Car park charges	
Time t (hours)	*Charge*
$0 < t \leqslant 1$ hours	$5.00
$1 < t \leqslant 2$ hours	$9.00
$2 < t \leqslant 3$ hours	$11.00
$3 < t \leqslant 6$ hours	$13.00
$6 < t \leqslant 9$ hours	$18.00
$9 < t \leqslant 12$ hours	$22.00
$12 < t \leqslant 24$ hours	$28.00

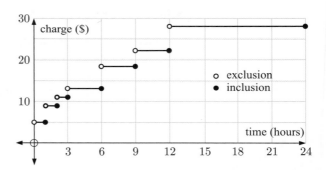

In mathematical terms, we have a relationship between two variables *time* and *charge*, so the schedule of charges is an example of a **relation**.

A relation may consist of a finite number of ordered pairs, such as $\{(1, 5), (-2, 3), (4, 3), (1, 6)\}$, or an infinite number of ordered pairs.

The parking charges example is clearly the latter as any real value of time in the interval $0 < t \leqslant 24$ hours is represented.

The set of possible values of the variable on the horizontal axis is called the **domain** of the relation.

For example:
- the domain for the car park relation is $\{t \mid 0 < t \leqslant 24\}$
- the domain of $\{(1, 5), (-2, 3), (4, 3), (1, 6)\}$ is $\{-2, 1, 4\}$.

The set of possible values on the vertical axis is called the **range** of the relation.

For example:
- the range of the car park relation is $\{5, 9, 11, 13, 18, 22, 28\}$
- the range of $\{(1, 5), (-2, 3), (4, 3), (1, 6)\}$ is $\{3, 5, 6\}$.

We will now look at relations and functions more formally.

RELATIONS

> A **relation** is any set of points which connect two variables.

A relation is often expressed in the form of an **equation** connecting the **variables** x and y. In this case the relation is a set of points (x, y) in the **Cartesian plane**.

For example $y = x + 3$ and $x = y^2$ are the equations of two relations. Each equation generates a set of ordered pairs, which we can graph:

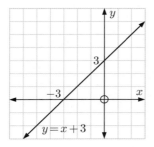 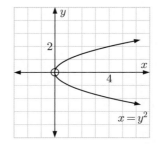

However, a relation may not be able to be defined by an equation. For example:

(1)
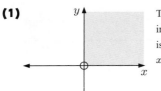
The set of all points in the first quadrant is a relation.
$x > 0, \quad y > 0$

(2)

These 13 points form a relation.

FUNCTIONS

> A **function**, sometimes called a **mapping**, is a relation in which no two different ordered pairs have the same x-coordinate or first component.

We can see from the above definition that a function is a special type of relation.

Every function is a relation, but not every relation is a function.

This can be represented in set form as shown.

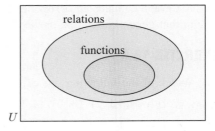

TESTING FOR FUNCTIONS

Algebraic Test:

> If a relation is given as an equation, and the substitution of any value for x results in one and only one value of y, then the relation is a function.

For example:

$y = 3x - 1$ is a function, as for any value of x there is only one corresponding value of y

$x = y^2$ is not a function, since if $x = 4$ then $y = \pm 2$.

Geometric Test   or   Vertical Line Test:

> If we draw all possible vertical lines on the graph of a relation, the relation:
> - is a function if each line cuts the graph no more than once
> - is not a function if at least one line cuts the graph more than once.

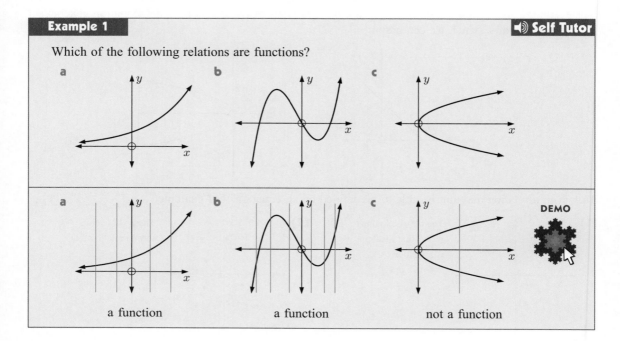

| **Example 1** | ◀)) **Self Tutor** |

Which of the following relations are functions?

a   b   c

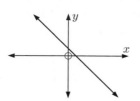   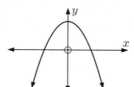   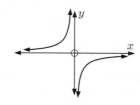

a function   a function   not a function

GRAPHICAL NOTE

- If a graph contains a small **open circle** such as ──o── , this point is **not included**.
- If a graph contains a small **filled-in circle** such as ──● , this point **is included**.
- If a graph contains an **arrow head** at an end such as ───▶ , then the graph continues indefinitely in that general direction, or the shape may repeat as it has done previously.

EXERCISE 16A

1 Which of the following sets of ordered pairs are functions? Give reasons.

    a $\{(1, 3), (2, 4), (3, 5), (4, 6)\}$ **b** $\{(1, 3), (3, 2), (1, 7), (-1, 4)\}$

    c $\{(2, -1), (2, 0), (2, 3), (2, 11)\}$ **d** $\{(7, 6), (5, 6), (3, 6), (-4, 6)\}$

    e $\{(0, 0), (1, 0), (3, 0), (5, 0)\}$ **f** $\{(0, 0), (0, -2), (0, 2), (0, 4)\}$

2 Use the vertical line test to determine which of the following relations are functions:

    a   b   c

d

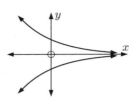

e

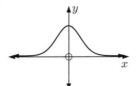

f

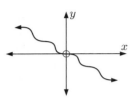

g

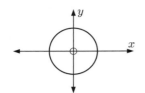

h

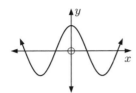

i

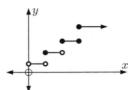

3 Will the graph of a straight line always be a function? Give evidence to support your answer.

4 Give algebraic evidence to show that the relation $x^2 + y^2 = 9$ is not a function.

B · FUNCTION NOTATION

Function machines are sometimes used to illustrate how functions behave.

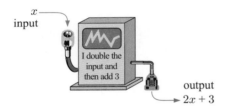

If 4 is the input fed into the machine, the output is $2(4) + 3 = 11$.

The above 'machine' has been programmed to perform a particular function.

If f is used to represent that particular function we can say that

"f is the function that will convert x into $2x + 3$".

In **function notation** we write: $f(x) = 2x + 3$ or $y = 2x + 3$.

$f(x)$ is read as "f of x".

$f(x)$ is the value of y for a given value of x, so $y = f(x)$.

$y = f(x)$ is sometimes called the **function value** or **image** of x.

For $f(x) = 2x + 3$:

$f(2) = 2(2) + 3 = 7$ indicates that the point $(2, 7)$ lies on the graph of the function.

$f(-4) = 2(-4) + 3 = -5$ indicates that the point $(-4, -5)$ also lies on the graph.

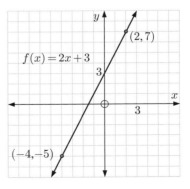

Example 2   ◀ Self Tutor

If $f(x) = 2x^2 - 3x$,   find the value of: **a** $f(5)$ **b** $f(-4)$

$f(x) = 2x^2 - 3x$

   a $f(5) = 2(5)^2 - 3(5)$ {replacing x with (5)}
       $= 2 \times 25 - 15$
       $= 35$

   b $f(-4) = 2(-4)^2 - 3(-4)$ {replacing x with (-4)}
        $= 2(16) + 12$
        $= 44$

Example 3   ◀ Self Tutor

If $f(x) = 5 - x - x^2$,   find in simplest form: **a** $f(-x)$ **b** $f(x+2)$

   a $f(-x) = 5 - (-x) - (-x)^2$ {replacing x with $(-x)$}
        $= 5 + x - x^2$

   b $f(x+2) = 5 - (x+2) - (x+2)^2$ {replacing x with $(x+2)$}
        $= 5 - x - 2 - [x^2 + 4x + 4]$
        $= 3 - x - x^2 - 4x - 4$
        $= -x^2 - 5x - 1$

EXERCISE 16B

1 If $f(x) = 3x + 2$,   find the value of:

  a $f(0)$ **b** $f(2)$ **c** $f(-1)$ **d** $f(-5)$ **e** $f(-\frac{1}{3})$

2 If $f(x) = 3x - x^2 + 2$,   find the value of:

  a $f(0)$ **b** $f(3)$ **c** $f(-3)$ **d** $f(-7)$ **e** $f(\frac{3}{2})$

3 If $g(x) = x - \dfrac{4}{x}$,   find the value of:

  a $g(1)$ **b** $g(4)$ **c** $g(-1)$ **d** $g(-4)$ **e** $g(-\frac{1}{2})$

4 If $f(x) = 7 - 3x$,   find in simplest form:

  a $f(a)$ **b** $f(-a)$ **c** $f(a+3)$ **d** $f(b-1)$ **e** $f(x+2)$ **f** $f(x+h)$

5 If $F(x) = 2x^2 + 3x - 1$,   find in simplest form:

  a $F(x+4)$ **b** $F(2-x)$ **c** $F(-x)$ **d** $F(x^2)$ **e** $F(x^2-1)$ **f** $F(x+h)$

6 Suppose $G(x) = \dfrac{2x+3}{x-4}$.

  a Evaluate: **i** $G(2)$ **ii** $G(0)$ **iii** $G(-\frac{1}{2})$

  b Find a value of x such that $G(x)$ does not exist.

  c Find $G(x+2)$ in simplest form.

  d Find x if $G(x) = -3$.

7 f represents a function. What is the difference in meaning between f and $f(x)$?

8 The value of a photocopier t years after purchase is given by $V(t) = 9650 - 860t$ euros.

    a Find $V(4)$ and state what $V(4)$ means.

    b Find t when $V(t) = 5780$ and explain what this represents.

    c Find the original purchase price of the photocopier.

9 On the same set of axes draw the graphs of three different functions $f(x)$ such that $f(2) = 1$ and $f(5) = 3$.

10 Find a function $f(x) = ax + b$ for which $f(2) = 1$ and $f(-3) = 11$.

11 Given $f(x) = ax + \dfrac{b}{x}$, $f(1) = 1$, and $f(2) = 5$, find constants a and b.

12 If $f(x) = 2^x$, show that $f(a)\,f(b) = f(a + b)$.

C   DOMAIN AND RANGE

> The **domain** of a relation is the set of values of x in the relation.
>
> The **range** of a relation is the set of values of y in the relation.

The domain and range of a relation are often described using **set notation**.

For example:

(1)

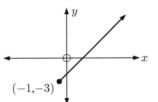

All values of $x \geqslant -1$ are included, so the domain is $\{x \mid x \geqslant -1\}$.
All values of $y \geqslant -3$ are included, so the range is $\{y \mid y \geqslant -3\}$.

(2)

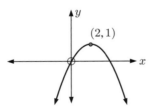

x can take any value, so the domain is $\{x \mid x \in \mathbb{R}\}$.
y cannot be > 1, so the range is $\{y \mid y \leqslant 1\}$.

(3)

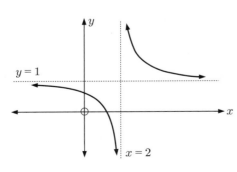

x can take all values except 2, so the domain is $\{x \mid x \neq 2\}$.
y can take all values except 1, so the range is $\{y \mid y \neq 1\}$.

The dotted lines in **(3)** represent asymptotes. The graph gets closer and closer to these lines, but never reaches them.

Click on the icon to obtain software for finding the domain and range of different functions.

DOMAIN AND RANGE

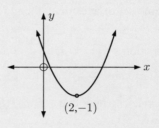

Example 4   🔊 **Self Tutor**

For each of the following graphs state the domain and range:

a

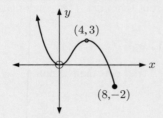

(4, 3)

(8, −2)

b

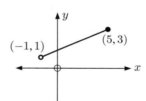

a   Domain is $\{x \mid x \leqslant 8\}$
       Range is $\{y \mid y \geqslant -2\}$

b   Domain is $\{x \mid x \in \mathbb{R}\}$
       Range is $\{y \mid y \geqslant -1\}$

EXERCISE 16C

1   For each of the following graphs, find the domain and range:

a

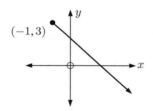

(−1, 3)

b

(−1, 1)

(5, 3)

c

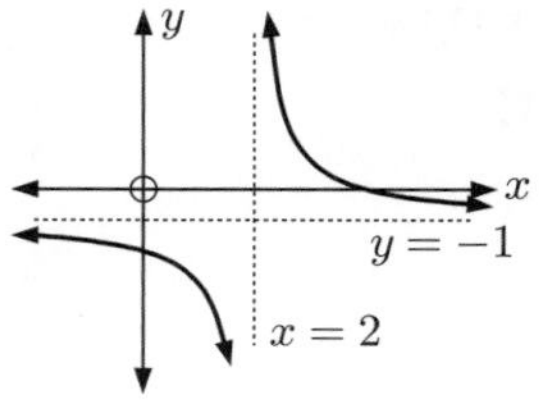

$y = -1$

$x = 2$

d

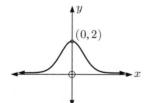

(0, 2)

e

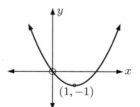

(1, −1)

f

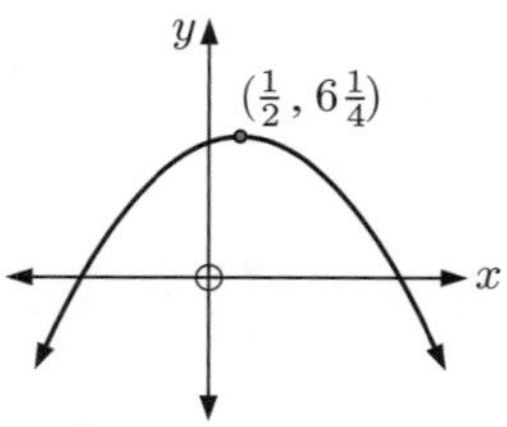

$(\frac{1}{2}, 6\frac{1}{4})$

g

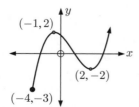

(−1, 2)

(2, −2)

(−4, −3)

h

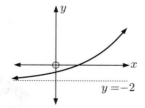

$y = -2$

i

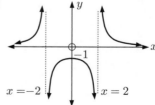

−1

$x = -2$ $x = 2$

Example 5 ◄》 **Self Tutor**

Use technology to help sketch the graph of $f(x) = 1 - x^2 + 4x$. Hence, determine the domain and range of $f(x)$.

Casio fx-CG20

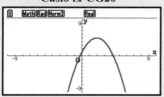

TI-84 Plus

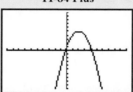

TI-nspire

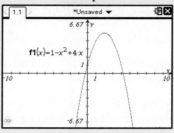

It appears that there is an upper limit or maximum to the set of permissible y values. We use technology to find the point at which this occurs:

Casio fx-CG20

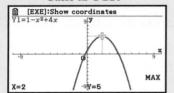

TI-84 Plus

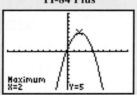

TI-nspire

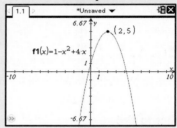

We can now sketch the graph of $f(x) = 1 - x^2 + 4x$.

The domain is $\{x \mid x \in \mathbb{R}\}$.

The range is $\{y \mid y \leqslant 5\}$.

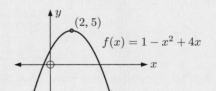

2 Use technology to help sketch graphs of the following functions. Find the domain and range of each.

DOMAIN AND RANGE

a $f(x) = 2x + 4$

b $f(x) = x^2 - 4x + 7$

c $y = (x - 3)(x + 1)$

d $f(x) = \sqrt{x}$

e $y = 5x - 3x^2$

f $f(x) = \dfrac{1}{x^2}$

g $f(x) = (x + 3)^4 - 1$

h $f(x) = \sqrt{x^2 + 4}$

i $f(x) = \sqrt{4 - x^2}$

j $f(x) = x + \dfrac{1}{x}$

k $y = \dfrac{x + 4}{x - 2}$

l $y = x^3 - 3x^2 - 9x + 10$

m $y = x^2 + x^{-2}$

n $y = x^3 + \dfrac{1}{x^3}$

o $f(x) = x^4 + 4x^3 - 16x + 3$

D   LINEAR MODELS

A **linear function** is a function of the form $f(x) = mx + c$ where m and c are constants, $m \neq 0$.

GRAPHS OF LINEAR FUNCTIONS

Consider the function $f(x) = mx + c$.

The graph of $y = f(x)$ is a **straight line** with gradient m and y-intercept c.

The x-intercept is where the graph cuts the x-axis. It is found by solving the equation $f(x) = 0$.

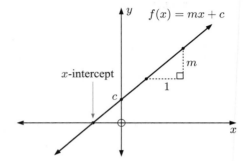

INVESTIGATION   MODELLING BAMBOO GROWTH

Bamboo is the fastest growing plant in the world, with some species growing up to 1 metre per day.

Xuanyu planted a 30 cm high bamboo plant in her garden bed. She found that with consistent weather it grew 10 cm each day.

What to do:

1 Copy and complete this table of values which gives the height H of the bamboo after t days.

t (days)	0	1	2	3	4	5	6
H (cm)	30	40					

2 Plot the points on a set of axes and connect them with straight line segments.

3 Explain why it is reasonable to connect the points with straight line segments.

4 Discuss whether it is reasonable to continue the line for $t < 0$ and for $t > 6$ days. Hence state the domain of the function $H(t)$.

5 Find the 'H-intercept' and gradient of the line.

6 Find an equation for the function $H(t)$.

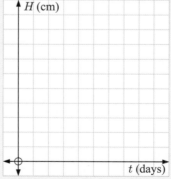

7 Use your equation to find the value of $H(10)$. Explain what this value represents.

8 How long will it take for the bamboo to be 1 m high?

Example 6 ◄⦂ **Self Tutor**

The cost of hiring a tennis court for h hours is given by the formula $C(h) = 5h + 8$ dollars.
Find the cost of hiring the tennis court for: **a** 4 hours **b** 10 hours.

a Substituting $h = 4$ we get
$$C(4) = 5(4) + 8$$
$$= 20 + 8$$
$$= 28$$
It costs \$28 to hire the court for 4 hours.

b Substituting $h = 10$ we get
$$C(10) = 5(10) + 8$$
$$= 50 + 8$$
$$= 58$$
It costs \$58 to hire the court for 10 hours.

Example 7 ◄⦂ **Self Tutor**

Ace taxi services charge \$3.30 for stopping to pick up a passenger and then \$1.75 for each kilometre of the journey.

a Copy and complete:

Distance (d km)	0	2	4	6	8	10
Cost (\$$C$)						

b Graph C against d.

c Find the function $C(d)$ which connects the variables.

d Find the cost of a 9.4 km journey.

a

Distance (d km)	0	2	4	6	8	10
Cost (\$$C$)	3.30	6.80	10.30	13.80	17.30	20.80

adding $2 \times \$1.75 = \$3.50$ each time.

b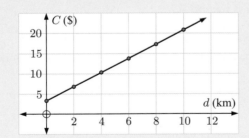

c The 'y-intercept' is 3.30 and
the gradient $= \dfrac{20.80 - 17.30}{10 - 8}$
$$= 1.75$$
$$\therefore \ C(d) = 1.75d + 3.3$$

d $C(9.4) = 1.75 \times 9.4 + 3.3$
$$= 19.75$$
$$\therefore \ \text{the cost is } \$19.75$$

You can use a **graphics calculator** or **graphing package** to help you in the following exercise.

GRAPHING PACKAGE

EXERCISE 16D

1 The cost of staying at a hotel for d days is given by the formula $C(d) = 50d + 20$ euros.
Find the cost of staying for:

   a 3 days   **b** 6 days   **c** 2 weeks.

2 The thermometer on Charlotte's kitchen oven uses the Celsius scale, but her recipe book gives temperatures in degrees Fahrenheit. The formula which links the two temperature scales is $T_C(F) = \frac{5}{9}(F - 32)$ where T_C is the temperature in degrees Celsius and F is the temperature in degrees Fahrenheit.

Convert the following Fahrenheit temperatures into Celsius:

a $212°F$ b $32°F$ c $104°F$ d $374°F$

3 The value of a car t years after its purchase is given by $V(t) = 25\,000 - 3000t$ pounds.

a Find $V(0)$ and explain its meaning.

b Find $V(3)$ and explain its meaning.

c Find t when $V(t) = 10\,000$, and explain what this represents.

4 An electrician charges $60 for getting to a job and $45 per hour he spends working on it.

a From a table of values, plot the amount $C the electrician charges against the time t hours he works, for $t = 0, 1, 2, 3, 4$, and 5.

b Use your graph to determine the cost function $C(t)$.

c Use the cost function to determine the electrician's total cost for a job lasting $6\frac{1}{2}$ hours. Use your graph to check your answer.

5 A rainwater tank contains 265 litres. The tap is left on and 11 litres escape per minute.

a Construct a table of values for the volume V litres left in the tank after t minutes, for $t = 0, 1, 2, 3, 4$, and 5.

b Use your table to graph V against t.

c Use your graph to determine the function $V(t)$.

d Use your function to determine:

  i how much water is left in the tank after 15 minutes

  ii the time taken for the tank to empty.

e Use your graph to check your answers to **d i** and **d ii**.

6 The cost of running a truck is €158 plus €365 for every one thousand kilometres driven.

a Without using a graph, write a formula for the cost €C in terms of the number of thousands of kilometres n.

b Find the cost of running the truck a distance of 3750 km.

c How far could the truck travel for €5000?

7 A salesperson's wage is calculated using the graph alongside.

a Determine the salesperson's weekly wage $W in terms of the sales s thousand dollars.

b Find the weekly wage if the salesperson makes $33\,500 worth of sales.

c Determine the sales necessary for a weekly wage of $830.

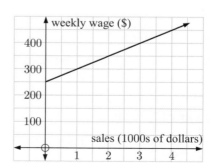

Example 8   ◀》 **Self Tutor**

It costs an appliance manufacturer $12 000 to set up the machinery to produce a new line of toaster. Following this initial setup cost, every 100 toasters produced will cost a further $1000. The toasters are sold to a distributor for $25 each.

a Determine the cost of production function $C(n)$ where n is the number of toasters manufactured.

b Determine the income or revenue function $R(n)$.

c Graph $C(n)$ and $R(n)$ on the same set of axes for $0 \leqslant n \leqslant 1500$.

d How many toasters need to be produced and sold in order to 'break even'?

e Calculate the profit or loss made when:

    i 400 toasters   ii 1500 toasters   are produced and sold.

---

a After the fixed cost of $12 000, each toaster costs $10 to produce.

    $\therefore$ $C(n) = 10n + 12\,000$ dollars   {gradient = cost/item = $10}

b Each toaster is sold for $25, so $R(n) = 25n$ dollars.

c

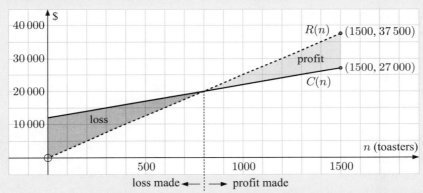

loss made ◀— ⋮ —▶ profit made

d To the left of the point of intersection, $C(n) > R(n)$, so a loss is made.

The manufacturer 'breaks even' where $C(n) = R(n)$

$$\therefore \quad 10n + 12\,000 = 25n$$

$$\therefore \quad 12\,000 = 15n$$

$$\therefore \quad n = 800$$

800 toasters must be produced and sold in order to 'break even'.

e   Profit $= R(n) - C(n)$

    $\therefore$ $P(n) = 25n - (10n + 12\,000)$

            $= 15n - 12\,000$

i $P(400) = 15 \times 400 - 12\,000$

           $= -\$6000$

This is a loss of $6000.

ii $P(1500) = 15 \times 1500 - 12\,000$

             $= \$10\,500$

This is a profit of $10 500.

8 Self adhesive label packs are produced with cost function $C(n) = 3n + 20$ dollars and revenue function $R(n) = 5n + 10$ dollars, where n is the number of packs produced.

   a Graph each function on the same set of axes, clearly labelling each graph.

   b Determine the number of packs which must be produced and sold to 'break even'. Check your answer algebraically.

   c For what values of n is a profit made?

   d How many self adhesive label packs need to be produced and sold to make a profit of $100?

9 Two way adaptors sell for £7 each. The adaptors cost £2.50 each to make, with fixed costs of £300 per day regardless of the number made.

   a Find revenue and cost functions in terms of the number n of adaptors manufactured per day.

   b Graph the revenue and cost functions on the same set of axes.

   c Determine the 'break even' level of production and check your answer algebraically.

   d How many adaptors must be made and sold each day to make a profit of £1000?

10 A new novel is being printed. The plates required for the printing process cost €6000, after which the printing costs €3250 per thousand books. The books are to sell at €9.50 each with an unlimited market.

   a Determine cost and revenue functions for the production of the novel.

   b Graph the cost and revenue functions on the same set of axes.

   c How many books must be sold in order to 'break even'? Check your answer algebraically.

   d What level of production and sale will produce a €10 000 profit?

11 Waverley Manufacturing produces carburettors for motor vehicles. Each week there is a fixed cost of $2100 to keep the factory running. Each carburettor costs $13.20 in materials and $14.80 in labour to produce. Waverley is able to sell the carburettors to the motor vehicle manufacturers at $70 each.

   a Determine Waverley's cost and revenue functions in terms of the number n manufactured per week.

   b Draw graphs of the cost and revenue functions on the same set of axes. Use your graph to find the 'break even' point.

   c Determine the profit function $P(n)$.

   d Use your profit function to:

     i check your answer for the 'break even' value of n

     ii find the weekly profit for producing and selling 125 carburettors

     iii find the number of carburettors required to make a profit of at least $1300.

THEORY OF KNOWLEDGE

In mathematics we clearly define terms so there is no misunderstanding of their exact meaning.

We can understand the need for specific definitions by considering integers and rational numbers:

- 2 is an integer, and is also a rational number since $2 = \dfrac{4}{2}$.

- $\dfrac{4}{2}$ is a rational number, and is also an integer since $\dfrac{4}{2} = 2$.

- $\dfrac{4}{3}$ is a rational number, but is *not* an integer.

Symbols are frequently used in mathematics to take the place of phrases. For example:

- $=$ is read as "is equal to"
- $\sum$ is read as "the sum of all"
- $\in$ is read as "is an element of" or "is in".

> **1** Is mathematics a language?
>
> **2** Why is it important that mathematicians use the same notation?
>
> **3** Does a mathematical argument need to read like a good piece of English?

The word *similar* is used in mathematics to describe two figures which are in proportion. This is different from how *similar* is used in everyday speech.

Likewise the words *function*, *domain*, *range*, *period*, and *wave* all have different or more specific mathematical meanings.

> **4** What is the difference between *equal*, *equivalent*, and *the same*?
>
> **5** Are there any words which we use only in mathematics? What does this tell us about the nature of mathematics and the world around us?

REVIEW SET 16A

1 If $f(x) = 2x - x^2$, find: **a** $f(2)$ **b** $f(-3)$ **c** $f(-\tfrac{1}{2})$

2 Suppose $f(x) = ax + b$ where a and b are constants. If $f(1) = 7$ and $f(3) = -5$, find a and b.

3 If $g(x) = x^2 - 3x$, find in simplest form: **a** $g(x+1)$ **b** $g(x^2 - 2)$

4 For each of the following graphs determine:

> **i** the domain and range **ii** the x and y-intercepts
>
> **iii** whether it is a function.

a
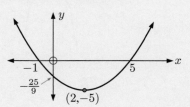

b
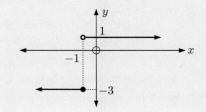

5 Consider $f(x) = \dfrac{1}{x^2}$.

   a For what value of x is $f(x)$ meaningless?

   b Sketch the graph of this function using technology.

   c State the domain and range of the function.

6 A marquee hire company charges £130 for setting up and packing down, and £80 per day of use.

   a Construct a table of values showing the cost £C of hiring a marquee for d days, for $d = 0$, 1, 2, 3, 4.

   b Use your table to graph C against d.

   c Use your graph to find the function $C(d)$.

   d The company offers a special deal in which the total cost of a week's hire is £650. How much money does this save?

REVIEW SET 16B

1 Use the vertical line test to determine which of the following relations are functions:

a 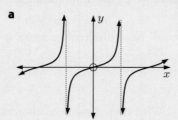   **b** 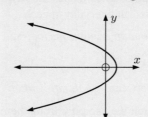   **c**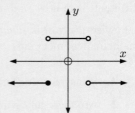

2 If $f(x) = 3x - 5$, find:

   a $f(2)$ **b** $f(0)$ **c** $f(x+1)$ **d** $f(x^2 - x)$

3 Find constants a and b such that $f(x) = \dfrac{a}{x-2} + b$, $f(1) = -4$, and $f(5) = 0$.

4 For each of the following graphs, find the domain and range:

a 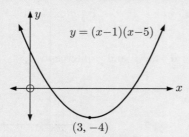   **b**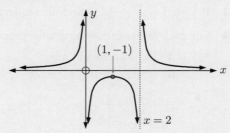

5 **a** Use technology to help sketch the graph of $f(x) = (x+2)^4 - 3$.

   b Hence determine the domain and range of $f(x)$.

6 The amount of oil O left in a leaky barrel after t minutes is shown on the graph alongside.

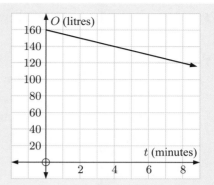

   a Write a formula for the amount of oil left after t minutes.

   b How much oil is left after 15 minutes?

   c How long will it take before:

   i there are only 50 litres of oil left

   ii the barrel is empty?

REVIEW SET 16C

1 Which of these sets of ordered pairs are functions? Give reasons for your answers.

   a $\{(1, 2), (-1, 2), (0, 5), (2, -7)\}$ **b** $\{(0, 1), (1, 3), (2, 5), (0, 7)\}$

   c $\{(6, 1), (6, 2), (6, 3), (6, 4)\}$

2 For each of the following graphs, find the domain and range:

   a

   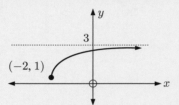

   b

   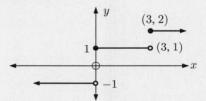

3 Draw a possible graph of a function $g(x)$ where $g(2) = 5$, $g(4) = 7$, and $g(6) = -1$.

4 For each of the following graphs determine:

   i the domain and range   **ii** whether it is a function.

   a

   b

5 Rohan's lawn mower cuts grass to a height of 17 mm. The grass grows 3 mm each day.

   a Construct a table of values for the height H of the lawn d days after it is cut, for $d = 0, 1, 2, 3, 4$.

   b Use your table to graph H against d.

   c Determine the linear function $H(d)$.

   d Find the height of the lawn after 12 days.

   e Rohan mows the lawn again when it is 8 cm high. How often does he mow the lawn?

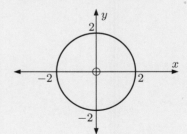

6 Use technology to graph the following, and hence determine its domain and range:

    a $y = x^3 - 3x^2 + x - 4$ **b** $y = \sqrt{9 - 4x^2}$

7 Tennis balls are sold in packs of 3 for \$11 per pack. The balls cost \$2.40 each to produce, with factory running costs of \$1750 per day.

    a Find the cost and revenue functions for making n tennis balls in a day.

    b Graph the cost and revenue functions on the same set of axes.

    c Determine the 'break even' production level. Check your answer algebraically.

    d How many tennis ball packs must be sold to make \$400 profit per day?

Chapter **17**

Quadratic functions

Syllabus reference: 1.6, 6.3

OPENING PROBLEM

An athlete throws a javelin. Its height above the ground after it has travelled a horizontal distance of x metres, is given by $H(x) = -\frac{1}{60}x^2 + x$ metres.

Things to think about:

a What would the graph of H against x look like?

b How high is the javelin after it has travelled 20 metres horizontally?

c What is the maximum height reached by the javelin?

d How far does the javelin travel before it hits the ground?

The height function in the **Opening Problem** is an example of a **quadratic function**. In this chapter we will look at the properties of quadratic functions, and how to draw their graphs.

We will use the techniques for solving quadratic equations which we studied in **Chapter 4**, to solve problems involving quadratic functions.

A   QUADRATIC FUNCTIONS

> A **quadratic function** is a relationship between two variables which can be written in the form $y = ax^2 + bx + c$ where x and y are the variables and a, b, and c are constants, $a \neq 0$.

Using function notation, $y = ax^2 + bx + c$ can be written as $f(x) = ax^2 + bx + c$.

FINDING y GIVEN x

For any value of x, the corresponding value of y can be found by substitution.

Example 1	◀) Self Tutor

If $y = 2x^2 + 4x - 5$ find the value of y when: **a** $x = 0$ **b** $x = 3$

a When $x = 0$,
$$y = 2(0)^2 + 4(0) - 5$$
$$= 0 + 0 - 5$$
$$= -5$$

b When $x = 3$,
$$y = 2(3)^2 + 4(3) - 5$$
$$= 2(9) + 12 - 5$$
$$= 18 + 12 - 5$$
$$= 25$$

SUBSTITUTING POINTS

We can test whether an ordered pair (x, y) satisfies a quadratic function by substituting the x-coordinate into the function, and seeing whether the resulting value matches the y-coordinate.

Example 2   ◀)) **Self Tutor**

State whether the following quadratic functions are satisfied by the given ordered pairs:

  a $y = 3x^2 + 2x$ $(2, 16)$ **b** $f(x) = -x^2 - 2x + 1$ $(-3, 1)$

  a When $x = 2$,
$$y = 3(2)^2 + 2(2)$$
$$= 12 + 4$$
$$= 16$$
$$\therefore \ (2, 16) \text{ does satisfy}$$
$$y = 3x^2 + 2x$$

  b $f(-3) = -(-3)^2 - 2(-3) + 1$
$$= -9 + 6 + 1$$
$$= -2$$
So, $f(-3) \neq 1$
$$\therefore \ (-3, 1) \text{ does not satisfy}$$
$$f(x) = -x^2 - 2x + 1$$

FINDING x GIVEN y

When we substitute a value for y into a quadratic function, we are left with a quadratic equation. Solving the quadratic equation gives us the values of x corresponding to that y-value. There may be 0, 1, or 2 solutions.

Example 3   ◀)) **Self Tutor**

If $y = x^2 - 6x + 8$, find the value(s) of x when: **a** $y = 15$ **b** $y = -1$

  a If $y = 15$ then
$$x^2 - 6x + 8 = 15$$
$$\therefore \ x^2 - 6x - 7 = 0$$

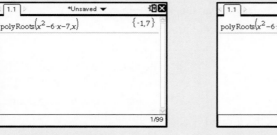

$$\therefore \ x = -1 \ \text{or} \ x = 7$$
So, there are 2 solutions.

  b If $y = -1$ then
$$x^2 - 6x + 8 = -1$$
$$\therefore \ x^2 - 6x + 9 = 0$$

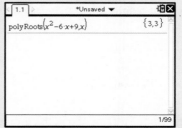

$$\therefore \ x = 3$$
So, there is only one solution.

EXERCISE 17A

1 Which of the following are quadratic functions?

    a $y = 2x^2 - 4x + 10$ **b** $y = 15x - 8$ **c** $y = -2x^2$

    d $y = \frac{1}{3}x^2 + 6$ **e** $3y + 2x^2 - 7 = 0$ **f** $y = 15x^3 + 2x - 16$

2 For each of the following functions, find the value of y for the given value of x:

    a $y = x^2 + 5x - 14$ when $x = 2$ **b** $y = 2x^2 + 9x$ when $x = -5$

    c $y = -2x^2 + 3x - 6$ when $x = 3$ **d** $y = 4x^2 + 7x + 10$ when $x = -2$

3 **a** If $f(x) = x^2 + 3x - 7$, find $f(2)$ and $f(-1)$.

   b If $f(x) = 2x^2 - x + 1$, find $f(0)$ and $f(-3)$.

   c If $g(x) = -3x^2 - 2x + 4$, find $g(3)$ and $g(-2)$.

4 State whether the following quadratic functions are satisfied by the given ordered pairs:

   a $f(x) = 6x^2 - 10$ $(0, 4)$ **b** $y = 2x^2 - 5x - 3$ $(4, 9)$

   c $y = -4x^2 + 6x$ $(-\frac{1}{2}, -4)$ **d** $y = -7x^2 + 9x + 11$ $(-1, -6)$

   e $f(x) = 3x^2 - 11x + 20$ $(2, -10)$ **f** $f(x) = -3x^2 + x + 6$ $(\frac{1}{3}, 4)$

5 For each of the following quadratic functions, find any values of x for the given value of y:

   a $y = x^2 + 6x + 10$ when $y = 1$ **b** $y = x^2 + 5x + 8$ when $y = 2$

   c $y = x^2 - 5x + 1$ when $y = -3$ **d** $y = 3x^2$ when $y = -3$.

6 Find the value(s) of x for which:

   a $f(x) = 3x^2 - 3x + 6$ takes the value 6

   b $f(x) = x^2 - 2x - 7$ takes the value -4

   c $f(x) = -2x^2 - 13x + 3$ takes the value -4

   d $f(x) = 2x^2 - 10x + 1$ takes the value -11.

Example 4   ◀) **Self Tutor**

A stone is thrown into the air. Its height above the ground t seconds after it is thrown is given by the function $h(t) = -5t^2 + 30t + 2$ metres.

   a How high is the stone above the ground at time $t = 3$ seconds?

   b From what height above the ground was the stone released?

   c At what time is the stone 27 m above the ground?

a $h(3) = -5(3)^2 + 30(3) + 2$ **b** The stone was released when $t = 0$ s.

   $\quad\quad = -45 + 90 + 2$ $h(0) = -5(0)^2 + 30(0) + 2 = 2$

   $\quad\quad = 47$ $\therefore$ the stone was released from 2 m above

   $\therefore$ the stone is 47 m above the ground.   ground level.

c When $h(t) = 27$,

   $\quad\quad -5t^2 + 30t + 2 = 27$

   $\therefore\quad -5t^2 + 30t - 25 = 0$

   $\quad\quad\quad\quad\therefore\quad t = 1$ or 5

   $\quad\quad\quad$ {using technology}

Casio fx-CG20

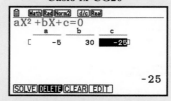

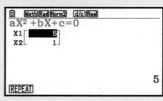

   $\therefore$ the stone is 27 m above the ground after
   1 second and after 5 seconds.

7 An object is projected into the air with speed 80 m s^{-1}. Its height after t seconds is given by the function $h(t) = 80t - 5t^2$ metres.

   a Calculate the height after: **i** 1 second   **ii** 3 seconds   **iii** 5 seconds.

   b Calculate the time(s) at which the height is: **i** 140 m   **ii** 0 m.

   c Explain your answers to part **b**.

   d Over what domain is the model $h(t)$ valid?

8 A cake manufacturer determines that the profit from making x cakes per day is given by the function

     $P(x) = -\frac{1}{2}x^2 + 36x - 40$ dollars.

   a Calculate the profit if: **i** 0 cakes   **ii** 20 cakes are made per day.

   b How many cakes need to be made per day for the profit to be $270?

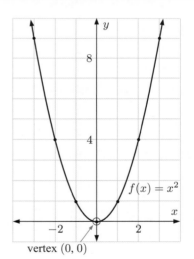

B   GRAPHS FROM TABLES OF VALUES

Consider the quadratic function $f(x) = x^2$.

The table below shows the values of $f(x)$ corresponding to x-values from -3 to 3.

x	-3	-2	-1	0	1	2	3
$f(x)$	9	4	1	0	1	4	9

These points can be used to draw the graph of $f(x) = x^2$.

The shape formed is a **parabola**. The graphs of all quadratic functions have this same basic shape.

Notice that the curve $f(x) = x^2$:

- opens upwards
- has a **vertex** or **turning point** at $(0, 0)$
- is **symmetric** about the y-axis.

   For example, we can see from the table of values that: $f(-3) = f(3)$
                                     $f(-2) = f(2)$
                                     $f(-1) = f(1)$

vertex $(0, 0)$

$f(x) = x^2$

The **vertex** is the point where the graph is at its maximum or minimum.

Example 5   ◀)) **Self Tutor**

Draw the graph of $y = x^2 - 2x - 5$ from a table of values.

Consider $f(x) = x^2 - 2x - 5$.
$$\therefore \quad f(-3) = (-3)^2 - 2(-3) - 5$$
$$= 9 + 6 - 5$$
$$= 10$$

We can do the same for the other values of x.

The table of values is:

x	-3	-2	-1	0	1	2	3
y	10	3	-2	-5	-6	-5	-2

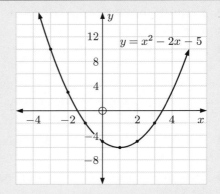

EXERCISE 17B

1 Construct a table of values for $x = -3, -2, -1, 0, 1, 2, 3$ for each of the following functions. Use the table to graph each function.

> When drawing a graph from a table of values, plot the points then join them with a smooth curve.

  a $y = x^2 + 2x - 2$

  b $y = x^2 - 3$

  c $y = x^2 - 2x$

  d $f(x) = -x^2 + x + 2$

  e $y = x^2 - 4x + 4$

  f $f(x) = -2x^2 + 3x + 10$

Use the **graphing package** or your **graphics calculator** to check your answers.

GRAPHING PACKAGE

2 **a** Copy and complete the following table of values:

x	-3	-2	-1	0	1	2	3
x^2	9	4	1	0	1	4	9
$x^2 + 2$	11	6	3	2	3	6	11
$x^2 - 2$							

  b Hence sketch $y = x^2$, $y = x^2 + 2$, and $y = x^2 - 2$ on the same set of axes.

  c Comment on your results.

3 **a** Copy and complete the following table of values:

x	-3	-2	-1	0	1	2	3
x^2	9	4	1	0	1	4	9
$(x+2)^2$							
$(x-2)^2$							

  b Hence sketch $y = x^2$, $y = (x+2)^2$, and $y = (x-2)^2$ on the same set of axes.

  c Comment on your results.

C   AXES INTERCEPTS

The axes intercepts are an important property of quadratic functions. If we know the axes intercepts, we can graph the function very easily.

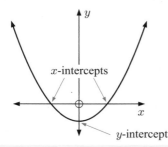

x-intercepts

y-intercept

> The **x-intercepts** are values of x where the graph meets the x-axis.

> The **y-intercept** is the value of y where the graph meets the y-axis.

INVESTIGATION 1   AXES INTERCEPTS

What to do:

1   For the following quadratic functions, use a graphing package or graphics calculator to:

   GRAPHING PACKAGE

   i draw the graph   **ii** find the y-intercept   **iii** find any x-intercepts

   a $y = x^2 - 3x - 4$ **b** $y = -x^2 + 2x + 8$ **c** $y = 2x^2 - 3x$

   d $y = -2x^2 + 2x - 3$ **e** $y = (x - 1)(x - 3)$ **f** $y = -(x + 2)(x - 3)$

   g $y = 3(x + 1)(x + 4)$ **h** $y = 2(x - 2)^2$ **i** $y = -3(x + 1)^2$

2   From your observations in question **1**:

   a State the y-intercept of a quadratic function in the form $y = ax^2 + bx + c$.

   b State the x-intercepts of a quadratic function in the form $y = a(x - \alpha)(x - \beta)$.

   c What do you notice about the x-intercepts of quadratic functions in the form $y = a(x - \alpha)^2$?

THE y-INTERCEPT

You will have noticed that for a quadratic function of the form $y = ax^2 + bx + c$,   the y-intercept is the constant term c. This is because any curve cuts the y-axis when $x = 0$.

We can see this since, letting $x = 0$, $y = a(0)^2 + b(0) + c$
$$= 0 + 0 + c$$
$$= c$$

FINDING x-INTERCEPTS FROM THE FACTORISED FORM

When a quadratic function is given in the factorised form $y = a(x - \alpha)(x - \beta)$,   we can find the x-intercepts by letting $y = 0$ and using the Null Factor law:

> The x-intercepts are also called the **zeros** of the function.

$$0 = a(x - \alpha)(x - \beta) \quad \text{where } a \neq 0$$
$$\therefore \quad x - \alpha = 0 \quad \text{or} \quad x - \beta = 0 \quad \{\text{Null Factor law}\}$$
$$\therefore \quad x = \alpha \quad \text{or} \quad x = \beta$$

> The x-intercepts of $y = a(x - \alpha)(x - \beta)$ are α and β.

Example 6   🔊 **Self Tutor**

Find the x-intercepts of:

a $y = 3(x-4)(x+2)$ **b** $y = (x-5)^2$

a We let $y = 0$
$\therefore\ 3(x-4)(x+2) = 0$
$\therefore\ x = 4\ \text{or}\ x = -2$
So, the x-intercepts are 4 and -2.

b We let $y = 0$
$\therefore\ (x-5)^2 = 0$
$\therefore\ x = 5$
So, the only x-intercept is 5.

FINDING x-INTERCEPTS FROM THE EXPANDED FORM

For quadratic functions written in the expanded form $y = ax^2 + bx + c$, finding the x-intercepts is not so easy.

The x-intercepts are the **zeros** of the quadratic function, and we find them by solving the quadratic equation $ax^2 + bx + c = 0$.

In **Chapter 4** we saw that the quadratic equation can have two, one, or zero solutions. This means that quadratic functions can have two, one, or zero x-intercepts.

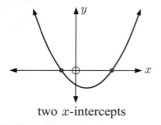 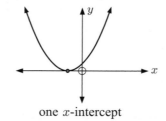 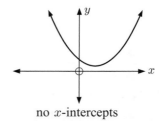

two x-intercepts   one x-intercept   no x-intercepts

Example 7   🔊 **Self Tutor**

Find the x-intercepts of the quadratic function $y = x^2 - 2x - 15$.

We use technology to graph $y = x^2 - 2x - 15$, then find where the graph meets the x-axis.

Casio fx-CG20   **TI-84 Plus**   **TI-nspire**

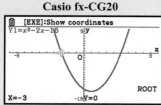 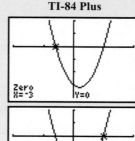 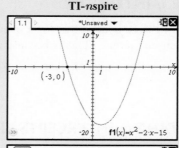

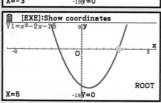 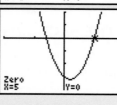 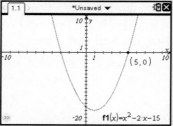

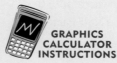 **GRAPHICS CALCULATOR INSTRUCTIONS**

So, the x-intercepts are -3 and 5.

EXERCISE 17C

1 State the y-intercept for the following functions:

a $y = x^2 + 2x + 3$ **b** $y = 2x^2 + 5x - 1$ **c** $y = -x^2 - 3x - 4$

d $f(x) = 3x^2 - 10x + 1$ **e** $y = 3x^2 + 5$ **f** $y = 4x^2 - x$

g $y = 8 - x - 2x^2$ **h** $f(x) = 2x - x^2 - 5$ **i** $y = 6x^2 + 2 - 5x$

2 Find the y-intercept for the following functions:

a $y = (x + 1)(x + 3)$ **b** $y = (x - 2)(x + 3)$ **c** $y = (x - 7)^2$

d $y = (2x + 5)(3 - x)$ **e** $y = x(x - 4)$ **f** $y = -(x + 4)(x - 5)$

3 Find the x-intercepts of the following functions:

a $y = (x - 2)(x - 5)$ **b** $y = (x - 3)(x + 4)$ **c** $y = 2(x + 6)(x + 3)$

d $y = -(x - 7)(x + 1)$ **e** $y = x(x - 8)$ **f** $y = -3(x + 5)(x - 5)$

g $y = (x + 4)^2$ **h** $y = 7(x - 2)^2$ **i** $y = -4(x + 1)^2$

4 How many zeros has a quadratic function which:

a cuts the x-axis twice   **b** *touches* the x-axis

c lies entirely below the x-axis?

5 Find the x-intercepts of the following functions:

a $y = x^2 - x - 6$ **b** $y = x^2 - 16$ **c** $y = x^2 + 5$

d $y = 3x - x^2$ **e** $y = x^2 - 12x + 36$ **f** $y = x^2 + x - 7$

g $y = -x^2 - 4x + 21$ **h** $y = 2x^2 - 20x + 50$ **i** $y = 2x^2 - 7x - 15$

j $y = -2x^2 + x - 5$ **k** $y = -6x^2 + x + 5$ **l** $y = 3x^2 + x - 1$

6 Find the axes intercepts of the following functions:

a $y = x^2 + x - 2$ **b** $y = (x + 3)^2$ **c** $y = (x + 5)(x - 2)$

d $y = x^2 + x + 4$ **e** $y = -x^2 + 7x - 8$ **f** $y = -x^2 - 8x - 16$

g $y = x^2 - 7x$ **h** $y = -2x^2 + 3x + 7$ **i** $y = 2x^2 - 18$

j $y = -x^2 + 2x - 9$ **k** $y = 4x^2 - 4x - 3$ **l** $y = -5x^2 + 2x + 11$

D   GRAPHS OF THE FORM $y = ax^2$

INVESTIGATION 2   GRAPHS OF THE FORM $y = ax^2$

In this investigation we consider graphs of functions of the form $y = ax^2$. We consider the meaning of the size and sign of a.

GRAPHING PACKAGE

What to do:

1 Use the **graphing package** or your **graphics calculator** to graph each pair of functions on the same set of axes.

a $y = x^2$ and $y = 2x^2$ **b** $y = x^2$ and $y = 4x^2$ **c** $y = x^2$ and $y = \frac{1}{2}x^2$

d $y = x^2$ and $y = -x^2$ **e** $y = x^2$ and $y = -2x^2$ **f** $y = x^2$ and $y = -\frac{1}{2}x^2$

2 Use the interactive demonstration to explore other functions of the form $y = ax^2$.

DEMO

3 What effect does a have on:

    a the direction in which the graph opens   **b** the shape of the graph?

From the **Investigation** we make the following observations:

> If $a > 0$, $y = ax^2$ opens upwards. It has the shape
>
> If $a < 0$, $y = ax^2$ opens downwards. It has the shape
>
> If $a < -1$ or $a > 1$, $y = ax^2$ is 'thinner' than $y = x^2$.
>
> If $-1 < a < 1$, $a \neq 0$, $y = ax^2$ is 'wider' than $y = x^2$.
>
> The vertex of $y = ax^2$ is $(0, 0)$. The graph is always symmetrical.

Example 8   ◀) **Self Tutor**

Sketch $y = x^2$ on a set of axes and hence sketch:

    a $y = 3x^2$ **b** $y = -3x^2$

a $y = 3x^2$ is 'thinner' than $y = x^2$.

b $y = -3x^2$ has the same shape as $y = 3x^2$ but opens downwards.

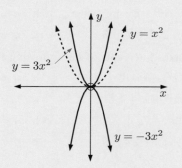

EXERCISE 17D

1 For each of the following functions, sketch $y = x^2$ and the function on the same set of axes. In each case comment on the direction in which the graph opens, and the shape of the graph.

GRAPHING PACKAGE

    a $y = 5x^2$ **b** $y = -5x^2$ **c** $y = \frac{1}{3}x^2$

    d $y = -\frac{1}{3}x^2$ **e** $y = -4x^2$ **f** $y = \frac{1}{4}x^2$

Use the **graphing package** or your **graphics calculator** to check your answers.

2 State the coordinates of the vertex of the following functions, and explain whether the vertex is at a maximum or a minimum of the function.

    a $y = 3x^2$ **b** $y = -6x^2$

E GRAPHS OF QUADRATIC FUNCTIONS

If we know the value of a and the axes intercepts of a quadratic function, we can use them to sketch its graph.

Example 9 ◀) **Self Tutor**

Sketch the graph of $y = x^2 - 2x - 3$ by considering:

a the value of a **b** the y-intercept **c** the x-intercepts.

a Since $a = 1$ which is > 0, the parabola has shape .

b The y-intercept occurs when $x = 0$

∴ $y = (0)^2 - 2(0) - 3$

 $= -3$

∴ the y-intercept is -3.

c The x-intercepts occur when $y = 0$.

∴ $x^2 - 2x - 3 = 0$

Casio fx-CG20	TI-84 Plus	TI-*n*spire
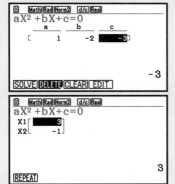	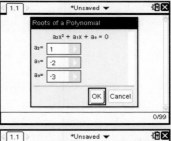	
	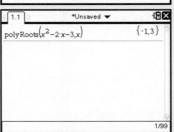	

∴ the x-intercepts are 3 and -1.

Sketch:

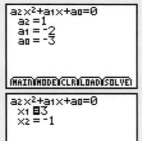

$y = x^2 - 2x - 3$

A sketch must show the general shape and key features of the graph.

Example 10

Sketch the graph of $y = -2(x+1)(x-2)$ by considering:

  a the value of a **b** the y-intercept   **c** the x-intercepts.

a Since $a = -2$ which is < 0, the parabola has shape 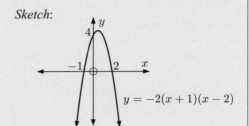.

b The y-intercept occurs when $x = 0$

$$\therefore \quad y = -2(0+1)(0-2)$$
$$= -2 \times 1 \times -2$$
$$= 4$$

$\therefore$ the y-intercept is 4

c The x-intercepts occur when $y = 0$

$$\therefore \quad -2(x+1)(x-2) = 0$$
$$\therefore \quad x = -1 \text{ or } x = 2$$

$\therefore$ the x-intercepts are -1 and 2.

Sketch:

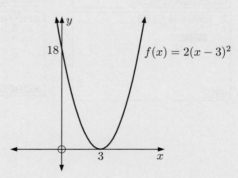

Example 11

Sketch the graph of $f(x) = 2(x-3)^2$ by considering:

  a the value of a **b** the y-intercept   **c** the x-intercepts.

a Since $a = 2$ which is > 0, the parabola has shape .

b The y-intercept occurs when $x = 0$.
Now $f(0) = 2(0-3)^2 = 18$
$\therefore$ the y-intercept is 18.

c The x-intercepts occur when $f(x) = 0$

$$\therefore \quad 2(x-3)^2 = 0$$
$$\therefore \quad x = 3$$

$\therefore$ the x-intercept is 3.

There is only one x-intercept, which means the graph *touches* the x-axis.

EXERCISE 17E

1 Sketch the graph of the quadratic function with:

  a x-intercepts -1 and 1, and y-intercept -1

  b x-intercepts -3 and 1, and y-intercept 2

  c x-intercepts 2 and 5, and y-intercept -4

  d x-intercept 2 and y-intercept 4.

> If a quadratic function has only one x-intercept then its graph must *touch* the x-axis.

2 Sketch the graphs of the following by considering:

    i the value of a **ii** the y-intercept   **iii** the x-intercepts.

  a $y = x^2 - 4x + 4$ **b** $f(x) = (x-1)(x+3)$ **c** $y = 2(x+2)^2$

  d $y = -(x-2)(x+1)$ **e** $y = -3(x+1)^2$ **f** $f(x) = -3(x-4)(x-1)$

  g $y = 2(x+3)(x+1)$ **h** $f(x) = 2x^2 + 3x + 2$ **i** $y = -2x^2 - 3x + 5$

F   AXIS OF SYMMETRY

The graph of any quadratic function is symmetric about a vertical line called the **axis of symmetry**.

Since the axis of symmetry is vertical, its equation will have the form $x = k$.

If a quadratic function has two x-intercepts, then the axis of symmetry lies halfway between them.

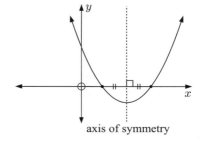

axis of symmetry

Example 12   **◄》 Self Tutor**

Find the equation of the axis of symmetry for the following quadratic functions:

  a

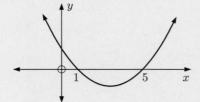

  b

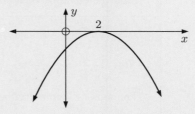

  a The x-intercepts are 1 and 5, and 3 is halfway between 1 and 5.
So, the axis of symmetry has equation $x = 3$.

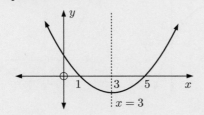

  b The only x-intercept is 2, so the axis of symmetry has equation $x = 2$.

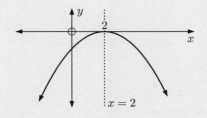

AXIS OF SYMMETRY OF $y = ax^2 + bx + c$

When quadratic functions are given in expanded form, for example $y = 2x^2 + 9x + 4$, we cannot easily identify the x-intercepts. We have also seen that some quadratic functions do not have any x-intercepts.

So, we need a method for finding the axis of symmetry of a function without using x-intercepts.

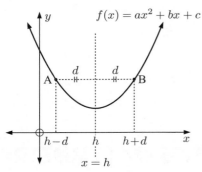

Consider the quadratic function $f(x) = ax^2 + bx + c$ alongside, with axis of symmetry $x = h$.

Suppose A and B are two points on $f(x)$ which are d units either side of the axis of symmetry. A and B have x-coordinates $h - d$ and $h + d$ respectively.

Since the function is *symmetric* about $x = h$,   A and B will have the same y-coordinate.

$$\therefore \quad f(h - d) = f(h + d)$$

$$\therefore \quad a(h - d)^2 + b(h - d) + c = a(h + d)^2 + b(h + d) + c$$

$$\therefore \quad a(h^2 - 2hd + d^2) + bh - bd = a(h^2 + 2hd + d^2) + bh + bd$$

$$\therefore \quad -4ahd = 2bd$$

$$\therefore \quad h = \frac{-b}{2a}$$

The equation of the axis of symmetry of $y = ax^2 + bx + c$ is $x = \dfrac{-b}{2a}$.

Example 13
◀)) **Self Tutor**

Find the equation of the axis of symmetry of $y = 3x^2 + 4x - 5$.

$y = 3x^2 + 4x - 5$ has $a = 3, \ b = 4, \ c = -5$.

Now $\dfrac{-b}{2a} = \dfrac{-4}{2 \times 3} = -\dfrac{2}{3}$

The axis of symmetry has equation $x = -\dfrac{2}{3}$.

EXERCISE 17F

1 For each of the following, find the equation of the axis of symmetry:

a
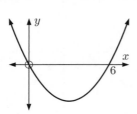

b
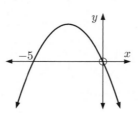

c
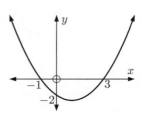

d
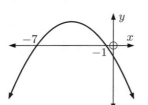

e
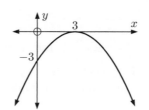

f
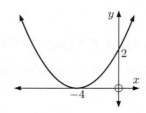

2 Find the equation of the axis of symmetry for the following functions:

a $y = (x - 2)(x - 6)$

b $y = x(x + 4)$

c $y = -(x + 3)(x - 5)$

d $y = (x - 3)(x - 8)$

e $y = 2(x - 5)^2$

f $y = -3(x + 2)^2$

3 Determine the equation of the axis of symmetry of:

a $y = x^2 + 6x + 2$

b $y = x^2 - 8x - 1$

c $f(x) = 2x^2 + 5x - 3$

d $y = -x^2 + 3x - 7$

e $y = 2x^2 - 5$

f $y = -5x^2 + 7x$

g $f(x) = x^2 - 6x + 9$

h $y = 10x - 3x^2$

i $y = \frac{1}{8}x^2 + x - 1$

G   VERTEX

The **vertex** or **turning point** of a parabola is the point at which the function has:

- a **maximum value** for $a < 0$. We call this point a **local maximum**.

  or

- a **minimum value** for $a > 0$. We call this point a **local minimum**.

The vertex of a quadratic function always lies on the **axis of symmetry**, so the axis of symmetry gives us the x-coordinate of the vertex.

The y-coordinate can be found by substituting this value of x into the function.

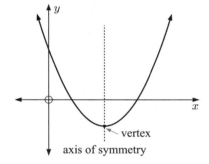

vertex

axis of symmetry

Example 14   🔊 **Self Tutor**

Determine the coordinates of the vertex of $f(x) = x^2 + 6x + 4$.

$f(x) = x^2 + 6x + 4$ has $a = 1$, $b = 6$, $c = 4$.

Now $\dfrac{-b}{2a} = \dfrac{-6}{2 \times 1} = -3$

So, the axis of symmetry has equation $x = -3$.

$$f(-3) = (-3)^2 + 6(-3) + 4$$
$$= 9 - 18 + 4$$
$$= -5$$

So, the vertex is $(-3, -5)$.

> The vertex is a local minimum since $a > 0$.

Example 15 ◀) Self Tutor

Use technology to find the vertex of $f(x) = -2x^2 + 2x + 3$.

We first graph the function $f(x) = -2x^2 + 2x + 3$.

We see that the vertex is a *local maximum*, and use the optimisation feature to find its coordinates.

GRAPHICS
CALCULATOR
INSTRUCTIONS

GRAPHING
PACKAGE

Casio fx-CG20

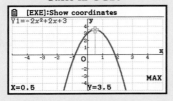

TI-84 Plus

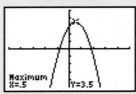

TI-nspire

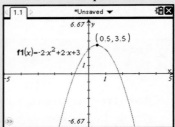

So, the vertex is $(0.5, 3.5)$.

Example 16 ◀) Self Tutor

Consider the quadratic function $y = -x^2 - 4x + 5$.

a Find the axes intercepts.
b Find the equation of the axis of symmetry.
c Find the coordinates of the vertex.
d Sketch the function, showing all important features.
e State the domain and range of the function.

a When $x = 0$, $y = 5$
So, the y-intercept is 5.

TI-nspire

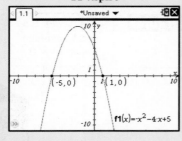

The x-intercepts are -5 and 1.

b $a = -1$, $b = -4$, $c = 5$
$$\therefore \quad \frac{-b}{2a} = \frac{4}{-2} = -2$$
So, the axis of symmetry is $x = -2$.

c When $x = -2$,
$$\begin{aligned} y &= -(-2)^2 - 4(-2) + 5 \\ &= -4 + 8 + 5 \\ &= 9 \end{aligned}$$
So, the vertex is $(-2, 9)$.

d

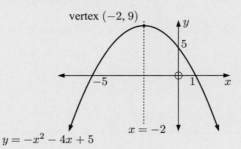

e The domain is $\{x \mid x \in \mathbb{R}\}$.
The range is $\{y \mid y \leqslant 9\}$.

EXERCISE 17G

1 Find the vertex of each of the following quadratic functions. In each case state whether the vertex is a local maximum or a local minimum.

a $y = x^2 - 4x + 7$

b $y = x^2 + 2x + 5$

c $f(x) = -x^2 + 6x - 1$

d $y = x^2 + 3$

e $f(x) = 2x^2 + 12x$

f $y = -3x^2 + 6x - 4$

g $y = x^2 - x - 1$

h $y = -2x^2 + 3x - 2$

i $y = -\frac{1}{4}x^2 + 3x - 2$

2 Use technology to find the vertex of:

a $y = x^2 - 3x - 10$

b $f(x) = -x^2 + 4x - 8$

c $y = 4x^2 + 20x + 25$

d $f(x) = (x - 3)^2 + 1$

e $f(x) = 9 - x^2$

f $y = -3x^2 - 7x + 1$

3 For each of the following functions:

   i find the axes intercepts

   ii find the equation of the axis of symmetry

   iii find the coordinates of the vertex

   iv sketch the function, showing all important features

   v state the domain and range of the function.

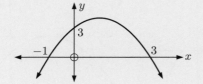

a $y = x^2 - 4x + 3$

b $y = -(x + 2)(x - 6)$

c $f(x) = x^2 + 2x$

d $y = (x + 5)(x - 3)$

e $y = x^2 - 10x + 25$

f $f(x) = -4x^2 - 8x - 3$

g $y = x(x - 8)$

h $y = 2x^2 - 2x - 12$

i $f(x) = -(x + 4)^2$

j $y = 9x^2 - 1$

k $y = 3x^2 - 4x + 1$

l $f(x) = -\frac{1}{2}x^2 - x + 12$

H   FINDING A QUADRATIC FROM ITS GRAPH

So far in this chapter we have learned how to draw a graph given a function. To reverse this process we need to use information on or about a graph to determine the quadratic function which generates it.

Example 17   ◀ⁱ⁾ **Self Tutor**

Find the quadratic function with graph:

a

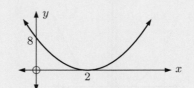

b

a Since the x-intercepts are -1 and 3,
$y = a(x + 1)(x - 3)$, $a < 0$.
But when $x = 0$, $y = 3$
∴ $3 = a(1)(-3)$
∴ $a = -1$
So, $y = -(x + 1)(x - 3)$.

b Since it touches the x-axis when $x = 2$,
$y = a(x - 2)^2$, $a > 0$.
But when $x = 0$, $y = 8$
∴ $8 = a(-2)^2$
∴ $a = 2$
So, $y = 2(x - 2)^2$.

Example 18 ◀) **Self Tutor**

Find the quadratic function with graph:

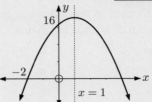

The axis of symmetry is $x = 1$, so the other x-intercept is 4.
$$\therefore \quad y = a(x+2)(x-4)$$
But when $x = 0$, $y = 16$
$$\therefore \quad 16 = a(2)(-4)$$
$$\therefore \quad a = -2$$
$\therefore$ the quadratic function is $y = -2(x+2)(x-4)$.

EXERCISE 17H

1 Find the quadratic function with graph:

a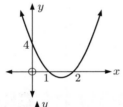

b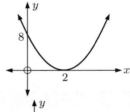

c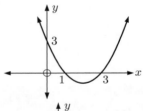

d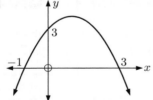

e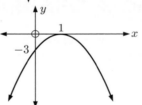

f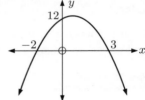

2 Find the quadratic function with graph:

a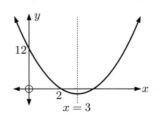

b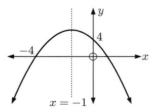

c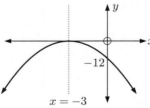

d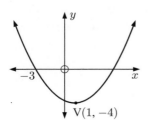

e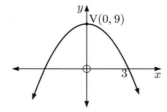

f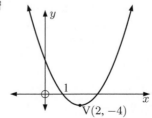

Example 19   ◀)) **Self Tutor**

Find, in the form $y = ax^2 + bx + c$, the quadratic function whose graph cuts the
x-axis at 4 and -3, and which passes through the point $(2, -20)$.

Since the x-intercepts are 4 and -3, the equation is $y = a(x - 4)(x + 3)$, $a \neq 0$.

But when $x = 2$, $y = -20$ $\quad \therefore \quad -20 = a(2 - 4)(2 + 3)$
$$\therefore \quad -20 = a(-2)(5)$$
$$\therefore \quad a = 2$$

$\therefore$ the equation is $y = 2(x - 4)(x + 3)$ or $y = 2x^2 - 2x - 24$.

3 Find, in the form $y = ax^2 + bx + c$, the quadratic function whose graph:

a cuts the x-axis at 5 and 1, and passes through $(2, -9)$

b cuts the x-axis at 2 and $-\frac{1}{2}$, and passes through $(3, -14)$

c touches the x-axis at 3, and passes through $(-2, -25)$

d touches the x-axis at -2, and passes through $(-1, 4)$

e cuts the x-axis at 3, passes through $(5, 12)$, and has axis of symmetry $x = 2$

f cuts the x-axis at 5, passes through $(2, 5)$, and has axis of symmetry $x = 1$.

4 Consider the quadratic function $f(x) = ax^2 + bx + c$ alongside.

a State the value of c.

b The graph passes through $(1, 1)$ and $(2, 6)$. Use this information to write two equations in terms of a and b.

c Solve these equations simultaneously, and hence state the equation of the quadratic.

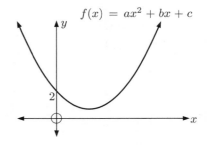

5 The quadratic function $f(x) = ax^2 + bx + c$ has y-intercept -2 and axis of symmetry $x = 3$. The graph also passes through $(5, 3)$.

a State the value of c.

b Use the remaining information to write two equations in terms of a and b.

c Solve these equations simultaneously, and hence state the equation of the quadratic.

d Graph the quadratic using technology.

ACTIVITY

Click on the icon to run a card game for quadratic functions.   **CARD GAME**

WHERE FUNCTIONS MEET

Consider the graphs of a quadratic function and a linear function on the same set of axes.

We could have:

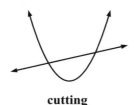   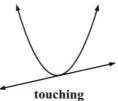   

cutting   **touching**   **missing**
2 points of intersection   1 point of intersection   no points of intersection

We can use technology to find the intersection points of two functions.

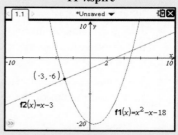

GRAPHICS CALCULATOR INSTRUCTIONS

GRAPHING PACKAGE

Example 20   ◀)) **Self Tutor**

Find the coordinates of the points of intersection of the graphs with equations $y = x^2 - x - 18$
and $y = x - 3$.

We graph $Y_1 = X^2 - X - 18$ and $Y_2 = X - 3$ on the same set of axes.

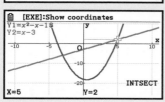

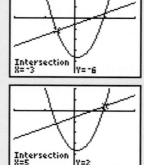

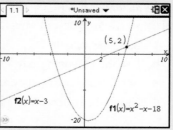

The graphs intersect at $(-3, -6)$ and $(5, 2)$.

EXERCISE 17I

1 Find the coordinates of the point(s) of intersection of the graphs with equations:

a $y = x^2 + x - 1$ and $y = 2x - 1$ **b** $y = -x^2 + 2x + 3$ and $y = 2x - 1$

c $y = x^2 - 2x + 8$ and $y = x + 6$ **d** $y = -x^2 + 3x + 9$ and $y = 2x - 3$

e $y = x^2 - 4x + 3$ and $y = 2x - 6$ **f** $y = -x^2 + 4x - 7$ and $y = 5x - 4$

2 Find the coordinates of the points of intersection, to 3 significant figures, of the graphs with equations:

a $y = x^2 - 3x + 7$ and $y = x + 5$

b $y = x^2 - 5x + 2$ and $y = x - 7$

c $y = -x^2 - 2x + 4$ and $y = x + 8$

d $y = -x^2 + 4x - 2$ and $y = 5x - 6$

e $y = x^2 + 5x - 4$ and $y = -\frac{1}{2}x - 3$

f $y = -x^2 + 7x + 1$ and $y = -3x + 2$

g $y = 3x^2 - x - 2$ and $y = 2x - \frac{11}{4}$

Example 21   ◀⧽ Self Tutor

Find the coordinates of the points of intersection of the graphs with equations $y = x^2 + 2x - 1$ and $y = -x^2 - 4x + 7$.

We graph $Y_1 = X^2 + 2X - 1$ and $Y_2 = -X^2 - 4X + 7$ on the same set of axes.

Casio fx-CG20	TI-84 Plus	TI-nspire
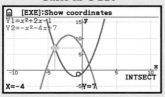	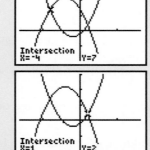	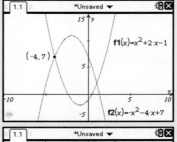
		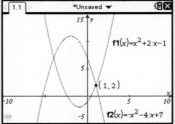

The graphs intersect at $(-4, 7)$ and $(1, 2)$.

---

3 Find the coordinates of the points of intersection, to 3 significant figures, of the graphs with equations:

a $y = x^2 - 8x + 15$ and $y = -x^2 - 4x + 7$

b $y = x^2 - 3x + 4$ and $y = -x^2 + x + 2$

c $y = x^2 - 4x + 9$ and $y = -x^2 + 8x - 12$

d $y = -2x^2 - 3x + 15$ and $y = -x^2 + 5$

e $y = x^2 + 5x + 7$ and $y = 3x^2 - 5x + 6$

f $y = 7x^2 - 14x$ and $y = x^2 - 12x + 36$

A quadratic may miss, touch, or intersect another quadratic.

J   QUADRATIC MODELS

There are many situations in the real world where the relationship between two variables is a quadratic function.

The graph of such relationships will have shape or and the function will have a minimum or maximum value.

We have already seen that this maximum or minimum point lies on the axis of symmetry.

For the quadratic function $y = ax^2 + bx + c$:

- If $a > 0$,
  the **minimum**
  value of y occurs
  at $x = -\dfrac{b}{2a}$.

  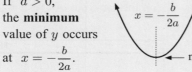

- If $a < 0$,
  the **maximum**
  value of y occurs
  at $x = -\dfrac{b}{2a}$.

  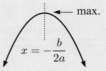

The process of finding the maximum or minimum value of a function is called **optimisation**.

Example 22   ◀》 Self Tutor

A baseballer hits the ball straight up. Its height above the ground after t seconds is given by $H(t) = 30t - 5t^2$ metres, $t \geqslant 0$.

a How long does it take for the ball to reach its maximum height?

b What is the maximum height reached by the ball?

c How long does it take for the ball to hit the ground?

a $H(t) = 30t - 5t^2$ has $a = -5$ which is < 0, so the shape of the graph is .

The maximum height occurs when $t = \dfrac{-b}{2a} = \dfrac{-30}{2 \times (-5)} = 3$

So, the maximum height is reached after 3 seconds.

b $H(3) = 30(3) - 5(3)^2$
$ = 90 - 45$
$ = 45$

So, the maximum height reached is 45 metres.

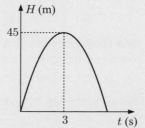

c The ball hits the ground when
$ H(t) = 0$
$\therefore \ 30t - 5t^2 = 0$
$\therefore \ \ t = 0$ or 6
 {using technology}

So, the ball hits the ground after 6 seconds.

TI-84 Plus

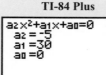

EXERCISE 17J

1 Andrew dives off a jetty.   His height above the water t seconds after diving is given by
$H(t) = -4t^2 + 4t + 3$ metres, $t \geqslant 0$.

  a How high above the water is the jetty?

  b How long does it take for Andrew to reach the maximum height of his dive?

  c How far is Andrew above the water at his highest point?

  d How long does it take for Andrew to hit the water?

2 Jasmine makes necklaces for her market stall. Her daily profit from making x necklaces is given
by $P(x) = -x^2 + 20x$ dollars.

  a How many necklaces should Jasmine make per day to maximise her profit?

  b Find the maximum daily profit that Jasmine can make.

3 The average cost of making x televisions per week is
$C(x) = x^2 - 40x + 500$ dollars *per television*.

  a How many televisions should be made per week to
minimise the *average* cost?

  b Find the minimum average cost.

  c How many televisions are made per week if the average
cost is $200 per television?

4 Answer the questions in the **Opening Problem** on page **502**.

Example 23

    🔊 **Self Tutor**

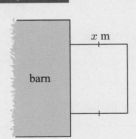

A farmer has 20 metres of fencing to create a rectangular
enclosure next to his barn.

The two equal sides of the enclosure are x metres long.

  a Show that the area of the enclosure is given by
$A = x(20 - 2x)$ m^2.

  b Find the dimensions of the enclosure of maximum area.

---

a The side XY has length $y = 20 - 2x$ m

The area of the enclosure = length × width

$\therefore \quad A = x(20 - 2x)$ m^2

b $A = 20x - 2x^2$

$= -2x^2 + 20x$

which has $a = -2, \ b = 20$

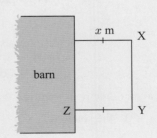

Since $a < 0$, the shape is $\frown$.

So, the maximum area occurs when $x = \dfrac{-b}{2a} = \dfrac{-20}{-4} = 5$ m

The area is maximised when YZ = 5 m and XY = $20 - 2(5) = 10$ m.

5 A rectangular plot is enclosed by 200 m of fencing and has an area of A square metres. Show that:

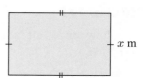

  a if one of the sides is x m long, then $A = 100x - x^2$

  b the area is maximised when the rectangle is a square.

6 A rectangular field is to be fenced on three sides, the fourth being a straight water drain. If 1000 m of fencing is available for the 3 sides, what dimensions should be used for the field to enclose the maximum possible area?

7 1800 m of fencing is available to fence six identical pens as shown.

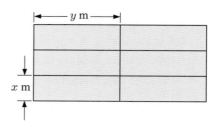

  a Explain why $9x + 8y = 1800$.

  b Show that the total area of each pen is given by $A = -\frac{9}{8}x^2 + 225x$ m^2.

  c If the area enclosed is to be maximised, what is the shape of each pen?

8 500 m of fencing is available to make 4 rectangular pens of identical shape. Find the dimensions that maximise the area of each pen if the plan is:

  a

  b

Example 24 ◀») **Self Tutor**

A manufacturer of pot-belly stoves has the following situation to consider.

If x stoves are made per week, each one will cost $\left(50 + \dfrac{400}{x}\right)$ dollars. The total income per week for selling them will be $(550x - 2x^2)$ dollars.

How many pot-belly stoves should be made per week to maximise the profit?

The total profit $P = \text{income} - \text{costs}$

$$\therefore \ P = (550x - 2x^2) - \underbrace{\left(50 + \dfrac{400}{x}\right)}_{\text{cost for one}} \ \overset{\diagdown}{x}$$

$$\text{cost for one} \qquad \text{number made}$$

$\therefore \ P = 550x - 2x^2 - 50x - 400$

$\therefore \ P = -2x^2 + 500x - 400$ dollars

This is a quadratic in x, with $a = -2$, $b = 500$, $c = -400$.

Since $a < 0$, the shape is .

P is maximised when $x = \dfrac{-b}{2a} = \dfrac{-500}{-4} = 125$

$\therefore$ 125 stoves should be made per week to maximise the profit.

9 The total cost of producing x toasters per day is given by $C = (\frac{1}{10}x^2 + 20x + 25)$ euros, and the selling price of each toaster is $(44 - \frac{1}{5}x)$ euros. How many toasters should be produced each day to maximise the total profit?

10 If x barbeques are made each week then each one will cost $\left(60 + \dfrac{800}{x}\right)$ pounds, and the total income will be $(1000x - 3x^2)$ pounds.

How many barbeques should be made per week to maximise profits?

INVESTIGATION 3   TUNNELS AND TRUCKS

A tunnel is parabolic in shape with the dimensions shown.

A truck carrying a wide load is 4.8 m high and 3.9 m wide. Your task is to determine if the truck will fit through the tunnel.

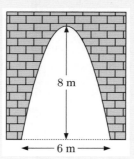

What to do:

1 Suppose a set of axes is fitted to the parabolic tunnel as shown. Each grid unit represents 1 m. State the coordinates of A, B and C.

2 The tunnel has equation $y = ax^2 + bx + c$.

   a Use the coordinates of the vertex A to find the values of b and c.

   b Use the coordinates of B to find the value of a.

3 What is the equation of the truck's roofline?

4 Graph the equations of the tunnel and the truck's roofline on the same set of axes. Calculate the points of intersection of the graphs of these functions.

5 Will the truck pass through the tunnel? Explain your answer.

6 What is the maximum width of a truck 4.8 m high, that can pass through the tunnel?

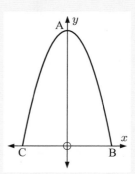

REVIEW SET 17A

1 If $f(x) = x^2 - 3x - 15$ find:

   a $f(0)$ **b** $f(1)$ **c** x such that $f(x) = 3$.

2 On the same set of axes, sketch $y = x^2$ and the function:

   a $y = 3x^2$ **b** $y = -\frac{1}{2}x^2$

3 Consider the quadratic function $y = -2(x-1)(x+3)$.

   a Find the:

      i direction the parabola opens   **ii** y-intercept

      iii x-intercepts   **iv** equation of the axis of symmetry.

   b Sketch a graph of the function showing all of the above features.

   c State the domain and range of the function.

4 Consider the function $y = x^2 - 2x - 15$.

   a Find the:

      i y-intercept   **ii** x-intercepts

      iii equation of the axis of symmetry   **iv** coordinates of the vertex.

   b Sketch a graph of the function showing all of the above features.

5 Find the x-intercepts of the following functions:

   a $y = 3x^2 - 12x$ **b** $y = 3x^2 - x - 10$ **c** $f(x) = x^2 - 11x - 60$

6 Match the function with the correct graph:

   a $y = x^2$

   b $y = -\frac{1}{2}x^2$

   c $y = 3x^2$

   d $y = -2x^2$

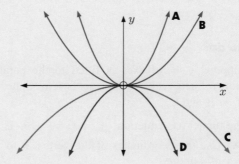

7 Find, in the form $y = ax^2 + bx + c$, the quadratic function whose graph:

   a touches the x-axis at 4 and passes through $(2, 12)$

   b has x-intercepts 3 and -2, and y-intercept 3.

8 Find the maximum or minimum value of the function $y = -2x^2 + 4x + 3$, and the value of x for which the maximum or minimum occurs.

9 A stone was thrown from the top of a cliff 60 metres above sea level. The height of the stone above sea level t seconds after it was released, is given by $H(t) = -5t^2 + 20t + 60$ metres.

   a Find the time taken for the stone to reach its maximum height.

   b Find the maximum height above sea level reached by the stone.

   c How long did it take before the stone struck the water?

REVIEW SET 17B

1   **a** Is $f(x) = -2x^2 + 13x - 4$ satisfied by the ordered pair $(1, 5)$?

   b Find the value(s) of x for which $g(x) = x^2 - 5x - 9$ takes the value 5.

2 Consider the function $y = 3(x - 2)^2$.

   a Find the:

   i direction the parabola opens   **ii** y-intercept

   iii x-intercepts   **iv** equation of the axis of symmetry.

   b Sketch a graph of the function showing all of the above features.

   c State the domain and range of the function.

3 Consider the function $y = -x^2 + 7x - 10$.

   a Find the:

   i y-intercept   **ii** x-intercepts

   iii equation of the axis of symmetry   **iv** coordinates of the vertex.

   b Sketch a graph of the function showing all of the above features.

4 Find the coordinates of the vertex of $y = -3x^2 + 8x + 7$.

5 Find the equation of the quadratic function with graph:

   a

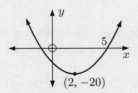

   b

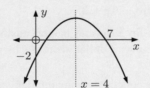

   c

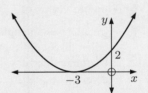

6 Find the coordinates of the point(s) of intersection of the graphs with equations
$y = x^2 + 13x + 15$ and $y = 2x - 3$.

7 Determine the values of a and b:

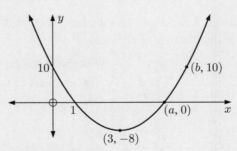

8 A farmer has 2000 m of fencing to enclose two identical adjacent fields.

   a Find an expression for the total area of the fields in terms of x.

   b What is the maximum possible total area of the two fields?

   c What dimensions give this maximum total area?

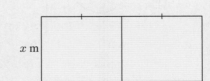

REVIEW SET 17C

1 Suppose $g(x) = x^2 + 5x - 2$. Find:

   a $g(-1)$ **b** $g(4)$ **c** x such that $g(x) = -6$.

2 Consider the quadratic function $y = 2x^2 + 6x - 3$.

   a Find the coordinates of the vertex.   **b** Find the y-intercept.

   c Sketch the graph of the function.   **d** State the range of the function.

3 Draw the graph of $y = -x^2 + 2x$.

4 Find the equation of the quadratic function with graph:

   a

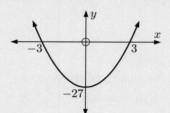

   b

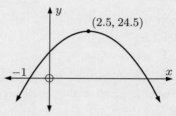

5 Use your calculator to find the coordinates of the point(s) of intersection of the graphs with equations $y = 2x - 9$ and $y = 2x^2 - 3x - 8$.

6 Find the vertex of $y = 2x^2 - 6x + 3$.

7 A retailer sells sunglasses for \$15, and has 50 customers per day. From market research, the retailer discovers that for every dollar increase in the price of the sunglasses, he will lose 2 customers per day.

   a Show that the revenue collected by the retailer each day is $R = (15+x)(50-2x)$ dollars, where x is the price increase of the sunglasses in dollars.

   b Find the price the retailer should set for his sunglasses in order to maximise daily revenue.

   c How much revenue is made per day at this price?

8 Find the quadratic function which cuts the x-axis at 3 and -2, and has y-intercept 24. Give your answer in the form $y = ax^2 + bx + c$.

9

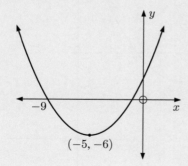

For the quadratic function shown, find:

   a the axis of symmetry

   b the second x-intercept

Chapter **18**

Exponential functions

Syllabus reference: 6.4, 6.6

OPENING PROBLEM

Bacteria reproduce by dividing themselves into two 'daughter' cells. A Petri dish contains a colony of 10 million bacteria. It takes one hour for each of these bacteria to divide into two bacteria, so every hour the total number of bacteria doubles. We can construct a table to show the population b million bacteria after time t hours.

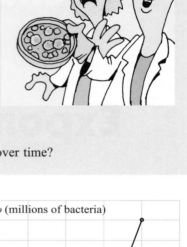

t (hours)	0	1	2	3	4
b (millions)	10	20	40	80	160

Things to think about:

a What type of series do these values form?

b If b is plotted against t, what shape do these points form on a graph?

c Is it reasonable to connect the points with a smooth curve?

d What function can be used to model the bacteria population over time?

The growth pattern in the **Opening Problem** can be shown on a graph like the one alongside.

Since not all the bacteria will divide at the same time, but rather throughout the hour, it is reasonable to join the points with a smooth curve.

We can use the curve to estimate how many bacteria are alive at times other than on the hour. For example, after $1\frac{1}{2}$ hours there are about 28 million bacteria present.

However, drawing a curve on a graph and then reading off values is not a very precise way to investigate the colony. It would be better to have an equation linking t and b.

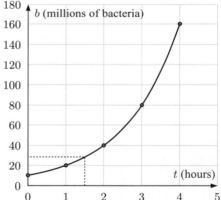

Using our knowledge from **Chapter 5**, we see that the population after each hour forms a geometric sequence with common ratio 2. The general term of the sequence is $b_t = 20 \times 2^{t-1}$.

However, we are also interested in what happens when t is not an integer.

We therefore use the function $b(t) = 20 \times 2^{t-1}$

$$= 10 \times 2 \times 2^{t-1}$$
$$= 10 \times 2^t$$

We call this an **exponential function** because the variable appears in an **exponent**.

The simplest **exponential functions** have the form $y = a^x$ where $a > 0$, $a \neq 1$.

A   EVALUATING EXPONENTIAL FUNCTIONS

> **Example 1**   ◀) **Self Tutor**
>
> For the function $f(x) = 3^x + 5$, find:
>
>   **a** $f(6)$ **b** $f(0)$ **c** $f(-2)$
>
> ---
>
> **a** $f(6) = 3^6 + 5$ **b** $f(0) = 3^0 + 5$ **c** $f(-2) = 3^{-2} + 5$
> $\quad\quad = 729 + 5$ $= 1 + 5$ $= \dfrac{1}{3^2} + 5$
> $\quad\quad = 734$ $= 6$ $= 5\frac{1}{9}$

EXERCISE 18A

1 If $f(x) = 2^x - 3$, find:

  a $f(2)$ **b** $f(1)$ **c** $f(0)$ **d** $f(-1)$ **e** $f(-2)$

2 If $f(x) = 5 \times 3^x$, find:

  a $f(1)$ **b** $f(3)$ **c** $f(0)$ **d** $f(-4)$ **e** $f(-1)$

3 If $f(x) = 2^{x+1}$, find:

  a $f(4)$ **b** $f(0)$ **c** $f(1)$ **d** $f(-1)$ **e** $f(-5)$

4 If $g(x) = 5^{-x}$, find:

  a $g(1)$ **b** $g(3)$ **c** $g(0)$ **d** $g(-2)$ **e** $g(-3)$

5 If $h(x) = 3 \times (1.1)^x$, use your calculator to evaluate:

  a $h(0)$ **b** $h(1)$ **c** $h(5)$ **d** $h(-2)$ **e** $h(3.8)$

B   GRAPHS OF EXPONENTIAL FUNCTIONS

For example, $y = 2^x$ is an exponential function.

We construct a table of values from which we graph the function:

x	-3	-2	-1	0	1	2	3
y	$\frac{1}{8}$	$\frac{1}{4}$	$\frac{1}{2}$	1	2	4	8

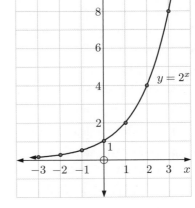

When $x = -10$, $y = 2^{-10} \approx 0.001$ and when $x = -50$,
$y = 2^{-50} \approx 8.88 \times 10^{-16}$.

As x becomes large and negative, the graph of $y = 2^x$
approaches the x-axis, but never quite reaches it.

We say 'as x approaches minus infinity, y approaches 0' and
write: as $x \to -\infty$, $y \to 0$.

We also say that $y = 2^x$ is '**asymptotic** to the x-axis' or
'$y = 0$ is a **horizontal asymptote**'.

As x becomes large and positive, y also becomes large and positive. As $x \to \infty$, $y \to \infty$.

THEORY OF KNOWLEDGE

The word "infinity" comes from the Latin word "infinitas" which means "unbounded". The symbol ∞ was first used to represent infinity by **John Wallis** in 1655 in his *De sectionibus conicis*.

We can construct a table of values for the exponential function $y = 10^x$ as follows:

x	-5	-4	-3	-2	-1	0	1	2	3	4	5
y	0.00001	0.0001	0.001	0.01	0.1	1	10	100	1000	10000	100000

For a postive integer value of x, y is written as a '1' with x '0s' after it.

As x moves to the right on the number line, we need to write more and more '0s'.

If x is positive and *infinitely* big, we need to write a '1' followed by infinitely many '0s'. We can never finish writing the number down, and y is *infinitely* big.

For this reason we say, "As $x \to \infty$, $y \to \infty$."

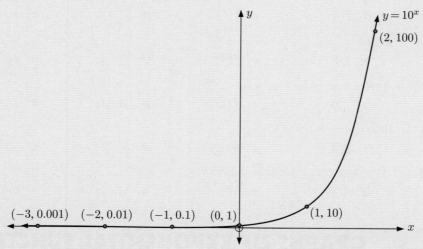

For a negative integer value of x, y has a decimal point followed by $(x-1)$ '0s', then a '1'.

As x moves to the left on the number line, we need to write more and more '0s' before the '1'.

If x is negative and *infinitely* big, we need to write infinitely many '0s' before we can put the '1' on the end. We can never finish writing the number down, and we say y is *infinitesimally* small.

On the graph of $y = 10^x$, y never quite reaches 0, but it gets indistinguishably close to it.

For this reason we say, "As $x \to -\infty$, $y \to 0$."

1 What do you understand by the term *infinity*?

2 Is ∞ a real number?

3 Is *infinity* a natural thing, or is it a creation of mathematics?

4 If the entire world were made of grains of sand, could you count them? Would the number of grains of sand be infinite?

5 Is the universe infinite?

EXERCISE 18B.1

1 Consider the exponential function $y = 4^x$.

   a Copy and complete the table of values.

   b Complete the following statements:

x	-3	-2	-1	0	1	2	3
y			$\frac{1}{4}$	1	4		

      i As we increase x by 1, the value of y is ......

      ii As we decrease x by 1, the value of y is ......

   c Use your table of values to draw the graph of $y = 4^x$.

   d Copy and complete:

      i As $x \to \infty$, $y \to$ ......   **ii** As $x \to -\infty$, $y \to$ ......

   e Find the horizontal asymptote of $y = 4^x$.

2 Consider the exponential function $y = (\frac{1}{3})^x$.

   a Copy and complete the table of values alongside.

   b Use your table of values to draw the graph of $y = (\frac{1}{3})^x$.

x	-3	-2	-1	0	1	2	3
y							

   c Is the graph of $y = (\frac{1}{3})^x$ increasing or decreasing?

   d Copy and complete:

      i As $x \to \infty$, $y \to$ ......   **ii** As $x \to -\infty$, $y \to$ ......

   e Find the horizontal asymptote of $y = (\frac{1}{3})^x$.

3 Given the graph of $y = 2^x$ we can estimate values of 2^x for various values of x.

For example:

- $2^{1.8} \approx 3.5$ (point A)
- $2^{2.3} \approx 5$ (point B)

Use the graph to determine approximate values of:

   a $2^{\frac{1}{2}}$ $(= \sqrt{2})$ **b** $2^{0.8}$

   c $2^{1.5}$ **d** $2^{-1.6}$

   e $2^{\sqrt{2}}$ **f** $2^{-\sqrt{2}}$

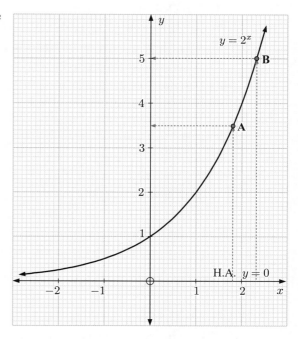

INVESTIGATION 1   EXPONENTIAL GRAPHS

In this investigation we consider the graphs of exponential equations of the
form $y = ka^x + c$ and $y = ka^{-x} + c$.

GRAPHING PACKAGE

What to do:

1   **a**   On the same set of axes, graph the functions:
$$y = 2^x, \quad y = 3^x, \quad y = 10^x, \quad \text{and} \quad y = (1.3)^x.$$

     b   The functions in **a** are all members of the family $y = a^x$.
For $a > 1$, what effect does changing a have on the shape of the graph?

2   **a**   On the same set of axes, graph the functions:
$$y = 2^x, \quad y = 2^x + 1, \quad \text{and} \quad y = 2^x - 2.$$

     b   The functions in **a** are all members of the family $y = 2^x + c$ where c is a constant.

       i   What effect does changing c have on the position of the graph?

       ii   What effect does changing c have on the shape of the graph?

       iii   What is the horizontal asymptote of each graph?

       iv   What is the horizontal asymptote of $y = 2^x + c$?

3   **a**   On the same set of axes, graph the functions:

       i $y = 2^x$ and $y = 2^{-x}$ **ii** $y = 5^x$ and $y = 5^{-x}$

       iii $y = (\frac{1}{2})^x$ and $y = (\frac{1}{2})^{-x}$.

     b   **i**   What is the y-intercept of each graph?

       ii   What is the horizontal asymptote of each graph?

       iii   Describe how the graphs of $y = 2^x$ and $y = 2^{-x}$ are related.

4   **a**   On the same set of axes, graph the following functions:

       i $y = 2^x, \; y = 3 \times 2^x, \; y = \frac{1}{2} \times 2^x$

       ii $y = -1 \times 2^x, \; y = -3 \times 2^x, \; y = -\frac{1}{2} \times 2^x$

     b   The functions in **a** are all members of the family $y = k \times 2^x$ where k is a constant.
Comment on the effect on the graph when:

       i $k > 0$ **ii** $k < 0$

     c   What is the horizontal asymptote of each graph? Explain your answer.

From your **Investigation** you should have discovered that:

For the general exponential functions $y = ka^x + c$ and $y = ka^{-x} + c$:

- a and k control the steepness of the curve, and whether the curve increases or decreases
- c controls the vertical position of the curve
- $y = c$ is the equation of the horizontal asymptote.

We can sketch reasonably accurate graphs of exponential functions using:

- the horizontal asymptote
- the y-intercept
- two other points, for example, when $x = 2$ and $x = -2$.

All exponential graphs are similar in shape and have a horizontal asymptote.

Example 2   ◀) Self Tutor

Sketch the graph of $y = 2^{-x} - 3$.

For $y = 2^{-x} - 3$,
the horizontal asymptote is $y = -3$.

When $x = 0$, $\quad y = 2^0 - 3$
$$= 1 - 3$$
$$= -2$$

∴ the y-intercept is -2

When $x = 2$, $\quad y = 2^{-2} - 3$
$$= \tfrac{1}{4} - 3$$
$$= -2\tfrac{3}{4}$$

When $x = -2$, $\quad y = 2^2 - 3 = 1$

horizontal
asymptote
$y = -3$

$y = 2^{-x} - 3$

EXERCISE 18B.2

1 Draw freehand sketches of the following pairs of graphs using your observations from the previous investigation:

  a $y = 2^x$ and $y = 2^x + 3$ **b** $y = 2^x$ and $y = 2^{-x}$

  c $y = 2^x$ and $y = 5^x$ **d** $y = 2^x$ and $y = 2(2^x)$

GRAPHING
PACKAGE

2 Draw freehand sketches of the following pairs of graphs:

  a $y = 3^x$ and $y = 3^{-x}$ **b** $y = 3^x$ and $y = 3^x + 1$

  c $y = 3^x$ and $y = -3^x$

3 For each of the following exponential functions:

  i calculate the y-intercept
  ii write down the equation of the horizontal asymptote
  iii determine the value of y when $x = 2$ and $x = -2$
  iv sketch the function
  v state the domain and range of the function.

  a $y = 2^x + 1$ **b** $y = 3^{-x} + 4$ **c** $y = (\tfrac{2}{5})^x$ **d** $y = (\tfrac{1}{2})^x - 3$

  e $y = 2 - 2^x$ **f** $y = 4^{-x} + 3$ **g** $y = 3 - 2^{-x}$ **h** $y = (0.8)^{-x} + 1$

C   EXPONENTIAL EQUATIONS

An **exponential equation** is an equation in which the unknown occurs as part of the exponent or index.

For example, $2^x = 50$ and $7^{1-x} = 40$ are both exponential equations.

We can use technology to solve exponential equations. We graph each side of the equation on the same set of axes, and the x-coordinate of the intersection point gives us the solution to the equation.

Example 3   ◀》 Self Tutor

Use technology to solve the equation $3^x = 100$.

We graph $Y1 = 3^X$ and $Y2 = 100$ on the same set of axes, and find the point of intersection.

Casio fx-CG20	TI-84 Plus	TI-*n*spire
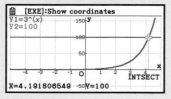	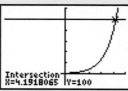	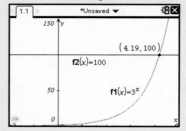

So, the solution is $x \approx 4.19$.

EXERCISE 18C

1   Solve using technology:

   a $2^x = 20$ **b** $2^x = 100$ **c** $3^x = 30$

   d $(1.2)^x = 3$ **e** $(1.04)^x = 4.238$ **f** $(0.9)^x = 0.5$

2   Solve using technology:

   a $3 \times 2^x = 93$ **b** $40 \times (0.8)^x = 10$ **c** $8 \times 3^x = 120$

   d $21 \times (1.05)^x = 34$ **e** $500 \times (0.95)^x = 350$ **f** $250 \times (1.125)^x = 470$

D   GROWTH AND DECAY

In this section we will examine situations where quantities are either increasing or decreasing exponentially. These situations are known as **growth** and **decay**, and occur frequently in the world around us.

For example, populations of animals, people, and bacteria usually *grow* in an exponential way. Radioactive substances, and items that depreciate in value, usually *decay* exponentially.

> **Exponential growth** occurs for $y = a^x$ if $a > 1$.
> **Exponential decay** occurs for $y = a^x$ if $0 < a < 1$.

GROWTH

A population of 100 mice is increasing by 20% each week. To increase a quantity by 20%, we multiply it by 120% or 1.2.

If $P(n)$ is the population after n weeks, then

$P(0) = 100$ {the original population}

$P(1) = P(0) \times 1.2 = 100 \times 1.2$

$P(2) = P(1) \times 1.2 = 100 \times (1.2)^2$

$P(3) = P(2) \times 1.2 = 100 \times (1.2)^3$, and so on.

From this pattern we see that $P(n) = 100 \times (1.2)^n$,   which is an exponential function.

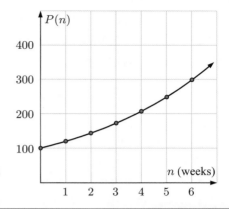

Example 4   ◀))) **Self Tutor**

An entomologist monitoring a grasshopper plague notices that the area affected by the grasshoppers is given by $A(n) = 1000 \times (1.15)^n$ hectares, where n is the number of weeks after the initial observation.

   a   Find the original affected area.

   b   Find the affected area after: **i**   5 weeks   **ii**   12 weeks.

   c   Draw the graph of $A(n)$ against n.

   d   How long will it take for the area affected to reach $10\,000$ hectares?

---

   a $A(0) = 1000 \times 1.15^0$

           $= 1000 \times 1$

           $= 1000$ $\therefore$ the original affected area was 1000 ha.

   b   **i** $A(5) = 1000 \times 1.15^5$

             ≈ 2010

           $\therefore$ after 5 weeks, the affected area is about 2010 ha.

      ii $A(12) = 1000 \times 1.15^{12}$

              ≈ 5350

           $\therefore$ after 12 weeks, the affected area is about 5350 ha.

   c

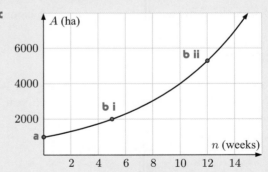

   d   We need to find when $A(n) = 10\,000$

         $\therefore$ $1000 \times (1.15)^n = 10\,000$

Casio fx-CG20	TI-84 Plus	TI-*n*spire

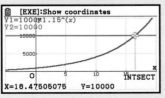
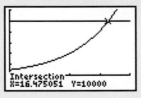
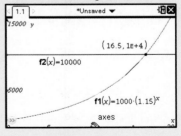

So, it will take about 16.5 weeks.

EXERCISE 18D.1

1 A weed in a field covers an area of $A(t) = 3 \times (1.08)^t$ square metres after t days.

  a Find the initial area the weed covered.

  b Find the area after: **i** 2 days   **ii** 10 days   **iii** 30 days.

  c Sketch the graph of $A(t)$ against t using the results of **a** and **b** only.

  d Use technology to graph $A(t)$ and check your answers to **a**, **b**, and **c**.

2 A breeding program to ensure the survival of pygmy possums was established with an initial population of 50. From a previous program, the expected population $P(n)$ in n years' time is given by $P(n) = 50 \times (1.23)^n$.

  a What is the expected population after: **i** 2 years   **ii** 5 years   **iii** 10 years?

  b Sketch the graph of $P(n)$ against n.

  c How long will it take for the population to reach 600?

3 The speed of a chemical reaction is given by $V(t) = 5 \times (1.03)^t$ units, where t is the temperature in °C.

  a Find the speed of the reaction at: **i** 0°C   **ii** 20°C.

  b Find the percentage increase in speed from 0°C to 20°C.

  c Draw the graph of $V(t)$ against t.

  d At what temperature will the speed of the reaction reach 15 units?

4 Six pairs of bears were introduced to a large island off Alaska where previously there were no bears. It is expected that the population will increase by 14% each year after the introduction.

  a Find a model for the number of bears $B(t)$ on the island t years after the introduction.

  b Find the bear population after 7 years.

  c How long will it take for the population to reach 100?

DECAY

Consider a radioactive substance with original weight 20 grams. It *decays* or reduces by 5% each year. The multiplier is thus 95% or 0.95.

If $W(n)$ is the weight after n years, then:

$$W(0) = 20 \text{ grams}$$
$$W(1) = W(0) \times 0.95 = 20 \times 0.95 \text{ grams}$$
$$W(2) = W(1) \times 0.95 = 20 \times (0.95)^2 \text{ grams}$$
$$W(3) = W(2) \times 0.95 = 20 \times (0.95)^3 \text{ grams}$$
$$\vdots$$
$$W(20) = 20 \times (0.95)^{20} \approx 7.2 \text{ grams}$$
$$\vdots$$
$$W(100) = 20 \times (0.95)^{100} \approx 0.1 \text{ grams}$$

From this pattern we see that $W(n) = 20 \times (0.95)^n$.

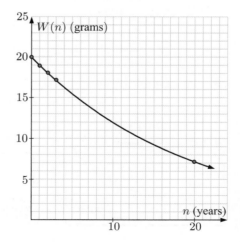

Example 5   ◀)) **Self Tutor**

When medication is taken by a patient, it is slowly used by their body. After t hours, the amount of drug remaining in the body is given by $D(t) = 120 \times (0.9)^t$ mg.

a Find $D(t)$ when $t = 0$, 4, 12, and 24 hours.

b What was the original drug dose?

c Graph $D(t)$ against t for $t \geqslant 0$ using the information from **a**.

d Use the graph or technology to find when there is only 25 mg of the drug left in the body.

a $D(t) = 120 \times (0.9)^t$ mg

$$D(0) \qquad\qquad D(4)$$
$$= 120 \times (0.9)^0 \qquad = 120 \times (0.9)^4$$
$$= 120 \text{ mg} \qquad\qquad \approx 78.7 \text{ mg}$$
$$D(12) \qquad\qquad D(24)$$
$$= 120 \times (0.9)^{12} \qquad = 120 \times (0.9)^{24}$$
$$\approx 33.9 \text{ mg} \qquad\qquad \approx 9.57 \text{ mg}$$

c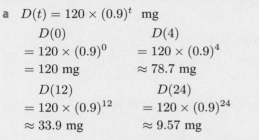

b $D(0) = 120$, so the original dose was 120 mg.

d From the graph, the time to reach 25 mg is about 15 hours.

or

By finding the point of intersection of
$Y_1 = 120 \times (0.9)\text{\^{}}X$ and $Y_2 = 25$
on a graphics calculator, the solution is ≈ 14.9 hours.

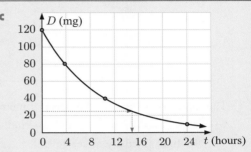

EXERCISE 18D.2

1 The weight of a radioactive substance t years after being buried is given by
$W(t) = 250 \times (0.998)^t$ grams.

a How much radioactive substance was initially buried?

b Determine the weight of the substance after:

    i 400 years   **ii** 800 years   **iii** 1200 years.

c Sketch the graph of $W(t)$ for $t \geqslant 0$, using the above information.

d Use your graph or graphics calculator to find how long it takes for the substance to decay to 125 grams.

2 The current in a radio t seconds after it is switched off is given by $I(t) = 0.6 \times (0.03)^t$ amps.

a Find the initial current.

b Find the current after: **i** 0.1 seconds   **ii** 0.5 seconds   **iii** 1 second.

c Graph $I(t)$ against t using **a** and **b** only.

3 The temperature of a liquid t minutes after it has been placed in a refrigerator, is given by
$T(t) = 100 \times (1.02)^{-t}$ °C.

a Find the initial temperature.

b Find the temperature after: **i** 15 minutes   **ii** 20 minutes   **iii** 78 minutes.

c Sketch the graph of $T(t)$ for $t \geqslant 0$ using **a** and **b** only.

Example 6

🔊 **Self Tutor**

The weight of radioactive material remaining after t years is given by $W(t) = W_0 \times 2^{-0.001t}$ grams.

Find the percentage remaining after 200 years.

When $t = 0$, $W(0) = W_0 \times 2^0 = W_0$

When $t = 200$, $W(200) = W_0 \times 2^{-0.001 \times 200}$

$$= W_0 \times 2^{-0.2}$$

$$\approx W_0 \times 0.8706$$

$$\approx 87.06\% \text{ of } W_0$$

After 200 years, 87.1% of the material remains.

4 The intensity of light in the ocean d metres below the surface is given by $L(d) = L_0 \times (0.9954)^d$ candelas. Find:

   a the light intensity at sea level

   b the percentage intensity decrease at 1000 metres.

5 The value of a car depreciates according to the formula $C(t) = 4500 \times (0.68)^t + 500$ euros, where t is the age of the car in years.

   a Sketch a graph of $C(t)$ against t.   **b** What was the initial cost of the car?

   c How much is the car worth after $4\frac{1}{2}$ years?

   d State the equation of the horizontal asymptote of $C(t)$. What does this mean?

   e How long will it take for the car's value to drop to €1000?

6 The population of turtles in a lake decreases by 7% each year. In 2005 there were 340 turtles in the lake.

   a Find an exponential model for the number of turtles T in the lake, n years after 2005.

   b Graph your model from **a**.

   c How many turtles were in the lake in 2010?

   d If the population falls as low as 10, conservationists will not be able to save the turtle colony. According to your model, when will this occur?

INVESTIGATION 2   **CONTINUOUS COMPOUND INTEREST**

In **Chapter 5** we used the compound interest formula $FV = PV \left(1 + \frac{r}{100k}\right)^{kn}$

where FV is the final amount, PV is the initial amount,

        r is the interest rate per annum,

        k is the number of times the interest is compounded per year,

        n is the number of years.

We can see now that this is an exponential function.

In this investigation we look at the final value of an investment for various values of k, and allow k to get extremely large.

What to do:

1 Suppose $1000 is invested for one year at a fixed rate of 6% per annum. Use your calculator to find the final amount if the interest is paid:

   a annually
   b quarterly
   c monthly
   d daily
   e by the second
   f by the millisecond.

   Comment on your answers.

2 Suppose we let $a = \dfrac{100k}{r}$.   Show that $FV = PV\left[\left(1+\dfrac{1}{a}\right)^a\right]^{\frac{r}{100}n}$.

3 For *continuous* compound growth, the number of interest payments per year k gets very large.

   a Explain why a gets very large as k gets very large.

   b Copy and complete, giving your answers as accurately as technology permits:

a	10	100	1000	10 000	100 000
$\left(1+\dfrac{1}{a}\right)^a$					

4 You should have found that for very large values of a,
$$\left(1+\frac{1}{a}\right)^a \approx 2.718\,281\,828\,459\,....$$

   This is a special number in mathematics called e. e is an irrational number like π.

   Use the $\boxed{e^x}$ key of your calculator to find the value of e^1.

5 For continuous growth, $FV = PV \times e^{\frac{r}{100}n}$ where PV is the initial amount
r is the annual percentage rate
n is the number of years.

   Use this formula to find the final value if $1000 is invested for 4 years at a fixed rate of 6% per annum, where the interest is calculated continuously.

REVIEW SET 18A

1 If $f(x) = 3 \times 2^x$, find the value of:

   a $f(0)$
   b $f(3)$
   c $f(-2)$

2 Consider the function $f(x) = 2 + 3^{-x}$.

   a For the graph of $y = f(x)$, determine:

   i the y-intercept
   ii the equation of the horizontal asymptote
   iii $f(-2)$ and $f(2)$.

   b Sketch $y = f(x)$, showing the details found in **a**.

   c Write down the domain and range of $y = f(x)$.

3 Use technology to solve:

   a $5^x = 1000$
   b $15 \times (1.6)^x = 80$
   c $400 \times (0.98)^x = 70$

4 An autograph by Marilyn Monroe had value $V = 20 \times (1.12)^t$ dollars, where t is the number of years after 1960.

   a Find the original value of the autograph.

   b How much was the autograph worth in: **i** 1970   **ii** 1990   **iii** 2010?

   c Draw the graph of V against t.

   d When was the autograph worth \$1000?

5 The graph opposite shows the temperature of a pie put in the fridge immediately after it is cooked. The temperature after t minutes is given by $T(t) = T_0 \times (1.097)^{-t}$ °C.

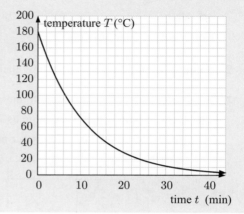

   a Use the graph to find T_0.

   b What is the temperature of the pie after 20 minutes?

   c The pie is to be served at 5°C. How long after cooking can it be served?

REVIEW SET 18B

1 If $f(x) = 5^{x+1}$, find: **a** $f(2)$ **b** $f(0)$ **c** $f(-4)$

2 On the same set of axes, draw the graphs of: **a** $y = 2^x$ **b** $y = 2^x - 4$.
In each case state the y-intercept and the equation of the horizontal asymptote.

3 The weight of a lump of radioactive plutonium after t years is given by $W(t) = 60 \times (0.95)^t$ grams.

   a Find the original weight of the plutonium.

   b Find the weight remaining after: **i** 10 years   **ii** 50 years.

   c How long will it take for the plutonium to decay to 1 gram?

4 Consider the function $f(x) = -2 \times 3^x - 4$.

   a For the graph of $y = f(x)$, determine:

     i the y-intercept   **ii** the equation of the horizontal asymptote

     iii $f(-2)$ and $f(2)$.

   b Sketch $y = f(x)$, showing the details found in **a**.

   c Write down the domain and range of $y = f(x)$.

5 8 pairs of rhinoceroses are introduced onto an Indonesian island. The expected population after n years is given by $P(n) = P_0 \times (1.03)^n$.

   a State the value of P_0.

   b Find the expected population after 25 years.

   c Once there are 40 pairs of rhinoceroses, a new colony can be formed. When is this expected to occur?

Chapter **19**

Unfamiliar functions

OPENING PROBLEM

Regina owns a company that manufactures oil tanks. She needs a cylindrical tank with capacity 10 kL, and wants to choose the base radius for the cylinder which minimises the material needed.

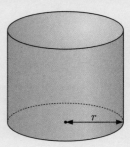

The surface area of the tank is given by $A(r) = 2\pi r^2 + \dfrac{20}{r}$ m^2

where r is the base radius of the cylinder in metres.

Things to think about:

a   What is the domain of $A(r)$?

b   What does the graph of $A(r)$ look like?

c   What are the coordinates of the minimum turning point of $A(r)$? Explain the significance of this point.

A   PROPERTIES OF FUNCTIONS

Real world situations are not always modelled by simple linear or quadratic functions that we are familiar with. However, we can use technology to help us graph and investigate the key features of an unfamiliar function.

The main features we are interested in are:

- the axes intercepts where the graph cuts the x and y-axes
- turning points (local maxima and local minima)
- the domain and range
- values of x where the function does not exist
- the presence of asymptotes, or lines that the graph approaches.

When graphing a function using technology, it is important to start with a large viewing window. This ensures we do not miss any key features of the function.

Example 1   ◀ Self Tutor

Consider the function $y = 2x^3 - 17x^2 + 42x - 30$.

a   Use technology to help sketch the function.   **b**   Find the axes intercepts.

c   Find the coordinates and nature of any turning points.

d   Discuss the behaviour of the function as $x \to \infty$ and $x \to -\infty$.

e   Add to your graph in **a** the key features found in **b** and **c**.

a

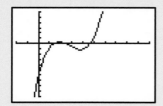

Using technology, we can sketch the graph:

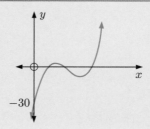

b When $x = 0$, $y = -30$. So, the y-intercept is -30.

From our sketch, there appear to be three x-intercepts.

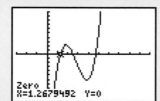 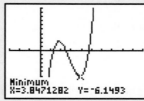 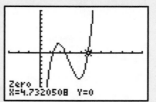

The x-intercepts are 1.27, 2.5, and 4.73.

c From our sketch, the graph has one local maximum and one local minimum.

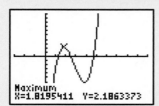

So, we have a local maximum at $(1.82, \ 2.19)$ and a local minimum at $(3.85, -6.15)$.

d As $x \to \infty$, $y \to \infty$; as $x \to -\infty$, $y \to -\infty$.

e

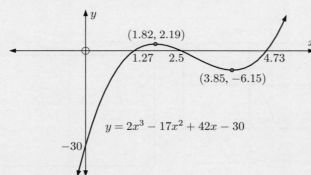

$(1.82, 2.19)$

$1.27 \quad 2.5$

4.73

$(3.85, -6.15)$

$y = 2x^3 - 17x^2 + 42x - 30$

-30

When using technology, always start with a large viewing window.

EXERCISE 19A

1 Consider the function $y = -x^3 + 7x^2 - 3x - 12$.

  a By first graphing the function on your calculator, sketch the function.

  b Find the axes intercepts.

  c Find the coordinates and nature of any turning points.

  d Discuss the behaviour of the function as $x \to \infty$ and $x \to -\infty$.

  e Add to your graph in **a** the key features found in **b** and **c**.

2 Consider the function $y = x^4 - 4x^3 + x^2 + 3x - 5$.

  a By first graphing the function on your calculator, sketch the function.

  b Find the axes intercepts.

  c Find the coordinates and nature of any local maxima or minima.

  d Discuss the behaviour of the function as $x \to \infty$ and $x \to -\infty$.

  e Add to your graph in **a** the key features found in **b** and **c**.

  f State the range of the function.

3 For each of the following:

      i sketch the function   **ii** find the axes intercepts   **iii** find any turning points

      iv add to your graph in **i** all key features found in **ii** and **iii**.

  a $y = \frac{1}{2}x(x-4)(x+3)$ **b** $y = -3x^3 - 24x^2 - 48x$

  c $y = \frac{4}{5}x^4 + 5x^3 + 5x^2 + 2$ **d** $y = 3x^3 - 7x^2 - 28x + 10$

  e $y = 4(x-1)^3(2x+3)$ **f** $y = -x(x+2)(x-1)(x-4)$

Example 2   ◄)) **Self Tutor**

Sketch the graph of $f(x) = x^3 - 3x^2 + 4x + 2$ on the domain $-2 \leqslant x \leqslant 3$.

We first calculate the endpoints for the function:

$$f(-2) = (-2)^3 - 3(-2)^2 + 4(-2) + 2 = -26$$
$$f(3) = (3)^3 - 3(3)^2 + 4(3) + 2 = 14$$

So, the endpoints of the function are $(-2, -26)$ and $(3, 14)$.

$f(0) = 2$, so the y-intercept is 2.

The x-intercepts are when $f(x) = 0$.

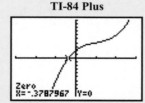

Casio fx-CG20	TI-84 Plus	TI-*nspire*

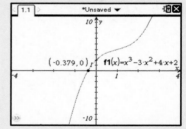

So, the x-intercept is -0.379.

The function has no turning points.

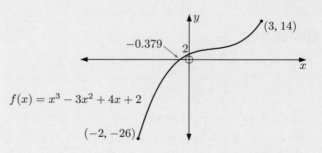

---

4 Sketch the graph of each of the following functions on the given domain. Identify all axes intercepts and turning points.

  a $y = 2x^3 - 6x^2$ on the domain $-1 \leqslant x \leqslant 2.5$

  b $y = -x^3 + \frac{7}{2}x^2 + \frac{7}{2}x - 6$ on the domain $-3 \leqslant x \leqslant 5$

  c $f(x) = 2x^3 - x$ where $-2 \leqslant x \leqslant 2$

  d $y = 2 - x^4 + 2x^2$ where $-2 \leqslant x \leqslant 2$

B   ASYMPTOTES

An **asymptote** is a line which a function gets closer and closer to but never quite reaches.

In this course we consider asymptotes which are **horizontal** or **vertical**.

HORIZONTAL ASYMPTOTES

In **Chapter 18** we observed exponential functions such as $f(x) = 2^x$.

We saw that as $x \to -\infty$, $f(x) \to 0$ from above.

Since $f(x)$ approaches, but never quite reaches, the line $y = 0$, we say that $y = 0$ is a **horizontal asymptote** of the function.

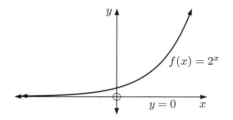

In general, to determine the equation of a horizontal asymptote, we must consider the behaviour of the function as $x \to \pm\infty$. To do this on a calculator, we adjust the viewing window to show a very wide domain. We then use the **trace** feature to investigate y for extreme values of x.

For example, consider the function $g(x) = 3 + \dfrac{2}{x - 1}$.

Using technology, obtain a graph for the domain $-100 \leqslant x \leqslant 100$.

Using the trace feature, we observe:

- as $x \to -\infty$, $g(x) \to 3$ from below
- as $x \to \infty$, $g(x) \to 3$ from above.

We can check this by examining the function. As x gets very large, $\dfrac{2}{x - 1}$ gets very small, so $g(x)$ approaches 3.

So, $g(x)$ has the horizontal asymptote $y = 3$.

Casio fx-CG20

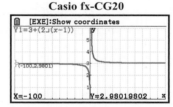

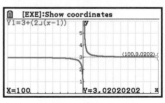

VERTICAL ASYMPTOTES

The graph of $g(x) = 3 + \dfrac{2}{x - 1}$ is now given for the domain $-5 \leqslant x \leqslant 5$.

We observe there is a 'jump' or *discontinuity* in the graph when $x = 1$.

This occurs because $g(1) = 3 + \dfrac{2}{1 - 1} = 3 + \dfrac{2}{0}$ which is undefined.

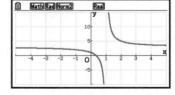

As $x \to 1$ from the left, $g(x) \to -\infty$. As $x \to 1$ from the right, $g(x) \to \infty$.

Since $g(x)$ approaches, but never reaches, the line $x = 1$, we say that $x = 1$ is a **vertical asymptote** of the function.

For functions which contain a fraction, a vertical asymptote occurs when the denominator is zero.

We can now display a complete graph of the function
$g(x) = 3 + \dfrac{2}{x-1}$, including both horizontal and vertical
asymptotes.

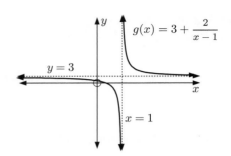

Example 3

◀)) **Self Tutor**

Consider the function $y = \dfrac{1}{x+2} + 4$.

a Find the asymptotes of the function.   **b** Find the axes intercepts.

c Sketch the function, including the features from **a** and **b**.

---

a Graphing the function on the domain $-5 \leqslant x \leqslant 5$, we see
there is a vertical asymptote at $x = -2$.
This is confirmed by substituting $x = -2$ into the function:

$$y = \frac{1}{-2+2} + 4 = \frac{1}{0} + 4 \quad \text{which is undefined.}$$

Graphing the function on the domain $-100 \leqslant x \leqslant 100$, we
see there is a horizontal asymptote at $y = 4$.
So, the graph has the vertical asymptote $x = -2$ and the
horizontal asymptote $y = 4$.

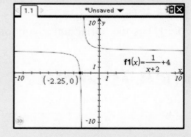

b When $x = 0$, $y = \dfrac{1}{2} + 4 = 4.5$.

So, the y-intercept is 4.5.

We can use technology to find the x-intercept:

Casio fx-CG20	TI-84 Plus	TI-*nspire*

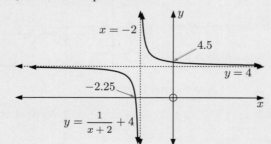

So, the x-intercept is -2.25.

c

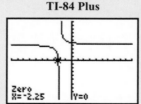

EXERCISE 19B

1 Consider the function $y = \dfrac{6}{x-3} - 2$.

    a Find the asymptotes of the function.   **b** Find the axes intercepts.

    c Sketch the function, including the features from **a** and **b**.

    d State the domain and range of the function.

2 For each of the following functions:

    i find any asymptotes   **ii** find the axes intercepts

    iii sketch the function, including the features you have found.

    a $y = \dfrac{3}{x-1} + 2$ **b** $y = \dfrac{6}{x+2} - 4$ **c** $y = 3 - \dfrac{2}{4+x}$

    d $y = \dfrac{x-6}{x+3}$ **e** $y = \dfrac{2x+3}{1-x}$ **f** $y = \dfrac{-5x+1}{2x-1}$

3 Use technology to help graph $y = \dfrac{2^x}{x}$. Your graph should include any axes intercepts, turning points, and asymptotes.

C   COMBINED POWER FUNCTIONS

A **power function** is a function of the form $y = kx^n$ where $k \neq 0$ and n is a non-zero rational number.

INVESTIGATION 1   GRAPHS OF POWER FUNCTIONS

In this investigation we explore the graphs of simple power functions of the form $y = x^n$, $n \in \mathbb{Z}$, $n \neq 0$.

What to do:

1 Use technology to sketch the following sets of functions. Sketch each set on its own set of axes.

    a $y = x$, $y = x^3$, $y = x^5$, $y = x^7$

    b $y = x^2$, $y = x^4$, $y = x^6$, $y = x^8$

    Comment on any similarities or differences between the graphs in each set and between the sets of graphs.

2 Use technology to sketch the following sets of functions. Sketch each set on its own set of axes.

    a $y = x^{-1}$, $y = x^{-3}$, $y = x^{-5}$, $y = x^{-7}$

    b $y = x^{-2}$, $y = x^{-4}$, $y = x^{-6}$, $y = x^{-8}$

    Comment on any similarities or differences between the graphs in each set and between the sets of graphs.

3 What graphical features are found in the graphs in **2** but *not* in the graphs in **1**? Explain this difference.

You should have observed the following features of functions of the form $y = x^n$, $n \in \mathbb{Z}$:

- $n > 0$ and odd

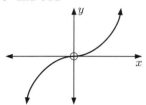

- $n > 0$ and even

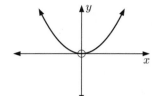

- $n < 0$ and odd

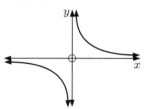

- $n < 0$ and even

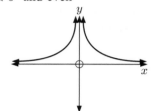

Asymptotic to $x = 0$ and $y = 0$.

Asymptotic to $x = 0$ and $y = 0$.

In this course we also consider the sum of power functions where the exponents can be negative.

INVESTIGATION 2   COMBINED POWER FUNCTIONS

In this investigation we observe the features of the graph when two power functions are added together.

Consider the *linear* function $y = x$ and the *reciprocal* function $y = \dfrac{1}{x}$.

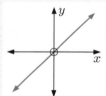

The graph of $y = x$ has:

- one section
- x-intercept 0
- y-intercept 0
- no asymptotes

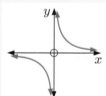

The graph of $y = \dfrac{1}{x}$ has:

- two sections
- no axes intercepts
- a vertical asymptote $x = 0$
- a horizontal asymptote $y = 0$

What to do:

1 Graph $y = x$ and $y = \dfrac{1}{x}$ on the same set of axes.

2 Think about the combined function $y = x + \dfrac{1}{x}$. Predict whether the graph of this function will have:
   a one or two sections
   b any axes intercepts
   c a vertical asymptote
   d a horizontal asymptote.

3 Use technology to sketch $y = x + \dfrac{1}{x}$. Discuss the features of this graph with your class.

Example 4   ◀) **Self Tutor**

Consider the function $f(x) = x^2 + \dfrac{1}{x}$.

  a Find any vertical asymptotes of the function.   **b** Find the axes intercepts.

  c Find the turning points.   **d** Sketch the function.

  a Using technology to graph the function, we see there is a vertical asymptote at $x = 0$. We can check this by finding $f(0) = 0^2 + \frac{1}{0}$, which is undefined.

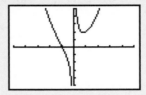

If a function contains a negative power of x such as $\dfrac{1}{x} = x^{-1}$, the y-axis $x = 0$ is a vertical asymptote.

  b There is no y-intercept, as the function is undefined when $x = 0$.

Casio fx-CG20	TI-84 Plus	TI-*n*spire

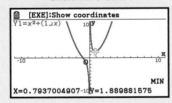
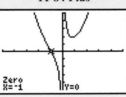
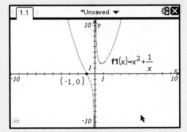

The x-intercept is -1.

  c

Casio fx-CG20	TI-84 Plus	TI-*n*spire

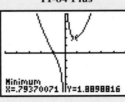
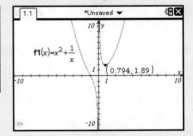

There is a local minimum at $(0.794, 1.89)$.

  d

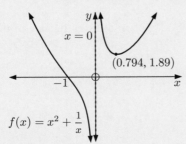

$f(x) = x^2 + \dfrac{1}{x}$

EXERCISE 19C

1 For each of the functions below:

> **i**   find any vertical asymptotes
> **ii** determine the axes intercepts
> **iii** determine the position of any turning points
> **iv** sketch the graph of $y = f(x)$, clearly showing the features you have found.

a $f(x) = x^3 + x^{-1}$

b $f(x) = x^3 - x^{-1}$

c $f(x) = \dfrac{4}{x^2} + x^3$

d $f(x) = x^2 - 2x + \dfrac{1}{x}$

e $f(x) = \left(x - \dfrac{1}{x}\right)^2$

f $f(x) = x^2 + 4x + \dfrac{1}{x^3}$

2 A theme park water slide is constructed according to the function $W(x) = -0.0125x^3 + 0.3x^2 - 2.35x + 12$, where W is the height of the slide above the ground x metres from the starting platform.

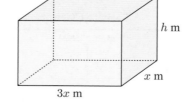

> **a** How high is the starting platform above the ground?
>
> **b** The water slide ends in a pool which is at ground level. How far away is the pool from the starting platform?
>
> **c** Supporting structures hold up the water slide at the turning points of $W(x)$.
>
> > **i**   How far from the starting platform are they?
> > **ii** How tall are the columns?
>
> **d** Sketch the water slide, showing the information you have found.

3 A closed box is to be constructed with length three times its width. The volume of the box must be 6 m³.

> **a** If the box is x metres wide and h metres high, show that $h = \dfrac{2}{x^2}$.

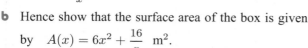

> **b** Hence show that the surface area of the box is given by $A(x) = 6x^2 + \dfrac{16}{x}$ m².
>
> **c** Find the vertical asymptote of $y = A(x)$.
>
> **d** Draw the graph of $y = A(x)$.
>
> **e** **i**   Use your graph to predict the surface area of a box with width 2 metres.
> > **ii** Use technology to check your answer.
>
> **f** Find the coordinates of the turning point of $y = A(x)$. Explain the significance of this point.

D

COMBINED FUNCTIONS

We can **combine** the exponential functions studied in **Chapter 18**, with functions involving powers of x, to obtain functions such as $f(x) = 2^x + x^{-3}$.

These combined functions often exhibit some of the features of their individual components.

For example:

- since $y = x^{-3}$ has the vertical asymptote $x = 0$, so does $f(x) = 2^x + x^{-3}$

- as $x \to \infty$, $x^{-3} \to 0$, so as $x \to \infty$, $f(x) = 2^x + x^{-3}$ takes on the shape of $y = 2^x$.

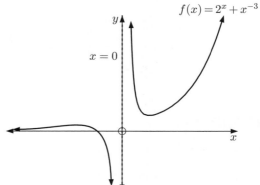

Example 5   ◀ᴵ)) **Self Tutor**

Consider the function $y = x^3 + 3^{-x}$.

  a Find the axes intercepts.   **b** Find the position and nature of any turning points.

  c Sketch the graph of the function.

a When $x = 0$, $y = 0^3 + 3^0 = 1$.
   So, the y-intercept is 1.

TI-nspire

Casio fx-CG20	TI-84 Plus	TI-nspire
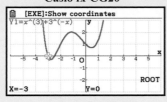	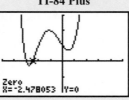	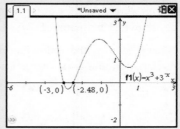

The x-intercepts are -3 and -2.48.

b From the graph, there are two local minima and one local maximum.

TI-nspire

Casio fx-CG20	TI-84 Plus	TI-nspire
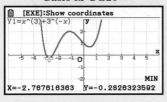	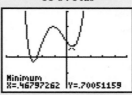	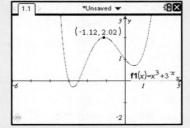

The graph has local minima at $(-2.77, -0.283)$ and $(0.468, 0.701)$, and a local maximum at $(-1.12, 2.02)$.

c

$$y = x^3 + 3^{-x}$$

$(-1.12, 2.02)$

$(0.468, 0.701)$

-3 -2.48

$(-2.77, -0.283)$

EXERCISE 19D

1 Consider the function $\ f(x) = \dfrac{1}{x} - x + 2^x.$

    a Find the equation of the vertical asymptote.

    b Find any axes intercepts.

    c Find the position and nature of any turning points.

    d Sketch the graph of the function.

2 Sketch the following graphs, clearly identifying any axes intercepts, turning points, and asymptotes.

    a $y = 2^x + \dfrac{3}{x^2}$
        b $y = 5^{-x} + x^2 - 4$
        c $y = 2^{-x} - 3x^{-2}$

    d $y = 2 - x + 3^{-x}$
        e $y = 2x^3 + 3^{-x}$
        f $y = \dfrac{3}{x} + 3^{-x}$

    g $y = x^2 - 2^x$
        h $y = \dfrac{2}{x} + 3^x - 3x^2$

3 By drawing the graph of $\ f(x) = 2^{-x} + x,\ $ show that $\ 2^{-x} + x > 0\ $ for all x.

4 Sketch each of the following graphs over the specified domain. Clearly label all turning points, asymptotes, and axes intercepts.

    a $y = 2x^2 + 3x - 4 + 3^x\ $ where $\ -8 \leqslant x \leqslant 4$

    b $y = 2^x - x^2 - 3x - 4\ $ on the domain $\ -6 \leqslant x \leqslant 6$

    c $f(x) = 2^x - 3x - 2x^{-2}\ $ where $\ -5 \leqslant x \leqslant 5$

    d $f(x) = -3^x + 0.1x^3 + 5x\ $ on the domain $\ -8 \leqslant x \leqslant 4$

5 When a new pain killing injection is administered, the effect of the injection is given by

$$E(t) = 640t \times 4^{-t}\ \text{ units,}$$

where $\ t \geqslant 0\ $ is the time in hours after the injection of the drug.

    a Find $E(1)$ and $E(4)$. Interpret your answers.

    b Sketch the graph of $E(t)$ for $t \geqslant 0$, and find the axes intercepts.

    c Find the turning point of $E(t)$. Explain the significance of this point.

E   WHERE FUNCTIONS MEET

We have previously seen that when a quadratic function and a linear function are graphed on the same set of axes, there are three situations which could occur:

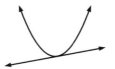

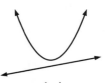

cutting
(2 points of intersection)

touching
(1 point of intersection)

missing
(no points of intersection)

For other combinations of functions, there may be three or more points of intersection.

For example, the functions $f(x) = x^3 - 5x$ and $g(x) = x - 1$ have three points of intersection: $(-2.53, -3.53)$, $(0.167, -0.833)$, and $(2.36, 1.36)$.

This means that the equation $x^3 - 5x = x - 1$ has three solutions: $x \approx -2.53$, 0.167, or 2.36.

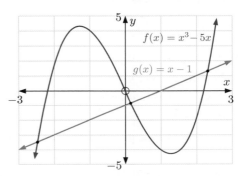

EXERCISE 19E

1 **a** Use technology to find the intersection point of $f(x) = x^3 - 3x^2 - 5x$ and $g(x) = 4x - 2$.

  b Hence, solve the equation $x^3 - 3x^2 - 5x = 4x - 2$.

2 Solve the following equations:

  a $x^3 + 4x^2 - 2 = 2x - 5$
    b $3^x = 2x + 1$
    c $2x = (1.5)^x$

  d $2^{-x} = 2 + \dfrac{6}{x-3}$
    e $4^x - 3x + \dfrac{1}{x} = x^3$
    f $3x^2 - \dfrac{2}{x^2} = 6$

  g $x^2 = 2^x$
    h $3 + \dfrac{1}{x} = 5^x$
    i $x^3 - (1.6)^x = 5$

3 Which of these equations has the   **a** most   **b** least   solutions?

  A $x^4 - 4x^2 + x = -1$
      B $x^5 - x^2 + \dfrac{1}{x^3} = 4x^2$

  C $5^x + 3^{-x} = x^6$
      D $x^4 + 8x^3 - 3x^2 - 8x = 3^x$

4 The graphs of $f(x) = 5 - 3^x$, $g(x) = x^3$, and $h(x) = -\dfrac{32}{x^2}$ are shown alongside.

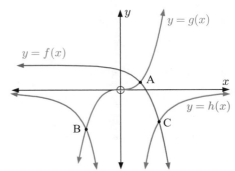

  a Use technology to find the coordinates of A, B, and C.

  b Hence, solve the equations:

    i $x^3 = -\dfrac{32}{x^2}$
      ii $x^3 + 3^x = 5$

5 **a** Using the 'solver' mode of your calculator, find a solution to $x^3 = \dfrac{2}{x}$.

    b Using the 'graph' mode of your calculator, find the points of intersection of $y = x^3$ and $y = \dfrac{2}{x}$.

    c Comment on the advantages and disadvantages of using 'graph' mode compared to 'solver' mode.

6 **a** Solve the equation $x^3 - 2x^2 - 5x = 7$.

    b Find the values of k such that $x^3 - 2x^2 - 5x = k$ has three distinct solutions.

7 **a** Solve the equation $x^4 + 3x^3 - 2x^2 - 8x = -4$.

    b Find the values of k such that $x^4 + 3x^3 - 2x^2 - 8x = k$ has:

      i no solutions   **ii** one solution   **iii** two solutions

      iv three solutions   **v** four solutions.

8 The volume of usable wood produced by a forest is given by $V(t) = 178 \times 2^{1 - \frac{80}{t}}$ thousand cubic metres, where t is the time in years since the forest was planted, $0 < t \leqslant 80$.

    a Graph $V(t)$ against t.

    b What is the volume of wood after   **i** 20 years   **ii** 40 years?

    c At what time does the volume of usable wood reach $100\,000$ m^3?

REVIEW SET 19A

1 For each of the following functions:

    i Use technology to help sketch the function.

    ii Find the axes intercepts and include them on your sketch.

    a $y = x^3 - 4x^2 + 3$ **b** $y = -2x^3 - 8x^2$

2 For each of the following functions:

    i Determine the axes intercepts.

    ii Determine the position of any turning points.

    iii Find the equation(s) of any asymptotes.

    iv Sketch $y = f(x)$ showing all of the information you have found.

    a $f(x) = x^3 + \dfrac{2}{x} + 7$ **b** $f(x) = 3^{-x} - x^2 + 5x$

3 Draw the graph of $y = x^4 - x^3 - 3x^2 + x + 2$ on the interval $-2 \leqslant x \leqslant 2$.

4 **a** Draw the graph of $y = 3^x + 3^{-x}$.

    b Hence, show that $3^x + 3^{-x} \geqslant 2$ for all x.

5 Consider the function $f(x) = 1 + \dfrac{8}{x + 2}$.

    a Find the asymptotes of the function.   **b** Find the axes intercepts.

    c Sketch the function, including the features you have found.

    d State the domain and range of $f(x)$.

6 Consider the function $y = 5x^3 + 15 + \dfrac{3}{x}$.

    a Use technology to help sketch the function.   **b** Find any asymptotes.

    c Find the axes intercepts.   **d** Find any turning points.

    e Add to your graph in **a** all of the features you have found.

7 Solve the following equations:

    a $\dfrac{3}{x} = 2x + 5$ **b** $2^x = -\frac{1}{2}x^2 - 4x$

8 The height of a seedling t days after planting is given by $H(t) = \dfrac{10}{1 + 4 \times (1.5)^{-1.2t}}$ cm
for $t \geqslant 0$.

    a Sketch the graph of $H(t)$ for $0 \leqslant t \leqslant 15$.

    b How high was the seedling when it was planted?

    c How high was the seedling after 1 week?

    d How long did it take for the seedling to reach a height of 5 cm?

    e Is there a limit to how high the seedling can grow? If so, what is it?

REVIEW SET 19B

1 For each of the following functions:

    i Determine the axes intercepts.

    ii Determine the position of any turning points.

    iii Find the equation(s) of any asymptotes.

    iv Sketch $y = f(x)$ showing all of the information you have found.

    a $f(x) = 5x - \frac{4}{5}x^2 - x^{-2}$ **b** $y = 3^{x-2} + \dfrac{4}{x^2}$

2 Draw the graph of $y = x^3 + 2x^2 + 3x - 1$ on the domain $-3 \leqslant x \leqslant 2$.

3   **a** Use technology to find the point(s) of intersection of the graphs with equations
$y = x^2 - 5x + 6$ and $y = 2^x - 1$.

    b Hence solve the equation $x^2 - 5x + 6 = 2^x - 1$.

4 Consider the function $y = \dfrac{2}{x + 1} - 3$.

    a What is the vertical asymptote?   **b** What is the horizontal asymptote?

    c What is the x-intercept?   **d** What is the y-intercept?

    e Using only **a** to **d**, sketch the graph of the function.

5 Consider the function $f(x) = 2^{-x} - \dfrac{1}{x^3}$.

    a Using technology, find:

        i the equation of the vertical asymptote

        ii the equation of the horizontal asymptote

        iii $f(-3)$ and $f(3)$.

    b Sketch $y = f(x)$, showing all of the features found above.

6 Sketch each of the following on the given domain. Clearly identify all axes intercepts, turning points, and asymptotes.

    a $y = x^4 - 3x^3 - 5x^2$ on the domain $-2 \leqslant x \leqslant 4.3$

    b $f(x) = x^4 - 6x^2 - \dfrac{1}{x}$ where $-2.6 \leqslant x \leqslant 2.6$

7 An open-topped cylindrical bin is designed with capacity 10 L. Suppose the bin has radius x cm and height h cm.

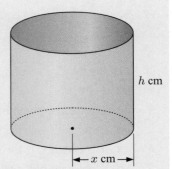

    a Show that $h = \dfrac{10\,000}{\pi x^2}$.

    b Hence show that the surface area of the bin is given by

        $S(x) = \pi x^2 + \dfrac{20\,000}{x}, \quad x > 0.$

    c Find the coordinates of the turning point of $S(x)$. Explain the significance of this result.

8 The number of people infected with a virus t days after an outbreak is given by

    $N(t) = 100t \times (1.3)^{-t}$ for $t \geqslant 0$.

    a Sketch the graph of $N(t)$ for $0 \leqslant t \leqslant 20$.

    b How many people were infected after 1 day?

    c At what time was the outbreak greatest? How many people were infected at this time?

    d How long did it take before the outbreak was contained to 15 people?

Chapter 20

Differential calculus

OPENING PROBLEM

Valentino is riding his motorbike around a racetrack. A computer chip on his bike measures the distance Valentino has travelled as time goes on. This data is used to plot a graph of Valentino's progress.

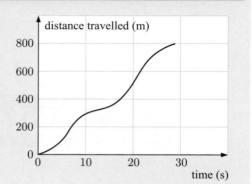

Things to think about:

a What is meant by a *rate*?

b What do we call the rate at which Valentino is travelling?

c What is the difference between an *instantaneous* rate and an *average* rate?

d How can we read a rate from a graph?

e How can we identify the fastest part of the racetrack?

A   RATES OF CHANGE

A **rate** is a comparison between two quantities of different kinds.

Rates are used every day to measure performance.

For example, we measure:

- the **speed** at which a car is travelling in $km\,h^{-1}$ or $m\,s^{-1}$.
- the **fuel efficiency** of a car in $km\,L^{-1}$ or litres per 100 km travelled.
- the **scoring rate** of a basketballer in points per game.

Example 1	◀)) Self Tutor

Josef typed 213 words in 3 minutes and made 6 errors, whereas Marie typed 260 words in 4 minutes and made 7 errors. Compare their performance using rates.

Josef's typing rate $= \dfrac{213 \text{ words}}{3 \text{ minutes}} = 71$ words per minute.

Josef's error rate $= \dfrac{6 \text{ errors}}{213 \text{ words}} \approx 0.0282$ errors per word.

Marie's typing rate $= \dfrac{260 \text{ words}}{4 \text{ minutes}} = 65$ words per minute.

Marie's error rate $= \dfrac{7 \text{ errors}}{260 \text{ words}} \approx 0.0269$ errors per word.

∴   Josef typed at a faster rate, but Marie typed with greater accuracy.

EXERCISE 20A.1

1 Karsten's pulse rate was measured at 67 beats per minute.

a Explain exactly what this rate means.

b How many heart beats would Karsten expect to have each hour?

2 Jana typed a 14 page document and made eight errors. If an average page of typing has 380 words, find Jana's error rate in:

    a errors per word   **b** errors per 100 words.

3 Niko worked 12 hours for $148.20, whereas Marita worked 13 hours for $157.95. Who worked for the better hourly rate of pay?

4 New tyres have a tread depth of 8 mm. After driving for 32 178 km, the tread depth on Joanne's tyres was reduced to 2.3 mm. What was the wearing rate of the tyres in:

    a mm per km travelled   **b** mm per 10 000 km travelled?

5 We left Kuala Lumpur at 11:43 am and travelled to Penang, a distance of 350 km. We arrived there at 3:39 pm. What was our average speed in: **a** $km\,h^{-1}$ **b** $m\,s^{-1}$?

INVESTIGATION 1   CONSTANT AND VARIABLE RATES OF CHANGE

When water is added at a **constant rate** to a cylindrical container, the depth of water in the container is a linear function of time.

The depth-time graph for a cylindrical container is shown alongside.

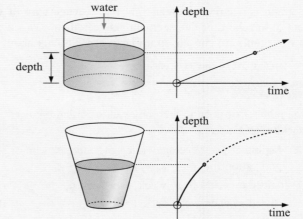

In this investigation we explore the changes in the graph for different shaped containers such as a conical vase.

What to do:

1 What features of the graph indicate a rate of change in water level that is:

    a constant   **b** variable?

2 For each of the following containers, draw a depth-time graph as water is added:

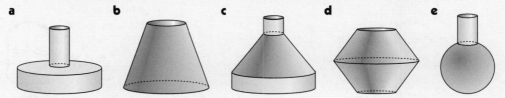

    a   **b**   **c**   **d**   **e**

Use the water filling demonstration to check your answers.   **DEMO**

3 Write a brief report on the connection between the shape of a vessel and the shape of its depth-time graph. You may wish to discuss this in parts. For example, first examine cylindrical containers, then conical, then other shapes.

4 Suggest possible container shapes that will have the following depth-time graphs:

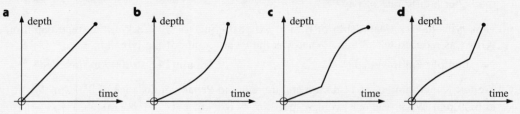

AVERAGE RATE OF CHANGE

If the graph which compares two quantities is a **straight line**, there is a constant rate of change in one quantity with respect to the other. This constant rate is the gradient of the straight line.

If the graph is a **curve**, we can find the **average rate of change** between two points by finding the gradient of the chord or line segment between them. The average rate of change will vary depending on which two points are chosen, so it makes sense to talk about the average rate of change over a particular interval.

Example 2   ◀) **Self Tutor**

The number of mice in a colony was recorded on a weekly basis.

  a Estimate the average rate of increase in population for:

    i the period from week 3 to week 6

    ii the seven week period.

  b What is the overall trend in the population growth over this period?

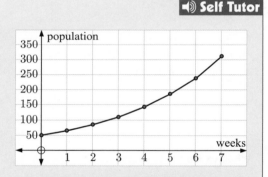

  a   **i**   population growth rate

$$= \frac{\text{increase in population}}{\text{increase in time}}$$

$$= \frac{(240 - 110) \text{ mice}}{(6 - 3) \text{ weeks}}$$

$$\approx 43 \text{ mice per week}$$

    ii   population growth rate

$$= \frac{(315 - 50) \text{ mice}}{(7 - 0) \text{ weeks}}$$

$$\approx 38 \text{ mice per week}$$

> The **average rate of change** between two points on the graph is the **gradient of the chord** between them.

  b The graph is increasing over the period by larger and larger amounts, so the population is increasing at an ever increasing rate.

EXERCISE 20A.2

1 For the travel graph given alongside, estimate the average speed:

   a in the first 4 seconds

   b in the last 4 seconds

   c in the 8 second interval.

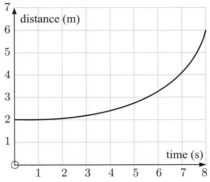

2 The numbers of surviving beetles per m² of lawn after various doses of poison, are shown in the graph alongside.

   a Estimate the rate of beetle decrease when:

      i the dose increases from 0 to 10 g

      ii the dose increases from 4 to 8 g.

   b Describe the effect on the rate of beetle decline as the dose goes from 0 to 14 g.

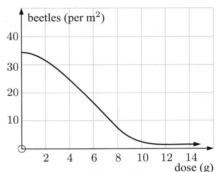

B   INSTANTANEOUS RATES OF CHANGE

The speed of a moving object such as a motor car, an aeroplane, or a runner, will vary over time. The speed of the object at a particular instant in time is called its **instantaneous speed**. We examine this concept in the following investigation.

INVESTIGATION 2   INSTANTANEOUS SPEED

A ball bearing is dropped from the top of a tall building. The distance it has fallen after t seconds is recorded, and the following graph of distance against time obtained.

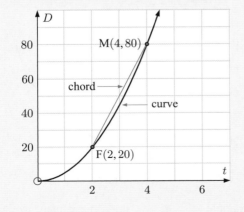

The *average* speed in the time interval $2 \leqslant t \leqslant 4$ is

$$= \frac{\text{distance travelled}}{\text{time taken}}$$

$$= \frac{(80 - 20) \text{ m}}{(4 - 2) \text{ s}}$$

$$= \frac{60}{2} \text{ m s}^{-1}$$

$$= 30 \text{ m s}^{-1}$$

However, this does not tell us the *instantaneous* speed at any particular time.

In this investigation we will try to measure the speed of the ball at the instant when $t = 2$ seconds.

What to do:

DEMO

1 Click on the icon to start the demonstration.
   F is the point where $t = 2$ seconds, and M is another point on the curve.
   To start with, M is at $t = 4$ seconds.
   The number in the box marked *gradient* is the gradient of the chord FM. This is the *average speed* of the ball bearing in the interval from F to M. For M at $t = 4$ seconds, you should see the average speed is 30 m s^{-1}.

2 Click on M and drag it slowly towards F. Copy and complete the table alongside with the gradient of the chord FM for various times t.

t	gradient of FM
3	
2.5	
2.1	
2.01	

3 Observe what happens as M reaches F. Explain why this is so.

4 When $t = 2$ seconds, what do you suspect the instantaneous speed of the ball bearing is?

5 Move M to the origin, and then slide it towards F from the left. Copy and complete the table alongside with the gradient of the chord FM for various times t.

t	gradient of FM
0	
1.5	
1.9	
1.99	

6 Do your results agree with those in **4**?

From the investigation you should have discovered that:

> The **instantaneous rate of change** of a variable at a particular instant is given by the **gradient of the tangent** to the graph at that point.

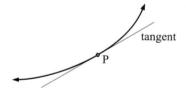

tangent

P

For example, the graph alongside shows how a cyclist accelerates away from an intersection.

The average speed over the first 8 seconds is

$$\frac{100 \text{ m}}{8 \text{ sec}} = 12.5 \text{ m s}^{-1}.$$

Notice that the cyclist's early speed is quite small, but it increases as time goes by.

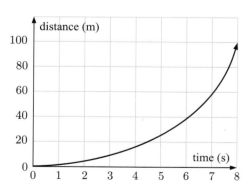

To find the instantaneous speed at any time instant, for example $t = 4$, we draw the tangent to the graph at that time and find its gradient.

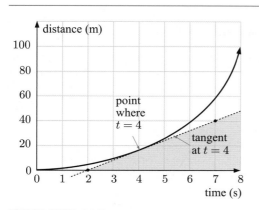

The tangent passes through $(2, 0)$ and $(7, 40)$.

$\therefore$ the instantaneous speed at $t = 4$

$\qquad$ = the gradient of the tangent

$\qquad = \dfrac{(40 - 0)\text{ m}}{(7 - 2)\text{ s}}$

$\qquad = \frac{40}{5}\text{ m s}^{-1}$

$\qquad = 8\text{ m s}^{-1}$

EXERCISE 20B.1

PRINTABLE GRAPHS

1 For each of the following graphs, estimate the rate of change at the point shown by the arrow. Make sure your answer has the correct units.

a

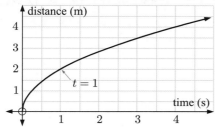

b

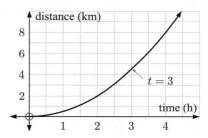

c

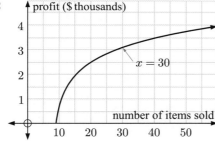

d

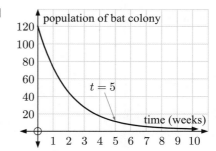

2 Water is leaking from a tank. The volume of water left in the tank over time is given in the graph alongside.

 a How much water was in the tank originally?

 b How much water was in the tank after 1 hour?

 c How quickly was the tank losing water initially?

 d How quickly was the tank losing water after 1 hour?

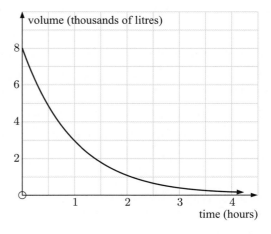

FINDING THE GRADIENT OF A TANGENT ALGEBRAICALLY

In the previous exercise we found the instantaneous rate of change at a given point by drawing the tangent at that point and finding its gradient. The problem with this method is that it is difficult to draw an accurate tangent by hand, and the result will vary from one person to the next. So, we need a better method for finding the gradient of a tangent.

Consider the curve $y = f(x)$. We wish to find the gradient of the tangent to the curve at the fixed point F. To do this we add a moving point M to the curve, and observe what happens to the gradient of the chord FM as M is moved closer and closer to F.

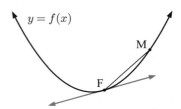

INVESTIGATION 3   THE GRADIENT OF A TANGENT

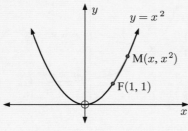

Given the curve $y = x^2$, we wish to find the gradient of the tangent at the point F(1, 1).

What to do:

1

Suppose M lies on $y = x^2$ and M has coordinates (x, x^2).

Copy and complete the table below:

x	Point M	gradient of FM
5	(5, 25)	$\frac{25-1}{5-1} = 6$
3		
2		
1.5		
1.1		
1.01		
1.001		

2 Comment on the gradient of FM as x gets closer to 1.

3 Repeat the process as x gets closer to 1, but from the left of F.

4 Click on the icon to view a demonstration of the process.

DEMO

5 What do you suspect is the gradient of the tangent at F?

Fortunately we do not have to use a graph and table of values each time we wish to find the gradient of a tangent. Instead we can use an algebraic approach.

THE ALGEBRAIC METHOD

To illustrate the algebraic method we will once again consider the curve $y = x^2$ and the tangent at F(1, 1).

Let the moving point M have x-coordinate $1 + h$, where $h \neq 0$.

So, M is at $(1 + h, (1 + h)^2)$.

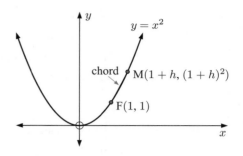

The gradient of chord FM is

$$\frac{y\text{-step}}{x\text{-step}} = \frac{(1+h)^2 - 1}{1 + h - 1}$$

$$= \frac{1 + 2h + h^2 - 1}{h}$$

$$= \frac{2h + h^2}{h}$$

$$= \frac{h(2 + h)}{h}$$

$$= 2 + h \qquad \{\text{as } h \neq 0\}$$

Now as M approaches F, h approaches 0, and so $2 + h$ approaches 2.

Since the gradient of the chord FM gets closer and closer to 2 as M approaches F, we conclude that the tangent at $(1, 1)$ has gradient 2.

Therefore, the tangent at $(1, 1)$ has gradient 2.

Example 3 ◀) **Self Tutor**

Use the algebraic method to find the gradient of the tangent to $y = x^2$ at the point where $x = 2$.

When $x = 2$, $y = 2^2 = 4$, so the fixed point F is $(2, 4)$.

Let $M(2 + h, (2 + h)^2)$ be a point on $y = x^2$ which is close to F.

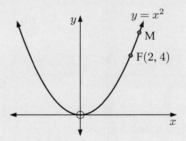

The gradient of FM $= \dfrac{y\text{-step}}{x\text{-step}}$

$$= \frac{(2+h)^2 - 4}{2 + h - 2}$$

$$= \frac{4 + 4h + h^2 - 4}{h} \qquad \{\text{using } (a + b)^2 = a^2 + 2ab + b^2\}$$

$$= \frac{h(4 + h)}{h}$$

$$= 4 + h \qquad \{\text{as } h \neq 0\}$$

Now as M approaches F, h approaches 0, and $4 + h$ approaches 4.

So, the tangent at $(2, 4)$ has gradient 4.

EXERCISE 20B.2

1 Use the algebraic method to find the gradient of the tangent to:

  a $y = x^2$ at the point where $x = 3$ **b** $y = 3x^2$ at the point where $x = 2$

  c $y = -x^2 - 2x$ at the point where $x = 0$ **d** $y = x^2 + 3x$ at the point where $x = 1$

  e $y = 2x - x^2$ at the point where $x = 3$.

2 **a** Using $(x+h)^3 = (x+h)^2(x+h)$, show that $(x+h)^3 = x^3 + 3x^2h + 3xh^2 + h^3$.

  b Find $(1+h)^3$ in expanded form using **a**.

  c Consider finding the gradient of the tangent to $y = x^3$ at the point $F(1, 1)$. If the x-coordinate of a moving point M, which is close to F, has value $1 + h$, state the coordinates of M.

  d Find the gradient of the chord FM in simplest form.

  e What is the gradient of the tangent to $y = x^3$ at the point $(1, 1)$?

3 Find the gradient of the tangent to $y = x^3$ at the point $(2, 8)$.

4 Consider the graph of $y = \dfrac{1}{x}$ alongside.

  a Show that $\dfrac{1}{x+h} - \dfrac{1}{x} = \dfrac{-h}{x(x+h)}$.

  b Suppose M has x-coordinate $1 + h$.

    i State the y-coordinate of M.

    ii Find the gradient of FM in terms of h.

  c Find the gradient of the tangent to $y = \dfrac{1}{x}$ at the point where $x = 1$.

  d Find the gradient of the tangent to $y = \dfrac{1}{x}$ at the point where $x = 3$.

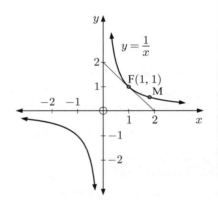

C   THE DERIVATIVE FUNCTION

For a non-linear function, the gradient of the tangent changes as we move along the graph.

We can hence describe a **gradient function** which, for any given value of x, gives the gradient of the tangent at that point. We call this gradient function the **derived function** or **derivative function** of the curve.

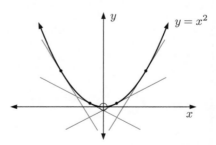

If we are given y in terms of x, we represent the derivative function by $\dfrac{dy}{dx}$. We say this as 'dee y by dee x'.

If we are given the function $f(x)$, we represent the derivative function by $f'(x)$. We say this as 'f dashed x'.

INVESTIGATION 4   THE DERIVATIVE OF $y = x^2$

The graphs below show $y = x^2$ with tangents drawn at the points where $x = -3, -2, ..., 3$.

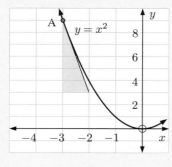
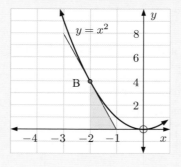
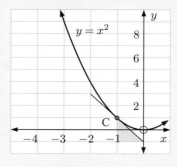

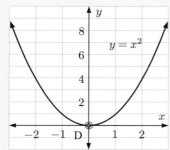
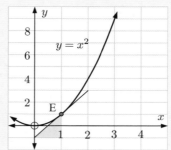
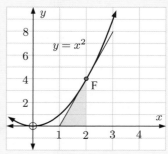

What to do:

1 Use the shaded triangles to find the gradients of the tangents to $y = x^2$ at the seven different points. Hence complete the following table:

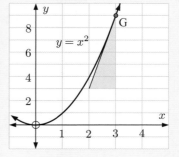

x-coordinate	-3						
gradient of tangent							

2 Use your table to help complete:
"the gradient of the tangent to $y = x^2$ at $(x,\ y)$ is $m = $ ...."

DEMO

3 Click on the icon to check the validity of your statement in **2**.
Click on the bar at the top to drag the point of contact of the tangent along the curve.

You should have found that the gradient of the tangent to $y = x^2$ at the point $(x,\ y)$ is given by $2x$.

So, $y = x^2$ has the derivative function $\dfrac{dy}{dx} = 2x$.

Alternatively, if $f(x) = x^2$ then $f'(x) = 2x$.

INVESTIGATION 5   THE DERIVATIVE OF $y = x^n$

In this investigation we seek derivative functions for other functions of the form $y = x^n$ where $n \in \mathbb{Z}$.

DERIVATIVE DETERMINER

What to do:

1 Click on the icon to run the derivative determiner software.

2 Choose the function $y = x$. By sliding the point along the graph, we can observe the changing gradient of the tangent.

   a Use the software to complete the table:

x	-3	-2	-1	0	1	2	3
$\dfrac{dy}{dx}$							

   b Graph $\dfrac{dy}{dx}$ against x.

   Hence predict a formula for the derivative function $\dfrac{dy}{dx}$.

3 Repeat **2** for the functions:

   a $y = x^3$ **b** $y = x^4$ **c** $y = \dfrac{1}{x} = x^{-1}$ **d** $y = \dfrac{1}{x^2} = x^{-2}$

   Hint: When $x = 0$, the derivatives of both $y = x^{-1}$ and $y = x^{-2}$ are undefined.

4 Use your results to complete this table of derivative functions:

Function	Derivative function
x	
x^2	$2x$
x^3	
x^4	
x^{-1}	
x^{-2}	

5 For $y = x^n$, $n \in \mathbb{Z}$, predict the form of $\dfrac{dy}{dx}$.

You should have discovered that:

$$\text{If}\quad y = x^n \quad \text{then} \quad \frac{dy}{dx} = nx^{n-1}.$$

DISCUSSION

Does the rule "if $y = x^n$ then $\dfrac{dy}{dx} = nx^{n-1}$" work when $n = 0$?

Example 4 ◀) **Self Tutor**

Find the gradient function for:

  a $y = x^8$ **b** $f(x) = \dfrac{1}{x^3}$

a	$y = x^8$	**b**	$f(x) = \dfrac{1}{x^3} = x^{-3}$
	$\therefore \ \dfrac{dy}{dx} = 8x^7$		$\therefore \ f'(x) = -3x^{-4}$

Remember that
$$\dfrac{1}{x^n} = x^{-n}.$$

Once we have found the derivative function, we can substitute a value of x to find the gradient of the tangent at that point.

Example 5 ◀) **Self Tutor**

Consider $f(x) = \dfrac{1}{x^2}$.

  a Find $f'(x)$.   **b** Find and interpret $f'(1)$.

a $f(x) = \dfrac{1}{x^2} = x^{-2}$

     $\therefore \ f'(x) = -2x^{-3} = -\dfrac{2}{x^3}$

b $f'(1) = -\dfrac{2}{1^3} = -2$

    The tangent to $f(x) = \dfrac{1}{x^2}$

    at the point where $x = 1$,
    has gradient -2.

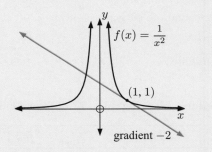

$f'(1)$ gives the gradient of the tangent to $y = f(x)$ at the point where $x = 1$.

EXERCISE 20C

1 Find the gradient function $\dfrac{dy}{dx}$ for:

  a $y = x^6$ **b** $y = \dfrac{1}{x^5}$ **c** $y = x^9$ **d** $y = \dfrac{1}{x^7}$

2 For $f(x) = x^5$, find:

  a $f(2)$ **b** $f'(2)$ **c** $f(-1)$ **d** $f'(-1)$

3 Consider $f(x) = \dfrac{1}{x^4}$.

  a Find $f'(x)$.   **b** Find and interpret $f'(1)$.

4 The graph of $f(x) = x^3$ is shown alongside, and its tangent at the point $(-1, -1)$.

  a Use the graph to find the gradient of the tangent.

  b Check your answer by finding $f'(-1)$.

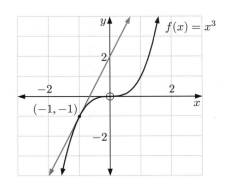

D   RULES OF DIFFERENTIATION

Differentiation is the process of finding a derivative or gradient function.

There are a number of rules associated with differentiation, which can be used to differentiate more complicated functions.

INVESTIGATION 6   RULES OF DIFFERENTIATION

In this investigation we attempt to differentiate functions of the form ax^n where a is a constant, and functions which are a sum or difference of terms of the form ax^n.

DERIVATIVE DETERMINER

What to do:

1 Use the software to find the derivatives of:

   a x^2 **b** $4x^2$ **c** x^3 **d** $2x^3$

   Hence copy and complete: "If $f(x) = ax^n$ then $f'(x) = ...$"

2 Use the software to find the derivatives of:

   a $f(x) = x^2 + 3x$ **b** $f(x) = x^3 - 2x^2$

   Hence copy and complete: "If $f(x) = u(x) + v(x)$ then $f'(x) = ...$"

We have now determined the following rules for differentiating:

Function	$f(x)$	$f'(x)$
a constant	a	0
x^n	x^n	nx^{n-1}
a constant multiple of x^n	ax^n	anx^{n-1}
multiple terms	$u(x) + v(x)$	$u'(x) + v'(x)$

Using the rules we have now developed we can differentiate sums of powers of x.

For example,   if $f(x) = 3x^4 + 2x^3 - 5x^2 + 7x + 6$ then

$$f'(x) = 3(4x^3) + 2(3x^2) - 5(2x) + 7(1) + 0$$
$$= 12x^3 + 6x^2 - 10x + 7$$

Example 6   ◀) Self Tutor

Find $f'(x)$ for $f(x)$ equal to:

   a $5x^3 + 6x^2 - 3x + 2$ **b** $7x - \dfrac{4}{x} + \dfrac{3}{x^3}$ **c** $\dfrac{x^2 + 4x - 5}{x}$

   a $f(x) = 5x^3 + 6x^2 - 3x + 2$

    ∴ $f'(x) = 5(3x^2) + 6(2x) - 3(1)$

           $= 15x^2 + 12x - 3$

b $f(x) = 7x - \dfrac{4}{x} + \dfrac{3}{x^3}$

$= 7x - 4x^{-1} + 3x^{-3}$

$\therefore \ f'(x) = 7(1) - 4(-1x^{-2}) + 3(-3x^{-4})$

$= 7 + 4x^{-2} - 9x^{-4}$

$= 7 + \dfrac{4}{x^2} - \dfrac{9}{x^4}$

Remember that
$\dfrac{1}{x^n} = x^{-n}.$

c $f(x) = \dfrac{x^2 + 4x - 5}{x}$

$= \dfrac{x^2}{x} + 4 - \dfrac{5}{x}$

$= x + 4 - 5x^{-1}$

$\therefore \ f'(x) = 1 + 5x^{-2}$

EXERCISE 20D

1 Find $f'(x)$ given that $f(x)$ is:

    a x^3
    b $2x^3$
    c $7x^2$
    d $x^2 + x$

    e $4 - 2x^2$
    f $x^2 + 3x - 5$
    g $5x^4 - 6x^2$
    h $x^3 + 3x^2 + 4x - 1$

    i $3 - 6x^{-1}$
    j $\dfrac{2x - 3}{x^2}$
    k $\dfrac{x^3 + 5}{x}$
    l $\dfrac{x^3 + x - 3}{x}$

2 Suppose $f(x) = 4x^3 - x$.   Find:

    a $f'(x)$
    b $f'(2)$
    c $f'(0)$ −1

3 Suppose $g(x) = \dfrac{x^2 + 1}{x}$.   Find:

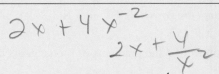

    a $g'(x)$ $1 - x^{-2}$
    b $g'(3)$ $8/9$
    c $g'(-2)$ $13T4^x$ −2

Example 7	🔊 **Self Tutor**

Find the gradient function of $f(x) = x^2 - \dfrac{4}{x}$. $x^2 - 4x^{-1}$

Hence find the gradient of the tangent to the function at the point where $x = 2$.

$f(x) = x^2 - \dfrac{4}{x}$

$= x^2 - 4x^{-1}$

$\therefore \ f'(x) = 2x - 4(-1x^{-2})$

$= 2x + 4x^{-2}$

$= 2x + \dfrac{4}{x^2}$

$2x + 4x^{-2}$

$2x + \dfrac{4}{x^2}$

Now $f'(2) = 2(2) + \dfrac{4}{2^2} = 5$.

So, the tangent has gradient $= 5$.

---

4 Find the gradient of the tangent to:

    a $y = x^2$ at $x = 2$
    b $y = \dfrac{8}{x^2}$ at $x = 9$

    c $y = 2x^2 - 3x + 7$ at $x = -1$
    d $y = 2x - 5x^{-1}$ at $x = 2$

    e $y = \dfrac{x^2 - 4}{x^2}$ at $x = 4$
    f $y = \dfrac{x^3 - 4x - 8}{x^2}$ at $x = -1$

Example 8

Use technology to find the gradient of the tangent to $y = x^3 + 3$ at the point where $x = -2$.

Casio fx-CG20	TI-84 Plus	TI-*n*spire

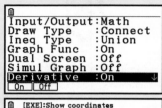
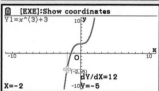

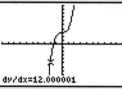
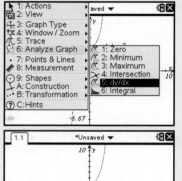
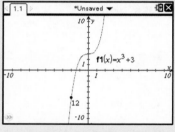

So, the gradient of the tangent is 12.

---

5 Consider the function $f(x) = (3x + 1)^2$.

   a Expand the brackets of $(3x + 1)^2$.

   b Hence find $f'(x)$.

   c Hence find the gradient of the tangent to $y = f(x)$ at the point where $x = -2$.

Check your answer to **c** using technology.

6 The graph of $f(x) = \frac{1}{3}x^3 + \frac{3}{4}x^2 - \frac{5}{2}x - \frac{1}{4}$ is shown alongside. The tangents at A$(-3, 5)$ and B$(1, -\frac{5}{3})$ are also given.

   a Use the graph to find the gradients of the tangents at A and B.

   b Calculate the gradients in **a** exactly by finding $f'(-3)$ and $f'(1)$.

Check your answers using technology.

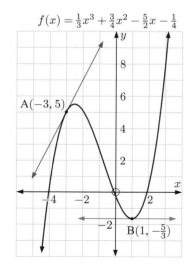

$f(x) = \frac{1}{3}x^3 + \frac{3}{4}x^2 - \frac{5}{2}x - \frac{1}{4}$

Example 9   ◀) **Self Tutor**

If $y = 3x^2 - 4x$, find $\dfrac{dy}{dx}$ and interpret its meaning.

As $y = 3x^2 - 4x$, $\dfrac{dy}{dx} = 6x - 4$.

$\dfrac{dy}{dx}$ is:

- the gradient function or derivative function of $y = 3x^2 - 4x$, from which the gradient at any point can be found
- the instantaneous rate of change in y as x changes.

7 If $y = 4x - \dfrac{3}{x}$, find $\dfrac{dy}{dx}$ and interpret its meaning.

8 The position of a car moving along a straight road is given by $S = 2t^2 + 4t$ metres, where t is the time in seconds.

Find $\dfrac{dS}{dt}$ and interpret its meaning.

9 The cost of producing and selling x toasters each week is given by
$C = 1785 + 3x + 0.002x^2$ dollars.

Find $\dfrac{dC}{dx}$ and interpret its meaning.

Example 10   ◀) **Self Tutor**

At what point on the graph of $y = 2x^2 + 5x - 3$ does the tangent have gradient 13?

Since $y = 2x^2 + 5x - 3$, $\dfrac{dy}{dx} = 4x + 5$

$\therefore$ the tangent has gradient 13 when $4x + 5 = 13$
$$\therefore \quad 4x = 8$$
$$\therefore \quad x = 2$$

When $x = 2$, $y = 2(2)^2 + 5(2) - 3 = 15$

So, the tangent has gradient 13 at the point $(2, 15)$.

10 At what point on the graph of $y = x^2 - 4x + 7$ does the tangent have gradient 2? Draw a diagram to illustrate your answer.

11 Find the coordinates of the point(s) on:

a $y = x^2 + 5x + 1$ where the tangent has gradient 3

b $y = 3x^2 + 11x + 5$ where the tangent has gradient -7

c $f(x) = 2x^{-2} + x$ where the tangent has gradient $\frac{1}{2}$

d $f(x) = 3x^3 - 5x + 2$ where the tangent has gradient 4

e $f(x) = ax^2 + bx + c$ where the tangent is horizontal.

12 Find the coordinates of P on the graph shown.

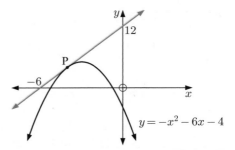

| **Example 11** | ◀) **Self Tutor** |

The tangent to $f(x) = 2x^2 - ax + b$ at the point $(2, 7)$ has a gradient of 3.

Find a and b.

Since $f(x) = 2x^2 - ax + b,$ $f'(x) = 4x - a$

Now, $f'(2) = 3,$ so $4(2) - a = 3$

$$\therefore \quad a = 5$$

Also, $f(2) = 7,$ so $2(2)^2 - 5(2) + b = 7$

$$\therefore \quad b = 9$$

---

13 The tangent to $f(x) = x^3 + ax + 5$ at the point where $x = 1,$ has a gradient of 10. Find a.

14 The tangent to $f(x) = -3x^2 + ax + b$ at the point $(-3, 8)$ has a gradient of 9. Find a and b.

15 The tangent to $f(x) = 2x^2 + a + \dfrac{b}{x}$ at the point $(1, 11)$ has a gradient of -2. Find a and b.

16 **a** Find the gradient of the tangent line L.
    b Hence, find a and b.

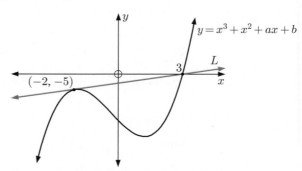

| **E** | **EQUATIONS OF TANGENTS** |

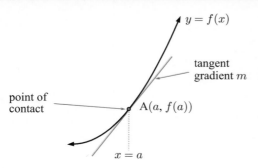

Consider a curve $y = f(x)$.

If the point A has x-coordinate a, then its y-coordinate is $f(a)$, and the gradient of the tangent at A is $f'(a)$.

The equation of the tangent is

$$\frac{y - f(a)}{x - a} = f'(a) \quad \{\text{equating gradients}\}$$

or $y - f(a) = f'(a)(x - a)$.

The equation of the tangent at the point A(a, b) is

$$\frac{y - b}{x - a} = f'(a) \qquad \text{or} \qquad y - b = f'(a)(x - a).$$

The equation can then be rearranged into gradient-intercept form.

Example 12 · Self Tutor

Find the equation of the tangent to $f(x) = x^2 + 1$ at the point where $x = 1$.

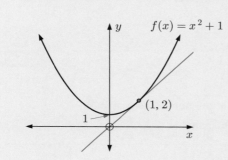

Since $f(1) = 1^2 + 1 = 2$,
the point of contact is $(1, 2)$.

Now $f'(x) = 2x$,   so $f'(1) = 2$

$\therefore$ the tangent has equation

$$\frac{y - 2}{x - 1} = 2$$

which is $y - 2 = 2x - 2$

or $y = 2x$.

Example 13 · Self Tutor

Use technology to find the equation of the tangent to $y = x^3 - 7x + 3$
at the point where $x = 2$.

GRAPHICS
CALCULATOR
INSTRUCTIONS

Casio fx-CG20	TI-84 Plus	TI-*n*spire

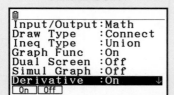

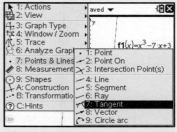

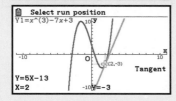

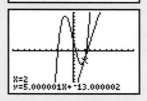

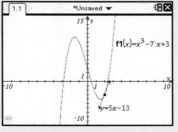

So, the tangent has equation $y = 5x - 13$.

EXERCISE 20E

1 Find the equation of the tangent to:

    a $y = x^2$ at $x = 4$

    b $y = x^3$ at $x = -2$

    c $y = 3x^{-1}$ at $x = -1$

    d $y = \dfrac{4}{x^3}$ at $x = 2$

    e $y = x^2 + 5x - 4$ at $x = 1$

    f $y = 2x^2 + 5x + 3$ at $x = -2$

    g $y = x^3 + 2x$ at $x = 0$

    h $y = x^2 + x^{-1}$ at $x = 0$

    i $y = x + 2x^{-1}$ at $x = 2$

    j $y = \dfrac{x^2 + 4}{x}$ at $x = -1$

Check your answers using technology.

Example 14   ◀) Self Tutor

Consider the curve $y = x^3 - 4x^2 - 6x + 8$.

    a Find the equation of the tangent to this curve at the point where $x = 0$.

    b At what point does this tangent meet the curve again?

a When $x = 0$, $y = 8$. So, the point of contact is $(0, 8)$.

$\dfrac{dy}{dx} = 3x^2 - 8x - 6$, so when $x = 0$, $\dfrac{dy}{dx} = -6$.

$\therefore$ the tangent has equation $\dfrac{y - 8}{x - 0} = -6$

$\therefore y = -6x + 8$

b We use technology to find where the tangent meets the curve again:

Casio fx-CG20   **TI-84 Plus**   **TI-nspire**

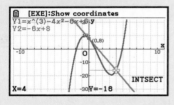
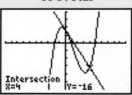
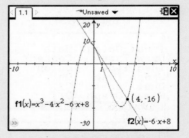

The tangent meets the curve again at $(4, -16)$.

---

2 For each of the following curves:

    i find the equation of the tangent at the given point

    ii find the point at which this tangent meets the curve again.

    a $f(x) = 2x^3 - 5x + 1$ at $x = -1$

    b $y = x^2 + \dfrac{3}{x} + 2$ at $x = 3$

    c $f(x) = x^3 + 5$ at $x = 1.5$

    d $y = x^3 + \dfrac{1}{x}$ at $x = -1$

    e $f(x) = 3x^3 + 2x^2 - x + 2$ at $x = 0.5$

3   **a**   Find the point where the tangent to $y = 2x^3 + 3x^2 - x + 4$ at $x = -1$ meets the x-axis.

   b   Find the point where the tangent to $y = x^3 + 5$ at $(-2, -3)$ meets the line $y = 2$.

   c   Find the point where the tangent to $y = \dfrac{2}{x} + 1$ at $(-2, 0)$ meets the line $y = 2x - 3$.

   d   Find the point where the tangent to $y = 3x^3 - 2x + 1$ at $x = 1$ meets the y-axis.

4   The graph of $f(x) = x^4 - 2x^3 - x^2 + 4$ is shown alongside. The tangents at $P(-1, 6)$ and $Q(2, 0)$ intersect at R.

Find the coordinates of R.

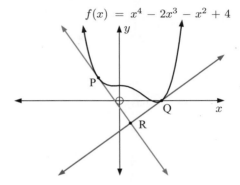

5   Consider the function $f(x) = x^4 - 2x^2 + 2x + 3$.

   a   Find the equation of the line which is the tangent to the curve at the point where $x = 1$.

   b   Find the point at which this line meets the curve again.

   c   Show that the line is the tangent to the curve at this point also.

F   NORMALS TO CURVES

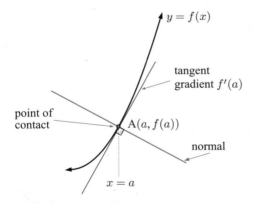

A **normal** to a curve is a line which is perpendicular to the tangent at the point of contact.

The gradients of perpendicular lines are negative reciprocals of each other, so:

The gradient of the **normal** at $x = a$ is $-\dfrac{1}{f'(a)}$.

Example 15   ◀))） **Self Tutor**

Find the equation of the normal to $f(x) = x^2 - 4x + 3$ at the point where $x = 4$.

Since $f(4) = (4)^2 - 4(4) + 3 = 3$,
the point of contact is $(4, 3)$.

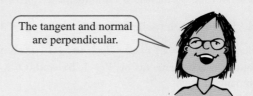

The tangent and normal
are perpendicular.

Now $f'(x) = 2x - 4$,

so $f'(4) = 2(4) - 4$
$= 4$

So, the normal at $(4, 3)$ has gradient $-\frac{1}{4}$.

∴   the normal has equation

$$\frac{y - 3}{x - 4} = -\frac{1}{4}$$

which is $y - 3 = -\frac{1}{4}x + 1$

or $y = -\frac{1}{4}x + 4$

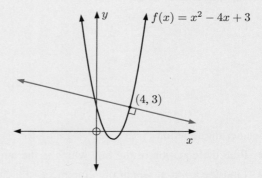

Example 16   ◀))） **Self Tutor**

Find the coordinates of the point where the normal to $y = x^2 - 3$ at $(1, -2)$ meets the curve
again.

$\dfrac{dy}{dx} = 2x$,   so when $x = 1$, $\dfrac{dy}{dx} = 2$

So, the normal at $(1, -2)$ has gradient $-\frac{1}{2}$.

∴   the normal has equation $\dfrac{y - (-2)}{x - 1} = -\frac{1}{2}$

$$\therefore \ y + 2 = -\frac{1}{2}x + \frac{1}{2}$$

$$\therefore \ y = -\frac{1}{2}x - \frac{3}{2}$$

We use technology to find where the normal meets the curve again:

Casio fx-CG20	TI-84 Plus	TI-*n*spire

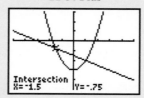
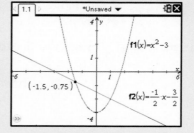

The normal meets the curve again at $(-1.5, -0.75)$.

EXERCISE 20F

1 Find the equation of the normal to:

 a $y = x^2$ at the point $(3, 9)$ **b** $y = x^3 - 5x + 2$ at $x = -2$

 c $y = \dfrac{1}{x} + 2$ at the point $(-1, 1)$ **d** $y = 2x^3 - 3x + 1$ at $x = 1$

 e $y = x^2 - 3x + 2$ at $x = 3$ **f** $y = 3x + \dfrac{1}{x} - 4$ at $x = 1$.

2 Consider the graph of $y = \dfrac{2}{x}$ alongside.

 a Find the equation of:

  i the tangent at P   **ii** the normal at P.

 b Sketch the graph of $y = \dfrac{2}{x}$, including the tangent and normal at P.

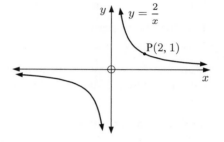

3 For each of the following curves, find the coordinates of the point where the normal to the curve at the given point, meets the curve again.

 a $y = x^2$ at $(2, 4)$ **b** $y = \dfrac{1}{x} + 2$ at $(-1, 1)$

 c $y = x^3$ at $x = -1$ **d** $y = x^3 - 12x + 2$ at $(3, -7)$.

4 **a** Find where the normal to $y = x^3 - 12x + 2$ at $x = -2$ meets the x-axis.

 b Find where the normal to $y = x^3$ at $(-1, -1)$ meets the line $y = 3$.

 c Find where the normal to $y = \dfrac{1}{x} - 3$ at $(-1, -4)$ meets the line $y = -2x + 1$.

 d Find where the normal to $y = 2x^3 - 3x + 1$ at $x = 1$ meets the y-axis.

5 The normal to $y = 5 - \dfrac{a}{x}$ at the point where $x = -2$, has a gradient of 1. Find a.

6 In the graph alongside, P is the point with x-coordinate 2.

 a The tangent at P has a gradient of 1. Find:

  i a **ii** the coordinates of P.

 b Find the equation of the normal at P.

 c Find the coordinates of the point Q where the normal at P meets the curve again.

 d Find the equation of the tangent at Q. Comment on your answer.

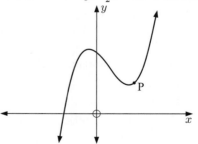

$y = \tfrac{1}{2}x^3 - x^2 + ax + 4$

THEORY OF KNOWLEDGE

The Greek philosopher Zeno of Elea lived in what is now southern Italy, in the 5th century BC. He is most famous for his paradoxes, which were recorded in Aristotle's work *Physics*.

The arrow paradox

"If everything when it occupies an equal space is at rest, and if that which is in locomotion is always occupying such a space at any moment, the flying arrow is therefore motionless."

This argument says that if we fix an instant in time, an arrow appears motionless. Consequently, how is it that the arrow actually moves?

The dichotomy paradox

"That which is in locomotion must arrive at the half-way stage before it arrives at the goal."

If an object is to move a fixed distance then it must travel half that distance. Before it can travel a half the distance, it must travel a half *that* distance. With this process continuing indefinitely, motion is impossible.

Achilles and the tortoise

"In a race, the quickest runner can never overtake the slowest, since the pursuer must first reach the point whence the pursued started, so that the slower must always hold a lead."

According to this principle, the athlete Achilles will never be able to catch the slow tortoise!

1 A paradox is a logical argument that leads to a contradiction or a situation which defies logic or reason. Can a paradox be the truth?

2 Are Zeno's paradoxes really paradoxes?

3 Are the three paradoxes essentially the same?

4 We know from experience that things *do* move, and that Achilles *would* catch the tortoise. Does that mean that logic has failed?

5 What do Zeno's paradoxes have to do with rates of change?

REVIEW SET 20A

1 The total number of televisions sold over many months is shown on the graph alongside.

Estimate the rate of sales:

   a from 40 to 50 months

   b from 0 to 50 months

   c at 20 months.

PRINTABLE GRAPH

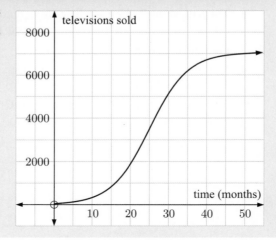

2 Use the rules of differentiation to find $f'(x)$ for $f(x)$ equal to:

    a $7x^3$ **b** $3x^2 - x^3$ **c** $(2x - 3)^2$ **d** $\dfrac{7x^3 + 2x^4}{x^2}$

3 Consider $f(x) = x^4 - 3x - 1$. Find: **a** $f'(x)$ **b** $f'(2)$ **c** $f'(0)$.

4 Find the equation of the tangent to $y = -2x^2$ at the point where $x = -1$.

5 Consider the function $f(x) = -2x^2 + 5x + 3$. Find:

    a the average rate of change from $x = 2$ to $x = 4$

    b the instantaneous rate of change at $x = 2$.

6 Find the equation of the normal to $y = x^3 + 3x - 2$ at the point where $x = 2$.

7 The tangent shown has gradient -4.
Find the coordinates of P.

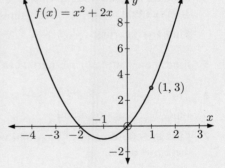

$y = -x^2 + 8x - 7$

8 The tangent to $y = ax^3 - 3x + 3$ at the point where $x = 2$, has a gradient of 21. Find a.

REVIEW SET 20B

1 Consider the function $f(x) = x^2 + 2x$, which has the graph shown.

    a Find the gradient of the line which passes through $(1, 3)$ and the point on $f(x)$ with x-coordinate:

        i 2   **ii** 1.5   **iii** 1.1

    b Find $f'(x)$.

    c Find the gradient of the tangent to $f(x)$ at $(1, 3)$.
Compare this with your answers to **a**.

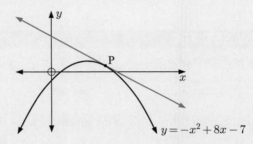

2 Find $\dfrac{dy}{dx}$ for:

    a $y = 3x^2 - x^4$ **b** $y = \dfrac{x^3 - x}{x^2}$ **c** $y = 2x + x^{-1} - 3x^{-2}$

3 Find the equation of the tangent to $y = x^3 - 3x + 5$ at the point where $x = 2$.

4 Find all points on the curve $y = 2x + x^{-1}$ where the tangent is horizontal.

5 If $f(x) = 7 + x - 3x^2$, find: **a** $f(3)$ **b** $f'(3)$.

6 Find the coordinates of the point where the normal to $y = x^2 - 7x - 44$ at $x = -3$ meets the curve again.

7 The tangent to $f(x) = a - \dfrac{b}{x^2}$ at $(-1, -1)$ has equation $y = -6x - 7$.   Find the values of a and b.

8 The tangent shown has a gradient of 1.

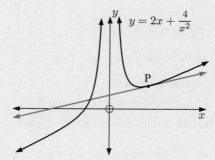

   a Find the coordinates of P.

   b Find the equation of the tangent.

   c Find where the tangent cuts the x-axis.

   d Find the equation of the normal at P.

REVIEW SET 20C

1 Use the rules of differentiation to find $f'(x)$ for $f(x)$ equal to:

   a $x^4 + 2x^3 + 3x^2 - 5$ **b** $2x^{-3} + x^{-4}$ **c** $\dfrac{1}{x} - \dfrac{4}{x^2}$

2 Find the gradient of $f(x)$ at the given point for the following functions:

   a $f(x) = x^2 - 3x$ at $x = -1$ **b** $f(x) = -3x^2 + 4$ at $x = 2$

   c $f(x) = x + \dfrac{2}{x}$ at $x = 3$ **d** $f(x) = x^3 - x^2 - x - 2$ at $x = 0$

3 Find the equation of the tangent to $y = \dfrac{12}{x^2}$ at the point $(1, 12)$.

4 Sand is poured into a bucket for 30 seconds.   After t seconds, the weight of sand is $S(t) = 0.3t^3 - 18t^2 + 550t$ grams.

Find and interpret $S'(t)$.

5 Find the equation of the normal to $y = 2 + \dfrac{1}{x} + 3x$ at the point where $x = 1$.

6 The tangent to $y = x^3 - 2x^2 + ax - b$ at $(2, -1)$ has equation $y = 7x - 15$.
Find the values of a and b.

7 Find the coordinates of the point where the normal to $y = -3x^3 + 5x - 1$ at $x = 0$ meets the curve again.

8 The graph of $f(x) = x^3 - 4x^2 + 4x + 1$ is shown alongside.

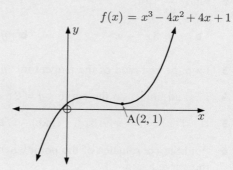

   a Find $f'(x)$.

   b Find and interpret $f'(1)$.

   c The graph has a minimum turning point at A(2, 1).

      i Find the gradient of the tangent at A.

      ii Find the equation of the tangent at A.

Chapter 21

Applications of differential calculus

Syllabus reference: 7.4, 7.5, 7.6

Contents:
- A Increasing and decreasing functions
- B Stationary points
- C Rates of change
- D Optimisation

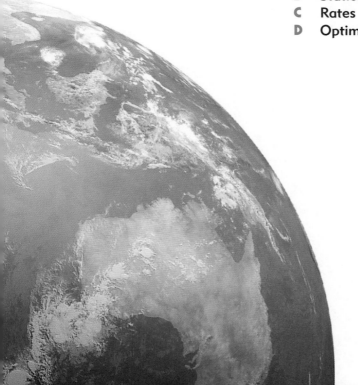

OPENING PROBLEM

A skatepark designer proposes to build a bowl with cross-section given by
$h(x) = 0.014x^4 - 0.196x^3 + 1.039x^2 - 2.471x + 2.225$ metres, $0 \leqslant x \leqslant 7$.

Things to think about:

a How high is the wall of the bowl?

b Is the lowest point exactly in the middle of the bowl?

c How steep are the sides? What units could we use to measure this?

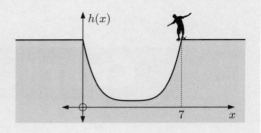

We saw in the previous chapter how differential calculus can be used to find the equation of a tangent to a curve. In this chapter we consider other uses, including:

- increasing and decreasing functions
- rates of change
- stationary points
- optimisation

A   INCREASING AND DECREASING FUNCTIONS

If we are given the equation of a function, we can find where the function is **increasing** and where it is **decreasing**.

The concepts of increasing and decreasing are closely linked to **intervals** of a function's domain.

Some examples of intervals and their graphical representations are shown in the table.

Algebraic form	Geometric form
$x \geqslant 2$	●——→ x (2)
$x > 2$	○——→ x (2)
$x \leqslant 4$	←——● x (4)
$x < 4$	←——○ x (4)
$2 \leqslant x \leqslant 4$	●——● x (2, 4)
$2 \leqslant x < 4$	●——○ x (2, 4)

On an interval where the function is **increasing**, an increase in x produces an **increase** in y.

On an interval where the function is **decreasing**, an increase in x produces a **decrease** in y.

increase in y

increase in x

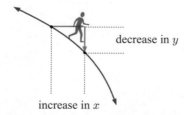

decrease in y

increase in x

Suppose S is an interval in the domain of $f(x)$, so $f(x)$ is defined for all x in S.

- $f(x)$ is **increasing** on S if $f(a) < f(b)$ for all $a, b \in S$ such that $a < b$.
- $f(x)$ is **decreasing** on S if $f(a) > f(b)$ for all $a, b \in S$ such that $a < b$.

For example:

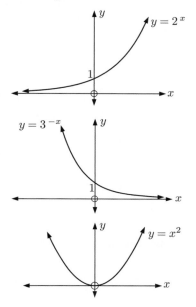

$y = 2^x$ is increasing for all x.

We say $y = 2^x$ is an **increasing function**.

$y = 3^{-x}$ is decreasing for all x.

We say $y = 3^{-x}$ is a **decreasing function**.

$y = x^2$ is decreasing for $x \leqslant 0$ and increasing for $x \geqslant 0$.

Important: For the curve $y = x^2$, people often get confused about the point $x = 0$. They wonder how the curve can be both increasing and decreasing at the same point. The answer is that increasing and decreasing are associated with *intervals*, not particular values for x. We must clearly state that $y = x^2$ is decreasing *on the interval* $x \leqslant 0$ and increasing *on the interval* $x \geqslant 0$.

Example 1 🔊 **Self Tutor**

Find intervals where $f(x)$ is:

a increasing

b decreasing.

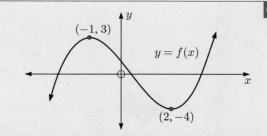

a $f(x)$ is increasing for $x \leqslant -1$ and for $x \geqslant 2$.

b $f(x)$ is decreasing for $-1 \leqslant x \leqslant 2$.

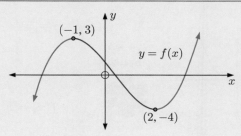

We can deduce when a curve is increasing or decreasing by considering $f'(x)$ on the interval in question.

> For the functions that we deal with in this course:
>
> - $f(x)$ is **increasing** on S if $f'(x) \geqslant 0$ for all x in S.
> - $f(x)$ is **strictly increasing** if $f'(x) > 0$ for all x in S.
> - $f(x)$ is **decreasing** on S if $f'(x) \leqslant 0$ for all x in S.
> - $f(x)$ is **strictly decreasing** if $f'(x) < 0$ for all x in S.

SIGN DIAGRAMS

Sign diagrams for the derivative are extremely useful for determining intervals where a function is increasing or decreasing.

The **critical values** for $f'(x)$ are the values of x for which $f'(x) = 0$ or $f'(x)$ is undefined. When $f'(x) = 0$, the critical values are shown on a number line using tick marks.

When $f'(x)$ is undefined, the critical values are shown with a vertical dotted line.

We complete the sign diagram by marking positive or negative signs, depending on whether $f'(x)$ is positive or negative, in the intervals between the critical values.

Consider the following examples:

- $f(x) = x^2$

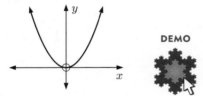

DEMO

$f'(x) = 2x$ which has sign diagram

$$\begin{array}{c} \quad - \quad\quad | \quad\quad + \\ \hline \quad\quad 0 \quad\quad\quad\quad x \\ \text{decreasing} \quad \text{increasing} \end{array}$$

$\therefore \ f(x) = x^2$ is decreasing for $x \leqslant 0$
and increasing for $x \geqslant 0$.

- $f(x) = -x^2$

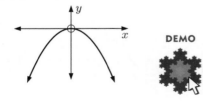

DEMO

$f'(x) = -2x$ which has sign diagram

$$\begin{array}{c} \quad + \quad\quad | \quad\quad - \\ \hline \quad\quad 0 \quad\quad\quad\quad x \\ \text{increasing} \quad \text{decreasing} \end{array}$$

$\therefore \ f(x) = -x^2$ is increasing for $x \leqslant 0$
and decreasing for $x \geqslant 0$.

- $f(x) = x^3$

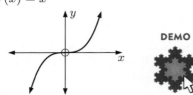

DEMO

$f'(x) = 3x^2$ which has sign diagram

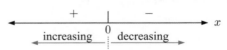

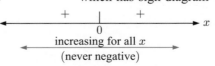

$\therefore \ f(x) = x^3$ is increasing for all x.

- $f(x) = \dfrac{1}{x^2}$

$f'(x) = -2x^{-3} = -\dfrac{2}{x^3}$ which has sign diagram

$\therefore$ $f(x) = \dfrac{1}{x^2}$ is   increasing for $x < 0$

and   decreasing for $x > 0$.

Example 2   ◀)) Self Tutor

Find the intervals where $f(x) = 2x^3 + 3x^2 - 12x - 5$ is increasing or decreasing.

$f(x) = 2x^3 + 3x^2 - 12x - 5$

$\therefore$ $f'(x) = 6x^2 + 6x - 12$

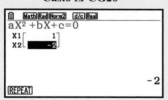   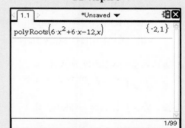   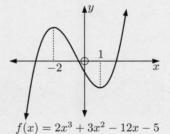

Using technology, $f'(x) = 0$ when $x = -2$ or 1.

So, $f'(x)$ has sign diagram

$\therefore$ $f(x)$ is increasing for $x \leqslant -2$ and for $x \geqslant 1$,
and decreasing for $-2 \leqslant x \leqslant 1$.

$f(x) = 2x^3 + 3x^2 - 12x - 5$

Remember that $f(x)$ must be defined for all x on an interval before we can classify the interval as increasing or decreasing. We must exclude points where a function is undefined, and need to take care with vertical asymptotes.

EXERCISE 21A

1   Find intervals where the graphed function is: **i**   increasing   **ii**   decreasing.

a
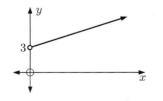

b
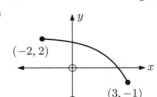

c
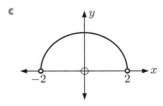

d 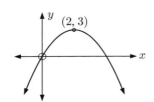   **e** 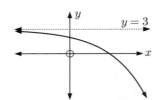   **f**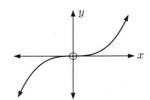

g 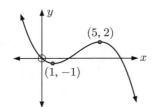   **h** 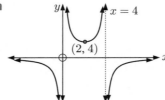   **i**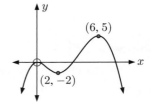

2 For each of the following functions:

    i find $f'(x)$

    ii draw a sign diagram for $f'(x)$

    iii find intervals where $f(x)$ is increasing or decreasing.

a $f(x) = 2x + 1$ **b** $f(x) = -3x + 2$

c $f(x) = x^2$ **d** $f(x) = -x^3$

e $f(x) = 2x^2 + 3x - 4$ **f** $f(x) = x^3 - 6x^2$

g $f(x) = \dfrac{1}{x^4}$ **h** $f(x) = \dfrac{1}{x}$

i $f(x) = -2x^3 + 4x$ **j** $f(x) = -4x^3 + 15x^2 + 18x + 3$

k $f(x) = 2x^3 + 9x^2 + 6x - 7$ **l** $f(x) = 2x + \dfrac{8}{x}$

B   STATIONARY POINTS

A **stationary point** of a function is a point such that $f'(x) = 0$.

A stationary point could be a **local maximum**, a **local minimum**, or a **horizontal inflection**.

MAXIMUM AND MINIMUM POINTS

Consider the following graph which has a restricted domain of $-5 \leqslant x \leqslant 6$.

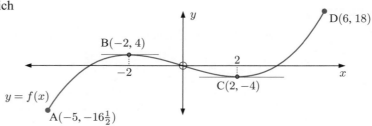

A is a **global minimum** as it is the minimum value of y on the entire domain.

B is a **local maximum** as it is a turning point where $f'(x) = 0$ and the curve has shape .

C is a **local minimum** as it is a turning point where $f'(x) = 0$ and the curve has shape .

D is a **global maximum** as it is the maximum value of y on the entire domain.

For many functions, a local maximum or minimum is also the global maximum or minimum.

For example, for $y = x^2$ the point $(0, 0)$ is a local minimum and is also the global minimum.

HORIZONTAL OR STATIONARY POINTS OF INFLECTION

A value of x where $f'(x) = 0$ does not always indicate a local maximum or minimum.

For example,   if $f(x) = x^3$ then $f'(x) = 3x^2$
$\therefore$ $f'(x) = 0$ when $x = 0$.

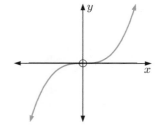

The tangent to the curve at $x = 0$ is the x-axis, and it actually crosses over the curve at O(0, 0). This tangent is horizontal, but O(0, 0) is neither a local maximum nor a local minimum.

It is called a **horizontal inflection** (or **inflexion**) as the curve changes its curvature or shape.

SIGN DIAGRAMS

Consider the graph alongside.

The sign diagram of its gradient function is shown directly beneath it.

We can use the sign diagram to describe the stationary points of the function.

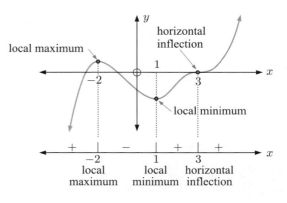

Stationary point	Sign diagram of $f'(x)$ near $x = a$	Shape of curve near $x = a$
local maximum	$\xrightarrow{\quad +\ \mid\ -\quad}{a} x$	
local minimum	$\xrightarrow{\quad -\ \mid\ +\quad}{a} x$	
horizontal inflection or stationary inflection	$\xrightarrow{\ +\ \mid\ +\ }{a} x$ or $\xrightarrow{\ -\ \mid\ -\ }{a} x$	

Example 3   ◀) **Self Tutor**

Find and classify all stationary points of $f(x) = x^3 - 3x^2 - 9x + 5$.

$f(x) = x^3 - 3x^2 - 9x + 5$

$\therefore \ f'(x) = 3x^2 - 6x - 9$

TI-$n$spire

Casio fx-CG20	**TI-84 Plus**	

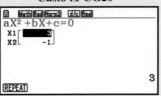

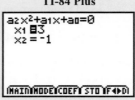

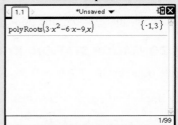

Using technology, $f'(x) = 0$ when $x = -1$ or 3.

$\therefore$ the sign diagram for $f'(x)$ is

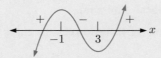

So, we have a local maximum at $x = -1$ and a local minimum at $x = 3$.

$f(-1) = (-1)^3 - 3(-1)^2 - 9(-1) + 5$ $f(3) = 3^3 - 3 \times 3^2 - 9 \times 3 + 5$

$\qquad = 10$ $\qquad = -22$

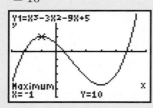

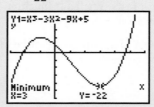

There is a local maximum at $(-1, \ 10)$.   There is a local minimum at $(3, \ -22)$.

If we are asked to find the greatest or least value on an interval, we should always check the endpoints also. We seek the *global* maximum or minimum on the given domain.

Example 4   ◀) **Self Tutor**

Find the greatest and least value of $x^3 - 6x^2 + 5$ on the interval $-2 \leqslant x \leqslant 5$.

First we graph $f(x) = x^3 - 6x^2 + 5$ on $-2 \leqslant x \leqslant 5$.

In this case the greatest value is at the local maximum when $f'(x) = 0$.

Now $f'(x) = 3x^2 - 12x$

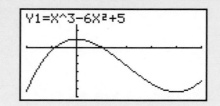

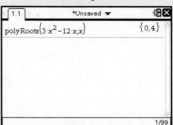

Using technology, $f'(x) = 0$ when $x = 0$ or 4.

So, the greatest value is $f(0) = 5$ when $x = 0$.

The least value is either $f(-2)$ or $f(4)$, whichever is smaller.

Now $f(-2) = -27$ and $f(4) = -27$

$\therefore$ the least value is -27 when $x = -2$ *and* when $x = 4$.

EXERCISE 21B

1 The tangents at points A, B, and C are horizontal.

   a Classify points A, B, and C.

   b Draw a sign diagram for the gradient function $f'(x)$ for all x.

   c State intervals where $y = f(x)$ is:

      i increasing   **ii** decreasing.

   d Draw a sign diagram for $f(x)$ for all x.

   e Comment on the differences between the sign diagrams found above.

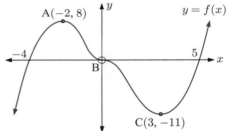

2 Consider the graph of $y = f(x)$ on the domain $-8 \leqslant x \leqslant 6$.

   a How many stationary points does the graph have?

   b Write down the coordinates of the:

      i local maximum

      ii horizontal inflection.

   c Find the   **i** greatest   **ii** least value of $f(x)$ on $-8 \leqslant x \leqslant 6$.

   d Find the greatest value of $f(x)$ on $-8 \leqslant x \leqslant 4$.

   e Find the least value of $f(x)$ on $-5 \leqslant x \leqslant 2$.

3 Consider the quadratic function $f(x) = 2x^2 - 5x + 1$.

   a Use quadratic theory to find the equation of the axis of symmetry.

   b Find $f'(x)$, and hence find x such that $f'(x) = 0$. Explain your result.

4 a Using technology to help, sketch a graph of $f(x) = x + \dfrac{1}{x}$.

   b Find $f'(x)$.

   c Find the values of x for which $f'(x) = 0$.

   d Draw a sign diagram for $f'(x)$.

   e Determine the position and nature of any stationary points.

5 For each of the following functions:

    i find $f'(x)$

   ii draw a sign diagram for $f'(x)$

  iii determine the position and nature of all stationary points

   iv sketch $y = f(x)$, showing all key features.

  a $f(x) = x^2 - 2$ **b** $f(x) = x^3 + 1$ **c** $f(x) = x^3 - 3x + 2$

  d $f(x) = x^4 - 2x^2$ **e** $f(x) = x^3 - 6x^2 + 12x + 1$ **f** $f(x) = 4x - x^3$

  g $f(x) = 2x + \dfrac{1}{x^2}$ **h** $f(x) = -x - \dfrac{9}{x}$ **i** $f(x) = x^2 + \dfrac{16}{x}$

6 At what value of x does the quadratic function $f(x) = ax^2 + bx + c$, $a \neq 0$, have a stationary point? Under what conditions is the stationary point a local maximum or a local minimum?

7 $f(x) = 2x^3 + ax^2 - 24x + 1$ has a local maximum at $x = -4$. Find a.

8 $f(x) = x^3 + ax + b$ has a stationary point at $(-2, 3)$. Find:

  a a and b **b** $f'(x)$ **c** the position and nature of all stationary points.

9 Find the greatest and least value of:

  a $x^3 - 12x - 2$ for $-3 \leqslant x \leqslant 5$ **b** $4 - 3x^2 + x^3$ for $-2 \leqslant x \leqslant 3$

  c $x^3 + x^2 - 4x$ for $-3 \leqslant x \leqslant 2$ **d** $-2x^3 - 2x^2 + 8x + 3$ for $-2 \leqslant x \leqslant 2$.

10 A manufacturing company makes door hinges. They have a standing order filled by producing 50 each hour, but production of more than 150 per hour is useless as they will not sell. The cost function for making x hinges per hour is:

$$C(x) = 0.0007x^3 - 0.1796x^2 + 14.663x + 160 \text{ dollars where } 50 \leqslant x \leqslant 150.$$

  a Find $C'(x)$.

  b Find the values of x for which $C'(x) = 0$.

  c Find the minimum and maximum hourly costs, and the production levels when each occurs.

C   RATES OF CHANGE

When we first introduced derivative functions, we discussed how

$\dfrac{dy}{dx}$ gives the **rate of change in y with respect to x**.

If y increases as x increases, then $\dfrac{dy}{dx}$ will be positive.

If y decreases as x increases, then $\dfrac{dy}{dx}$ will be negative.

TIME RATES OF CHANGE

There are countless quantities in the real world that vary with time.

For example:
- temperature varies continuously
- the height of a tree increases as it grows
- the prices of stocks and shares vary with each day's trading.

Varying quantities can be modelled using functions of time.

For example:

- Suppose $s(t)$ models the distance travelled by a runner.

  $\dfrac{ds}{dt}$ or $s'(t)$ is the instantaneous *speed* of the runner.

  It might have units metres per second or $m\,s^{-1}$.

- Suppose $H(t)$ models the height above the ground of a person riding in a Ferris wheel.

  $\dfrac{dH}{dt}$ or $H'(t)$ is the instantaneous rate of ascent of the person in the Ferris wheel.

  It might also have units metres per second or $m\,s^{-1}$.

- Suppose $C(t)$ models the capacity of a person's lungs, which changes when the person breathes.

  $\dfrac{dC}{dt}$ or $C'(t)$ is the person's instantaneous rate of change in lung capacity.

  It might have units litres per second or $L\,s^{-1}$.

Example 5 ◀)) **Self Tutor**

The volume of air in a hot air balloon after t minutes is given by
$V = 2t^3 - 3t^2 + 10t + 2$ m^3 where $0 \leqslant t \leqslant 8$.

Find:

a the initial volume of air in the balloon

b the volume when $t = 8$ minutes **c** $\dfrac{dV}{dt}$

d the rate of increase in volume when $t = 4$ minutes.

a When $t = 0$, $V = 2$ m^3
Initially there were 2 m^3 of air in the balloon.

b When $t = 8$, $V = 2(8)^3 - 3(8)^2 + 10(8) + 2$
$= 914$ m^3

After 8 minutes there were 914 m^3 of air in the balloon.

c $\dfrac{dV}{dt} = 6t^2 - 6t + 10$ m^3 min^{-1}

d When $t = 4$, $\dfrac{dV}{dt} = 6(4)^2 - 6(4) + 10$
$= 82$ m^3 min^{-1}

Since $\dfrac{dV}{dt} > 0$, V is increasing.

V is increasing at 82 m^3 min^{-1} when $t = 4$.

EXERCISE 21C.1

1 Find:

   a $\dfrac{dM}{dt}$ if $M = t^3 - 3t^2 + 1$
            b $\dfrac{dR}{dt}$ if $R = (2t + 1)^2$

2 **a** If A is measured in cm^2 and t is measured in seconds, what are the units for $\dfrac{dA}{dt}$?

    b If V is measured in m^3 and t is measured in minutes, what are the units for $\dfrac{dV}{dt}$?

3 The number of bacteria in a dish is modelled by $B(t) = 0.3t^2 + 30t + 150$ thousand, where t is in days, and $0 \leqslant t \leqslant 10$.

   a Find $B'(t)$ and state its meaning.
   b Find $B'(3)$ and state its meaning.
   c How do we know that $B(t)$ is increasing over the first 10 days?

4 Water is draining from a swimming pool such that the remaining volume of water after t minutes is $V = 2(50 - t)^2$ m^3. Find:

   a the average rate at which the water leaves the pool in the first 5 minutes
   b the instantaneous rate at which the water is leaving at $t = 5$ minutes.

5 When a ball is thrown, its height above the ground is given by $s(t) = 1.2 + 28.1t - 4.9t^2$ metres, where t is the time in seconds.

   a From what distance above the ground was the ball released?
   b Find $s'(t)$ and explain what it means.
   c Find t when $s'(t) = 0$. What is the significance of this result?
   d What is the maximum height reached by the ball?
   e Find the ball's speed:
      i when released   **ii** at $t = 2$ s   **iii** at $t = 5$ s.
     State the significance of the sign of the derivative $s'(t)$ for each of these values.
   f How long will it take for the ball to hit the ground?

6 The height of a palm tree is given by $H = 20 - \dfrac{18}{t}$ metres, where
t is the number of years after the tree was planted from an established potted juvenile tree, and $t \geqslant 1$.

   a How high was the palm after 1 year?
   b Find the height of the palm at $t = 2, 3, 5, 10$, and 50 years.
   c Find $\dfrac{dH}{dt}$ and state its units.
   d At what rate is the tree growing at $t = 1, 3$, and 10 years?
   e Explain why $\dfrac{dH}{dt} > 0$ for all $t \geqslant 1$. What does this mean in terms of the tree's growth?

GENERAL RATES OF CHANGE

Other rate problems can be treated in the same way as those involving time. However, we must always pay careful attention to the *units* of the quantities involved.

For example:

- The cost of manufacturing x items has a **cost function** $C(x)$ dollars associated with it.

  $\dfrac{dC}{dx}$ or $C'(x)$ is the **instantaneous rate of change in cost** with respect to the number of items made. In this case $\dfrac{dC}{dx}$ has the units dollars per item.

- The **profit** $P(x)$ in making and selling x items is given by $P(x) = R(x) - C(x)$ where $R(x)$ is the **revenue function** and $C(x)$ is the **cost function**.

  $\dfrac{dP}{dx}$ or $P'(x)$ represents the rate of change in profit with respect to the number of items sold.

Example 6   ◀)) **Self Tutor**

The cost of producing x items in a factory each day is given by

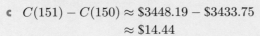

$$C(x) = \underbrace{0.000\,13x^3 + 0.002x^2}_{\substack{\text{cost of}\\\text{labour}}} + \underset{\substack{\uparrow\\\text{raw material}\\\text{costs}}}{5x} + \underset{\substack{\uparrow\\\text{fixed or overhead costs such as}\\\text{heating, cooling, maintenance, rent}}}{2200}$$

a Find $C'(x)$.   **b** Find $C'(150)$. Interpret this result.

c Find $C(151) - C(150)$. Compare this with the answer in **b**.

---

a $C'(x) = 0.000\,39x^2 + 0.004x + 5$

b $C'(150) = \$14.38$ per item

This is the rate at which the costs are increasing with respect to the production level x, when 150 items are made per day.

c $C(151) - C(150) \approx \$3448.19 - \$3433.75$
$ \approx \$14.44$

This is the actual cost of making the 151st item each day, and is similar to the answer from **b**.

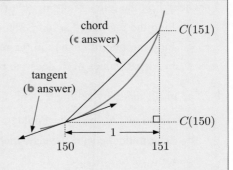

EXERCISE 21C.2

1 Find: **a** $\dfrac{dT}{dr}$ if $T = r^2 - \dfrac{100}{r}$ **b** $\dfrac{dA}{dh}$ if $A = 2\pi h + \frac{1}{4}h^2$

2 If C is measured in pounds and x is the number of items produced, what are the units for $\dfrac{dC}{dx}$?

3 The cost function for producing x items each day is
$$C(x) = 0.000\,072x^3 - 0.000\,61x^2 + 0.19x + 893 \text{ dollars.}$$

   a Find $C'(x)$ and explain what it represents.

   b Find $C'(300)$ and explain what it estimates.

   c Find the actual cost of producing the 301st item.

4 Seablue make denim jeans. The cost model for making x pairs per day is
$$C(x) = 0.0003x^3 + 0.02x^2 + 4x + 2250 \text{ dollars.}$$

    a Find $C'(x)$.   **b** Find $C'(220)$. What does it estimate?

    c Find $C(221) - C(220)$. What does this represent?

5 The total cost of running a train from Paris to Marseille is given by $C(v) = \frac{1}{5}v^2 + \dfrac{200\,000}{v}$ euros, where v is the average speed of the train in km h^{-1}.

    a Find the total cost of the journey if the average speed is:

        i 50 km h^{-1} **ii** 100 km h^{-1}.

    b Find the rate of change in the cost of running the train at speeds of:

        i 30 km h^{-1} **ii** 90 km h^{-1}.

6

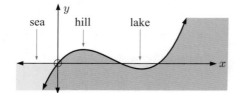

Alongside is a land and sea profile where the x-axis is sea level.

The function $y = \frac{1}{10}x(x-2)(x-3)$ km gives the height of the land or sea bed relative to sea level.

    a Find where the lake is located relative to the shore line of the sea.

    b Find $\dfrac{dy}{dx}$ and interpret its value when $x = \frac{1}{2}$ and when $x = 1\frac{1}{2}$ km.

    c Find the point at which the lake floor is level, and the depth at this point.

7 The resistance to the flow of electricity in a metal is given by $R = 20 + \frac{1}{10}T - \frac{1}{200}T^2$ ohms, where T is the temperature in °C of the metal.

    a Find the resistance at temperatures $0°C$, $20°C$, and $40°C$.

    b Find the rate of change in the resistance at any temperature T.

    c For what values of T does the resistance increase as the temperature increases?

8 The profit made by selling x items is given by $P(x) = 5x - 2000 - \dfrac{x^2}{10\,000}$ dollars.

    a Graph $P(x)$ using technology.

    b Determine the sales levels which produce a profit.

    c Find $P'(x)$.

    d Hence find x such that the profit is increasing.

9 The cost of producing x items is given by $C(x) = 0.0002x^3 + 0.04x^2 + 10x + 3000$ dollars. If each item sells for $70, find:

    a the revenue function $R(x)$ **b** the profit function $P(x)$

    c $P'(x)$ **d** $P'(120)$, and explain the significance of this result.

D   OPTIMISATION

There are many problems for which we need to find the **maximum** or **minimum** value for a function. We can often solve such problems using differential calculus techniques. The solution is referred to as the **optimum** solution, and the process is called **optimisation**.

Important: The maximum or minimum value does not always occur when the first derivative is zero. It is essential to also examine the values of the function at the endpoint(s) of the domain for global maxima and minima.

For example:

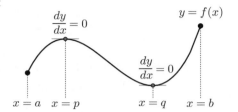

The maximum value of y occurs at the endpoint $x = b$.

The minimum value of y occurs at the local minimum $x = q$.

TESTING OPTIMAL SOLUTIONS

If we find a value of x such that $f'(x) = 0$, there are two tests we can use to see whether we have a maximum or a minimum solution:

1) SIGN DIAGRAM TEST

Suppose $f'(a) = 0$. If, near to $x = a$, the sign diagram of $f'(x)$ is:

- $\xleftarrow{\quad + \quad | \quad - \quad}_{\;a\;\quad\; x}$ then we have a **local maximum**

- $\xleftarrow{\quad - \quad | \quad + \quad}_{\;a\;\quad\; x}$ then we have a **local minimum**.

2) GRAPHICAL TEST

If the graph of $y = f(x)$ shows:

- $\frown$ then we have a **local maximum**

- $\smile$ then we have a **local minimum**.

OPTIMISATION PROBLEM SOLVING METHOD

Step 1:   If necessary, draw a large, clear diagram of the situation.

Step 2:   Construct a formula with the variable to be optimised as the subject. It should be written in terms of a single variable such as x. You should write down what restrictions there are on x.

Step 3:   Find the **first derivative** and find the values of x where it is **zero**.

Step 4:   If there is a restricted domain such as $a \leqslant x \leqslant b$, the maximum or minimum may occur either when the derivative is zero or else at an endpoint.

Show using the **sign diagram test** or the **graphical test**, that you have a maximum or a minimum.

Example 7   ◀)) **Self Tutor**

A 4 litre container must have a square base, vertical sides, and an open top. Find the most economical shape which minimises the surface area of material needed.

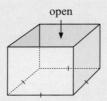

Step 1:

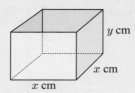

Let the base lengths be x cm and the depth be y cm.

The volume $V = \text{length} \times \text{width} \times \text{depth}$

$\therefore \ V = x^2 y$

$\therefore \ 4000 = x^2 y \ \dots \ (1) \quad \{\text{as 1 litre} \equiv 1000 \text{ cm}^3\}$

Step 2: The total surface area

$A = \text{area of base} + 4(\text{area of one side})$

$\quad = x^2 + 4xy$

$\quad = x^2 + 4x \left(\dfrac{4000}{x^2} \right) \qquad \{\text{using } (1)\}$

$\therefore \ A(x) = x^2 + 16\,000x^{-1} \quad \text{where } x > 0$

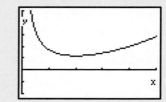

Step 3: $A'(x) = 2x - 16\,000x^{-2}$

$\therefore \ A'(x) = 0 \quad \text{when} \quad 2x = \dfrac{16\,000}{x^2}$

$\therefore \ 2x^3 = 16\,000$

$\therefore \ x = \sqrt[3]{8000} = 20$

Step 4: **Sign diagram test**

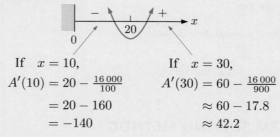

If $x = 10,$ If $x = 30,$

$A'(10) = 20 - \dfrac{16\,000}{100}$ $A'(30) = 60 - \dfrac{16\,000}{900}$

$\qquad\quad = 20 - 160$ $\qquad\quad \approx 60 - 17.8$

$\qquad\quad = -140$ $\qquad\quad \approx 42.2$

The material used to make the container is minimised when $x = 20$ and

$y = \dfrac{4000}{20^2} = 10.$

The most economical shape is shown alongside.

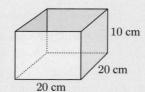

EXERCISE 21D.1

1 The cost of making x tennis racquets each day is given by $C(x) = x^2 - 20x + 120$ dollars per racquet.

How many racquets should be made per day to minimise the cost per racquet?

2 When a stone is thrown vertically upwards, its height above the ground is given by $h(t) = 49t - 9.8t^2$ metres. Find the maximum height reached.

3 A small business which employs x workers earns a profit given by $P(x) = -x^3 + 300x + 1000$ pounds.

How many workers should be employed to maximise the profit?

4 A manufacturer can produce x fittings per day where $0 \leqslant x \leqslant 10\,000$. The production costs are:

- €1000 per day for the workers
- €2 per day per fitting
- €$\dfrac{5000}{x}$ per day for running costs and maintenance.

How many fittings should be produced daily to minimise costs?

5 For the cost function $C(x) = 720 + 4x + 0.02x^2$ dollars and revenue function $R(x) = 15x - 0.002x^2$ dollars, find the production level that will maximise profits.

6 The total cost of producing x blankets per day is $(\frac{1}{4}x^2 + 8x + 20)$ dollars, and for this production level each blanket may be sold for $(23 - \frac{1}{2}x)$ dollars.

How many blankets should be produced per day to maximise the total profit?

7 An open rectangular box has a square base, and a fixed inner surface area of 108 cm².

  a Explain why $x^2 + 4xy = 108$.   **b** Hence show that $y = \dfrac{108 - x^2}{4x}$.

  c Find a formula for the capacity C of the container, in terms of x only.

  d Find $\dfrac{dC}{dx}$. Hence find x when $\dfrac{dC}{dx} = 0$.

  e What size must the base be in order to maximise the capacity of the box?

8 Radioactive waste is to be disposed of in fully enclosed lead boxes of inner volume 200 cm³. The base of the box has dimensions in the ratio $2 : 1$.

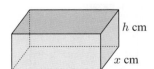

  a What is the inner length of the box?

  b Explain why $x^2h = 100$.

  c Explain why the inner surface area of the box is given by $A(x) = 4x^2 + \dfrac{600}{x}$ cm².

  d Use technology to help sketch the graph of $y = 4x^2 + \dfrac{600}{x}$.

  e Find $\dfrac{dA}{dx}$. Hence find x when $\dfrac{dA}{dx} = 0$.

  f Find the minimum inner surface area of the box.

  g Sketch the optimum box shape, showing all dimensions.

9 Consider the manufacture of cylindrical tin cans of 1 L capacity. The cost of the metal used is to be minimised, so the surface area must be as small as possible.

a If the radius is r cm, explain why the height h is given by $h = \dfrac{1000}{\pi r^2}$ cm.

b Show that the total surface area A is given by $A = 2\pi r^2 + \dfrac{2000}{r}$ cm².

c Use technology to help sketch the graph of A against r.

d Find $\dfrac{dA}{dr}$.   Hence find the value of r which makes A as small as possible.

e Sketch the can of smallest surface area.

Example 8   ◀)) **Self Tutor**

A square sheet of metal 12 cm × 12 cm has smaller squares cut from its corners as shown.

What sized square should be cut out so that when the sheet is bent into an open box it will hold the maximum amount of liquid?

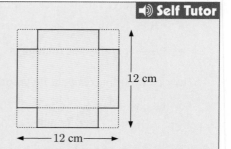
12 cm

12 cm

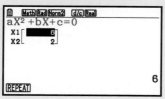

x cm

$(12 - 2x)$ cm

Suppose x cm by x cm squares are cut out.

∴   the base of the box is a square with side length $(12 - 2x)$ cm.

Volume $V(x) = \text{length} \times \text{width} \times \text{depth}$
$$= (12 - 2x) \times (12 - 2x) \times x$$
$$= x(12 - 2x)^2$$
$$= x(144 - 48x + 4x^2)$$
$$= 4x^3 - 48x^2 + 144x \ \ \text{cm}^3$$
∴ $V'(x) = 12x^2 - 96x + 144$

Casio fx-CG20	**TI-84 Plus**	**TI-*n*spire**
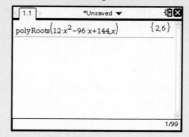		

Using technology, $V'(x) = 0$ when $x = 2$ or 6

However, $12 - 2x$ must be > 0 and so $x < 6$

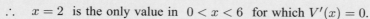

∴ $x = 2$ is the only value in $0 < x < 6$ for which $V'(x) = 0$.

Conclusion: The resulting container has maximum capacity when 2 cm × 2 cm squares are cut from its corners.

10 Sam has a sheet of metal which is 36 cm by 36 cm square. He will cut out identical squares which are x cm by x cm from the corners of the sheet. He will then bend the sheet along the dashed lines to form an open container.

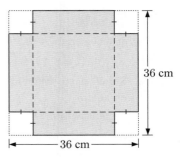

  a Show that the capacity of the container is given by $V(x) = x(36 - 2x)^2$ cm^3.

  b What sized squares should be cut out to produce the container of greatest capacity?

11 An athletics track has two 'straights' of length l m and two semi-circular ends of radius x m. The perimeter of the track is 400 m.

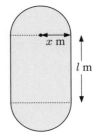

  a Show that $l = 200 - \pi x$ and hence write down the possible values that x may have.

  b Show that the area inside the track is given by $A = 400x - \pi x^2$ m^2.

  c What values of l and x produce the largest area inside the track?

12 Answer the **Opening Problem** on page **586**.

13

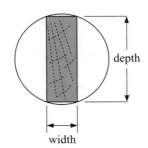

A beam with rectangular cross-section is to be cut from a log of diameter 1 m.

The strength of the beam is given by $S = kwd^2$, where w is the width and d is the depth.

  a Show that $d^2 = 1 - w^2$ using Pythagoras' theorem.

  b Write S in terms of w only. Hence find $\dfrac{dS}{dw}$.

  c Find the dimensions of the strongest beam that can be cut from the log.

14 A water tank has the dimensions shown. The capacity of the tank is 300 kL.

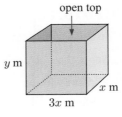

  a Explain why $x^2 y = 100$.

  b Hence find y in terms of x.

  c Show that the area of plastic used to make the tank is given by $A = 3x^2 + 800x^{-1}$ m^2.

  d Find $\dfrac{dA}{dx}$. Hence find the value of x which minimises the surface area A.

  e Sketch the tank, showing the dimensions which minimise A.

OPTIMISATION USING TECHNOLOGY

We have seen how to use calculus to solve optimisation problems. However, we only know how to differentiate a limited number of functions.

If we do not know how to differentiate a function, we can use technology to find the optimum solution.

GRAPHING PACKAGE

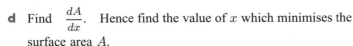

In the following exercise, use the **graphing package** or your **graphics calculator** to help solve the problems.

Example 9	◀ Self Tutor

The distance from A to P is given by
$D = \sqrt{(5-x)^2 + (y-1)^2}$ units.

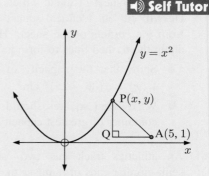

a Show, using triangle PQA, how this formula was obtained.

b Explain why $D = \sqrt{(5-x)^2 + (x^2-1)^2}$.

c Sketch the graph of D against x for $0 \leqslant x \leqslant 6$.

d Find the smallest value of D and the value of x where it occurs.

e Interpret the results from **d**.

a

$QA = 5 - x$ and $PQ = y - 1$
$\therefore\ D^2 = (5-x)^2 + (y-1)^2$
$\therefore\ D = \sqrt{(5-x)^2 + (y-1)^2}$

b Since P is on the curve $y = x^2$, $D = \sqrt{(5-x)^2 + (x^2-1)^2}$.

c

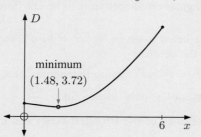

d Using technology, the coordinates of the turning point are $(1.48,\ 3.72)$.
So, the smallest value of D is 3.72 units when $x \approx 1.48$.

e The shortest distance from A(5, 1) to the graph of $y = x^2$ is 3.72 units.
The closest point on the graph to A(5, 1) is when $x \approx 1.48$.

EXERCISE 21D.2

1 The distance from A to P can be found using triangle ABP.

a Show that $D = \sqrt{(x-1)^2 + (4-y)^2}$ units.

b Explain why $D = \sqrt{(x-1)^2 + (4-\sqrt{x})^2}$.

c Sketch the graph of D against x for $0 \leqslant x \leqslant 8$.

d Find the smallest value of D and the value of x where it occurs.

e Interpret the results from **d**.

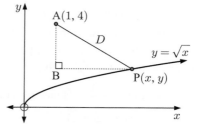

2

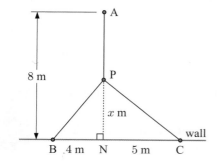

A, B, and C are computers. A printer P is networked to each computer as shown.

a Find, in terms of x, the lengths of AP, BP, and CP.

b Let $D = AP + BP + CP$ be the total length of cable needed to connect the three computers to the printer. Use **a** to write D in terms of x.

c Draw the graph of D against x.

d Where should the printer be placed so that the total cable length used is minimised?

3 A closed pizza box is folded from a sheet of cardboard 64 cm by 40 cm. To do this, equal squares of side length x cm are cut from two corners of the short side, and two equal rectangles of width x cm are cut from the long side as shown.

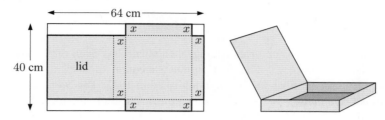

    a Find the dimensions of the lid and the base of the box in terms of x.

    b Find the volume of the box in terms of x.

    c What is the maximum possible volume of the box?

    d What are the dimensions of the box which has the maximum volume?

4 Three towns and their grid references are marked on the diagram alongside. A pumping station is to be located at P on the pipeline, to pump water to the three towns. The grid units are kilometres.

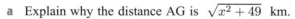

    a The distance PC can be found using the distance formula: $PC = \sqrt{(x-3)^2 + (8-11)^2}$

        $\therefore \;\; PC = \sqrt{(x-3)^2 + 9}$

    Find formulae for the distances PA and PB.

    b Write a formula for the sum of the distances $S = PA + PB + PC$ in terms of x.

    c Draw the graph of S against x.

    d Where should P be located to minimise the total length of connecting pipe needed?

5 G is a natural gas rig which is 7 km from the straight shore PB. B is a collection station which is 13 km from P.

A pipeline is to be laid from G underwater to A, and then from A to B along the shoreline. The cost of the pipeline is $6 million per km underwater, and $4 million per km along the shore.

We are to locate point A on the shoreline so that the cost of the pipeline will be minimised.

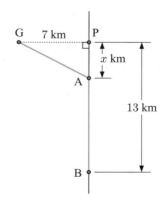

    a Explain why the distance AG is $\sqrt{x^2 + 49}$ km.

    b Find the distance from A to B in terms of x.

    c Explain why the total cost of the pipeline is
$C = 6\sqrt{x^2 + 49} + 52 - 4x$ million dollars.

    d Graph C against x and find the minimum turning point.

    e Where should A be located to minimise the cost?

THEORY OF KNOWLEDGE

"Aristotle is recognized as the inventor of scientific method because of his refined analysis of logical implications contained in demonstrative discourse, which goes well beyond natural logic and does not owe anything to the ones who philosophized before him."

– Riccardo Pozzo

A **scientific method** of inquiry for investigating phenomena has been applied in varying degrees throughout the course of history. The first formal statement of such a method was made by René Descartes in his *Discourse on the Method* published in 1637. This work is perhaps best known for Descartes' quote, *"Je pense, donc je suis"* which means "I think, therefore I am". In 1644 in his *Principles of Philosophy* he published the same quote in Latin: *"Cogito ergo sum"*.

The scientific method involves a series of steps:

Step 1:   asking a question (how, when, why, ...)

Step 2:   conducting appropriate research

Step 3:   constructing a hypothesis, or possible explanation why things are so

Step 4:   testing the hypothesis by a fair experiment

Step 5:   analysing the results

Step 6:   drawing a conclusion

Step 7:   communicating your findings

Snell's law states the relationship between the angles of incidence and refraction when a ray of light passes from one homogeneous medium to another.

It was first discovered in 984 AD by the Persian scientist Ibn Sahl, who was studying the shape of lenses. However, it is named after Willebrord Snellius, one of those who rediscovered the law in the Renaissance. The law was published by Descartes in the *Discourse on the Method*.

In the figure alongside, a ray passes from A to B via point X. The refractive indices of the two media are n and m. The angle of incidence is α and the angle of refraction is β.

Snell's law is: $n \sin \alpha = m \sin \beta$.

The law follows from Fermat's principle of least time. It gives the path of least time for the ray travelling from A to B.

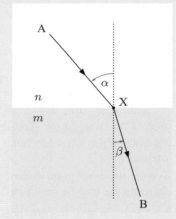

1 Is optimisation unique to mathematics?

2 How does mathematics fit into the scientific method?

3 Does mathematics have a prescribed method of its own?

4 Is mathematics a science?

REVIEW SET 21A

1 Find intervals where the graphed function is increasing or decreasing.

a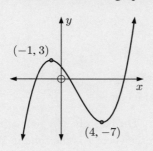

b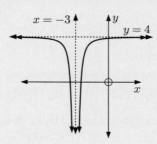

c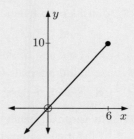

2 Consider the function $f(x) = x^3 - 3x$.

    a Determine the y-intercept of the function.

    b Find $f'(x)$.

    c Hence find the position and nature of any stationary points.

    d Sketch the graph of the function, showing the features you have found.

3 Consider the function $f(x) = 3x + 2 + \dfrac{48}{x}$.

    a Find $f'(x)$ and draw its sign diagram.

    b Find and classify all stationary points of the function.

    c Sketch the graph of $y = f(x)$.

4 An open box is made by cutting squares out of the corners of a 24 cm by 24 cm square sheet of tinplate. Use calculus techniques to determine the size of the squares that should be removed to maximise the volume of the box.

5 The graph of $f(x) = x^3 - 12x + 4$ is shown.

    a Find $f'(x)$.

    b Find the gradient of the tangent to the graph at P.

    c The graph has a local minimum at Q.
       Find the coordinates of Q.

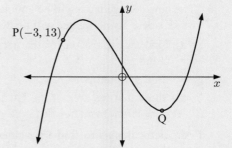

6 A factory makes x thousand chopsticks per day with a cost of $C(x) = 0.4x^2 + 1.6x + 150$ dollars. Packs of 1000 chopsticks sell for \$28.

    a Using calculus, find the production level that maximises daily profit.

    b Determine the profit at that production level.

REVIEW SET 21B

1 Find the maximum and minimum values of $x^3 - 3x^2 + 5$ for $-1 \leqslant x \leqslant 4$.

2 Consider the function $f(x) = 2x^3 - 3x^2 - 36x + 7$.

  a Find $f'(x)$.

  b Find and classify all stationary points.

  c Find intervals where the function is increasing or decreasing.

  d Sketch the graph of $y = f(x)$, showing all important features.

3 An astronaut standing on the moon throws a ball into the air. The ball's height above the surface of the moon is given by $H(t) = 1.5 + 19t - 0.8t^2$ metres, where t is the time in seconds.

  a Find $H'(t)$ and state its units.

  b Calculate $H'(0)$, $H'(10)$, and $H'(20)$. Interpret these values, including their sign.

  c How long is the ball in the 'air' for?

4 For the function $y = f(x)$ shown, draw a sign diagram of:

  a $f(x)$ **b** $f'(x)$.

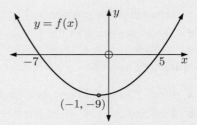

5 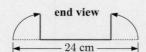 A rectangular gutter is formed by bending a 24 cm wide sheet of metal as illustrated. Where must the bends be made to maximise the capacity of the gutter?

6 The new college lawn will be a rectangle with a semi-circle on one of its sides. Its perimeter will be 200 m.

  a Find an expression for the perimeter of the lawn in terms of r and x.

  b Find x in terms of r.

  c Show that the area of the lawn A can be written as $A = 200r - r^2 \left(2 + \frac{\pi}{2}\right)$.

  d Use calculus to find the values of x and r which maximise the area of the lawn.

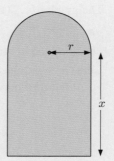

7 At time t years after mining begins on a mountain of iron ore, the rate of mining is given by $R(t) = \dfrac{1000 \times 3^{0.03t}}{25 + 2^{0.25t-10}}$ million tonnes per year, $t \geqslant 0$.

  a Graph $R(t)$ against t for $0 \leqslant t \leqslant 100$.

  b At what rate will the ore be mined after $t = 20$ years?

  c What will be the maximum rate of mining, and at what time will it occur?

  d When will the rate of mining be 100 million tonnes per year?

REVIEW SET 21C

1 $f(x) = x^3 + Ax + B$ has a stationary point at $(1, 5)$.

   a Find A and B.   **b** Find the nature of all the stationary points of $f(x)$.

2 Consider the function $f(x) = x^3 - 4x^2 + 4x$.

   a State the y-intercept.

   b Find $f'(x)$ and draw its sign diagram.

   c State intervals where the function is increasing or decreasing.

   d Find the position and nature of any stationary points.

   e Sketch the function, showing the features you have found.

3 The cost per hour of running a barge up the Rhein is given by $C(v) = 10v + \dfrac{90}{v}$ euros, where v is the average speed of the barge.

   a Find the cost of running the barge for:

      i two hours at 15 km h^{-1} **ii** 5 hours at 24 km h^{-1}.

   b Find the rate of change in the cost of running the barge at speeds of:

      i 10 km h^{-1} **ii** 6 km h^{-1}.

   c At what speed will the cost per hour be a minimum?

4 A manufacturer of open steel boxes has to make one with a square base and a volume of 1 m^3. The steel costs \$2 per square metre.

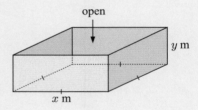

   a If the base measures x m by x m and the height is y m, find y in terms of x.

   b Hence, show that the total cost of the steel is
$C(x) = 2x^2 + \dfrac{8}{x}$ dollars.

   c Find $C'(x)$.

   d Hence find the dimensions which minimise the cost of the box.

   e How much will the steel for the box cost in this case?

5 The cost of running an advertising campaign for x days is $C(x) = 6900 + 950x$ pounds.

Research shows that after x days, $7500 - \dfrac{98\,000}{x}$ people will have responded, bringing an average profit of £17 per person.

   a Show that the profit from running the campaign for x days is $P(x) = 120\,600 - \dfrac{1\,666\,000}{x} - 950x$ pounds.

   b Find how long the campaign should last to maximise profit.

6 Find the maximum and minimum values of $y = \frac{1}{3}x^3 + x^2 - 3x$ for $-4 \leqslant x \leqslant 4$.

7 Max throws a stone into the air. It lands 5.9 seconds later. Over the course of its flight, the distance of the stone from Max after t seconds is given by

$$D(t) = \sqrt{24.01t^4 - 294t^3 + 936t^2} \quad \text{metres}.$$

   a State the domain of $D(t)$.

   b What is the maximum distance of the stone from Max?

   c How far away does the stone land?

Chapter 22

Miscellaneous problems

Contents: A Short questions
B Long questions

A **SHORT QUESTIONS**

EXERCISE 22A

1 Calculate the value of $\dfrac{(1.2 \times 10^{-1})^2}{4.72 \times 10^{-2}}$, giving your answer:

  a correct to two decimal places   **b** correct to 3 significant figures

  c in scientific notation correct to 6 significant figures.

2 Two propositions p and q are defined as follows:

    p: Farouk studies for the test. q: Farouk scores a good mark.

  a Write in words: **i** $p \Rightarrow q$ **ii** the inverse of $p \Rightarrow q$.

  b Write in symbols: **i** the converse of $p \Rightarrow q$ **ii** the contrapositive of $p \Rightarrow q$.

  c Use a truth table to show that the contrapositive of $p \Rightarrow q$ is equivalent to the original statement $p \Rightarrow q$.

3 A random variable X is normally distributed with mean 2.5 and standard deviation 6.7.

  a Find the probability that a randomly chosen item from this population has a negative value.

  b Given that $P(X \geqslant k) = 0.3$, find k.

4 The line $3x + 2y = 18$ cuts the axes at A and B. M is the midpoint of the line segment AB as shown.

  a Find the coordinates of A and B.

  b Find the coordinates of M.

  c Find the gradient of the line AB.

  d Find the equation of the perpendicular bisector of AB in the form $ax + by = c$, where $a, b \in \mathbb{Z}$ and $a > 0$.

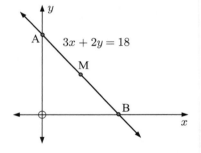

5 The lengths of a random sample of 200 fish caught one day from the local jetty are displayed in the cumulative frequency curve.

  a Write down the median length of fish caught.

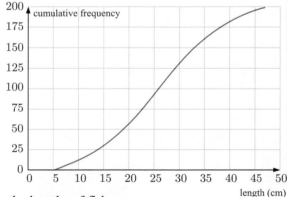

  b Complete the following table of values for the lengths of fish. Give your answers to the nearest 5 fish.

Length (cm)	$0 < x \leqslant 10$	$10 < x \leqslant 20$	$20 < x \leqslant 30$	$30 < x \leqslant 40$	$40 < x \leqslant 50$
Frequency	15	$55 - 15 = 40$	$130 - 55 = 75$		

  c Use your table in **b** to estimate the mean length of fish caught from the jetty.

6 Consider the function $f(x) = 2x^5 - 5x^2 + 1$.

   a Find $f'(x)$.   **b** Find the equation of the tangent to $y = f(x)$ at the point $(1, -2)$.

7 Romeo has \$12 000 which he would like to invest for four years until he finishes his University degree. The following options are available:

        Option A: 5.8% p.a. interest compounding monthly.
        Option B: 5.9% p.a. interest compounding quarterly.

   a For each option, calculate the value of the investment after four years.

   b Which option is better, and by how much?

8 A *light-year* (ly) is the distance light travels in a vacuum in one year.

   a Light travels at 2.998×10^5 km s^{-1}. Assuming there are 365.25 days in a year, calculate the distance light travels in 1 year. Write your answer correct to 3 significant figures, in the form $a \times 10^k$ km where $1 \leqslant a < 10$ and $k \in \mathbb{Z}$.

   b The Andromeda Galaxy is approximately 2.2×10^5 ly wide. Write this distance in kilometres, in the form $a \times 10^k$ where $1 \leqslant a < 10$ and $k \in \mathbb{Z}$.

9 Let U be the universal set $\{x \mid 1 \leqslant x \leqslant 10,\ x \in \mathbb{Z}\}$.
   P and Q are subsets of U, as shown in the Venn diagram.
   Let p and q be the propositions:

      p: x is an element of P.
      q: x is an element of Q.

   a For what values of x are the following statements true:

      i $\neg p$ **ii** $\neg p \wedge q$ **iii** $p \veebar q$?

   b Complete the truth table:

p	q	$\neg p$	$\neg p \wedge q$	$p \veebar q$
T	T			
T	F			
F	T			
F	F			

10 Consider the spinner alongside.

   a Find the probability that the next spin will finish on green.

   b How many 'reds' would you expect if the spinner was spun 300 times?

   c A game is played with this spinner where green pays \$1.50, blue pays \$2, red pays \$6, and yellow pays \$15. It costs \$5 to play the game.

      i Calculate the expected gain from this game.

      ii Determine whether the game is fair.

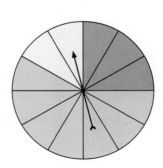

11 Line V is vertical and passes through A(5, 6) as shown.

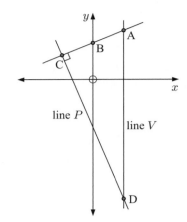

a Write down the equation of line V.

b B(0, 4) is the midpoint of line segment AC. Write down the coordinates of point C.

c Line P passes through C and is perpendicular to AC. Write down the equation of line P, giving your answer in the form $ax + by + d = 0$.

d Write down the coordinates of D, the point of intersection of lines P and V.

12 A high school principal believes that academic success is related to the students' involvement with co-curricular activities. To investigate this further, the principal compiled the following information.

Grade average	Total time spent on co-curricular activities		
	Less than 2 hours	From 2 to 5 hours	More than 5 hours
1 or 2	15	14	17
3, 4, or 5	31	26	18
6 or 7	22	24	31

The principal performs a χ^2 test on the data at a 1% significance level.

a For this χ^2 test:

  i write down the null hypothesis H_0

  ii explain why there are 4 degrees of freedom

  iii calculate the value of the χ^2 test statistic.

b Given the critical value is ≈ 13.3 at a 1% significance level, comment on whether H_0 is rejected.

c Discuss whether this χ^2 test at a 1% significance level supports the principal's belief.

13 Consider the graph of $y = f(x)$ shown opposite. B is a local minimum, D is a local maximum, and the tangent at C is horizontal.

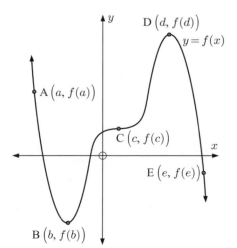

a Write down the equation of the tangent at C.

b Write down all solutions to $f'(x) = 0$.

c For what values of x is $f(x)$ decreasing?

d Comment on whether $\dfrac{f(b) - f(a)}{b - a}$ is positive, negative, or zero.

e What can be said about the tangent lines at A and E if $f'(a) = f'(e)$?

14 Mr Bond receives £200 000 in retirement money. He decides to spend £10 000 on a holiday to France, leaving the remainder of his retirement fund in the bank.

   a When Mr Bond converts his holiday money from British pounds (GBP) to euros (EUR), the exchange rate is 1 GBP = 1.21 EUR. A 3% commission is paid on the transaction. How many euros does Mr Bond receive?

   b The remainder of Mr Bond's retirement money is left in an account offering 5.6% p.a. interest, compounding monthly. Calculate the value of his retirement fund after 2 years.

15 A rectangular field is 91.4 m long and 68.5 m wide.

   a Calculate the exact area of the field in m^2.

   b Round your answer in **a** to two significant figures.

   c Calculate the percentage error of your answer in **b**.

16 Suppose $U = \{x \mid 1 \leqslant x \leqslant 11, \ x \in \mathbb{Z}\}$, p: x is a prime number, and q: x is an even number.

   a Represent the information on a Venn diagram.

   b Write down the truth set for: **i** $p \wedge q$ **ii** $p \vee \neg q$.

17 The graph alongside shows $y = x^2 - 3x - 18$. It cuts the x-axis at A, and its vertex is at B.

   a Write down the coordinates of:

      i A   **ii** B.

   b Find the coordinates of the points where the curve $y = x^2 - 3x - 18$ meets the line $y = -8$.

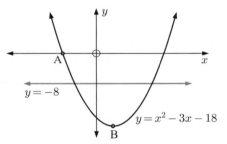

18 A house is x metres from a 190 m high radio tower. The angle of elevation from the house to the top of the tower is 16°.

   a Draw a diagram to show this information.   **b** Find x.

   c Find the straight line distance from the top of the tower to the house.

19 The histogram shows the times a group of students spent travelling to school in the morning.

   a Construct a frequency table for this data.

   b Estimate the mean and standard deviation for the travel time.

   c Find the percentage of students who spend more than 40 minutes travelling to school in the morning.

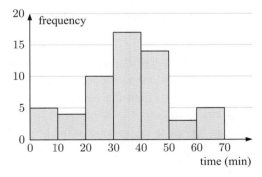

20   **a** Expand the expression $2(x - 1)(x + 5)$.

   b Differentiate $f(x) = 2(x - 1)(x + 5)$ with respect to x.

   c The tangent to $y = f(x)$ at the point where $x = a$ has gradient -5.

      i Find the value of a.

      ii Hence, find the coordinates of the point on the curve where the gradient is -5.

21 The table alongside shows exchange rates for the Malaysian ringgit (MYR).

Currency	1 MYR
Euro (EUR)	0.249 715
Chinese yuan (CNY)	2.004 38

   a   **i** Calculate how many Chinese yuan can be exchanged for 1000 MYR.

        ii If this transaction is subject to a 1.5% commission, calculate the amount of yuan received by the purchaser. Give your answer correct to the nearest yuan.

   b A tourist exchanges 5000 CNY into Malaysian ringgit. The money is left over after the holiday, however, so it is exchanged into euros ready for the next trip. A 1.5% commission applies to each transaction. Determine the amount of euros received, giving your answer correct to the nearest cent.

22 A ball is dropped from a height of 4 metres. After each bounce, the ball reaches 80% of its previous height.

   a Find the height reached by the ball after the:

        i first bounce   **ii** second bounce.

   b Assuming this trend continues, write an expression for the height reached by the ball after the nth bounce.

   c Determine the height reached by the ball after the 20th bounce. Write your answer correct to the nearest millimetre.

23 The probability of event A occurring in any given trial of an experiment is $P(A) = a$.

   a Write down $P(A')$.

   b Suppose two trials of the experiment are performed independently. Write in terms of a, the probability of:

        i A occurring exactly once   **ii** A occurring twice.

   c The probability of A occurring at least once in two independent trials is 0.94. Determine the value of a.

24 Consider the function $f(x) = -2 \times 3^x + 6$, where $x \in \mathbb{R}$.

   a Find the y-intercept.

   b Determine the value of y when $x = 2$ and when $x = -2$.

   c Determine the equation of the horizontal asymptote.

   d Sketch $y = -2 \times 3^x + 6$, showing the features you have found.

25 A solid metal spinning top is constructed by joining a hemispherical top to a cone-shaped base.

The radius of both the hemisphere and the base of the cone is 3 cm.

   a Calculate the volume of the hemispherical top.

   b Calculate the height of the cone-shaped base if its volume is half that of the hemisphere.

   c Hence, calculate the total outer surface area of the spinning top.

26   **a** Find the equation of the normal to $y = x^2 + \dfrac{3}{x} - 2$ at the point where $x = 1$.

   b Write down the coordinates of the point where this normal meets the curve again.

27 A small confectionery company produces x candy bars per day, where $x \leqslant 1500$.
For a given day, the cost per candy bar C depends on x, such that
$C(x) = 0.000\,004x^2 - 0.008x + 5$ dollars.

    a Calculate $C(1500)$, and interpret this value.   **b** Find $C'(x)$.

    c Solve $C'(x) = 0$.   **d** Determine the minimum daily cost per candy bar.

28 In July 2007, Fari purchased a car for €12 000. In July 2010, the car was valued at €8600.

    a Calculate the average annual rate of depreciation on the car.

    b If the car continued to depreciate at this same rate, find its value in July 2012.

29 The speed of sound in dry air at 20°C is 343 m s^{-1}. Calculate how many metres sound travels in one hour, giving your answer:

    a correct to two significant figures   **b** in scientific notation.

30 Propositions p and q are defined as follows: p: Antonio plays football.
                                                q: Antonio is good at kicking a ball.

    a Write the following in words:

        i $p \wedge \neg q$ **ii** $\neg q \Rightarrow p$

    b Write the following in symbolic language:

        i Antonio plays football or is good at kicking a ball, but not both.

        ii If Antonio does not play football, then he is not good at kicking a ball.

    c Use a truth table to show that the implication in **a ii** is not a tautology.

31 The sides of a right angled triangle are x cm, $(x + 3)$ cm, and $(x + 6)$ cm long.

    a Write a quadratic equation in x which links the three sides.

    b Solve the equation.

    c Hence find the area of the triangle.

32 A sail in the shape of a rhombus has sides of length 8 metres, and the longer diagonal has length 13 metres.

    a Draw a diagram and label the given information.

    b Find the length of the shorter diagonal of the rhombus.

    c Find the measure of the smaller angle in the rhombus.

33 The ages in months of 20 students are:

                     198, 192, 195, 194, 205, 208, 210, 200, 206, 203,
                     196, 198, 196, 201, 194, 198, 197, 195, 209, 204.

    a Find the:

        i median   **ii** range   **iii** interquartile range of the data.

    b Draw a box and whisker plot for the ages of the students.

34 Consider the function $f(x) = 2x^3 - 3x^{-2} - 24x + \frac{3}{4}$.

    a Find $f'(x)$.   **b** Write down the value of $f'(2)$.

    c Given $f(2) = -32$, find the equation of the tangent to $y = f(x)$ at the point where $x = 2$.
Write your answer in the form $ax + by = c$ where $a > 0$.

35 Last Tuesday, 48.47 Indian rupee (INR) was equivalent to 70.71 Japanese yen (JPY).

  a If the exchange rate of INR to JPY is written in the form $1 : a$, find the value of a. Give your answer correct to 5 significant figures.

  b Calculate the value of 2000 rupees in yen, correct to the nearest yen.

  c Calculate the value of 15 000 yen in rupees, correct to 2 decimal places.

36 The set $X = \{\frac{2}{7}, \sqrt{7}, 0, 2^{-4}, 0.\overline{1}, -1.2 \times 10^4\}$ is a subset of $\mathbb{R}$.

The Venn diagram alongside shows subsets of the real numbers.

Place each element of X on the Venn diagram.

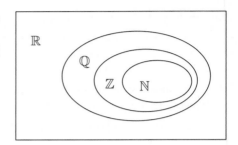

37 Two events A and B are independent. $P(A) = 0.1$ and $P(B) = 0.5$.

  a Calculate: **i** $P(A \cap B)$ **ii** $P(A \cup B)$ **iii** $P((A \cup B)')$

  b State, giving a reason, whether events A and B are mutually exclusive.

38 Triangle ABC has $A\widehat{C}B = 35°$, $AC = 14$ cm, and $AB = 17$ cm.

  a Sketch triangle ABC, showing all of the information provided. Your diagram does not need to be drawn to scale.

  b Calculate $A\widehat{B}C$ correct to 2 decimal places.

  c Determine the area of triangle ABC, correct to the nearest cm².

39 A group of students took an IQ test to measure their intelligence. The results were:

   119, 102, 89, 84, 85, 120, 90, 104, 95, 94, 89, 132

  a For this data, calculate the:

   i range   **ii** mean   **iii** standard deviation.

  b A result of two standard deviations above the mean is classified as "superior intelligence". What proportion of the students within this group have superior intelligence?

40 The graph of $y = f(x)$ is shown opposite, where $f(x) = ax^2 + bx + c$.

  a Copy and complete the table below using either *positive*, *negative*, or *zero*.

Constant	a	b	c
Value			

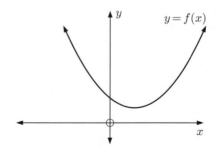

  b How many real zeros does $f(x)$ possess?

  c Another function $g(x)$ has the form $g(x) = px^2 + qx + r$, where p, q, and r are real constants with signs as follows:

Constant	p	q	r
Value	negative	positive	negative

Given that $g(x)$ has exactly one real zero, sketch a possible graph of $y = g(x)$.

41 A drug in the bloodstream of a patient t hours after being administered, has concentration $C(t) = 2t \times 3^{-t}$, where $0 \leqslant t \leqslant 8$.

    a Using your calculator, sketch the graph of $C(t)$ for the domain specified. Clearly show the coordinates of the local maximum.

    b For what time interval is the concentration of the drug:

        i decreasing   **ii** greater than 0.5?

42 £20 000 is to be invested for 4 years.

    a Calculate the final value of this investment if interest is offered at:

        i 5% p.a. compounded annually   **ii** 5% p.a. compounded monthly.

    b What is the percentage increase in the final value of the investment when the interest is compounded on a monthly basis, rather than annually?

43 Consider the Venn diagram shown.

    a List the letters in:

        i $A \cap B$ **ii** $(A \cup B)'$

        iii $A \cup B'$ **iv** $A' \cap B$

    b Determine:

        i $n(A \cup B)$ **ii** $n(A \cap B')$

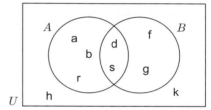

44 A bag contains 5 red, 3 yellow, and 2 green balloons. Without looking, Mary takes one balloon out of the bag and blows it up. She then takes out a second balloon. Find the probability that:

    a Mary selects a red balloon and then a yellow balloon

    b the second balloon is green, given that the first balloon is green

    c the first balloon is not red and the second balloon is red.

45 A quadratic function has x-intercepts -2 and 3, and the graph of the function passes through $(-3, 18)$.

    a Find the equation of the function. Write your answer in the form $y = ax^2 + bx + c$.

    b Write down the y-intercept.

    c Find the coordinates of the vertex of the graph.

46 The diagram shows the plan of a triangular garden bed. The garden bed will be enclosed by a 50 cm high wall and then filled with soil.

    a Calculate the length BC.

    b Calculate the area of the garden bed.

    c Find the volume of soil needed to fill the garden bed.

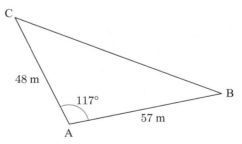

47 The following results were recorded in a recent Mathematical Studies test.

Score (%)	$50 \leqslant S < 60$	$60 \leqslant S < 70$	$70 \leqslant S < 80$	$80 \leqslant S < 90$	$90 \leqslant S < 100$
Frequency	6	15	20	10	4

    a Draw a table of cumulative frequencies.

    b Draw a cumulative frequency curve for this information.

    c Estimate the median score.

48 A and B are points on the curve $f(x) = 2x^3 - 5x^2 - 4x + 3$ at which the tangents to the curve are parallel to the x-axis.

   a Write down the gradient of the tangent at A.

   b Find the gradient function of the curve.

   c Find exactly the x-coordinates of points A and B.

49 $7000 is invested at 7.5% p.a. interest, compounding monthly.

   a Calculate the interest earned on this investment after 18 months.

   b How long will it take for the investment to earn $1700 in interest?

50 A running track consists of two straight segments joined by semi-circular ends, as shown.

   a If the total perimeter of the track is 1600 metres, determine the diameter of the semi-circular ends.

   b Jason takes 4 minutes and 25 seconds to complete a single lap of the track. Calculate Jason's average speed in $m\,s^{-1}$.

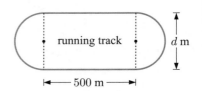

51 A group of 250 students of ages 13, 14, and 15 were asked to choose which of Art and Music they preferred. The results are shown in the table alongside.

	13	14	15	Total
Music	35	p	65	120
Art	55	q	r	130
Total	90	50	110	250

   a Calculate the values of p, q, and r.

   b A student from the group is selected at random. Calculate the probability that this student:

     i is 13 years old   **ii** is not 13 years old, and Music is their preferred subject

     iii is not 15 given that their preferred subject is Art.

52 The vertex of a quadratic function is $(2, -25)$, and one of the x-intercepts is -3.

   a Sketch the function, showing the information provided.

   b Write down the other x-intercept.

   c The quadratic function can be written in the form $y = a(x - p)(x - q)$.
Determine the values of: **i** p and q **ii** a.

53 Triangle ACH is isosceles with altitude 25 cm and base angles $\widehat{HAC} = \widehat{HCA} = 65°$.

   a Calculate the length of:

     i AH   **ii** AC

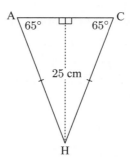

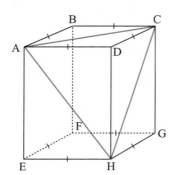

   b Triangle ACH lies within the square-based rectangular prism shown. Determine the volume of this square-based prism.

54 The curve with equation $y = x^3 - 4x^2 + 3x + 1$ passes through A(3, 1).

   a Find $\dfrac{dy}{dx}$.

   b Determine the equation of the tangent to this curve at A.

55 The straight line graph shows the relationship between Australian dollars and euros.

   a Estimate the value of:

     i 20 Australian dollars in euros

     ii 24 euros in Australian dollars.

   b Write down the exchange rate from Australian dollars to euros.

   c The sum of 75 000 AUD is converted into euros.   If the transaction is charged 2% commission, how many euros are actually received?

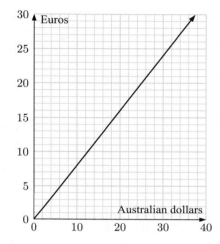

56 During a darts competition, players record their best 3-dart score out of 180. The results are shown below:

      132   146   154   113   126   140   137   148   156   133   121   102

      117   142   168   135   170   138   161   146   159   115   122   126

   a Determine the median score.   **b** Calculate the interquartile range.

   c Draw a box and whisker plot to display the data.

   d Use technology to find the standard deviation of the data.

57 A sequence is specified by the formula $t_n = 7n - 12$.

   a List the first three terms of the sequence.

   b Determine whether these terms form an arithmetic or geometric sequence.

   c Find the 100th term of the sequence.

   d Hence, or otherwise, find the sum of the first 100 terms.

58 Use Venn diagrams like the one alongside to illustrate the truth set for the compound propositions:

   a $p \wedge q$ **b** $\neg(p \vee q)$ **c** $p \veebar q$

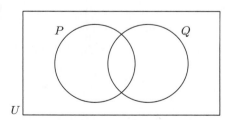

59 **a** The normal to $y = 3x^2 - ax + 2b$ at the point (1, 5) has equation $y = -\frac{1}{2}x + \frac{11}{2}$.
      Find a and b.

   b Find the coordinates of the point where the normal meets the x-axis.

60 The amount of petrol bought by customers at a service station is normally distributed with a mean of 33 litres and a standard deviation of 6.5 litres.

   a Copy and complete the values on the normal distribution curve below.

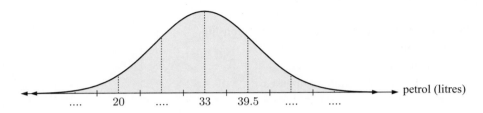

                 20   33   39.5   ....

   b Find the probability that a randomly chosen customer bought:

      i between 35 and 40 litres   **ii** at most 25 litres.

   c 30% of customers bought k or more litres of petrol. Find k.

   d In one day the service station had 500 customers. How many of these customers would be expected to buy less than 20 litres of petrol?

61 Nunu performs a chi-squared test to see if there is any association between the *time taken to travel to work* in the morning (short time or long time) and the *quality of work* she accomplishes in the day (good or poor). She performs this test at the 5% level of significance.

   a Write down the null and alternate hypotheses.

   b Determine the number of degrees of freedom for this test.

   c The p-value for Nunu's test is 0.082. What conclusion can be drawn? Justify your answer.

62 Consider $f(x) = x^3 - 4x^2 + 4x - 2$.

   a Find $f'(x)$.

   b Solve $f'(x) = 0$.

   c Draw a sign diagram for $f'(x)$.

   d Find intervals where $f(x)$ is increasing or decreasing.

63 **a** On the same set of axes, draw the graphs of $y = 2x - 12$ and $2x - 3y = 24$.

   b Find the coordinates of A, the intersection point of the two lines.

   c Find the equation of the line perpendicular to $2x - 3y = 24$ and passing through A.

64 Triangle LMO has $\widehat{LMO} = 120°$, $LM = 3$ cm, $LO = 21$ cm, and $MO = x$ cm.

   a Evaluate $\cos 120°$.

   b Using the cosine rule, show that $x^2 + 3x - 432 = 0$.

   c Hence, find x correct to 3 significant figures.

   d Find the perimeter of triangle LMO.

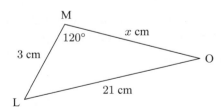

65 A circle has area 300 cm^2.

   a Find the radius of the circle correct to 3 decimal places.

   b Find the circumference of the circle correct to 2 significant figures.

66 For two events A and B, it is known that $P(A) = \frac{2}{5}$, $P(B) = \frac{3}{10}$, and $P(B \mid A) = \frac{1}{2}$.

   a Calculate $P(A \cap B)$.

   b Show that A and B are not independent.

   c Calculate $P(A \mid B)$.

67 The weekly income $£I$ of an employee varies depending on their total weekly sales $£S$. The chart alongside shows the relationship between I and S.

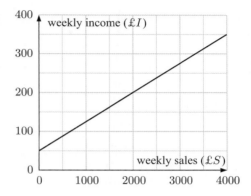

   a Use the graph to determine the employee's weekly income if:

   i no sales are made

   ii £2000 in sales are made.

   b In a given week an employee earns £275. Use the graph to estimate their total sales for that week.

   c The formula connecting I and S has the form $I = rS + t$, where r and t are both constants. Calculate the values of r and t.

68 A function f is defined by $f(x) = x^2 + \dfrac{2}{x}$ for $-4 \leqslant x \leqslant 4$.

   a Sketch $y = f(x)$ for the region $-4 \leqslant x \leqslant 4$, $-15 \leqslant y \leqslant 15$.

   b Using technology, write down the coordinates of the local minimum.

   c Hence, find the intervals in the given domain where $f(x)$ is decreasing.

69

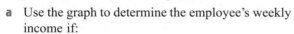

The examination marks for 200 students are displayed on the cumulative frequency graph shown. The pass mark for the examination was 30.

   a What percentage of the students passed?

   b A box and whisker plot for the examination data is:

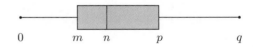

Use the graph to estimate:

   i m **ii** n **iii** p **iv** q

70 A geometric sequence has its general term given by $u_n = 6(1.2)^{n-1}$.

   a Write down the first two terms of the sequence.

   b Find the first term of the sequence which is greater than 30.

   c Another geometric sequence has first term 2 and common ratio 1.35. Find the first term of this sequence which is greater than the equivalent term of the first sequence.

71 Consider a game in which the player rolls a single die once. The player wins \$2 for rolling a 1, \$3 for rolling a 2, 3, or 4, and \$5 for rolling a 5 or 6. The game costs \$4 to play.

   a If the game is played 150 times, how many times would you expect the player to roll a 5 or 6?

   b Calculate the expected result from playing this game once.

   c Determine whether the game is fair.

72 Use logic symbols to describe the shaded area on the following Venn diagrams:

   a
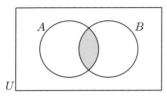

   b
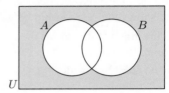

   c
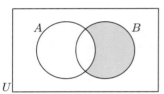

   d
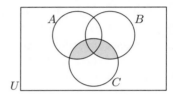

73 The functions f and g are defined for $-5 \leqslant x \leqslant 5$ by $f(x) = \dfrac{x}{x-2}$, $x \neq 2$ and $g(x) = x$.

   a Sketch the graphs of $y = f(x)$ and $y = g(x)$ on the same set of axes.

   b Write down the equations of the horizontal and vertical asymptotes of $y = f(x)$.

   c Find the solutions of $\dfrac{x}{x-2} = x$.

74 For the solid shown, find:

   a the length of AE

   b the length of BE

   c the angle BE makes with the base ADEF.

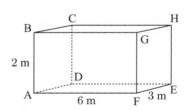

75 Consider the following data regarding the time to complete a task compared with a person's age.

Age x (years)	12	18	26	31	36	42
Time y (minutes)	22	30	24	28	26	23

   a Use your graphics calculator to find the equation of the regression line for y in terms of x.

   b Use your equation to estimate the time for a person aged 28 years to complete the task.

   c Use your graphics calculator to find the correlation coefficient r.

   d Comment on the reliability of your answer to **b**.

76 The profit when m machines are sold by a firm each month can be determined by the function $P(m) = 60m - 800 - m^2$ thousand dollars, where $0 \leqslant m \leqslant 40$.

   a Write down a function for the rate of change in the profit for a given change in the number of machines sold by the firm.

   b Show that the monthly profit is maximised when 30 machines are sold.

   c Calculate the maximum monthly profit.

77 Consider the function $f(x) = \frac{1}{2}x^3 - 2x^2 - 4x + 6$.

    a Find the axes intercepts.
    b Find the position and nature of any turning points.

    c Find $f(-3)$ and $f(6)$.
    d Sketch the function on the domain $-3 \leqslant x \leqslant 6$.

    e Find the greatest and least value of $f(x)$ on the domain $-3 \leqslant x \leqslant 6$.

78 A student has access to two printers, A and B. The probability that printer A malfunctions is 1%, and the probability that printer B malfunctions is 2%. When attempting to print, the student always tries printer A first. Printer B is only used if printer A malfunctions.

    a Complete the tree diagram by filling in the missing values.

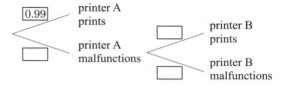

    b When the student tries to print a one page document, determine the probability that:
      i both printers malfunction
      ii printer B prints the document
      iii printer A prints the document, given that the document is printed.

79 The speed of sound can be found using the formula $S = 331.3 + 0.606T$ $\mathrm{m\,s^{-1}}$, where T is the temperature of the air in degrees Celsius.

    a Determine the speed of sound at 20°C. Do not round your answer.

    b Determine the distance sound travels in 10 minutes at 20°C. Write your answer in the form $a \times 10^k$, where $1 \leqslant a < 10$ and $k \in \mathbb{Z}$.

    c On a hot day, the temperature rises from 20°C to 45°C. Calculate the percentage increase in the speed of sound which results from this change in air temperature.

80 **a** Sketch the graph of $y = \dfrac{3}{x} - 2$ on the domain $-5 \leqslant x \leqslant 5$.

    b Write down the equation of the vertical asymptote.

    c Find the equation of the normal at the point where $x = 3$.

81 Line A has equation $y = 2x + 5$.   Line B has equation $x - 4y = 8$.   Point P is the y-intercept of line A and point Q is the x-intercept of line B.

    a Write down the coordinates of:
      i P
      ii Q.

    b Calculate the gradient of PQ.

    c Hence, or otherwise, calculate the *acute* angle PQ makes with the x-axis.

    d Line A and line B intersect at R. Find the coordinates of R.

82 Line S has equation $2x + y = -2$.

    a Write down the gradient of S.

    b Line T is parallel to line S and passes through A(1, 4).
      Find the equation of line T.

    c Line T is a tangent to the quadratic $y = x^2 + bx + c$ at A.
      Find b and c.

83 Consider the scatter diagrams shown below.

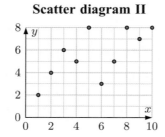

a For each of the cases shown, is the association between x and y positive, negative, or zero?

b Complete the table by matching each description with scatter diagram I, II, or III.

Strength of correlation	Scatter diagram
Weak	
Moderate	
Strong	

84 A teacher recorded the number of children who used the school's playground each day for 50 days. The results are displayed alongside.

Number of children	Frequency
21 - 30	8
31 - 40	16
41 - 50	14
51 - 60	12
Total	50

a On how many days was the playground used by more than 40 children?

b Find the modal class.

c Draw a column graph to display the data.

d Estimate the   **i** mean   **ii** standard deviation of the data.

85 Usain Bolt set a world record at the Beijing Olympics by running the 100 m sprint in 9.69 seconds.

a Calculate his average speed for this race in metres per second, giving your answer correct to 2 decimal places.

b Convert this speed to kilometres per hour.

86 The Venn diagram shows the number of students in a group who play soccer (S), rugby (R), or do track (T).

a Find the total number of students in the group.

b Find the probability that a randomly chosen student:

   i plays only rugby

   ii takes soccer and track only

   iii plays soccer, given that he or she plays rugby.

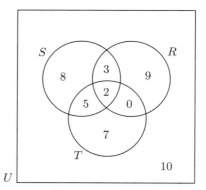

87 The value of a car over time is calculated using the function $v = 24\,000r^t$ dollars, where t is the number of years after it was first purchased, $t \geqslant 0$, and r is a constant, $0 < r < 1$.

a Write down the value of the car when it was first purchased.

b The value of the car after one year was $20\,400. Find the value of r.

c How long will it take for the value of the car to reduce to $8000? Give your answer to the nearest year.

88 ABCD is a trapezium with BC parallel to AD.
AD = 22 cm, BC = 12 cm, AB = 13 cm, and
AE = 5 cm.

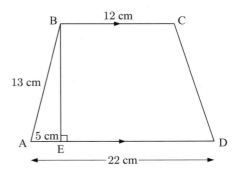

   a Calculate the height BE of the trapezium.

   b Calculate:

      i $B\widehat{A}E$ **ii** $A\widehat{B}C$

   c Calculate the length of the diagonal AC.

89 The diagram alongside shows the graphs of
$f(x) = -\frac{1}{2}x^2 + 3$ and $y = x - 1$.

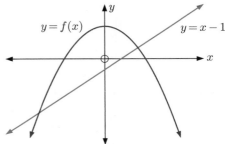

   a Find $f'(x)$.

   b Find the coordinates of the point on $f(x)$
where the tangent is parallel to $y = x - 1$.

90 Ten students were given aptitude tests on language skills and mathematics. The table below shows
the results:

Language (x)	12.5	15.0	10.5	12.0	9.5	10.5	15.5	10.0	14.0	12.0
Mathematics (y)	32	45	27	38	18	25	35	22	40	40

   a Plot the data on a scatter diagram.

   b Find the correlation coefficient r.

   c Use your results to comment on the statement:

      "Those who do well in language also do well in mathematics."

91 Consider the function $f(x) = \dfrac{8}{x^2} + 2x - 3$.

   a Differentiate $f(x)$ with respect to x.   **b** Find $f'(1)$ and explain what it represents.

   c Find the coordinates of the point where the gradient of the curve is zero.

92 **a** Complete the truth table for the compound proposition $\neg b \wedge (c \Rightarrow (b \wedge a)) \Rightarrow \neg c$

a	b	c	$\neg b$	$b \wedge a$	$c \Rightarrow (b \wedge a)$	$\neg b \wedge (c \Rightarrow (b \wedge a))$	$\neg c$	$\neg b \wedge (c \Rightarrow (b \wedge a)) \Rightarrow \neg c$
T	T	T						
T	T	F						
T	F	T						
T	F	F						
F	T	T						
F	T	F						
F	F	T						
F	F	F						

   b Is the proposition $\neg b \wedge (c \Rightarrow (b \wedge a)) \Rightarrow \neg c$ a tautology, a contradiction, or neither?

93 Melissa deposits €5000 into a bank account which pays 6% p.a. interest compounding quarterly. No extra money is deposited or withdrawn.

   a Determine the total value of the investment after:

      i 1 year   **ii** 2 years.

   b Write down a formula for the total value of the investment after n years.

   c Calculate the number of years required for Melissa to double her original deposit.

94 Let $a = 3.5$, $b = 1.2$, $c = 0.4$, and $d = -8$. Find the value of $\dfrac{5(a - d)^2}{b - c}$, giving your answer:

   a to 3 decimal places   **b** to 2 significant figures

   c in the form $a \times 10^k$, where $1 \leqslant a < 10$ and $k \in \mathbb{Z}$.

95 Consider A$(-4, 2)$ and B$(6, 6)$.

   a Write down the coordinates of M, the midpoint of the line segment AB.

   b Find the gradient of AB.

   c Line L is perpendicular to AB and passes through M. Determine the equation of line L, giving your answer in the form $ax + by + d = 0$.

   d Calculate the x-intercept of line L.

96 Greg needs to travel from Australia to Sweden for work. Prior to leaving, he converts Australian dollars (AUD) into Swedish kronor (SEK). The bank offers the rates in the table shown.

1 AUD	Buy	Sell
SEK	7.08	7.11

   a If Greg exchanges 1000 Australian dollars into Swedish kronor, how much will he receive?

   b If Greg immediately exchanged his Swedish kronor back into Australian dollars, how much would he receive?

   c Calculate the percentage loss if Greg converted his money from AUD into SEK and immediately back into AUD.

97 The manager of a bank decides to investigate the time customers wait to be served. Most of the results are shown in the table below, and they are illustrated in the cumulative frequency graph alongside it.

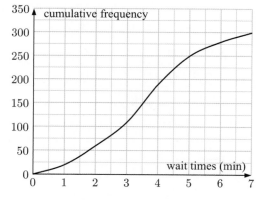

Waiting time (t) in minutes	Frequency
$0 \leqslant t < 1$	p
$1 \leqslant t < 2$	40
$2 \leqslant t < 3$	50
$3 \leqslant t < 4$	80
$4 \leqslant t < 5$	60
$5 \leqslant t < 6$	q
$6 \leqslant t < 7$	20

   a Use the graph to estimate the median waiting time.

   b Determine the values of p and q.

   c Hence, draw a frequency histogram for the data.

98 The graph shows $y = \dfrac{4}{x}$ for $x > 0$.

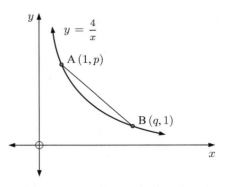

Points $A(1, p)$ and $B(q, 1)$ lie on the curve.

  a Determine the value of:

   i p **ii** q

  b Evaluate the gradient of line segment AB.

  c Point C also lies on $y = \dfrac{4}{x}$. The tangent at C is parallel to AB. Determine the coordinates of C.

99 A woman deposits $100 into her son's savings account on his first birthday. She deposits $125 on his second birthday, $150 on his third birthday, and so on.

  a Calculate the amount of money she will deposit into her son's account on his 15th birthday.

  b Find the total amount she will have deposited over the 15 years.

100 The table shows the frequencies of the ages of students at a school.

  a If a student is randomly selected from this school, find the probability that the student is:

   i 13 or 14 years old

   ii 15 years of age or older.

  b Given that a randomly selected student is older than 14, find the probability that the student is not 17.

Age (years)	Frequency
13	48
14	75
15	84
16	60
17	33
Total	300

101 The graph shows the function $f(x) = 3.5 - k^{-x}$, where k is a positive constant.

The point $(-1, 2)$ lies on the graph.

  a Write down the coordinates of the y-intercept, P.

  b Find the value of k.

  c Find the equation of the horizontal asymptote, L.

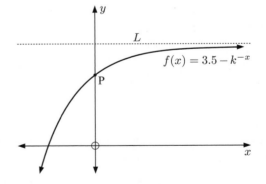

102 The table shows the amount of petrol remaining in a motorbike's fuel tank and the number of kilometres travelled. The capacity of the tank is 10 litres.

Remaining fuel x (litres)	10	8	6	4	2	1
Distance y (km)	0	90	190	260	330	370

  a Plot this data on a scatter diagram.

  b Write down the equation of the straight line of regression for y against x.

  c The motorbike has travelled 220 km since its tank was refilled. Use your regression equation to estimate the amount of fuel left in the tank.

  d Find the average distance travelled per litre over the 220 km.

103

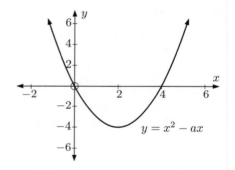

The figure shows two adjacent triangular fields ABC and ACD. AD = 30 m, CD = 80 m, BC = 75 m, $A\widehat{D}C = 60°$, and $B\widehat{A}C = 60°$.

  a Calculate the length of AC.

  b Calculate the size of $A\widehat{B}C$.

  c Find the total area of the fields.

104 $10\,000 is invested at 8.5% p.a. interest compounded monthly over 5 years. Find:

  a the value of the investment after 5 years

  b the amount of interest earned

  c how much more interest would have been earned if the interest rate had been 9.5% p.a.

105 The diagram shows the graph of $y = x^2 - ax$.

  a Find the value of a.

  b Find $\dfrac{dy}{dx}$.

  c Find the coordinates of the minimum point.

  d Find the gradient of the tangent to the curve at $x = 3$.

106 Suppose $a = \frac{3}{7}$, $b = 8$, $c = \sqrt{2}$, and $d = 1 \times 10^{-2}$. Classify each of the following statements as true or false:

  a $7a \in \mathbb{N}$ **b** $c^2 - b \notin \mathbb{N}$ **c** $\dfrac{1}{d} \geqslant c^b$

  d $\dfrac{c}{b} \in \mathbb{Q}$ **e** $\sqrt{a - b} \in \mathbb{R}$ **f** $\dfrac{b}{d} \in \mathbb{Z}$

107 For the two events A and B, $P(A) = \frac{3}{7}$ and $P(B') = \frac{2}{3}$.

  a Determine $P(B)$.

  b Calculate $P(A \cup B)$ if A and B are:

    i mutually exclusive   **ii** independent.

108 Margaret picked some mandarins from a tree, and counted the number of seeds in each. Her results are shown in the boxplot below.

Find the:

  a median   **b** interquartile range   **c** range of the data.

109 A χ^2 test at a 5% significance level is used to determine whether *intelligence* is independent of *income level*. For this test, intelligence and income were each split into three classes. The resulting χ^2 test statistic was 8.23.

    a State the null and alternative hypotheses.

    b Determine the number of degrees of freedom.

    c Given that the critical value for this test is ≈ 9.49, what conclusion can be drawn regarding *intelligence* and *income level*?

110 Let $f(x) = \frac{1}{4}x^4 - 2x^2$.

    a Find $f'(x)$.

    b Evaluate $f'(-3)$, $f'(-2)$, and $f'(-1)$.

    c Hence, describe what happens to $f(x)$ at $x = -2$.

    d The graph of $y = f(x)$ has exactly 3 turning points. Given $(0,\,0)$ is a local maximum and $(2,\,-4)$ is a local minimum, write down the intervals for which $f(x)$ is increasing.

111 $P(-3,\,0)$, $Q(0,\,4)$, and $R(8,\,0)$ are the vertices of a triangle. The length of QR is $\sqrt{80}$ units.

    a Calculate the length of: **i** PR   **ii** PQ.

    b Determine the size of angle QPR, giving your answer correct to 2 decimal places.

    c Calculate the area of triangle PQR.

112 Consider the following currency conversions between US dollars (USD), Mexican pesos (MXN), and euros (EUR).

$$1 \text{ USD} = 14 \text{ MXN}$$
$$1 \text{ USD} = 0.79 \text{ EUR}$$

    a Convert 2750 US dollars into:

        i Mexican pesos   **ii** euros.

    b Write down the exchange rate from euros to:

        i US dollars   **ii** Mexican pesos.

    c Hence, convert 5100 euros into Mexican pesos.

113 The graph alongside shows the curve $y = a(2^x) + b$, where a and b are constants.

    a Find the values of a and b.

    b Find y when $x = 6$.

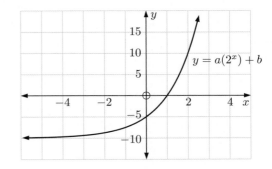

114 The fourth term of an arithmetic sequence is 22 and the tenth term is 70. Suppose the first term is u_1 and the common difference is d.

    a Write down two equations in u_1 and d that satisfy this information.

    b Solve the equations to find the values of u_1 and d.

    c Find the sum of the first 10 terms of the sequence.

115 The table shows the number of left and right handed writers in a sample of 50 students.

	Left handed	Right handed	Total
Male	4	26	30
Female			20
Total	7		50

    a Complete the table.

    b If a student is selected at random from the group, find the probability that the student is:

       i left handed   **ii** male and right handed

       iii right handed, given that the student is female.

116 Find the value of k if the lines $4x - 5y = 11$ and $2x + ky = -8$ are:

    a parallel   **b** perpendicular.

117 The scatter diagram displays the amount James spends on coffee in the cafeteria against the number of hours he works in the week.

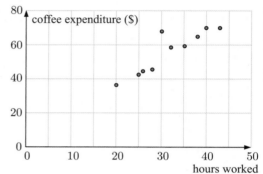

    a Over a period of weeks, James worked an average of 32 hours, and his average expenditure was $56 per week. Plot the mean point P(32, 56) on the graph.

    b Draw the line of best fit passing through P.

    c Use this line to predict the amount James will spend on coffee if he works a 35 hour week.

    d Describe the nature and strength of the linear relationship between the length of time James works and the amount he spends on coffee. Comment on whether the predicted quantity found in **c** is a reliable estimate.

118 A straight line L has equation $54x - 2y = 17$.

    a Find the gradient of the line.

    b A curve has equation $y - x^3 = -12$, $0 \leqslant x \leqslant 5$. Find the gradient function for the curve.

    c A tangent to the curve at point P is parallel to the straight line L. Find the coordinates of P.

119 Consider the function $f(x) = x^3 + \dfrac{5}{x}$.

    a Find $f'(x)$.   **b** Find $f'(1)$, and interpret your answer.

    c Hence, find the equation of the tangent to $f(x)$ when $x = 1$.

    d Find the equation of the normal to $f(x)$ when $x = 1$.

    e Use technology to find the point where the normal meets the graph of $y = f(x)$ again.

120 A group of 50 employees were surveyed regarding their interest in music, sport, and computers. The number of employees interested in each area is shown in the Venn diagram.

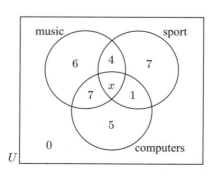

    a Write down the value of x.

    b If an employee is selected at random, determine the probability that they are:

       i interested in music

      ii interested in music, sport, and computers

      iii not interested in computers

      iv interested in sport, given that they are interested in music.

121 The tangent to the curve $y = ax^2 - \dfrac{b}{x}$ at $x = -0.5$ is horizontal.

a Show that $a = 4b$.

b Given that the tangent at $x = -0.5$ has the equation $y = 3$,   show that $a + 8b = 12$.

c Use the equations from a and b to determine the values of a and b.

122 Brian deposits £x into his daughter's bank account on her 1st birthday. On her second birthday, he deposits £$1.5x$ into the account, and he continues to add £$0.5x$ to the amount deposited for each subsequent birthday. The final deposit is made on her 20th birthday.

a Write down, in terms of x, the amount Brian deposits into his daughter's bank account on her 3rd birthday.

b Show that the total amount of birthday money Brian deposits is £$115x$.

c For the total amount of birthday money to reach £20 000, find the value of x. Round your answer to the next whole number.

123 Consider the triangle alongside.

a Find the perimeter of the triangle.

b Find the area of the triangle, giving your answer in:

i square metres   ii hectares.

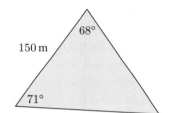

124 Line L_1 passes through $(0, 3)$ and $(6, 0)$.

Line L_2 has equation $y = -\frac{1}{2}x - 4$.

a Show that L_1 is parallel to L_2.

b Line L_3 is perpendicular to L_1 and meets L_1 at $(0, 3)$. Write down the equation of L_3, giving your answer in the form $y = ax + b$.

c At what point does line L_2 meet L_3?

d Calculate the perpendicular distance d between L_1 and L_2.

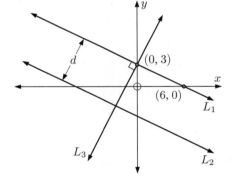

125 The table and histogram below represent the same set of data.

Score (s)	Frequency (f)	$s \times f$
11	2	22
12	w	x
13	5	65
14	2	28
15	4	60
Totals	y	z

a Determine the mode of the data.

b Determine the value of:

i w ii x iii y iv z

c Evaluate $\dfrac{z}{y}$ and interpret its meaning.

126 ¥600 000 is to be invested for 6 years.

   a Society Bank offers a return of 7% p.a. interest compounding annually. Calculate the amount of interest this account will generate over the 6 year period.

   b Corporate Credit Union offers a return of r% p.a. interest compounded monthly. What rate r is needed for Corporate Credit Union to match the amount of interest offered by Society Bank?

127 The nth term of an arithmetic sequence is given by $u_n = 63 - 4n$.

   a Calculate the first two terms of this sequence.

   b Which term of the sequence is -13?

   c Two consecutive terms of this sequence, u_k and u_{k+1}, have the sum 34. Find k.

128 A box contains 8 red pens and 12 green pens. Juanita takes one pen from the box and notes its colour. She then takes a second pen from the box without replacing the first pen.

   a Complete the tree diagram alongside to show all probabilities.

   b Find the probability that she chooses:

     i two red pens

     ii at least one green pen.

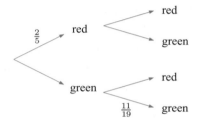

129 A flu virus spreads in a school according to the exponential model $N = 4 \times 1.332^t$ where N is the number of people who have caught the virus, and t is the number of days after the virus was first detected, $t \geqslant 0$.

   a Find the number of people who were initially infected.

   b Calculate the number of people who were infected after 16 days.

   c There are 1200 people in the school. Estimate the time it will take for everybody in the school to catch the flu.

130 OABCD is a square based pyramid with base sides of length 4 cm. Each slant edge of the pyramid is 7 cm long. OX is the perpendicular height of the pyramid.

   a Calculate the length of BX.

   b Calculate the angle between the line OB and the base ABCD. Give your answer to the nearest degree.

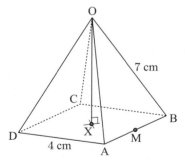

131 A 60 cm length of wire is bent into a rectangle with length x cm and width y cm.

   a Write an expression for y in terms of x.

   b Write an expression for the area $A(x)$ of the rectangle enclosed by the wire.

   c Find $A'(x)$.

   d Hence determine the value of x which maximises the area. What are the dimensions of the rectangle in this case?

132 The table shows the sizes of drinks purchased from a store at different times of the day.

	Small	Medium	Large
Morning	15	23	4
Afternoon	24	24	11
Evening	6	18	8

    a Write a suitable null hypothesis for a χ^2 test on this data.

    b Use technology to find the value of χ^2.

    c Determine the number of degrees of freedom.

    d Given that the critical value at the 5% level of significance is 9.488, what conclusion can be drawn from this test? Justify your answer.

133 A car was purchased 5 years ago for $21 000. It depreciated in value by 15% in the first year, 12.5% in the second year, and 10% in the third year.

    a Find the value of the car after 3 years.

    b Find the average annual rate of depreciation for the first 3 years. Give your answer correct to 3 decimal places.

    c If the car depreciated over the 5 years by the average rate found in **b**, find the current value of the car.

134 Consider the following argument:

    Jane ate an apple or a banana, but not both.

    Jane did not eat a banana.

    Therefore, Jane ate an apple.

    a Use the propositions a: Jane ate an apple   and b: Jane ate a banana   to write the argument in logical form.

    b Construct a truth table to show that the argument is valid.

135 The histogram shows the frequencies of a set of lengths.

    a Copy and complete the table below using information from the histogram.

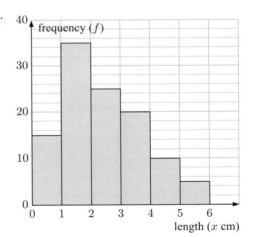

Length x (cm)	Frequency (f)	Cumulative frequency
$0 \leqslant x < 1$	15	15
$1 \leqslant x < 2$	35	50
$2 \leqslant x < 3$	25	75
$3 \leqslant x < 4$	20	95
$4 \leqslant x < 5$		
$5 \leqslant x < 6$		

    b Draw a cumulative frequency graph to represent this data.

    c Hence, estimate Q_3, the 75th percentile.

136 Suppose A and B are two events such that $P(A) = 0.7$, $P(B) = 0.5$, and $P(A \cup B) = 0.9$.

    a Find:

        i $P(A \cap B)$ **ii** $P(A \mid B)$ **iii** $P(B \mid A)$

    b Are A and B independent?

137 The statement *"If I watch a movie then I will relax"* consists of two propositions p and q such that $p \Rightarrow q$.

   a State p and q in words.

   b Under what conditions is the statement $p \Rightarrow q$ false?

   c In words, write down the contrapositive to $p \Rightarrow q$.

   d By completing the truth table below, show that the implication $p \Rightarrow q$ is logically equivalent to its contrapositive.

					Contrapositive to $p \Rightarrow q$
p	q	$\neg p$	$\neg q$	$p \Rightarrow q$	
T	T				
T	F				
F	T				
F	F				

138 BCDE is the square base of the pyramid ABCDE. O is the centre of BCDE, and the vertex A sits directly above O. M is the midpoint of CD.

   a If A sits 12 cm directly above O, and AM is 13 cm in length, calculate the length of OM.

   b Calculate the volume of the pyramid.

   c What angle do the triangular sides of the pyramid make with the square base?

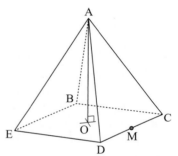

139 An arithmetic sequence begins with the terms 21, 29, 37, 45, ...

   a Write an expression for:

   i the nth term   **ii** the sum of the first n terms.

   b Hence, determine the exact value of:

   i the 50th term   **ii** the sum of the first 50 terms.

140 A tightrope connects two elevated platforms A and B. The curve of a tightrope between these platforms is given by the equation $y = 0.008x^2 - 0.8x + 50$. The units are metres.

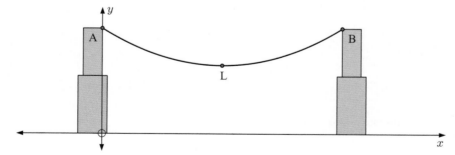

   a Find the height of the platform at A.

   b Given that platform B has the same height as platform A, determine:

   i the distance between the two platforms

   ii the domain for which $y = 0.008x^2 - 0.8x + 50$ represents the tightrope.

   c L is the lowest point along the tightrope. Determine the coordinates of L.

B   LONG QUESTIONS

EXERCISE 22B

1 A competition offers three options for the first prize, each of which pays the winner a monthly sum for 24 months.

   Option 1: $8000 per month.

   Option 2: $1000 in the first month, then each successive month pays $600 more than the previous month.

   Option 3: $500 in the first month, then each successive month pays 20% more than the previous month.

   a Calculate the total prize value for *Option 1*.

   b For *Option 2*:

       i write down the amount won in each of the first three months

       ii calculate the total amount won over the 24 month period.

   c For *Option 3*:

       i write down the amount won in each of the first three months

       ii calculate the total amount won over the 24 month period.

   d Which option is worth the greatest amount of money overall?

   e The amount won in the first month under *Option 3* is to be altered so that the total prize over 24 months is $250 000. Calculate the new initial amount, writing your answer to the nearest cent.

2 A jukebox contains 100 different songs, 60 of which are classified as rock songs. Songs from the jukebox are played at random and can be repeated.

   a If two songs are played, what is the probability that:

       i both are rock songs   **ii** one is a rock song   **iii** neither is a rock song?

   b Explain why the sum of the results in **a** is 1.

   c If three songs are played consecutively, determine the probability that they are all rock songs.

   d The jukebox is altered so that once a song has been played, it cannot be repeated until all the songs are played. Using R to represent the event of a rock song being played, complete a tree diagram showing the possible outcomes for the first three songs.

   Hence, or otherwise, determine the probability that:

       i exactly one of the first three songs is a rock song

       ii at least one of the first three songs is a rock song.

3 Consider the function $f(x) = \dfrac{4}{x-1} + 2$.

   a Find the axes intercepts for the graph $y = f(x)$.

   b Determine the equations of the horizontal and vertical asymptotes of the function.

   c Hence, write down the domain and range of the function.

   d Draw the graphs of $y = f(x)$ and $y = x + 1$ on the same set of axes.

   e Hence solve the equation $\dfrac{4}{x-1} + 2 = x + 1$.

4 Line S has equation $3x + 4y = 24$. It intersects the x-axis at A and the y-axis at B.

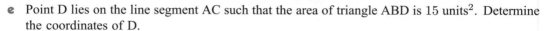

  a Write down the coordinates of:

    i A   **ii** B.

  b Determine the:

    i gradient of AB

    ii distance between A and B.

  c Line T is drawn through point B perpendicular to line S. Determine the equation of line T.

  d Line T cuts the x-axis at C. Calculate the area of triangle ABC.

  e Point D lies on the line segment AC such that the area of triangle ABD is 15 units^2. Determine the coordinates of D.

5 To test the difficulty level of a new computer game, a company measures the time taken for a group of players to complete the game. Their results are displayed in the table opposite.

Completion time (minutes)	Number of players
$0 \leqslant t < 30$	1
$30 \leqslant t < 60$	4
$60 \leqslant t < 90$	12
$90 \leqslant t < 120$	18
$120 \leqslant t < 150$	7
$150 \leqslant t < 180$	2

  a How many players were surveyed?

  b Write down the modal class.

  c Using graph paper, draw a cumulative frequency graph for the data. Use 1 cm to represent 15 minutes on the horizontal axis, and 1 cm to represent 4 individuals on the vertical axis.

  d The game is considered too easy if either the mean or median completion time is below 90 minutes.

    i Estimate the median completion time using your cumulative frequency graph.

    ii Estimate the mean completion time using your calculator.

    iii Hence, comment on whether the game is too easy.

  e Complete the sentence below:

  The middle 50% of players completed the game in times between .... and .... minutes.

6 Let $f(x) = x^3 - 6x^2 + px + q$, where p and q are real constants.

  a Find $f'(x)$.

  b The graph $y = f(x)$ has a local maximum at $(1, 7)$. Find the values of p and q.

  c By solving $f'(x) = 0$, determine the coordinates of a local minimum of the function.

  d Sketch $y = f(x)$ on the region $-1 \leqslant x \leqslant 5$, $-10 \leqslant y \leqslant 25$. Clearly show all turning points and axes intercepts.

  e Consider the tangent to $y = f(x)$ at $(1, 7)$.

    i Add this tangent to your sketch from **d**.

    ii Write down the equation of this tangent.

    iii At what other point does the tangent meet the curve?

7 A cylinder with base radius r cm has volume 250π cm^3.

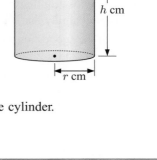

h cm

r cm

  a Show that $h = \dfrac{250}{r^2}$.

  b Hence show that the surface area of the cylinder is
    $$S = 2\pi r^2 + \frac{500\pi}{r} \quad \text{cm}^2.$$

  c Find $\dfrac{dS}{dr}$.

  d Find r such that $\dfrac{dS}{dr} = 0$.

  e Hence, find the radius which minimises the surface area of the cylinder.

  f Find the surface area of the cylinder in this case.

8 The racquet sports offered at a local club are tennis (T), badminton (B), and squash (S). The Venn diagram shows the number of members involved in these activities. All of the members play at least one racquet sport.

  a Write down the number of members in the club.

  b Write down the number of members who:

    i only play badminton

    ii do not play tennis

    iii play both tennis and squash, but not badminton.

  c Is $\{\ \} \subset B$?

  d Copy the diagram above, and shade the region that represents $S \cap (T \cup B)$.

  e Write down the number of members in $S \cap (T \cup B)'$.

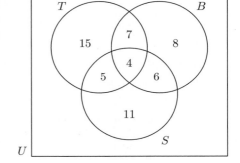

9 A bag contains 5 red marbles and 3 green marbles.

  a One marble is taken out of the bag. Find the probability that the marble is:

    i not red   **ii** red or green.

  b One marble is taken out and its colour noted before it is returned to the bag. A second marble is then taken out of the bag. Find the probability that:

    i both marbles are red   **ii** at least one marble is red.

  c Two marbles are taken out of the bag at the same time. Find the probability that:

    i both marbles are green   **ii** exactly one marble is green.

  d Three marbles are taken out of the bag at the same time. Find the probability that exactly two of them are red.

10 The vertices of a triangle are P(3, 5), Q(10, 6), and R(a, 4). R is in the first quadrant. The distance PR equals the distance PQ.

  a Calculate the distance PQ.   **b** Find the value of a.

  c Find the gradient of the line PQ.   **d** Find the equation of the line PQ.

  e The line PQ meets the x-axis at S. Write down the coordinates of S.

  f Find the angle between the x-axis and the line RS.

11 Scientists are monitoring a population of wild ferrets. Their lengths are normally distributed with mean 50 cm and standard deviation 2.2 cm.

a A scientist captures one of the ferrets at random. Find the probability that the ferret is no more than 45 cm long.

b Find the proportion of ferrets measuring between 52 cm and 56 cm long.

c In a colony of 150 ferrets, how many would you expect to measure at least 48 cm in length?

d The longest 10% of ferrets are at least k cm long. Find k.

12 The lengths and weights of 10 melons are shown in the table below.

Length x (cm)	32	40	43	36	42	35	38	46	36	44
Weight y (kg)	1.9	2.8	2.8	2.4	2.5	2.3	2.6	2.8	2.0	2.5

a Plot this information on a scatter diagram. Use a scale of 1 cm to represent 5 cm on the x-axis, and 1 cm to represent 0.25 kg on the y-axis.

b Use your graphics calculator to calculate the linear correlation coefficient r. What does this value tell you about the relationship between the two variables?

c Use your graphics calculator to determine the equation of the least squares regression line. Draw this line on your graph.

d Use the line on your graph to estimate:

   i the weight of a melon of length 35 cm   ii the length of a melon of weight 2.5 kg.

13 Consider the function $f(x) = x^3 - 4x^2 + 3x - 4$.

a Evaluate $f(0)$, $f(1)$, and $f(2)$.   b Find $f'(x)$.

c Write down the coordinates of the points where $f'(x) = 0$.

d Describe the nature of each point found in c.

e Sketch the graph of $y = f(x)$ for $-2 \leqslant x \leqslant 4$.

14 A group of friends meet each week for a games night. The number of people attending ranges from 4 to 8, with the probabilities shown alongside.

Number of people	4	5	6	7	8
Probability	0.1	0.19	0.35	a	0.08

a Find a.

b Find the probability that on a randomly chosen week, less than 6 people attend.

c Over a period of 25 weeks, how many times would you expect at least 7 people to attend?

d Find the average number of people attending the games night each week.

15 a The 5th term of an arithmetic sequence is 50, and the sum of the first 15 terms is 1200.

   i Determine two linear equations involving the first term u_1 and the common difference d.

   ii Solve these equations simultaneously to find u_1 and d.

   iii Write down the first 5 terms of the arithmetic sequence.

b A geometric sequence begins at 100, and each subsequent term is half of the previous one.

   i Write down the first 5 terms of the geometric sequence.

    ii Find the sum of the first 10 terms of the sequence correct to 3 significant figures.

    iii Find the sum of the first 15 terms of the sequence correct to 3 significant figures.

    iv Explain why your answers to parts **ii** and **iii** are so similar.

  c Hence, or otherwise, determine the sum of the first 15 terms of the sequence
$110 + 70 + 55 + 52.5 + \ldots$ Round your answer to the **nearest hundred**.

16 Consider the universal set $U = \{x \mid 1 \leqslant x \leqslant 15, \; x \in \mathbb{Z}\}$.

P, Q, and R are subsets of U, where $P = \{$factors of 12$\}$, $Q = \{$multiples of 3$\}$, and $R = \{$prime numbers$\}$.

  a Construct a Venn diagram showing the relationship between P, Q, and R. Show each element of U in an appropriate position.

  b Consider the following propositions: p: x is a factor of 12.

                                       q: x is a multiple of 3.

                                       r: x is a prime number.

For what values of $x \in U$ are the following statements true:

    i $p \wedge q$ **ii** $q \veebar r$ **iii** $q \wedge \neg r$ **iv** $\neg p \wedge \neg q \wedge \neg r$?

  c Consider the statement $(p \wedge q) \wedge \neg r$.

    i Write the statement in words.

    ii Using an appropriate truth table, show that there is only one set of truth values for p, q, and r which make this statement true. State the truth values of p, q, and r in this case.

    iii For what values of x is $(p \wedge q) \wedge \neg r$ true?

17 A function f is defined by $f(x) = x^2 + x - 2$.

  a Find the x-intercepts of $y = f(x)$.

  b Determine the coordinates of the vertex of $y = f(x)$.

  c Draw the graph $y = f(x)$ for $-5 \leqslant x \leqslant 5$.

  d On the same axes, draw the graph of $y = 6 - x$.

  e Use your graph to solve $x^2 + x - 2 = 6 - x$.

18 A university lecturer is investigating the association between attendance at lectures and performance in first year mathematics examinations. The lecturer collects the following information:

		Percentage attendance at lectures		
		0 - 39	40 - 79	80 - 100
Exam	Pass	12	50	78
result	Fail	18	20	22

  a What proportion of students:

    i attended less than 80% of lectures and failed the examination

    ii missed more than 60% of the lectures but still passed?

  b The university lecturer performs a χ^2 test for independence using this data. Write down the:

    i null and alternative hypotheses   **ii** number of degrees of freedom

    iii critical value if the test is run at a 10% significance level.

  c Construct the expected frequency table.

  d Find χ^2_{calc}.

  e What conclusion should the lecturer draw from these results? Explain your response.

19 Consider the figure shown.

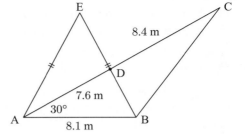

   a Find the length of:
       i DB   **ii** BC

   b Find the measure of:
       i $A\hat{B}E$ **ii** $D\hat{B}C$

   c Find the area of triangle BCD.

   d Find the length of AE.

20 Consider the function $y = \dfrac{3}{2-x} + 1$.

   a Determine the axes intercepts of the graph of the function.

   b Sketch the graph of $y = \dfrac{3}{2-x} + 1$.

   c Write down the equation of the:
       i horizontal asymptote   **ii** vertical asymptote.

   d Points $A(3, -2)$ and $B(p, q)$ lie on $y = \dfrac{3}{2-x} + 1$ for some $p > 3$.

   Suppose the gradient of line segment AB is m_{AB}.

       i Using your graph, explain why $m_{AB} > 0$.

       ii Show that $m_{AB} = \dfrac{-3}{2-p}$ for $p > 3$.

       iii Calculate the missing values a and b in the table below.

p	5	4	3.5	3.1	3.01	3.001
m_{AB}	1.0000	a	2.0000	2.7273	2.9703	b

       iv Hence, or otherwise, comment on the likely value of $\dfrac{dy}{dx}$ at $x = 3$.

21 The table opposite shows exchange rates between Japanese yen (JPY), Swiss francs (CHF), and British pounds (GBP).

The shaded box shows 1 GBP $= 1.6000$ CHF.

	GBP	CHF	JPY
1 GBP =	1	1.6000	c
1 CHF =	b	1	80.000
1 JPY =	d	0.0125	a

   a Using this table, convert:
       i 10 000 GBP to CHF   **ii** 2500 CHF to JPY.

   b Determine the value of:
       i a **ii** b

   c Write down the value of:
       i 1 CHF in JPY   **ii** 1 CHF in GBP.

   d Calculate the value of c.

   e Convert 9000 British pounds into Japanese yen assuming there is a charge of 1.5% commission on the transaction.

   f Find d correct to 4 significant figures. Give your answer in the form $a \times 10^k$ where $1 \leqslant a < 10$ and $k \in \mathbb{Z}$.

22 **a** Consider $P = \{x \mid 3 \leqslant x < 10, \ x \in \mathbb{Z}\}$, $Q = \{2, 9, 15\}$, and
$R = \{\text{multiples of 3 less than 12}\}$.

  i List the elements of P.

  ii Write down $n(P)$.

  iii State whether P is finite or infinite.

  iv Explain why:

    (1) $Q \not\subset P$ **(2)** $R \subset P$

  v List the elements of:

    (1) $P \cap Q$ **(2)** $R \cap Q$ **(3)** $R \cup Q$

  b On Venn diagrams like the one shown, shade
the regions which are described by:

  i $(A \cup B)' \cap C$

  ii $C' \cap B$

  iii $B' \cap (A \cap C)$.

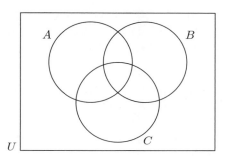

23 Consider the following propositions:

  p: Pepin lives in Jakarta.

  q: Pepin rides a motorbike.

  r: Pepin plays the guitar.

  a Write each of the following statements in symbols:

  i If Pepin does not ride a motorbike, then he does not live in Jakarta.

  ii If Pepin rides a motorbike, then he either lives in Jakarta or plays the guitar.

  b Consider the compound proposition $\neg r \Rightarrow \neg(q \wedge p)$.

  i Write the compound proposition in words.

  ii Complete the following truth table for the compound proposition.

p	q	r	$\neg r$	$(q \wedge p)$	$\neg(q \wedge p)$	$\neg r \Rightarrow \neg(q \wedge p)$
T	T	T				
T	T	F				
T	F	T				
T	F	F				
F	T	T				
F	T	F				
F	F	T				
F	F	F				

  iii State whether the compound statement is a tautology.

  iv Describe in words, for the given propositions p, q, and r, the situation where the compound
proposition is false.

24 The daily profit made by a local baker selling x homemade pies is given by
$$P = -0.05x^2 + 9x - 60 \text{ dollars.}$$

a Copy and complete the table alongside.

x	0	20	40	60	80	100
P		100		300		340

b Plot the points in **a** with x on the horizontal axis and P on the vertical axis. Use these points to sketch the graph of P against x.

c Find:

  i the number of pies that need to be sold to maximise the profit

  ii the maximum possible daily profit

  iii the number of pies that need to be sold to make a profit of $200

  iv the amount of money the baker loses if no pies are sold.

25 In the diagram opposite, ABEF, ABCD, and CDFE are all rectangles.
AD = 12 cm, DC = 20 cm, and DF = 5 cm.
M is the midpoint of EF, and N is the midpoint of CD.

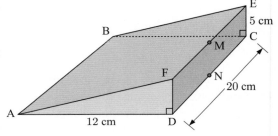

a Calculate the length of AN.

b Calculate the length of AM.

c Calculate the size of the angle AM makes with the base ABCD.

d Calculate the area of triangle AMN.

e Find the surface area of the solid.   f Find the volume of the solid.

26 The maximum daily temperature and the number of cups of coffee sold at a kiosk that day are given in the following table:

Temperature T (°C)	21	20.7	20	19	18	17.3	17	17.3	18	19
Coffees sold, n	120	110	105	125	120	150	140	130	120	120

a Find the mean temperature.

b Find the standard deviation of the temperatures.

c Find the correlation coefficient r and interpret this value.

d Find the equation of the least squares regression line.

e Hence estimate how many cups of coffee will be sold when the temperature is 19.6°C.

f On a day when the temperature is forecast to be 30°C, the owner estimates that only 40 cups of coffee will be sold. Discuss this estimate by comparison with the regression line.

27 a The curve $y = x^3 + ax + b$ has a local minimum at the point $(2, -10)$.
Find the values of a and b.

b The function f is defined by $f(x) = px^2 + qx + c$ where $p, q, c \in \mathbb{R}$.
$f(x)$ has a minimum value of -6.8 at the point A.

  i Given that $f'(x) = 10x - 4$, find the values of p and q.

  ii Find the x-coordinate of A.   iii Find the value of c.

28 Consider the propositions p: Peter is going to the zoo.

q: Quentin is going to the zoo.

r: Ryan is going to the zoo.

a Write the statement "If Peter is going to the zoo, then Ryan is going to the zoo" in symbolic form.

b Write, in words, the converse of the statement in **a**.

c Consider the following argument:

Peter is going to the zoo if and only if Ryan is going to the zoo.

Either Peter or Quentin is going to the zoo, but not both.

Therefore, Ryan is not going to the zoo.

    i Write the argument in logical form.

    ii Use a truth table to determine whether the argument is valid.

29 Let $U = \{\text{positive integers} \leqslant 20\}$,

$X = \{\text{factors of 24 which are} \leqslant 20\}$,

and $Y = \{\text{multiples of 4 which are} \leqslant 20\}$.

a List the elements of: i X ii Y

b Complete the Venn diagram alongside by placing each element of U in an appropriate position.

c Hence, write down the elements of:

    i $X \cap Y$ ii $(X \cup Y)'$

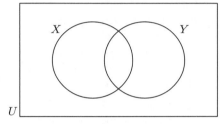

30 A game is played where tickets are randomly selected from a bag. To begin with the bag contains five tickets, one of which is yellow. Tickets are selected one at a time, without replacement, until the yellow ticket is selected. At this point, the game ends.

a A tree diagram is used to illustrate the first two possible selections in the game. Copy and complete the tree diagram by filling in the probability values.

b Use the tree diagram to determine the probability that the game ends in two selections or less.

c If the game was played 250 times, how many times would you expect the game to end in two selections or less?

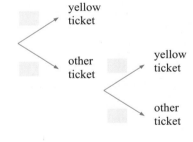

d Determine the probability that the game ends within:

    i four selections   ii five selections.

e The game is altered so that tickets are now **replaced** after each selection. Determine the probability that the game ends on the:

    i 1st selection   ii 2nd selection   iii 3rd selection.

f Using the results from **e**, determine the probability that the game ends within three selections.

g The values found in **e** form a geometric sequence. For this geometric sequence:

    i write down the common ratio

    ii show that the sum of the first n terms is $1 - \left(\frac{4}{5}\right)^n$.

h Hence, determine the probability that the game ends within fifteen selections. Write your answer as a percentage, correct to 3 significant figures.

31 The graph of $y = 2x + \dfrac{1}{x} + 3$ is shown for $-5 \leqslant x \leqslant 5$.

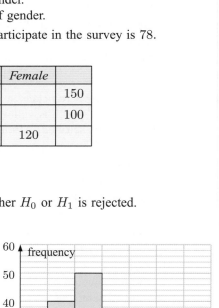

$y = 2x + \dfrac{1}{x} + 3$

    a Write down the equation of the vertical asymptote.

    b Find $\dfrac{dy}{dx}$.

    c Hence find the gradient of the tangent to the curve at the point where $x = 1$.

    d Write down the coordinates of the points where the tangent to the curve is horizontal.

    e State the range of the function.

32 A group of 250 IB students were given the option to participate in a survey. The table alongside shows participation levels according to gender.

	Male	Female
Participated	69	81
Did not participate	61	39

A χ^2 test at a 5% significance level is performed to investigate the following hypotheses:

    H_0: Participation in the survey was independent of gender.

    H_1: Participation in the survey was not independent of gender.

    a Show that the expected number of male students to participate in the survey is 78.

    b Hence, complete the table of expected values below:

	Male	Female	
Participated	78		150
Did not participate			100
	130	120	

    c Write down the number of degrees of freedom.

    d Determine the value of χ^2_{calc}.

    e Given that the critical value is ≈ 3.84, discuss whether H_0 or H_1 is rejected.

    f What conclusion can be drawn from this χ^2 test?

The 150 completed surveys provided information on how far students travelled to get to school each day. This information is shown in the histogram alongside.

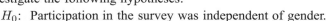

    g Is *distance* a discrete or continuous variable?

    h Using your calculator, estimate the:

        i mean

        ii standard deviation of the data.

    i A student is selected at random. Given that this student completed a survey, determine the probability the student travels no more than 10 kilometres to school.

33 The points $A(0, 3)$ and $B(4, 0)$ form two vertices of triangle ABC.

    a On a grid showing the region $-2 \leqslant x \leqslant 12$, $-2 \leqslant y \leqslant 12$, plot points A and B.

    b Calculate the distance between A and B.

    c Find the gradient of the line segment AB.

d Given that $\widehat{ABC} = 90°$, calculate:

    i the gradient of line BC   **ii** the equation of line BC.

e Point C has coordinates $(11.2, b)$.

    i Find b.   **ii** Add point C to your diagram from **a**.

f Calculate the area of triangle ABC.

g Determine the measure of $\widehat{ACB}$.

34 4800 cm^2 of material is used to construct a hollow, square based cuboid with an open top. The cuboid has base width x cm and height h cm.

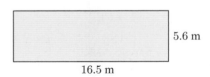

open top

a Show that $h = \dfrac{4800 - x^2}{4x}$.

b Hence, show that the volume of the cuboid is given by $V = 1200x - \frac{1}{4}x^3$ cm^3.

c The table alongside shows values of x and V. Find the value of:

    i a **ii** b

x	10	30	60
V	a	b	18 000

d Find $\dfrac{dV}{dx}$.

e Determine the dimensions x and h which maximise the volume of the cuboid.

f Write down the maximum volume of the cuboid.

35 Marinda invests €12 000 in a bank account offering 4.2% p.a. interest, compounded quarterly.

a Calculate the interest earned after:

    i 1 year   **ii** 3 years.

b Write a formula for the value of Marinda's investment after x years.

c How long will it take for Marinda's investment to reach €30 000? Give your answer to the nearest year.

d What rate of interest compounded annually would be needed for Marinda's investment to reach €30 000 in the same time as found in **c**?

36 A rectangular field needs to be top-dressed. We need to know the area of the field so we can order the correct amount of soil. The tape measure used to measure the field has marks on it every 10 cm.

5.6 m

16.5 m

a Use the measurements given to estimate the area of the field.

b The measurements in the diagram involved some inaccuracy. Write down the maximum possible length and width of the field correct to 2 decimal places.

c Calculate the maximum possible area of the field, correct to 3 significant figures.

d The top-dressing of soil will be 2 cm thick across the field. Calculate the amount of soil that needs to be ordered to make sure there is sufficient. Give your answer in cubic metres.

e The soil costs $120 per cubic metre, plus a delivery fee of $27.50 per kilometre travelled. The labour for spreading the soil costs $60 per cubic metre. The field is 5 km from the supplier's depot. Find the maximum total cost for top-dressing the field.

f Find the difference in cost if the amount of soil ordered was based on your answer to **a**.

37 There are 60 senior students in a school. Each of these students studies History, Geography, or both of these subjects. 38 students study History, 31 study Geography, and n study both.

   a Find the value of n.

   b Draw a fully labelled Venn diagram to illustrate this information.

   c Find the probability that a student selected at random studies only one of these subjects.

   d 28 of the 60 students are female. 17 females study History, and 15 females study Geography. Find the probability that a student selected at random:

   i is female and studies exactly one of these subjects

   ii is male and studies both of these subjects.

   e One of the History students is randomly selected. Calculate the probability that this student:

   i is female   **ii** also studies Geography.

38 The intensity of light L diminishes below the surface of the sea according to the formula $L = L_0 \times (0.95)^d$ units, where d is the depth in metres measured from the surface of the sea.

   a If the intensity of light at the surface is 10 units, calculate the value of L_0.

   b Find the intensity of light 25 m below the surface.

   c A light intensity of 4 units is considered adequate for divers to be able to see clearly. Calculate the depth corresponding to this intensity of light.

   d The table gives some values for the intensity of light at different depths.

Depth d (metres)	10	20	30	50
Intensity L (units)	5.99	3.58	2.15	0.769

   Using these values and your answers to **a**, **b**, and **c**, graph the intensity of light against depth for $0 \leqslant d \leqslant 50$.

   e Calculate the range of depths for which the light intensity is between 1 and 3 units.

39 The diagram shows a cuboid which measures 22.5 cm by 30 cm by 40 cm.

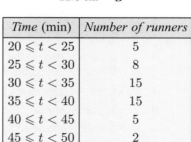

   a Find the length of AC.

   b Find the area of the plane ACGE.

   c Find the volume of the triangular prism ACGEFB.

   d Find the length of CE.

   e Find $A\widehat{C}E$.

   f Let M be the midpoint of CE. Find the area of triangle AMC.

40 The table shows the time taken for a group of runners to finish a cross country race.

   a Construct a cumulative frequency table for this data.

   b Draw the corresponding cumulative frequency curve.

   c Use the graph to estimate the:

   i median finishing time   **ii** interquartile range

   iii number of runners who finished in under 38 minutes

   iv time it took for the fastest 40% of the runners to complete the course.

Time (min)	Number of runners
$20 \leqslant t < 25$	5
$25 \leqslant t < 30$	8
$30 \leqslant t < 35$	15
$35 \leqslant t < 40$	15
$40 \leqslant t < 45$	5
$45 \leqslant t < 50$	2

   d The first 3 runners will be awarded medals. Estimate the time that was needed to be awarded a medal.

41 The cost of producing a pair of shoes is $15, and they are then sold for $$x$.

    a Write an expression for the profit made on each pair sold.

    b In a given period, a total of $(1500 - 9x)$ pairs of shoes are sold. Show that the total profit made on the shoes sold is $P = 1635x - 9x^2 - 22\,500$ dollars.

    c Calculate the profit made when the shoes are sold for $100 per pair.

    d Find $\dfrac{dP}{dx}$.

    e Calculate to the nearest dollar, the selling price that will maximise the profit, and find the maximum profit in this case.

42 The lines L_1 and L_2 are tangents to the graph of $y = f(x)$.

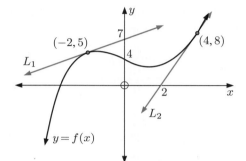

    a Find:

        i $f(0)$ **ii** $f'(-2)$ **iii** $f'(4)$

    b Find the equation of:

        i L_1 **ii** L_2

    c Find where the lines L_1 and L_2 intersect.

    d Find the equation of the normal to $y = f(x)$ at the point where $x = -2$.

43   **a** Consider the sum of the first n positive integers $1 + 2 + 3 + \ldots + n$.

        i Find the sum of the first 10 positive integers.

        ii Show that the sum of the first n positive integers is given by the formula $\dfrac{n(n+1)}{2}$.

        iii Using this formula, calculate the sum of the first 1000 integers.

        iv Determine n such that the sum of the first n positive integers is $11\,325$.

    b Consider the sequence $7, 14, 21, 28, \ldots$.

        i Write an expression for the nth term.

        ii Find the largest term which is no greater than 1000.

        iii Determine a formula for the sum of the first n terms.

    c Calculate the sum of all positive integers which are no greater than 1000 and which are *not* divisible by 7.

44 A survey is conducted regarding the types of cardio equipment used by the 300 members of a fitness club.

    134 members use rowers (R), 92 use treadmills (T), and 144 use spin-bikes (S).

    19 members use rowers, treadmills, and spin-bikes.

    23 members use rowers and treadmills only.

    28 members use treadmills and spin-bikes only.

    41 members use spin-bikes and rowers only.

    a Construct a Venn diagram to represent this information.

    b Determine the number of fitness club members who do not use any type of cardio equipment.

    c Find the proportion of the members that use:

        i all three types of cardio equipment

        ii exactly two of the three types of cardio equipment.

    d Of the members who use at least one type of cardio equipment, what proportion use spin-bikes?

45 A study measured the bone density (in g/cm^3) of a group of 25 year old adults, and a group of 60 year old adults. The results are shown below.

25 year old group: 1.35   1.15   1.3   1.3   1.15   1.25   1.3   1.15   1.3   1.45
                       1.25   1.4   1.45   1.35   1.2   1.2   1.3   1.45   1.2   1.3

60 year old group: 0.85   0.9   0.85   1.0   0.95   1.05   0.9   0.9   0.95   0.95
                       1.2   1.2   0.9   1.0   1.1   1.05   1.1   0.95   1.0   0.95

  a Calculate the five-number summary for each of the data sets.

  b Display the data in a parallel boxplot.

  c Compare the measures of the centre of each distribution.

  d Compare the measures of spread of each distribution.

  e What conclusions can be drawn from the data?

46 Consider the quadratic function $f(x) = x^2 - 8x + 12$.

  a Find the axes intercepts.

  b Find the equation of the axis of symmetry.

  c Find the coordinates of the vertex.

  d Sketch the graph of the function, showing the features found in **a**, **b**, and **c**.

  e State the intervals where the function is increasing or decreasing.

  f Find the equation of the tangent to $y = f(x)$ at $x = 3$.

  g Find the equation of the normal to $y = f(x)$ at $x = 6$.

47 QS is a diagonal of quadrilateral PQRS where $PQ = 3$ cm, $RS = 6$ cm, $PS = 5$ cm, $Q\widehat{S}R = 50°$, and $Q\widehat{P}S = 60°$.

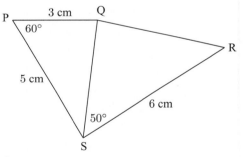

  a Show that $QS = \sqrt{19}$ cm.

  b Find the length of QR correct to 4 significant figures.

  c Hence find, correct to 3 significant figures, the:

    i perimeter of PQRS   **ii** area of PQRS.

48 Aaron purchased a new car for $40 000. The car depreciates at 25% p.a.

  a Let V_n represent the value of the car after n years.

    i Find V_1.

    ii Show that $V_3 = \$16\,875$.

    iii Deduce a formula for V_n using the sequence of values $V_1, V_2, V_3, ...$

    iv Plot V_n for $0 \leqslant n \leqslant 15$.

  b Aaron insured his car immediately after it was purchased. Initially, the annual cost of the insurance was $1200. One year later, the annual insurance cost increased to $1260.

    i Find the percentage increase in the annual insurance cost.

    ii Let P_n represent the annual insurance cost after n years, so $P_1 = \$1260$. Assuming the insurance cost increases by the same percentage each year, calculate P_2 and P_3.

    iii Write down a formula for P_n in terms of n.

  c After how many whole years will the annual cost of car insurance be more than the depreciated value of the car?

49 A group of students compare their average test results for Physics (x) and Chemistry (y).

Physics Test ($x\%$)	43	45	50	51	55	56	59	63	65	72	77	93
Chemistry Test ($y\%$)	52	53	57	57	58	62	63	70	72	87	88	100

    a Draw a scatter diagram for this data.

    b Find the mean point $(\overline{x},\ \overline{y})$.

    c Draw a line of best fit by eye on the scatter diagram drawn in **a**.

    d Using your graphics calculator, determine:

        i the product-moment correlation coefficient r

        ii the equation of the least squares regression line for y on x.

    e Hence, predict to the nearest 1% the average test result in Chemistry for a student who achieved an average test result of 85% in Physics.

50 The table alongside shows the number of balloons in a giant party pack.

	Red	Yellow	Blue
Large	12	5	9
Medium	15	8	10
Small	24	11	6

    a State the:

        i total number of balloons in the pack.

        ii number of medium balloons in the pack.

    b One balloon is chosen at random from the pack. Find the probability that:

        i the balloon is not yellow   **ii** the balloon is either medium or small.

    c Two balloons are selected at random from the pack. Find the probability that:

        i both balloons are red   **ii** neither of the balloons are large

        iii exactly one of the balloons is blue   **iv** at least one of the balloons is blue.

    d Three balloons are selected at random from the pack. Find the probability that:

        i all three balloons are small and yellow   **ii** exactly two balloons are medium and red.

51 Consider the function $f(x) = 3x^2 - 5x - 2^x - 10$.

    a Using technology:

        i find the axes intercepts   **ii** find the position and nature of any turning points

        iii discuss the behaviour of the function as $x \to \infty$ and $x \to -\infty$

        iv sketch the function.

    b Add the graph of $g(x) = 3^{-x}$ to your graph in **a iv**.

    c Solve for x: $3x^2 - 5x - 2^x - 10 = 3^{-x}$.

52 A yachting course is illustrated in the diagram alongside. The yachts start and finish at O, and travel in the direction indicated.

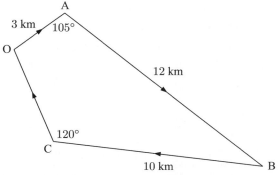

    a Find the distance from O to B in a straight line.

    b Find $B\widehat{O}C$.

    c Find the length of OC.

    d Calculate the area enclosed by the course OABC.

    e The course designer stated the length of the course is 30 km. Calculate the percentage error in this approximation.

53 Felicity is offered a new job and is given two salary options to choose from:

Option A: $40 000 in the first year, and 5% extra each subsequent year.

Option B: $60 000 in the first year, and $1000 more each subsequent year.

a If Felicity believed that she would work for 3 years in this new job, explain why *Option B* would be best for her.

b Write down a formula for the amount of money earned in the *n*th year if she selects:

   i *Option A*   **ii** *Option B*

c Determine the minimum length of time Felicity would need to work before the amount of money earned per year from *Option A* exceeds that of *Option B*.

d Felicity decides that the best way to compare the two options is to consider the total income accumulated after the first *n* years in each case. If T_A and T_B represent the total income earned over *n* years for *Options A* and *B* respectively, show that:

   i $T_A = 800\,000(1.05^n - 1)$ dollars   **ii** $T_B = 500n^2 + 59\,500n$ dollars

e The graph alongside shows T_A and T_B graphed against *n*.

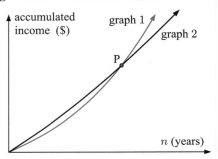

   i Write down which graph represents T_A and which graph represents T_B.

   ii Find the coordinates of the point P, where T_A meets T_B.

f Hence, write down a time interval, in whole years, for which *Option B* provides the greater accumulated income.

54 A club of beagle owners records the number of pups born per litter over a one year period. The results are shown in the frequency table.

a Is this data discrete or continuous?

b Calculate the total number of litters for this one year period.

c Determine the value of: **i** *s*   **ii** *t*

d How many beagle pups were born over this one year period?

e Calculate the average number of pups per litter.

f Using your graphics calculator, draw a boxplot to represent this data.

Number of pups per litter (x)	Frequency (f)	$x \times f$
2	1	2
3	3	9
4	7	28
5	15	*s*
6	21	126
7	17	*t*
8	9	72
9	4	36
10	2	20

g Hence, determine the: **i** range   **ii** interquartile range   **iii** median.

55 A furniture manufacturer constructs and sells wooden stools. The number N of stools sold depends on the selling price per stool, €x. The relationship between N and x is illustrated alongside.

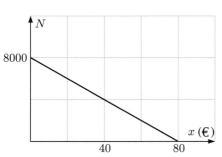

a Calculate the gradient of this line, and interpret its meaning.

b Write down the equation of the line, giving your answer in the form $N = ax + b$.

c If each wooden stool costs €50 to build, write an expression for the manufacturer's profit per stool.

d Using the results of **b** and **c**, show that the total profit for the sale of N chairs is given by
$P = -100x^2 + 13\,000x - 400\,000$ euros.

e Find $\dfrac{dP}{dx}$.

f Calculate the selling price required to produce the maximum profit, and the maximum profit in this case.

56 PQRS is a square and forms the base of a pyramid. O is the centre of the base, and the vertex A is 30 cm directly above O. M is the midpoint of RS. The volume of the pyramid is 4000 cm^3.

a Calculate the width of the square base.

b Calculate the distance OR.

c The triangular face ARS forms an angle θ with the square base.

   i Using a well labelled diagram, draw a triangle showing the correct position of angle θ.

   ii Hence, calculate the measure of θ.

d Calculate the total surface area of the pyramid.

e A wire frame is placed along the edges of the pyramid. If the wire costs $0.12 per cm, find the total cost of the frame.

57 Michael is saving to buy a house and needs $200\,000.

a Three years ago, he invested a sum of money in an account paying 6.5% p.a. interest compounded half-yearly. This investment has just matured at $50\,000. How much did Michael invest three years ago?

b Michael decides to reinvest his $50\,000 lump sum into an account for a period of n years at 6.0% p.a. interest compounded annually.

Copy and complete the table below showing the value V_n of Michael's investment after n years.

n (years)	0	1	2	3	4
V_n ($)	50 000	53 000	56 180		

c Write a formula for V_n in terms of n.

d Michael also decides to start an additional saving plan, whereby he deposits $3000 into a safe at the end of each year. Write down a formula for S_n, the amount of money in Michael's safe after n years.

e The total amount of money Michael has for his house after n years is given by $T_n = V_n + S_n$. Calculate the missing values in the table below.

n (years)	0	1	2	3	4
T_n ($)	50 000	56 000	62 180		

f After how many whole years will Michael have the $200\,000 needed to buy his house?

58 Mr Hilditch makes a cup of coffee in the staff room of his school, but accidentally leaves it behind. The approximate temperature of the coffee t minutes after it is made is $A(t) = 95 - 3t$ °C   for $0 \leqslant t \leqslant 30$ minutes.

   a Based on this model, estimate the temperature of Mr Hilditch's coffee:

      i initially   **ii** after 30 minutes.

   b Sketch $A(t)$ for $0 \leqslant t \leqslant 30$.   Clearly show the information obtained in **a**.

   c Discuss whether the use of $A(t)$ to represent the temperature of the coffee could be valid beyond $t = 30$ minutes. Give evidence to support your response.

   d The actual temperature of the coffee t minutes after being made is

      $C(t) = 80 \times (0.8)^t + 15$ °C, $\ t \geqslant 0$.

      Determine the actual temperature of the coffee:

      i initially   **ii** after 30 minutes.

   e Add the graph of $C(t)$ to your graph from **b**.

   f Mr Hilditch will drink his coffee provided its temperature does not drop below 20°C. How long will it take for the coffee to become too cold to drink?

   g If left for a long time, the temperature of the coffee will eventually reach the temperature of the surrounding environment. Based on the model $C(t)$, find the temperature of the staff room where Mr Hilditch left his cup of coffee.

   h Consider the function $D(t) = A(t) - C(t)$.

      i Solve $D(t) = 0$, and interpret this result.

      ii Determine the maximum value of $D(t)$ for $0 \leqslant t \leqslant 30$.

      iii Interpret the value found in **ii**.

59 Jose conducts a survey of 200 people to see which type of movie they prefer to watch. The results are shown in the table. Jose will conduct a χ^2 test at the 5% level of significance to determine whether the preferred movie type is independent of gender.

	Adventure	Comedy	Action	Drama
Men	25	25	40	15
Women	18	34	12	31

   a State the null and alternative hypotheses.

   b Calculate the expected frequency for the number of females who prefer comedies. Give your answer to the nearest whole number.

   c Using your graphics calculator or otherwise, find the χ^2 statistic for Jose's data.

   d Determine the number of degrees of freedom available for this calculation.

   e Write down the critical value for the test.

   f Give a conclusion for Jose's test, including reasons for your decision.

   g Jose realised after he had completed the test that he entered some information incorrectly. The adventure and drama numbers for males had been reversed. Perform the test again with the correct data, and state whether the conclusion drawn in **f** is still valid.

ANSWERS

EXERCISE 1A

1 a 23 **b** 18 **c** 78 **d** 168 **2 a** 503 **b** 3076
3 €27 **4** Yes **5** $24 149 **6 a** 437 **b** 28 **c** 720
7 82 buckets **8** 38 400 apples **9** 25 laps
10 a 840 apartments **b** $2 856 000 **11** 63

EXERCISE 1B.1

1 a 3, 9, 27, 81 **b** 5, 25, 125, 625
  c 6, 36, 216, 1296 **d** 7, 49, 343, 2401
2 a 2×3^2 **b** $3^2 \times 7^2$ **c** $2^2 \times 5^2 \times 7$
  d $3 \times 5^3 \times 11$ **e** $2^2 \times 3^3$ **f** $3^2 \times 5 \times 7^3$
3 a 70 **b** 18 **c** 135 **d** 108 **e** 600 **f** 48 400
4 a 3888 **b** 590 625 **c** 104 544
  d 41 544 503 **e** 36 450 **f** 857 500
5 8
6 a $2^1 = 2$ $\qquad 2^2 - 2 = 2$
  $2^1 + 2^2 = 6$ $\qquad 2^3 - 2 = 6$
  $2^1 + 2^2 + 2^3 = 14$ $\qquad 2^4 - 2 = 14$
  $2^1 + 2^2 + 2^3 + 2^4 = 30$ $\qquad 2^5 - 2 = 30$
  b 254 $(= 2^8 - 2)$
7 a 2^{n-1}, where n is the number of the square
  b 2^{39} grains **c** $1 + 2^1 + 2^2 + ... + 2^{63} = 2^{64} - 1$
8 a 9 **b** 27 **c** 81 **d** combinations $= 3^n$ **e** 6561

EXERCISE 1B.2

1 a 1 **b** −1 **c** 1 **d** −1 **e** 1 **f** −1
  g −1 **h** 9 **i** −64 **j** −64 **k** −49 **l** 27
2 a 512 **b** −243 **c** −3125 **d** 729 **e** 1296
  f 6561 **g** −6561 **h** 5.117 264 691
  i −0.764 479 956 4 **j** −20.361 584 96

EXERCISE 1C.1

1 a 1, 3, 5, 15 **b** 1, 2, 4, 8, 16 **c** $21 = 3 \times 7$
  d 1 and 21
2 a 1, 3, 9 **b** 1, 17 **c** 1, 2, 11, 22
  d 1, 2, 3, 4, 6, 8, 12, 24 **e** 1, 2, 4, 7, 14, 28
  f 1, 2, 3, 6, 7, 14, 21, 42
  g 1, 2, 3, 4, 5, 6, 10, 12, 15, 20, 30, 60
  h 1, 2, 3, 4, 6, 9, 12, 18, 27, 36, 54, 108
3 a $36 = 6 \times 6$ **b** $38 = 2 \times 19$ **c** $48 = 12 \times 4$
  d $90 = 5 \times 18$ **e** $88 = 8 \times 11$ **f** $54 = 3 \times 18$
  g $72 = 12 \times 6$ **h** $60 = 12 \times 5$
4 a 9 **b** 15 **c** 7 **d** 7
  e 44 **f** 13 **g** 63 **h** 73
5 a 6, 8, 10 **b** 11, 13, 15, 17, 19
6 a 16, 18 **b** 1, 7 **c** 1 and 15, 3 and 13, 5 and 11
7 a even **b** even **c** even **d** odd **e** odd
  f odd **g** even **h** odd **i** even

EXERCISE 1C.2

1 a 2, 3, 5, 7, 11, 13, 17, 19, 23, 29, 31, 37, 41, 43, 47, 53, 59
  b one, 2

2 (other answers are possible) **a** 5 **b** 3 **c** 10 **d** 11
3 a 2×7 **b** $2^2 \times 5$ **c** $2^2 \times 7$ **d** 2^5 **e** $2^3 \times 5$
4 a 3 **b** 15, 21, 25, 27 **c** 29

EXERCISE 1C.3

1 a 4 **b** 3 **c** 7 **d** 9 **e** 13 **f** 6 **g** 3 **h** 4
2 8

EXERCISE 1D

1 a 4, 8, 12, 16, 20, 24 **b** 5, 10, 15, 20, 25, 30
  c 7, 14, 21, 28, 35, 42 **d** 11, 22, 33, 44, 55, 66
2 a 24 **b** 54
3 a,b 1   2   ③   4   ⑤   ⑥   7   8   ⑨   ⑩
  11   ⑫   13   14   ⑮   16   17   ⑱   19   ⑳
  ㉑   22   23   ㉔   ㉕   26   ㉗   28   29   ㉚
  31   32   ㉝   34   ㉟   ㊱   37   38   ㊴   ㊵
  c 15, 30
4 a 36, 72, 108 **b** 60, 120
  c none in the list (first one is 180)
5 a 10 **b** 21 **c** 20 **d** 24
  e 18 **f** 60 **g** 140 **h** 36
6 a 105 **b** 198 **7** in 12 hours' time **8** 14.4 km

EXERCISE 1E.1

1 a 7 **b** 14 **c** 13 **d** 5 **e** 8 **f** 5
  g 7 **h** 5 **i** 2 **j** 4 **k** 1 **l** 8
2 a 15 **b** 3 **c** 3 **d** 16 **e** 32 **f** 2
  g 17 **h** 4 **i** 8 **j** 8 **k** 6 **l** 36
  m 4 **n** 2 **o** 14
3 a 12 **b** 7 **c** 14 **d** 6 **e** 5 **f** 64
4 a 8 **b** $\frac{1}{4}$ **c** 3 **d** 2
5 a 28 **b** 31 **c** 13 **d** 1 **e** 12 **f** 38
6 a 12 **b** −12 **c** 38 **d** 2 **e** −12 **f** −6
  g 30 **h** 3 **i** −11 **j** 4 **k** −1 **l** −2

EXERCISE 1E.2

1 a 45 **b** 6 **c** 14 **d** 10 **e** 10 **f** 1
  g 4 **h** 25 **i** 1 **j** 18 **k** 2 **l** 1

EXERCISE 1F.1

1 $8 = \frac{8}{1}$, $-11 = -\frac{11}{1}$
2 $\frac{4}{0}$ cannot be written in the form $\frac{p}{q}$ where p and q are integers and $q \neq 0$.
3 a $0.8 = \frac{8}{10}$ **b** $0.71 = \frac{71}{100}$ **c** $0.45 = \frac{45}{100}$
  d $0.219 = \frac{219}{1000}$ **e** $0.864 = \frac{864}{1000}$
4 a false **b** true **c** false
5 a $0.444\,444.... = \frac{4}{9}$ **b** $0.212\,121.... = \frac{21}{99}$
  c $0.325\,325\,325.... = \frac{325}{999}$
6

	$\mathbb{Q}$	$\mathbb{Q}^+$	$\mathbb{Z}$	$\mathbb{Z}^+$	$\mathbb{N}$
3	✓	✓	✓	✓	✓
−2	✓	✗	✓	✗	✗
1.5	✓	✓	✗	✗	✗
0	✓	✗	✓	✗	✓
$-\frac{1}{2}$	✓	✗	✗	✗	✗

EXERCISE 1F.2

1 a rational   b irrational   c rational   d rational

2 $\sqrt{\frac{9}{25}} = \frac{\sqrt{9}}{\sqrt{25}} = \frac{3}{5}$

   $\therefore$ is rational

3

	$\mathbb{Q}$	$\mathbb{R}$	$\mathbb{Z}$	$\mathbb{Q}'$	$\mathbb{N}$
$\sqrt{2}$	✗	✓	✗	✓	✗
5	✓	✓	✓	✗	✓
$-\frac{1}{3}$	✓	✓	✗	✗	✗
2.17	✓	✓	✗	✗	✗
-9	✓	✓	✓	✗	✗

REVIEW SET 1A

1 a 46   b 25   c 165   d 348   2 111 situps

3 a $2^2 \times 5^3 \times 7$ b 3500

4 a 9   b 25   c -49 d -8

5 a 4 times   b 32 times

6 a 84, 91, 98   b 31, 37

   c 2 and 20, 4 and 18, 6 and 16, 8 and 14, 10 and 12

7 a 1, 2, 17, 34   b 1, 31

   c 1, 2, 3, 4, 6, 9, 12, 18, 36   d 1, 3, 5, 9, 15, 45

8 a 4   b 18   c 14   9 a 30   b 56   c 60

10 a 21   b 9   c 42   11 a 12   b 29   c -15

12 a rational   b rational, $= \frac{165}{1000}$

   c neither, undefined (not a real number)

   d rational, $= \frac{56}{1}$ e irrational   f rational, $= \frac{18}{99}$

REVIEW SET 1B

1 $271   2 4600 bars

3 a 1   b -1 c 32   d -50.41 4 375

5 divisible by 3   6 a 3×11 b $2^2 \times 3 \times 5$ c $2^3 \times 7$

7 a 1 and 42, 2 and 21, 3 and 14, 6 and 7

   b 1, 2, 3, 6, 9, 18

8 a 3   b 60   9 the 12 000th

10 a 15   b 3   c 22   11 a -36 b -4 c 12

12

	$\mathbb{Q}$	$\mathbb{R}$	$\mathbb{Z}$	$\mathbb{Q}'$	$\mathbb{N}$
3.91	✓	✓	✗	✗	✗
$\sqrt{4}$	✓	✓	✓	✗	✓
-18	✓	✓	✓	✗	✗
π	✗	✓	✗	✓	✗
0	✓	✓	✓	✗	✓

EXERCISE 2A

1 a 2700 s   b 4200 s   c 7528 s

2 a 210 mins   b 24 mins   c 313 mins

   d 4428 mins

3 a 4 hours 50 minutes   b 3 hours 37 minutes

   c 6 hours 14 minutes   d 14 hours 26 minutes

4 a 53 minutes   b 9:03 am

5 a 10:15 am   b 4:56 am   c 4:20 pm

   d 8:05 pm the previous day

6 6:50 am   7 3 hours 17 minutes

EXERCISE 2B

1 a 16°C   b 82°C   c -12°C

2 a 140°F   b 104°F   c 59°F

3 a -17.8°C   b 37.8°C   c -6.67°C

4 a 158°F   b 14°F   c 752°F

6 a $-26\frac{2}{3}$°C   b 77°F   7 -40°

EXERCISE 2C

1 c and d   2 $1000 = 10^3$ $0.1 = 10^{-1}$

                $100 = 10^2$ $0.01 = 10^{-2}$

                $10 = 10^1$ $0.001 = 10^{-3}$

                $1 = 10^0$ $0.0001 = 10^{-4}$

3 a 82 000   b 36   c 8.7   d 490

   e 0.0078   f 0.055   g 0.376   h 0.002 02

4 a 3.9×10^3 b 1.7×10^4 c 4×10^{-2} d 7.1×10^{-5}

   e 8.5×10^1 f 6.3×10^0 g 2.48×10^6 h 1.08×10^{-7}

5 a 4.5×10^7 b 3.8×10^{-4} c 2.1×10^5

   d 4×10^{-3} e 6.1×10^3 f 1.6×10^{-6}

   g 3.9×10^4 h 6.7×10^{-2}

6 a 45 000 000   b 0.000 38   c 210 000   d 0.004

   e 6100   f 0.000 001 6   g 39 000   h 0.067

7 a 4.964×10^{13} b 6.561×10^{11} c 4×10^{-8}

   d 3.43×10^{-10} e 3.392×10^{14} f 9.62×10^{-5}

   g 4.8×10^{-8} h 4.375×10^{-11}

8 a 7 400 000 000 people   b 0.000 000 1 Pa

   c 140 000 light years

   d 0.000 000 000 000 000 000 000 000 001 67 kg

9 a 5.44×10^7 years   b 3×10^{-3} m

   c 3.119×10^8 hands   d 4.7×10^{-7} m

10 7.5×10^7 peanuts

EXERCISE 2D

1 1 000 000 mL   2 a 1000   b 1 000 000 000   3 10^{12}

4 a 25 mL   b 26.58 μs   c 45 000 000 mm

   d 5.84 t   e 194.4 MJ   f $16\frac{2}{3}$ m s^{-1}

   g 140 000 mm^2 h 57.6 km h^{-1} i 66.672 km h^{-1}

5 a 7×10^3 mL   b 3.8×10^6 mm   c 9.86×10^{-3} kg

   d 5.6×10^5 m^2 e 1.08×10^7 μs   f 2.58×10^{-7} GL

6 3.3 ha   7 216 000 000 J   8 8.64 knots   9 1 kg m^{2}s^{-2}

EXERCISE 2E.1

1 a 80   b 80   c 300   d 640

   e 3990   f 1650   g 9800   h 1020

   i 780   j 840   k 2120   l 2000

2 a 100   b 500   c 900   d 1000

   e 5400   f 4800   g 13 100   h 44 000

3 a 1000   b 6000   c 10 000   d 4000

   e 65 000   f 123 000   g 435 000   h 571 000

4 a $15 000   b 470 kg   c €600   d 5700 km

   e 117 000 L   f £29 000   g $6 500 000   h 32 000 ha

   i 36 000 000 times   j $1 000 000 000

EXERCISE 2E.2

1 a 3.5   b 5.36   c 7.2   d 15.23   e 9.025

   f 12.6   g 0.44   h 9.28   i 0.01

2 a 499.32   b 228.84   c 9.11   d 31.75   e 26.67

   f 0.88   g 7.41   h 5.93   i 0.48

3 1.74 goals per game

EXERCISE 2E.3

1 a 570   b 16 000   c 71   d 3.0   e 0.72

   f 50   g 3.0   h 1800   i 0.041   j 46 000

2 a 43 600 **b** 10 100 **c** 0.667 **d** 0.0368 **e** 0.319
   f 0.720 **g** 0.636 **h** 0.0637 **i** 19.0 **j** 257 000
3 a 28.04 **b** 0.005 362 **c** 23 680 **d** 42 370 000
   e 0.038 79 **f** 0.006 378 **g** 0.000 899 9 **h** 43.08
4 a i 6000 people **ii** 5800 people **b** 6000
5 a 0.691 **b** 455 000 **c** 4.12 **d** 7.28
   e 0.152 **f** 0.000 304
6 a 140 000 km **b** 670 000 km **c** 250 000 000 km
7 a 4.00×10^{13} **b** 2.59×10^7 **c** 7.08×10^{-9}
   d 4.87×10^{-11} **e** 8.01×10^6 **f** 3.55×10^{-9}
8 a i 2.88×10^8 km **ii** 7.01×10^{10} km
   b 2.5×10^8 km h^{-1} **c** 0.9 s **d** 3.94 times
   e i Microbe C **ii** 32.9 times

EXERCISE 2F.1

1 a 83.8 km h^{-1} **b** 83.3 km h^{-1} **2** 442 km h^{-1}
3 30 m s^{-1} (= 108 km h^{-1}) **4 a** 321 km **b** 32.7 km
5 7 hours 25 minutes 16 seconds

EXERCISE 2F.2

1 a \$2.76 per kg **b** 14.5 km per litre **c** 27 L min^{-1}
   d \$14.50 per hour **e** 4° per h **f** 5.5 kg m^{-2}
   g 10.45 cents per kWh **h** 55 words/min
2 a €586.80 **b** €16.77 per hour
3 B, 11.6 bags per hectare **4** Jo, 26.3 goals/match
5 a 511 L per day **b i** \$29.90 **ii** 33.2 cents
6 a 10 minutes **b** 4 minutes 17 seconds
7 a \$219.85 **b** 10.72 cents per kWh
8 a 13°C **b** 1.16°C per h
9 a 20 cents per min **b** 4 kL per s **c** 108 L per h
   d \$2730 per kg **e** 52 596 deaths per year

EXERCISE 2G

1 a $\pm\frac{1}{2}$ cm **b** $\pm\frac{1}{2}$ mL **c** ± 50 mL **d** ± 250 g
2 between 67.5 kg and 68.5 kg
3 a 26.5 mm - 27.5 mm **b** 38.25 cm - 38.35 cm
   c 4.75 m - 4.85 m **d** 1.45 kg - 1.55 kg
   e 24.5 g - 25.5 g **f** 3.745 kg - 3.755 kg
4 between 36.35°C and 36.45°C
5 a 6.4 m **b** 6.05 m **c** 10 cm **6** 246 cm - 250 cm
7 788 cm and 792 cm **8 a** 55.25 cm^2 **b** 41.25 cm^2
9 Upper boundary = 1126.25 cm^2
   Lower boundary = 1058.25 cm^2
10 Upper: 40.375 cm^2, Lower: 31.875 cm^2
11 Upper: 248.625 cm^3, Lower: 144.375 cm^3
12 Upper: 1545.69 cm^3, Lower: 1502.11 cm^3
13 Upper: 1473.01 cm^3, Lower: 922.45 cm^3
14 Upper: 347.69 cm^3, Lower: 332.21 cm^3

EXERCISE 2H

1 a i €2460 **ii** 0.180% **b i** −467 people **ii** 1.48%
   c i \$1890 **ii** 0.413% **d i** 189 cars **ii** 6.72%
2 a i −1.238 kg **ii** 19.8% **b i** 2.4 m **ii** 2.46%
   c i −3.8 L **ii** 16.0% **d i** −22 hours **ii** 30.6%
3 a 100 m^2 **b** 99.91 m^2 **c** 0.09 m^2 **d** 0.0901%
4 a 3254.224 cm^3 **b** 3240 cm^3 **c** −14.224 cm^3
   d 0.437%

5 a 72 m^2 **b** \$6120 **c** 77.08 m^2 **d** 6.59%
   e No **f** \$7650
6 a 1.7 m **b** 5.1 m^2 **c** 5 m^2 **d** 2%
7 a 65.25 km h^{-1} **b** 4.75 km h^{-1} **c** 7.28%

EXERCISE 21.1

1 a i 19 500 ZAR **ii** 2925 ZAR
   b i 3230.77 SGD **ii** 0.21 SGD
2 a i 6075.30 TWD **ii** 1161.50 NOK
   iii 1272.54 CNY
   b i 860.96 USD **ii** 5478.00 CNY
   c i 3.29 USD **ii** 20.95 CNY
3 a i 1924.65 CNY **ii** 9454.725 RUB
   b i 1 CNY = 8.1833 INR **ii** 1 RUB = 0.2036 CNY
   c 6106.95 CNY
4 a i 1349.50 ZAR **ii** 2242 MXN **b** 44 600 RUB
   c i 1.6617 **ii** 3.7051 **iii** 1 **d** 1 peso
5 a i 210 AUD **ii** 380 AUD
   b i 250 GBP **ii** 75 GBP

EXERCISE 21.2

1 a i 7.50 GBP **ii** 769.09 USD
   b i 5.25 GBP **ii** €400.08
   c i 18 GBP **ii** \$2476.76 NZ
2 a i 4.50 SGD **ii** 120.47 GBP
   b i 12.60 SGD **ii** 539.47 AUD
   c i 27 SGD **ii** €838.87

EXERCISE 21.3

1 a 220.62 EUR **b** 190.20 GBP **c** 387.54 SGD
   d 304.08 AUD
2 a 388.05 USD **b** 806.18 USD **c** 163.00 USD
   d 860.71 USD
3 a 907.37 USD **b** 26.32 USD **c** 255.61 USD
4 a 3332.44 USD **b** 6697.92 USD **c** 255.10 USD
   d 2733.40 USD
5 a 880 baht **b** 389.38 pesos **c** 10.62 pesos
6 a 3458.95 rupees **b** 416.23 yuan **c** 8.77 yuan
7 a 39 379.20 kwanza **b** 3126.57 pula **c** 73.43 pula

REVIEW SET 2A

1 6 hours 17 minutes
2 a 3:35 am the next day **b** 9:50 am **3** 440 000 g
4 95°F **5 a** 143 000 km **b** 0.000 004 5 m
6 a 1.96×10^{-5} s **b** 0.0110 s
7 a i 6.4 **ii** 6.38 **b i** 0.05 **ii** 0.047
8 a ± 0.5 cm **b** between 35.5 cm and 36.5 cm
   c Upper: 1332.25 cm^2, Lower: 1260.25 cm^2
9 a 25.3 km h^{-1} **b** 5 hours 35 minutes
10 a i −\$590 **ii** 22.8%
   b i −0.109 cm **ii** 0.417%
11 Upper: 52 cm, Lower: 48 cm
12 a i 419.40 CAD **ii** 1907.40 TJS
   b 8093.66 TJS **c** 5147.34 TJS

REVIEW SET 2B

1 165 minutes **2** 11 hours 4 minutes **3** $28\frac{8}{9}$°C

4 168 cm   **5** **a** 460 000 000 000   **b** 1.9   **c** 0.0032
6 **a** 1.276×10^7 m   **b** 4.2×10^{-7} cm   **7** 313 sheets
8 **a** **i** 59.4   **ii** 59.40   **b** **i** 0.01   **ii** 0.0084
9 $569.48   **10** **a** -2.3 m   **b** 6.71%
11 **a** £8.75/h   **b** Increases by £26.25
12 **a** 3834.88 krone   **b** 624.47 francs   **c** 15.53 francs

REVIEW SET 2C

1 5 hours 52 minutes   **2** **a** 2:47 pm   **b** 9:33 am   **3** $10°C$
4 24.1 km h^{-1} **5** **a** 0.005 73   **b** 3020   **c** 987.5
6 **a** 4.13   **b** 2.97
7 **a** 2 hours 9 minutes (2.15 hours)   **b** 50 km h^{-1}
8 Store B, 0.88 cents per g
9 Upper: 27.625 cm^2,   Lower: 20.625 cm^2
10 **a** Actual area ≈ 6.16 m^2,   Calculated area ≈ 7.07 m^2
   b 0.911 m^2 **c** 14.8%
11 **a** **i** 2 m   **ii** 2.24 m   **iii** 2.236 m
   b **i** 1   **ii** 3   **iii** 4   **c** 2.24 m and 2.236 m
12 **a** 99 yuan   **b** 65 560.04 yen

EXERCISE 3A.1

1 **a** k^6 **b** 5^8 **c** d^{10} **d** 11^{4+a}
   e p^7 **f** c^{8+m} **g** x^{k+2} **h** r^{11}
2 **a** 7^5 **b** b^2 **c** 5^3 **d** m^6
   e k^{12-a} **f** y^5 **g** t^{m-4} **h** x^{3a-2}
3 **a** 5^6 **b** c^{12} **c** 3^{32} **d** v^{25}
   e 7^{6d} **f** g^{8k} **g** m^{3t} **h** 11^{2xy}
4 **a** b^{12} **b** t^7 **c** p^{18} **d** 7^{6-n}
   e x^{6s} **f** d^{k-3} **g** 3^{13} **h** j^{12x}
   i 11^7 **j** z^{7-4t} **k** 13^{5cd} **l** w^{7p-1}
5 **a** 2^2 **b** 2^{-2} **c** 2^3 **d** 2^{-3} **e** 2^5
   f 2^{-5} **g** 2^1 **h** 2^{-1} **i** 2^6 **j** 2^{-6}
   k 2^7 **l** 2^{-7}
6 **a** 3^2 **b** 3^{-2} **c** 3^3 **d** 3^{-3} **e** 3^1
   f 3^{-1} **g** 3^4 **h** 3^{-4} **i** 3^0 **j** 3^5
   k 3^{-5}
7 **a** 2^{1+a} **b** 2^{2+b} **c** 2^{3+t} **d** 2^{2x} **e** 2^n
   f 2^{c-2} **g** 2^{2m} **h** 2^{n+1} **i** 2^1 **j** 2^{3x-1}
8 **a** 3^{2+p} **b** 3^{3a} **c** 3^{1+2n} **d** 3^{3+d} **e** 3^{2+3t}
   f 3^{y-1} **g** 3^{1-y} **h** 3^{2-3t} **i** 3^{3a-1} **j** 3^3
9 **a** 2^5 **b** 7^2 **c** 5^6 **d** 2^{10} **e** 2^{4p}
   f 3^{3t} **g** 5^{a+2} **h** 2^{5n}
10 **a** 2^{3m-4n} **b** 5^{2p-4} **c** 2^3 **d** 3^{2t+4}
   e 2^{10-5r} **f** 3^{3-y} **g** 2^{2k} **h** 5^{4-3a}
11 **a** $4a^2$ **b** $9n^2$ **c** $125m^3$ **d** m^3n^3
   e $\dfrac{a^3}{8}$ **f** $\dfrac{9}{m^2}$ **g** $\dfrac{p^4}{q^4}$ **h** $\dfrac{t^2}{25}$
12 **a** 1   **b** $\frac{1}{3}$ **c** $\frac{1}{49}$ **d** $\dfrac{1}{x^3}$
   e $\frac{6}{5}\left(1\frac{1}{5}\right)$ **f** 1   **g** $\frac{4}{7}$ **h** 6
   i $\frac{9}{16}$ **j** $\frac{5}{2}\left(2\frac{1}{2}\right)$ **k** $\frac{27}{125}$ **l** $\frac{151}{5}\left(30\frac{1}{5}\right)$
13 **a** $\dfrac{5}{n}$ **b** $\dfrac{1}{5n}$ **c** $\dfrac{n}{5}$ **d** $\dfrac{25}{n^2}$
   e $\dfrac{1}{mn}$ **f** $\dfrac{n}{m}$ **g** $\dfrac{m}{n}$ **h** $\dfrac{n}{m}$

EXERCISE 3A.2

1 **a** $25p^2$ **b** $36b^4$ **c** $\dfrac{25k^2}{m^2}$ **d** $\dfrac{t^3}{8s^3}$ **e** $8a^3$
   f $27m^6n^6$ **g** $\dfrac{y^6}{27z^3}$ **h** 1, $c \neq 0$, $d \neq 0$
   i $16a^4b^{16}$ **j** $\dfrac{8a^6}{b^6}$ **k** $\dfrac{16a^6}{b^2}$ **l** $\dfrac{9p^4}{q^6}$
2 **a** $4b^3$ **b** $6w^5$ **c** $4p^2$ **d** $30c^{11}$ **e** d^4 **f** $3ab^2$
   g $4n^3$ **h** t^7 **i** $20s^2t^4$ **j** k^{11} **k** $\dfrac{3xy^3}{2}$ **l** b^9
3 **a** $\dfrac{a}{b^2}$ **b** $\dfrac{1}{a^2b^2}$ **c** $\dfrac{4a^2}{b^2}$ **d** $\dfrac{1}{25m^4}$
   e $\dfrac{9b^2}{a^4}$ **f** $\dfrac{1}{27x^3y^{12}}$ **g** $\dfrac{a^2}{bc^2}$ **h** $\dfrac{a^2c^2}{b}$
   i a^3 **j** $\dfrac{b^3}{a^2}$ **k** $\dfrac{2}{ad^2}$ **l** $12am^3$
4 **a** a^{-n} **b** b^n **c** 3^{n-2} **d** a^nb^m **e** a^{-2n-2}
5 **a** $1 + 3x^{-1}$ **b** $3x^{-1} - 2$ **c** $5x^{-2} - x^{-1}$
   d $x^{-2} + 2x^{-3}$ **e** $x + 5x^{-1}$ **f** $x + 1 - 2x^{-1}$
   g $2x - 3 + 4x^{-1}$ **h** $x - 3x^{-1} + 5x^{-2}$
   i $5x^{-1} - 1 - x$ **j** $8x^{-1} + 5 - 2x^2$
   k $16x^{-2} - 3x^{-1} + x$ **l** $5x^2 - 3 + x^{-1} + 6x^{-2}$
6 **a** $4x + 2x^2$ **b** $5x^2 - 4x^3$ **c** $6x^3 + 3x^4$ **d** $x^3 + 3x$
   e $x^4 + x^3 - 4x^2$ **f** $x^6 - 3x^4 + 6x^3$ **g** $x^5 - 6x^3 + 10x^2$

EXERCISE 3B

1 **a** Each row is made up of $(b + c)$ balls in total, and there are
   a rows. $\therefore$ total number of balls is $a \times (b + c) = a(b + c)$
   b **i** ab **ii** ac
2 **a** $4x + 12$ **b** $5x - 10$ **c** $24 - 8x$
   d $-2x - 5$ **e** $-3x + 21$ **f** $2x^2 + 12x$
   g $-6x^2 - 30x$ **h** $12x^2 - 20x$ **i** $-5x^2 + 10x$
   j $-18x + 15x^2$ **k** $7x^3 - 28x^2$ **l** $-36x^3 + 81x$
3 **a** $19x + 11$ **b** $22x - 15$ **c** $7x + 2$ **d** $7x - 30$
   e $5x^2 + 11x$ **f** $3x^2 - 2x + 10$ **g** $8x^2 - 23x - 7$
   h $22x^2 - 12x$ **i** $9x^2 - 22x$ **j** $-12x^2 + 30x - 20$

EXERCISE 3C

1 **a** $x^2 + 9x + 14$ **b** $x^2 + 5x - 24$ **c** $x^2 - x - 20$
   d $x^2 - 9x + 18$ **e** $2x^2 - 5x - 12$ **f** $6x^2 + 11x - 35$
   g $20x^2 - 33x + 10$ **h** $4x^2 + 11x - 3$
   i $-3x^2 - 7x + 20$ **j** $-18x^2 + 51x - 8$
   k $-3x^2 + 23x + 36$ **l** $-35x^2 + 43x - 12$
2 **a** $x^2 - 16$ **b** $a^2 - 36$ **c** $49 - x^2$
   d $9x^2 - 1$ **e** $16k^2 - 9$ **f** $25 - 36a^2$
3 **a** $x^2 + 14x + 49$ **b** $x^2 - 10x + 25$
   c $4x^2 - 12x + 9$ **d** $25 + 30x + 9x^2$
   e $49 - 28x + 4x^2$ **f** $16x^2 + 8xy + y^2$

EXERCISE 3D

1 **a** $x^2 - 9$ **b** $x^2 - 1$ **c** $36 - x^2$
   d $100 - x^2$ **e** $x^2 - 100$ **f** $a^2 - 49$
   g $81 - y^2$ **h** $k^2 - 25$ **i** $x^2 - y^2$
2 **a** $4x^2 - 1$ **b** $25x^2 - 9$ **c** $16x^2 - 49$
   d $36x^2 - 25$ **e** $64t^2 - 1$ **f** $25 - 81x^2$
   g $49 - 16k^2$ **h** $100 - 9m^2$ **i** $1 - 144z^2$

3 **a** $9x^2 - y^2$ **b** $m^2 - 16n^2$ **c** $9p^2 - 49q^2$
  d $64c^2 - 25d^2$ **e** $81x^2 - 4y^2$ **f** $36y^2 - 25x^2$

EXERCISE 3E

1 **a** $x^2 + 6x + 9$ **b** $x^2 + 12x + 36$ **c** $x^2 + 4x + 4$
  d $a^2 + 18a + 81$ **e** $25 + 10k + k^2$ **f** $49 + 14t + t^2$

2 **a** $x^2 - 6x + 9$ **b** $x^2 - 2x + 1$ **c** $x^2 - 16x + 64$
  d $b^2 - 4b + 4$ **e** $16 - 8x + x^2$ **f** $49 - 14y + y^2$

3 **a** $9x^2 + 30x + 25$ **b** $16a^2 - 16a + 4$ **c** $4b^2 + 28b + 49$
  d $9k^2 + 6k + 1$ **e** $25y^2 - 40y + 16$ **f** $9 - 12x + 4x^2$
  g $16 + 24y + 9y^2$ **h** $1 + 10z + 25z^2$ **i** $4 - 12n + 9n^2$

4 **a** $x^4 + 6x^2 + 9$ **b** $y^4 - 14y^2 + 49$
  c $25z^4 + 10z^2 + 1$ **d** $9 - 12a^2 + 4a^4$
  e $m^4 + 2m^2n^2 + n^4$ **f** $x^4 - 2x^2y^2 + y^4$

5 **a** $-x^2 - 2x + 1$ **b** $x^2 - 5x + 5$ **c** $2x^2 + 4x - 5$
  d $-8x - 65$ **e** $-11x + 31$ **f** $10x^2 - 15x$
  g $10x^2 - 14x + 48$ **h** $x^2 + 3x - 16$
  i $10x^2 - 28x + 20$ **j** $7 - 2x$

6 **a**

b	$(5+b)^2$	$(5-b)^2$	$(5+b)^2 - (5-b)^2$
0	25	25	0
1	36	16	20
2	49	9	40
3	64	4	60
4	81	1	80
5	100	0	100

  b Expand and simplify the algebraic expression
  $(5 + b)^2 - (5 - b)^2$.

EXERCISE 3F

1 **a** $x^3 + 5x^2 + 11x + 10$ **b** $x^3 - x^2 - 10x + 6$
  c $x^3 + 6x^2 + 7x + 10$ **d** $x^3 + x^2 - 10x + 8$
  e $2x^3 - x^2 - 4x + 3$ **f** $4x^3 - 5x^2 - 3x + 1$
  g $-x^3 - 5x^2 + 17x - 6$ **h** $6x^3 - 11x^2 - x + 6$

2 **a** $x^3 + 6x^2 + 12x + 8$ **b** $x^3 + 3x^2 + 3x + 1$
  c $x^3 - 3x^2 + 3x - 1$ **d** $x^3 - 6x^2 + 12x - 8$
  e $27x^3 + 27x^2 + 9x + 1$ **f** $8x^3 - 36x^2 + 54x - 27$

3 **a** $x^3 + 3x^2 + 2x$ **b** $x^3 + x^2 - 6x$ **c** $x^3 - 5x^2 + 4x$
  d $2x^3 + 6x^2 + 4x$ **e** $2x^3 - 14x^2 + 24x$
  f $-x^3 + x^2 + 6x$ **g** $-3x^3 + 3x^2 + 60x$
  h $-3x^3 + 9x^2 - 6x$ **i** $x^3 + 5x^2 - 6x$

4 **a** $x^3 + 6x^2 + 11x + 6$ **b** $x^3 - 2x^2 - 5x + 6$
  c $x^3 - 12x^2 + 44x - 48$ **d** $x^3 - 2x^2 - x + 2$
  e $2x^3 - x^2 - 7x + 6$ **f** $4x^3 - 8x^2 - 9x + 18$
  g $-4x^3 - 11x^2 + 43x - 10$ **h** $-3x^3 + 8x^2 + 33x + 10$

5 **a** 4 **b** 6 **c** 6 **d** 9 **e** 8 **f** 12 **g** 8 **h** 12

REVIEW SET 3A

1 **a** x^6 **b** 2^{-7} **c** a^6b^{18} **2** **a** $\frac{1}{27}$ **b** $\frac{y}{x}$ **c** $\frac{b}{a}$

3 **a** 3^3 **b** 3^{2t} **c** 2^{3-m} **4** **a** $\frac{5x}{y^2}$ **b** $\frac{1}{j^7}$ **c** $3g^3h^3$

5 **a** $\frac{t^3}{64s^3}$ **b** $1, \ m \neq 0, \ n \neq 0$ **c** $25p^6q^2$

6 **a** $x + 8x^{-1}$ **b** $4x^2 + x^3 + x^5$ **c** k^{-2x-6}

7 **a** $7x^2 - 49x$ **b** $-8x^2 - 32x$

8 **a** $x^2 - 9$ **b** $2x^2 + 7x - 30$ **c** $49x^2 - 14xy + y^2$

9 **a** $2x^2 + 13x$ **b** $x^3 + 2x^2 - 37x + 10$ **10** **a** 6 **b** 8

REVIEW SET 3B

1 **a** m^4 **b** $1, \ y \neq 0$ **c** $\frac{w^2}{49z^2}$

2 **a** k^{x-2} **b** 11^{r-4} **c** 3^{2+b}

3 **a** 11^{-1} **b** ab^{-2} **c** jk^4l^{-a}

4 **a** 2^{-4} **b** 3^{k+4} **c** 5^{3a-b}

5 **a** $\frac{1}{8}$ **b** 1   **c** $\frac{10}{3} \ (3\frac{1}{3})$

6 **a** $\frac{a^{18}}{64b^6}$ **b** $\frac{25}{d^8}$ **c** $2z^4$

7 **a** $20x - 4x^2$ **b** $6x^2 + 13x + 6$

8 **a** $x^2 - 5x - 36$ **b** $x^2 + 14x + 49$ **c** $-x^2 - x + 6$

9 **a** $-x^2 - 8x - 9$ **b** $7x^2 + 27x + 9$

10 **a** $2x^3 + 13x^2 - 13x - 42$ **b** $x^3 - 12x^2 + 48x - 64$

EXERCISE 4A

1 **a** 8   **b** 1   **c** 6   **d** 6
  e 1   **f** -18 **g** -4 **h** -8

2 **a** $-\frac{3}{4}$ **b** -2 **c** -1 **d** $\frac{2}{7}$
  e -5 **f** $-\frac{3}{2}$ **g** -1 **h** -5

3 **a** 1   **b** -27 **c** 25   **d** 1
  e 63   **f** 27   **g** 36   **h** 18

4 **a** 1 **b** 4 **c** 3 **d** 5 **e** $\sqrt{53} \approx 7.28$
  f $\sqrt{2} \approx 1.41$ **g** $\sqrt{42} \approx 6.48$ **h** 6

EXERCISE 4B.1

1 **a** $x = -2$ **b** $x = 7$ **c** $x = 6$ **d** $x = -4$
  e $x = \frac{11}{2}$ **f** $x = -3$ **g** $x = 7$ **h** $x = \frac{4}{3}$

2 **a** $x = 45$ **b** $x = 64$ **c** $x = -3$ **d** $x = 22$
  e $x = 1$ **f** $x = 7$ **g** $x = \frac{23}{2}$ **h** $x = 17$

EXERCISE 4B.2

1 **a** $x = 1$ **b** $x = -4$ **c** $x = 9$ **d** $x = -2$
  e $x = \frac{1}{2}$ **f** $x = 6$

2 **a** $x = 6$ **b** $x = 3$ **c** $x = 2$ **d** $x = -4$
  e $x = \frac{1}{2}$ **f** $x = \frac{10}{3}$

3 **a** $x = 1$ **b** $x = 4$ **c** $x = -2$ **d** $x = -\frac{7}{10}$

4 **a** $x \in \mathbb{R}$ **b** no solution
  So, **a** has infinitely many solutions and **b** has no solutions.

EXERCISE 4B.3

1 **a** $x = 1$ **b** $x = 2$ **c** $x = \frac{22}{9}$ **d** $x = -\frac{9}{5}$
  e $x = -\frac{2}{3}$ **f** $x = -\frac{19}{6}$ **g** $x = -9$ **h** $x = \frac{5}{4}$

EXERCISE 4C

1 **a** $x = \frac{10}{3}$ **b** $x = \frac{25}{6}$ **c** $x = \frac{17}{5}$
  d $x = -4$ **e** $x = \frac{10}{29}$ **f** $x = \frac{7}{29}$
  g $x = -\frac{5}{13}$ **h** $x = \frac{51}{23}$ **i** $x = -1$

2 **a** $x = \frac{15}{2}$ **b** $x = 6$ **c** $x = \frac{28}{3}$
  d $x = \frac{9}{20}$ **e** $x = \frac{5}{6}$ **f** $x = -\frac{3}{2}$
  g $x = \frac{7}{5}$ **h** $x = -\frac{13}{2}$ **i** $x = 6$

3 no solution $(x \neq 0)$

4 **a** $x = 1$ **b** $x = \frac{3}{5}$ **c** $x = -7$
  d $x = \frac{5}{7}$ **e** $x = 5$ **f** $x = \frac{16}{17}$
  g $x = -2$ **h** $x = -\frac{21}{38}$ **i** $x = -\frac{6}{41}$

EXERCISE 4D

1 a $x \approx 1.56$ b $x = 262$ c $x \approx 1.09$ d $x \approx -26.0$
2 a $x \approx -2.33$ b $x \approx -0.0769$ c $x \approx 2.43$
3 a $w = 55$ b $w = 92.5$
4 a $\approx 4.44°C$ b $\approx -17.8°C$ c $\approx 93.3°C$
5 a 110 m   b 190 m
6 a $x = 9.5$ b $x \approx 6.56$ c $x \approx 10.5$ d $x \approx 37.3$

EXERCISE 4E

1 7   2 13   3 9   4 18 cm
5 a 85 cm   b 13 m by 6.5 m   6 11 years old
7 18 years old   8 6   9 10   10 10

EXERCISE 4F

1 a 35.8 cm   b 79.6 cm   c 15.9 m
2 a 44.1 m   b 129 m
3 a 80 km h^{-1} b 260 km   c 7 h 52 min
4 a 98.5 cm^2 b 7.98 m   5   a 0.48 volts b 60 ohms
6 a 7920 cm^3 b 1.59 cm   c 0.399 mm
7 a 11.3 km   b 71.0 m   8   a 598 cm^2 b 28.2 cm

EXERCISE 4G.1

1 a $y = \dfrac{4 - x}{2}$ b $y = \dfrac{7 - 2x}{6}$ c $y = \dfrac{11 - 3x}{4}$

   d $y = \dfrac{8 - 5x}{4}$ e $y = \dfrac{20 - 7x}{2}$ f $y = \dfrac{38 - 11x}{15}$

2 a $y = \dfrac{x - 4}{2}$ b $y = \dfrac{2x - 7}{6}$ c $y = \dfrac{3x + 12}{4}$

   d $y = \dfrac{4x - 18}{5}$ e $y = \dfrac{7x - 42}{6}$ f $y = \dfrac{12x + 44}{13}$

3 a $x = b - a$ b $x = \dfrac{b}{a}$ c $x = \dfrac{d - a}{2}$

   d $x = t - c$ e $x = \dfrac{d - 3y}{7}$ f $x = \dfrac{c - by}{a}$

   g $x = \dfrac{c + y}{m}$ h $x = \dfrac{c - p}{2}$ i $x = \dfrac{a - t}{3}$

   j $x = \dfrac{n - 5}{k}$ k $x = \dfrac{a - n}{b}$ l $x = \dfrac{a - p}{n}$

4 a $x = ab$ b $x = \dfrac{a}{d}$ c $x = \dfrac{2}{p}$

   d $x = 2n$ e $x = \dfrac{5z}{y}$ f $x = \pm\sqrt{mn}$

5 $y = -\frac{5}{3}x + 6$; $m = -\frac{5}{3}$; $c = 6$

EXERCISE 4G.2

1 a $s = \dfrac{R - 2t}{5}$ b i $s = 2$ ii $s = -4$ iii $s = 2.4$

2 a $a = \dfrac{d}{2bK}$ b i $a = \frac{3}{56}$ ii $a = \frac{9}{40}$

3 a $d = st$ km
      i 180 km   ii 120 km   iii $126\frac{2}{3}$ km

   b $t = \dfrac{d}{s}$ h
      i 3 hours   ii 4 hours   iii 2 hours 12 minutes

4 a $n = \dfrac{100I}{Cr}$ b 2.05 years   c 10 years

EXERCISE 4H.1

1 a $x = 3$, $y = -2$ b $x = -4$, $y = \frac{1}{2}$
   c $x = 2.75$, $y = -3.5$ d $x = -3.5$, $y = 1.5$
   e $x = 4$, $y = 3$ f $x = -2.4$, $y = 3.9$
2 a $x = 4$, $y = 11$ b $x = -3$, $y = -2$
   c $x \approx 2.92$, $y \approx -1.15$ d $x = 0$, $y = 1.5$
   e $x \approx 0.986$, $y \approx -0.314$ f $x = 0.75$, $y = 3.75$
3 no solution, the equations represent parallel lines

EXERCISE 4H.2

1 a $x = 4$, $y = 2$ b $x = -1$, $y = 3$
   c $x = 3$, $y = -1.5$
2 a $x = 4$, $y = -3$ b $x = -2$, $y = 0$
   c $x = 3$, $y = 1$ d $x = 1.5$, $y = -2.5$
   e $x \approx 1.06$, $y \approx 2.29$ f $x \approx -0.154$, $y \approx 0.615$
3 a none   b infinitely many solutions

EXERCISE 4H.3

1 a $x = 5$, $y = 2$ b $x = 3$, $y = 4$ c $x = -1$, $y = 5$
   d $x = 2$, $y = -4$ e $x = -3$, $y = 0$ f $x = \frac{1}{3}$, $y = \frac{2}{3}$
2 a $5 \neq 1$, so cannot solve   b no solution
3 a $x \in \mathbb{R}$ b infinitely many solutions

EXERCISE 4H.4

1 a $4x = 15$ b $2y = 12$ c $5x = 10$
2 a $x = 2$, $y = 1$ b $x = 3$, $y = 2$ c $x = 3$, $y = 2$
   d $x = 2$, $y = -1$ e $x = \frac{1}{2}$, $y = 2$ f $x = \frac{4}{3}$, $y = -\frac{1}{3}$
3 a $3x - 3y = 6$ b $-2x - y = 1$ c $-2x + 6y = 4$
   d $9x - 6y = 12$
4 a $x = 2$, $y = 1$ b $x = -1$, $y = 3$ c $x = 2$, $y = 4$
   d $x = 3$, $y = -2$ e $x = -2$, $y = \frac{1}{2}$ f $x = 7$, $y = -3$

EXERCISE 4I

1 40 and 18   2 27 and 55
3 Small can = 240 mL, Large can = 420 mL
4 Waltz = 3 minutes, Sonatina = 7 minutes
5 Short cable = 2.5 m, Long cable = 4.2 m
6 a 10 points   b 6 points   7 a 9 m   b 50 cm
8 12 of 3 L cans, 7 of 5 L cans   9 6 two hour lessons
10 33 km

EXERCISE 4J.1

1 a $x = \pm 2$ b $x = \pm 4$ c $x = \pm 1$
   d $x = \pm\sqrt{7}$ e no real solutions   f $x = 0$
   g $x = \pm\sqrt{5}$ h no real solutions
2 a $x = 7$ or -1 b $x = 2$ or -4 c no real solutions
   d $x = 2 \pm \sqrt{10}$ e $x = -4 \pm \sqrt{13}$ f $x = 7$
   g $x = 4$ or -1 h $x = \dfrac{-1 \pm \sqrt{14}}{3}$

EXERCISE 4J.2

1 a $x = 0$ b $a = 0$ c $y = 0$ d $a = 0$ or $b = 0$
   e $x = 0$ or $y = 0$ f $a = 0$
2 a $x = 0$ or 5   b $x = 0$ or -3 c $x = -1$ or 3
   d $x = 0$ or 7   e $x = 0$ or -1 f $x = -6$ or $\frac{3}{2}$
   g $x = -\frac{1}{2}$ or $\frac{1}{2}$ h $x = -2$ or 7   i $x = 5$ or $-\frac{2}{3}$
   j $x = 0$ k $x = 5$ l $x = \frac{1}{3}$

EXERCISE 4J.3

1　a　$x = 3$ or 2　　　　b　$x = -2$ or -7
　　c　$x = 4$　　　　　　　d　$x = 4$ or 0.5
　　e　$x = 0.25$ or -1.5　f　$x \approx 1.29$ or -1.54

2　a　$x = 1$ or -7　　　　b　$x = 1.5$ or -2.5
　　c　$x = 3.5$ or 1.8　　　d　$x \approx 1.18$ or 2.82
　　e　$x \approx -2.27$ or 1.77　f　no real solutions

3　a　$x = -3$ or -4　　　b　$x = 1$ or -3
　　c　$x \approx 1.85$ or -4.85　d　$x \approx 0.847$ or -1.18
　　e　$x = -0.5$　　　　　f　no real solutions

4　a　$x = 5$ or -0.75　　　b　$x = 1.5$ or ≈ -0.667
　　c　$x \approx 0.775$ or 3.22　d　$x = 4$ or -3
　　e　$x = -5$　　　　　　f　$x \approx 1.24$ or -3.24

5　a　$x = -1$ or 5　　　　b　$x = 2$
　　c　no solution　　　　　d　$x = -2.5$ or 0.6
　　e　$x \approx -0.155$ or ≈ 2.16　f　$x \approx -0.906$ or 1.66

6　a　$x \approx -0.667$ or 4　　b　$x \approx -7.21$ or 0.208
　　c　$x \approx -6.54$ or -0.459

7　a　$x \approx -1.22$ or 8.22　　b　$x = -0.25$
　　c　$x \approx -1.69$ or 1.19　　d　$x \approx 0.0783$ or 0.811

EXERCISE 4J.4

1　a　$x = 2 \pm \sqrt{7}$　　b　$x = -3 \pm \sqrt{2}$　　c　$x = 2 \pm \sqrt{3}$
　　d　$x = -2 \pm \sqrt{5}$　　e　$x = 2 \pm \sqrt{2}$　　f　$x = \frac{1 \pm \sqrt{17}}{2}$
　　g　$x = \frac{-4 \pm \sqrt{7}}{9}$　　h　$x = \frac{-7 \pm \sqrt{97}}{4}$　　i　$x = \frac{5 \pm 2\sqrt{10}}{3}$

2　a　$x = -2 \pm 2\sqrt{2}$　b　$x = \frac{-5 \pm \sqrt{57}}{8}$　c　$x = \frac{5 \pm \sqrt{13}}{2}$
　　d　$x = \frac{1 \pm \sqrt{7}}{2}$　　e　$x = \frac{1 \pm \sqrt{5}}{2}$　　f　$x = \frac{3 \pm \sqrt{17}}{4}$

EXERCISE 4K

1　-5 and 7, or -7 and 5　　2　5 or $\frac{1}{5}$　　3　14
4　18 and 20, or -18 and -20
5　15 and 17, or -15 and -17　　6　15　　7　3.48 cm
8　7 m by 10 m, or 5 m by 14 m　　9　No
10　b　6 cm $\times$ 6 cm $\times$ 7 cm　　11　≈ 11.2 cm $\times$ 11.2 cm
12　c　1.5 m　　13　61.8 km h^{-1}　　14　2.03 m

REVIEW SET 4A

1　a　100　　b　$\frac{1}{3}$　　c　3　　2　a　$x = -1$　　b　$x = 8$
3　a　$x = -4$　　b　$x = 4$　　4　a　$x = -\frac{1}{4}$　　b　$x = 8$
5　11　　6　11　　7　a　$x = 4$　　b　$x = -3$
8　a　224 000 J　　b　1.19°C
9　a　$y = \frac{4x - 28}{3}$　　b　$y = \frac{k - d}{c}$　　c　$y = \frac{p}{q}$
10　a　$x = 7$ or -3　　b　$x = 3$ or 2
11　a　$x = \pm\sqrt{28}$　　b　$x = 1$ or -2
12　20 cm by 13 cm　　13　£10

REVIEW SET 4B

1　a　-33　　b　$\frac{1}{5}$　　c　4
2　a　$x = 20$　　b　$x = \frac{25}{4}$　　c　$x = -\frac{14}{3}$
3　a　$x = \frac{7}{4}$　b　$x = -2$　　4　a　$k = 4.7$　　b　$a = \frac{10}{11}$
5　$1.98　　6　a　222 people per km^2　　b　3 280 000 km^2
7　a　$x = -2$, $y = 3$　　b　$x = 4$, $y = -1$　　8　25 people
9　a　$x = 3$ or -8　　b　$x = 3$ or -3　　c　$x = \frac{1}{2}$ or $-\frac{3}{4}$

10　a　$x = 4$ or -5　　　b　$x = 9$ or -6
11　a　$x \approx 0.317$ or -6.32　　　b　$x \approx -1.48$ or 3.15
12　BC $= 5$ cm or 16 cm　　13　5 or 2

REVIEW SET 4C

1　a　36　　b　$-\frac{5}{4}$　　c　2　　2　a　$x = 2$　　b　$x = 2$
3　a　$w = \frac{5q - 12}{2}$　　b　$w = \frac{3t}{2s}$
4　a　$n = \frac{P}{S - C}$　　b　97 watches　　c　$S = \frac{P + Cn}{n}$
　　d　€29.30
5　a　$x = \frac{5}{2}$, $y = \frac{13}{4}$　　b　$x = 5$, $y = -8$
6　3　　7　24 m, 51 m
8　a　$x = 0$ or $\frac{5}{2}$　　b　$x = 6$ or -2　　c　$x = 2$ or $-\frac{3}{4}$
9　a　$x = 3$ or -9　　b　$x = -1$ or -5　　c　$x = \frac{1}{3}$ or -2
10　Richard is 7 years old.　　11　1.17 seconds
12　28.4 km h^{-1}　　13　1620 adults, 1370 children

EXERCISE 5A

1　a　4, 13, 22, 31　　　b　45, 39, 33, 27
　　c　2, 6, 18, 54　　　d　96, 48, 24, 12

2　a　Start with 8, add 8 each time. 40, 48
　　b　Start with 2, add 3 each time. 14, 17
　　c　Start with 36, subtract 5 each time. 16, 11
　　d　Start with 96, subtract 7 each time. 68, 61
　　e　Start with 1, multiply by 4 each time. 256, 1024
　　f　Start with 2, multiply by 3 each time. 162, 486
　　g　Start with 480, divide by 2 each time. 30, 15
　　h　Start with 243, divide by 3 each time. 3, 1
　　i　Start with 50 000, divide by 5 each time. 80, 16

3　a　Each term is the square of its term number in the sequence.
　　　25, 36, 49
　　b　Each term is the cube of its term number in the sequence.
　　　125, 216, 343
　　c　Each term is $n(n + 1)$, where n is the term number.
　　　30, 42, 56

4　a　79, 75　　　b　1280, 5120　　c　625, 1296
　　d　1, $\frac{1}{2}$　　　e　13, 17　　　f　16, 22

EXERCISE 5B

1　a　1　　b　13　　c　79
2　a　7, 9, 11, 13　　b

3　a　2, 4, 6, 8, 10　　b　4, 6, 8, 10, 12　　c　1, 3, 5, 7, 9
　　d　-1, 1, 3, 5, 7　　e　5, 7, 9, 11, 13　　f　13, 15, 17, 19, 21
　　g　4, 7, 10, 13, 16　　h　1, 5, 9, 13, 17

4　a　2, 4, 8, 16, 32　　　b　6, 12, 24, 48, 96
　　c　3, $\frac{3}{2}$, $\frac{3}{4}$, $\frac{3}{8}$, $\frac{3}{16}$　　　d　-2, 4, -8, 16, -32

5　17, 11, 23, -1, 47

6 **a** 5, 8, 11, 14, 17, ...   **b** 5, 8, 11, 14, 17, ...
   c 100, 93, 86, 79, 72, ...   **d** 100, 93, 86, 79, 72, ...
   e 5, 10, 20, 40, 80, ...   **f** 5, 10, 20, 40, 80, ...
   g 48, 24, 12, 6, 3, ...   **h** 48, 24, 12, 6, 3, ...

   Each pair describes the same sequence. (**a** and **b**, **c** and **d**, ...)

EXERCISE 5C

1 **a** 73   **b** 65   **c** 21.5
2 **a** 101   **b** -107 **c** $a + 14d$
3 **b** $u_n = 11n - 5$ **c** 545   **d** Yes   **e** No
4 **b** $u_n = 91 - 4n$ **c** -69 **d** the 97th term
5 **b** $u_1 = 1$, $d = 3$ **c** 169   **d** $u_{150} = 448$
6 **b** $u_1 = 32$, $d = -\frac{7}{2}$ **c** -227 **d** $n \geqslant 68$
7 **a** $k = 17\frac{1}{2}$ **b** $k = 4$ **c** $k = 4$ **d** $k = 0$
   e $k = 7$ **f** $k = -4$
8 **a** $k = 3$ or -2 **b** $k = 1$ or -3 **c** $k = 3$ or -1
9 **a** $u_n = 6n - 1$ **b** $u_n = -\frac{3}{2}n + \frac{11}{2}$
   c $u_n = -5n + 36$ **d** $u_n = -\frac{3}{2}n + \frac{1}{2}$
10 **a** 6.25, 7.5, 8.75   **b** $3\frac{5}{7}, 8\frac{3}{7}, 13\frac{1}{7}, 17\frac{6}{7}, 22\frac{4}{7}, 27\frac{2}{7}$
11 **a** $u_1 = 36$, $d = -\frac{2}{3}$ **b** u_{100} **12** $u_{7692} = 100\,006$
13 **a** Month 1 = 5 cars   Month 4 = 44 cars
      Month 2 = 18 cars   Month 5 = 57 cars
      Month 3 = 31 cars   Month 6 = 70 cars
   b The constant difference $d = 13$.   **c** 148 cars
   d 20 months
14 **b** 111 online friends   **c** 18 weeks
15 **a** Day 1 = 97.3 tonnes,   Day 2 = 94.6 tonnes
      Day 3 = 91.9 tonnes
   b $d = -2.7$, the cattle eat 2.7 tonnes of hay each day.
   c $u_{25} = 32.5$. After 25 days (i.e., July 25th) there will be
      32.5 tonnes of hay left.
   d 16.3 tonnes

EXERCISE 5D.1

1 **a** $b = 18$, $c = 54$ **b** $b = \frac{5}{2}$, $c = \frac{5}{4}$ **c** $b = 3$, $c = -\frac{3}{2}$
2 **a** 96   **b** 6250   **c** 16
3 **a** 6561   **b** $\frac{19\,683}{64}$ $(307\frac{35}{64})$ **c** 16   **d** ar^8
4 **a** $u_1 = 5$, $r = 2$ **b** $u_n = 5 \times 2^{n-1}$ **c** $u_{15} = 81\,920$
5 **a** $u_1 = 12$, $r = -\frac{1}{2}$ **b** $u_n = 12 \times (-\frac{1}{2})^{n-1}$
   c $u_{13} = \frac{3}{1024}$
6 $u_{10} \approx -0.601$ **7** $u_n = 8\left(\frac{1}{\sqrt{2}}\right)^{n-1}$
8 **a** $k = \pm 14$ **b** $k = 2$ **c** $k = -2$ or 4
9 **a** $u_n = 3 \times 2^{n-1}$ **b** $u_n = 32 \times (-\frac{1}{2})^{n-1}$
   c $u_n = 3 \times (\sqrt{2})^{n-1}$ or $u_n = 3 \times (-\sqrt{2})^{n-1}$
   d $u_n = 10 \times \left(\frac{1}{\sqrt{2}}\right)^{n-1}$ or $u_n = 10\left(-\frac{1}{\sqrt{2}}\right)^{n-1}$
10 **a** $u_9 = 13\,122$ **b** $u_{14} = 2916\sqrt{3}$ **c** $u_{18} \approx 0.000\,091\,6$

EXERCISE 5D.2

1 **a** **i** ≈ 1550 ants   **ii** ≈ 4820 ants   **b** ≈ 12.2 weeks
2 **a** **i** ≈ 73 **ii** ≈ 167 **b** 30.5 years
3 **a** ≈ 220 members   **b** ≈ 11.2 years
4 **a** **i** ≈ 2860 **ii** $\approx 184\,000$ **b** 14.5 years
5 **a** ≈ 319 **b** ≈ 52 years

EXERCISE 5E.1

1 **a** 91   **b** 91   **c** 91   **2** 203   **3** $-115\frac{1}{2}$
4 **a** 160   **b** 820   **c** $3087\frac{1}{2}$ **d** -1460
   e -150 **f** -740
5 **a** $d = 6$ **b** $n = 12$ **c** $S_{12} = 504$
6 **a** 1749   **b** 2115   **c** $1410\frac{1}{2}$
7 **a** 65   **b** 1914   **c** 47\,850
8 **a** 14\,025   **b** 71\,071   **c** 3367
9 **a** **i** $u_{10} = 38$ **ii** $u_{30} = 78$ **b** 1470
10 8 terms   **11** **a** $d = 3$ **b** $n = 11$
12 15 terms   **13** 18 layers   **14** $-2, 4, 10$ or $10, 4, -2$

EXERCISE 5E.2

1 **a** 93   **b** 93
2 **a** 6560   **b** 5115   **c** $\frac{3069}{128}$ **d** $\approx 189\,134$
   e ≈ 4.00 **f** ≈ 0.585
3 **a** $S_n = \dfrac{\sqrt{3}\left((\sqrt{3})^n - 1\right)}{\sqrt{3} - 1}$ **b** $S_n = 24\left(1 - (\frac{1}{2})^n\right)$
   c $S_n = 1 - (0.1)^n$ **d** $S_n = \frac{40}{3}\left(1 - (-\frac{1}{2})^n\right)$
4 **c** \$26\,361.59   **5** $n = 5$
6 **a** $u_8 = 1.25$ **b** $S_8 = 318.75$ **c** 12 terms

EXERCISE 5F.1

1 \$6945.75   **2** **a** £17\,496   **b** £2496
3 **a** ¥1\,284\,045   **b** ¥404\,045   **4** £13\,373.53
5 \$546.01   **6** Bank A

EXERCISE 5F.2

2 £6629.65   **3** \$4079.77   **4** €4159.08   **5** ¥199\,713
6 \$20\,836.86   **7** €80\,000   **8** 2 years 5 months
9 2 years 9 months   **10** 13 years 3 months   **11** 14.5% p.a.
12 6.00% p.a.   **13** 5.25% p.a.

EXERCISE 5G

1 €1280   **2** **a** €26\,103.52   **b** €83\,896.48
3 **a** ¥30\,013   **b** ¥57\,487   **4** 24.8%   **5** 18.4%

REVIEW SET 5A

1 **a** arithmetic   **b** arithmetic and geometric
   c geometric   **d** neither   **e** arithmetic
2 $k = -\frac{11}{2}$ **3** $u_n = 33 - 5n$, $S_n = \frac{n}{2}(61 - 5n)$
4 $k = 4$ or -4 **5** $u_n = \frac{1}{6} \times 2^{n-1}$ or $u_n = -\frac{1}{6} \times (-2)^{n-1}$
6 21, 19, 17, 15, 13, 11
7 **a** $u_8 = \frac{1}{15\,625}$ **b** $u_8 = 6\frac{1}{2}$ **c** $u_8 = a - 7d$
8 **a** Week 1: 2817 L   Week 3: 2451 L
      Week 2: 2634 L   Week 4: 2268 L
   b Amount in tank decreases by the same amount (183 L) each
      week.
   c after 17 weeks
9 **a** -492 **b** 7\,324\,218
10 **a** $u_8 = 61$ **b** $S_{10} = 435$ **c** $n = 15$
11 Bank A: \$231\,995.25,   Bank B: \$220\,787.17
   Val should deposit her money in Bank A.
12 \$657.26   **13** **a** \$59\,900.22   **b** \$75\,099.78
14 in 3 years

REVIEW SET 5B

1 **b** $u_1 = 6$, $r = \frac{1}{2}$ **c** $0.000\,183$

2 **a** 81 **b** $u_{35} = -1\frac{1}{2}$ **c** -486 **3** **a** 1587 **b** $47\frac{253}{256}$

4 **a** $\frac{1}{3}, \frac{1}{9}, \frac{1}{27}, \frac{1}{81}, \frac{1}{243}$ **b** $17, 22, 27, 32, 37$

c $\frac{4}{3}, 1, \frac{4}{5}, \frac{2}{3}, \frac{4}{7}$

5 **a** €8415.31   **b** €2415.31   **6** $u_{11} \approx 0.000\,406$

7 **a** $u_n = (\frac{3}{4})2^{n-1}$ **b** $49\,152$ **c** $24\,575\frac{1}{4}$

8 **a** 33 **b** $4(n+1) - 7 - (4n - 7) = 4$

c The difference between terms is always the same.   **d** 1328

9 **a** 17 terms   **b** $255\frac{511}{512}$

10 **a** $r = \frac{1}{3}$ **b** $u_6 = \frac{20}{27}$ **c** $n = 8$ **11** €970.26

12 4.80% p.a.   **13** **a** 12.5% per year   **b** $10\,966.45

REVIEW SET 5C

1 **b** $u_1 = 63$, $d = -5$ **c** $u_{37} = -117$ **d** $u_{54} = -202$

2 **b** $u_n = 3 \times 4^{n-1}$, $u_9 = 196\,608$

3 $u_n = 73 - 6n$, $u_{34} = -131$

4 **a** $a = 15$ **b** $a = 12$ or -12

5 **a** $u_{10} = -31$ **b** $u_{10} = 243$

6 **a** ≈ 3470 **b** 11 years

7 **a** $u_n = 89 - 3n$ **b** $u_n = \dfrac{2n+1}{n+3}$

c $u_n = 100 \times (0.9)^{n-1}$

8 $u_{12} = 10\,240$ **9** $k = -2$ or 4

10 **a** 2001: $630\,000$, 2002: $567\,000$ **b** $\approx 4\,560\,000$ sheets

11 €9838.99   **12** £13\,125.36   **13** $\approx 13.3\%$

EXERCISE 6A

1 **a** quantitative discrete   **b** categorical

c quantitative continuous   **d** quantitative continuous

e categorical   **f** quantitative discrete   **g** categorical

h quantitative discrete   **i** quantitative continuous

j quantitative continuous   **k** quantitative continuous

l categorical   **m** quantitative discrete

2 **a** $0, 1, 2, 3, ..., 8$ **b** red, yellow, orange, green, ...

c 0 - 15 minutes   **d** 0 - 25 m

e Ford, BMW, Renault, ...   **f** $1, 2, 3, ..., 20$

g Australia, Hawaii, Dubai, ...   **h** 0.0 - 10.0

i 0 - 4 L   **j** 0 - 80 hours   **k** $-20°C - 35°C$

l cereal, toast, fruit, rice, eggs, ...   **m** $0, 1, 2, ..., 10$

EXERCISE 6B

1 **a** the number of goals scored in a game

b variable is counted, not measured

c

Goals scored	Tally	Frequency	Rel. Frequency
0	|||||	5	0.208
1	|||| ||||	9	0.375
2	|||||	5	0.208
3	|||	3	0.125
4			1	0.042
5		0	0
6			1	0.042
	Total	24	

d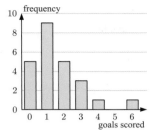

e 1 goal

f positively skewed, one outlier, (6 goals)

g $\approx 20.8\%$

2 **a**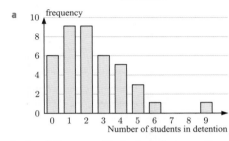

b 1 and 2   **c** positively skewed, one outlier, (9 students)

d $12\frac{1}{2}\%$

3 **a**

No. of commercials	Tally	Frequency
4				2
5						5
6										10
7										9
8						5
9					3
	Total	34

b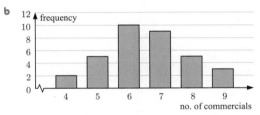

c 6 commercials   **d** symmetrical, no outliers   **e** $\approx 79.4\%$

4 **a** 45   **b** 1 time   **c** 8   **d** 20%

e positively skewed, no outliers

5 **a**

Peas in pod	Tally	Freq.
3						4
4													13
5											11
6																									28
7																																								47
8																								27
9														14
10						4
11			1
12		0
13			1
	Total	150

b

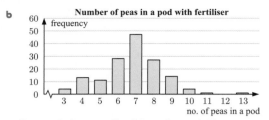

Number of peas in a pod with fertiliser

c Symmetrical, one outlier (13 peas)   **d** Yes
e Not necessarily.   (Consider factors like the cost of the fertiliser, changing prices, etc.)

EXERCISE 6C

1 a

People waiting	Tally	Frequency	Rel. Freq.
0 - 9	||	2	0.067
10 - 19	ЖŤ |	6	0.200
20 - 29	ЖŤ ЖŤ |	11	0.367
30 - 39	ЖŤ ||	7	0.233
40 - 49	||||	4	0.133
	Total	30	

b 2 days   **c** ≈ 36.7%   **e** 20 - 29 people
d

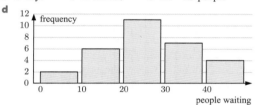

2 a 37   **b** 40 - 49 employees   **c** negatively skewed
d ≈ 37.8%
e No, only that it was in the interval 50 - 59 employees.

3 a

Number of houses	Tally	Frequency
0 - 9	ЖŤ	5
10 - 19	ЖŤ |||	8
20 - 29	ЖŤ |||	8
30 - 39	ЖŤ ЖŤ ||||	14
40 - 49	||||	4
50 - 59	|	1
	Total	40

b

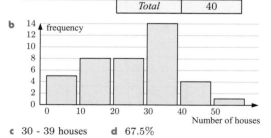

c 30 - 39 houses   **d** 67.5%

EXERCISE 6D

1 a Height is measured on a continuous scale.
b

Heights of a volleyball squad

c $185 \leqslant H < 190$ cm. This is the class of values that appears most often.
d slightly positively skewed

2 a column graph

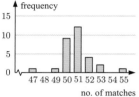

frequency

no. of matches

b frequency histogram

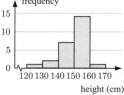

frequency

height (cm)

3 a continuous
b

Travel time (min)	Tally	Frequency
$0 \leqslant t < 10$	ЖŤ |	6
$10 \leqslant t < 20$	ЖŤ ЖŤ ЖŤ ЖŤ ЖŤ |	26
$20 \leqslant t < 30$	ЖŤ ЖŤ |||	13
$30 \leqslant t < 40$	ЖŤ ||||	9
$40 \leqslant t < 50$	ЖŤ |	6
	Total	60

c

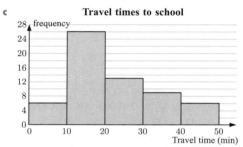

Travel times to school

d positively skewed   **e** $10 \leqslant t < 20$ minutes

4 a, b

Distance (m)	Tally	Frequency
$0 \leqslant d < 10$	||	2
$10 \leqslant d < 20$	ЖŤ	5
$20 \leqslant d < 30$	ЖŤ ||||	9
$30 \leqslant d < 40$	ЖŤ |	6
$40 \leqslant d < 50$	|||	3
	Total	25

c

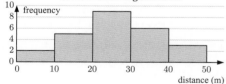

Javelin throwing distances

d $20 \leqslant d < 30$ m   **e** 36%

5 a

Heights of 6-month old seedlings at a nursery

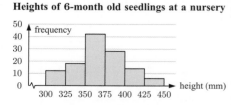

b 20   **c** ≈ 58.3%   **d** **i** 1218   **ii** 512

6 a, b

Weight (g)	Tally	Frequency
$100 \leqslant w < 125$	⅏	5
$125 \leqslant w < 150$	⅏	5
$150 \leqslant w < 175$	⅏ ⅏ I	11
$175 \leqslant w < 200$	IIII	4
$200 \leqslant w < 225$	⅏	5
$225 \leqslant w < 250$	⅏ II	7
$250 \leqslant w < 275$	⅏ IIII	9
$275 \leqslant w < 300$	IIII	4
	Total	50

c

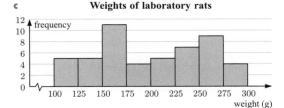

Weights of laboratory rats

d 50%

EXERCISE 6E.1

1 a 1 cup   **b** 2 cups   **c** 1.8 cups   **2** 9

3 a i 5.61 **ii** 6 **iii** 6   **b i** 16.3 **ii** 17 **iii** 18

   c i 24.8   **ii** 24.9   **iii** 23.5

4 a data set A: 6.46, data set B: 6.85

   b data set A: 7, data set B: 7

   c The data are the same except for the last value, which pushes the mean of set B up.

   d 7 is the middle value in both data sets. It is not affected by extreme values.

5 Ruth (164)

6 a i Pies: 67.1, Pasties: 53.6

     ii Pies: 69, Pasties: 52

   b Pies, higher mean (more sold), higher median (higher data values)

7 a Bus: mean = 39.7, median = 40.5,

     Tram: mean ≈ 49.1, median = 49

   b Tram has higher mean and median, but there are more bus trips per day and more people travel by bus in a day, so bus is more popular.

8 a 44 points   **b** 44 points   **c** 40.2 points

   d increase, 40.3 points

9 \$185 604   **10** 3144 km   **11** 17.25 goals   **12** $x = 15$

13 $a = 5$ **14** 37   **15** 14.8   **16** 6, 12   **17** 7, 9

EXERCISE 6E.2

1 a Mean: \$163 770, median: \$147 200

     Mean has been affected by the extreme values (the two values greater than \$200k).

   b i the mean   **ii** the median

2 a mean: \$29 300, median: \$23 500, mode: \$23 000

   b It is the lowest value in the data set.

   c No, it is too close to the lower end of the distribution.

3 a mean: 3.19 mm, median: 0 mm, mode: 0 mm

   b The median is not in the centre as the data is positively skewed.

   c The mode is the lowest value.

   d Yes, 42 and 21.   **e** No

EXERCISE 6E.3

1 a 1 head   **b** 1 head   **c** 1.43 heads

2 a i 2.61 children   **ii** 2 children   **iii** 2 children

   b This school has more children per family than average.

   c positive   **d** mean is higher than the median, mode

3 a i 2.96 calls   **ii** 2 calls   **iii** 2 calls

   b

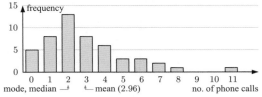

Phone calls made by teenagers

   c positively skewed   **d** Because of the skewness.

   e mean

4 a i 49 matches   **ii** 49 matches   **iii** 49.0 matches

   b No   **c** Need a larger sample.

5 a i 5.63 peas   **ii** 6 peas   **iii** 6 peas

   b i 6.81 peas   **ii** 7 peas   **iii** 7 peas

   c all of them   **d** It has improved it.

EXERCISE 6E.4

1 31.7   **2 a** 70   **b** ≈ 411 000 L   **c** ≈ 5870 L

3 a 11.5 points   **b i** 11.3 points   **ii** 11.4 points

   c ii is closer to the actual mean than **i**. Smaller class intervals give better estimates.

4 90.1 km h^{-1} **5** 768 m^2

6 a 125 people   **b** 119 marks   **c** $\frac{3}{25}$ **d** 137

EXERCISE 6F

1 a i 6   **ii** $Q_1 = 4$, $Q_3 = 7$ **iii** 7   **iv** 3

   b i 17.5   **ii** $Q_1 = 15$, $Q_3 = 19$ **iii** 14   **iv** 4

   c i 24.9   **ii** $Q_1 = 23.5$, $Q_3 = 26.1$ **iii** 7.7   **iv** 2.6

2 a median = 2.45 min, $Q_1 = 1.45$ min, $Q_3 = 3.8$ min

   b range = 5.2 minutes, IQR = 2.35 minutes

   c i 2.45 min   **ii** 3.8 min   **iii** 0, 5.2, 5.2

3 a 6   **b** 28   **c** 15   **d** 12   **e** 21   **f** 22   **g** 9

4 a i 124 cm   **ii** $Q_1 = 116$ cm, $Q_3 = 130$ cm

   b i 124 cm   **ii** 130 cm   **c i** 29 cm   **ii** 14 cm

   d 14 cm

5 a i 7 peas   **ii** 6 peas   **iii** 5 peas   **iv** 7 peas   **v** 2 peas

   b i 10 peas   **ii** 7 peas   **iii** 6 peas   **iv** 8 peas

     v 2 peas

   c The fertiliser does improve the yield of peas.

EXERCISE 6G.1

1 a i 35 points   **ii** 78 points   **iii** 13 points

     iv 53 points   **v** 26 points

   b i 65 points   **ii** 27 points

2 a i 98, 25 marks   **ii** 70 marks   **iii** 85 marks

     iv 55, 85 marks

   b 73 marks   **c** 30 marks   **d** 67 marks

3 a i min = 3; $Q_1 = 5$; med = 6; $Q_3 = 8$; max = 10

ii

iii 7
iv 3

b i min = 0, Q_1 = 4; med = 7; Q_3 = 8, max = 9
ii

iii 9
iv 4

c i min = 17, Q_1 = 26; med = 31; Q_3 = 47, max = 51
ii

iii 34
iv 21

4 a median = 6, Q_1 = 5, Q_3 = 8   **b** 3
c

no. of beans in a pod

5 a min = 33, Q_1 = 35, med = 36, Q_3 = 37, max = 40
b i 7   **ii** 2
c

no. of bolts

d No

EXERCISE 6G.2

1 a

Statistic	Year 9	Year 12
minimum	1	6
Q_1	5	10
median	7.5	14
Q_3	10	16
maximum	12	17.5

b i Year 9: 11,
   Year 12: 11.5

ii Year 9: 5,
   Year 12: 6

c i cannot tell   **ii** true since Year 9 Q_1 < Year 12 min.

2 a Friday: min = $20, Q_1 = $50, med = $70,
      Q_3 = $100, max = $180

   Saturday: min = $40, Q_1 = $80, med = $100,
      Q_3 = $140, max = $200

b i Friday: $160, Saturday: $160
ii Friday: $50, Saturday: $60

3 a i Class 1 (96%)   **ii** Class 1 (37%)   **iii** Class 1
b 18   **c** 55   **d i** 25%   **ii** 50%
e i slightly positively skewed   **ii** negatively skewed
f .... class 2, ... class 1

4 a Paul: min = 0.8 min; Q_1 = 1.3 min; med = 2.3 min;
      Q_3 = 3.3 min; max = 6.9 min

   Redmond: min = 0.2 min; Q_1 = 2.2 min;
      med = 3.7 min; Q_3 = 5.7 min;
      max = 11.5 min

b

Mobile Phone call duration

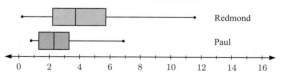

Redmond

Paul

c Both are positively skewed (Redmond's more so than Paul's).
Redmond's phone calls were more varied in duration.

5 a discrete
c

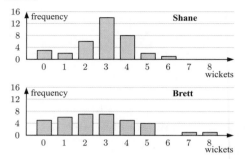

d Shane: approximately symmetrical Brett: positively skewed.
e Shane: mean ≈ 2.89, median = 3, mode = 3
Brett: mean ≈ 2.67, median = 2.5, mode = 2, 3
Shane's mean and median are slightly higher.
Shane has a clear mode of 3, whereas Brett has two modes
(2 and 3)
f Shane: Range = 6, IQR = 2
Brett: Range = 8, IQR = 3
Shane's data set demonstrates less variability than Brett's.

g

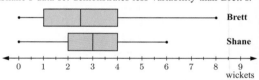

Brett

Shane

wickets

h Shane is more consistent with his bowling (in terms of wickets
taken) than Brett.

6 a continuous (the data is measured)
c Old: mean = 107, median = 110.5, range = 56,
      IQR = 19, min = 75, max = 131
New: mean = 134, median = 132, range = 84,
      IQR = 18.5, min = 107, max = 191
The 'new' type of light globe has a higher mean and median
than the 'old' type.
The IQR is relatively unchanged going from 'old' to 'new',
however, the range of the 'new' type is greater, suggesting
greater variability.

d

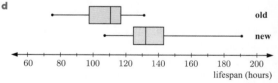

old

new

lifespan (hours)

e Old type: negatively skewed, New type: positively skewed
f The 'new' type of light globes do last longer than the old
type. Each number in the 5-number summary is at least 20%
greater in the 'new' type. The manufacturer's claim appears
to be valid.

EXERCISE 6G.3

1 a 12   **b** lower: 13.5, upper: 61.5   **c** 13
d

2 a median = 10, Q_1 = 8, Q_3 = 13   **b** 5
c lower = 0.5, upper = 20.5   **d** Yes, 22

e

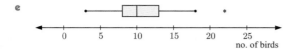

EXERCISE 6H

1

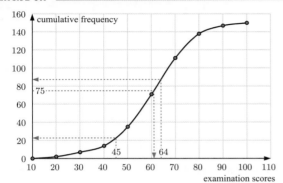

a ≈ 61 marks   **b** ≈ 87 students   **c** ≈ 76 students
d ≈ 23 students   **e** ≈ 75 marks

2   **a** 9   **b** $\approx 28.3\%$ **c** 7.1 cm   **d** ≈ 2.4 cm
    e 90% of the seedlings are shorter than 10 cm.

3

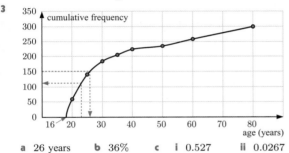

a 26 years   **b** 36%   **c i** 0.527   **ii** 0.0267

4   **a**

Length (cm)	Frequency	Cumulative frequency
$24 \leqslant x < 27$	1	1
$27 \leqslant x < 30$	2	3
$30 \leqslant x < 33$	5	8
$33 \leqslant x < 36$	10	18
$36 \leqslant x < 39$	9	27
$39 \leqslant x < 42$	2	29
$42 \leqslant x < 45$	1	30

b

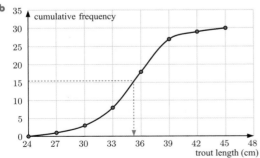

c median ≈ 35 cm
d median $= 34.5$. Median from graph is a good approximation.

5   **a** 27 min   **b** 29 min   **c** 31.3 min
    d 4.3 min   **e** ≈ 28 min

6

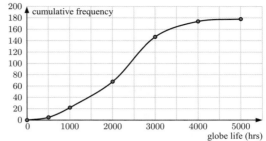

a ≈ 2270 hours   **b** $\approx 69\%$ **c** ≈ 63

7   **a** $19.5 \leqslant l < 20.5$

b

Foot length (cm)	Frequency	Cumulative frequency
$19.5 \leqslant l < 20.5$	1	1
$20.5 \leqslant l < 21.5$	1	2
$21.5 \leqslant l < 22.5$	0	2
$22.5 \leqslant l < 23.5$	3	5
$23.5 \leqslant l < 24.5$	5	10
$24.5 \leqslant l < 25.5$	13	23
$25.5 \leqslant l < 26.5$	17	40
$26.5 \leqslant l < 27.5$	7	47
$27.5 \leqslant l < 28.5$	2	49
$28.5 \leqslant l < 29.5$	0	49
$29.5 \leqslant l < 30.5$	1	50

c

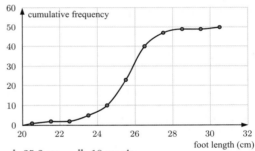

d i 25.2 cm   **ii** 18 people

EXERCISE 6I.1

1   **a** ≈ 1.49 **b** ≈ 4.73
2   mean $= 55$ L, standard deviation ≈ 10.9 L
3   mean ≈ 1.69 kg, standard deviation ≈ 0.182 kg
4   **a** $\overline{x} = 169$ cm, $s \approx 6.05$ cm **b** $\overline{x} = 174$ cm, $s \approx 6.05$ cm
    c The distribution has simply shifted by 5 cm. The mean
        increases by 5 cm and the standard deviation remains the
        same.
5   **a** $\overline{x} = 1.01$ kg; $s = 0.17$ kg **b** $\overline{x} = 2.02$ kg; $s = 0.34$ kg
    c Doubling the values doubles the mean and standard deviation.
6   **a** ≈ 0.809 **b** 2.8, from volunteer F   **c** ≈ 0.150
    d the extreme value greatly increases the standard deviation

EXERCISE 6I.2

1 $\overline{x} \approx 1.72$ children, $s_n \approx 1.67$ children
2 $\overline{x} \approx 14.5$ years, $s_n \approx 1.75$ years
3 $\overline{x} = 45$ clients, $s_n \approx 3.28$ clients
4 $\overline{x} \approx 48.3$ cm, $s_n \approx 2.66$ cm   **5** $\overline{x} \approx \$390.30$, $s_n \approx \$15.87$
6   **a** $\overline{x} \approx 40.4$ hours $s_n \approx 4.23$ hours
    b $\overline{x} = 40.6$ hours $s_n \approx 4.10$ hours
    The mean increases slightly, the standard deviation decreases
    slightly. These are good approximations.

c

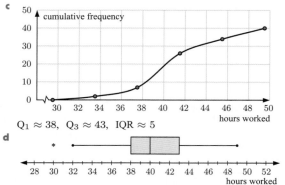

$Q_1 \approx 38$, $Q_3 \approx 43$, $IQR \approx 5$

d

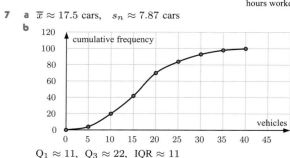

7 **a** $\overline{x} \approx 17.5$ cars, $s_n \approx 7.87$ cars

b

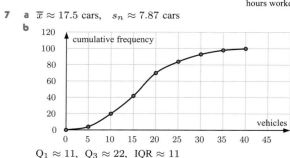

$Q_1 \approx 11$, $Q_3 \approx 22$, $IQR \approx 11$

EXERCISE 61.3

1 **a** Sample A
   b Sample A: mean = 8,   Sample B: mean = 8
   c Sample A: $s_n = 2$,   Sample B: $s_n \approx 1.06$
      Sample B's standard deviation is smaller than Sample A's.
      The graph shows the data to be less 'spread out' in Sample B.
2 **a** Andrew: $\overline{x} = 25$, $s_n \approx 4.97$ **b** Andrew
      Brad: $\overline{x} = 30.5$, $s_n \approx 12.6$
3 **a** Rockets: mean = 5.7, range = 11
      Bullets: mean = 5.7, range = 11
   b We suspect the Rockets, they have two zeros.
   c Rockets: $s_n = 3.9$ ⟵ greater variability
      Bullets: $s_n \approx 3.29$
   d Standard deviation, as it takes into account all data values.
4 **a** No, because of random variation
   b   **i** the sample mean $\overline{x}$
       ii the sample standard deviation s_n
   c Less variability in the volume of soft drink per can.

REVIEW SET 6A

1 **a** quantitative discrete   **b** quantitative continuous
   c categorical   **d** categorical   **e** categorical
   f quantitative continuous   **g** quantitative continuous
   h quantitative discrete   **i** quantitative discrete
2 **a**

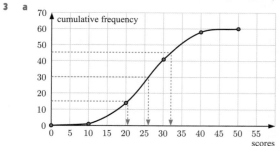

   b   **i** median = 14.5 m   **ii** range = 17.3 m
   c The data is positively skewed.

3 $a = 2$
4 **a** negatively skewed   **b** 47.5%   **c** 7.5%
   d We do not know all the data values exactly, only the class
      intervals they fall into.
5

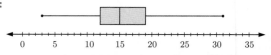

6 **a** 77 days   **b** 12 days
7 **a** $\overline{x} \approx 122$, $s_n \approx 7.94$ **b** $\overline{x} \approx 7.01$, $s_n \approx 0.984$
8 **a** min = 3; $Q_1 = 12$; med = 15; $Q_3 = 19$; max = 31
   b range = 28; IQR = 7
   c

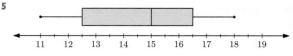

REVIEW SET 6B

1 **a** quantitative continous   **b** categorical   **c** categorical
   d quantitative continous   **e** quantitative continous
   f quantitative discrete   **g** categorical
2 **a** minimum = 64.6 m,   maximum = 97.5 m
   b   **i** mean ≈ 81.1 m   **ii** median ≈ 83.1 m
   c, d

Distance (m)	Tally	Frequency
$60 \leqslant d < 65$	|	1
$65 \leqslant d < 70$	|||	3
$70 \leqslant d < 75$	⦀⦀	5
$75 \leqslant d < 80$	||	2
$80 \leqslant d < 85$	⦀⦀ |||	8
$85 \leqslant d < 90$	⦀⦀ |	6
$90 \leqslant d < 95$	|||	3
$95 \leqslant d < 100$	||	2
Total		30

   e

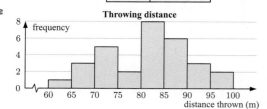

3 **a**

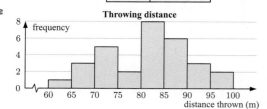

   b   **i** median ≈ 26.0 **ii** IQR ≈ 12
       iii $\overline{x} \approx 26.0$ **iv** $s_n \approx 8.31$
4 **a**   **i** £352.50   **ii** £336   **iii** £365.50
   b £29.50   **c** $\overline{x} \approx$ £350, $s_n \approx$ £17.80
5 **a** 88 students   **b** $m = 24$

6 a $\bar{x} \approx 48.6$ min, $s_n \approx 7.63$ min

b

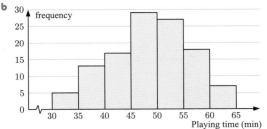

c negatively skewed

7 range $= 19$; $Q_1 = 119$; $Q_3 = 130$; $s_n \approx 6.38$

8 a $\bar{x} \approx 29.6$ allsorts, $s_n \approx 1.61$ allsorts

b More investigation is needed.

REVIEW SET 6C

1 $p = 7$, $q = 9$ (or $p = 9$, $q = 7$)

2

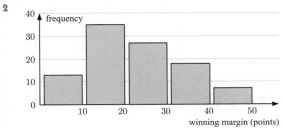

3 $\bar{x} \approx 414$ patrons

4 a A: min $= 11$ s; $Q_1 = 11.6$ s; med $= 12$ s;
   $Q_3 = 12.6$ s; max $= 13$ s
   B: min $= 11.2$ s; $Q_1 = 12$ s; med $= 12.6$ s;
   $Q_3 = 13.2$ s; max $= 13.8$ s

b i A: range $= 2.0$ s   **ii** A: IQR $= 1.0$ s
   B: range $= 2.6$ s B: IQR $= 1.2$ s

c i A, the median time is lower.
   ii B, the range and IQR are higher.

5 $\bar{x} \approx €104$, $s_n \approx €19.40$

6 a 120 students   **b** 65 marks   **c** 54 and 75
   d 21 marks   **e** $\approx 73\%$ **f** 82 marks

7 a

	Brand X	Brand Y
min	871	891
Q_1	888	898
median	896.5	903.5
Q_3	904	910
max	916	928
IQR	16	12

b

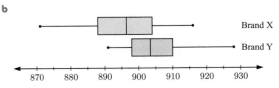

c i Brand Y, as the median is higher.
   ii Brand X, as the IQR is lower, so less variations.

EXERCISE 7A

1 a $5 \in D$ **b** $6 \notin G$ **c** $d \notin \{a, e, i, o, u\}$
   d $\{2, 5\} \subseteq \{1, 2, 3, 4, 5, 6\}$
   e $\{3, 8, 6\} \nsubseteq \{1, 2, 3, 4, 5, 6\}$

2 a i $\{9\}$ **ii** $\{5, 6, 7, 8, 9, 10, 11, 12, 13\}$
   b i $\varnothing$ **ii** $\{1, 2, 3, 4, 5, 6, 7, 8\}$
   c i $\{1, 3, 5, 7\} = A$ **ii** $\{1, 2, 3, 4, 5, 6, 7, 8, 9\} = B$

3 a 5   **b** 6   **c** 2   **d** 9

4 a True   **b** True   **c** False   **d** True
   e False   **f** True   **g** True   **h** False

5 a finite   **b** infinite   **c** infinite   **d** infinite

6 a True   **b** True   **c** False   **d** True

7 a disjoint   **b** not disjoint   **8** True

9 a i $\varnothing$, $\{a\}$, $\{b\}$, $\{c\}$, $\{a, b\}$, $\{a, c\}$, $\{b, c\}$, $\{a, b, c\}$,
      so 8 subsets
   ii $\varnothing$, $\{a\}$, $\{b\}$, $\{c\}$, $\{d\}$, $\{a, b\}$, $\{a, c\}$, $\{a, d\}$, $\{b, c\}$,
      $\{b, d\}$, $\{c, d\}$, $\{a, b, c\}$, $\{a, b, d\}$, $\{a, c, d\}$, $\{b, c, d\}$,
      $\{a, b, c, d\}$, so 16 subsets
   b 2^n, $n \in \mathbb{Z}^+$

EXERCISE 7B

1 a finite   **b** infinite   **c** infinite   **d** infinite

2 a i A is the set of all x such that x is an integer between
      -1 and 7, including -1 and 7.
   ii $\{-1, 0, 1, 2, 3, 4, 5, 6, 7\}$ **iii** 9
   b i A is the set of all x such that x is a natural number
      between -2 and 8.
   ii $\{0, 1, 2, 3, 4, 5, 6, 7\}$ **iii** 8
   c i A is the set of all x such that x is a real number between
      0 and 1, including 0 and 1.
   ii not possible   **iii** infinite
   d i A is the set of all x such that x is a rational number
      between 5 and 6, including 5 and 6.
   ii not possible   **iii** infinite

3 a $A = \{x \mid -100 < x < 100,\ x \in \mathbb{Z}\}$
   b $A = \{x \mid x > 1000,\ x \in \mathbb{R}\}$
   c $A = \{x \mid 2 \leqslant x \leqslant 3,\ x \in \mathbb{Q}\}$

4 a $A \subseteq B$ **b** $A \nsubseteq B$ **c** $A \subseteq B$ **d** $A \subseteq B$
   e $A \nsubseteq B$ **f** $A \nsubseteq B$

EXERCISE 7C

1 a $C' = \{\text{consonants}\}$ **b** $C' = \mathbb{N}$
   c $C' = \{x \mid x \geqslant -4,\ x \in \mathbb{Z}\}$
   d $C' = \{x \mid 2 < x < 8,\ x \in \mathbb{Q}\}$

2 a $\{2, 3, 4, 5, 6, 7\}$ **b** $\{0, 1, 8\}$ **c** $\{5, 6, 7, 8\}$
   d $\{0, 1, 2, 3, 4\}$ **e** $\{5, 6, 7\}$ **f** $\{2, 3, 4, 5, 6, 7, 8\}$
   g $\{2, 3, 4\}$

3 a 9   **b** 11   **4 a** False   **b** True

5 a $\{1, 2, 10, 11, 12\}$ **b** $\{1, 2, 3, 4, 12\}$
   c $\{1, 8, 9, 10, 11, 12\}$ **d** $\{3, 4, 5, 6, 7\}$
   e $\{1, 2, 8, 9, 10, 11, 12\}$ **f** $\{8, 9, 10, 11\}$
   g $\{1, 2, 5, 6, 7, 8, 9, 10, 11, 12\}$ **h** $\{2, 10, 11\}$

6 a $P = \{2, 3, 5, 7, 11, 13, 17, 19, 23\}$ **b** $\{2, 5, 11\}$
   c $\{2, 3, 4, 5, 7, 11, 12, 13, 15, 17, 19, 23\}$
   d $12 = 9 + 6 - 3$ ✓

7 a $P = \{1, 2, 4, 7, 14, 28\}$, $Q = \{1, 2, 4, 5, 8, 10, 20, 40\}$
   b $\{1, 2, 4\}$ **c** $\{1, 2, 4, 5, 7, 8, 10, 14, 20, 28, 40\}$
   d $11 = 6 + 8 - 3$ ✓

8 a $M = \{32, 36, 40, 44, 48, 52, 56\}$, $N = \{36, 42, 48, 54\}$

b {36, 48}　　**c** {32, 36, 40, 42, 44, 48, 52, 54, 56}
d $9 = 7 + 4 - 2$　✓

9　**a** $R = \{-2, -1, 0, 1, 2, 3, 4\}$,　$S = \{0, 1, 2, 3, 4, 5, 6\}$
b {0, 1, 2, 3, 4}　　**c** {-2, -1, 0, 1, 2, 3, 4, 5, 6}
d $9 = 7 + 7 - 5$　✓

10　**a** $C = \{-4, -3, -2, -1\}$
$D = \{-7, -6, -5, -4, -3, -2, -1\}$
b {-4, -3, -2, -1}　　**c** {-7, -6, -5, -4, -3, -2, -1}
d $7 = 4 + 7 - 4$　✓

11　**a** $P = \{1, 2, 3, 4, 6, 12\}$,　$Q = \{1, 2, 3, 6, 9, 18\}$,
$R = \{1, 3, 9, 27\}$
b　**i** {1, 2, 3, 6}　　**ii** {1, 3}　　**iii** {1, 3, 9}
iv {1, 2, 3, 4, 6, 9, 12, 18}　**v** {1, 2, 3, 4, 6, 9, 12, 27}
vi {1, 2, 3, 6, 9, 18, 27}
c　**i** {1, 3}　　　　**ii** {1, 2, 3, 4, 6, 9, 12, 18, 27}

12　**a** $A = \{4, 8, 12, 16, 20, 24, 28, 32, 36\}$
$B = \{6, 12, 18, 24, 30, 36\}$,　$C = \{12, 24, 36\}$
b　**i** {12, 24, 36}　　　　**ii** {12, 24, 36}
iii {12, 24, 36}　　　　**iv** {12, 24, 36}
v {4, 6, 8, 12, 16, 18, 20, 24, 28, 30, 32, 36}
c $12 = 9 + 6 + 3 - 3 - 3 - 3 + 3$　✓

13　**a** $A = \{6, 12, 18, 24, 30\}$,　$B = \{1, 2, 3, 5, 6, 10, 15, 30\}$
$C = \{2, 3, 5, 7, 11, 13, 17, 19, 23, 29\}$
b　**i** {6, 30}　　**ii** {2, 3, 5}　　**iii** ∅　　　**iv** ∅
v {1, 2, 3, 5, 6, 7, 10, 11, 12, 13, 15, 17, 18, 19, 23, 24, 29, 30}
c $18 = 5 + 8 + 10 - 2 - 3 - 0 + 0$　✓

EXERCISE 7D

1　**a**
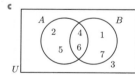

b

c
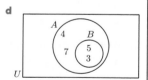

d

2　**a** $A = \{1, 3, 5, 7, 9\}$
$B = \{2, 3, 5, 7\}$
b $A \cap B = \{3, 5, 7\}$
$A \cup B = \{1, 2, 3, 5, 7, 9\}$
c
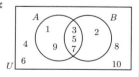

3　**a** $A = \{1, 2, 3, 6\}$
$B = \{1, 3, 9\}$
b $A \cap B = \{1, 3\}$
$A \cup B = \{1, 2, 3, 6, 9\}$
c

4　**a** $P = \{4, 8, 12, 16, 20, 24, 28\}$
$Q = \{6, 12, 18, 24\}$
b $P \cap Q = \{12, 24\}$
$P \cup Q = \{4, 6, 8, 12, 16, 18, 20, 24, 28\}$
c

5　**a** $R = \{2, 3, 5, 7, 11, 13, 17, 19, 23, 29\}$
$S = \{4, 6, 8, 9, 10, 12, 14, 15, 16, 18, 20, 21, 22, 24, 25, 26, 27, 28\}$
b $R \cap S = \varnothing$
$R \cup S = \{2, 3, 4, 5, 6, 7, 8, 9, 10, 11, 12, 13, 14, 15, 16, 17, 18, 19, 20, 21, 22, 23, 24, 25, 26, 27, 28, 29\}$
c

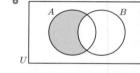

6　**a** {b, d, e, h}　**b** {e, f, h, i, j}　**c** {a, c, f, g, i, j, k}
d {a, b, c, d, g, k}　**e** {e, h}　**f** {b, d, e, f, h, i, j}
g {a, c, g, k}　**h** {a, b, c, d, f, g, i, j, k}

7　**a**　**i** {a, b, c, d, h, j}　　　**ii** {a, c, d, e, f, g, k}
iii {a, b, e, f, i, l}　　　**iv** {a, c, d}
v {a, b, c, d, e, f, g, h, j, k}　　　**vi** {a, e, f}
vii {a}　　　　**viii** {a, b, c, d, e, f, g, h, i, j, k, l}
b　**i** 12　　**ii** 12

EXERCISE 7E

1　**a**
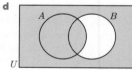
b

c
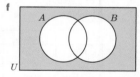
d

e
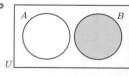
f

2　**a**
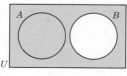
b

c
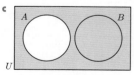
d

e

f

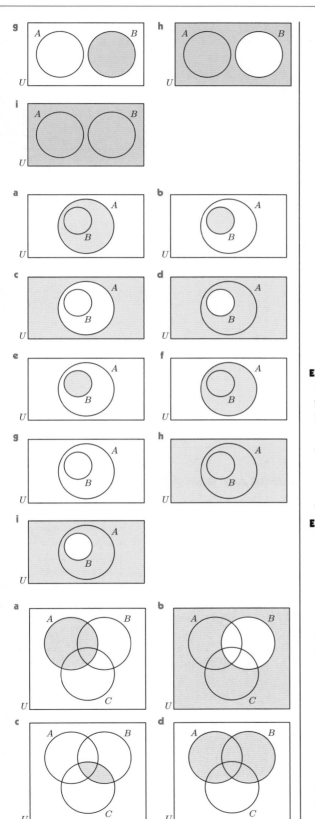

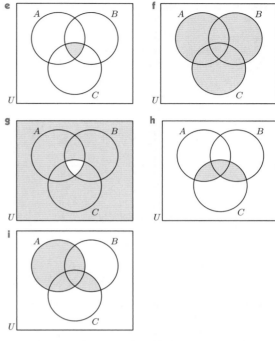

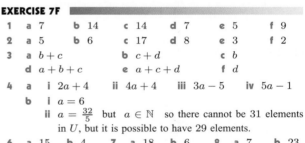

EXERCISE 7F

1 **a** 7   **b** 14   **c** 14   **d** 7   **e** 5   **f** 9
2 **a** 5   **b** 6   **c** 17   **d** 8   **e** 3   **f** 2
3 **a** $b + c$ **b** $c + d$ **c** b
    d $a + b + c$ **e** $a + c + d$ **f** d
4 **a** **i** $2a + 4$ **ii** $4a + 4$ **iii** $3a - 5$ **iv** $5a - 1$
    b **i** $a = 6$
        ii $a = \frac{32}{5}$ but $a \in \mathbb{N}$ so there cannot be 31 elements
        in U, but it is possible to have 29 elements.
6 **a** 15   **b** 4   **7** **a** 18   **b** 6   **8** **a** 7   **b** 23

EXERCISE 7G

1 **a**   2 **a**

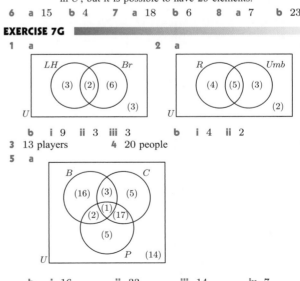

    b **i** 9   **ii** 3   **iii** 3   **b** **i** 4   **ii** 2
3 13 players   4 20 people
5 **a**

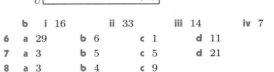

    b **i** 16   **ii** 33   **iii** 14   **iv** 7
6 **a** 29   **b** 6   **c** 1   **d** 11
7 **a** 3   **b** 5   **c** 5   **d** 21
8 **a** 3   **b** 4   **c** 9

REVIEW SET 7A

1 **a** $S = \{3, 4, 5, 6, 7\}$ **b** 5

2 **a** Yes   **b** Yes   **c** No   **d** Yes

3 **a** $X' = \{\text{orange, yellow, green, blue}\}$
  b $X' = \{-5, -3, -2, 0, 1, 2, 5\}$
  c $X' = \{x \mid x \geqslant -8, \ x \in \mathbb{Q}\}$

4 **a**   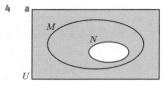   **b**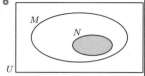

  c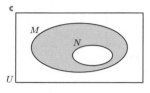

5 **a** **i** $\{s, p, r, i, n, g, b, o, k, w, a, t, e, u, c\}$
  ii $\{r, b, k\}$ **iii** $\{g, i, n, o, p, s\}$
  b **i** {the letters in 'springbok' or 'waterbuck'}
  ii {the letters common to both 'springbok' and 'waterbuck'}
  iii {the letters in 'springbok' but not 'waterbuck'}
  c

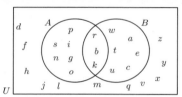

6 **a** **i** $\{1, 2, 3, 4, 6, 8, 12, 24\}$
  ii $\{1, 2, 3, 5, 6, 10, 15, 30\}$ **iii** $\{1, 2, 3, 6\}$
  iv $\{1, 2, 3, 4, 5, 6, 8, 10, 12, 15, 24, 30\}$
  b

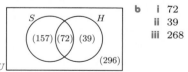

7 **a**

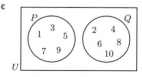

  b **i** 72
  ii 39
  iii 268

8 8   **9** **a** 9   **b** 7   **c** 17

10 **a** $P = \{1, 3, 5, 7, 9\}$ **c**
  $Q = \{2, 4, 6, 8, 10\}$
  b They are disjoint.

REVIEW SET 7B

1 **a** True   **b** False   **c** True   **d** False   **e** False

2 **a** **i** $\{x \mid 5 < x < 12, \ x \in \mathbb{R}\}$
  ii $\{x \mid -4 \leqslant x < 7, \ x \in \mathbb{Z}\}$ **iii** $\{x \mid x > 45, \ x \in \mathbb{N}\}$
  b **i** infinite   **ii** finite   **iii** infinite

3 $\varnothing, \{1\}, \{3\}, \{5\}, \{1, 3\}, \{3, 5\}, \{1, 5\}, \{1, 3, 5\}$

4 **a** **i** $\{2, 4, 6, 8\}$ **b**
  ii $\{2, 4, 8\}$
  iii $\{3, 5, 7, 9\}$

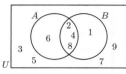

5 **a** $\varnothing$ **b** $s + t$

6 **a** C' **b** $(A \cap B) \cup (A \cap C)$ or $A \cap (B \cup C)$

7 **a**   **b** **i** 27
  ii 8
  iii 14

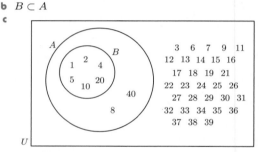

8 4

9 **a** $A = \{1, 2, 4, 5, 8, 10, 20, 40\}, \quad B = \{1, 2, 4, 5, 10, 20\}$
  b $B \subset A$
  c

10 **a** 1   **b** 7   **c** 15

EXERCISE 8A.1

1 **a** proposition, false   **b** proposition, false
  c proposition, true   **d** proposition, false
  e proposition, true   **f** proposition, true
  g not a proposition   **h** proposition, true
  i not a proposition   **j** proposition, false
  k proposition, indeterminate   **l** not a proposition
  m proposition, indeterminate   **n** proposition, indeterminate
  o proposition, indeterminate   **p** proposition, false

2 **a** **i** $\neg p$: not all rectangles are parallelograms
  ii p is true.
  b **i** $\neg m$: $\sqrt{5}$ is a rational number.   **ii** m is true.
  c **i** $\neg r$: 7 is an irrational number.   **ii** r is true.
  d **i** $\neg q$: $23 - 14 \neq 12$ **ii** $\neg q$ is true.
  e **i** $\neg r$: $52 \div 4 \neq 13$ **ii** r is true.
  f **i** $\neg s$: The difference between two odd numbers is not always even.
  ii s is true.
  g **i** $\neg t$: The product of consecutive integers is not always even.
  ii t is true.
  h **i** $\neg u$: Not all obtuse angles are equal.   **ii** $\neg u$ is true.
  i **i** $\neg p$: Not all trapeziums are parallelograms.
  ii $\neg p$ is true.

j **i** $\neg q$: Not all triangles with two equal angles are isosceles.
  ii q is true.

3 **a** $x \geqslant 5$ **b** $x < 3$ **c** $y \geqslant 8$ **d** $y > 10$

4 **a** **i** No **ii** $\neg r$: Kania scored 60% or less.   **b** **i** Yes
  c **i** No **ii** $\neg r$: Fari is not at soccer practice.
  d **i** Yes   **e** **i** No **ii** I did not drink black tea today.

5 **a** $x \in \{1, 2, 3, 4\}$ **b** $x < 0, \ x \in \mathbb{Z}$
  c $x \in \{\text{horses, sheep, goats, deer}\}$
  d x is a female student   **e** x is a female non-student

EXERCISE 8A.2

1 **a** $P = \{21, 24, 27\}$ **b** $P = \{2, 4, 6, 8, 10\}$

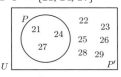 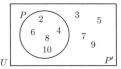

  c $P = \{1, 2, 3, 6, 7, 14, 21, 42\}$

2 **a**   **b**

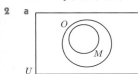

  c

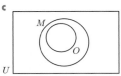

3 **a**

  b $P' = \{9, 10, 11, 12, 13, 14\}$

4 **a**   **b** $P' = \{1, 3, 5, 7, 9\}$

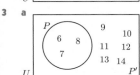

EXERCISE 8B.1

1 **a** $p \wedge q$: Ted is a doctor and Shelly is a dentist.
  b $p \wedge q$: x is greater than 15 and less than 30.
  c $p \wedge q$: It is windy and it is raining.
  d $p \wedge q$: Kim has brown hair and blue eyes.

2 **a** True   **b** False   **c** False   **d** True   **e** False

3 **a**   **b** $\{2, 4, 6\}$

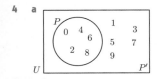

EXERCISE 8B.2

1 **a** $p \vee q$: Tim owns a bicycle or a scooter.
  b $p \vee q$: x is a multiple of 2 or a multiple of 5.
  c $p \vee q$: Dana studies Physics or Chemistry.

2 **a** True   **b** True   **c** False   **d** True

3 **a** $p \veebar q$: Meryn will visit Japan or Singapore, but not both, next year.
  b $p \veebar q$: Ann will invite Kate or Tracy, but not both, to her party.
  c $p \veebar q$: x is a factor of 56 or 40, but not both.

4 **a** False   **b** True   **c** False   **d** True

5 **a** $\neg r$ **b** $r \wedge s$ **c** $\neg s \wedge \neg r$ **d** $r \vee s$

6 **a** $\neg x$ **b** $x \wedge y$ **c** $x \vee y$ **d** $\neg(x \wedge y)$ **e** $x \veebar y$

7 **a** p: Phillip likes icecream. q: Phillip likes jelly.
    $p \wedge q$: Phillip likes icecream and jelly.
  b p: Phillip likes icecream. q: Phillip likes jelly.
    $p \vee \neg q$: Phillip likes icecream or Phillip does not like jelly.
  c p: x is greater than 10. q: x is a prime number.
    $p \wedge q$: x is both greater than 10 and a prime number.
  d p: Tuan can go to the mountains.
    q: Tuan can go to the beach.
    $p \veebar q$: Tuan can go to the mountains or to the beach, but not both.
  e p: The computer is on. $\neg p$: The computer is not on.
  f p: Angela has a watch. q: Angela has a mobile phone.
    $\neg p \wedge q$: Angela does not have a watch but does have a mobile phone.
  g p: Maya studied Spanish. q: Maya studied French.
    $p \veebar q$: Maya studied one of Spanish or French.
  h p: I can hear thunder. q: I can hear an aeroplane.
    $p \vee q$: I can hear thunder or an aeroplane.

8 $p \veebar q$ is false $\Rightarrow$ p and q are true or p and q are false.
  $\therefore$ p is true and q is true

9 **a**

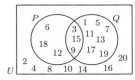

  b **i** $\{2, 4, 6, 8, 10, 12, 14, 16, 18, 20\}$
    ii $\{1, 3, 5, 6, 7, 9, 11, 12, 13, 15, 17, 18, 19\}$
    iii $\{3, 9, 15\}$ **iv** $\{1, 5, 6, 7, 11, 12, 13, 17, 18, 19\}$

10 **a**

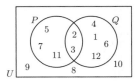

  b **i** x is both prime and a factor of 12.
    ii x is prime or a factor of 12.
    iii x is prime or factor of 12, but not both.
  c **i** $\{2, 3\}$ **ii** $\{1, 2, 3, 4, 5, 6, 7, 11, 12\}$
    iii $\{1, 4, 5, 6, 7, 11, 12\}$

11 **a** False   **b** True   **c** True   **d** True
  e True   **f** False   **g** True   **h** False

12 **a** $P \cup Q$ **b** $P' \cup Q$

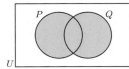 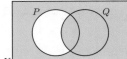

c $(P \cap Q') \cup (Q \cap P')$ **d** $P' \cap Q'$

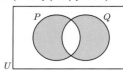 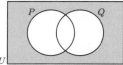

13 a $p \wedge q$ **b** $p \veebar q$ **c** $\neg p$

14 a The captain is old, but not male.
  b The captain is old or male.   **c** The captain is old.

EXERCISE 8C.1

1 a

p	q	$\neg p$	$\neg p \wedge q$
T	T	F	F
T	F	F	F
F	T	T	T
F	F	T	F

b

p	q	$p \veebar q$	$\neg(p \veebar q)$
T	T	F	T
T	F	T	F
F	T	T	F
F	F	F	T

c

p	q	$\neg p$	$\neg q$	$\neg p \vee \neg q$
T	T	F	F	F
T	F	F	T	T
F	T	T	F	T
F	F	T	T	T

d

p	$p \vee p$
T	T
F	F

2 a i

p	q	$\neg p$	$\neg q$	$\neg p \wedge \neg q$
T	T	F	F	F
T	F	F	T	F
F	T	T	F	F
F	F	T	T	T

ii neither

b i

p	q	$p \vee q$	$\neg p$	$(p \vee q) \vee \neg p$
T	T	T	F	T
T	F	T	F	T
F	T	T	T	T
F	F	F	T	T

ii tautology

c i

p	q	$p \veebar q$	$p \wedge (p \veebar q)$
T	T	F	F
T	F	T	T
F	T	T	F
F	F	F	F

ii neither

d i

p	q	$p \wedge q$	$p \veebar q$	$(p \wedge q) \wedge (p \veebar q)$
T	T	T	F	F
T	F	F	T	F
F	T	F	T	F
F	F	F	F	F

ii logical contradiction

3 a It requires both p and $\neg p$ to be true at the same time, which cannot occur.

b

p	$\neg p$	$p \wedge \neg p$
T	F	F
F	T	F

4 a

p	$\neg p$	$\neg(\neg p)$
T	F	T
F	T	F

b

p	$p \wedge p$
T	T
F	F

c

p	q	$\neg p$	$\neg p \wedge q$	$p \vee (\neg p \wedge q)$	$p \vee q$
T	T	F	F	T	T
T	F	F	F	T	T
F	T	T	T	T	T
F	F	T	F	F	F

d

p	q	$p \veebar q$	$\neg(p \veebar q)$	$\neg q$	$p \veebar \neg q$
T	T	F	T	F	T
T	F	T	F	T	F
F	T	T	F	F	F
F	F	F	T	T	T

e

p	q	$\neg p$	$q \vee \neg p$	$\neg(q \vee \neg p)$	$\neg q$	$p \vee q$	$\neg q \wedge (p \vee q)$
T	T	F	T	F	F	T	F
T	F	F	F	T	T	T	T
F	T	T	T	F	F	T	F
F	F	T	T	F	T	F	F

f

p	q	$\neg p$	$p \vee q$	$\neg p \veebar (p \vee q)$	$\neg q$	$p \vee \neg q$
T	T	F	T	T	F	T
T	F	F	T	T	T	T
F	T	T	T	F	F	F
F	F	T	F	T	T	T

5 a

p	q	$\neg p$	$\neg q$	$\neg p \wedge q$	$p \wedge \neg q$	$(\neg p \wedge q) \vee (p \wedge \neg q)$
T	T	F	F	F	F	F
T	F	F	T	F	T	T
F	T	T	F	T	F	T
F	F	T	T	F	F	F

b $p \veebar q$

6 a i I like apples or bananas.
  ii I do not like apples or bananas.
  iii I do not like apples.
  iv I do not like apples and I do not like bananas.

b

p	q	$p \vee q$	$\neg(p \vee q)$	$\neg p$	$\neg q$	$\neg p \wedge \neg q$
T	T	T	F	F	F	F
T	F	T	F	F	T	F
F	T	T	F	T	F	F
F	F	F	T	T	T	T

7 a

p	q	$p \veebar q$	$q \wedge (p \veebar q)$	$(p \veebar q) \vee p$
T	T	F	F	T
T	F	T	F	T
F	T	T	T	T
F	F	F	F	F

b i $-3 \leqslant x < 2$ or $x > 7$ **ii** $x > 7$ **iii** $x \geqslant -3$

8 a Any tautology has all the values in its truth table column as true.
  b Any logical contradiction has all the values in its truth table column as false.

9 a It is a tautology.   **b** It is a logical contradiction.
  c It is a tautology.

EXERCISE 8C.2

1 a

p	q	r	$\neg p$	$q \wedge r$	$\neg p \vee (q \wedge r)$
T	T	T	F	T	T
T	T	F	F	F	F
T	F	T	F	F	F
T	F	F	F	F	F
F	T	T	T	T	T
F	T	F	T	F	T
F	F	T	T	F	T
F	F	F	T	F	T

b

p	q	r	$\neg q$	$p \vee \neg q$	$(p \vee \neg q) \wedge r$
T	T	T	F	T	T
T	T	F	F	T	F
T	F	T	T	T	T
T	F	F	T	T	F
F	T	T	F	F	F
F	T	F	F	F	F
F	F	T	T	T	T
F	F	F	T	T	F

c

p	q	r	$p \vee q$	$\neg r$	$p \wedge \neg r$	$(p \vee q) \vee (p \wedge \neg r)$
T	T	T	T	F	F	T
T	T	F	T	T	T	T
T	F	T	T	F	F	T
T	F	F	T	T	T	T
F	T	T	T	F	F	T
F	T	F	T	T	F	T
F	F	T	F	F	F	F
F	F	F	F	T	F	F

2 a

p	q	r	$p \vee q$	$r \wedge p$	$\neg(r \wedge p)$	$(p \vee q) \vee \neg(r \wedge p)$
T	T	T	T	T	F	T
T	T	F	T	F	T	T
T	F	T	T	T	F	T
T	F	F	T	F	T	T
F	T	T	T	F	T	T
F	T	F	T	F	T	T
F	F	T	F	F	T	T
F	F	F	F	F	T	T

$\therefore$ tautology

b

p	q	r	$p \veebar r$	$\neg q$	$(p \veebar r) \wedge \neg q$
T	T	T	F	F	F
T	T	F	T	F	F
T	F	T	F	T	F
T	F	F	T	T	T
F	T	T	T	F	F
F	T	F	F	F	F
F	F	T	T	T	T
F	F	F	F	T	F

$\therefore$ neither

c

p	q	r	$q \wedge r$	$p \vee q$	$\neg(p \vee q)$	$(q \wedge r) \wedge \neg(p \vee q)$
T	T	T	T	T	F	F
T	T	F	F	T	F	F
T	F	T	F	T	F	F
T	F	F	F	T	F	F
F	T	T	T	T	F	F
F	T	F	F	T	F	F
F	F	T	F	F	T	F
F	F	F	F	F	T	F

$\therefore$ logical contradiction

3 a
  i Jake owns a phone and a TV.
  ii Jake owns a phone, a TV and a laptop.
  iii Jake owns a TV and a laptop.
  iv Jake owns a phone, a TV and a laptop.

b

p	q	r	$p \wedge q$	$(p \wedge q) \wedge r$	$q \wedge r$	$p \wedge (q \wedge r)$
T	T	T	T	T	T	T
T	T	F	T	F	F	F
T	F	T	F	F	F	F
T	F	F	F	F	F	F
F	T	T	F	F	T	F
F	T	F	F	F	F	F
F	F	T	F	F	F	F
F	F	F	F	F	F	F

4

p	q	r	$p \vee q$	$(p \vee q) \vee r$	$q \vee r$	$p \vee (q \vee r)$
T	T	T	T	T	T	T
T	T	F	T	T	T	T
T	F	T	T	T	T	T
T	F	F	T	T	F	T
F	T	T	T	T	T	T
F	T	F	T	T	T	T
F	F	T	F	T	T	T
F	F	F	F	F	F	F

5 a
  i Mary will study French or German next year.
  ii Mary will study Mathematics, and French or German next year.
  iii Mary will study Mathematics and French next year.
  iv Mary will study Mathematics and German next year.
  v Mary will study Mathematics and French, or Mathematics and German, next year.

b

p	q	r	$q \vee r$	$p \wedge (q \vee r)$	$p \wedge q$	$p \wedge r$	$(p \wedge q) \vee (p \wedge r)$
T	T	T	T	T	T	T	T
T	T	F	T	T	T	F	T
T	F	T	T	T	F	T	T
T	F	F	F	F	F	F	F
F	T	T	T	F	F	F	F
F	T	F	T	F	F	F	F
F	F	T	T	F	F	F	F
F	F	F	F	F	F	F	F

6 a

p	q	r	$q \wedge r$	$p \vee (q \wedge r)$	$p \vee q$	$p \vee r$	$(p \vee q) \wedge (p \vee r)$
T	T	T	T	T	T	T	T
T	T	F	F	T	T	T	T
T	F	T	F	T	T	T	T
T	F	F	F	T	T	T	T
F	T	T	T	T	T	T	T
F	T	F	F	F	T	F	F
F	F	T	F	F	F	T	F
F	F	F	F	F	F	F	F

b
  i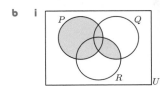
  ii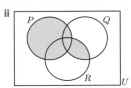

They are equivalent statements.

EXERCISE 8D

1 a antecedent: I miss the bus.
    consequent: I will walk to school.
  b antecedent: The temperature is low enough.
    consequent: The lake will freeze.
  c antecedent: $x > 20$.   consequent: $x > 10$.
  d antecedent: You jump all 8 hurdles.
    consequent: You may win the race.

2 a If the sun is shining, then I will go swimming.
  b If x is a multiple of 6, then x is even.
  c If there are eggs in the fridge, then Jan will bake a cake.

3 a
  i Rome is the capital of Italy if and only if Paris is the capital of France.
  ii True
  b
  i $2x + 3 = 10$ is an expression if and only if $2x + 3$ is an expression.
  ii False.

c **i** Cows have nine legs if and only if horses have five heads.
   ii True.

4 **a** $p \Rightarrow q$ **b** $q \Rightarrow p$ **c** $\neg q$ **d** $\neg p$
   e $\neg p \Rightarrow \neg q$ **f** $p \Rightarrow \neg q$ **g** $\neg q \Rightarrow p$ **h** $p \Leftrightarrow q$

5 **a**

p	q	$\neg q$	$p \Rightarrow \neg q$
T	T	F	F
T	F	T	T
F	T	F	T
F	F	T	T

b

p	q	$\neg q$	$\neg p$	$\neg q \Rightarrow \neg p$
T	T	F	F	T
T	F	T	F	F
F	T	F	T	T
F	F	T	T	T

c

p	q	$p \wedge q$	$(p \wedge q) \Rightarrow p$
T	T	T	T
T	F	F	T
F	T	F	T
F	F	F	T

d

p	q	$p \Rightarrow q$	$q \wedge (p \Rightarrow q)$
T	T	T	T
T	F	F	F
F	T	T	T
F	F	T	F

e

p	q	$\neg q$	$p \Leftrightarrow \neg q$
T	T	F	F
T	F	T	T
F	T	F	T
F	F	T	F

f

p	q	$p \Leftrightarrow q$	$\neg p$	$(p \Leftrightarrow q) \wedge \neg p$
T	T	T	F	F
T	F	F	F	F
F	T	F	T	F
F	F	T	T	T

g

p	q	$\neg q$	$p \wedge \neg q$	$p \Rightarrow (p \wedge \neg q)$
T	T	F	F	F
T	F	T	T	T
F	T	F	F	T
F	F	T	F	T

h

p	q	$p \Rightarrow q$	$\neg p$	$(p \Rightarrow q) \Rightarrow \neg p$
T	T	T	F	F
T	F	F	F	T
F	T	T	T	T
F	F	T	T	T

6 **a**

p	q	$p \veebar q$	$p \Leftrightarrow q$	$\neg(p \Leftrightarrow q)$
T	T	F	T	F
T	F	T	F	T
F	T	T	F	T
F	F	F	T	F

b

p	q	$\neg p$	$\neg p \Rightarrow q$	$p \vee q$
T	T	F	T	T
T	F	F	T	T
F	T	T	T	T
F	F	T	F	F

c

p	q	$p \veebar q$	$q \Rightarrow (p \veebar q)$	$p \wedge q$	$\neg(p \wedge q)$
T	T	F	F	T	F
T	F	T	T	F	T
F	T	T	T	F	T
F	F	F	T	F	T

d

p	q	$p \Leftrightarrow q$	$p \wedge q$	$\neg p$	$\neg q$	$\neg p \wedge \neg q$	$(p \wedge q) \vee (\neg p \wedge \neg q)$
T	T	T	T	F	F	F	T
T	F	F	F	F	T	F	F
F	T	F	F	T	F	F	F
F	F	T	F	T	T	T	T

7 **D**

8 **a**

p	q	$\neg p$	$\neg p \wedge q$	$p \Rightarrow (\neg p \wedge q)$
T	T	F	F	F
T	F	F	F	F
F	T	T	T	T
F	F	T	F	T

∴ neither

b

p	q	$p \wedge q$	$p \vee q$	$(p \wedge q) \Rightarrow (p \vee q)$
T	T	T	T	T
T	F	F	T	T
F	T	F	T	T
F	F	F	F	T

∴ tautology

c

p	q	$\neg q$	$p \Rightarrow \neg q$	$\neg p$	$\neg p \Rightarrow q$	$(p \Rightarrow \neg q) \vee (\neg p \Rightarrow q)$
T	T	F	F	F	T	T
T	F	T	T	F	T	T
F	T	F	T	T	T	T
F	F	T	T	T	F	T

∴ tautology

EXERCISE 8E

1 **a** Converse: If Nicole is warm, then she is wearing a jumper.
   Inverse: If Nicole is not wearing a jumper, then she is not warm.
   b Converse: If two triangles are equiangular, then they are similar.
   Inverse: If two triangles are not similar, then they are not equiangular.
   c Converse: If $x = \pm\sqrt{6}$, then $2x^2 = 12$.
   Inverse: If $2x^2 \neq 12$, then $x \neq \pm\sqrt{6}$.
   d Converse: If Alex is having fun, he is in the playground.
   Inverse: If Alex is not in the playground, then he is not having fun.
   e Converse: If a triangle has its three sides equal in length, then it is equilateral.
   Inverse: If a triangle is not equilateral, then its three sides are not equal in length.

2 **a** If a person is not a doctor, then the person is not fair and clever.
   b If a bush does not have thorns, then it is not a rose bush.
   c If a person does not make correct decisions all the time, then he or she is not an umpire.
   d If a person does not have good kicking skills, then he or she is not a good soccer player.
   e If a substance does not take the shape of the container in which it is placed, then it is not a liquid.

3 **a** If a person does not study Mathematics, then he or she is not a high school student.
   b **i** Keong studies Mathematics.
      ii Tamra is not a high school student.
      iii Nothing can be deduced.

4 **a** If x^2 is not divisible by 9, then x is not divisible by 3.
   b If x is not even, then x is not a number ending in 2.
   c If PQ $\nparallel$ SR or PS $\nparallel$ QR, then PQRS is not a rectangle.
   d If $\widehat{\text{KML}}$ does not measure $60°$, then KLM is not an equilateral triangle.

5 **a** **i** If a house has a chimney, then it has at least 3 windows.
      ii If a house does not have at least 3 windows, then it does not have a chimney.
      iii If a house does not have a chimney, then it does not have at least 3 windows.

b **i** Implication: True   Converse: False
Inverse: False   Contrapositive: True
ii Implication: True   Converse: True
Inverse: True   Contrapositive: True
iii Implication: False   Converse: True
Inverse: True   Contrapositive: False

6 **a** **i** No weak students are in Year 11.
ii No Year 11 students are weak.
b **i** If $x \in W$ then $x \notin E$.   **ii** If $x \in E$ then $x \notin W$.
c They are contrapositives.

EXERCISE 8F.1

1 **a** $p \Leftrightarrow q$
$\dfrac{\neg q}{\neg p}$

b $(p \Leftrightarrow q) \wedge \neg q \Rightarrow \neg p$

c

p	q	$p \Leftrightarrow q$	$\neg q$	$(p \Leftrightarrow q) \wedge \neg q$	$\neg p$	$(p \Leftrightarrow q) \wedge \neg q \Rightarrow \neg p$
T	T	T	F	F	F	T
T	F	F	T	F	F	T
F	T	F	F	F	T	T
F	F	T	T	T	T	T

We have a tautology, $\therefore$ argument is valid.

2 **a** **i** $(p \Rightarrow q) \wedge \neg q \Rightarrow \neg p$ **ii** $(p \vee q) \wedge \neg p \Rightarrow q$
iii $(p \vee q) \Rightarrow p$ **iv** $(p \Rightarrow q) \wedge \neg p \Rightarrow \neg q$
v $(p \Rightarrow q) \wedge (q \Rightarrow p) \Rightarrow p$

b **i**

p	q	$p \Rightarrow q$	$\neg q$	$(p \Rightarrow q) \wedge \neg q$	$\neg p$	$(p \Rightarrow q) \wedge \neg q \Rightarrow \neg p$
T	T	T	F	F	F	T
T	F	F	T	F	F	T
F	T	T	F	F	T	T
F	F	T	T	T	T	T

$\therefore$ argument is valid.

ii

p	q	$p \vee q$	$\neg p$	$(p \vee q) \wedge \neg p$	$(p \vee q) \wedge \neg p \Rightarrow q$
T	T	T	F	F	T
T	F	T	F	F	T
F	T	T	T	T	T
F	F	F	T	F	T

$\therefore$ argument is valid.

iii

p	q	$p \vee q$	$(p \vee q) \Rightarrow p$
T	T	T	T
T	F	T	T
F	T	T	F
F	F	F	T

$\therefore$ argument is not valid.

iv

p	q	$p \Rightarrow q$	$\neg p$	$(p \Rightarrow q) \wedge \neg p$	$\neg q$	$(p \Rightarrow q) \wedge \neg p \Rightarrow \neg q$
T	T	T	F	F	F	T
T	F	F	F	F	T	T
F	T	T	T	T	F	F
F	F	T	T	T	T	T

$\therefore$ argument is not valid.

v

p	q	$p \Rightarrow q$	$q \Rightarrow p$	$(p \Rightarrow q) \wedge (q \Rightarrow p)$	$(p \Rightarrow q) \wedge (q \Rightarrow p) \Rightarrow p$
T	T	T	T	T	T
T	F	F	T	F	T
F	T	T	F	F	T
F	F	T	T	T	F

$\therefore$ argument is not valid.

3 **a** valid   **b** not valid   **c** valid   **d** not valid

5 **b** Don has visited Australia and New Zealand.
6 **a** valid   **b** not valid   **c** valid
d not valid   **e** valid   **f** not valid

EXERCISE 8F.2

1 **a** It is sunny and I am warm. Hence, I feel happy.
b It is sunny and I am not warm. Hence, I do not feel happy.
c I am warm and I feel happy. Hence, it is sunny.
2 **B**   **3** **b** p, q, r are all true.
4 **a** p: I do not like the subject. q: I do not work hard.
r: I fail.
b $(p \Rightarrow q) \wedge (q \Rightarrow r) \wedge \neg r \Rightarrow \neg p$
c Argument is valid, $\therefore$ conclusion is a result of valid reasoning.
5 not valid (he can be tall and fast, but not on the team)

REVIEW SET 8A

1 **a** proposition, true   **b** not a proposition
c proposition, indeterminate   **d** not a proposition
e not a proposition   **f** proposition, true
g not a proposition   **h** proposition, false
i proposition, indeterminate   **j** proposition, true
2 **a** x is not an even number.
b x is an even number or is divisible by 3.
c x is an even number or is divisible by 3, but not both.
d If x is an even number, then x is divisible by 3.
e x is not an even number and is divisible by 3.
f x is not an even number or x is divisible by 3, but not both.
g If x is an even number then x is not divisible by 3.
h If x is not an even number then x is not divisible by 3.
3 **a** $p \Rightarrow q$, 7   **b** $\neg p$, 4   **c** $q \wedge \neg p$, 14
d $p \veebar q$, 2   **e** $\neg p \wedge \neg q$, 6
Note: There are other numbers that satisfy these statements.
4 **a** Implication: If I love swimming, then I live near the sea.
$p \Rightarrow q$
Inverse: If I do not love swimming, then I do not
$\neg p \Rightarrow \neg q$ live near the sea.
Converse: If I live near the sea, then I love swimming.
$q \Rightarrow p$
Contrapositive: If I do not live near the sea, then I do not
$\neg q \Rightarrow \neg p$ love swimming.
b Implication: If I like food, then I eat a lot.
$p \Rightarrow q$
Inverse: If I do not like food, then I do not eat a lot.
$\neg p \Rightarrow \neg q$
Converse: If I eat a lot, then I like food.
$q \Rightarrow p$
Contrapositive: If I do not eat a lot, then I do not like food.
$\neg q \Rightarrow \neg p$

5 **a** 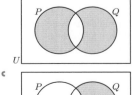   **b**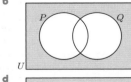

c 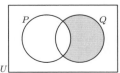   **d**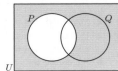

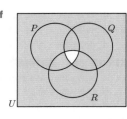

6 a $\{1, 2, 3, 4, 6, 12\}$ b $\{1, 3, 5, 7, 9\}$ c $\{1, 3\}$
  d $\{1, 2, 3, 4, 5, 6, 7, 9, 12\}$

7 a invalid b invalid c invalid

REVIEW SET 8B

1 a $P = \{20, 24, 28\}$, $Q = \{1, 2, 3, 4, 6, 8, 12, 24\}$
    $R = \{20, 22, 24, 26, 28\}$

  b i $\{24\}$ ii $\{24\}$ iii $\{20, 24, 28\}$
   iv $P \cap Q \cap R = \{24\}$

2 a Eddy is not good at football.
  b The maths class includes 10 or less boys.
  c The writing is legible.   d Ali does not own a new car.

3 a If a creature is a bird, then it has two legs.
  b If a creature is a snake, then it is not a mammal.
  c If a polygon is a rectangle, then it does not have five sides.
  d If this equation has solutions, then they are not real solutions.

4 a It is neither.   b x is zero or a positive rational number.

5 a $\neg(p \vee q)$ b $p \wedge \neg q$ c $p \wedge q \wedge r$

6 a logically equivalent   b logically equivalent
  c not logically equivalent   d logically equivalent

7 a p: The sun is shining. q: I will wear my shorts.
    $(p \Rightarrow q) \wedge p \Rightarrow q$
    The argument is valid.
  b p: Marty is a teacher. q: Marty works hard.
    $(p \Rightarrow q) \wedge \neg p \Rightarrow \neg q$
    The argument is not valid.

REVIEW SET 8C

1 a $x > 3$ for $x \in \mathbb{Z}$ b $x \in \{$brush, hairclip, bobby pin$\}$
  c x is a woman, but is not tall.

2 a

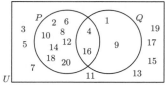

  b i $\{4, 16\}$ ii $\{1, 3, 4, 5, 7, 9, 11, 13, 15, 16, 17, 19\}$
   iii $\{3, 4, 5, 7, 11, 13, 15, 16, 17, 19\}$

3 Inverse: If a parallelogram is not a rhombus, then its diagonals
       are not equal in length.
   Converse: If the diagonals of a parallelogram are equal in length,
       then the paralellogram is a rhombus.
   Contrapositive: If the diagonals of a parallelogram are not
       equal in length, then the parallelogram is not a
       rhombus.

4 a $\neg p \Rightarrow \neg q$ b $\neg p \Rightarrow q$ c $q \wedge \neg p$ d $\neg p \vee q$

5 a If the plane leaves from gate 5, then it leaves this morning
    and it does not leave from gate 2.
  b $\neg r \Leftrightarrow q \vee p$

6 a

p	q	$p \Rightarrow q$	$(p \Rightarrow q) \wedge q$	$(p \Rightarrow q) \wedge q \Rightarrow p$
T	T	T	T	T
T	F	F	F	T
F	T	T	T	F
F	F	T	F	T

  $\therefore$ it is neither

  b

p	q	$p \wedge q$	$p \vee q$	$\neg(p \vee q)$	$(p \wedge q) \wedge \neg(p \vee q)$
T	T	T	T	F	F
T	F	F	T	F	F
F	T	F	T	F	F
F	F	F	F	T	F

  $\therefore$ logical contradiction

  c

p	q	$\neg p$	$\neg p \Leftrightarrow q$
T	T	F	F
T	F	F	T
F	T	T	T
F	F	T	F

  $\therefore$ it is neither

  d

p	q	$\neg q$	$p \vee \neg q$	$(p \vee \neg q) \Rightarrow q$
T	T	F	T	T
T	F	T	T	F
F	T	F	F	T
F	F	T	T	F

  $\therefore$ it is neither

  e

p	q	r	$\neg p$	$\neg p \vee q$	$(\neg p \vee q) \Rightarrow r$
T	T	T	F	T	T
T	T	F	F	T	F
T	F	T	F	F	T
T	F	F	F	F	T
F	T	T	T	T	T
F	T	F	T	T	F
F	F	T	T	T	T
F	F	F	T	T	F

  $\therefore$ it is neither

  f

p	q	$p \wedge q$	$(p \wedge q) \Rightarrow q$
T	T	T	T
T	F	F	T
F	T	F	T
F	F	F	T

  $\therefore$ tautology

7 a p: Fred is a dog. q: Fred has fur.
    r: Fred has a cold nose.
    $(p \Rightarrow q) \wedge (q \Rightarrow r) \wedge p \Rightarrow r$
    The argument is valid.
  b p: Viv is a judge. q: Viv wears a robe.
    r: Viv wears a wig.
    $(p \Rightarrow (q \vee r)) \wedge (\neg r \wedge \neg p) \Rightarrow \neg q$
    Argument is not valid.

EXERCISE 9A.1

1 a 0.78 b 0.22   **2** a 0.487 b 0.051 c 0.731
3 a 43 days b i 0.0465 ii 0.186 iii 0.465
4 a 0.0895 b 0.126

EXERCISE 9A.2

1 a 0.265 b 0.861 c 0.222
2 a 0.146 b 0.435 c 0.565
3 a i 0.189 ii 0.55 b 0.381 c 0.545

EXERCISE 9B

1 a $\{A, B, C, D\}$ b $\{BB, BG, GB, GG\}$

c {ABCD, ABDC, ACBD, ACDB, ADBC, ADCB, BACD, BADC, BCAD, BCDA, BDAC, BDCA, CABD, CADB, CBAD, CBDA, CDAB, CDBA, DABC, DACB, DBAC, DBCA, DCAB, DCBA}

d {BBB, BBG, BGB, GBB, BGG, GBG, GGB, GGG}

2 a

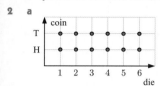

b

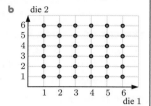

c

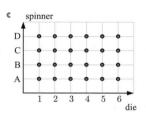

d

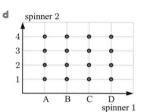

3 a

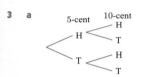

5-cent   10-cent

b

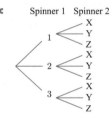

coin   spinner

c

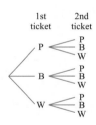

Spinner 1   Spinner 2

d

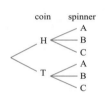

1st ticket   2nd ticket

EXERCISE 9C.1

1 a $\frac{3}{15} = \frac{1}{5}$ **b** $\frac{5}{15} = \frac{1}{3}$ **c** $\frac{7}{15}$ **d** $\frac{12}{15} = \frac{4}{5}$

   e $\frac{3}{15} = \frac{1}{5}$ **f** $\frac{8}{15}$

2 a 4   **b i** $\frac{8}{12} = \frac{2}{3}$ **ii** $\frac{4}{12} = \frac{1}{3}$

3 a $\frac{9}{36} = \frac{1}{4}$ **b** $\frac{4}{36} = \frac{1}{9}$ **c** $\frac{16}{36} = \frac{4}{9}$ **d** $\frac{1}{36}$

   e $\frac{2}{36} = \frac{1}{18}$ **f** $\frac{6}{36} = \frac{1}{6}$ **g** $\frac{3}{36} = \frac{1}{12}$ **h** $\frac{12}{36} = \frac{1}{3}$

4 a $\frac{1}{7}$ **b** $\frac{2}{7}$ **c** $\frac{124}{1461}$

   d $\frac{237}{1461}$ {remember leap years}

5 a AKN, ANK, KAN, KNA, NAK, NKA

   b i $\frac{2}{6} = \frac{1}{3}$ **ii** $\frac{2}{6} = \frac{1}{3}$ **iii** $\frac{4}{6} = \frac{2}{3}$ **iv** $\frac{4}{6} = \frac{2}{3}$

6 a BBB, BBG, BGB, GBB, BGG, GBG, GGB, GGG

   b i $\frac{1}{8}$ **ii** $\frac{1}{8}$ **iii** $\frac{1}{8}$ **iv** $\frac{3}{8}$ **v** $\frac{4}{8} = \frac{1}{2}$ **vi** $\frac{7}{8}$

7 a ABCD, ABDC, ACBD, ACDB, ADBC, ADCB, BACD, BADC, BCAD, BCDA, BDAC, BDCA, CABD, CADB, CBAD, CBDA, CDAB, CDBA, DABC, DACB, DBAC, DBCA, DCAB, DCBA.

   b i $\frac{12}{24} = \frac{1}{2}$ **ii** $\frac{12}{24} = \frac{1}{2}$ **iii** $\frac{12}{24} = \frac{1}{2}$ **iv** $\frac{12}{24} = \frac{1}{2}$

EXERCISE 9C.2

1

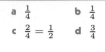

5-cent / 10-cent

   a $\frac{1}{4}$ **b** $\frac{1}{4}$

   c $\frac{2}{4} = \frac{1}{2}$ **d** $\frac{3}{4}$

2 a

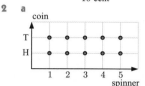

   b 10   **c i** $\frac{1}{10}$

   ii $\frac{2}{10} = \frac{1}{5}$

   iii $\frac{6}{10} = \frac{3}{5}$

   iv $\frac{6}{10} = \frac{3}{5}$

3 a $\frac{1}{36}$ **b** $\frac{2}{36} = \frac{1}{18}$ **c** $\frac{20}{36} = \frac{5}{9}$ **d** $\frac{11}{36}$

   e $\frac{10}{36} = \frac{5}{18}$ **f** $\frac{25}{36}$

EXERCISE 9C.3

1 a

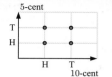

die 2 / die 1

   b i $\frac{2}{36} = \frac{1}{18}$

   ii $\frac{9}{36} = \frac{1}{4}$

   iii $\frac{10}{36} = \frac{5}{18}$

2 a

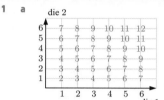

die 2 / die 1

   b i $\frac{6}{36} = \frac{1}{6}$

   ii $\frac{8}{36} = \frac{2}{9}$

   iii $\frac{6}{36} = \frac{1}{6}$

3 a

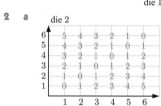

spinner 1 / spinner 2

   b i $\frac{2}{15}$

   ii $\frac{7}{15}$

   iii $\frac{6}{15} = \frac{2}{5}$

EXERCISE 9D.1

1 a $\frac{1}{36}$ **b** $\frac{1}{6}$ **c** $\frac{25}{36}$ **2 a** $\frac{1}{8}$ **b** $\frac{1}{8}$

3 a $\frac{6}{625}$ **b** $\frac{506}{625}$ **4 a** $\frac{1}{16}$ **b** $\frac{15}{16}$

5 a 0.56   **b** 0.06   **c** 0.14   **d** 0.24

6 a $\frac{8}{125}$ **b** $\frac{12}{125}$ **c** $\frac{27}{125}$

EXERCISE 9D.2

1 a $\frac{14}{55}$ **b** $\frac{1}{55}$ **2 a** $\frac{7}{15}$ **b** $\frac{7}{30}$

3 a $\frac{3}{100}$ **b** $\frac{1}{1650}$ **c** $\frac{1}{161\,700}$ **d** $\frac{7372}{8085}$

4 a $\frac{4}{7}$ **b** $\frac{2}{7}$ **5 a** $\frac{10}{21}$ **b** $\frac{1}{21}$

EXERCISE 9E

1 a

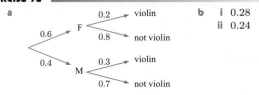

   b i 0.28

   ii 0.24

2 a

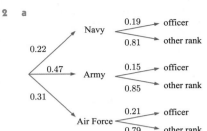

b i 0.177
ii 0.958
iii 0.864

3 a

b $\frac{1}{4}$
c $\frac{1}{16}$
d $\frac{5}{8}$
e $\frac{3}{4}$

4

$$P(\text{win}) = \frac{7}{50}$$

5

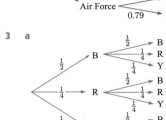

$$P(\text{spoiled}) = 0.032$$

6 $\frac{17}{40}$ **7** $\frac{9}{38}$ **8 a** $\frac{11}{30}$ **b** $\frac{19}{30}$

EXERCISE 9F

1 a $\frac{20}{49}$ **b** $\frac{10}{21}$

2 a

draw 1   draw 2

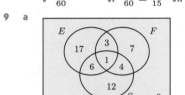

b i $\frac{3}{10}$
ii $\frac{1}{10}$
iii $\frac{3}{5}$

3 a $\frac{2}{9}$ **b** $\frac{5}{9}$

4 a i $\frac{1}{3}$ **ii** $\frac{2}{15}$ **iii** $\frac{4}{15}$ **iv** $\frac{4}{15}$
   b These are all the possible outcomes.

5 a $\frac{1}{5}$ **b** $\frac{3}{5}$ **c** $\frac{4}{5}$ **6** $\frac{19}{45}$

7 a $\frac{1}{4950}$ **b** $\frac{4753}{4950}$ **c** $\frac{197}{4950}$ **8** $\frac{7}{33}$

EXERCISE 9G.1

1 27   **2 a** $\frac{2}{3}$ **b** 2   **3 a** $\frac{1}{8}$ **b** 25

4 15 days   **5** 30 times

6 a i $\frac{11}{20}$ **ii** $\frac{29}{100}$ **iii** $\frac{4}{25}$
   b i 4125   **ii** 2175   **iii** 1200

EXERCISE 9G.2

1 11.7 points   **2** 1.57 fish   **3** 3.13 books
4 5.25 lollies   **5 a** $\frac{4}{15}$ **b** 8.93 pins

EXERCISE 9G.3

1 fair   **2 a** €3.50   **b** −€0.50. No
3 a −$0.05   **b** lose $5   **4** −£0.75
5 a −$0.67 ≠ 0   **b** $30   **6** $4.75

EXERCISE 9H

1 a $\frac{3}{17}$ **b** $\frac{14}{17}$ **2 a** $\frac{17}{29}$ **b** $\frac{26}{29}$ **c** $\frac{5}{29}$

3 a $\frac{9}{65}$ **b** $\frac{4}{65}$ **c** $\frac{52}{65} = \frac{4}{5}$

4 a $\frac{19}{40}$ **b** $\frac{20}{40} = \frac{1}{2}$ **c** $\frac{32}{40} = \frac{4}{5}$ **d** $\frac{25}{40} = \frac{5}{8}$
   e $\frac{13}{40}$

5 a $\frac{38}{50} = \frac{19}{25}$ **b** $\frac{26}{50} = \frac{13}{25}$ **c** $\frac{12}{50} = \frac{6}{25}$

6 a $\frac{14}{30} = \frac{7}{15}$ **b** $\frac{2}{30} = \frac{1}{15}$ **c** $\frac{4}{30} = \frac{2}{15}$

7 a i $\dfrac{b+c}{a+b+c+d}$ **ii** $\dfrac{b}{a+b+c+d}$
   iii $\dfrac{a+b+c}{a+b+c+d}$ **iv** $\dfrac{a+b+c}{a+b+c+d}$
   b $P(A \text{ or } B) = P(A) + P(B) - P(A \text{ and } B)$

8 a $k = 5$
   b i $\frac{14}{60} = \frac{7}{30}$ **ii** $\frac{11}{60}$ **iii** $\frac{7}{60}$ **iv** $\frac{53}{60}$
   v $\frac{7}{60}$ **vi** $\frac{8}{60} = \frac{2}{15}$ **vii** $\frac{41}{60}$ **viii** $\frac{31}{60}$

9 a

   b i $\frac{27}{50}$
   ii $\frac{15}{50} = \frac{3}{10}$
   iii $\frac{16}{50} = \frac{8}{25}$
   iv $\frac{10}{50} = \frac{1}{5}$
   v $\frac{4}{50} = \frac{2}{25}$

10 a $a = 3,\ b = 3$
   b i $\frac{12}{40} = \frac{3}{10}$ **ii** $\frac{4}{40} = \frac{1}{10}$ **iii** $\frac{7}{40}$
   iv $\frac{15}{40} = \frac{3}{8}$ **v** $\frac{25}{40} = \frac{5}{8}$

EXERCISE 9I

1 0.6   **2** 0.2   **3** 0.35
4 a Yes   **b i** $\frac{4}{15}$ **ii** $\frac{7}{15}$ **iii** $\frac{11}{15}$
5 a $\frac{11}{25}$ **b** $\frac{12}{25}$ **c** $\frac{8}{25}$ **d** $\frac{7}{25}$ **e** $\frac{4}{25}$ **f** $\frac{23}{25}$
   g not possible   **h** $\frac{11}{25}$ **i** not possible   **j** $\frac{12}{25}$

EXERCISE 9J

1 a

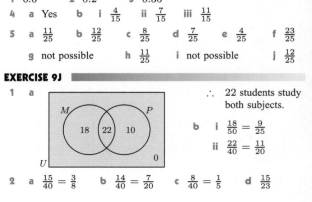

∴ 22 students study both subjects.

b i $\frac{18}{50} = \frac{9}{25}$
ii $\frac{22}{40} = \frac{11}{20}$

2 a $\frac{15}{40} = \frac{3}{8}$ **b** $\frac{14}{40} = \frac{7}{20}$ **c** $\frac{8}{40} = \frac{1}{5}$ **d** $\frac{15}{23}$

3 a $\frac{28}{50} = \frac{14}{25}$ **b** $\frac{40}{50} = \frac{4}{5}$ **c** $\frac{10}{50} = \frac{1}{5}$ **d** $\frac{5}{23}$

e $\frac{18}{28} = \frac{9}{14}$

4 $\frac{5}{6}$

5 a $\frac{13}{20}$ **b** $\frac{7}{20}$ **c** $\frac{11}{50}$ **d** $\frac{7}{25}$ **e** $\frac{4}{7}$ **f** $\frac{1}{4}$

6 a $\frac{3}{5}$ **b** $\frac{2}{3}$ **7 a** 0.46 **b** ≈ 0.609 **8** 0.429

9 a 0.45 **b** 0.75 **c** 0.65 **10 a** 0.0484 **b** 0.393

11 a $\frac{20}{95} = \frac{4}{19}$ **b** $\frac{22}{95}$ **c** $\frac{83}{95}$

d $\frac{22}{34} = \frac{11}{17}$ **e** $\frac{14}{34} = \frac{7}{17}$ **f** $\frac{12}{39} = \frac{4}{13}$

12 a

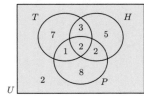

b i $\frac{5}{30} = \frac{1}{6}$

ii $\frac{13}{30}$

iii $\frac{4}{13}$

iv $\frac{23}{30}$

v $\frac{8}{18} = \frac{4}{9}$

vi $\frac{2}{12} = \frac{1}{6}$

EXERCISE 9K

1 Yes

2 a i $\frac{7}{30}$ **ii** $\frac{7}{12}$ **iii** $\frac{7}{10}$

b A and B are **not** independent events.

3 a 0.35 **b** 0.85 **c** 0.15 **d** 0.15 **e** 0.5

4 $\frac{14}{15}$ **6** 0.9

REVIEW SET 9A

1 ABCD, ABDC, ACBD, ACDB, ADBC, ADCB, BACD, BADC, BCAD, BCDA, BDAC, BDCA, CABD, CADB, CBAD, CBDA, CDAB, CDBA, DABC, DACB, DBAC, DBCA, DCAB, DCBA

a $\frac{12}{24} = \frac{1}{2}$ **b** $\frac{8}{24} = \frac{1}{3}$

2 a $1 - m$ **b** $0 \leqslant m \leqslant 1$

3 a $\frac{3}{8}$ **b** $\frac{1}{8}$ **c** $\frac{5}{8}$ **4 a** $\frac{2}{5}$ **b** $\frac{13}{15}$ **c** $\frac{4}{15}$

5 a 0 **b** 0.45 **c** 0.8

6 a Events are independent if the occurrence of one event does not affect the probability of the other event occurring.

b Mutually exclusive events have no common outcomes.

7 die 2

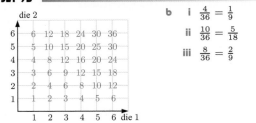

a $\frac{8}{36} = \frac{2}{9}$

b $\frac{15}{36} = \frac{5}{12}$

8 4350 seeds **9 a** $\frac{10}{40} = \frac{1}{4}$ **b** $\frac{37}{40}$ **c** $\frac{10}{25} = \frac{2}{5}$ **10** $\frac{5}{9}$

REVIEW SET 9B

1 a die 2

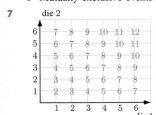

b i $\frac{4}{36} = \frac{1}{9}$

ii $\frac{10}{36} = \frac{5}{18}$

iii $\frac{8}{36} = \frac{2}{9}$

2

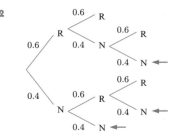

P(N wins) = 0.352

3 a $\frac{7}{39}$ **b** $\frac{21}{74}$ **c** $\frac{108}{402} = \frac{18}{67}$

4 a $\frac{1}{5\,177\,125}$ **b** ≈ 0.0239 **5 a** 0.259 **b** 0.703

6 a

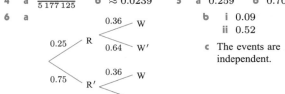

b i 0.09

ii 0.52

c The events are independent.

7 0.496

8 a $\frac{20}{42} = \frac{10}{21}$ **b** $\frac{5}{42}$ **c** $\frac{30}{42} = \frac{5}{7}$ **d** $\frac{29}{42}$

e $\frac{9}{42} = \frac{3}{14}$ **f** $\frac{12}{24} = \frac{2}{7}$ **g** $\frac{5}{20} = \frac{1}{4}$ **h** $\frac{3}{15} = \frac{1}{5}$

9 1.18 goals

REVIEW SET 9C

1 BBBB, BBBG, BBGB, BGBB, GBBB, BBGG, BGBG, GBBG, BGGB, GBGB, GGBB, BGGG, GBGG, GGBG, GGGB, GGGG
$\therefore$ P(2 boys, 2 girls) $= \frac{6}{16} = \frac{3}{8}$

2 a $\frac{5}{33}$ **b** $\frac{19}{66}$ **c** $\frac{5}{11}$ **d** $\frac{16}{33}$

3 a $\frac{12}{25}$ **b** $\frac{12}{25}$ **c** $\frac{7}{8}$ **4 a** $\frac{5}{8}$ **b** $\frac{1}{4}$

5 0.9975 **6 a** $\frac{31}{70}$ **b** $\frac{21}{31}$ **7** Yes

8 a $\frac{5}{50} = \frac{1}{10}$ **b** $\frac{14}{50} = \frac{7}{25}$ **c** $\frac{13}{50}$

EXERCISE 10A

1 a, b The manufacturer wants a particular volume of drink (or diameter of bolt), and so that value is generally the mean. However, minor variations in the filling of the can (or machining of the bolt) lead to some volumes (or diameters) being slightly larger than the mean, and some being slightly less than the mean. However, it is unlikely that the volumes (or diameters) will be *much* larger, or *much* smaller.

2 a 0.683 **b** 0.477

3 a 15.9% **b** 84.1% **c** 97.6% **d** 0.13%

4 3 times **5 a** 459 babies **b** 446 babies

6 a i 34.1% **ii** 47.7%

b i 0.136 **ii** 0.159 **iii** 0.0228 **iv** 0.841

7 a 0.341 **b** 0.159 **c** 0.0228

8 a 84.1% **b** 2.28% **c i** 2.15% **ii** 95.4%

d i 97.7% **ii** 2.28%

9 a 41 days **b** 254 days **c** 213 days

EXERCISE 10B

1 a 0.341 **b** 0.383 **c** 0.106

2 a 0.341 **b** 0.264 **c** 0.212 **d** 0.945

e 0.579 **f** 0.383

3 a 0.248 **b** 0.798 **c** 0.205 **d** 0.427
e 0.0859 **f** 0.457
4 a 0.334 **b** 0.166
5 a 0.585 **b** 0.805 **c** 0.528 **6** 0.378
7 a i 0.904 **ii** 0.0912 **b** ≈ 11 weeks
8 a 0.0509 **b** 52.1% **c** ≈ 47 eels
9 a 0.303 **b** 0.968 **c** 0.309

EXERCISE 10C

1 a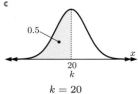

    $k \approx 18.8$

b

    $k \approx 23.5$

c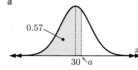

    $k = 20$

2 a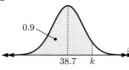

    $k \approx 49.2$

b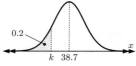

    $k \approx 31.8$

3 a

    $\therefore \ a > 30$

b $a \approx 30.9$
c i 0.43
  ii 0.07

4 a 21.4 **b** 21.8 **c** 2.82
5 83 **6** 24.7 cm **7** 75.2 mm
8 a 1.98 kg **b** 1.40 kg **9** 502 mL to 504 mL

REVIEW SET 10A

1 a 2.28% **b** 95.4% **c** 68.3%
2 a i 2.28% **ii** 84.0% **b** 0.341
3 a 0.683 **b** 0.954 **c** 0.401 **d** 0.894 **4** 31.2 mm
5 a $\mu = 29, \ \sigma \approx 10.7$ **b i** 0.713 **ii** 0.250
6 a 6.68% **b** 137 bags **7** 162 seconds

REVIEW SET 10B

1 a 0.136 **b** 0.341 **2 a** 0.364 **b** 0.356 **c** $k = 18.2$
3 a 2.28% **b** 84.1% **c** 81.9%
4 a 0.341 **b** 0.0228 **c** 0.238 **d** 0.225
5 a 0.260 **b** 29.3 weeks
6 0 to 18.6 words per minute **7** 17.5°C to 30.8°C

REVIEW SET 10C

1 a ≈ 0.279 **b** ≈ 0.238 **c** ≈ 0.415
2 a ≈ 0.274 **b i** ≈ 0.726 **ii** ≈ 0.226
3 a ≈ 0.758 **b** ≈ 0.115 **c** ≈ 0.285

4 a $k \approx 19.7$ **b** $k \approx 28.0$
5 a ≈ 0.258 **b** about 243 suitcases **c** 23.0 kg
6 a k is greater than 25. **b** $k \approx 26.8$
7 a ≈ 0.0478 **b i** 1446 **ii** 57.4 mins

EXERCISE 11A

1 a weak positive correlation, linear, no outliers
  b strong negative correlation, linear, one outlier
  c no correlation
  d strong negative correlation, not linear, one outlier
  e moderate positive correlation, linear, no outliers
  f weak positive correlation, not linear, no outliers

2 a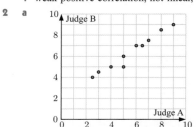

  b There appears to be **strong**, **positive**, **linear** correlation between Judge A's scores and Judge B's scores. This means that as Judge A's scores increase, Judge B's scores **increase**.
  c No, the scores are related to the quality of the ice-skaters' performances.

3 a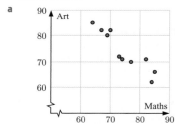

  b There is a strong, negative, linear correlation between Mathematics and Art marks.

4 a **D** **b** **A** **c** **B** **d** **C**
5 a There is a moderate, positive, linear correlation between *hours of study* and *marks obtained*.
  b The test is out of 50 marks, so the outlier (> 50) appears to be an error. It should be discarded.
6 a Not causal, dependent on genetics and/or age.
  b Not causal, dependent on the size of the fire. **c** Causal
  d Causal **e** Not causal, dependent on population of town.

EXERCISE 11B.1

1 weak/moderate positive correlation
2 a **B** **b** **A** **c** **D** **d** **C** **e** **E**
3 a i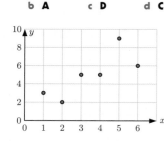

  ii $r \approx 0.786$ **iii** moderate positive correlation

b **i**

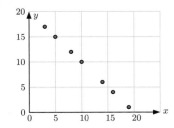

ii $r = -1$ **iii** perfect negative correlation

c **i**

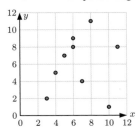

ii $r \approx 0.146$ **iii** weak positive correlation

4 **a**

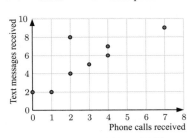

b $r \approx 0.816$ **c** moderate positive correlation

5 **a** $r \approx 0.917$

b strong positive correlation.
In general, the greater the young athlete's age, the further they can throw a discus.

6 **a**

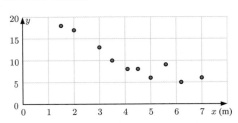

b negative   **c** $r \approx -0.911$

d strong negative correlation   **e** decreases   **f** yes

EXERCISE 11B.2

1 **a** $\overline{x} = 6$, $\overline{y} = 6$

b

x	y	$x - \overline{x}$	$y - \overline{y}$	$(x - \overline{x})(y - \overline{y})$	$(x - \overline{x})^2$	$(y - \overline{y})^2$
2	10	-4	4	-16	16	16
4	7	-2	1	-2	4	1
7	5	1	-1	-1	1	1
11	2	5	-4	-20	25	16
Totals: 24	24	0	0	-39	46	34

c $r \approx -0.986$

2 **a** $r = 1$, the data is perfectly positively linearly correlated.

b $r = -1$, the data is perfectly negatively linearly correlated.

c $r = 0$, there is no correlation.

3 **a**

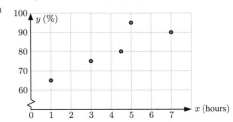

b $r \approx 0.881$ **c** strong positive correlation

EXERCISE 11B.3

1 57.8% of the variation in the number of visitors can be explained by the variation in maximum temperature.

2 $r^2 \approx 0.224$. 22.4% of the variation in money lost can be explained by the variation in time spent gambling.

3 $r^2 \approx 0.133$. 13.3% of the variation in heart rate can be explained by the variation in age.

4 **a**

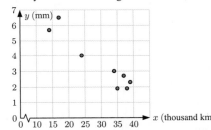

b $r^2 \approx 0.904$. 90.4% of the variation in tread depth can be explained by the variation in number of kilometres travelled.

EXERCISE 11C

1 **a, e**

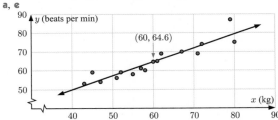

b $r \approx 0.929$

c There is a strong positive correlation between *weight* and *pulse rate*.

d $(60, 64.6)$

f 68 beats per minute. This is an interpolation, so the estimate is reliable.

2 **a, d**

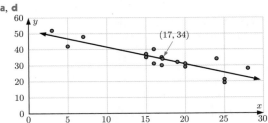

b $r \approx -0.878$

c There is a strong negative correlation between *number of speed cameras* and *number of car accidents*.

e At $y \approx 52$. This means that we would expect a city with no speed cameras to have approximately 52 car accidents in a week.

3 a, e

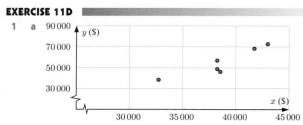

b (20, 22)   **c** moderate height, and thinner.   **d** (45, 15.7)
f ≈ 37.4 m. This is an extrapolation, so the prediction may not be reliable.

EXERCISE 11D

1 a

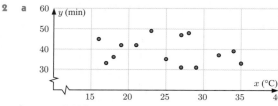

b $r \approx 0.921$
c There is a strong, positive, linear correlation between the starting salaries for Bachelor degrees and the starting salaries for PhDs.
d $y \approx 3.44x - 78\,300$
e i $59\,300
   ii This is an interpolation, so the prediction is likely to be reliable.

2 a

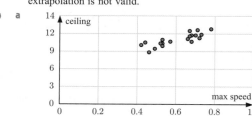

b $r \approx -0.219$
c There is a weak negative correlation between *temperature* and *time*.
d No, as there is almost no correlation.

3 a $r \approx -0.924$
b There is a strong, negative, linear correlation between the *petrol price* and the *number of customers*.
c $y \approx -4.27x + 489$
d gradient ≈ -4.27, for every 1 cent per litre increase in the price of petrol, a service station will lose 4.27 customers.
e -5.10 customers
f It is impossible to have a negative number of customers. This extrapolation is not valid.

4 a

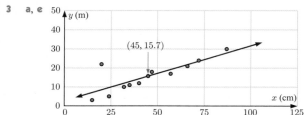

b $r \approx 0.840$ **c** moderate positive linear correlation
d $y \approx 8.12x + 6.09$ **e** 11.0 km

5 a

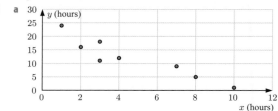

b $r \approx -0.927$
c There is a strong negative linear correlation between time exercising and time watching television.
d $y \approx -2.13x + 22.1$
e gradient ≈ -2.13, for every hour the children spend exercising, they watch 2.13 hours less television.
   y-intercept ≈ 22.1 We would expect a child who does not exercise at all to watch 22.1 hours of television per week.
f 11.5 hours each week

6 a

(50, 4.4) is the outlier.
b i $r \approx 0.798$ **ii** $r \approx 0.993$
c i $y \approx 0.0672x + 2.22$ **ii** $y \approx 0.119x + 1.32$
d The one which excludes the outlier.
e Too much fertiliser often kills the plants, or makes them sick.

EXERCISE 11E.1

1 a

	Likes chicken	Dislikes chicken	sum
Likes fish	45	15	60
Dislikes fish	30	10	40
sum	75	25	100

b

	Drove to work	Cycled to work	Public transport	sum
Male	25.3	7.7	11	44
Female	20.7	6.3	9	36
sum	46	14	20	80

c

	Junior school	Middle school	High school	sum
Plays sport	38.28	56.76	69.96	165
Does not play sport	19.72	29.24	36.04	85
sum	58	86	106	250

d

	Wore hat and sunscreen	Wore hat or sunscreen	Wore neither	sum
Sunburnt	10.92	6.16	3.92	21
Not sunburnt	28.08	15.84	10.08	54
sum	39	22	14	75

2 a

	Pass Maths test	Fail Maths test	sum
Male	30	20	50
Female	30	20	50
sum	60	40	100

b In a sample of 100 students, we would expect 30 to be male and pass the Maths test.

c

f_o	f_e	$f_o - f_e$	$(f_o - f_e)^2$	$\dfrac{(f_o - f_e)^2}{f_e}$
24	30	−6	36	1.2
26	20	6	36	1.8
36	30	6	36	1.2
14	20	−6	36	1.8
			Total	6

$\chi^2_{calc} = 6$

3 a i

	Likes football	Dislikes football	sum
Male	14.56	11.44	26
Female	13.44	10.56	24
sum	28	22	50

ii $\chi^2_{calc} \approx 13.5$

b i

	Full-time job	Part-time job	Unemployed	sum
Left handed	16	14	10	40
Right handed	144	126	90	360
sum	160	140	100	400

ii $\chi^2_{calc} \approx 1.05$

c i

	\multicolumn{3}{c}{Age}	
	18 - 29	30 - 39	40+	sum
Married	13.99	15.67	17.35	47
Single	11.01	12.33	13.65	37
sum	25	28	31	84

ii $\chi^2_{calc} \approx 4.35$

d i

	Visits Art Gallery			
	Often	Rarely	Never	sum
Visits Museum — Often	37.60	37.95	35.45	111
Rarely	36.58	36.93	34.49	108
Never	30.82	31.12	29.06	91
sum	105	106	99	310

ii $\chi^2_{calc} \approx 25.1$

EXERCISE 11E.2

1 $\chi^2_{calc} \approx 6.61$, df = 2, $p \approx 0.0368$
As $\chi^2_{calc} > 5.99$, we reject H_0, and conclude that the variables *weight* and *suffering diabetes* are not independent.

2 a 4.61
b $\chi^2_{calc} \approx 8.58$, df = 2, $p \approx 0.0137$
As $\chi^2_{calc} > 4.61$, we reject H_0. So at a 10% level, we conclude that *age* and the *party to vote for* are not independent.

3 $\chi^2_{calc} \approx 2.56$, df = 3, $p \approx 0.456$
As $\chi^2_{calc} < 11.34$, we do not reject H_0. So at a 1% level, *gender* and *favourite season* are independent.

4 a $\chi^2_{calc} \approx 23.6$, df = 3, $p \approx 0.000\,029\,9$
As $\chi^2_{calc} > 7.81$, we reject H_0. So at a 5% level, *reason for travelling* and *rating* are not independent.
b Guests travelling for a holiday are more likely to give a higher rating.

5 $\chi^2_{calc} \approx 18.4$, df = 6, $p \approx 0.005\,28$
As $\chi^2_{calc} > 12.59$, we reject H_0. So at a 5% level, *hair colour* and *eye colour* are not independent.
6 $\chi^2_{calc} \approx 7.94$, df = 6, $p \approx 0.242$
As $\chi^2_{calc} < 10.64$, we do not reject H_0. So at a 10% level, *position* and *injury type* are independent.

EXERCISE 11E.3

1 a

	Own a pet?		
	Yes	No	sum
Age — 0 - 19	4.02	3.98	8
20 - 29	27.1	26.9	54
30 - 49	50.2	49.8	100
50+	36.7	36.3	73
sum	118	117	235

b Yes, 4.02 and 3.98.

c Combine the 0 - 19 and 20 - 29 rows.

2 a $\chi^2_{calc} \approx 16.9$, df = 6, $p = 0.009\,59$
As $\chi^2_{calc} > 16.81$, we reject H_0. So at a 1% level, we conclude that *intelligence level* and *cigarette smoking* are not independent.

b

	Intelligence level				
	low	average	high	very high	sum
Non smoker	262	383	114	4.69	763
Medium level smoker	133	194	57.7	2.38	387
Heavy smoker	107	157	46.6	1.93	313
sum	502	734	218	9	1463

c Combine the *high* and *very high* data columns.

d $\chi^2_{calc} \approx 13.2$, df = 4, $p = 0.0104$
As $\chi^2_{calc} < 13.28$, we do not reject H_0. So at a 1% level, *intelligence level* and *cigarette smoking* are independent. This is a different conclusion from the one in **a**.

EXERCISE 11E.4

1 a

	Result		
	Heads	Tails	sum
Guess — Heads	49.4	54.6	104
Tails	45.6	50.4	96
sum	95	105	200

b $\chi^2_{calc} \approx 1.35$
c As $\chi^2_{calc} < 3.84$, we do not reject H_0. So at a 5% level, Horace's *guess* and *result* are independent.
d According to this test, Horace's claim is not valid.

2 a

	Result		
	Pass	Fail	sum
Country — France	63.8	21.2	85
Germany	168.2	55.8	224
sum	232	77	309

b 2.71 **c** $\chi^2_{calc} \approx 4.62$
d As $\chi^2_{calc} > 2.71$, we reject H_0. So at a 10% level, *motorbike test result* and *country* are not independent.

REVIEW SET 11A

1 a

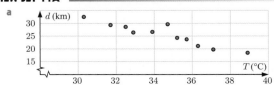

b $r \approx -0.928$, a strong negative linear relationship exists between the variables.

c $d = -1.64T + 82.3$ **d** $50.0°C$

2 $\chi^2_{calc} \approx 7.37$,   df $= 2$, $p \approx 0.0251$

As $\chi^2_{calc} > 5.99$ we reject H_0. So, at a 5% level, *wearing a seat belt* and *severity of injury* are not independent.

3   **a, e**

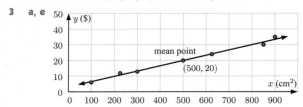

b $r \approx 0.994$

c There is a very strong positive correlation between *area* and *price*.

d $y \approx 0.0335x + 3.27$

f $43.42, this is an extrapolation, so it may be unreliable.

4   **a, c**

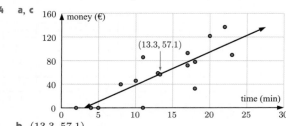

b $(13.3, 57.1)$

d There is a moderate positive linear correlation between *time in the store* and *money spent*.

e €66.80. This is an interpolation, so the estimate is reliable.

5   **a**

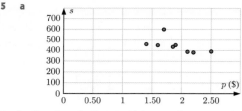

b Yes, the point $(1.7, 597)$ is an outlier. It should not be deleted as there is no evidence that it is a mistake.

c $s \approx -116p + 665$

d No, the prediction would not be accurate, as that much extrapolation is unreliable.

6   **a** number of waterings, n **b** $f \approx 34.0n + 19.3$

c Yes, plants need water to grow, so it is expected that an increase in watering will result in an increase in flowers.

d

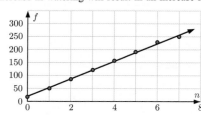

e   **i** $104 \, (n = 2.5)$, $359 \, (n = 10)$

    ii $n = 10$ is unreliable as it is outside the poles and over watering could be a problem. $n = 2.5$ is reliable.

7 $\chi^2_{calc} \approx 13.0$,   df $= 6$, $p \approx 0.0433$

   a As $\chi^2_{calc} > 12.59$, we reject H_0. So, at a 5% level, P and Q are not independent.

   b As $\chi^2_{calc} < 16.81$, we do not reject H_0. So, at a 1% level, P and Q are independent.

REVIEW SET 11B

1   **a**

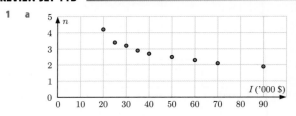

b $r \approx -0.908$ **c** $n \approx -0.0284I + 4.12$

d   **i** 2.84 children   **ii** 0.144 children

e The first is interpolation, so the estimate is reliable. The second is extrapolation, so the estimate may not be reliable.

2   **a**   **i** Negative correlation. As prices increase, the number of tickets sold is likely to decrease.

     ii Causal. Less people will be able to afford tickets as the prices increase.

   b   **i** Positive correlation. As icecream sales increase, number of drownings is likely to increase.

     ii Not causal. Both these variables are dependent on the number of people at the beach.

3 $\chi^2_{calc} \approx 42.1$,   df $= 2$, $p \approx 7.37 \times 10^{-10}$

As $\chi^2_{calc} > 4.61$, we reject H_0. So at a 10% level, *age of driver* and *increasing the speed limit* are not independent.

4 $\chi^2_{calc} \approx 25.6$,   df $= 9$, $p \approx 0.00241$

As $\chi^2_{calc} > 21.67$, we reject H_0. So at a 1% level, *intelligence level* and *business success* are not independent.

5   **a**

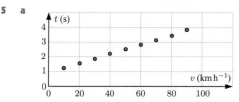

b $t \approx 0.0322v + 0.906$

c   **i** 2.68 seconds   **ii** 4.44 seconds

d The driver's reaction time.

6   **a**

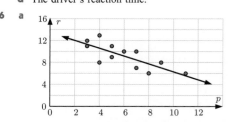

b $r \approx -0.706p + 13.5$ dozen maidens

c $r \approx -0.763$. There is a moderate negative relationship. This supports Superman's suspicions.

d 9.25 dozen (111 maidens)

e This would predict that Silent Predator would abduct a negative number of maidens, which is unrealistic.

f r-int ≈ 13.5, p-int ≈ 19.1 These represent how many dozen maidens we would expect one villain to abduct if the other villain did not abduct any.

g Silent Predator

EXERCISE 12A

1 a $\sqrt{34}$ **b** $\sqrt{20}$ **c** $\sqrt{72}$ **d** $\sqrt{233}$ **e** $\sqrt{392}$
f $\sqrt{250}$ **g** 1.12 **h** 21.5 **i** 8.38

2 a 8 **b** $\sqrt{15}$ **c** $\sqrt{24}$ **d** 2.53 **e** $\sqrt{3}$ **f** 8.98

3 a $x = \sqrt{7}$ **b** $x = \sqrt{2}$ **c** $x = \sqrt{7}$
d $x = \sqrt{5}$ **e** $x = \sqrt{5}$ **f** $x = \sqrt{8}$

4 a $x = \sqrt{\frac{10}{9}}$ **b** $x = \sqrt{\frac{5}{4}}$ **c** $x = \sqrt{\frac{7}{4}}$
d $x = \sqrt{\frac{13}{16}}$ **e** $x = 1$ **f** $x = \frac{1}{2}$

5 a $x = \sqrt{48}$ **b** $x = \sqrt{13}$ **c** $x = \sqrt{3}$
d $x = \sqrt{7}$ **e** $x = \sqrt{3}$ **f** $x = 1$

6 a $x = \sqrt{21}$, $y = \sqrt{5}$ **b** $x = 4$, $y = \sqrt{17}$
c $x = \sqrt{2}$, $y = \sqrt{3}$

7 a $x = \sqrt{14}$ **b** $x = -1 + \sqrt{7}$ **8** $AC \approx 4.92$ m $\left(\sqrt{\frac{97}{4}}\right)$

9 a $AB = \sqrt{10}$ cm **b** $AB = 2\sqrt{5}$ cm **c** $AB = \sqrt{33}$ m

EXERCISE 12B.1

1 a 10 cm **b** $\sqrt{18}$ m ≈ 4.24 m **2** 20 mm
3 a $\sqrt{96}$ mm ≈ 9.80 mm **b** $5\sqrt{96}$ mm$^2 \approx 49.0$ mm^2
4 10 m $\times 30$ m **5** $\sqrt{5}$ cm **6** $\sqrt{162}$ cm ≈ 12.7 cm
7 a $2\sqrt{39}$ m ≈ 12.5 m **b** $10\sqrt{39}$ m$^2 \approx 62.4$ m^2
8 a $\sqrt{20}$ cm ≈ 4.47 cm **b** $2\sqrt{20}$ cm$^2 \approx 17.9$ cm^2
9 5 cm **10** 12 mm

EXERCISE 12B.2

1 a $90°$ **b** $a^2 + b^2 = c^2$
2 a 4 **b** 5 **c** $\sqrt{208} \approx 14.4$
3 5 cm **4** 29 mm
5 a 100 cm **b** 357 cm **c** 457 cm

EXERCISE 12C

1 a not right angled **b** right angled **c** not right angled
d not right angled **e** right angled **f** right angled
2 a right angle at A **b** right angle at B **c** right angle at C
3 Check if the diagonal^2 = height^2 + width^2.

EXERCISE 12D

1 a $x \approx 0.663$ **b** $x \approx 4.34$ **c** $x \approx 2.23$
2 46.3 m **3** Yes **4** 88.2 km
5 a
b 87.1 km

6 a 26.6 km **b** 2 hours 40 minutes (2.66 hours)
7 8.62 m **8 a** 92.4 cm **b** $18\,500$ cm^2 **9** 5.97 m
10 a Jack 30 km, Will 38 km **b** 48.4 km **11** 0.697 m
12 a 73.9 m **b** 30.9 m

13 a 44.0 km to A and 61.6 km to B **b** $\$248\,000$
14 64 diagonal braces **15** 72 m **16** 55.0 cm
17 a 2 hours 45 minutes (2.74 hours)
b 2 hours 31 minutes (2.52 hours) **c** the train
18 Francisca 2.68 km h^{-1}, Gisela 5.37 km h^{-1}

EXERCISE 12E

1 6 cm **2** 33.1 m **3** 14.6 cm **4** 16.6 cm
5 3.46 cm **6** 8.37 m **7** 2.45 m **8 a** No **b** Yes
9 a 28.3 cm **b** 22.4 cm **c** 17.5 cm
10 a 8.54 cm **b** 13 cm **11** 3.5 m **12** 1.92 m
13 a 7 m **b** 14.5 m **c** 9.22 m **d** 8.25 m

REVIEW SET 12A

1 3.53 m **2** 1.79 m **3** $2^2 + 5^2 = 29$, right angle at B.
4 42.4 m **5** 41.2 m
6 a $AR = 8.062$ km, $BR = 13.038$ km **b** €$538\,050$
7 28.3 m **8 a** Kate 2.5 km, Ric 3.25 km **b** 4.10 km
9 11.4 cm

REVIEW SET 12B

1 1950 mm **2** 7.79 m **3** No, $4^2 + 5^2 \neq 8^2$
4 No, $8^2 + 5^2 + 3^2 < 10^2$ **5** 18.1 cm
6 a 11.3 m **b** 45.3 m^2 **7** 35.2 m
8 $3.2^2 + 2.1^2 \approx 3.83^2$ ✓ ∴ the concrete is rectangular.
9 17.3 m **10** 1.73 cm

REVIEW SET 12C

1 6 m **2** $4^2 + (\sqrt{33})^2 = 7^2$, right angle at A
3 Hint: Let the inner square have side length $2x$.
4 12.5 cm **5** Yes **6** 1.2 km **7** 3.74 cm
8 20.6 m **9** 15.1 cm **10** 21.2 cm

EXERCISE 13A

1 a $\sqrt{10}$ units **b** $\sqrt{13}$ units **c** $\sqrt{58}$ units **d** $\sqrt{20}$ units
e 2 units **f** $\sqrt{20}$ units **g** 5 units **h** $\sqrt{53}$ units
2 a $\sqrt{45}$ km (≈ 6.71 km) **b** $\sqrt{97}$ km (≈ 9.85 km)
c 5 km **d** 10 km
3 a $AB = \sqrt{10}$, $BC = \sqrt{10}$, $AC = \sqrt{32}$
Triangle ABC is isosceles.
b $AB = \sqrt{73}$, $BC = \sqrt{50}$, $AC = \sqrt{17}$
Triangle ABC is scalene.
c $AB = 2$, $BC = 2$, $AC = 2$
Triangle ABC is equilateral.
d $AB = \sqrt{28}$, $BC = \sqrt{48}$, $AC = \sqrt{28}$
Triangle ABC is isosceles.
4 a $AB = \sqrt{13}$, $BC = \sqrt{65}$, $AC = \sqrt{52}$
Triangle ABC is right angled at A.
b $AB = \sqrt{20}$, $BC = \sqrt{20}$, $AC = \sqrt{40}$
Triangle ABC is right angled at B.
c $AB = \sqrt{10}$, $BC = \sqrt{40}$, $AC = \sqrt{10}$
Triangle ABC is not right angled.
d $AB = \sqrt{85}$, $BC = \sqrt{17}$, $AC = \sqrt{68}$
Triangle ABC is right angled at C.
5 a $AB = \sqrt{50}$, $BC = \sqrt{50}$, $AC = \sqrt{180}$
Triangle ABC is isosceles.
b $AB = \sqrt{65}$, $BC = \sqrt{13}$, $AC = \sqrt{52}$
Triangle ABC is a scalene right angled triangle, with right angle at C.

c $AB = \sqrt{10}$, $BC = \sqrt{20}$, $AC = \sqrt{10}$
Triangle ABC is an isosceles right angled triangle, with right angle at A.

d $AB = \sqrt{12}$, $BC = \sqrt{12}$, $AC = \sqrt{12}$
Triangle ABC is equilateral.

6 a $q = -1$ or 5 b $q = 0$ or -4 c $q = \pm 2$ d $q = 8$

7 Triangle ABC is:
- equilateral when $a = 1 \pm b\sqrt{3}$
- isosceles otherwise.

EXERCISE 13B

2 a $(2, 3)$ b $(1, -3)$ c $(-2, 3)$ d $(1, 1)$
  e $(3, 1)$ f $(0, -1)$ g $(0, \frac{1}{2})$ h $(3, -1)$

3 a $(3, 6)$ b $(\frac{5}{2}, 4)$ c $(1, 1\frac{1}{2})$ d $(3, 0)$
  e $(\frac{1}{2}, 3)$ f $(-1, 1)$ g $(-\frac{1}{2}, -1\frac{1}{2})$ h $(-2\frac{1}{2}, 4)$

4 a $(3, -5)$ b $(-2, 3)$ c $(-1, 5)$ d $(4, -2)$
  e $(4, -1)$ f $(3, -\frac{1}{2})$

6 a $(0, -9)$ b $(5, -5)$ 7 $(1, -5)$ 8 $(5, -2)$

9 a $(-5, 4)$ b ≈ 3.16 km 10 $(0, 1)$

11 a $(1, 3\frac{1}{2})$ b 5.85 m

12 a $(9, -2)$ b $(3, 7)$ c $(2, 5)$

13 a i $P(2, 5)$ ii $Q(9, 4)$ iii $R(4, -1)$ iv $S(-3, 0)$
   b i $\sqrt{50}$ units ii $\sqrt{50}$ units iii $\sqrt{50}$ units
     iv $\sqrt{50}$ units
   c PQRS is a rhombus.

EXERCISE 13C.1

1 a $\frac{3}{2}$ b -1 c 0 d $\frac{2}{5}$
  e $-\frac{2}{3}$ f 3 g undefined h $-\frac{4}{3}$

2 a 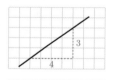 b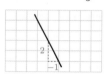

  c  d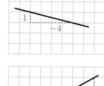

  e   f

3 a **A** and **D** b **B**

4

5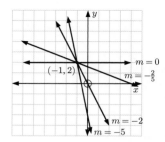

EXERCISE 13C.2

1 a 1 b $-\frac{1}{4}$ c $\frac{5}{3}$ d $-\frac{7}{3}$ e $-\frac{1}{3}$ f 0
  g $-\frac{2}{3}$ h undefined i $\frac{3}{2}$

2 a 3 b 1 c $\frac{1}{4}$ d 0 e $-\frac{2}{3}$ f -5

3 a $a = 11$ b $a = 6$ c $a = 15$

4 Cuts the x-axis at $(4, 0)$.

EXERCISE 13D

1 a i $\frac{3}{4}$ ii $-\frac{4}{3}$ b i $\frac{1}{5}$ ii -5
  c i 4 ii $-\frac{1}{4}$ d i -3 ii $\frac{1}{3}$
  e i $-\frac{3}{7}$ ii $\frac{7}{3}$ f i $-4\frac{1}{2}$ ii $\frac{2}{9}$
  g i 0 ii undefined h i -1 ii 1

2 a not perpendicular b not perpendicular
  c perpendicular d not perpendicular
  e perpendicular f not perpendicular

3 a **A** and **E** b **C** and **F**, **B** and **D**

4 a $t = -3$ b $t = -10$

5 a $k = 2$ b $k = 1\frac{1}{2}$ c $k = 7$ d $k = -\frac{10}{3}$

6 a $AB = \sqrt{20}$, $BC = \sqrt{5}$, $AC = 5$
    and $(\sqrt{20})^2 + (\sqrt{5})^2 = 25 = AC^2$
  b gradient of $AB = \frac{1}{2}$, gradient of $BC = -2$
    $m_{AB} \times m_{BC} = -1$
    $\therefore$ AB is perpendicular to BC.

7 a collinear b not collinear c collinear d not collinear

8 a $n = 7$ b $n = 0$

EXERCISE 13E

1 a $-\frac{3}{20}$ For every 20 metres we move horizontally, we drop 3 metres vertically.
  b $\frac{1}{50}$ For every 50 metres we move horizontally, we rise 1 metre vertically.
  c $-\frac{11}{20}$ For every 20 metres we move horizontally, we drop 11 metres vertically.
  d $\frac{3}{10}$ For every 10 metres we move horizontally, we rise 3 metres vertically.

2 a $\frac{27}{200}$ For every 200 metres the train moves horizontally, it will rise 27 metres vertically.
  b 108 m

3 17.6 cm

4 a $10\frac{1}{2}$ b The density of silver is $10\frac{1}{2}$ g per cm^3
  c i 31.5 g ii ≈ 9.52 cm^3

5 a 82.2 km h^{-1} b i 80 km h^{-1} ii 110 km h^{-1}
  c From 5 hours to 6 hours.

6 a €3000

b 0.18. This represents the cost (in euros per kilometre) of running the car for the first 500 km.

c 0.23. This represents the average cost (in euros per km) of running the car.

7 a Biodiesel $= 33\frac{1}{3}$ MJ L^{-1},   Ethanol $= 24$ MJ L^{-1}

b the biodiesel

8 a No tax is paid on incomes of $6000 or less.

b gradient of AB ≈ 0.33,   gradient of BC $= 0.35$
These represent the tax rates for the brackets $6k - $15k and $15k - $42k respectively (in cents per dollar earned).

c The tax rate would increase again.

EXERCISE 13F

1 a **A**: $y = -3$, **B**: $y = -1$ **b** **A**: $x = -2$, **B**: $x = 0$
   C: $y = 0$, **D**: $y = 4$ **C**: $x = 1$, **D**: $x = 4$

2 a vertical   **b** horizontal

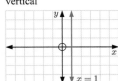

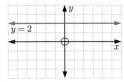

c vertical   **d** horizontal

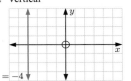

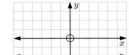

3 a $y = -4$ **b** $x = 5$ **c** $x = -1$
   d $y = 2$ **e** $y = 0$ **f** $x = 0$

4 a $x = 2$ **b** $y = -2$

EXERCISE 13G.1

1 a $y = x - 2$ **b** $y = -x + 4$ **c** $y = 2x$
   d $y = -\frac{1}{2}x + 3$

2 a $y = 4x - 13$ **b** $y = -3x - 5$ **c** $y = -5x + 32$
   d $y = \frac{1}{2}x + \frac{7}{2}$ **e** $y = -\frac{1}{3}x + \frac{8}{3}$ **f** $y = 6$

3 a $2x - 3y + 11 = 0$ **b** $3x - 5y + 23 = 0$
   c $x + 3y - 5 = 0$ **d** $2x + 7y + 2 = 0$
   e $4x - y + 11 = 0$ **f** $2x + y - 7 = 0$
   g $7x + 2y - 18 = 0$ **h** $6x - y + 40 = 0$

4 a $y = \frac{5}{2}x - 2$ **b** $y = -2x + 3$ **c** $y = -2$
   d $y = -\frac{1}{5}x + \frac{2}{5}$ **e** $y = \frac{1}{6}x - \frac{11}{6}$ **f** $y = -\frac{2}{3}x - \frac{11}{3}$

5 a $x - 3y + 3 = 0$ **b** $5x - y - 1 = 0$
   c $x - y - 3 = 0$ **d** $4x - 5y - 10 = 0$
   e $x - 2y + 1 = 0$ **f** $2x + 3y + 5 = 0$

6 a $y = \frac{4}{3}x - 1$ **b** $y = \frac{2}{3}x + \frac{13}{3}$ **c** $y = x + 1$
   d $y = -2x - 2$ **e** $y = -\frac{2}{3}x + 2$ **f** $y = -\frac{3}{7}x - \frac{9}{7}$

7 a $M = \frac{1}{3}p + 2$ **b** $R = -\frac{5}{4}n + 2$ **c** $T = \frac{1}{2}x - 1$
   d $F = \frac{1}{10}x + 1$ **e** $H = -\frac{1}{2}z + 2$ **f** $W = -\frac{1}{6}t - 2$

EXERCISE 13G.2

1 a 3   **b** -2 **c** 0   **d** undefined   **e** $\frac{2}{3}$ **f** $-\frac{4}{5}$

2 a -3 **b** $\frac{2}{7}$ **c** $-\frac{2}{7}$ **d** $\frac{3}{4}$ **e** $-\frac{4}{11}$ **f** $\frac{7}{9}$

---

3 a gradient $= -\dfrac{a}{b}$, $b \neq 0$

b **i** $-\frac{2}{5}$ **ii** $\frac{3}{2}$ **iii** $-\frac{5}{4}$ **iv** $\frac{1}{3}$ **v** 2   **vi** $\frac{1}{4}$

EXERCISE 13G.3

1 a Yes   **b** No   **c** Yes   **d** Yes

2 a $k = -5$ **b** $k = -6$ **c** $k = 41$ **d** $k = 1$

3 a $a = 2$ **b** $a = 7$ **c** $a = \frac{1}{3}$

4 a **i** $(3, 5\frac{1}{2})$ **ii** $(4\frac{1}{5}, 4)$
   b $\{(x, y) \mid 5x + 4y = 37,\ 1 < x < 5\}$ **c** No

EXERCISE 13H.1

1 a $y = \frac{1}{2}x + 2$ **b** $y = 2x + 1$

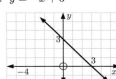

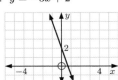

c $y = -x + 3$ **d** $y = -3x + 2$

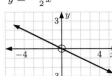

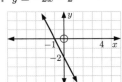

e $y = -\frac{1}{2}x$ **f** $y = -2x - 2$

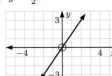

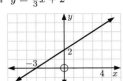

g $y = \frac{3}{2}x$ **h** $y = \frac{2}{3}x + 2$

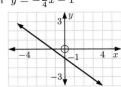

i $y = -\frac{3}{4}x - 1$

2 a $x + 2y = 8$ **b** $4x + 3y - 12 = 0$

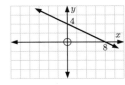

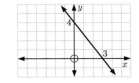

c $2x - 3y = 6$

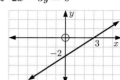

d $3x - y - 6 = 0$

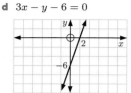

e $x + y = 5$

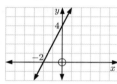

f $x - y = -5$

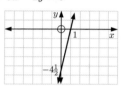

g $2x - y + 4 = 0$

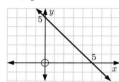

h $9x - 2y = 9$

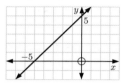

i $3x + 4y = -15$

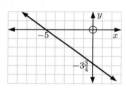

EXERCISE 13H.2

1 a

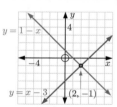

$y = 1 - x$, $y = x - 3$, $(2, -1)$

b

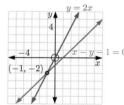

$y = 2x$, $x - y - 1 = 0$, $(-1, -2)$

c

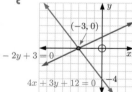

$x - 2y + 3 = 0$, $4x + 3y + 12 = 0$, $(-3, 0)$

d

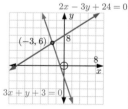

$2x - 3y + 24 = 0$, $3x + y + 3 = 0$, $(-3, 6)$

e

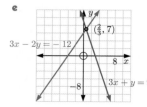

$3x - 2y = -12$, $3x + y = 9$, $(\frac{2}{3}, 7)$

f

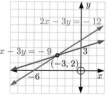

$2x - 3y = -12$, $x - 3y = -9$, $(-3, 2)$

g

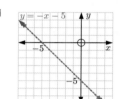

$x + 2y = 8$, $2x - y = 6$, $(4, 2)$

h

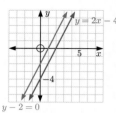

$y = 2x - 4$, $2x - y - 2 = 0$
Lines are parallel,
$\therefore$ do not intersect.

i

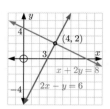

$y = -x - 5$, $2x + 2y = -10$

Infinitely many points of
intersection (lines are
coincident).

2 a No points of intersection (same gradient, different y-intercept, parallel).

b Infinitely many points of intersection (same gradient, same y-intercept, $\therefore$ same line).

c If $k = 5$, the lines are coincident, and $\therefore$ have infinitely many points of intersection.
If $k \neq 5$, the lines are parallel, and there are no points of intersection.

3 a $(-3, 2)$ **b** $(1, 4)$ **c** $(2.3, 1.4)$ **d** $(0.9, -3.1)$

4 a No points of intersection (lines are parallel).

b Infinitely many points of intersection (lines are coincident).

5 a $(15.4, 262)$

b The potter must make 16 pots to make a profit.

6 a $5x + 2y = 8.30$, $8x + y = 8.00$ **b** $(0.7, 2.4)$

c Gives the cost of each item that satisfies both equations. An orange costs 70 cents and a rockmelon costs $2.40.

EXERCISE 13I

1 a $y = x - 4$ **b** $y = 2x + 6$ **c** $y = \frac{6}{5}x + \frac{7}{2}$ **d** $y = 1$

2 $y = \frac{2}{3}x + \frac{5}{3}$

3 a Hospital S   **b** $(-1, -2)$ **c** $y = x - 1$

4 a Perpendicular bisector of PQ: $y = -x + 6$
Perpendicular bisector of QR: $y = \frac{1}{3}x + 2$

b Centre of circle $= (3, 3)$

5 a P(5, 3),   Q(4, 0),   R(2, 2)

b i $y = x - 2$ **ii** $y = -3x + 12$ **iii** $y = -\frac{1}{3}x + \frac{8}{3}$

c X$(3\frac{1}{2}, 1\frac{1}{2})$ **d** Yes

e They will meet at a single point (are concurrent).

f It is the point equidistant from all three vertices.

REVIEW SET 13A

1 a 5 units   **b** $-\frac{4}{3}$ **c** $(1, 4)$

2 x-intercept is -2, y-intercept is 5, gradient is $\frac{5}{2}$

3 $y = -2x + 6$ **4** $a = 7\frac{1}{5}$ **5** $c = 2$

6 a $y = -3x + 4$ **b** $x + 2y - 5 = 0$

7

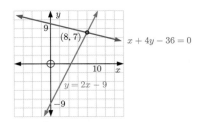

8 a -4 **b** $\frac{1}{4}$ **c** $x - 4y + 6 = 0$ **9** C(3, 0)

10 $k = 4 \pm \sqrt{24}$ **11 a** $-\frac{4}{25}$ **b** 48 m

REVIEW SET 13B

1 $(5, 1\frac{1}{2})$ **2 a** $y = -3x + 5$ **b** $y = -\frac{3}{2}x + \frac{5}{2}$

3 a $\frac{2}{3}$ **b** 4   **c** $-\frac{3}{2}$ **d** undefined

4 a x-intercept $\frac{14}{3}$, y-intercept 7
   b x-intercept $\frac{12}{5}$, y-intercept -4

5 Yes   **6 a** $k = \frac{3}{4}$ **b** $k = -12$

7

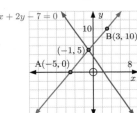

8 a $y = 3$ **b** $x = -6$ **9** $5x - 3y - 4 = 0$
10 a $(7, 0)$ **b** $x + 2y - 7 = 0$ **c** $3 + 2(2) - 7 = 0$ ✓
11 a AC has gradient 0,   MN has gradient 0
      $\therefore$ AC and MN are parallel.
   b AC has length 6,   MN has length 3
      $\therefore$ MN $= \frac{1}{2}$AC

REVIEW SET 13C

1 a $2x - 3y - 17 = 0$ **b** $x - 3y - 11 = 0$

2 a $k = -\frac{21}{5}$ **b** $k = \frac{15}{7}$

3 a T$(0, 2 + \sqrt{8})$ or T$(0, 2 - \sqrt{8})$
   b $y = \sqrt{8}x + (2 + \sqrt{8})$

4 a 50   **b** 82
   c The gradient of AB is the average speed of the truck between A and B, in km h^{-1}.
   The gradient of OC is the average speed of the truck over the whole day, in km h^{-1}.

5 Triangle KLM is a right angled isosceles triangle.

6 Z$(2, -2)$

7 a $y = -\frac{1}{3}x + 4$ **b** $5x - 2y + 1 = 0$

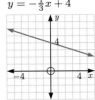   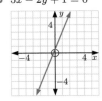

8 $x - 2y + 9 = 0$

9 a i gradient of AB $= -\frac{1}{4}$,   gradient of DC $= -\frac{1}{4}$
      The gradients are equal, $\therefore$ AB $\parallel$ DC.
   ii gradient of BC $= \frac{3}{5}$,   gradient of AD $= \frac{3}{5}$
      The gradients are equal, $\therefore$ BC $\parallel$ AD.
   b parallelogram
   c AB $=$ DC $= \sqrt{68}$,   BC $=$ AD $= \sqrt{306}$
   d i $(2\frac{1}{2}, 2\frac{1}{2})$ **ii** $(2\frac{1}{2}, 2\frac{1}{2})$
   e The diagonals of a parallelogram bisect each other.

10

Equation of line	Gradient	x-intercept	y-intercept
a $5x - 2y - 10 = 0$	$\frac{5}{2}$	2	-5
b $4x + 5y = 20$	$-\frac{4}{5}$	5	4
c $y = -2x + 5$	-2	$\frac{5}{2}$	5
d $x = 8$	undefined	8	none
e $y = 5$	0	none	5
f $x + y = 11$	-1	11	11

11 a AB $=$ BC $=$ CD $=$ DA $= 5$ units   **b** $(2, 1)$ for both
   c $m_{AC} = -2$, $m_{BD} = \frac{1}{2}$

REVIEW SET 13D

1 a $\sqrt{34}$ units   **b** $-\frac{3}{5}$ **c** $3x + 5y + 12 = 0$
2 scalene   **3** $k = -5$ **4** K$(10, 15)$
5 a 330 L   **b** from B to C   **c** 18 L per minute
   d 20.5 L per minute
6 $c = \frac{11}{2}$ **7 a** $-\frac{3}{2}$ **b** $-\frac{5}{3}$
8 a $r = \frac{5}{7}a + 2$ **b** $K = \frac{3}{5}s + 3$
9 a $t = -32$ **b** $t = -\frac{13}{5}$
10 a PQ $=$ PR $= \sqrt{20}$ units   **b** M$(4, 4)$
   c gradient of PM $= -\frac{1}{3}$, gradient of QR $= 3$
   d

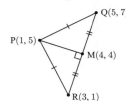

11 a i $y = 2$ **ii** $x = 0$ **iii** $4x - 3y + 18 = 0$
   b i $(-3, 2)$ **ii** $(0, 6)$

EXERCISE 14A

1 a 82.5 m   **b** 29.5 cm   **c** 6.25 km
   d 7380 cm   **e** 0.2463 m   **f** 0.009 761 km
2 a 4130 mm   **b** 3 754 000 m   **c** 482 900 cm
   d 26 900 mm   **e** 47 000 cm   **f** 3 880 000 mm
3 7.26 km   **4** 18 000 candles
5 a 5900 g   **b** 2.6 kg   **c** 0.003 75 t
   d 15 000 000 mg   **e** 4 800 000 g   **f** 0.0016 kg
   g 1738.5 mg   **h** 0.046 218 t   **i** 36 100 mg
6 20 000 nails   **7 a** 6.21 t   **b** 9

EXERCISE 14B

1 a 11.7 m   **b** 35 mm   **c** 6.2 km
   d 172 cm   **e** $(4x - 4)$ cm   **f** $(4x + 2)$ m
   g $(13x + 2)$ km   **h** $(6y - 8)$ cm   **i** $8x$ km

2 a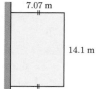
(rectangle, 220 m by 300 m)

b 1040 m

3 17.5 km

4 a 132 m   **b** 650 m   **c** 66 posts   **d** €1009.70

5 a 20.2 m   **b** $22.32

6 a 7.97 cm   **b** 44.3 m   **c** 410 mm   **7** 481 m

8 a 48.6 m   **b** 221 bricks   **c** $1038.70

9 a 91.5 m   **b** 156 m

10 a 11.9 m   **b** 5.20 m   **11** 1.27 m

EXERCISE 14C.1

1 a 0.056 m^2 **b** 480 ha   **c** 0.55 cm^2
   d 130 000 m^2 **e** 0.046 17 m^2 **f** 0.0721 km^2
   g 0.000 008 43 km^2 **h** 59 m^2 **i** 0.000 989 km^2

2 a 845 m^2 **b** 180 panels

EXERCISE 14C.2

1 a 280 km^2 **b** 910 m^2 **c** 1780 m^2 **d** 66.7 m^2

2 a $(2x^2 + 9x + 4)$ cm^2 **b** (πy^2) mm^2

   c $\left(\dfrac{5x^2 + 3x}{2}\right)$ m^2 **d** $\left(\dfrac{3x^2 + 3x}{2}\right)$ cm^2

   e $(y^2 + 2y)$ cm^2 **f** $(2\pi x^2)$ cm^2

3 a $\left(\dfrac{x^2 - x}{2}\right)$ m^2 **b** $(3y^2 + 4y - 4)$ cm^2

4 a 83 cm^2 **b** 506 cm^2 **c** 143 cm^2

5 a 125 cm^2 **b** 76.0 cm^2 **c** 90 cm^2

6 a $A = 2k^2$ **b** $A = \dfrac{\pi(z^2 - y^2)}{2}$ **c** $A = (\pi - 2)x^2$

7 99.5 m^2 **8** medium size

9 a 43.2 m^2
   b Type B slab is half the area of type A slab. Every 2nd row you need 2 type B slabs, so you need 4 type B slabs in total.

   c 118 type A   **d** 2.6 t   **e** $835.20

10 a 4 m   **b** 50.3 m^2 **c** $160.85
   d When opened out, the curved wall is a rectangle. The width is h (the height of the cylinder), and the length is $2\pi r$ (the circumference of the end). The area is therefore $2\pi r \times h$.
   e 151 m^2 **f** $678.58   **g** $840

11 a $BC = \dfrac{100}{x}$ m   **b** Length of netting $= AB + BC + CD$
   c $x \approx 7.07$ $\therefore\ L = x + \dfrac{100}{x} + x$
   d

(rectangle 7.07 m by 14.1 m)
$= 2x + \dfrac{100}{x}$ m

12 a $A = 3xy$ m^2 **d** $x \approx 11.55$ m
   e
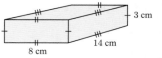
(diagram 17.32 m by 11.55 m)

EXERCISE 14D.1

1 a 413 cm^2 **b** 5.78 m^2 **c** $78x^2$ mm^2

2 a 84 cm^2 **b** 392 m^2

3 a
(cube, 2.5 cm)   surface area $= 37.5$ cm^2

   b
(rectangular prism, 3 cm, 14 cm, 8 cm)   surface area $= 356$ cm^2

   c
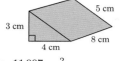
(triangular prism, 5 cm, 3 cm, 4 cm, 8 cm)   surface area $= 108$ cm^2

4 a 11 907 cm^2
   b
(rectangle 81 cm by 34 cm)   area $= 2754$ cm^2

(rectangle 219 cm by 34 cm)   area $= 7446$ cm^2

(rectangle 75 cm by 34 cm)   area $= 2550$ cm^2

(rectangle $\sqrt{27297}$ cm by 34 cm)   area ≈ 5617 cm^2

   c $540

5 $239.10   **6** 2310 cm^2

EXERCISE 14D.2

1 a 1005.3 cm^2 **b** 145.3 cm^2 **c** 188.5 cm^2
   d 549.8 m^2 **e** 1068.1 cm^2 **f** 63.6 km^2

2 84.8 cm^2

3 a $8\pi x^2$ cm^2 **b** $16\pi x^2$ cm^2 **c** $12\pi x^2$ cm^2
   d $24\pi x^2$ cm^2

4 a 19.4 m^2 **b** £883.38   **c** £21 201.23

5 a 5.39 m   **b** 46.4 m^2 **c** $835.79

6 a 12.6 m^2 **b** €483.81   **7 a** $4\pi r^2$ **b** 5.40 m

8 a $3\pi r^2$ **b** 4.50 cm   **c** 4.24 cm

EXERCISE 14E.1

2 a 39.1 m^3 **b** 510 mm^3 **c** 0.469 m^3
   d 3 820 000 cm^3 **e** 0.005 27 cm^3 **f** 17 900 cm^3
   g 692 cm^3 **h** 0.183 46 m^3 **i** 5100 cm^3

3 a 5 000 000 ball bearings   **b** 0.216 m^3

EXERCISE 14E.2

1 **a** 5.54 m^3 **b** 373 cm^3 **c** 390 cm^3
   d 1180 cm^3 **e** 36.9 cm^3 **f** 2.62 m^3

2 **a** 25.1 cm^3 **b** 765 cm^3 **c** 2940 cm^3
   d 463 cm^3 **e** 4.60 cm^3 **f** 26.5 cm^3
   g 648 000 cm^3 **h** 72.6 cm^3 **i** 19.5 m^3
   j 1870 m^3 **k** 11.6 m^3 **l** 156 cm^3

3 **a** $V = \frac{32}{3}\pi x^3$ **b** $V = abc$ **c** $V = 3\pi y^2(y - 4)$

4 **a** 1.36 cm **b** 6 cm

5 **a**

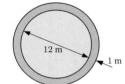

   b 40.8 m^2
   c 4.08 m^3

6 **a**   Uncooked cake   Cooked cake

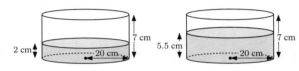

   b 2510 cm^3 **c** 6910 cm^3 **d** 175%

7 **a** 0.5 m **b** 0.45 m **c** 0.373 m^3

8 **a** 7.18 m^3 **b** €972 9 **a** 8.58 m^3 **c** 32.6%

10 **a** 2 **b** \$54.60 **c i** 2 **ii** \$35.90 **d** \$90.50

11 217 tonnes

12 **a** 2.67 cm **b** 3.24 cm **c** 4.46 cm
    d 2.60 m **e** 1.74 cm **f** 5.60 m

EXERCISE 14F

1 **a** 4210 mL **b** 8630 L **c** 4.6 L
   d 56.9 kL **e** 0.003 97 kL **f** 12 000 mL

2 **a** 40.8 kL **b** 1860 bottles

3 **a** 83 m^3 **b** 3200 cm^3 **c** 2.3 L
   d 7 154 000 L **e** 0.46 m^3 **f** 4 600 000 cm^3

4 **a** 12.9 kL **b** 61.2 kL **c** 68.0 kL

5 12.2 L 6 594 000 kL

7 **a** 1.32 m^3 **b** 1.32 kL **c** 10.5 cm

8 **a** 189 mL **b** 3.25 cm

9 **a** 954 mL **b** 4.92 kL **c** 5155 **d** €10 567.75

10 7.8 cm 11 35 truckloads

EXERCISE 14G

1 **a** 5 g cm^{-3} **b** 1.33 g cm^{-3}

2 **a** 2.25 g cm^{-3} **b** 20 g cm^{-3}

3 312 cm^3 4 569 g 5 19.3 g cm^{-3} 6 4.90 cm

7 472 000 beads 8 4 240 000 t

EXERCISE 14H

1 **a** Slant height ≈ 1.06 m
   b Hemisphere surface area ≈ 4.02 m^2 **d** ≈ 3890 kg
      Cylinder surface area ≈ 9.05 m^2
      Cone surface area ≈ 2.67 m^2

2 **a** 16.8 m **b** 2.16 m^3 **c** 8.04 m^2

3 **a** 11.9 m^3 **b** 5.8 m **c** 1.36 m^3 more

REVIEW SET 14A

1 **a** 0.0305 t **b** 93 000 mL **c** 8.033 cm^3

2 379 tiles 3 51.52 m 4 38.8 m

5 **a** 7.14 km^2 **b** 50.0 m^2 6 **a** 26 643 m^2 **b** 2.66 ha

7 **a** 67.45 m^2 **b** \$222.75 8 2670 m^2

9 **a** 4.99 m^3 **b** 853 cm^3 **c** 0.452 m^3 10 3.22 m^3

11 1.03 m 12 0.52 m^3 13 **a** 2.71 g cm^{-3} **b** 1.62 m^3

REVIEW SET 14B

1 13.6 m 2 **a** 0.023 m^3 **b** 50.62 km^2 **c** 534 mg

3 **a** 24.2 m **b** 11 posts

4 **a** 17.3 m^2 **b** Style 1: 900 cm^2, Style 2: 800 cm^2
   c Style 1: 192 tiles, Style 2: 216 tiles **d** Style 2

5 **a** $A = 3xy$ **b** $A = \dfrac{\pi r^2}{2} - r^2$ **c** $A = \dfrac{\pi a^2}{4} + 2a^2$

6 **a** 377.0 cm^2 **b** 339.8 cm^2 **c** 201.1 cm^2

7 8000 rectangles 8 13.6 m^2 9 16 300 spikes

10 82 400 cm^3

11 **a** 133 464 mm^3 ≈ 133 cm^3 **b** 74 cones

12 68.4 mm 13 **a** 4.10 kg

REVIEW SET 14C

1 **a** 0.0243 m **b** 32 000 cm^3 **c** 0.000 845 kg

2 25 000 erasers 3 1120 m

4 **a** $(8x - 8)$ km **b** $(3y + 1)$ mm **c** $(7x + 8)$ cm

5 **a** 3.77 cm **b** The circle, 3.09 cm

6 **a** 164 cm^3 **b** 120 m^3 **c** 10 300 mm^3 7 4.64 m^2

8 5.03 m^3 9 5680 L 10 434 cm^2 11 5 tanks

12 **a** 11 cm **b** 5.59 m **c** 11.0 cm 13 0.936 g cm^{-3}

EXERCISE 15A

1 **a i** BC **ii** AC **iii** AB **b i** QR **ii** PQ **iii** PR
   c i JL **ii** JK **iii** KL

2 **a** z cm **b** x cm **c** y cm **d** y cm **e** x cm

EXERCISE 15B.1

1 **a i** $\dfrac{q}{r}$ **ii** $\dfrac{p}{r}$ **iii** $\dfrac{q}{p}$ **b i** $\dfrac{l}{j}$ **ii** $\dfrac{k}{j}$ **iii** $\dfrac{l}{k}$

   c i $\dfrac{3}{5}$ **ii** $\dfrac{4}{5}$ **iii** $\dfrac{3}{4}$

2 **a i** $\dfrac{p}{r}$ **ii** $\dfrac{q}{r}$ **iii** $\dfrac{p}{q}$ **iv** $\dfrac{q}{r}$ **v** $\dfrac{p}{r}$ **vi** $\dfrac{q}{p}$

   b i $\dfrac{y}{x}$ **ii** $\dfrac{z}{x}$ **iii** $\dfrac{y}{z}$ **iv** $\dfrac{z}{x}$ **v** $\dfrac{y}{x}$ **vi** $\dfrac{z}{y}$

   c i $\dfrac{12}{13}$ **ii** $\dfrac{5}{13}$ **iii** $\dfrac{12}{5}$ **iv** $\dfrac{5}{13}$ **v** $\dfrac{12}{13}$ **vi** $\dfrac{5}{12}$

   d i $\dfrac{8}{17}$ **ii** $\dfrac{15}{17}$ **iii** $\dfrac{8}{15}$ **iv** $\dfrac{15}{17}$ **v** $\dfrac{8}{17}$ **vi** $\dfrac{15}{8}$

   e i $\dfrac{4}{7}$ **ii** $\dfrac{\sqrt{33}}{7}$ **iii** $\dfrac{4}{\sqrt{33}}$ **iv** $\dfrac{\sqrt{33}}{7}$ **v** $\dfrac{4}{7}$ **vi** $\dfrac{\sqrt{33}}{4}$

   f i $\dfrac{5}{\sqrt{34}}$ **ii** $\dfrac{3}{\sqrt{34}}$ **iii** $\dfrac{5}{3}$ **iv** $\dfrac{3}{\sqrt{34}}$ **v** $\dfrac{5}{\sqrt{34}}$ **vi** $\dfrac{3}{5}$

3 **a** XY ≈ 4.9 cm, XZ ≈ 3.3 cm, YZ = 5.9 cm
   b i 0.83 **ii** 0.56 **iii** 1.48

4 **a** base angles of an isosceles triangle are equal, sum of all angles
      in a triangle is 180°
   b $\sqrt{2}$ ≈ 1.41 m
   c i $\dfrac{1}{\sqrt{2}}$ ≈ 0.707 **ii** $\dfrac{1}{\sqrt{2}}$ ≈ 0.707 **iii** 1

EXERCISE 15B.2

1 **a** $\sin 21° = \dfrac{x}{k}$ **b** $\cos 50° = \dfrac{x}{m}$ **c** $\tan 38° = \dfrac{x}{t}$

d $\cos 56° = \dfrac{a}{x}$ **e** $\tan 41° = \dfrac{p}{x}$ **f** $\sin 36° = \dfrac{x}{n}$

g $\tan 73° = \dfrac{x}{l}$ **h** $\sin 21° = \dfrac{b}{x}$ **i** $\tan 46° = \dfrac{r}{x}$

2 **a** 7.00 cm **b** 7.50 m **c** 7.82 cm **d** 4.82 cm
e 5.55 m **f** 21.5 cm **g** 18.8 cm **h** 5.17 m
i 6.38 m **j** 4.82 cm **k** 7.22 cm **l** 43.3 m

3 **a** $x \approx 3.98$ **b** **i** $y \approx 4.98$ **ii** $y \approx 4.98$

4 **a** $x \approx 2.87, \ y \approx 4.10$ **b** $x \approx 16.40, \ y \approx 18.25$
c $x \approx 10.77, \ y \approx 14.50$

EXERCISE 15B.3

1 **a** $\theta \approx 36.9°$ **b** $\theta \approx 48.6°$ **c** $\theta \approx 40.6°$
d $\theta \approx 42.6°$ **e** $\theta \approx 13.7°$ **f** $\theta \approx 52.4°$
g $\theta \approx 76.1°$ **h** $\theta = 60°$ **i** $\theta \approx 36.0°$

2 **a** $\theta \approx 56.3°$ **b** **i** $\phi \approx 33.7°$ **ii** $\phi \approx 33.7°$

3 **a** $\theta \approx 39.7°, \ \phi \approx 50.3°$ **b** $\alpha \approx 38.9°, \ \beta \approx 51.1°$
c $\theta \approx 61.5°, \ \phi \approx 28.5°$

4 **a** The triangle cannot be drawn with the given dimensions.
b The triangle cannot be drawn with the given dimensions.
c The result is not a triangle, but a straight line of length 9.3 m.

EXERCISE 15C.1

1 **a** $x \approx 4.13$ **b** $\alpha \approx 75.5°$ **c** $\beta \approx 41.0°$
d $x \approx 6.29$ **e** $\theta \approx 51.9°$ **f** $x \approx 12.6$

2 22.4° **3** 11.8 cm **4** 119° **5** 36.5 cm
6 46.7 m **7** 45.4° **8** **a** $x \approx 3.44$ **b** $\alpha \approx 51.5°$
9 $\beta \approx 129°$

EXERCISE 15C.2

1 **a** $\theta \approx 36.9°$ **b** $r \approx 11.3$ **c** $\alpha \approx 61.9°$
2 7.99 cm **3** 89.2° **4** 47.2° **5** 13.9 cm

EXERCISE 15D

1 18.3 m **2** **a** 371 m **b** 1.62 km **3** 159 m
4 1.58° **5** **a** 26.4° **b** 26.4° **6** 418 m
7 $\theta \approx 12.6°$ **8** 9.56 m **9** 10.9 m **10** 72.0 m
11 786 m **12** 962 m

EXERCISE 15E.1

1 **a** 18.4 cm **b** 35.3°
2 **a** 10.8 cm **b** 36.5° **c** 9.49 cm **d** 40.1°
3 **a** 82.4 cm **b** 77.7 L
4 **a** DC ≈ 2.01 m, CE = 2 m **b** 6.84°
5 **a** 10.2 m **b** No **6** **a** 45°

EXERCISE 15E.2

1 **a** **i** GF **ii** HG **iii** HF **iv** GM
b **i** MC **ii** MN
c **i** XW **ii** WZ **iii** XZ **iv** XM
2 **a** **i** $\widehat{DEH}$ **ii** $\widehat{CEG}$ **iii** $\widehat{AGE}$ **iv** $\widehat{BXF}$
b **i** $\widehat{PYS}$ **ii** $\widehat{QWR}$ **iii** $\widehat{QXR}$ **iv** $\widehat{QYR}$
c **i** $\widehat{AQX}$ **ii** $\widehat{AYX}$
3 **a** **i** 45° **ii** 35.3° **iii** 63.4° **iv** 41.8°
b **i** 21.8° **ii** 18.9° **iii** 21.0°

c **i** 36.9° **ii** 33.9° **iii** 33.9°
d **i** 58.6° **ii** 64.9°
4 **a** 109 m **b** 17.3°

EXERCISE 15F

1 **a** 28.9 cm^2 **b** 384 km^2 **c** 26.7 cm^2 **2** $x \approx 19.0$
3 **a** 166 cm^2 **b** 1407 cm^2 **4** 18.9 cm^2
5 137 cm^2 **6** **a** 71.616 m^2 **b** 8.43 m

EXERCISE 15G

1 **a** 28.8 cm **b** 3.38 km **c** 14.2 m
2 $\widehat{CAB} \approx 52.0°$, $\widehat{CBA} \approx 59.3°$, $\widehat{ACB} \approx 68.7°$
3 **a** 112° **b** 97.2° **4** **a** 40.3° **b** 107°
5 **a** $\cos \theta = \dfrac{13}{20}$ **b** $x \approx 3.81$ **6** 71.6°

EXERCISE 15H.1

1 **a** $x \approx 28.4$ **b** $x \approx 13.4$ **c** $x \approx 3.79$
d $x \approx 4.19$ **e** $x \approx 8.81$ **f** $x \approx 4.43$
2 **a** $a \approx 21.3$ cm **b** $b \approx 76.9$ cm **c** $c \approx 5.09$ cm
3 PQ ≈ 4.08 cm, PR ≈ 5.96 cm

EXERCISE 15H.2

1 **a** $x \approx 9.85°$ **b** $x \approx 41.3°$ **c** $x \approx 32.7°$
2 **a** 30.9° **b** 28.7° **c** 30.1°
3 **b** The triangle cannot be drawn with the given dimensions.

EXERCISE 15I

1 17.7 m **2** 207 m **3** 23.9° **4** 44.3° **5** 9.38°
6 69.1 m **7** **a** 29.5° **b** £9047.96
8 **a** 38.0 m **b** 94.0 m
9 CA ≈ 11.7 km, CB ≈ 8.49 km
10 **a** 74.9 km^2 **b** 7490 ha **11** 9.12 km **12** 85.0 mm

EXERCISE 15J

1 $C \approx 62.1°$ or 117.9° **2** $P \approx 23.0°$
3 **a** $A \approx 34.8°$ **b** $B \approx 53.5°$ or 126°
c $C \approx 84.1°$ or 95.9°
4 No. The ratios in the sine rule are not equal.

REVIEW SET 15A

1 **a** c **b** b **c** $\dfrac{b}{c}$ **d** $\dfrac{a}{b}$ **2** **a** $x \approx 14.0$ **b** $x \approx 35.2$
3 $x \approx 12.4, \ y \approx 21.0, \ \theta = 36°$ **4** 8.19°
5 14 km^2 **6** 8.74° **7** **a** $x \approx 34.1$ **b** $x \approx 25.2$
8 AC ≈ 12.6 cm, $\widehat{CAB} \approx 48.6°$, $\widehat{ACB} \approx 57.4°$
9 113 cm^2 **10** 17.7 m

REVIEW SET 15B

1 $\sin \theta = \dfrac{5}{13}$, $\cos \theta = \dfrac{12}{13}$, $\tan \theta = \dfrac{5}{12}$
2 AC ≈ 111 mm, AB ≈ 120 mm
3 **a** $x \approx 2.8$ **b** $x \approx 4.2$ **c** $x \approx 5.2$ **4** 80.9 m
5 **a** 90° **b** 33.9° **6** 31.6 mm **7** 125°
8 **a** 275 m **b** 2.86 ha **9** 7.32 m
10 **a** 49.9° **b** 56.8° or 123.2°

REVIEW SET 15C

1 a 0.2756   b 0.7431   c −8.1443

2 a $x \approx 38.7$ b $x \approx 37.1$

3 $x \approx 25.7$, $\theta \approx 53.6°$, $\alpha \approx 36.4°$ 4 124°

5 a VS   b $X\widehat{S}T$ c $W\widehat{U}S$ 6 a 58.4°   b 68.3°

7 a 10 600 m²   b 1.06 ha   8 204 m

9 a 15.4 km   b 10.3 km

10 a There are two possible values for $A\widehat{B}C$, which means two possible areas for △ABC.
    b 2.23 m³

EXERCISE 16A

1 a, d, e   2 a, b, c, e, g, i

3 No, all points on a vertical line have the same x-coordinate.

4 For example, $(0, 3)$ and $(0, -3)$ satisfy the relation.

EXERCISE 16B

1 a 2   b 8   c −1   d −13   e 1

2 a 2   b 2   c −16   d −68   e $\frac{17}{4}$

3 a −3   b 3   c 3   d −3   e $\frac{15}{2}$

4 a $7 - 3a$ b $7 + 3a$ c $-3a - 2$ d $10 - 3b$
   e $1 - 3x$ f $7 - 3x - 3h$

5 a $2x^2 + 19x + 43$ b $2x^2 - 11x + 13$
   c $2x^2 - 3x - 1$ d $2x^4 + 3x^2 - 1$
   e $2x^4 - x^2 - 2$ f $2x^2 + (4h + 3)x + 2h^2 + 3h - 1$

6 a i $-\frac{7}{2}$ ii $-\frac{3}{4}$ iii $-\frac{4}{9}$
   b $x = 4$ c $\frac{2x + 7}{x - 2}$ d $x = \frac{9}{5}$

7 f is the function which converts x into $f(x)$ whereas $f(x)$ is the value of the function at any value of x.

8 a 6210 euros, is the value of the photocopier after 4 years
   b $t = 4.5$ years, the time for the photocopier to reach a value of 5780 euros.
   c 9650 euros

9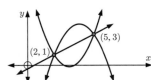

10 $f(x) = -2x + 5$
11 $a = 3$, $b = -2$

EXERCISE 16C

1 a Domain = $\{x \mid x \geqslant -1\}$, Range = $\{y \mid y \leqslant 3\}$
   b Domain = $\{x \mid -1 < x \leqslant 5\}$, Range = $\{y \mid 1 < y \leqslant 3\}$
   c Domain = $\{x \mid x \neq 2\}$, Range = $\{y \mid y \neq -1\}$
   d Domain = $\{x \mid x \in \mathbb{R}\}$, Range = $\{y \mid 0 < y \leqslant 2\}$
   e Domain = $\{x \mid x \in \mathbb{R}\}$, Range = $\{y \mid y \geqslant -1\}$
   f Domain = $\{x \mid x \in \mathbb{R}\}$, Range = $\{y \mid y \leqslant \frac{25}{4}\}$
   g Domain = $\{x \mid x \geqslant -4\}$, Range = $\{y \mid y \geqslant -3\}$
   h Domain = $\{x \mid x \in \mathbb{R}\}$, Range = $\{y \mid y > -2\}$
   i Domain = $\{x \mid x \neq \pm 2\}$,
      Range = $\{y \mid y \leqslant -1$ or $y > 0\}$

2 a Domain = $\{x \mid x \in \mathbb{R}\}$, Range = $\{y \mid y \in \mathbb{R}\}$
   b Domain = $\{x \mid x \in \mathbb{R}\}$, Range = $\{y \mid y \geqslant 3\}$
   c Domain = $\{x \mid x \in \mathbb{R}\}$, Range = $\{y \mid y \geqslant -4\}$
   d Domain = $\{x \mid x \geqslant 0\}$, Range = $\{y \mid y \geqslant 0\}$

e Domain = $\{x \mid x \in \mathbb{R}\}$, Range = $\{y \mid y \leqslant \frac{25}{12}\}$
f Domain = $\{x \mid x \neq 0\}$, Range = $\{y \mid y > 0\}$
g Domain = $\{x \mid x \in \mathbb{R}\}$, Range = $\{y \mid y \geqslant -1\}$
h Domain = $\{x \mid x \in \mathbb{R}\}$, Range = $\{y \mid y \geqslant 2\}$
i Domain = $\{x \mid -2 \leqslant x \leqslant 2\}$, Range = $\{y \mid 0 \leqslant y \leqslant 2\}$
j Domain = $\{x \mid x \neq 0\}$, Range = $\{y \mid y \leqslant -2$ or $y \geqslant 2\}$
k Domain = $\{x \mid x \neq 2\}$, Range = $\{y \mid y \neq 1\}$
l Domain = $\{x \mid x \in \mathbb{R}\}$, Range = $\{y \mid y \in \mathbb{R}\}$
m Domain = $\{x \mid x \neq 0\}$, Range = $\{y \mid y \geqslant 2\}$
n Domain = $\{x \mid x \neq 0\}$, Range = $\{y \mid y \leqslant -2$ or $y \geqslant 2\}$
o Domain = $\{x \mid x \in \mathbb{R}\}$, Range = $\{y \mid y \geqslant -8\}$

EXERCISE 16D

1 a €170   b €320   c €720

2 a 100°C   b 0°C   c 40°C   d 190°C

3 a $V(0) = 25\,000$ pounds.
      This is the purchase price of the car.
   b $V(3) = 16\,000$ pounds
      This is the value of the car 3 years after purchase.
   c $t = 5$. It will take 5 years for the value of the car to decrease to £10 000.

4 a

t	0	1	2	3	4	5
C	60	105	150	195	240	285

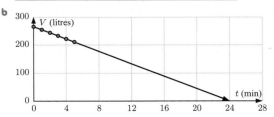

   b $C = 60 + 45t$ c $352.50

5 a

t	0	1	2	3	4	5
V	265	254	243	232	221	210

   b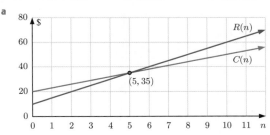

   c $V(t) = 265 - 11t$ d i 100 L   ii 24.1 minutes

6 a $C = 158 + 365n$ b €1526.75   c $\approx 13\,300$ km

7 a $W = 50s + 250$ b $1925   c $11 600

8 a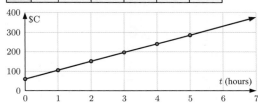

   b 5 packs   c $n > 5$ d 55 packs

9 a $R(n) = 7n$, $C(n) = 2.5n + 300$

b

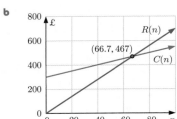

c 67 adaptors
d 289 adaptors

10 a $C(n) = 6000 + 3.25n$, $R(n) = 9.5n$

b

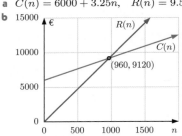

c 960 books
d 2560 books

11 a $C(n) = 2100 + 28n$, $R(n) = 70n$

b

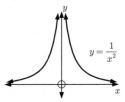

c $P(n) = 42n - 2100$
d **i** 50 carburettors
   ii \$3150
   iii 81 carburettors

REVIEW SET 16A

1 a 0   **b** -15 **c** $-\frac{5}{4}$ **2** $a = -6$, $b = 13$

3 a $x^2 - x - 2$ **b** $x^4 - 7x^2 + 10$

4 a i Domain $= \{x \mid x \in \mathbb{R}\}$,   Range $= \{y \mid y \geqslant -5\}$
   ii x-int $-1, 5$, y-int $-\frac{25}{9}$ **iii** is a function

b i Domain $= \{x \mid x \in \mathbb{R}\}$,   Range $= \{y \mid y = 1$ or $-3\}$
   ii no x-intercepts, y-intercept 1   **iii** is a function

5 a $x = 0$ **b**

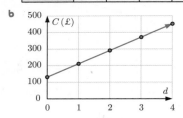

$y = \dfrac{1}{x^2}$

c Domain $= \{x \mid x \neq 0\}$,   Range $= \{y \mid y > 0\}$

6 a

d (days)	0	1	2	3	4
C (£)	130	210	290	370	450

b

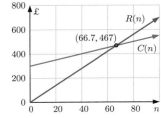

c $C = 130 + 80d$
d £40

REVIEW SET 16B

1 a is a function   **b** is not a function   **c** is a function

2 a 1   **b** -5 **c** $3x - 2$ **d** $3x^2 - 3x - 5$

3 $a = 3$, $b = -1$

4 a Domain $= \{x \mid x \in \mathbb{R}\}$,   Range $= \{y \mid y \geqslant -4\}$
   b Domain $= \{x \mid x \neq 0,\ x \neq 2\}$,
      Range $= \{y \mid y > 0$ or $y \leqslant -1\}$

5 a

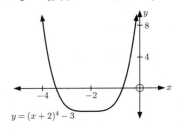

$y = (x + 2)^4 - 3$

b Domain $= \{x \mid x \in \mathbb{R}\}$,   Range $= \{y \mid y \geqslant -3\}$

6 a $O = 160 - 5t$ **b** 85 L
   c i 22 minutes   **ii** 32 minutes

REVIEW SET 16C

1 a function (x-coordinates are all different)
   b not a function (two points have the same x-coordinate)
   c not a function (x-coordinates are the same)

2 a Domain $= \{x \mid x \geqslant -2\}$,   Range $= \{y \mid 1 \leqslant y < 3\}$
   b Domain $= \{x \mid x \in \mathbb{R}\}$
      Range $= \{y \mid y = -1$ or $y = 1$ or $y = 2\}$

3

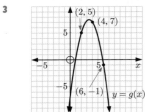

$y = g(x)$

(There are other answers.)

4 a i Domain $= \{x \mid x \neq 1\}$,   Range $= \{y \mid y > -1\}$
      ii is a function
   b i Domain $= \{x \mid -2 \leqslant x \leqslant 2\}$,
         Range $= \{y \mid -2 \leqslant y \leqslant 2\}$
      ii is not a function

5 a

d (days)	0	1	2	3	4
H (mm)	17	20	23	26	29

b

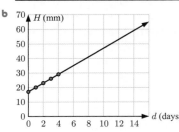

c $H(d) = 3d + 17$ **d** 53 mm
e Every 21 days (3 weeks)

6 a

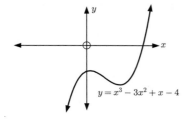

$$y = x^3 - 3x^2 + x - 4$$

Domain $= \{x \mid x \in \mathbb{R}\}$,   Range $= \{y \mid y \in \mathbb{R}\}$

b

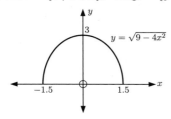

$$y = \sqrt{9 - 4x^2}$$

Domain $= \{x \mid -\frac{3}{2} \leqslant x \leqslant \frac{3}{2}\}$,   Range $= \{y \mid 0 \leqslant y \leqslant 3\}$

7 a $C(n) = 2.4n + 1750$, $R(n) = \frac{11}{3}n$

b

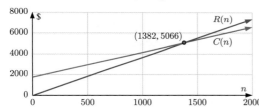

c 1383 tennis balls (461 complete packs)   **d** 566 packs

EXERCISE 17A

1 a Yes   **b** No   **c** Yes   **d** Yes   **e** Yes   **f** No

2 a $y = 0$ **b** $y = 5$ **c** $y = -15$ **d** $y = 12$

3 a $f(2) = 3$, $f(-1) = -9$ **b** $f(0) = 1$, $f(-3) = 22$
   c $g(3) = -29$, $g(-2) = -4$

4 a No   **b** Yes   **c** Yes   **d** No   **e** No   **f** No

5 a $x = -3$ **b** $x = -2$ or -3 **c** $x = 1$ or 4
   d no real solutions

6 a $x = 1$ or 0 **b** $x = 3$ or -1 **c** $x = -7$ or $\frac{1}{2}$
   d $x = 3$ or 2

7 a i 75 m   **ii** 195 m   **iii** 275 m
   b i $t = 2$ s or $t = 14$ s   **ii** $t = 0$ s or $t = 16$ s
   c These height levels are each obtained twice, once on the way up, and once on the way down.
   d Domain $= \{t \mid 0 \leqslant t \leqslant 16\}$

8 a i $-\$40$ **ii** $\$480$ **b** 10 cakes or 62 cakes

EXERCISE 17B

1 a

x	-3	-2	-1	0	1	2	3
y	1	-2	-3	-2	1	6	13

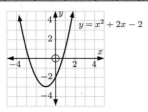

$$y = x^2 + 2x - 2$$

b

x	-3	-2	-1	0	1	2	3
y	6	1	-2	-3	-2	1	6

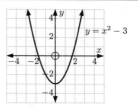

$$y = x^2 - 3$$

c

x	-3	-2	-1	0	1	2	3
y	15	8	3	0	-1	0	3

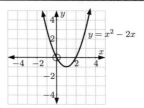

$$y = x^2 - 2x$$

d

x	-3	-2	-1	0	1	2	3
y	-10	-4	0	2	2	0	-4

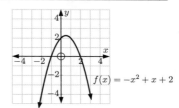

$$f(x) = -x^2 + x + 2$$

e

x	-3	-2	-1	0	1	2	3
y	25	16	9	4	1	0	1

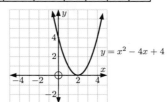

$$y = x^2 - 4x + 4$$

f

x	-3	-2	-1	0	1	2	3
y	-17	-4	5	10	11	8	1

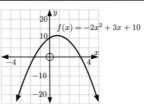

$$f(x) = -2x^2 + 3x + 10$$

2 a

x	-3	-2	-1	0	1	2	3
x^2	9	4	1	0	1	4	9
$x^2 + 2$	11	6	3	2	3	6	11
$x^2 - 2$	7	2	-1	-2	-1	2	7

b

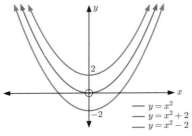

— $y = x^2$
— $y = x^2 + 2$
— $y = x^2 - 2$

c The graphs are all the same shape, but $y = x^2 + 2$ is $y = x^2$ translated 2 units up, and $y = x^2 - 2$ is $y = x^2$ translated 2 units down.

3 a

x	-3	-2	-1	0	1	2	3
x^2	9	4	1	0	1	4	9
$(x+2)^2$	1	0	1	4	9	16	25
$(x-2)^2$	25	16	9	4	1	0	1

b

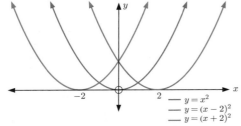

— $y = x^2$
— $y = (x-2)^2$
— $y = (x+2)^2$

c The graphs are all the same shape, but $y = (x+2)^2$ is $y = x^2$ translated 2 units left, and $y = (x-2)^2$ is $y = x^2$ translated 2 units right.

EXERCISE 17C

1 **a** 3   **b** -1 **c** -4 **d** 1   **e** 5   **f** 0
   g 8   **h** -5 **i** 2

2 **a** 3   **b** -6 **c** 49   **d** 15   **e** 0   **f** 20

3 **a** 2 and 5   **b** 3 and -4 **c** -6 and -3
   d 7 and -1 **e** 0 and 8   **f** -5 and 5
   g -4 **h** 2   **i** -1

4 **a** 2   **b** 1   **c** none

5 **a** -2 and 3   **b** 4 and -4 **c** no x-intercepts
   d 0 and 3   **e** 6   **f** 2.19 and -3.19 **g** -7 and 3
   h 5   **i** 5 and $-1\frac{1}{2}$ **j** no x-intercepts
   k 1 and -0.833 (or $-\frac{5}{6}$)   **l** 0.434 and -0.768

6 **a** x-intercepts 1 and -2, y-intercept -2
   b x-intercept -3, y-intercept 9
   c x-intercepts -5 and 2, y-intercept -10
   d no x-intercepts, y-intercept 4
   e x-intercepts 1.44 and 5.56, y-intercept -8
   f x-intercept -4, y-intercept -16
   g x-intercepts 0 and 7, y-intercept 0
   h x-intercepts -1.27 and 2.77, y-intercept 7
   i x-intercepts -3 and 3, y-intercept -18
   j no x-intercepts, y-intercept -9
   k x-intercepts $-\frac{1}{2}$ and $\frac{3}{2}$, y-intercept -3
   l x-intercepts -1.30 and 1.70, y-intercept 11

EXERCISE 17D

1 **a**

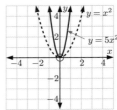

$y = 5x^2$ opens upwards and is 'thinner'.

b

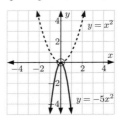

$y = -5x^2$ opens downwards and is 'thinner'.

c

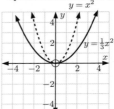

$y = \frac{1}{3}x^2$ opens upwards and is 'wider'.

d

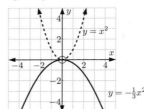

$y = -\frac{1}{3}x^2$ opens downwards and is 'wider'.

e

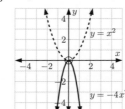

$y = -4x^2$ opens downwards and is 'thinner'.

f

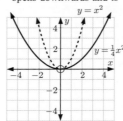

$y = \frac{1}{4}x^2$ opens upwards, and is 'wider'.

2 a $(0, 0)$, minimum **b** $(0, 0)$, maximum

EXERCISE 17E

1 a
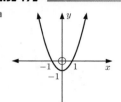

b
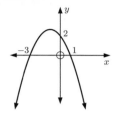

c
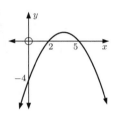

d
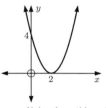

2 a
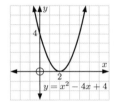

b $f(x) = (x-1)(x+3)$
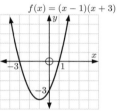

c
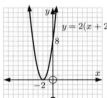 $y = 2(x+2)^2$

d $y = -(x-2)(x+1)$
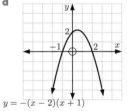

e $y = -3(x+1)^2$
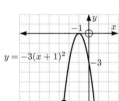

f $f(x) = -3(x-4)(x-1)$
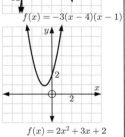

g $y = 2(x+3)(x+1)$
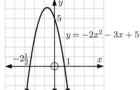

h $f(x) = 2x^2 + 3x + 2$

i $y = -2x^2 - 3x + 5$
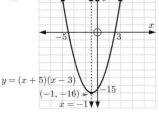

EXERCISE 17F

1 a $x = 3$ **b** $x = -\frac{5}{2}$ **c** $x = 1$ **d** $x = -4$
e $x = 3$ **f** $x = -4$

2 a $x = 4$ **b** $x = -2$ **c** $x = 1$ **d** $x = \frac{11}{2}$
e $x = 5$ **f** $x = -2$

3 a $x = -3$ **b** $x = 4$ **c** $x = -\frac{5}{4}$ **d** $x = \frac{3}{2}$
e $x = 0$ **f** $x = \frac{7}{10}$ **g** $x = 3$ **h** $x = \frac{5}{3}$
i $x = -4$

EXERCISE 17G

1 a $(2, 3)$, local minimum **b** $(-1, 4)$, local minimum
c $(3, 8)$, local maximum **d** $(0, 3)$, local minimum
e $(-3, -18)$, local minimum **f** $(1, -1)$, local maximum
g $(\frac{1}{2}, -\frac{5}{4})$, local minimum **h** $(\frac{3}{4}, -\frac{7}{8})$, local maximum
i $(6, 7)$, local maximum

2 a $(\frac{3}{2}, -\frac{49}{4})$ **b** $(2, -4)$ **c** $(-\frac{5}{2}, 0)$
d $(3, 1)$ **e** $(0, 9)$ **f** $(-\frac{7}{6}, \frac{61}{12})$

3 a **i** x-intercepts:
1 and 3
y-intercept: 3
ii $x = 2$
iii $(2, -1)$
iv
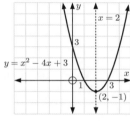 $y = x^2 - 4x + 3$

v Domain $= \{x \mid x \in \mathbb{R}\}$, Range $= \{y \mid y \geqslant -1\}$

b **i** x-intercepts:
-2 and 6
y-intercept: 12
ii $x = 2$
iii $(2, 16)$
iv
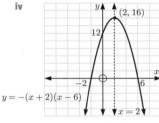 $y = -(x+2)(x-6)$

v Domain $= \{x \mid x \in \mathbb{R}\}$, Range $= \{y \mid y \leqslant 16\}$

c **i** x-intercepts:
-2 and 0
y-intercept: 0
ii $x = -1$
iii $(-1, -1)$
iv
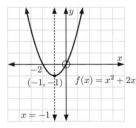 $f(x) = x^2 + 2x$

v Domain $= \{x \mid x \in \mathbb{R}\}$, Range $= \{y \mid y \geqslant -1\}$

d **i** x-intercepts:
-5 and 3
y-intercept: -15
ii $x = -1$
iii $(-1, -16)$
v Domain
$= \{x \mid x \in \mathbb{R}\}$,
Range
$= \{y \mid y \geqslant -16\}$
iv
$y = (x+5)(x-3)$

e i x-intercept: 5
    y-intercept: 25
ii $x = 5$
iii $(5, 0)$

iv

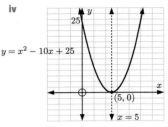

$y = x^2 - 10x + 25$

v Domain $= \{x \mid x \in \mathbb{R}\}$,   Range $= \{y \mid y \geqslant 0\}$

f i x-intercepts:
    $-\frac{3}{2}$ and $-\frac{1}{2}$,
    y-intercept: -3
ii $x = -1$
iii $(-1, 1)$

iv

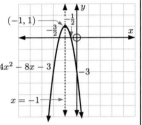

$f(x) = -4x^2 - 8x - 3$

v Domain $= \{x \mid x \in \mathbb{R}\}$,   Range $= \{y \mid y \leqslant 1\}$

g i x-intercepts:
    0 and 8
    y-intercept: 0
ii $x = 4$
iii $(4, -16)$

iv

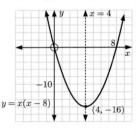

$y = x(x - 8)$

v Domain $= \{x \mid x \in \mathbb{R}\}$,   Range $= \{y \mid y \geqslant -16\}$

h i x-intercepts:
    -2 and 3
    y-intercept: -12
ii $x = \frac{1}{2}$
iii $(\frac{1}{2}, -12\frac{1}{2})$

iv

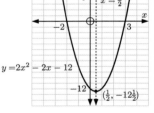

$y = 2x^2 - 2x - 12$

v Domain $= \{x \mid x \in \mathbb{R}\}$,   Range $= \{y \mid y \geqslant -12\frac{1}{2}\}$

i i x-intercept: -4,
    y-intercept: -16
ii $x = -4$
iii $(-4, 0)$

iv

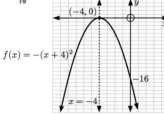

$f(x) = -(x + 4)^2$

v Domain $= \{x \mid x \in \mathbb{R}\}$,   Range $= \{y \mid y \leqslant 0\}$

j i x-intercepts:
    $-\frac{1}{3}$ and $\frac{1}{3}$
    y-intercept: -1
ii $x = 0$
iii $(0, -1)$

iv

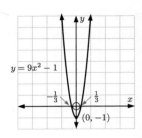

$y = 9x^2 - 1$

v Domain $= \{x \mid x \in \mathbb{R}\}$,   Range $= \{y \mid y \geqslant -1\}$

k i x-intercepts:
    $\frac{1}{3}$ and 1
    y-intercept: 1
ii $x = \frac{2}{3}$
iii $(\frac{2}{3}, -\frac{1}{3})$

iv

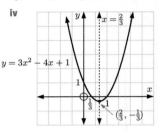

$y = 3x^2 - 4x + 1$

v Domain $= \{x \mid x \in \mathbb{R}\}$,   Range $= \{y \mid y \geqslant -\frac{1}{3}\}$

l i x-intercepts:
    4 and -6
    y-intercept: 12
ii $x = -1$
iii $(-1, 12\frac{1}{2})$

iv

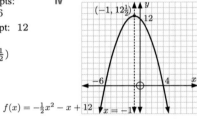

$f(x) = -\frac{1}{2}x^2 - x + 12$

v Domain $= \{x \mid x \in \mathbb{R}\}$,   Range $= \{y \mid y \leqslant 12\frac{1}{2}\}$

EXERCISE 17H

1 a $y = 2(x - 1)(x - 2)$
   b $y = 2(x - 2)^2$
   c $y = (x - 1)(x - 3)$
   d $y = -(x - 3)(x + 1)$
   e $y = -3(x - 1)^2$
   f $y = -2(x + 2)(x - 3)$

2 a $y = \frac{3}{2}(x - 2)(x - 4)$
   b $y = -\frac{1}{2}(x + 4)(x - 2)$
   c $y = -\frac{4}{3}(x + 3)^2$
   d $y = \frac{1}{4}(x + 3)(x - 5)$
   e $y = -(x + 3)(x - 3)$
   f $y = 4(x - 1)(x - 3)$

3 a $y = 3x^2 - 18x + 15$
   b $y = -4x^2 + 6x + 4$
   c $y = -x^2 + 6x - 9$
   d $y = 4x^2 + 16x + 16$
   e $y = \frac{3}{2}x^2 - 6x + \frac{9}{2}$
   f $y = -\frac{1}{3}x^2 + \frac{2}{3}x + 5$

4 a $c = 2$ **b** $a + b = -1$, $2a + b = 2$
   c $a = 3$, $b = -4$, $f(x) = 3x^2 - 4x + 2$

5 a $c = -2$ **b** $b = -6a$, $5a + b = 1$
   c $a = -1$, $b = 6$, $y = -x^2 + 6x - 2$
   d

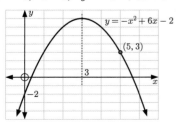

$y = -x^2 + 6x - 2$
$(5, 3)$

EXERCISE 17I

1 **a** $(1, 1)$ and $(0, -1)$ **b** $(-2, -5)$ and $(2, 3)$
   c $(1, 7)$ and $(2, 8)$ **d** $(-3, -9)$ and $(4, 5)$
   e $(3, 0)$ **f** graphs do not intersect

2 **a** $(0.586, 5.59)$ and $(3.41, 8.41)$ **b** $(3, -4)$
   c graphs do not intersect
   d $(-2.56, -18.8)$ and $(1.56, 1.81)$
   e $(0.176, -3.09)$ and $(-5.68, -0.162)$
   f $(9.90, -27.7)$ and $(0.101, 1.70)$ **g** $(0.5, -1.75)$

3 **a** do not intersect   **b** $(1, 2)$
   c do not intersect   **d** $(2, 1)$ and $(-5, -20)$
   e $(-0.0981, 6.52)$ and $(5.10, 58.5)$
   f $(-2.29, 68.7)$ and $(2.62, 11.4)$

EXERCISE 17J

1 **a** 3 m   **b** 0.5 s   **c** 4 m   **d** 1.5 s

2 **a** 10 necklaces   **b** $100

3 **a** 20 televisions   **b** $100   **c** 10 or 30

4 **a**
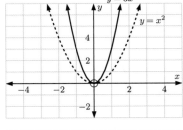
   b 13.3 m
   c 15 m
   d 60 m

6 250 m by 500 m

7 **a** **Hint:** Consider the total length of all the fencing.
   c 100 m by 112.5 m

8 **a** 41.7 m by 41.7 m   **b** 50 m by 31.25 m

9 40 toasters   **10** 157 barbecues

REVIEW SET 17A

1 **a** -15 **b** -17 **c** $x = -3$ or 6

2 **a**
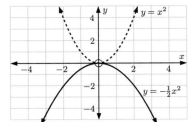
   b

3 **a** **i** downwards **ii** 6 **iii** -3 and 1 **iv** $x = -1$

b
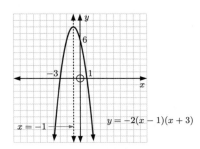

c Domain $= \{x \mid x \in \mathbb{R}\}$,   Range $= \{y \mid y \leqslant 8\}$

4 **a** **i** -15 **b**
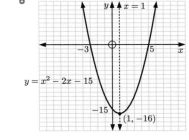
   ii -3 and 5
   iii $x = 1$
   iv $(1, -16)$

5 **a** 0 and 4   **b** $-1\frac{2}{3}$ and 2   **c** -4 and 15

6 **a** **B**   **b** **C**   **c** **A**   **d** **D**

7 **a** $y = 3x^2 - 24x + 48$ **b** $y = -\frac{1}{2}x^2 + \frac{1}{2}x + 3$

8 Maximum value is 5, when $x = 1$.

9 **a** 2 seconds   **b** 80 m   **c** 6 seconds

REVIEW SET 17B

1 **a** No   **b** $x = -2$ or 7

2 **a** **i** upwards   **b**
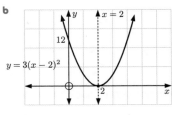
   ii 12
   iii 2 (touches)
   iv $x = 2$

c Domain $= \{x \mid x \in \mathbb{R}\}$,   Range $= \{y \mid y \geqslant 0\}$

3 **a** **i** -10 **b**
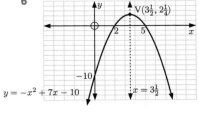
   ii 2 and 5
   iii $x = 3\frac{1}{2}$
   iv $(3\frac{1}{2}, 2\frac{1}{4})$

4 vertex is $\left(\frac{4}{3}, \frac{37}{3}\right)$

5 **a** $y = \frac{20}{9}(x - 5)(x + 1)$ **b** $y = -\frac{2}{7}(x - 7)(x - 1)$
   c $y = \frac{2}{9}(x + 3)^2$

6 $(-9, -21)$ and $(-2, -7)$ **7** $a = 5$, $b = 6$

8 **a** $\left(1000x - \frac{3}{2}x^2\right)$ m²   **b** ≈ 16.7 ha
   c Each field is 333 m by 250 m.

REVIEW SET 17C

1 a -6 **b** 34 **c** $x = -4$ or -1

2 a $\left(-\frac{3}{2}, -\frac{15}{2}\right)$ **b** -3

   c

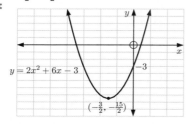

$y = 2x^2 + 6x - 3$

   d Range $= \{y \mid y \geqslant -\frac{15}{2}\}$

3

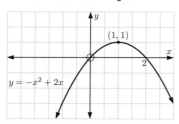

$y = -x^2 + 2x$

4 a $y = 3(x+3)(x-3)$ **b** $y = -2(x+1)(x-6)$

5 $(0.219, -8.56)$ and $(2.28, -4.44)$ **6** $(1.5, -1.5)$

7 b $\$20$ **c** $\$800$ **8** $y = -4x^2 + 4x + 24$

9 a $x = -5$ **b** -1

EXERCISE 18A

1 a 1 **b** -1 **c** -2 **d** $-2\frac{1}{2}$ **e** $-2\frac{3}{4}$

2 a 15 **b** 135 **c** 5 **d** $\frac{5}{81}$ **e** $1\frac{2}{3}$

3 a 32 **b** 2 **c** 4 **d** 1 **e** $\frac{1}{16}$

4 a $\frac{1}{5}$ **b** $\frac{1}{125}$ **c** 1 **d** 25 **e** 125

5 a 3 **b** 3.3 **c** 4.83 **d** 2.48 **e** 4.31

EXERCISE 18B.1

1 a

x	-3	-2	-1	0	1	2	3
y	$\frac{1}{64}$	$\frac{1}{16}$	$\frac{1}{4}$	1	4	16	64

   b i As we increase x by 1, the value of y is quadrupled.
   ii As we decrease x by 1, the value of y is divided by 4.

   c

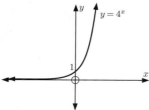

$y = 4^x$

   d i as $x \to \infty$, $y \to \infty$ **ii** as $x \to -\infty$, $y \to 0^+$
   e $y = 0$

2 a

x	-3	-2	-1	0	1	2	3
y	27	9	3	1	$\frac{1}{3}$	$\frac{1}{9}$	$\frac{1}{27}$

   b

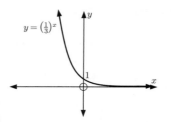

$y = \left(\frac{1}{3}\right)^x$

   c decreasing

   d i as $x \to \infty$, $y \to 0^+$ **ii** as $x \to -\infty$, $y \to \infty$
   e $y = 0$

3 a 1.4 **b** 1.7 **c** 2.8 **d** 0.3 **e** 2.7 **f** 0.4

EXERCISE 18B.2

1 a

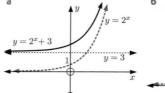

$y = 2^x$
$y = 2^x + 3$
$y = 3$

   b

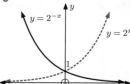

$y = 2^{-x}$
$y = 2^x$

   c

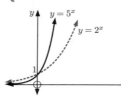

$y = 5^x$
$y = 2^x$

   d

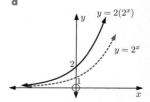

$y = 2(2^x)$
$y = 2^x$

2 a

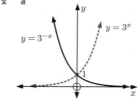

$y = 3^{-x}$
$y = 3^x$

   b

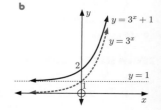

$y = 3^x + 1$
$y = 3^x$
$y = 1$

   c

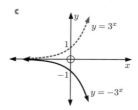

$y = 3^x$
$y = -3^x$

3 a i y-intercept is 2   **iv**

   ii $y = 1$
   iii When $x = 2$,
         $y = 5$
         When $x = -2$,
         $y = \frac{5}{4}$

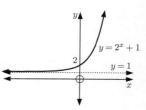

$y = 2^x + 1$
$y = 1$

   v Domain $= \{x \mid x \in \mathbb{R}\}$,   Range $= \{y \mid y > 1\}$

b **i** y-intercept is 5
   ii $y = 4$
   iii When $x = 2$,
        $y = \frac{37}{9}$
     When $x = -2$,
        $y = 13$

iv
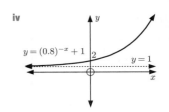

   v Domain $= \{x \mid x \in \mathbb{R}\}$, Range $= \{y \mid y > 4\}$

c **i** y-intercept is 1
   ii $y = 0$
   iii When $x = 2$,
        $y = \frac{4}{25}$
     When $x = -2$,
        $y = \frac{25}{4}$

iv
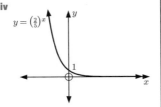

   v Domain $= \{x \mid x \in \mathbb{R}\}$, Range $= \{y \mid y > 0\}$

d **i** y-intercept is -2
   ii $y = -3$
   iii When $x = 2$,
        $y = -\frac{11}{4}$
     When $x = -2$,
        $y = 1$

iv
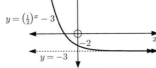

   v Domain $= \{x \mid x \in \mathbb{R}\}$, Range $= \{y \mid y > -3\}$

e **i** y-intercept is 1
   ii $y = 2$
   iii When $x = 2$,
        $y = -2$
     When $x = -2$,
        $y = \frac{7}{4}$

iv
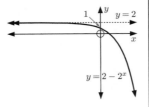

   v Domain $= \{x \mid x \in \mathbb{R}\}$, Range $= \{y \mid y < 2\}$

f **i** y-intercept is 4
   ii $y = 3$
   iii When $x = 2$,
        $y = \frac{49}{16}$
     When $x = -2$,
        $y = 19$

iv
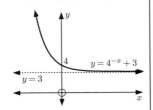

   v Domain $= \{x \mid x \in \mathbb{R}\}$, Range $= \{y \mid y > 3\}$

g **i** y-intercept is 2
   ii $y = 3$
   iii When $x = 2$,
        $y = \frac{11}{4}$
     When $x = -2$,
        $y = -1$

iv
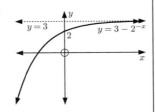

   v Domain $= \{x \mid x \in \mathbb{R}\}$, Range $= \{y \mid y < 3\}$

h **i** y-intercept is 2
   ii $y = 1$
   iii When $x = 2$,
        $y = \frac{41}{16}$
     When $x = -2$,
        $y = \frac{41}{25}$

iv

   v Domain $= \{x \mid x \in \mathbb{R}\}$, Range $= \{y \mid y > 1\}$

EXERCISE 18C

1 **a** $x \approx 4.32$ **b** $x \approx 6.64$ **c** $x \approx 3.10$
   d $x \approx 6.03$ **e** $x \approx 36.8$ **f** $x \approx 6.58$
2 **a** $x \approx 4.95$ **b** $x \approx 6.21$ **c** $x \approx 2.46$
   d $x \approx 9.88$ **e** $x \approx 6.95$ **f** $x \approx 5.36$

EXERCISE 18D.1

1 **a** 3 m^2
   b **i** 3.50 m^2
      ii 6.48 m^2
      iii 30.2 m^2

   c
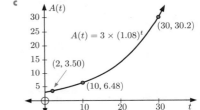

2 **a** **i** 76
      ii 141
      iii 396
   c ≈ 12 years

   b
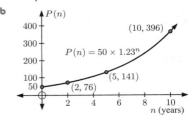

3 **a** **i** 5 units
      ii 9.03 units
   b an 80.6%
     increase
   d $37.2°$C

   c
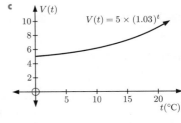

4 **a** $B(t) = 12 \times (1.14)^t$ **b** 30 bears   **c** 16.2 years

EXERCISE 18D.2

1 **a** 250 g   **b** **i** 112 g   **ii** 50.4 g   **iii** 22.6 g
   c   **d** ≈ 346 years

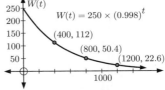

2 **a** 0.6 amps
   b **i** 0.423 amps   **ii** 0.104 amps   **iii** 0.018 amps

c

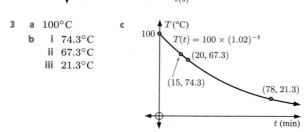

3 **a** 100°C

b **i** 74.3°C
ii 67.3°C
iii 21.3°C

c

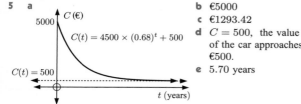

4 **a** L_0 candelas   **b** 99.0% decrease

5 **a**

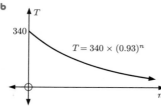

b €5000
c €1293.42
d $C = 500$, the value of the car approaches €500.
e 5.70 years

6 **a** $T = 340 \times (0.93)^n$ **b**
c 237 turtles
d In 2053

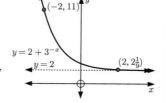

REVIEW SET 18A

1 **a** 3   **b** 24   **c** $\frac{3}{4}$

2 **a** **i** y-intercept is 3   **b**
ii $y = 2$
iii $f(-2) = 11$,
    $f(2) = \frac{19}{9}$

c Domain $= \{x \mid x \in \mathbb{R}\}$,
    Range $= \{y \mid y > 2\}$

3 **a** $x \approx 4.29$ **b** $x \approx 3.56$ **c** $x \approx 86.3$

4 **a** \$20   **c**

b **i** \$62.12
ii \$599.20
iii \$5780.04
d during 1994

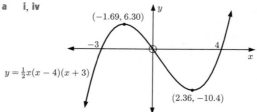

5 **a** $T_0 = 180$°C   **b** 28.3°C   **c** 38.7 min

REVIEW SET 18B

1 **a** 125   **b** 5   **c** $\frac{1}{125}$

2

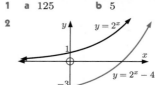

a $y = 2^x$ has y-intercept 1 and horizontal asymptote $y = 0$

b $y = 2^x - 4$ has y-intercept -3 and horizontal asymptote $y = -4$

3 **a** 60 grams   **b** **i** 35.9 g   **ii** 4.62 g
c after 79.8 years

4 **a** **i** y-intercept is -6 **b**
ii $y = -4$
iii $f(-2) = -\frac{38}{9}$,
    $f(2) = -22$

c Domain $= \{x \mid x \in \mathbb{R}\}$,
    Range $= \{y \mid y < -4\}$

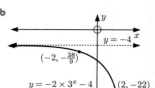

5 **a** $P(0) = 16$ **b** 34 rhinoceroses   **c** after 54.4 years

EXERCISE 19A

1 **a, e**

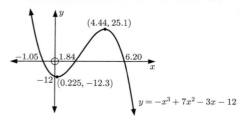

b x-intercepts are -1.05, 1.84, and 6.20, y-intercept is -12
c local maximum $(4.44, 25.1)$,
    local minimum $(0.225, -12.3)$
d As $x \to \infty$, $y \to -\infty$; as $x \to -\infty$, $y \to \infty$

2 **a, e**

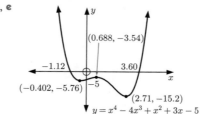

b x-intercepts are -1.12 and 3.60, y-intercept is -5
c local maximum $(0.688, -3.54)$,
    local minimum $(-0.402, -5.76)$ and $(2.71, -15.2)$
d as $x \to \infty$, $y \to \infty$; as $x \to -\infty$, $y \to \infty$
f Range $= \{y \mid y \geqslant -15.2\}$

3 **a** **i, iv**

ii x-intercepts are -3, 0, and 4, y-intercept is 0

iii local maximum $(-1.69, 6.30)$,
local minimum $(2.36, -10.4)$

b **i, iv**

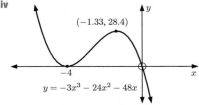

$(-1.33, 28.4)$

-4

$y = -3x^3 - 24x^2 - 48x$

ii x-intercepts are -4 and 0, y-intercept is 0
iii local minimum $(-4, 0)$,
local maximum $(-1.33, 28.4)$

c **i, iv**

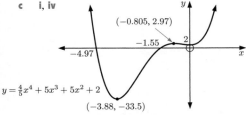

$(-0.805, 2.97)$

-1.55 2

-4.97

$y = \frac{4}{5}x^4 + 5x^3 + 5x^2 + 2$

$(-3.88, -33.5)$

ii x-intercepts are -4.97 and -1.55, y-intercept is 2
iii local minimum $(-3.88, -33.5)$ and $(0, 2)$,
local maximum $(-0.805, 2.97)$

d **i, iv**

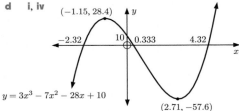

$(-1.15, 28.4)$

-2.32 10 0.333 4.32

$y = 3x^3 - 7x^2 - 28x + 10$

$(2.71, -57.6)$

ii x-intercepts -2.32, 0.333, and 4.32, y-intercept 10
iii local maximum $(-1.15, 28.4)$,
local minimum $(2.71, -57.6)$

e **i, iv**

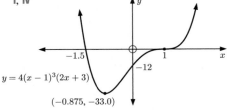

-1.5 1

-12

$y = 4(x-1)^3(2x+3)$

$(-0.875, -33.0)$

ii x-intercepts are -1.5 and 1, y-intercept is -12
iii local minimum $(-0.875, -33.0)$

f **i, iv**

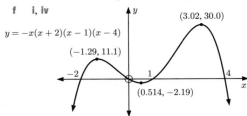

$y = -x(x+2)(x-1)(x-4)$

$(3.02, 30.0)$

$(-1.29, 11.1)$

-2 1 4

$(0.514, -2.19)$

ii x-intercepts are -2, 0, 1, and 4, y-intercept is 0
iii local maximum $(-1.29, 11.1)$ and $(3.02, 30.0)$,
local minimum $(0.514, -2.19)$

4 **a**

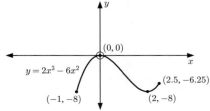

$(0,0)$

$y = 2x^3 - 6x^2$

$(2.5, -6.25)$

$(-1, -8)$ $(2, -8)$

b

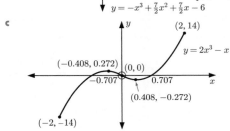

$(-3, 42)$

$(2.76, 9.30)$

-1.5 1 4

$(-0.423, -6.78)$ -6

$(5, -26)$

$y = -x^3 + \frac{7}{2}x^2 + \frac{7}{2}x - 6$

c

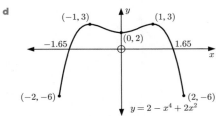

$(2, 14)$

$y = 2x^3 - x$

$(-0.408, 0.272)$ $(0, 0)$

-0.707 0.707

$(0.408, -0.272)$

$(-2, -14)$

d

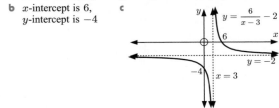

$(-1, 3)$ $(1, 3)$

$(0, 2)$

-1.65 1.65

$(-2, -6)$ $(2, -6)$

$y = 2 - x^4 + 2x^2$

EXERCISE 19B

1 **a** horizontal asymptote $y = -2$, vertical asymptote $x = 3$
b x-intercept is 6,   **c**
y-intercept is -4

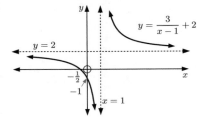

$y = \frac{6}{x-3} - 2$

6

$y = -2$

-4 $x = 3$

d Domain $= \{x \mid x \neq 3\}$,   Range $= \{y \mid y \neq -2\}$

2 **a** **i** vertical asymptote $x = 1$, horizontal asymptote $y = 2$
ii x-intercept is $-\frac{1}{2}$, y-intercept is -1
iii

$y = \frac{3}{x-1} + 2$

$y = 2$

$-\frac{1}{2}$

-1 $x = 1$

b **i** vert. asymptote $x = -2$, horiz. asymptote $y = -4$
ii x-intercept is $-\frac{1}{2}$, y-intercept is -1
iii

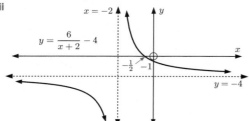

c **i** vert. asymptote $x = -4$, horiz. asymptote $y = 3$
ii x-intercept is $-\frac{10}{3}$, y-intercept is $\frac{5}{2}$
iii

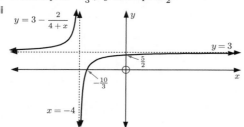

d **i** vert. asymptote $x = -3$, horiz. asymptote $y = 1$
ii x-intercept is 6, y-intercept is -2
iii

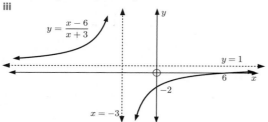

e **i** vert. asymptote $x = 1$, horiz. asymptote $y = -2$
ii x-intercept is $-\frac{3}{2}$, y-intercept is 3
iii

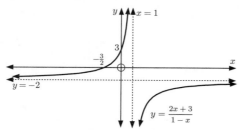

f **i** vert. asymptote $x = \frac{1}{2}$, horiz. asymptote $y = -2.5$
ii x-intercept is $\frac{1}{5}$, y-intercept is -1
iii

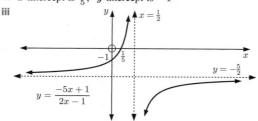

3

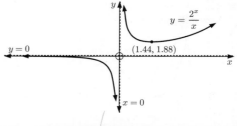

EXERCISE 19C

1 **a** **i** vertical asymptote $x = 0$ **ii** no axes intercepts
iii local maximum $(-0.760, -1.75)$,
local minimum $(0.760, 1.75)$
iv

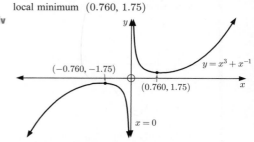

b **i** vertical asymptote $x = 0$
ii x-intercepts are -1 and 1, no y-intercepts
iii no turning points
iv

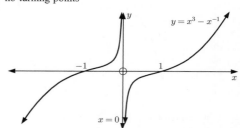

c **i** vertical asymptote $x = 0$ **ii** x-intercept -1.32
iii local minimum $(1.22, 4.50)$
iv

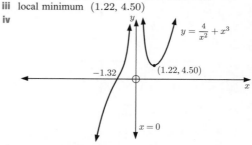

d **i** vertical asymptote $x = 0$
ii x-intercepts are -0.618, 1, and 1.62
iii local minimum $(1.30, -0.141)$
iv

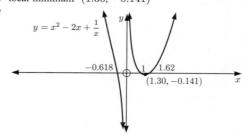

e **i** vertical asymptote $x = 0$
ii x-intercepts are -1 and 1
iii local minima $(-1, 0)$ and $(1, 0)$
iv

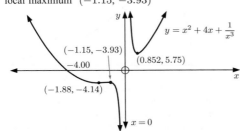

f **i** vertical asymptote $x = 0$ **ii** x-intercept is -4.00
iii local minima $(-1.88, -4.14)$ and $(0.852, 5.75)$,
local maximum $(-1.15, -3.93)$
iv

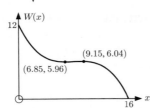

2 **a** 12 m
b 16 m
c **i** ≈ 6.85 m,
≈ 9.15 m
ii ≈ 5.96 m,
≈ 6.04 m
d

3 **c** vertical asymptote $x = 0$
d

e **i** ≈ 30 m^2 **ii** 32 m^2
f local minimum $(1.10, 21.8)$. The box will have minimum
surface area of ≈ 21.8 m^2 when $x \approx 1.10$.

EXERCISE 19D

1 **a** vertical asymptote $x = 0$ **b** x-intercept is -0.745
c local minimum $(1.25, 1.93)$
d

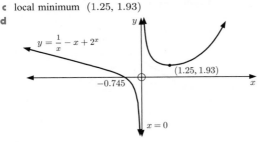

2 **a**

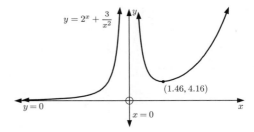

b

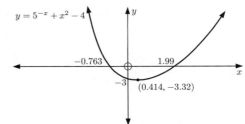

c

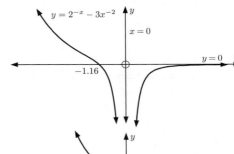

d

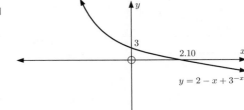

e

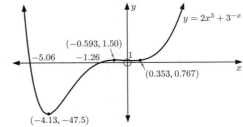

f

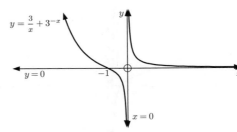

g

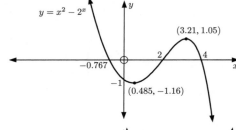

$y = x^2 - 2^x$

(3.21, 1.05)

-0.767

(0.485, -1.16)

h

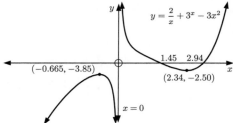

$y = \dfrac{2}{x} + 3^x - 3x^2$

($-0.665, -3.85$)   1.45 2.94

(2.34, -2.50)

$x = 0$

3

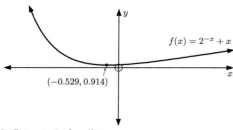

$f(x) = 2^{-x} + x$

($-0.529, 0.914$)

$\therefore \quad 2^{-x} + x > 0$ for all x.

4 a

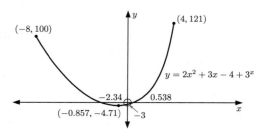

($-8, 100$)   (4, 121)

$y = 2x^2 + 3x - 4 + 3^x$

-2.34 0.538

($-0.857, -4.71$) -3

b

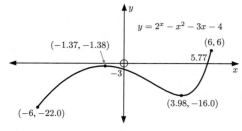

$y = 2^x - x^2 - 3x - 4$

($-1.37, -1.38$)   (6, 6)

5.77 -3

(3.98, -16.0)

($-6, -22.0$)

c

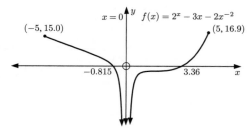

$x = 0$ $f(x) = 2^x - 3x - 2x^{-2}$

($-5, 15.0$)   (5, 16.9)

-0.815 3.36

d

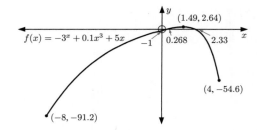

(1.49, 2.64)

$f(x) = -3^x + 0.1x^3 + 5x$ -1 0.268   2.33

(4, -54.6)

($-8, -91.2$)

5 a $E(1) = 160$, $E(4) = 10$. These are the effects of the injection 1 and 4 hours after it was administered.

b

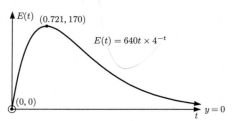

$E(t)$ (0.721, 170)

$E(t) = 640t \times 4^{-t}$

(0, 0) $y = 0$

x-intercept is 0, y-intercept is 0

c local maximum (0.721, 170). At $\approx$ 0.721 hours after the injection, the drug has reached maximum effect of $\approx$ 170 units and the effect will now begin to decrease.

EXERCISE 19E

1 a $(-2, -10)$, $(0.209, -1.17)$, and $(4.79, 17.2)$
   b $x \approx -2$, 0.209, or 4.79

2 a $x \approx -4.58$ **b** $x = 0$ or 1
   c $x \approx 0.651$ or 6.22   **d** no solution
   e $x \approx -0.483$ **f** $x \approx -1.51$ or 1.51
   g $x \approx -0.767$, 2 or 4   **h** $x \approx -0.404$ or 0.882
   i $x \approx 1.96$

3 a **A** and **D**   **b** **B** and **C**

4 a A(1.14, 1.49), B($-2, -8$), C(2.22, -6.48)
   b **i** $x = -2$ **ii** $x \approx 1.14$

5 a $x \approx 1.19$ **b** $(-1.19, -1.68)$, (1.19, 1.68)
   c 'solver' mode only gave the positive solution - it missed the second solution.
   $\therefore$ 'graph' mode is more reliable.

6 a $x \approx 3.80$ **b** $-10.1 < k < 2.21$ (3 s.f.)

7 (All answers to 3 s.f.)
   a $x \approx 0.491$ or 1.33
   b **i** $k < -6.02$ **ii** $k = -6.02$
   iii $-6.02 < k < -0.698$ or $k > 4.05$
   iv $k = -0.698$ or $k = 4.05$ **v** $-0.698 < k < 4.05$

8 a

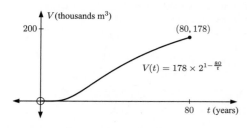

V (thousands m^3)

200   (80, 178)

$V(t) = 178 \times 2^{1 - \frac{80}{t}}$

80   t (years)

   b **i** 22 250 m^3 **ii** 89 000 m^3 **c** after 43.7 years

REVIEW SET 19A

1 a **i, ii**

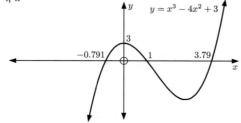

b

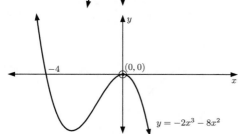

2 a **i** x-intercepts -1.81 and -0.287, no y-intercept
ii local minimum $(0.904, 9.95)$,
local maximum $(-0.904, 4.05)$
iii vertical asymptote $x = 0$
iv

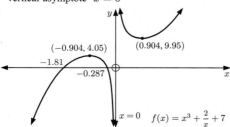

b **i** x-intercepts are -2.81, -0.251, and 5.00,
y-intercept is 1
ii local minimum $(-1.89, -5.05)$,
local maximum $(2.46, 6.32)$
iii no asymptote
iv

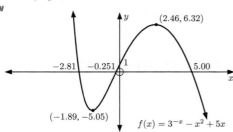

3

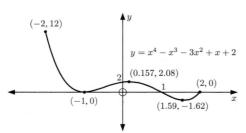

4 a

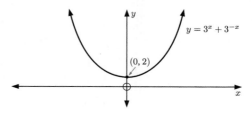

5 a vertical asymptote $x = -2$, horizontal asymptote $y = 1$
b x-intercept is -10, y-intercept is 5
c

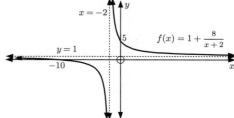

d Domain $= \{x \mid x \neq -2\}$, Range $= \{y \mid y \neq 1\}$

6 a, e

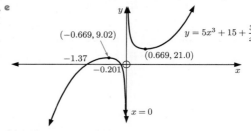

b vertical asymptote $x = 0$
c x-intercepts are -1.37 and -0.201, no y-intercept
d local maximum $(-0.669, 9.02)$,
local minimum $(0.669, 21.0)$

7 a $x = -3$ or 0.5 **b** $x \approx -8.00$ or -0.221

8 a

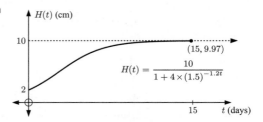

b 2 cm   **c** 8.83 cm   **d** 2.85 days   **e** yes, 10 cm

REVIEW SET 19B

1 a **i** x-intercepts are 0.605 and 6.24, no y-intercept
ii local maxima $(-0.689, -5.93)$ and $(3.16, 7.71)$
iii vertical asymptote $x = 0$
iv

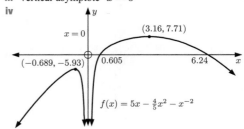

b   **i** no axes intercepts
    ii local minimum (1.96, 2.00)
    iii vertical asymptote $x = 0$, horizontal asymptote $y = 0$
    iv

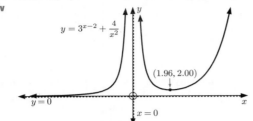

$y = 3^{x-2} + \dfrac{4}{x^2}$

(1.96, 2.00)

$y = 0$ $x = 0$

2

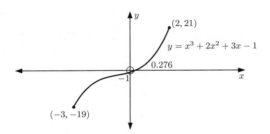

(2, 21)

$y = x^3 + 2x^2 + 3x - 1$

0.276

-1

$(-3, -19)$

3   **a** (1.23, 1.35)   **b** $x \approx 1.23$

4   **a** $x = -1$ **b** $y = -3$ **c** $-\frac{1}{3}$ **d** -1
    e

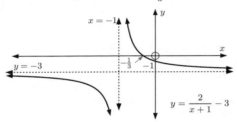

$x = -1$

$y = -3$ $-\frac{1}{3}$ -1

$y = \dfrac{2}{x+1} - 3$

5   **a** **i** vertical asymptote $x = 0$
    ii horizontal asymptote $y = 0$
    iii $f(-3) \approx 8.04$, $f(3) \approx 0.0880$
    b

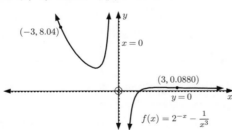

$(-3, 8.04)$

$x = 0$

$(3, 0.0880)$

$y = 0$

$f(x) = 2^{-x} - \dfrac{1}{x^3}$

6   **a**

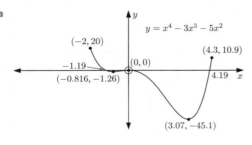

$y = x^4 - 3x^3 - 5x^2$

$(-2, 20)$

$(4.3, 10.9)$

-1.19 (0, 0)

$(-0.816, -1.26)$ 4.19

$(3.07, -45.1)$

b

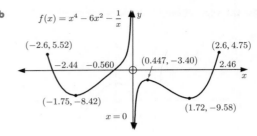

$f(x) = x^4 - 6x^2 - \dfrac{1}{x}$

$(-2.6, 5.52)$

$(2.6, 4.75)$

-2.44 -0.560 $(0.447, -3.40)$ 2.46

$(-1.75, -8.42)$

$(1.72, -9.58)$

$x = 0$

7   **c** local minimum at $\approx (14.7, 2039)$
    The minimum surface area of the bin is 2039 cm^2, when $r \approx 14.7$ cm.

8   **a**

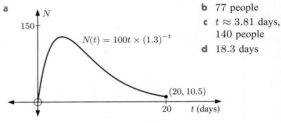

150

$N(t) = 100t \times (1.3)^{-t}$

(20, 10.5)

20   t (days)

b 77 people
c $t \approx 3.81$ days, 140 people
d 18.3 days

EXERCISE 20A.1

1   **a** In one minute, Karsten's heart is expected to beat 67 times.
    b 4020 beats per hour

2   **a** $\approx 0.001\,50$ errors per word
    b ≈ 0.150 errors per 100 words

3   Niko   ($12.35)

4   **a** 0.000 177 mm per km   **b** 1.77 mm per 10 000 km

5   **a** 89.0 km h^{-1} **b** 24.7 m s^{-1}

EXERCISE 20A.2

1   **a** 0.1 m s^{-1} **b** 0.9 m s^{-1} **c** 0.5 m s^{-1}

2   **a** **i** 3.1 beetles per g   **ii** 4.5 beetles per g
    b The decrease is slow at first, then becomes more rapid from 2 g until 8 g, when the decrease slows down.

EXERCISE 20B.1

1   **a** 1 m s^{-1} **b** 3 km h^{-1}
    c $44.40 per item sold   **d** -4.3 bats per week

2   **a** 8000 L   **b** 3000 L
    c 10 667 L per hour   **d** 3000 L per hour

EXERCISE 20B.2

1   **a** 6   **b** 12   **c** -2 **d** 5   **e** -4

2   **b** $(1 + h)^3 = 1 + 3h + 3h^2 + h^3$
    c M$(1 + h, 1 + 3h + 3h^2 + h^3)$ **d** $h^2 + 3h + 3$ **e** 3

3   12

4   **b** **i** $\dfrac{1}{1 + h}$ **ii** $-\dfrac{1}{1 + h}$ **c** -1 **d** $-\frac{1}{9}$

EXERCISE 20C

1   **a** $6x^5$ **b** $-\dfrac{5}{x^6}$ **c** $9x^8$ **d** $-\dfrac{7}{x^8}$

2   **a** 32   **b** 80   **c** -1 **d** 5

3   **a** $-\dfrac{4}{x^5}$ **b** -4 The gradient of the tangent at $x = 1$.

4   **a** 3

EXERCISE 20D

1 a $f'(x) = 3x^2$ b $f'(x) = 6x^2$
   c $f'(x) = 14x$ d $f'(x) = 2x + 1$
   e $f'(x) = -4x$ f $f'(x) = 2x + 3$
   g $f'(x) = 20x^3 - 12x$ h $f'(x) = 3x^2 + 6x + 4$
   i $f'(x) = 6x^{-2}$ j $f'(x) = -2x^{-2} + 6x^{-3}$
   k $f'(x) = 2x - 5x^{-2}$ l $f'(x) = 2x + 3x^{-2}$

2 a $f'(x) = 12x^2 - 1$ b 47   c -1

3 a $g'(x) = 1 - x^{-2}$ b $\frac{8}{9}$ c $\frac{3}{4}$

4 a 4   b $-\frac{16}{729}$ c -7 d $\frac{13}{4}$ e $\frac{1}{8}$ f -11

5 a $9x^2 + 6x + 1$ b $18x + 6$ c -30

6 a at A, gradient = 2;   at B, gradient = 0
   b $f'(x) = x^2 + \frac{3}{2}x - \frac{5}{2}$, $f'(-3) = 2$, $f'(1) = 0$

7 $\dfrac{dy}{dx} = 4 + \dfrac{3}{x^2}$ This is the instantaneous rate of change in y as x changes.

8 $\dfrac{dS}{dt} = 4t + 4$ This gives the speed of the car at time t, in metres per second.

9 $\dfrac{dC}{dx} = 3 + 0.004x$ This is the instantaneous rate of change in production cost as the number of toasters changes.

10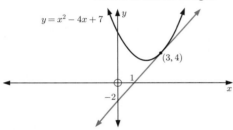

$y = x^2 - 4x + 7$

$(3, 4)$

The tangent has gradient 2 at the point $(3, 4)$.

11 a $(-1, -3)$ b $(-3, -1)$ c $(2, \frac{5}{2})$
    d $(-1, 4)$ or $(1, 0)$ e $\left(-\dfrac{b}{2a}, \dfrac{b^2}{4a} - \dfrac{b^2}{2a} + c\right)$

12 $P(-4, 4)$ 13 $a = 7$ 14 $a = -9$, $b = 8$
15 $a = 3$, $b = 6$ 16 a 1   b $a = -7$, $b = -15$

EXERCISE 20E

1 a $y = 8x - 16$ b $y = 12x + 16$ c $y = -3x - 6$
   d $y = -\frac{3}{4}x + 2$ e $y = 7x - 5$ f $y = -3x - 5$
   g $y = 2x$ h no tangent exists at $x = 0$
   i $y = \frac{1}{2}x + 2$ j $y = -3x - 8$

2 a i $y = x + 5$ ii $(2, 7)$
   b i $y = \frac{17}{3}x - 5$ ii $(-\frac{1}{3}, -\frac{62}{9}) \approx (-0.333, -6.89)$
   c i $y = 6.75x - 1.75$ ii $(-3, -22)$
   d i $y = 2x$ ii $(1, 2)$
   e i $y = 3.25x + 0.75$ ii $(-1.67, -4.67)$

3 a $(5, 0)$ b $(-1.58, 2)$ c $(0.8, -1.4)$ d $(0, -5)$
4 $R(0.5, -6)$ 5 a $y = 2x + 2$ b $(-1, 0)$

EXERCISE 20F

1 a $y = -\frac{1}{6}x + \frac{19}{2}$ b $y = -\frac{1}{7}x + \frac{26}{7}$ c $y = x + 2$
   d $y = -\frac{1}{3}x + \frac{1}{3}$ e $y = -\frac{1}{3}x + 3$ f $y = -\frac{1}{2}x + \frac{1}{2}$

2 a i $y = -\frac{1}{2}x + 2$ b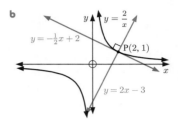
      ii $y = 2x - 3$

$y = \frac{2}{x}$

$y = -\frac{1}{2}x + 2$

$P(2, 1)$

$y = 2x - 3$

3 a $(-2.25, 5.06)$ b $(1, 3)$
   c normal does not meet curve again
   d $(-3.78, -6.55)$ and $(0.777, -6.85)$
4 a $(-2, 0)$ b $(-13, 3)$ c $(1.33, -1.67)$ d $(0, 0.333)$
5 $a = -4$
6 a i $a = -1$ ii $P(2, 2)$ b $y = -x + 4$ c $(0, 4)$
   d $y = -x + 4$. This is the same line as the normal to the curve at P.

REVIEW SET 20A

1 a 33 televisions per month   b 140 televisions per month
   c 250 televisions per month
2 a $f'(x) = 21x^2$ b $f'(x) = 6x - 3x^2$
   c $f'(x) = 8x - 12$ d $f'(x) = 7 + 4x$
3 a $f'(x) = 4x^3 - 3$ b 29   c -3
4 $y = 4x + 2$ 5 a -7 b -3
6 $y = -\frac{1}{15}x + \frac{182}{15}$ or $y \approx -0.0667x + 12.1$
7 $P(6, 5)$ 8 $a = 2$

REVIEW SET 20B

1 a i 5   ii $4\frac{1}{2}$ iii 4.1
   b $f'(x) = 2x + 2$ c gradient = 4, as $x \to 1$, $f'(x) \to 4$
2 a $\dfrac{dy}{dx} = 6x - 4x^3$ b $\dfrac{dy}{dx} = 1 + x^{-2}$
   c $\dfrac{dy}{dx} = 2 - x^{-2} + 6x^{-3}$
3 $y = 9x - 11$ 4 $\left(-\frac{1}{\sqrt{2}}, -2\sqrt{2}\right)$ and $\left(\frac{1}{\sqrt{2}}, 2\sqrt{2}\right)$
5 a -17 b -17 6 $(10.1, -13.0)$ 7 $a = 2$, $b = 3$
8 a $P(2, 5)$ b $y = x + 3$ c $(-3, 0)$ d $y = -x + 7$

REVIEW SET 20C

1 a $f'(x) = 4x^3 + 6x^2 + 6x$ b $f'(x) = -6x^{-4} - 4x^{-5}$
   c $f'(x) = -x^{-2} + 8x^{-3}$
2 a -5 b -12 c $\frac{7}{9}$ d -1 3 $y = -24x + 36$
4 $S'(t) = 0.9t^2 - 36t + 550$ g sec^{-1}
   This gives the instantaneous rate of change in weight, in grams per second, for a given value of t.
5 $y = -\frac{1}{2}x + \frac{13}{2}$ 6 $a = 3$, $b = 7$
7 $(-1.32, -0.737)$ and $(1.32, -1.26)$
8 a $f'(x) = 3x^2 - 8x + 4$
   b $f'(1) = -1$. This is the gradient of the tangent to the curve at the point $x = 1$.
   c i 0   ii $y = 1$

EXERCISE 21A

1 a i $x > 0$ ii never   b i never   ii $-2 \leqslant x \leqslant 3$
   c i $-2 < x \leqslant 0$ ii $0 \leqslant x < 2$

d **i** $x \leqslant 2$ **ii** $x \geqslant 2$
e **i** never   **ii** $x \in \mathbb{R}$ **f** **i** $x \in \mathbb{R}$ **ii** never
g **i** $1 \leqslant x \leqslant 5$ **ii** $x \leqslant 1, \ x \geqslant 5$
h **i** $2 \leqslant x < 4, \ x > 4$ **ii** $x < 0, \ 0 < x \leqslant 2$
i **i** $x \leqslant 0, \ 2 \leqslant x \leqslant 6$ **ii** $0 \leqslant x \leqslant 2, \ x \geqslant 6$

2 a **i** $f'(x) = 2$ **ii**

   iii increasing for all $x \in \mathbb{R}$
b **i** $f'(x) = -3$ **ii**

   iii decreasing for all $x \in \mathbb{R}$
c **i** $f'(x) = 2x$ **ii**

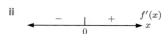

   iii increasing: $x \geqslant 0$, decreasing: $x \leqslant 0$
d **i** $f'(x) = -3x^2$ **ii**

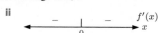

   iii decreasing for all $x \in \mathbb{R}$
e **i** $f'(x) = 4x + 3$ **ii**

   iii increasing: $x \geqslant -\frac{3}{4}$, decreasing: $x \leqslant -\frac{3}{4}$
f **i** $f'(x) = 3x^2 - 12x$ **ii**

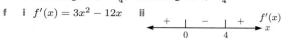

   iii increasing: $x \leqslant 0, \ x \geqslant 4$, decreasing: $0 \leqslant x \leqslant 4$
g **i** $f'(x) = -\dfrac{4}{x^5}$ **ii**

   iii increasing: $x < 0$, decreasing: $x > 0$
h **i** $f'(x) = -\dfrac{1}{x^2}$ **ii**

   iii decreasing: $x < 0, \ x > 0$, never increasing
i **i** $f'(x) = -6x^2 + 4$ **ii**

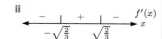

   iii increasing: $-\sqrt{\frac{2}{3}} \leqslant x \leqslant \sqrt{\frac{2}{3}}$,
   decreasing: $x \leqslant -\sqrt{\frac{2}{3}}, \ x \geqslant \sqrt{\frac{2}{3}}$
j **i** $f'(x) = -12x^2 + 30x + 18$
   ii

   $\begin{array}{ccc} - & + & - \\ \hline & -\frac{1}{2} \quad\quad 3 \end{array} \xrightarrow{\ f'(x)\ } x$

   iii increasing: $-\frac{1}{2} \leqslant x \leqslant 3$, decreasing: $x \leqslant -\frac{1}{2}, \ x \geqslant 3$
k **i** $f'(x) = 6x^2 + 18x + 6$
   ii

   $\begin{array}{ccc} + & - & + \\ \hline & -2.62 \quad -0.382 \end{array} \xrightarrow{\ f'(x)\ } x$

   iii increasing: $x \leqslant -2.62, \ x \geqslant -0.382$,
   decreasing: $-2.62 \leqslant x \leqslant -0.382$

l **i** $f'(x) = 2 - \dfrac{8}{x^2}$ **ii**

   $\begin{array}{cccc} + & - & - & + \\ \hline & -2 \quad\ 0 \quad\ 2 \end{array} \xrightarrow{\ f'(x)\ } x$

   iii increasing: $x \leqslant -2, \ x \geqslant 2$,
   decreasing: $-2 \leqslant x < 0, \ 0 < x \leqslant 2$

EXERCISE 21B

1 a A is a local maximum.   B is a horizontal inflection.
   C is a local minimum.
b

   $\begin{array}{cccc} + & - & - & + \\ \hline & -2 \quad\ 0 \quad\ 3 \end{array} \xrightarrow{\ f'(x)\ } x$

c **i** $x \leqslant -2, \ x \geqslant 3$ **ii** $-2 \leqslant x \leqslant 3$
d

   $\begin{array}{cccc} - & + & - & + \\ \hline & -4 \quad\ 0 \quad\ 5 \end{array} \xrightarrow{\ f(x)\ } x$

e For **b** we have intervals where the function is increasing
   ($+$) or decreasing ($-$). For **d** we have intervals where the
   function is above ($+$) or below ($-$) the x-axis.
2 a 4   **b** **i** $(-2, 9)$ **ii** $(2, -6)$
   c **i** 11, when $x = 6$ **ii** -10, when $x = 4$
   d 9, when $x = -2$ **e** -6, when $x = 2$
3 a $x = \frac{5}{4}$
   b $f'(x) = 4x - 5$. $f'(x) = 0$ when $x = \frac{5}{4}$
   The vertex of the quadratic (a local minimum here) is always
   on the axis of symmetry.
4 a

   b $f'(x) = 1 - \dfrac{1}{x^2}$ **c** $x = \pm 1$
   d

   $\begin{array}{cccc} + & - & - & + \\ \hline & -1 \quad\ 0 \quad\ 1 \end{array} \xrightarrow{\ f'(x)\ } x$

   e local maximum at $(-1, -2)$, local minimum at $(1, 2)$
5 a **i** $f'(x) = 2x$ **ii**

   $\begin{array}{cc} - & + \\ \hline & 0 \end{array} \xrightarrow{\ f'(x)\ } x$

   iii local minimum   **iv**
   at $(0, -2)$

   b **i** $f'(x) = 3x^2$ **ii**

   $\begin{array}{cc} + & + \\ \hline & 0 \end{array} \xrightarrow{\ f'(x)\ } x$

   iii stationary inflection at $(0, 1)$

iv

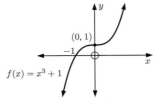

$(0, 1)$

$f(x) = x^3 + 1$

c i $f'(x) = 3x^2 - 3$ **ii**

$f'(x)$

-1 1

iii local maximum at $(-1, 4)$,
local minimum at $(1, 0)$

iv

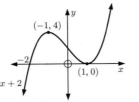

$(-1, 4)$

-2

$(1, 0)$

$f(x) = x^3 - 3x + 2$

d i $f'(x) = 4x^3 - 4x$ **ii**

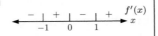

$f'(x)$

-1 0 1

iii local maximum at $(0, 0)$,
local minima at $(-1, -1)$ and $(1, -1)$

iv

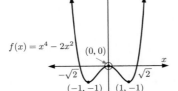

$f(x) = x^4 - 2x^2$ $(0, 0)$

$-\sqrt{2}$ $\sqrt{2}$

$(-1, -1)$ $(1, -1)$

e i $f'(x) = 3x^2 - 12x + 12$

ii

$f'(x)$

2

iii stationary inflection at $(2, 9)$

iv

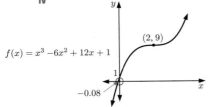

$(2, 9)$

$f(x) = x^3 - 6x^2 + 12x + 1$

1

-0.08

f i $f'(x) = 4 - 3x^2$ **ii**

$f'(x)$

$-\frac{2}{\sqrt{3}}$ $\frac{2}{\sqrt{3}}$

iii local minimum at $\left(-\frac{2}{\sqrt{3}}, -\frac{16}{3\sqrt{3}}\right)$,
local maximum at $\left(\frac{2}{\sqrt{3}}, \frac{16}{3\sqrt{3}}\right)$

iv

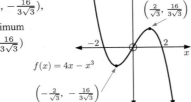

$\left(\frac{2}{\sqrt{3}}, \frac{16}{3\sqrt{3}}\right)$

-2 2

$f(x) = 4x - x^3$

$\left(-\frac{2}{\sqrt{3}}, -\frac{16}{3\sqrt{3}}\right)$

g i $f'(x) = 2 - \frac{2}{x^3}$ **ii**

$f'(x)$

$+$ $-$ $+$

0 1

iii local minimum at $(1, 3)$

iv

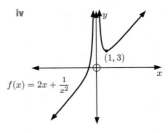

$(1, 3)$

$f(x) = 2x + \frac{1}{x^2}$

h i $f'(x) = -1 + \frac{9}{x^2}$ **ii**

$f'(x)$

$-$ $+$ $+$ $-$

-3 0 3

iii local minimum at $(-3, 6)$,
local maximum at $(3, -6)$

iv

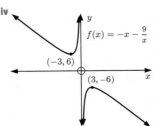

$f(x) = -x - \frac{9}{x}$

$(-3, 6)$

$(3, -6)$

i i $f'(x) = 2x - \frac{16}{x^2}$ **ii**

$f'(x)$

$-$ $-$ $+$

0 2

iii local minimum at $(2, 12)$

iv

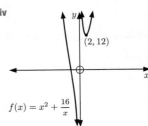

$(2, 12)$

$f(x) = x^2 + \frac{16}{x}$

6 $f(x)$ has a stationary point when $x = -\frac{b}{2a}$.
local maximum if $a < 0$, local minimum if $a > 0$

7 $a = 9$

8 a $a = -12$, $b = -13$ **b** $f'(x) = 3x^2 - 12$
c local maximum at $(-2, 3)$, local minimum at $(2, -29)$

9 a greatest value $= 63$, least value $= -18$
b greatest value $= 4$, least value $= -16$
c greatest value ≈ 4.88, least value $= -6$
d greatest value ≈ 7.13, least value ≈ -6.76

10 a $C'(x) = 0.0021x^2 - 0.3592x + 14.663$
b $x \approx 67.3$, $x \approx 104$
c Minimum hourly cost: \$529.80 when 104 hinges are made.
Maximum hourly cost: \$680.95 when 150 hinges are made.

EXERCISE 21C.1

1 a $\frac{dM}{dt} = 3t^2 - 6t$ **b** $\frac{dR}{dt} = 8t + 4$

2 a $cm^2\,s^{-1}$ **b** $m^3\,min^{-1}$

3 **a** $B'(t) = 0.6t + 30$ thousand per day
  $B'(t)$ is the instantaneous rate of growth of the bacteria.
 b $B'(3) = 31.8$ thousand per day
  After 3 days, the bacteria are increasing at a rate of
  31.8 thousand per day.
 c $B'(t)$ is always positive for $0 \leqslant t \leqslant 10$,
  $\therefore$ $B(t)$ is increasing for $0 \leqslant t \leqslant 10$.

4 **a** 190 m³ per minute   **b** 180 m³ per minute

5 **a** 1.2 m
 b $s'(t) = 28.1 - 9.8t$ This is the speed of the ball (in m s⁻¹).
 c $t \approx 2.87$ s. The ball has reached its maximum height.
 d 41.5 m
 e **i** 28.1 m s^{-1} **ii** 8.5 m s^{-1} **iii** -20.9 m s^{-1}
  The sign tells us whether the ball is travelling upwards $(+)$
  or downwards $(-)$.
 f 5.78 s

6 **a** 2 m
 b $t = 2,\ H = 11$ m; $t = 3,\ H = 14$ m;
  $t = 5,\ H = 16.4$ m; $t = 10,\ H = 18.2$ m;
  $t = 50,\ H = 19.64$ m
 c $\dfrac{dH}{dt} = \dfrac{18}{t^2}$ m per year
 d $t = 1,\ \dfrac{dH}{dt} = 18$ m per year
  $t = 3,\ \dfrac{dH}{dt} = 2$ m per year
  $t = 10,\ \dfrac{dH}{dt} = 0.18$ m per year
 e $\dfrac{18}{t^2}$ can never be negative, as $t^2 \geqslant 0$ for all real t.
  In addition, $t > 0$ or $H(t)$ is undefined.
  So, the tree is always growing.

EXERCISE 21C.2

1 **a** $\dfrac{dT}{dr} = 2r + \dfrac{100}{r^2}$ **b** $\dfrac{dA}{dh} = 2\pi + \tfrac{1}{2}h$

2 pounds per item produced

3 **a** $C'(x) = 0.000\,216x^2 - 0.001\,22x + 0.19$ dollars per item.
  This is the instantaneous rate of change in cost with respect
  to the production level x.
 b $C'(300) \approx \$19.26$
  It estimates the cost of producing the 301st item.
 c $\$19.33$

4 **a** $C'(x) = 0.0009x^2 + 0.04x + 4$ dollars per pair.
 b $C'(220) = \$56.36$
  This estimates the cost of making the 221st pair of jeans.
 c $C(221) - C(220) \approx \$56.58$
  This is the actual cost of making the 221st pair of jeans.

5 **a** **i** €4500   **ii** €4000
 b **i** decrease of €210.22 per km h⁻¹
  ii increase of €11.31 per km h⁻¹

6 **a** Near part is 2 km from the shore line, far part is 3 km away.
 b $\dfrac{dy}{dx} = \tfrac{3}{10}x^2 - x + \tfrac{3}{5}$
  At $x = \tfrac{1}{2}$, $\dfrac{dy}{dx} = 0.175$. The gradient of the hill at a
  point 500 m from the shoreline is 0.175 (going uphill).
  At $x = 1\tfrac{1}{2}$, $\dfrac{dy}{dx} = -0.225$. The gradient of the hill at a
  point 1.5 km from the shoreline is 0.225 (going down).

---

 c 2.55 km from the sea. The depth is 0.0631 km (63.1 m).

7 **a** $T = 0°C,\ R = 20$ ohms; $T = 20°C,\ R = 20$ ohms;
  $T = 40°C,\ R = 16$ ohms
 b $\dfrac{dR}{dt} = \tfrac{1}{10} - \tfrac{1}{100}T$ ohms per °C   **c** $T \leqslant 10$

8 **a**
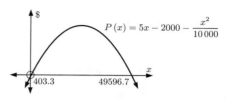

 b $404 \leqslant x \leqslant 49\,596$ **c** $P'(x) = 5 - \dfrac{x}{5000}$
 d $0 \leqslant x \leqslant 25\,000$

9 **a** $R(x) = 70x$
 b $P(x) = -0.0002x^3 - 0.04x^2 + 60x - 3000$
 c $P'(x) = -0.0006x^2 - 0.08x + 60$
 d $P'(120) = 41.76$ This means that producing 121 items
  instead of 120 increases profit by about $\$41.76$.

EXERCISE 21D.1

1 10 racquets   **2** 61.25 m   **3** 10 workers
4 50 fittings   **5** 250 items   **6** 10 blankets

7 **c** $C = 27x - \dfrac{x^3}{4}$
 d $\dfrac{dC}{dx} = 27 - \tfrac{3}{4}x^2$; $\dfrac{dC}{dx} = 0$ when $x = 6$
 e 6 cm by 6 cm

8 **a** $2x$ cm   **b** $V = 200 = 2x \times x \times h$
 c **Hint:** Show $h = \dfrac{100}{x^2}$ and substitute into the surface area
  equation.
 d
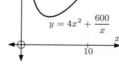
 e $\dfrac{dA}{dx} = 8x - \dfrac{600}{x^2}$,
  $\dfrac{dA}{dx} = 0$ when $x \approx 4.22$
 f $SA_{\min} \approx 213$ cm²
 g

9 **a** recall that $V_{\text{cylinder}} = \pi r^2 h$ and that 1 L $= 1000$ cm³
 b recall that $SA_{\text{cylinder}} = 2\pi r^2 + 2\pi rh$
 c
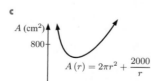
 d $\dfrac{dA}{dr} = 4\pi r - \dfrac{2000}{r^2}$,
  $r \approx 5.42$
 e

10 **b** 6 cm by 6 cm
11 **a** $0 \leqslant x \leqslant \dfrac{200}{\pi}$ **c** $x = \dfrac{200}{\pi}$, $l = 0$ (a circular track)
12 **a** 2.225 m   **b** Yes   **c** $h'(0) \approx -2.47$, $h'(7) \approx 2.47$

13 **b** $S = kw(1 - w^2)$, $\dfrac{dS}{dw} = k - 3kw^2$

  c $\frac{1}{\sqrt{3}}$ m by $\sqrt{\frac{2}{3}}$ m

14 **b** $y = \dfrac{100}{x^2}$ **d** $\dfrac{dA}{dx} = 6x - 800x^{-2}$, $x \approx 5.11$

  e

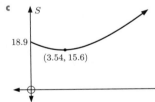

3.83 m

5.11 m

15.3 m

EXERCISE 21D.2

1 **c**

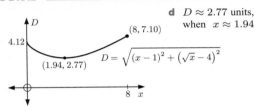

D

4.12

$(8, 7.10)$

$(1.94, 2.77)$

$D = \sqrt{(x-1)^2 + (\sqrt{x} - 4)^2}$

8 x

  d $D \approx 2.77$ units, when $x \approx 1.94$

  e The shortest distance from A$(1, 4)$ to the graph of $y = \sqrt{x}$ is 2.77 units. The closest point on the graph to A is the point with $x \approx 1.94$.

2 **a** AP $= (8 - x)$ m, BP $= \sqrt{x^2 + 16}$ m, CP $= \sqrt{x^2 + 25}$ m

  b $D = 8 - x + \sqrt{x^2 + 16} + \sqrt{x^2 + 25}$, $0 \leqslant x \leqslant 8$

  c

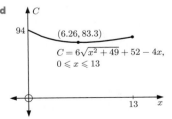

D

17

$(2.58, 15.8)$

8 x

  d 2.58 metres from N

3 **a** $(32 - x)$ cm by $(40 - 2x)$ cm

  b $V = x(32 - x)(40 - 2x)$ cm^3 **c** 4608 cm^3

  d 8 cm $\times$ 24 cm $\times$ 24 cm

4 **a** PA $= \sqrt{(x-1)^2 + 36}$, PB $= \sqrt{(x-7)^2 + 25}$

  b $S = \sqrt{(x-1)^2 + 36} + \sqrt{(x-7)^2 + 25}$
      $+ \sqrt{(x-3)^2 + 9}$

  c

S

18.9

$(3.54, 15.6)$

x

  d at $(3.54, 8)$

5 **b** $(13 - x)$ km   **d**

  e 6.26 km from P

C

94

$(6.26, 83.3)$

$C = 6\sqrt{x^2 + 49} + 52 - 4x$,
$0 \leqslant x \leqslant 13$

13 x

REVIEW SET 21A

1 **a** increasing: $x \leqslant -1$, $x \geqslant 4$, decreasing: $-1 \leqslant x \leqslant 4$

  b increasing: $x > -3$, decreasing: $x < -3$

  c increasing: $x \leqslant 6$, decreasing: never

2 **a** y-intercept is 0   **d**

  b $f'(x) = 3x^2 - 3$

  c local maximum at $(-1, 2)$, local minimum at $(1, -2)$

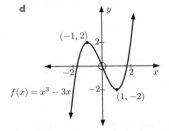

$(-1, 2)$

$f(x) = x^3 - 3x$

$(1, -2)$

3 **a** $f'(x) = 3 - \dfrac{48}{x^2}$

$f'(x)$

-4 0   4

  b local maximum at $(-4, -22)$, local minimum at $(4, 26)$

  c

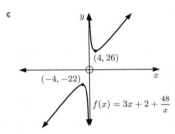

y

$(4, 26)$

$(-4, -22)$

$f(x) = 3x + 2 + \dfrac{48}{x}$

4 4 cm by 4 cm

5 **a** $f'(x) = 3x^2 - 12$ **b** $f'(-3) = 15$ **c** $(2, -12)$

6 **a** $x = 33$ (which is 33 000 chopsticks)

  b Maximum daily profit is \$285.60

REVIEW SET 21B

1 maximum value is 21, minimum value is 1

2 **a** $f'(x) = 6x^2 - 6x - 36$ **d**

  b local maximum at $(-2, 51)$, local minimum at $(3, -74)$

  c increasing for $x \leqslant -2$ and $x \geqslant 3$, decreasing for $-2 \leqslant x \leqslant 3$

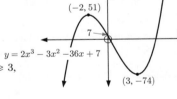

y

$(-2, 51)$

$y = 2x^3 - 3x^2 - 36x + 7$

$(3, -74)$

3 **a** $H'(t) = 19 - 1.6t$ m s^{-1}

  b $H'(0) = 19$ m s^{-1}, $H'(10) = 3$ m s^{-1}, $H'(20) = -13$ m s^{-1}
  These are the instantaneous speeds at $t = 0$, 10, and 20 s. A positive sign means the ball is travelling upwards. A negative sign means the ball is travelling downwards.

  c 23.8 s

4 **a**

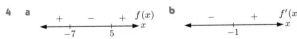

$f(x)$

-7 5 x

  b

$f'(x)$

-1 x

5 6 cm from each end

6 **a** $P = \pi r + 2x + 2r$ m   **b** $x = 100 - r - \frac{\pi}{2}r$ m

  d $x \approx 28.0$ m, $r \approx 28.0$ m

7 a

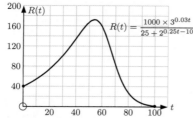

$R(t) = \dfrac{1000 \times 3^{0.03t}}{25 + 2^{0.25t-10}}$

b ≈ 77.2 million tonnes per year

c ≈ 170 million tonnes per year, ≈ 50.2 years after mining begins

d when $t ≈ 28.0$ years, and $t ≈ 63.1$ years

REVIEW SET 21C

1 a $A = -3$, $B = 7$

b local maximum at $(-1, 9)$, local minimum at $(1, 5)$

2 a y-intercept is 0   **b** $f'(x) = 3x^2 - 8x + 4$

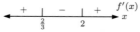

c increasing for $x \leqslant \frac{2}{3}$, $x \geqslant 2$, decreasing for $\frac{2}{3} \leqslant x \leqslant 2$

d local maximum at $(\frac{2}{3}, \frac{32}{27})$, local minimum at $(2, 0)$

e

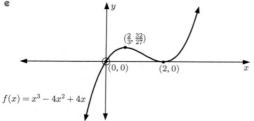

$f(x) = x^3 - 4x^2 + 4x$

3 a i €312   **ii** €1218.75

b i €9.10 per hour per km h^{-1}

ii €7.50 per hour per km h^{-1}

c 3 km h^{-1}

4 a $y = \dfrac{1}{x^2}$ m   **c** $C'(x) = 4x - \dfrac{8}{x^2}$

d 1.26 m by 1.26 m by 0.630 m   **e** $9.52

5 b 42 days

6 maximum value is $25\frac{1}{3}$, minimum value is $-1\frac{2}{3}$

7 a Domain $= \{t \mid 0 \leqslant t \leqslant 5.9\}$ **b** 49.8 m   **c** 36.0 m

EXERCISE 22A

1 a 0.31   **b** 0.305   **c** 3.05085×10^{-1}

2 a i If Farouk studies for the test, Farouk scores a good mark.

ii If Farouk does not study for the test, Farouk does not score a good mark.

b i $q \Rightarrow p$

ii $\neg q \Rightarrow \neg p$

c

p	q	$p \Rightarrow q$	$\neg p$	$\neg q$	$\neg q \Rightarrow \neg p$
T	T	T	F	F	T
T	F	F	F	T	F
F	T	T	T	F	T
F	F	T	T	T	T

same truth table column
∴ logically equivalent

3 a ≈ 0.355   **b** $k ≈ 6.01$

4 a $A(0, 9)$, $B(6, 0)$ **b** $M(3, 4.5)$ **c** $-\frac{3}{2}$

d $4x - 6y = -15$

5 a ≈ 26 cm   **c** 26 cm

b

Length (cm)	Frequency
$0 < x \leqslant 10$	15
$10 < x \leqslant 20$	40
$20 < x \leqslant 30$	75
$30 < x \leqslant 40$	50
$40 < x \leqslant 50$	20

6 a $f'(x) = 10x^4 - 10x$ **b** $y = -2$

7 a Option A: $15 124.98, Option B: $15 167.93

b Option B, by $42.95

8 a 9.46×10^{12} km   **b** 2.08×10^{18} km

9 a i $x = 3, 4, 5, 10$

ii $x = 3, 5$

iii $x = 1, 3, 5, 7, 8, 9$

b

p	q	$\neg p$	$\neg p \wedge q$	$p \vee q$
T	T	F	F	F
T	F	F	F	T
F	T	T	T	T
F	F	T	F	F

10 a $P(G) = \frac{1}{3}$ **b** 75 'reds'

c i $0   **ii** The game is fair.

11 a $x = 5$ **b** $C(-5, 2)$

c $5x + 2y + 21 = 0$ **d** $D(5, -23)$

12 a i H_0: *time spent on co-curricular activities* and *grade average* are independent.

ii df $= (3 - 1) \times (3 - 1) = 4$ **iii** $\chi^2_{calc} ≈ 5.31$

b H_0 is not rejected

c At a 1% level, the test does not support the principal's belief.

13 a $y = f(c)$ **b** $x = b, c, d$ **c** $x \leqslant b, x \geqslant d$

d negative   **e** The tangent lines are parallel.

14 a €11 737   **b** £212 462.09

15 a 6260.9 m^2 **b** 6300 m^2 **c** 0.625%

16 a

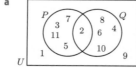

b i $\{2\}$

ii $\{1, 2, 3, 5, 7, 9, 11\}$

17 a i $A(-3, 0)$ **ii** $B(\frac{3}{2}, -\frac{81}{4})$ **b** $(-2, -8)$ and $(5, -8)$

18 a

tower, 190 m, 16°, House, x m

b $x ≈ 663$

c ≈ 689 m

19 a

Time (t min)	Frequency
$0 < t \leqslant 10$	5
$10 < t \leqslant 20$	4
$20 < t \leqslant 30$	10
$30 < t \leqslant 40$	17
$40 < t \leqslant 50$	14
$50 < t \leqslant 60$	3
$60 < t \leqslant 70$	5

b $\bar{x} ≈ 35.3$, $s ≈ 15.6$

c 37.9%

20 a $2x^2 + 8x - 10$ **b** $f'(x) = 4x + 8$

c i $a = -\frac{13}{4}$ **ii** $(-\frac{13}{4}, -\frac{119}{8})$

21 a i 2004.38 yuan   **ii** 1974 yuan   **b** €604.38

22 a i 3.2 m   **ii** 2.56 m   **b** $4 \times (0.8)^n$ m   **c** 4.6 cm

23 a $P(A') = 1 - a$ **b i** $2a(1-a)$ **ii** a^2 **c** $a ≈ 0.755$

24 a 4
  b When $x = 2$, $y = -12$. When $x = -2$, $y = 5\frac{7}{9}$.
  c $y = 6$ **d**

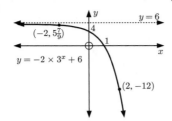

$y = -2 \times 3^x + 6$

25 a 56.5 cm³   **b** 3 cm   **c** 96.5 cm²
26 a $y = x + 1$ **b** $\approx (-1.73, -0.732)$ and $(1.73, 2.73)$
27 a $C(1500) = 2$, when 1500 bars are produced each day, the cost per bar is \$2.
  b $C'(x) = 0.000\,008x - 0.008$ **c** $x = 1000$ **d** \$1
28 a $\approx 10.5\%$ **b** $\approx €6887.21$
29 a 1 200 000 m   **b** 1.2348×10^6 m
30 a i Antonio plays football, and is not good at kicking a ball.
    ii If Antonio is not good at kicking a ball, then he plays football.
  b i $p \veebar q$ **c**
    ii $\neg p \Rightarrow \neg q$

p	q	$\neg q$	$\neg q \Rightarrow p$
T	T	F	T
T	F	T	T
F	T	F	T
F	F	T	Ⓕ

31 a $x^2 + (x + 3)^2 = (x + 6)^2$ **b** $x = 9$ {since $x > 0$}
  c 54 cm²
32 a

13 m
8 m
  b 9.33 m
  c 71.3°
33 a i 198 months   **ii** 18 months   **iii** 9 months
  b

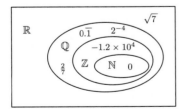

age (months)
190 195 200 205 210 215

34 a $f'(x) = 6x^2 + 6x^{-3} - 24$ **b** $f'(2) = \frac{3}{4}$
  c $3x - 4y = 134$
35 a $a \approx 1.4588$ **b** 2918 yen   **c** 10 282.14 rupees
36

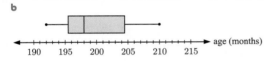

$\mathbb{R}$ $\sqrt{7}$
$0.\overline{1}$ 2^{-4}
$\mathbb{Q}$ -1.2×10^4
$\frac{2}{7}$ $\mathbb{Z}$ $\mathbb{N}$ 0

37 a i 0.05   **ii** 0.55   **iii** 0.45   **b** no, $P(A \cap B) \neq 0$
38 a

A
14 cm   17 cm
C   35°   B
  b $\widehat{ABC} \approx 28.19°$
  c 106 cm²

39 a i 48   **ii** 100.25   **iii** 15.0   **b** 8.33%
40 a

Constant	a	b	c
Value	positive	negative	positive

  b none   **c**

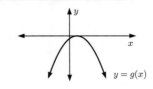

$y = g(x)$

41 a

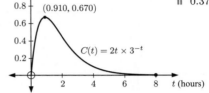

C
0.8   (0.910, 0.670)
0.6
0.4
0.2 $C(t) = 2t \times 3^{-t}$
   2   4   6   8 t (hours)
  b i $0.910 \leqslant t \leqslant 8$
    ii $0.379 < t < 1.79$
42 a i £24 310.13   **ii** £24 417.91   **b** 0.443%
43 a i $\{d, s\}$ **ii** $\{h, k\}$ **iii** $\{a, b, d, h, k, r, s\}$
    iv $\{f, g\}$
  b i 7   **ii** 3
44 a $\frac{1}{6}$ **b** $\frac{1}{9}$ **c** $\frac{5}{18}$
45 a $y = 3x^2 - 3x - 18$ **b** -18 **c** $(\frac{1}{2}, -\frac{75}{4})$
46 a 89.7 m   **b** 1220 m²   **c** 609 m³
47 a

Score (%)	Frequency	Cum. Freq.
$50 \leqslant S < 60$	6	6
$60 \leqslant S < 70$	15	21
$70 \leqslant S < 80$	20	41
$80 \leqslant S < 90$	10	51
$90 \leqslant S < 100$	4	55

  b

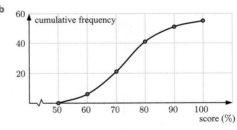

60   cumulative frequency
40
20
   50   60   70   80   90   100
   score (%)
  c ≈ 73
48 a 0   **b** $f'(x) = 6x^2 - 10x - 4$ **c** $-\frac{1}{3}$ and 2
49 a \$830.76   **b** ≈ 35 months
50 a 191 m   **b** 6.04 m s⁻¹
51 a $p = 20$, $q = 30$, $r = 45$
  b i 0.36   **ii** 0.34   **iii** 0.654
52 a

y
-3 x
$(2, -25)$
  b 7
  c i $p = -3$, $q = 7$
    ii $a = 1$

53 **a** **i** 27.6 cm **ii** 23.3 cm   **b** 6010 cm^3

54 **a** $\dfrac{dy}{dx} = 3x^2 - 8x + 3$ **b** $y = 6x - 17$

55 **a** **i** €16 **ii** $30   **b** 1 AUD = 0.8 EUR   **c** €58 800

56 **a** 137.5   **b** 27

c

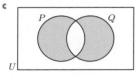

dart score

d ≈ 17.7

57 **a** $-5, 2, 9$ **b** arithmetic sequence   **c** 688   **d** 34 150

58 **a**   **b**

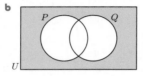

c

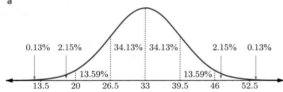

59 **a** $a = 4, \ b = 3$ **b** $(11, 0)$

60 **a**

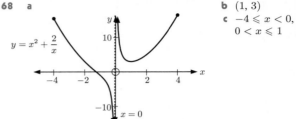

b **i** ≈ 0.238 **ii** ≈ 0.109

c $k \approx 36.4$ **d** about 11 customers

61 **a** H_0: *travel time* and *quality of work* are independent.
H_1: *travel time* and *quality of work* are not independent.

b 1

c Since $p > 0.05$, we do not reject H_0. At a 5% level of significance, *travel time* and *quality of work* are independent.

62 **a** $f'(x) = 3x^2 - 8x + 4$ **b** $x = \frac{2}{3}$ or 2

c

```
    +  |  −  |  +   f'(x)
    ───┼─────┼───►  x
      2/3    2
```

d increasing for $x \leqslant \frac{2}{3}$ or $x \geqslant 2$
decreasing for $\frac{2}{3} \leqslant x \leqslant 2$

63 **a**

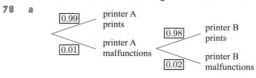

b A is $(3, -6)$ **c** $3x + 2y = -3$

64 **a** $-\frac{1}{2}$ **c** $x \approx 19.3$ **d** 43.3 cm

65 **a** 9.772 cm   **b** 61 cm

66 **a** $\frac{1}{5}$ **b** $P(B \mid A) \neq P(B)$ **c** $\frac{2}{3}$

67 **a** **i** £50 **ii** £200   **b** £3000   **c** $r = 0.075, \ t = 50$

68 **a**   **b** $(1, 3)$

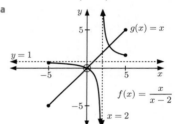

c $-4 \leqslant x < 0,$
$0 < x \leqslant 1$

69 **a** 70%

b **i** $m \approx 28$ **ii** $n \approx 35$ **iii** $p \approx 42$ **iv** $q = 100$

70 **a** 6, 7.2   **b** $u_{10} \approx 31.0$

c 40.2 (the 11th term, and $u_{11} \approx 37.2$)

71 **a** 50 times   **b** $3\frac{1}{2}$ ($3.50)   **c** No

72 **a** $a \wedge b$ **b** $\neg(a \vee b)$ **c** $b \wedge \neg a$ **d** $(a \vee b) \wedge c$

73 **a**

b horiz. asymptote $y = 1$, vert. asymptote $x = 2$

c $x = 0$ or 3

74 **a** $\sqrt{45}$ m   **b** 7 m   **c** $16.6°$

75 **a** $y \approx -0.0151x + 25.9$ **b** 25.5 min   **c** $r \approx -0.0550$

d Very unreliable, as there is almost no linear relationship between the variables.

76 **a** $P'(m) = 60 - 2m, \ 0 \leqslant m \leqslant 40$ **c** $100 000

77 **a** y-intercept is 6, x-intercepts are $\approx -2.18, 1.08, 5.11$

b local maximum at $\approx (-0.775, 7.67)$
local minimum at $\approx (3.44, -11.1)$

c $f(-3) = -13\frac{1}{2}$,   **d**
$f(6) = 18$

e greatest value of $f(x)$ is 18 (when $x = 6$)
least value of $f(x)$ is $-13\frac{1}{2}$ (when $x = -3$)

78 **a**

b **i** 0.0002   **ii** 0.0098   **iii** 0.990

79 **a** 343.42 m s^{-1} **b** 2.06×10^5 m   **c** 4.41%

80 **a**

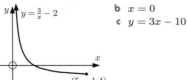

b $x = 0$
c $y = 3x - 10$

81 **a** **i** P(0, 5)   **ii** Q(8, 0)
b $-\frac{5}{8}$ **c** $32.0°$ **d** $(-4, -3)$

82 **a** -2 **b** $y = -2x + 6$ **c** $b = -4, \ c = 7$

83 **a** positive for each case   **b**

Strength of correlation	Scatter diagram
Weak	II
Moderate	I
Strong	III

84 **a** 26 days
b 31 - 40 children
d **i** $\mu = 41.5$ children,
     ii $\sigma \approx 10.2$ children
c

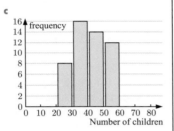

85 **a** 10.32 m s^{-1} **b** 37.2 km h^{-1}

86 **a** 44 students   **b** **i** $\frac{9}{44}$ **ii** $\frac{5}{44}$ **iii** $\frac{5}{14}$

87 **a** $\$24\,000$ **b** $r = 0.85$ **c** 7 years

88 **a** 12 cm   **b** **i** $67.4°$ **ii** $113°$ **c** 20.8 cm

89 **a** $f'(x) = -x$ **b** $(-1, 2\frac{1}{2})$

90 **a**

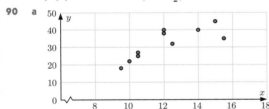

b $r \approx 0.819$ **c** The statement is true in general.

91 **a** $f'(x) = -\dfrac{16}{x^3} + 2$
b $f'(1) = -14$, the gradient of the tangent to $f(x)$ at the point where $x = 1$.
c (2, 3)

92 **a**

a	b	c	$\neg b$	$b \wedge a$	$c \Rightarrow (b \wedge a)$	$\neg b \wedge (c \Rightarrow (b \wedge a))$	$\neg c$	$\neg b \wedge (c \Rightarrow (b \wedge a)) \Rightarrow \neg c$
T	T	T	F	T	T	F	F	T
T	T	F	F	T	T	F	T	T
T	F	T	T	F	F	F	F	T
T	F	F	T	F	T	T	T	T
F	T	T	F	F	F	F	F	T
F	T	F	F	F	T	F	T	T
F	F	T	T	F	F	F	F	T
F	F	F	T	F	T	T	T	T

b tautology

93 **a** **i** €5306.82   **ii** €5632.46
b $V_n = 5000 \times (1.015)^{4n}$ **c** ≈ 11.6 years

94 **a** 826.563   **b** 830   **c** $8.265\,625 \times 10^2$

95 **a** M(1, 4)   **b** $\frac{2}{5}$ **c** $5x + 2y - 13 = 0$ **d** $\frac{13}{5}$

96 **a** 7080 SEK   **b** 995.78 AUD   **c** 0.422%

97 **a** 3.5 minutes   **b** $p = 20, \ q = 30$
c

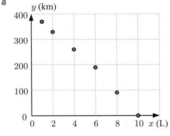

98 **a** **i** $p = 4$ **ii** $q = 4$ **b** -1 **c** C(2, 2)

99 **a** $\$450$ **b** $\$4125$

100 **a** **i** 0.41   **ii** 0.59   **b** ≈ 0.814

101 **a** (0, 2.5)   **b** $k = 1.5$ **c** $y = 3.5$

102 **a**

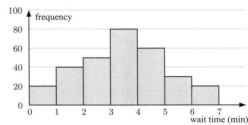

b $y \approx -40.7x + 417$
c 4.84 litres
d 42.6 km per litre

103 **a** 70 m   **b** $53.9°$ **c** 3440 m^2

104 **a** $\$15\,273.01$ **b** $\$5273.01$ **c** $\$777.09$

105 **a** $a = 4$ **b** $\dfrac{dy}{dx} = 2x - 4$ **c** $(2, -4)$ **d** 2

106 **a** true   **b** true   **c** true   **d** false   **e** false   **f** true

107 **a** $P(B) = \frac{1}{3}$ **b** **i** $\frac{16}{21}$ **ii** $\frac{13}{21}$

108 **a** 9 seeds   **b** 7 seeds   **c** 15 seeds

109 **a** H_0: *intelligence* and *income level* are independent.
     H_1: *intelligence* and *income level* are not independent.
b 4
c At a 5% significance level, *intelligence* and *income level* are independent.

110 **a** $f'(x) = x^3 - 4x$
b $f'(-3) = -15, \ f'(-2) = 0, \ f'(-1) = 3$
c local minimum   **d** $-2 \leqslant x \leqslant 0, \ x \geqslant 2$

111 **a** **i** 11 units   **ii** 5 units   **b** $53.13°$ **c** 22 units^2

112 **a** **i** 38 500 MXN   **ii** 2172.50 EUR
b **i** 1 EUR ≈ 1.2658 USD   **ii** 1 EUR ≈ 17.7215 MXN
c 90 379.65 MXN

113 **a** $a = 5, \ b = -10$ **b** $y = 310$

114 **a** $u_1 + 3d = 22, \ u_1 + 9d = 70$
b $u_1 = -2, \ d = 8$ **c** 340

115 a

	Left handed	Right handed	Total
Male	4	26	30
Female	3	17	20
Total	7	43	50

b **i** 0.14   **ii** 0.52   **iii** 0.85

116 a $k = -\frac{5}{2}$ **b** $k = \frac{8}{5}$

117 a, b

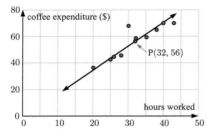

c $61
d strong positive relationship, the prediction in **c** is reliable

118 a 27   **b** $\frac{dy}{dx} = 3x^2$ **c** P(3, 15)

119 a $f'(x) = 3x^2 - \frac{5}{x^2}$

b $f'(1) = -2$
The gradient of the tangent to $f(x)$ when $x = 1$, is -2.
c $y = -2x + 8$ **d** $x - 2y = -11$
e meets the graph again at $\approx (1.35, 6.18)$

120 a $x = 20$ **b** **i** $\frac{37}{50}$ **ii** $\frac{2}{5}$ **iii** $\frac{17}{50}$ **iv** $\frac{24}{37}$

121 c $a = 4,\ b = 1$ **122 a** £2x   **c** $x = 174$

123 a $P \approx 578$ m   **b** **i** $\approx 15\,000$ m²   **ii** ≈ 1.50 ha

124 b $y = 2x + 3$ **c** $(-2.8, -2.6)$ **d** 6.26 units

125 a 13

b **i** $w = 3$ **ii** $x = 36$ **iii** $y = 16$ **iv** $z = 211$

c $\frac{z}{y} \approx 13.2$, the mean of the data set

126 a ¥300 438.21   **b** $\approx 6.78\%$

127 a $u_1 = 59,\ u_2 = 55$ **b** 19th term   **c** $k = 11$

128 a

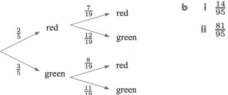

b **i** $\frac{14}{95}$

ii $\frac{81}{95}$

129 a 4 people   **b** 393 people   **c** $19.9 \approx 20$ days

130 a 2.83 cm   **b** 66°

131 a $y = 30 - x$ **b** $A(x) = x(30 - x)$ cm²
c $A'(x) = 30 - 2x$ **d** $x = 15$, 15 cm × 15 cm

132 a H_0: *drink size* and *time of day* are independent.
b $\chi^2 \approx 7.11$ **c** 4
d $\chi^2 < 9.488$, so at a 5% significance level *drink size* and *time of day* are independent.

133 a $14\,056.88   **b** 12.524%   **c** $10\,756.44

134 a $a \veebar b$
$\dfrac{\neg b}{a}$

b

a	b	$a \veebar b$	$\neg b$	$(a \veebar b) \wedge \neg b$	$(a \veebar b) \wedge \neg b \Rightarrow a$
T	T	F	F	F	T
T	F	T	T	T	T
F	T	T	F	F	T
F	F	F	T	F	T

∴   the argument is valid (we have a tautology).

135 a

Length (x cm)	Frequency	Cumulative frequency
$0 \leqslant x < 1$	15	15
$1 \leqslant x < 2$	35	50
$2 \leqslant x < 3$	25	75
$3 \leqslant x < 4$	20	95
$4 \leqslant x < 5$	10	105
$5 \leqslant x < 6$	5	110

b

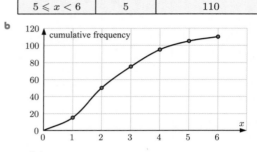

c ≈ 3.4 cm

136 a **i** 0.3   **ii** 0.6   **iii** $\frac{3}{7} \approx 0.429$ **b** No

137 a p: I watch a movie, q: I will relax.
b p true but q false (I watch a movie, but do not relax.)
c If I have not relaxed, then I have not watched a movie.

d

p	q	$\neg p$	$\neg q$	$p \Rightarrow q$	Contrapositive $\neg q \Rightarrow \neg p$
T	T	F	F	T	T
T	F	F	T	F	F
F	T	T	F	T	T
F	F	T	T	T	T

138 a OM = 5 cm   **b** 400 cm³   **c** 67.4°

139 a **i** $u_n = 13 + 8n$ **ii** $S_n = 4n^2 + 17n$
b **i** $u_{50} = 413$ **ii** $S_{50} = 10\,850$

140 a 50 m   **b** **i** 100 m   **ii** $0 \leqslant x \leqslant 100$ **c** L(50, 30)

EXERCISE 22B

1 a $192\,000
b **i** $1000, $1600, $2200   **ii** $189\,600
c **i** $500, $600, $720   **ii** $196\,242.12
d *Option 3*   **e** $636.97

2 a **i** 0.36   **ii** 0.48   **iii** 0.16
b All the possible outcomes are covered in **a**.   **c** 0.216
d

i 0.289
ii 0.939

Tree diagram:
$\frac{60}{100}$ R $\frac{40}{100}$ R′
$\frac{59}{99}$ R $\frac{40}{99}$ R′
$\frac{40}{99}$ R′ $\frac{60}{99}$ R
$\frac{39}{99}$ R′
$\frac{58}{98}$ R $\frac{40}{98}$ R′
$\frac{59}{98}$ R $\frac{39}{98}$ R′
$\frac{59}{98}$ R $\frac{39}{98}$ R′
$\frac{60}{98}$ R $\frac{38}{98}$ R′

3 **a** x-intercept is -1
   y-intercept is -2
   b horizontal asymptote $y = 2$,
     vertical asymptote $x = 1$
   c Domain $\{x \mid x \neq 1\}$,
     Range $\{y \mid y \neq 2\}$
   e $x = -1$ or 3

d

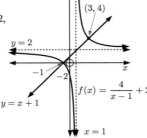

$f(x) = \dfrac{4}{x-1} + 2$

$y = x + 1$

$x = 1$

4 **a** **i** A(8, 0)   **ii** B(0, 6)   **b** **i** $-\frac{3}{4}$ **ii** 10 units
   c $y = \frac{4}{3}x + 6$ **d** 37.5 units^2 **e** D(3, 0)

5 **a** 44 players   **b** $90 \leqslant t < 120$
   c

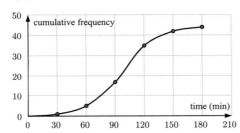

   d **i** ≈ 98 min   **ii** 96.8 min   **iii** no
   e ".... between 75 and 117 minutes."

6 **a** $f'(x) = 3x^2 - 12x + p$ **b** $p = 9$, $q = 3$ **c** (3, 3)
   d, e i

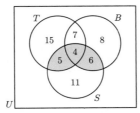

$y = x^3 - 6x^2 + 9x + 3$ (5, 23)

$y = 7$ (1, 7)

-0.279 3

(3, 3)

$(-0.869, -10)$

   e **ii** $y = 7$ **iii** (4, 7)

7 **c** $\dfrac{dS}{dr} = 4\pi r - \dfrac{500\pi}{r^2}$ **d** $r = 5$ cm   **e** 5 cm
   f ≈ 471 cm^2

8 **a** 56 members   **d**
   b **i** 8 members
     ii 25 members
     iii 5 members
   c yes
   e 11 members

9 **a** **i** $\frac{3}{8}$ **ii** 1   **b** **i** $\frac{25}{64}$ **ii** $\frac{55}{64}$
   c **i** $\frac{3}{28}$ **ii** $\frac{15}{28}$ **d** $\frac{15}{28}$

10 **a** PQ $= \sqrt{50}$ units   **b** $a = 10$ **c** $\frac{1}{7}$
   d $x - 7y + 32 = 0$ **e** S(-32, 0)   **f** 5.44°

11 **a** ≈ 0.0115 **b** $\approx 17.8\%$ **c** ≈ 123 ferrets
   d $k \approx 52.8$ cm

12 **a, c**

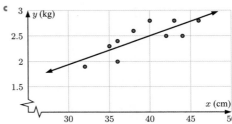

   b $r \approx 0.797$, there is a moderate positive relationship between
     the variables.
   c $y \approx 0.0565x + 0.244$ **d** **i** 2.2 kg   **ii** 40 cm

13 **a** $f(0) = -4$, $f(1) = -4$, $f(2) = -6$
   b $f'(x) = 3x^2 - 8x + 3$
   c $(0.451, -3.37)$ and $(2.22, -6.11)$
   d $(0.451, -3.37)$ is a local maximum,
     $(2.22, -6.11)$ is a local minimum
   e

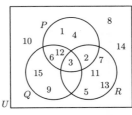

$y = x^3 - 4x^2 + 3x - 4$
(4, 8)
3.47
(2.22, -6.11)
-4
(0.451, -3.37)
$(-2, -34)$

14 **a** $a = 0.28$ **b** 0.29   **c** 9 times   **d** 6.05 people

15 **a** **i** $u_1 + 4d = 50$, $u_1 + 7d = 80$
     ii $u_1 = 10$, $d = 10$ **iii** 10, 20, 30, 40, 50
   b **i** 100, 50, 25, 12.5, 6.25   **ii** 200   **iii** 200
     iv The terms get successively smaller, and adding the extra
       terms does not alter the overall sum when rounded to
       3 significant figures.
   c 1400

16 **a**

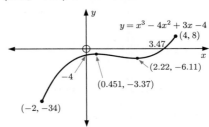

   b **i** $x = 3, 6, 12$ **ii** $x = 2, 5, 6, 7, 9, 11, 12, 13, 15$
     iii $x = 6, 9, 12, 15$ **iv** $x = 8, 10, 14$
   c **i** x is a factor of 12, and a multiple of 3, but is not prime.
     ii

p	q	r	$p \wedge q$	$\neg r$	$(p \wedge q) \wedge \neg r$
T	T	T	T	F	F
T	T	F	T	T	T
T	F	T	F	F	F
T	F	F	F	T	F
F	T	T	F	F	F
F	T	F	F	T	F
F	F	T	F	F	F
F	F	F	F	T	F

p is true, q is true, r is false.
     iii $x = 6, 12$

17 a 1 and -2 **b** $(-\frac{1}{2}, -\frac{9}{4})$

c, d

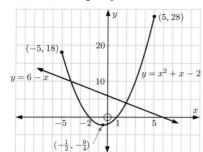

e $x = -4$ or 2

18 a i 0.19   **ii** 0.06

b i H_0: *attendance* and *performance* are independent.
   H_1: *attendance* and *performance* are not independent.
   ii 2   **iii** 4.61

c

% attendance at lectures

		0 - 39	40 - 79	80 - 100	*sum*
Exam	Pass	21	49	70	140
result	Fail	9	21	30	60
	sum	30	70	100	200

d $\chi^2_{calc} \approx 16.0$

e $\chi^2_{calc} > \chi^2_{crit}$, so at a 10% significance level *attendance* and *performance* are not independent.

19 a i DB ≈ 4.09 m   **ii** BC ≈ 9.86 m

b i A$\widehat{B}$E $\approx 68.2°$ **ii** D$\widehat{B}$C $\approx 57.5°$

c 17.0 m^2 **d** AE ≈ 10.9 m

20 a x-intercept is 5, y-intercept is $\frac{5}{2}$

b

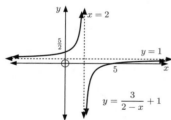

$y = \dfrac{3}{2 - x} + 1$

c i $y = 1$ **ii** $x = 2$

d i The graph is increasing for $x \geqslant 3$.

   iii $a = 1.5$, $b \approx 2.9970$ **iv** $\dfrac{dy}{dx} = 3$

21 a i 16 000 CHF   **ii** 200 000 JPY

b i $a = 1$ **ii** $b = 0.625$

c i 1 CHF = 80 JPY   **ii** 1 CHF = 0.625 GBP

d $c = 128$ **e** 1 134 720 JPY   **f** $\approx 7.813 \times 10^{-3}$

22 a i $P = \{3, 4, 5, 6, 7, 8, 9\}$ **ii** $n(P) = 7$ **iii** finite

   iv (1) 2 and 15 are in Q, but not P
   (2) $R = \{3, 6, 9\}$, all these elements are in P
   v (1) $\{9\}$ **(2)** $\{9\}$ **(3)** $\{2, 3, 6, 9, 15\}$

b i

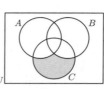

ii

iii

23 a i $\neg q \Rightarrow \neg p$ **ii** $q \Rightarrow p \veebar r$

b i If Pepin does not play the guitar, then he does not both ride a motorbike *and* live in Jakarta.

ii

p	q	r	$\neg r$	$q \wedge p$	$\neg(q \wedge p)$	$\neg r \Rightarrow \neg(q \wedge p)$
T	T	T	F	T	F	T
T	T	F	T	T	F	F
T	F	T	F	F	T	T
T	F	F	T	F	T	T
F	T	T	F	F	T	T
F	T	F	T	F	T	T
F	F	T	F	F	T	T
F	F	F	T	F	T	T

iii not a tautology

iv Pepin does not play the guitar, but he does ride a motorbike and he does live in Jakarta.

24 a

x	0	20	40	60	80	100
P	-60	100	220	300	340	340

b

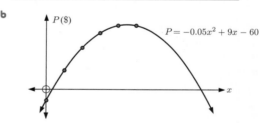

c i 90 pies   **ii** \$345   **iii** 37 or 143   **iv** \$60

25 a AN = $\sqrt{244} \approx 15.6$ cm   **b** AM = $\sqrt{269} \approx 16.4$ cm

c 17.7°   **d** 39.1 cm^2 **e** 660 cm^2 **f** 600 cm^3

26 a 18.7°C   **b** 1.38°C

c $r \approx -0.744$,   there is a moderate negative correlation between n and T.

d $n = -6.82T + 252$ **e** 118 cups of coffee

f Using the regression line, 47 should be sold, so the owner may be underestimating. However, this is an extrapolation, so the regression line estimate may be unreliable.

27 a $a = -12$, $b = 6$

b i $p = 5$, $q = -4$ **ii** $\frac{2}{5}$ **iii** $c = -6$

28 a $p \Rightarrow r$

b If Ryan is going to the zoo, then Peter is going to the zoo.

c i $p \Leftrightarrow r$

$\dfrac{p \veebar q}{\neg r}$

ii

p	q	r	$p \Leftrightarrow r$	$p \veebar q$	$(p \Leftrightarrow r) \wedge (p \veebar q)$	$\neg r$	$(p \Leftrightarrow r) \wedge (p \veebar q)$ $\Rightarrow \neg r$
T	T	T	T	F	F	F	T
T	T	F	F	F	F	T	T
T	F	T	T	T	T	F	F
T	F	F	F	T	F	T	T
F	T	T	F	T	F	F	T
F	T	F	T	T	T	T	T
F	F	T	F	F	F	F	T
F	F	F	T	F	F	T	T

∴ the argument is not valid.

29 a i $X = \{1, 2, 3, 4, 6, 8, 12\}$
   ii $Y = \{4, 8, 12, 16, 20\}$

b

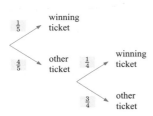

c i $X \cap Y = \{4, 8, 12\}$
   ii $(X \cup Y)' = \{5, 7, 9, 10, 11, 13, 14, 15, 17, 18, 19\}$

30 a

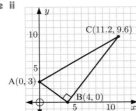

b $\frac{2}{5}$ **c** 100 times   **d** i $\frac{4}{5}$ ii 1
e i $\frac{1}{5}$ ii $\frac{4}{25}$ iii $\frac{16}{125}$ **f** $\frac{61}{125}$ **g** i $\frac{4}{5}$
h 96.5%

31 a $x = 0$ **b** $\frac{dy}{dx} = 2 - \frac{1}{x^2}$ **c** gradient $= 1$
d $(-0.707, 0.172)$ and $(0.707, 5.83)$
e $\{y \mid y \leqslant 0.172$ or $y \geqslant 5.83\}$

32 b

	Male	Female	Total
Participated	78	72	150
Did not participate	52	48	100
Total	130	120	250

c 1   **d** ≈ 5.41 **e** H_0 is rejected
f Participation in the survey was not independent of gender.
g continuous   **h** i 12.5 km   ii 6.19 km   i 0.367

33 a, e ii

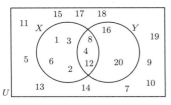

b 5 units
c $-\frac{3}{4}$
d i $\frac{4}{3}$
   ii $y = \frac{4}{3}x - \frac{16}{3}$
e i $b = 9.6$
f 30 units^2
g 22.6°

34 c i $a = 11\,750$ ii $b = 29\,250$
d $\frac{dV}{dx} = 1200 - \frac{3}{4}x^2$ **e** $x = 40$, $h = 20$ **f** $32\,000$ cm^3

35 a i €511.99   ii €1602.45
b $V = 12\,000(1.0105)^{4x}$ euros   **c** 22 years
d 4.27% (if $n = 21.9$; 4.25% if $n = 22$)

36 a 92.4 m^2
b maximum length 16.55 m, maximum width 5.65 m
c 93.5 m^2 **d** 1.87 m^3 **e** $474.13   **f** $3.99

37 a $n = 9$ **b**

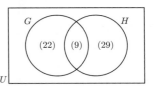

c $\frac{17}{20}$
d i $\frac{2}{5}$ ii $\frac{1}{12}$
e i $\frac{17}{38}$ ii $\frac{9}{38}$

38 a $L_0 = 10$ **b** 2.77 units   **c** 17.9 m
d

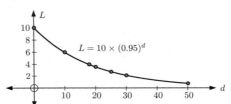

e Between 23.5 m and 44.9 m.

39 a 37.5 cm   **b** 1500 cm^2 **c** 13 500 cm^3
d 54.8 cm   **e** 46.8°   **f** 375 cm^2

40 a

Time (min)	Frequency	Cumulative frequency
$20 \leqslant t < 25$	5	5
$25 \leqslant t < 30$	8	13
$30 \leqslant t < 35$	15	28
$35 \leqslant t < 40$	15	43
$40 \leqslant t < 45$	5	48
$45 \leqslant t < 50$	2	50

b

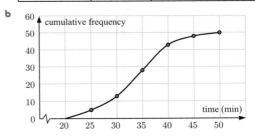

c i 34 min   ii 8 min   iii 37 runners   iv 32 min
d 23 min

41 a $(x - 15)$ **c** $51\,000   **d** $\frac{dP}{dx} = 1635 - 18x$
e $91 per pair, $51\,756 profit

42 a i 4   ii 1   iii 4
b i $y = x + 7$ ii $y = 4x - 8$ **c** $(5, 12)$
d $y = -x + 3$

43 a i 55   iii 500 500   iv $n = 150$
b i $u_n = 7n$ ii $u_{142} = 994$ iii $S_n = \frac{7n(n+1)}{2}$
c 429 429

44 a

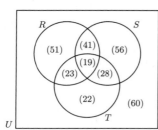

b 60

c **i** 6.33%
   ii 30.7%

d 60%

45 a 25 year old group:
   min = 1.15 $Q_1 = 1.2$ median = 1.3 $Q_3 = 1.35$
   max = 1.45

   60 year old group:
   min = 0.85 $Q_1 = 0.9$ median = 0.95 $Q_3 = 1.05$
   max = 1.2

b

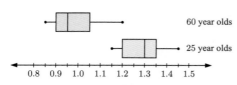

c The 25 year old group has a higher mean, median and mode than the 60 year old group.

d 25 year old group: IQR = 0.15, range = 0.3
   60 year old group: IQR = 0.15, range = 0.35
   The IQR is the same for both groups. The range is slightly greater for the 60 year old group.

e 60 year old adults will, in general, have a lower bone density than 25 year old adults.

46 a x-intercepts are 2 and 6,
   y-intercept is 12

b $x = 4$

c $(4, -4)$

e increasing for $x \geqslant 4$,
   decreasing for $x \leqslant 4$

f $y = -2x + 3$

g $y = -\frac{1}{4}x + \frac{3}{2}$

d

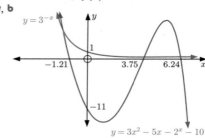

47 b QR ≈ 4.624 cm   **c** **i** 18.6 cm   **ii** 16.5 cm^2

48 a **i** $V_1 = \$30\,000$ **iii** $V_n = 40\,000(0.75)^n$
   iv

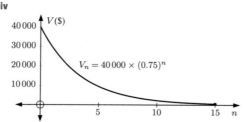

b **i** 5%   **ii** $P_2 = \$1323$, $P_3 = \$1389.15$
   iii $P_n = 1200(1.05)^n$

c 11 years

49 a, c

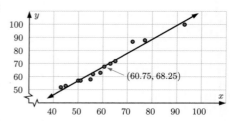

b $(60.75, 68.25)$

d **i** $r \approx 0.981$ **ii** $y \approx 1.06x + 3.61$ **e** 94%

50 a **i** 100   **ii** 33   **b** **i** 0.76   **ii** 0.74

c **i** 0.258   **ii** 0.546   **iii** 0.379   **iv** 0.439

d **i** 0.001 02   **ii** 0.0552

51 a **i** x-intercepts are -1.21, 3.75, and 6.24,
   y-intercept is -11

   ii local minimum at $(1.08, -14.0)$,
   local maximum at $(5.26, 8.38)$

   iii As $x \to \infty$, $f(x) \to -\infty$
   As $x \to -\infty$, $f(x) \to \infty$

   iv, b

$y = 3^{-x}$ $y = 3x^2 - 5x - 2^x - 10$

c $x \approx -3.38$, -1.65, 3.75, or 6.24

52 a 13.1 km   **b** 41.4°   **c** 4.83 km   **d** 38.3 km^2
   e 0.567%

53 a In 3 years she will earn \$183 000 under *Option B*, compared with \$126 100 under *Option A*.

b **i** $A_n = 40\,000 \times (1.05)^{n-1}$ **ii** $B_n = 59\,000 + 1000n$

c ≈ 13.1 years

e **i** graph 1 represents T_A, graph 2 represents T_B
   ii P(22.3, 1 580 000)

f $0 \leqslant n \leqslant 22$

54 a discrete   **b** 79   **c** **i** $s = 75$ **ii** $t = 119$
   d 487   **e** 6.16
   f

   no. of pups per litter

g **i** 8   **ii** 2   **iii** 6

55 a -100, for every €1 increase in the selling price, the number of stools sold decreases by 100.

b $N = -100x + 8000$ **c** €$(x - 50)$

e $\dfrac{dP}{dx} = -200x + 13\,000$ **f** $x = 65$, €22 500 profit

56 a 20 cm   **b** OR $= 10\sqrt{2}$ cm

c **i**

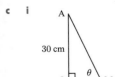

ii $\theta \approx 71.6°$

d 1660 cm^2 **e** $25.52

57 **a** $41 269.54

b

n (years)	0	1	2	3	4
V_n ($)	50 000	53 000	56 180	59 550.80	63 123.85

c $V_n = 50\,000 \times (1.06)^n$ dollars   **d** $S_n = 3000n$ dollars

e

n (years)	0	1	2	3	4
T_n ($)	50 000	56 000	62 180	68 550.80	75 123.85

f 19 years

58 **a**   **i** 95°C   **ii** 5°C

b, e

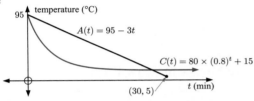

c No, we would not expect the temperature to drop at a constant rate in the long term.   The coffee's temperature should approach that of its surroundings.

d   **i** 95°C   **ii** 15.1°C   **f** 12.4 min   **g** 15°C

h   **i** $t = 0$ or 26.6, at these times the approximate temperature $A(t)$ is equal to the actual temperature $C(t)$.

ii 42.6°C

iii This is the maximum amount by which $A(t)$ overestimates the actual temperature.

59 **a** H_0: *movie type* and *gender* are independent.
H_1: *movie type* and *gender* are not independent.

b 28   **c** $\chi^2 \approx 22.7$ **d** 3   **e** 7.81

f $\chi^2 > 7.81$, so we reject H_0, and conclude that *movie type* and *gender* are not independent.

g $\chi^2 \approx 16.9$, which is still > 7.81, so the conclusion is still valid.

INDEX